D0617330

NONVOLATILE MEMORIES
Materials, Devices and Applications

Titles in Nanotechnology Book Series

Founding Editor

Dr. Hari Singh Nalwa

1. **Encyclopedia of Nanoscience and Nanotechnology, 10-Volume Set**
   Edited by Hari Singh Nalwa
2. **Handbook of Theoretical and Computational Nanotechnology, 10-Volume Set**
   Edited by Michael Rieth and Wolfram Schommers
3. **Bottom-up Nanofabrication: Supramolecules, Self-Assemblies, and Organized Films, 6-Volume Set**
   Edited by Katsuhiko Ariga and Hari Singh Nalwa
4. **Handbook of Semiconductor Nanostructures and Nanodevices, 5-Volume Set**
   Edited by A. A. Balandin and K. L. Wang
5. **Handbook of Organic-Inorganic Hybrid Materials and Nanocomposites, 2-Volume Set**
   Edited by Hari Singh Nalwa
6. **Handbook of Nanostructured Biomaterials and Their Applications in Nanobiotechnology, 2-Volume Set**
   Edited by Hari Singh Nalwa
7. **Handbook of Electrochemical Nanotechnology, 2-Volume Set**
   Edited by Yuehe Lin and Hari Singh Nalwa
8. **Polymeric Nanostructures and Their Applications, 2-Volume Set**
   Edited by Hari Singh Nalwa
9. **Soft Nanomaterials, 2-Volume Set**
   Edited by Hari Singh Nalwa
10. **Functional Nanomaterials**
    Edited by Kurt E. Geckeler and Edward Rosenberg
11. **Synthesis, Functionalization and Surface Treatment of Nanoparticles**
    Edited by I. M. Baraton
12. **Quantum Dots and Nanowires**
    Edited by S. Bandyopadhyay and Hari Singh Nalwa
13. **Nanoclusters and Nanocrystals**
    Edited by Hari Singh Nalwa
14. **Molecular Nanoelectronics**
    Edited by Mark A. Reed and T. Lee
15. **Magnetic Nanostructures**
    Edited by Hari Singh Nalwa
16. **Nanoparticles for Pharmaceutical Applications**
    Edited by J. Domb, Y. Tabata, M. N. V. Ravi Kumar, and S. Farber
17. **Cancer Nanotechnology**
    Edited by Hari Singh Nalwa and Thomas J. Webster
18. **Biochips Nanotechnology**
    Edited by Nongyue He and Hari Singh Nalwa
19. **Nanotoxicology**
    Edited by Yuliang Zhao and Hari Singh Nalwa
20. **Nanoscale Science and Engineering Education**
    Edited by Aldrin E. Sweeney and Sudipta Seal
21. **Packaging Nanotechnology**
    Edited by Amar Mohanty, Manjusri Misra, and Hari Singh Nalwa
22. **Chemistry of Carbon Nanotubes**
    Edited by Vladimir A. Basiuk and Elena V. Basiuk
23. **Encyclopedia of Nanoscience and Nanotechnology, 15-Volume Set (Vols. 11–25)**
    Edited by Hari Singh Nalwa
24. **Handbook of Nanoceramics and Their Based Nanodevices, 5-Volume Set**
    Edited by Tseung-Yuen Tseng and Hari Singh Nalwa
25. **Metal Oxide Nanostructures and Their Applications, 5-Volume Set**
    Edited by Ahmad Umar and Yoon Bong Hahn
26. **Doped Nanomaterials and Nanodevices, 3-Volume Set**
    Edited by Wei Chen
27. **Nanomanufacturing**
    Edited by Shaochen Chen
28. **Nanomaterials for Energy Storage Applications**
    Edited by Hari Singh Nalwa
29. **Magnetic Nanostructures (Second Edition)**
    Edited by Hari Singh Nalwa
30. **Nanoparticles: Synthesis, Characterization and Applications**
    Edited by R. S. Chaughule and R. V. Ramanujan
31. **Nanocrystals and Quantum Dots of Group IV Semiconductors**
    Edited by T. V. Torchynska and Yu. V. Vorobiev
32. **Nanoclusters and Nanostructured Surfaces**
    Edited by Asok K. Ray

Additional Volumes in Preparation

NONVOLATILE MEMORIES
Materials, Devices and Applications

Volume 2

Edited by

Tseung-Yuen Tseng, Simon Min Sze
National Chiao Tung University, Taiwan

AMERICAN SCIENTIFIC PUBLISHERS
25650 Lewis Way
Stevenson Ranch, California 91381-1439, USA

AMERICAN SCIENTIFIC PUBLISHERS
25650 Lewis Way, Stevenson Ranch, California 91381-1439, USA
Tel.: (661) 254-0807
Fax: (661) 254-1207
E-mail: order@aspbs.com
URL: http://www.aspbs.com

Nonvolatile Memories: Materials, Devices and Applications edited by Tseung-Yuen Tseng and Simon M. Sze

The schematic diagram on the cover of this book is courtesy of Professor Tseung-Yuen Tseng and Professor Simon M. Sze, National Chiao Tung University, Hsinchu, Taiwan.

This book is printed on acid free paper. ♾

Library of Congress Control Number: 2011945807

International Standard Book Number: 1-58883-249-X (2-Volume Set)
International Standard Book Number: 1-58883-250-3 (Volume 1)
International Standard Book Number: 1-58883-251-1 (Volume 2)

PRINTED IN THE UNITED STATES OF AMERICA
10 9 8 7 6 5 4 3 2 1

Preface

The nonvolatile semiconductor memory (NVSM) is one of the most important inventions in the electron-device field since the invention of the transistor. Today, NVSM is the technology driver of the electronics industry—the largest industry in the world. NVSM was invented in 1967 by D. Kahng and S. M. Sze. The memory device employed a floating gate for information storage and a tunneling current for programming and erasure. This seminal invention has subsequently given rise to a large family of memory devices, including the flash memory and electrically erasable programmable read-only memory (EEPROM). Since 1990, NVSM has enabled the development of all modern electronic systems, such as the mobile phone, notebook computer, digital camera, MP3 music player, personal digital assistant, digital television, automotive engine control unit, portable medical diagnostic system, universal serial bus (USB) flash personal disc, global positioning system, and many more.

In the past 20 years, NVSM's minimum feature length has been scaled down from 0.8 μm to $<$20 nm—a $>$40-fold reduction. This reduction has substantially increased its memory density, decreased its cost per bit, and broadened its applications to become ubiquitous. However, this relentless miniaturization of device size has resulted in significant reliability challenges that may hinder further scaling of the floating-gate memory device. Therefore, many alternative nonvolatile memory technologies are being developed to possibly continue the scaling to the sub-10-nm regime and to improve device performance. These alternative technologies include nanocrystal memory, semiconductor-oxide-nitride-oxide-semiconductor (SONOS) memory, ferroelectric memory, phase-change memory, magnetic memory, and resistive memory.

This two-volume book contains 32 chapters. They are written by 71 world experts on nonvolatile memories for a comprehensive coverage of the physics, materials science, device structures, and applications of the aforementioned memory devices. The book also summarizes their recent advances and future trends. It is intended as a reference book for engineers and scientists actively involved in semiconductor-device research and development. It may also serve as a textbook for senior undergraduate and graduate students in applied physics, materials science and engineering, and electrical and electronics engineering who have already acquired a basic understanding of semiconductor-device physics.

In the course of writing the book, many people have assisted us and offered their support. We would first like to express our appreciation to the management of our academic and industrial organizations in eight countries across three continents, for providing the environments in which we worked on the book project; without their support this book would not have been written. We, the editors, are grateful to our colleagues at the College of Electrical and Computer Engineering, National Chiao Tung University, for their encouragement and assistance. We wish also to thank Mr. M. C. Wu, Mr. D. Y. Lee, Mr. C. Y. Huang, and Mr. T. H. Wu for their literature searches and to Ms. M. L. Chen for her help in technical illustrations.

Tseung-Yuen Tseng, Simon M. Sze
National Chiao Tung University, Taiwan

Contents

CHAPTER 5. Metal-Oxide-Based Resistive-Switching Memory: Materials, Device Scaling, and Technology Design

Jinfeng Kang, Bin Gao, Bin Yu

CHAPTER 6. Resistance Switching Effects in Transition Metal Oxide Thin Films for Nonvolatile Memory Applications

Dinghua Bao

CHAPTER 7. Resistive-Random Access Memory Based on Amorphous Films

Yuchao Yang, Wei Lu

CHAPTER 8. Overview of Metal-Oxide Resistive Memory

ChiaHua Ho, Fu-Liang Yang

CHAPTER 9. Resistive-Switching Memory Devices Based on Metal Oxides: Modeling of Unipolar Switching, Reliability, and Scaling

Carlo Cagli, Daniele Ielmini

CHAPTER 10. Organic and Polymer Nonvolatile Memories: Materials, Devices, and Working Mechanisms

Wei Lek Kwan, Yang Yang

CHAPTER 11. Material, Device, and Circuit of Organic Nonvolatile Memory

Zingway Pei, Heng-Tien Lin

CHAPTER 12. Organic/Polymeric Films with Resistive-Switching Behavior and Their Application as Nonvolatile Memory Devices

Jianyong Ouyang

CHAPTER 13. Organic Resistive Switching for Nonvolatile Memory Application

Byungjin Cho, Tae-Wook Kim, Yongsung Ji, Sunghoon Song, Takhee Lee

About the Editors

Tseung-Yuen Tseng received his Ph.D. degree in electroceramics from the School of Materials Engineering, Purdue University, West Lafayette, USA in 1982. He was briefly associated with the University of Florida, Gainesville, before joining National Chiao-Tung University, Hsinchu, Taiwan in 1983, where he is now a University Chair Professor in the Department of Electronics Engineering and the Institute of Electronics. He was the Dean of College of Engineering (2005–2007), the Vice Chancellor and University Chair Professor of the National Taipei University of Technology, Taipei, Taiwan (2007–2009). Dr. Tseng's professional interests are electronic ceramics, nanoceramics, ceramic sensors, high-k dielectric films, ferroelectric thin films and their based devices, and resistive switching memory devices. He has published over 290 research papers in refereed international journals and 110 conference papers, several book chapters, and held 28 patents. He co-invented the base metal multilayer ceramic capacitor, which has become large scale commercial product. He is an Editor of the Handbook of Nanoceramics and Their Based Nanodevices (5-Vol. set), Guest Editor of a special issue of Ferroelectrics (6 Volumes), an Associate Editor of the Journal of Nanoscience and Nanotechnology, Advanced Science Letters and International Journal of Applied Ceramic Technology. He is Member of Board of Asia Ferroelectrics Association and General Chair of The 6th Asian Meeting of Ferroelectrics. He is a Chairperson, Session Chair, Keynote and Invited Speaker, and Member of Advisory Committee of many National and International Meetings. Dr. Tseng has received Distinguished Research Award from the National Science Council (1995–2001), Hou Chin-Tui Distinguished Honor Award (2002), Dr. Sun Yat-Sen Academic Award (2003), TECO Technology Award (2004), IEEE CPMT Exceptional Technical Achievement Award (2005), Distinguished Research Award of Pan Wen Yuan Foundation (2006), Academic Award of Ministry of Education (2006), Medal of Chih-Hung Lu (2010) and National Endowed Chair Professor (2011). He was elected a Fellow of the American Ceramic Society in 1998, IEEE Fellow in 2002 and MRS-T Fellow in 2009.

Simon M. Sze received his B.S. degree from the National Taiwan University, M.S. from the University of Washington, and Ph.D. from Standford University, all in Electrical Engineering. Dr. Sze was with Bell Telephone Laboratories from 1963 to 1989 as a member of the Technical Staff. He joined the National Chiao Tung University (NCTU) from 1990 to 2006 as a Distinguished Professor. At present, he is a Consulting Professor at Standford University and an Honorary Chair Professor at NCTU. Dr. Sze has served as a visiting professor to many academic institutions including the University of Cambridge, Delft University, Beijing Jiaotong University, Tokyo Institute of Technology, and Swiss Federal Institute of Technology. He has made fundamental and pioneering contributions to semiconductor devices, especially the metal-semiconductor contacts, microwave devices, and submicron MOSFET technology. Of particular important is his co-invention of the non-volatile semiconductor memory (NVSM) which has subsequently given rise to large family of memory devices including the Flash memory and the EEPROM. The NVSM has enabled the development or enhanced the performances of all modern electronic systems such as the cellular phone, notebook computer, personal digital assistant, digital camera, digital television, smart IC card, electronic book, portable DVD, MP3 music player, automatic braking system (ABS) and global positioning system (GPS). Dr. Sze has authored or coauthored over two hundred technical papers. He has written and edited 14 books. His book "Physics of Semiconductor Devices" (Wiley, 1969; 2nd Ed, 1981; 3rd Ed, 2007) is one of the most cited works in contemporary engineering and applied science publications(over 20,000 citations according to ISI Press). Dr. Sze has received the IEEE J.J. Ebers Award, the Sun Yet-sen Award, the National Endowed Chair Professor Award, and the National Science and Technology Prize. He is a Life Fellow of IEEE, an Academician of the Academia Sinica, a foreign member of the Chinese Academy of Engineering, and a member of the US National Academy of Engineering.

List of Contributors

Numbers in parenthesis indicate the pages on which the author's contribution begins.

Dinghua Bao (139)
State Key Laboratory of Optoelectronic Materials and Technologies,
School of Physics and Engineering, Sun Yat-Sen University, Guangzhou 510275,
People's Republic of China

Carlo Cagli (225)
Dipartimento di Elettronica e Informazione and IU.NET, Politecnico di Milano,
Piazza L. da Vinci 32, 20133 Milano (MI), Italy

Kuan-Neng Chen (1)
Department of Electronics Engineering, National Chiao Tung University,
Hsinchu 30010, Taiwan

Frederick T. Chen (1)
Nanoelectronic Technology Division, Electronics and Optoelectronics Research
Laboratories, Industrial Technology Research Institute, Hsinchu 31040, Taiwan

Huai-Yu Cheng (1)
Emerging Central Lab., Macronix International Co., Ltd., Hsinchu 30078, Taiwan

Byung-Ki Cheong (31)
Electronic Materials Center, Korea Institute of Science and Technology,
39-1 Hawolgok-Dong, Sungbuk-Ku, Seoul, 136-791, Korea

Byungjin Cho (309)
School of Materials Science and Engineering, Gwangju Institute of Science and
Technology, Gwangju 500-712, Korea

Bin Gao (111)
Institute of Microelectronics, Peking University, Beijing 100871, China

Alois Gutmann (401)
Infineon Technologies, 2070 Rt. 52, Hopewell Junction, NY 12533, USA

Jin-Ping Han (401)
Infineon Technologies, 2070 Rt. 52, Hopewell Junction, NY 12533, USA

Xiaoli He (335)
Institute of Microelectronics, Chinese Academy of Science, Beijing, 100079, China

ChiaHua Ho (185)
National Nano Device Laboratories (NDL), Hsinchu City 300, Taiwan

Daniele Ielmini (83, 225)
Dipartimento di Elettronica e Informazione and IU.NET, Politecnico di Milano,
Piazza L. da Vinci 32, 20133 Milano (MI), Italy

Hong-Sik Jeong (31)
Memory Division, Semiconductor Business, Samsung Electronics Corp. Ltd. Yongin-City, Kyungi-Do, 449-711, South Korea

Yongsung Ji (309)
School of Materials Science and Engineering, Gwangju Institute of Science and Technology, Gwangju 500-712, Korea

Jinfeng Kang (111)
Institute of Microelectronics, Peking University, Beijing 100871, China

Dae-Hwan Kang (31)
Memory Division, Semiconductor Business, Samsung Electronics Corp. Ltd. Yongin-City, Kyungi-Do, 449-711, South Korea

Tae-Wook Kim (309)
Korea Institute of Science and Technology, Jeollabuk-Do 565-902, Korea

Ki-Bum Kim (31)
Seoul National University, Department of Materials Science and Engineering, Seoul National University, 599 Gwanak-Ro, Gwanak-Gu, Seoul, 151-744, Korea

Wei Lek Kwan (249)
School of Electrical and Electronic Engineering, Singapore Polytechnic, Singapore 139651

Takhee Lee (309)
Department of Physics and Astronomy, Seoul National University, Seoul 151-744, Korea

Heng-Tien Lin (265)
Circuit and System Design Technology Department, Flexible Electronics Technology Division, Electronics and Optoelectronics Research Laboratories, Industrial Technology Research Institute (ITRI), 195, Sec. 4, Chung Hsing Rd., Chutung, Hsinchu, 31040, Taiwan, R.O.C.

Wei Lu (161)
Department of Electrical Engineering and Computer Science, The University of Michigan, Ann Arbor, Michigan 48109, USA

Hsiang-Lan Lung (1)
Emerging Central Lab., Macronix International Co., Ltd., Hsinchu 30078, Taiwan

Jianyong Ouyang (289)
Department of Materials Science and Engineering, National University of Singapore, Singapore 117574

Zingway Pei (265)
Graduate Institute of Optoelectronic Engineering, Department of Electrical Engineering, National Chung Hsing University, 250 Ku-Kang Rd., Taichung, 40227, Taiwan, R.O.C.

L. P. Shi (57)
Data Storage Institute, (A*STAR) Agency for Science Technology and Research, DSI Building, 5 Engineering Drive 1, Singapore 117608

Sunghoon Song (309)
School of Materials Science and Engineering, Gwangju Institute of Science and Technology, Gwangju 500-712, Korea

Oleksandr Voskoboynikov (377)
National Chiao Tung University, 1001 Ta Hsueh Rd., Hsinchu 30010, Taiwan

Wei Wang (335)
College of Nanoscale Science and Engineering, University at Albany, NY 12203, USA

Yuchao Yang (161)
Department of Electrical Engineering and Computer Science, The University of Michigan, Ann Arbor, Michigan 48109, USA

Yang Yang (249)
Department of Materials Science and Engineering, University of California, Los Angeles, CA 90095, USA

Fu-Liang Yang (185)
National Nano Device Laboratories (NDL), Hsinchu City 300, Taiwan

Bin Yu (111)
College of Nanoscale Science and Engineering, State University of New York, Albany, New York 12203, USA

R. Zhao (57)
Data Storage Institute, (A*STAR) Agency for Science Technology and Research, DSI Building, 5 Engineering Drive 1, Singapore 117608

Yu Zhu (1)
IBM T. J. Watson Research Center, Yorktown Heights, New York 10598, USA

CHAPTER 1

Phase Change Memory: Research Developments and Device Applications

Kuan-Neng Chen[1], Hsiang-Lan Lung[2], Yu Zhu[3], Huai-Yu Cheng[2], Frederick T. Chen[4]

[1]*Department of Electronics Engineering, National Chiao Tung University, Hsinchu 30010, Taiwan*
[2]*Emerging Central Lab., Macronix International Co., Ltd., Hsinchu 30078, Taiwan*
[3]*IBM T. J. Watson Research Center, Yorktown Heights, New York 10598, USA*
[4]*Nanoelectronic Technology Division, Electronics and Optoelectronics Research Laboratories, Industrial Technology Research Institute, Hsinchu 31040, Taiwan*

CONTENTS

ISBN: 1-58883-251-1

Nonvolatile Memories: Materials, Devices and Applications
Edited by Tseung-Yuen Tseng and Simon M. Sze
Volume 2: Pages: 1–30

1. INTRODUCTION

1.1. Historical Development of Phase Change Material Applications

The earliest instance of phase change memory (PCM) was the optical rewritable disc (DVD-RW) based on technology developed by Stanford Ovshinsky in the 1960s and used by Panasonic in drives in the late 1980s [1]. The memory effect is brought about by the distinct optical differences that result from the fundamental difference between the disordered, amorphous phase and the crystalline phase of certain materials, typically chalcogenides. The DVD-RW technology is now commonly used for the storage of large files, such as movies or library archives. However, the amorphous and crystalline phases are also profoundly different electrically, which forms the basis of storing randomly accessible data based on PCM (also known as PC-RAM). PCM devices are programmed into lower resistance, crystalline states by a SET operation (typically an annealing pulse on the order of a few hundred nanoseconds) or higher resistance, amorphous states by a RESET operation (a quick, melting pulse on the order of nanoseconds, followed by rapid cooling).

Although the concept of such a device had already been proposed by Ovshinsky [2], actual devices in production did not appear until much later. In 2004, Samsung demonstrated a 64-Mb array using $Ge_2Sb_2Te_5$ (GST) with nitrogen doping to suppress crystallization for a better retention of the amorphous state [3]. In 2006, BAE Systems began selling a 4-Mb chalcogenide random-access memory (*C*-RAM) part for radiation-hard and space applications [4]. The first PCM devices were generally layers composed of GST situated on a bottom contact heater that also served as an electrode contact. IBM also worked on PCM, demonstrating various novel structures such as the phase change bridge composed of GeSb, with only a 3 × 20 nm heating cross-section area [5]. Recently, Numonyx (now part of Micron) and Samsung have separately released products based on PCM. The Numonyx part [6] is a 128-Mb standalone NOR flash-compatible memory built on a 90-nm process, while the Samsung part [7] is a 512-Mb memory designed to replace an equivalent NOR flash memory component in a multichip package.

Two general considerations have driven the evolution of PCM toward higher density memory. First, the heating of the phase change material requires a very high current density (> 30 MA/cm^2). This would often require an extra fabrication step to confine the current from a driving source, e.g., a metal–oxide–semiconductor field-effect transistor (MOSFET) or diode, into a sufficiently small heating area. This has led to the development of sublithographic patterning techniques for the phase change heaters or the phase change elements themselves. Some notable examples are the lithography-independent "keyhole" structure [8] and the crossed spacer structure [9]. The second consideration is the a need to allow for the PCM threshold voltage in the overall voltage budget (Fig. 1) [10]. A certain threshold voltage (generally denoted as V_{th}) must be exceeded for the amorphous state to switch to the crystalline state. This V_{th} has a minimum value equal to roughly E_g/e, where E_g is the band gap of the material [11]. For GST, E_g is roughly 0.7 eV [12]. Additional voltage is required to drive the heating current, which often leads to an overall programming voltage exceeding 1 V and approaching 2 V. Such a high voltage may not be tolerated with gate oxide breakdown in advanced logic MOSFET devices [13]. As a result, alternative isolation/driving devices have been used. The current 128-Mb and next-generation 1-Gb Numonyx chips use bipolar junction transistor (BJT) devices [14], while Samsung uses *p–n* diodes [15]. The junction breakdown voltage in both cases is safe for at 3 V and above. An additional benefit offered by diodes or BJTs is the possibility to minimize the cell area, which allows for higher density.

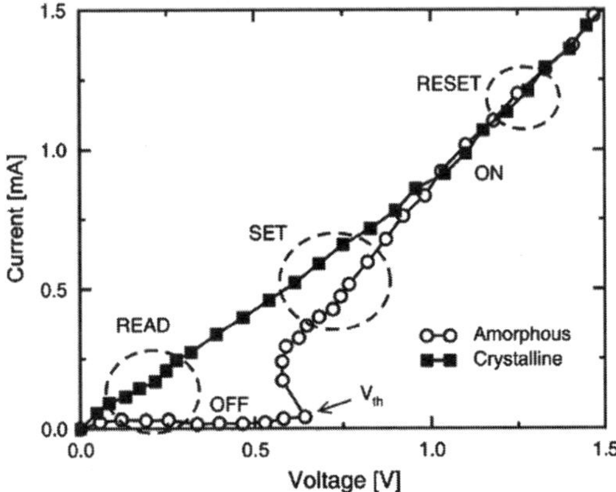

Figure 1. *I–V* curve from a typical GST-based phase change memory cell showing both amorphous and crystalline states. Reprinted with permission from [10], A. Pirovano et al., *IEEE Trans. Elec. Dev.* 51, 714 (2004). © 2004, IEEE.

Despite the trend of higher density, the combination of sublithographic patterning and additional process steps to form *p–n* junctions either for diodes or BJTs has led to additional costs compared with mainstream chip technologies such as flash memory or logic. Thus, although PCM has been a strong candidate to fulfil the role of a "universal memory" capable of serving all possible memory applications [16], its entry into the mainstream market has still been limited by its cost [17].

In this chapter, we briefly introduce the historical development of phase change materials and their applications. In the following sections, phase change materials, including material properties and physics, will be reviewed and discussed. Next, we will introduce the PCM device concept, electrical performance, and applications. The fabrication of phase change materials will also be reported. In the end, we will summarize the current status of phase change materials and their outlook. Readers are expected to have an overview about phase change materials, including research developments and device applications from this chapter.

2. PHASE CHANGE MATERIALS

2.1. Introduction and History

That differences in electrical resistance observed in phase change materials can be used to store information was recognized by Ovshinsky in the 1960s [18]. He demonstrated that Te–As–Si–Ge could be switched between a high conductivity and low conductivity state and he proposed possible solid-state memory device configurations based on this

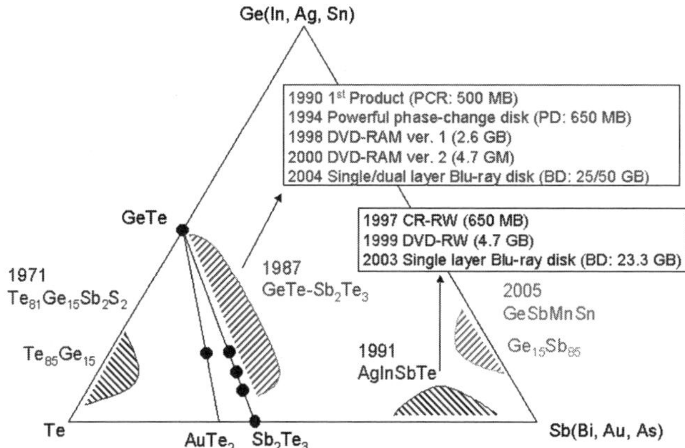

Figure 2. Ternary phase diagram depicting different phase-change alloys, their year of discovery as a phase-change alloy, and their use in different optical storage products. Reprinted with permission from [24], M. Wuttig and N. Yamada, *Nat. Mater.* 6, 824 (2007). © 2007, NPG.

switching behavior [19]. Although this material could show electrical switching and could be used for electronic storage, the crystallization time of the order of microseconds hindered earlier attempts to develop this concept into a viable technology.

The interest in phase change materials was renewed when Feinleib and colleagues [20] described a laser-induced phase change in a $Te_{81}Ge_{15}Sb_2S_2$ alloy and opened up a new chapter for the application of phase change materials. This is the basis of phase-change optical storage, where the difference in optical reflectivity between the amorphous and crystalline phases of phase change materials is utilized to store the information and a laser is applied to write and read the data. The crystallization time for the $Te_{81}Ge_{15}Sb_2S_2$ alloy was still in the microsecond range, which was too slow for a viable technology. As the first fast recrystallization materials, GeTe and $Ge_{11}Te_{60}Sn_4Au_{25}$, were reported (Refs. [21, 22]), they triggered the discovery of pseudobinary alloys along the $GeTe–Sb_2Te_3$ tie line, such as $Ge_1Sb_4Te_7$, $Ge_1Sb_2Te_4$ and $Ge_2Sb_2Te_5$ [23]. Figure 2 shows in a ternary phase diagram that demonstrates which alloys have been used for rewritable optical storage in the last few decades [24]. Nowadays, $Ge_2Sb_2Te_5$ is the most studied and most commonly applied material for both optical and electrical applications.

The operation principle of a memory cell based on phase change materials is accomplished by the phase transition of a chalcogenide material (i.e., material containing one or more elements of group VI, such as S, Se or Te) between two different states. These states include an amorphous one with very low electrical conductivity and a crystalline one that is highly conductive. The phase transition is triggered by electric pulses (or heat surges). To switch the memory cell to the crystalline state, a moderate magnitude voltage pulse ("SET" operation) is applied to the material within a cell to heat it above its crystallization temperature. Conversely, to switch the cell back to its amorphous state, a large and short electric pulse melts the crystalline phase into a transient liquid, which is then rapidly quenched by the cold surroundings into the amorphous state (called the "RESET" operation). The "read" operation can be performed nondestructively (read out) by measuring the memory cell resistance. The difference in resistance between the two states is known to be 3–6 orders of magnitude, which provides a sufficient data-sensing margin.

Device performance is directly related to the properties of phase change materials. For example, a material with a low melting point, a low heat capacity (C_p), a low heat of fusion (ΔH_f), a low thermal conductivity, and a high resistance in its crystalline state would lead to less power consumption for heating, thus resulting in a low reset current for the operation. Furthermore, a material with a high crystallization temperature (T_x) generally leads to a better thermal stability of the memory, significantly improving data retention. Fast switching speed is always desired, and it can be determined by the crystallization time of a phase change material. The material needs to be able to switch repeatedly for many cycles, such as 10^5 times for optical storage, 10^6–10^8 times to replace flash memory, which is more than 10^{12} to replace dynamic RAM (DRAM). Therefore, a requirement for good phase change materials is high stability of the chemical composition, which does not phase segregate and does not react with the surrounding and contact materials after many cycles. Unfortunately, the currently used GST material still has some drawbacks, including phase segregation after cycling, insufficient data retention at elevated operation temperatures, high reset current and relatively slow switching speed.

To optimize device performance, finding a material with a short crystallization time (τ_x), a high crystallization temperature (T_x) and good chemical composition stability without phase segregation is a formidable challenge for material scientists. The next sections describe what materials have been most successfully studied, as well as materials-oriented research in PCM to improve the reset current, thermal stability, endurance properties, and speed.

2.2. Current Phase Change Alloys and the Development of New Materials

GST is the most intensely studied material for PCM, and it has been used for DVD-RAM phase-change optical discs. Some of the material research is directed at modifying GST by changing the Ge:Sb:Te ratios to improve its properties; other research is probing into finding a new substitute. The material studies can be classified into two categories: (1) Modification of conventional GST by different dopants, such as N-doped or O-doped GST, and (2) the development of novel materials. Modifications of conventional GST material have been successful in improving the properties of phase change material and some companies, such as Samsung and Intel, use these modified GST materials as the memory material for high-density integrated PCM. An example of the effect of N-doped GST is shown in Figure 3, where the required reset current can be reduced by 50% using nitrogen-doped GST instead of undoped GST [25]. It is obvious that this simple modification of material can more effectively reduce the reset current of PCM than structural scaling alone. In addition, nitrogen suppresses grain growth of GST during heating. The grain size of N-doped GST was considerably smaller than undoped GST [26], which results in an improvement in cyclability. Besides, the crystallization temperature of N-doped GST

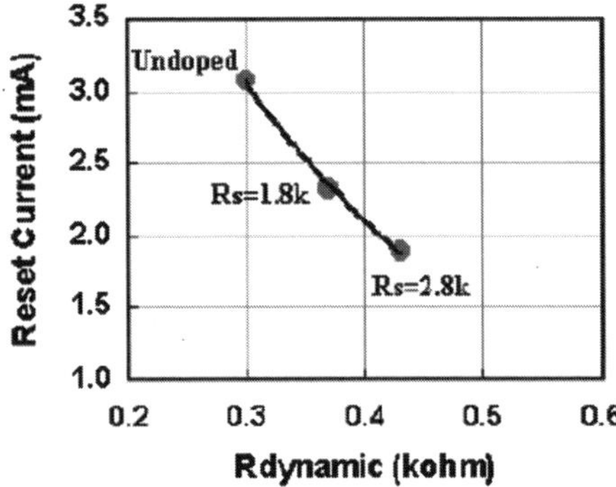

Figure 3. Doping nitrogen into GST increases the dynamic resistance, resulting in lower reset current. Reprinted with permission from [25], Y. N. Hwang et al., "International Electron Devices Meeting," p. 893, 2003. © 2003, IEEE.

(N = 7 at.%) increased by 50°C, resulting in better thermal stability [26]. Similarly, lower power PCM devices could be achieved with oxygen-doped GST stemming from the formation of high electrical resistance of the germanium oxides in this material [27]. The operation current of PCM cells enabled 100 μA through a tungsten-bottom-electrode contact with a diameter of 180 nm, representing a very low value for a PCM cell. Therefore, oxygen-doped GST with higher electrical resistance will improve the thermal efficiency and result in less power consumption. Alternatively, the grain size of oxygen-doped GST is much smaller than that in conventional GST (Fig. 4). By controlling the grain size of GST, thermal lifetime will be further improved [27]. Undoped GeSbTe material was developed to improve the crystallization speed and decrease the melting points, which could be as low as to 450°C for 18.8 at a %Sn doping into GST, which is significantly lower than GST and melts around 630°C [28]. To fulfill the requirements of phase change materials that are suitable for PCM, the search for new phase change alloys will vigorously proceed.

Nakayama is a pioneer who is devoted to developing new materials for PCM other than the conventional GST material [29]. This group successfully proposed new memory material based on As–Sb–Te for submicron nonvolatile memory in 2000 [29]. The crystallization temperature (T_x) of $As_xSb_{40-x}Te_{60}$ ($0 \leq x \leq 40$) shows a compositional

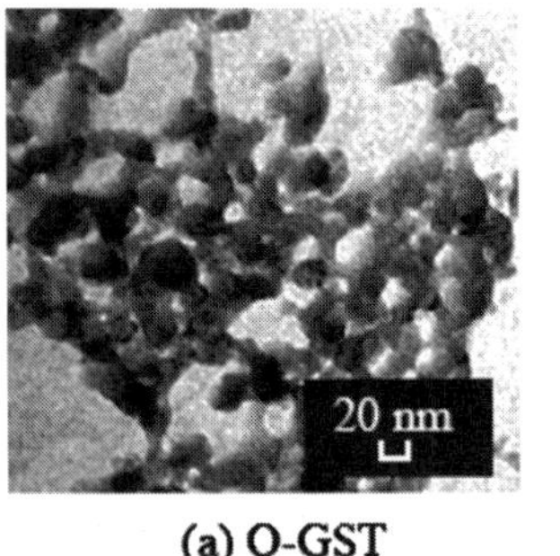

Figure 4. Comparison of TEM micrographs of films after annealing at 400°C with (a) showing oxygen-doped GST and (b) showing conventional GST. Reprinted with permission from [27], N. Matsuzaki et al., "International Electron Devices Meeting," p. 738, 2005. © 2005, IEEE.

Table 1. Melting points T_m of some chalcogenide semiconductors (K).

	T_m (K)
$Ge_2Sb_2Te_5$	889
$GeSb_2Te_4$	887
$GeSb_4Te_7$	880
$In_{49}Sb_{23}Te_{28}$	893
$As_{24}Sb_{16}Te_{60}$	650, 695, 710
$Se_{20}Sb_{20}Te_{60}$	669

Source: Reprinted with permission from [30], K. Nakayama et al., *Jpn. J. Appl. Phys.* 42, 404 (2003). © 2003, Japan Society of Applied Physics.

dependence from 74–146°C with increasing As concentration. However, the lower T_x of alloys from the As–Sb–Te system adversely affects the stability of the amorphous state and renders them unsuitable for PCM applications.

In 2003, this group proposed another new material based on the Se–Sb–Te system for improving PCM [30]. They chose Se to replace As in order to solve the problem of low crystallization speed of alloys from the As–Sb–Te system. The melting temperatures of typical chalcogenide semiconductors are listed in Table 1 [30]. The T_m of $Se_{20}Sb_{20}Te_{60}$ is as low as that of $As_{24}Sb_{16}Te_{60}$ and at least 200 K lower than that of the Ge–Sb–Te system. Therefore the operating current during amorphization could be successfully decreased. In fact, the current densities for amorphization of As–Sb–Te and Se–Sb–Te systems are lower than that of Ge–Sb–Te (Table 2) [30]. However, there are some problems with the As–Sb–Te and Se–Sb–Te systems. Oxidation occurs easily in As–Sb–Te, and both As–Sb–Te and Se–Sb–Te show slow speeds of crystallization. The crystallization time of the As–Sb–Te system is typically 100 μs while the Se–Sb–Te can be faster than 1 μs, which is still much longer compared with the Ge–Sb–Te system (10–100 ns). The Se–Sb–Te system with greatly reduced T_m, which suggested a lower energy for the amorphization, is more suitable for PCM applications.

Several approaches for lower power and higher speed operations of PCM were proposed using new materials, including compositions from the Sb–Se, Si–Sb, and Si–Sb–Te materials systems [31, 32]. Sb_xSe_{100-x} is a very attractive candidate because of its low melting temperature of about 540–560°C and low thermal conductivity of $Sb_{65}Se_{35}$ with 0.2 W/cm · K (GST with hexagonal structure is 0.46 W/cm · K). In a PCM device, heat confinement within the programming volume is very important for a lower power operation. For $Sb_{65}Se_{35}$ with lower thermal conductivity, it is expected that the generated heat will be more effectively utilized; thus, the reset current will be decreased. The Te-free environmental friendly SiSb phase change material was proposed to solve the problems of serious movement of Te atoms at the interface between the GST and bottom electrode [32]. The movement of Te causes problems not

Table 2. Current density for reset operation of some chalcogenide thin films.

	Se–Sb–Te	As–Sb–Te	Ge–Sb–Te
Current density (mA/μm^2)	20–30	20–30	80–110

Source: Reprinted with permission from [30], K. Nakayama et al., *Jpn. J. Appl. Phys.* 42, 404 (2003). © 2003, Japan Society of Applied Physics.

only by phase segregation of the GST material itself, but it also causes void formation and, thus, degrades the life cycles of the phase change memory cell [33]. In addition, the high T_x (~220°C for $Si_{16}Sb_{84}$) and low-density change on crystallization (~3.8%) compared with that of GST (~6.8%) makes this material more attractive.

The other new alloys, such as In–Ge–Te and Ga–Sb–Te, were investigated for PCM to optimize the device performances with respect to faster speed, longer data retention, and ultimate cycling ability [34–37]. The doped In–Ge–Te material has a very high T_x of 276°C, which was 130°C higher than that of GST (T_x = 148°C) and demonstrated a 10-year retention at temperatures above 150°C suitable for automotive applications [34]. In addition, the fine grains of doped In–Ge–Te (~20 nm), which prevented void formation, suggested a great potential for future scaling.

In the literature two composition classes have been proposed that show a growth-dominated crystallization mechanism and usually can exhibit fast crystallization. Figure 5 shows these two groups in the Ge, Sb and Te composition diagram, which are doped Sb–Te materials that have compositions close to the eutectic point of the Sb–Te phase diagram, and the alloys of antimony with 5%~30% germanium, gallium or indium, which are called doped Sb-based phase-change materials [38, 39]. However, high-speed materials usually show low amorphous phase stability and high media noise [40]. Thus, adding dopants into phase change materials is commonly employed to improve the amorphous phase stability. The effects of various dopants in eutectic.

SbTe and Sb-based materials are interesting topics and have been extensively studied [39]. Ga is an effective dopant that increases crystallization temperature greatly and still maintains a high crystallization speed. The $Ga_2Sb_5Te_3$ material has been demonstrated for PCM. Memory cells based on this new material system showed an excellent performance regarding data retention with 10 years at 160°C [35]. Since this material exhibits a high T_x (228°C) and high activation energy for crystallization (4.5 eV), excellent thermal stability can be expected.

The search for new materials for PCM is still rigorously proceeding. However, the optimization of phase change materials is largely an empirical process and still requires and considerable resources and enthusiastic endeavors from material scientists. Phase change materials play an important role in memory performance, and scientists are driven to solve all of the issues for PCM, thus making this new technology closer to commercialization.

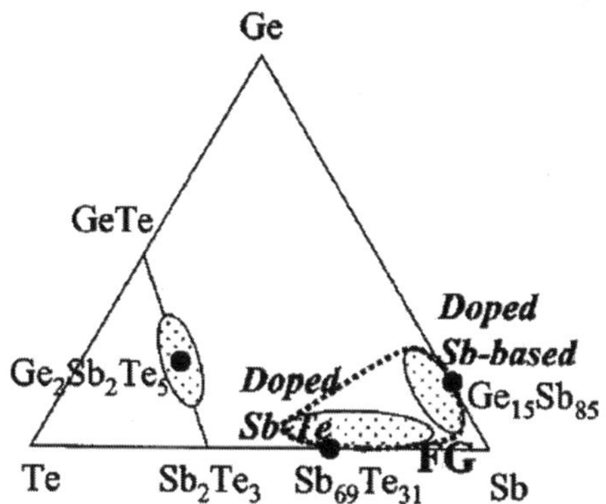

Figure 5. Ge–Sb–Te composition ternary diagram. Fast-growth materials like doped Sb–Te and doped Sb-based compositions are indicated. Reprinted with permission from [39], L. van Pieterson et al., *J. Appl. Phys.* 97, 083520 (2005). © 2005, AIP.

2.3. Materials Issues for PCM Development

Common device failure mechanisms include phase segregation after cycling and insufficient data retention at elevated operation temperatures. In particular, the endurance of resistance between SET and RESET under repetitive programming operation is still a main issue that impedes the attempts for DRAM replacement. Two typical failure modes have been observed. One is the "set-stuck" failure, in which the cell cannot be programmed to reset (high) its resistance state and remains at a low set resistance after repeated cycling. It was proposed that the phase separation of constituent elements might be the possible reason for this stuck-low failure [41]. The other is the "reset-stuck" failure, in which the cell resistance of set and reset merge together to become high resistance, and the set cannot be programmed any longer. The void generation by material movement or a serious degradation of the electrode material between phase change materials and the bottom electrodes are mentioned to be the main cause of this stuck high failure [41]. Figure 6(a) shows the scanning electron microscope (SEM) image of GST in bottleneck geometry line structures after a high voltage sweeping (0~20 V). The high-electric stress induces an atomic transport to create a nonuniform region (also called a river-delta region [42]). Under high-electric stress circumstances ($> 10^6$ A/cm^2), an asymmetric compositional separation between Sb and Te was observed. Sb moves toward the cathode (−), whereas the Te element is distributed toward the anode (+). The separation of Sb and Te is clearly observed at the river-delta region (Fig. 6(b); see the elemental maps detected by scanning Auger microscope [SAM]). This compositional separation tendency between Sb and Te coincides with the failure mechanisms that were observed in conventional PCM cells where the Sb-rich composition forms near the bottom electrode (biased with negative voltage) [43]. Yang and colleagues [44] investigated the electromigration behavior in molten and crystalline GST using a pulsed direct current (DC) stress to an isolated line structure. An electrostatic force induced the compositional variation after melting where the Ge and Sb drift toward the cathode and Te toward the anode. In addition, the Sb and Te atoms diffused prior to the diffusion of Ge atoms. The direction of migrating atoms can be explained by the valence difference of each atom in the molten state, in which Te has a higher electronegativity value than Ge; Sb indicates that Te atoms are more likely to attract electrons and become anions, but Ge and Sb atoms lose their electrons and become cations. Therefore, under the electrostatic forces, the anionic Te ions diffuse to the anode, and the cationic Ge ions and Sb ions diffuse to the cathode. In crystalline GST, the atomic flux of Te by electromigration is about twice as large as the flux of Ge and Sb due to wind force [44]. The reasons of compositional variations after many cycling operations of PCM cells can explained with this picture.

(a)

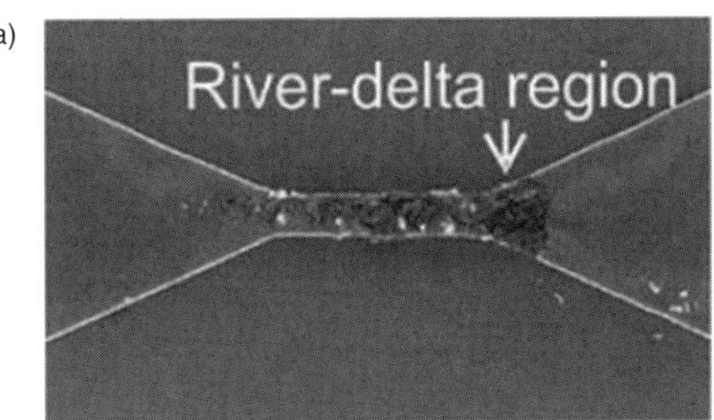

(b)

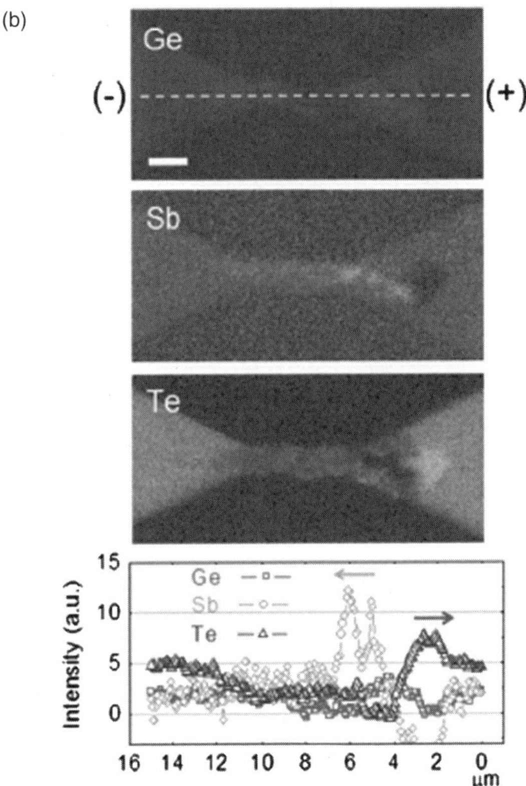

Figure 6. (a) SEM image of $Ge_2Sb_2Te_5$ bottleneck geometry line devices after 0–20 V *I–V* sweeping, (b) SAM elemental mapping analysis with respect to Ge, Sb, and Te. The separation of Sb and Te is clearly observed at the river-delta region. Reprinted with permission from [42], S. W. Nam et al., *Electrochem. Solid State Lett.* 12, 155 (2009) © 2009, ECS.

Other degradation phenomena of PCM cells were observed, such as drift phenomenon for the RESET operation and the degradation of set switching speed. The elemental phase segregation is typically the main cause for those failures. How to extend PCM cycle life will involve suppressing unwanted chemistry with electrodes at the interface as well as developing alloys with reduced or eliminated elemental migration, which will also be a challenging topic for material researchers.

2.4. Scaling Capability of Phase Change Materials

Scalability is a critical aspect of any data storage technology, i.e., its capability to continue shrinking following Moore's law. The optical storage based on phase change materials has been successful because the data density was increased from generation to generation. PCM is a promising technology because it is expected that the trend of increased storage density will also continue for several future lithography generations. In this section, we investigate how the properties of phase change materials themselves change with scaling. Several important parameters of phase change materials are affected as a function of film thickness, e.g., crystallization temperatures, optical band gaps are increased with decreasing film thickness, melting temperature, and mass density are decreased as film thickness is reduced. At some materials–dependent film, thickness crystallization does not occur any longer when the film thickness is below a critical value and materials stop being "phase change" materials. Figure 7(a) shows the intensity of the diffracted X-ray diffraction (XRD) peaks as a function of temperature for a 50-nm thick GST film and a 2-nm thick GST film. Figures 7(b and c) show θ–2θ scans for various film thicknesses after heating the films to 300°C and 450°C, respectively. The 50-nm thick film crystallizes into the metastable rock-salt phase at about 155°C and then undergoes a phase transformation into the stable hexagonal phase at about 370°C. For films thinner than 2 nm, the rock-salt phase was not observed any longer at all, while the hexagonal phase still formed for films as thin as 2 nm (Fig. 7(c)) Therefore, the thinnest films of GST that crystallize in the rock-salt phase were 3.5 nm, while the hexagonal phase still formed for films as thin as 2 nm [45]. This is, in fact, good news because it means that the materials still do crystallize down to such ultra-thin thicknesses. For the other materials, the smallest film thickness that still showed XRD peaks for N-GST, GeSb, Sb_2Te and AgIn–Sb_2Te (AIST) were 2 nm, 1.3 nm, 1.5 nm, and 1.5 nm, respectively. As a result, an ultra-scaled PCM device with only 3 nm thin doped $Ge_{15}Sb_{85}$ phase-change films has been fabricate using bridge structures, demonstrating the capability to scale down this technology for many more lithographic generations [5].

The crystallization times (τ_x) and crystallization temperatures (T_x) of phase change materials are two of its most important properties. They strongly influence data rate, data retention, and archival lifetime. The T_x depends on several factors such as the surrounding materials (substrate and capping layer), the heating ramp rate, and even the method used to measure it. The dependency of T_x on the film thickness is an imperative topic for scalability of PCM. Figures 8(a and b) summarize the crystallization behavior as a function of film thickness of thin layers of $Ge_{15}Sb_{85}$, Sb_2Te, nitrogen-doped GST, GST, and AIST sandwiched between SiO_2 and Al_2O_3, which was studied using time-resolved XRD during sample annealing [45]. Films with thicknesses between 10 and 50 nm exhibited very little thickness dependence of the crystallization temperature T_x, and the T_x values were comparable to those of bulk materials. As the film thickness was reduced below 10 nm, the increase in T_x was quite substantial for all materials and reached up to 200°C. This shows that phase change materials that scale down to very thin films still exhibit phase change behavior, and that the crystallization temperature is increased when the films are sandwiched between oxides. The results are promising for the scalability of PCM technology with respect

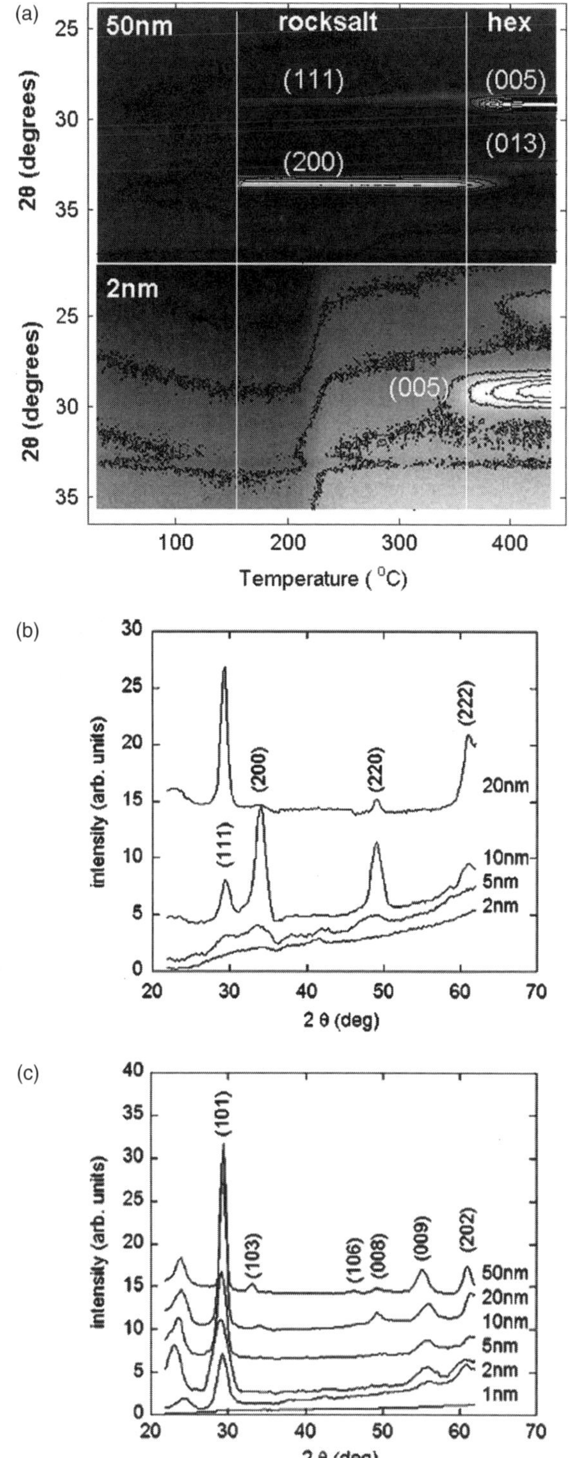

Figure 7. (a) Time-resolved XRD peak intensity for 50 nm (top) and 2 nm (bottom) thick GST films, and (b) and (c) θ–2θ scans of GST films of various thicknesses after heating to 300°C and 450°C, respectively at 1°C/s. Reprinted with permission from [45], S. Raoux et al., *J. Appl. Phys.* 103, 114310 (2008). © 2008, AIP.

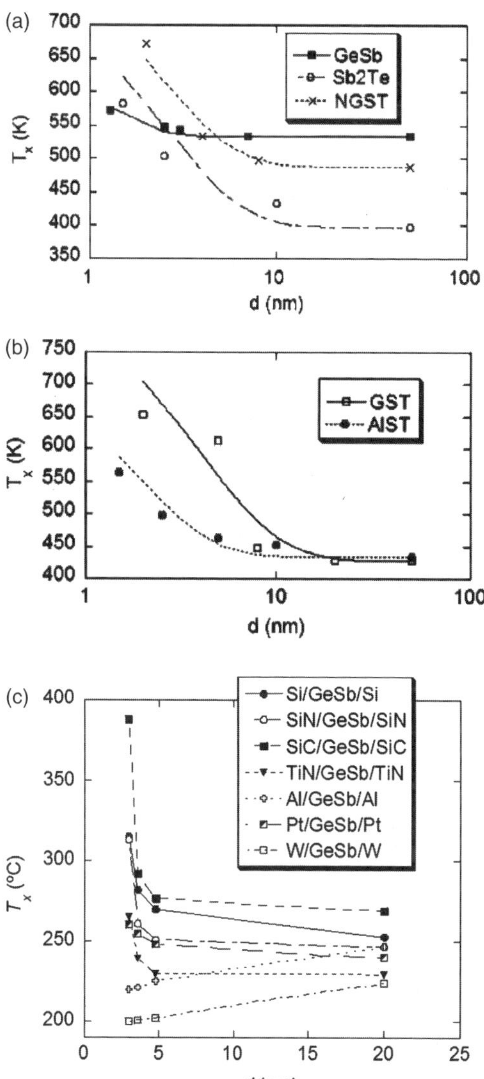

Figure 8. (a and b) show crystallization temperature T_x as a function of film thickness d for different materials, (c) T_x as a function of film thickness d for Ge–Sb thin films sandwiched between 10 nm of various materials. Reprinted with permission from [45], S. Raoux et al., *J. Appl. Phys.* 103, 114310 (2008). © 2008, AIP; from [46], S. Raoux et al., *Appl. Phys. Lett.* 94, 183114 (2009). © 2009, AIP.

to shrinking cell dimensions that should have better thermal stability of the materials. However, as device dimensions and film thicknesses are reduced, the crystallization behavior becomes a function of size, and interfaces and surfaces play more and more important roles. Figure 8(c) summarizes the effect of the cladding material and film thickness material, d, on T_x for $Ge_{15}Sb_{85}$ material [46]. T_x is not a strong function of film thickness between 5 and 20 nm. When the film thickness is reduced, T_x of the samples with cladding materials Si, SiN, SiC, and TiN increases substantially. For metallic interfaces, however, a decrease in T_x was observed as film thickness was reduced, with the exception of Pt. A plausible reason for the exceptional behavior of Pt cladding material is that most likely Pt reacted chemically with Sb, thus forming an intermediate phase. Time-resolved XRD showed the formation of PtSb and not the crystalline Sb structure, which was the case of the other $Ge_{15}Sb_{85}$ films. An exponential increase in T_x with reduced film thickness was also observed for GST sandwiched between TiN by Simpson and colleagues [47] using an extended X-ray absorption fines structure and ellipsometry to determine the crystallization temperature. However, a slight decrease in T_x with decreasing films thickness was found for GST sandwiched between $(ZnS)_{0.85}(SiO_2)_{0.15}$. It was mentioned that the influence of stress from the encapsulation material surrounding GST has an increasingly dominant influence on the phase change behavior. The increase in T_x originates from compressive stress exerted from the encapsulation material (e.g. TiN) whereas a negligible effect on T_x was observed from a lower stress $(ZnS)_{0.85}(SiO_2)_{0.15}$ encapsulation material. By minimizing the stress the GST films can maintain the bulk crystallization temperature for films as thin as 2 nm. However, a highly compressive cladding material, such as TiN, is suggested to be used in PCM since it has an advantage of leading to higher T_x, thus providing a better thermal stability with decreasing cell dimensions.

For the rewritable DVD media [48, 49], the complete erasure time (CET; the laser pulse duration that is required to completely recrystallize an amorphous mark in a crystalline film) was shown to strongly depend on the phase change material when film thickness was reduced. One study found that for the growth-dominated Ag–In–Sb–Te materials, the CET was decreased with a reduction of film thickness (10–25 nm), while the opposite trend was observed for the nucleation-dominated GST materials (15–35 nm) [48]. However, another study found an optimum layer thickness (~9 nm) where the crystallization time was minimum for SbTe-based (growth-dominated) material [49]. Figure 9 summarizes the crystallization times needed to complete 90% of the phase transformation as a function of film thickness, which is plotted for capped (SiO_2 capping) and uncapped GST in the as-deposited, amorphous, and melt-quenched amorphous states, respectively, and determined using a static laser tester [50]. The capped GST in the as-deposited state shows a monotonic increase of the crystallization time with decreasing film thickness, while the melt-quenched GST shows the opposite trend as a function of film thickness. In contrast, the uncapped GST has an optimum thickness with a shortest crystallization time for both as-deposited and melt-quenched amorphous materials. The difference in the thickness dependence for the same material between uncapped and capped condition again demonstrates the large role interfaces play in the crystallization behavior of very thin phase change films, which is similar to the large role it plays for crystallization temperatures.

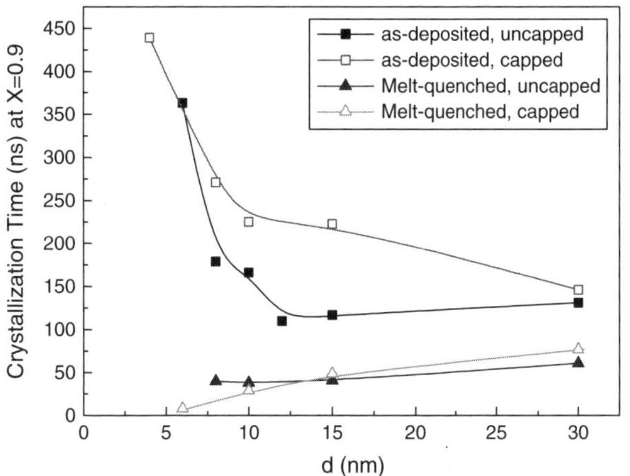

Figure 9. Crystallization and recrystallization times for a crystal fraction x of 0.9 as a function of film thickness for capped and uncapped GST films in the as-deposited amorphous state and melt-quenched amorphous from the rock-salt state, respectively. Reprinted with permission from [50], H.-Y. Cheng et al., *J. Appl. Phys.* 107, 074308 (2010). © 2010, AIP.

Typically, the melt-quenched amorphous materials have shorter recrystallization times than as-deposited amorphous materials. This is due to two effects: (1) crystallization from the as-deposited amorphous phase requires first nucleation of supercritical nuclei, which then grow in size, and (2) recrystallization of melt-quenched amorphous materials does not require nucleation because in PCM cells the melt-quenched area is surrounded by crystalline materials and the crystals can grow from this boundary. In addition, melt-quenched amorphous material often has a higher medium-range order than as-deposited amorphous material, thus leading to faster recrystallization. Due to required high-temperature (typically 400°C) back-end-of-the-line processes (BEOL) during fabrication of a real phase change memory chip, the GST material will be crystallized and transformed to the rock-salt or hexagonal phase after fabrication. Therefore, the phase transition between the melt-quenched amorphous state to the recrystallized state needs to be carefully explored. In this case, the crystallization behavior of melt-quenched GST is a more meaningful sign to predict device performance, and it shows a beneficial trend for crystallization speed when the films scales down.

Phase change nanowires and nanoparticles are investigated to study other aspects of scaling (two dimensions reduced in size for nanowires and three dimensions reduced in size for nanoparticles). PCM devices have been successfully fabricated using GST phase change nanowires [51]. Self-assembled GST nanowires are produced by a vapor–liquid–solid process using Au particles as catalysts, and the hexagonal single-crystalline structure of the nanowires along the [0001] direction was confirmed. The size-dependent switching behavior of this hexagonal GST nanowires was studied. It was found that the reset current was reduced as wire dimensions were reduced. The activation energy and data retention are also reduced for smaller wires. It was measured that the data retention time at 80°C for a 150-nm nanowire GST is 330 years and when nanowire scaled down to 20 nm thickness, it still can easily retain data for 1 year. Highly scalable properties of PCM by using nanowire were confirmed, and it was demonstrated that phase change nanowires can offer an important system for investigating nanoscale phase transition phenomena.

All studies according to the scaling indicate that PCM based on phase change materials can scale well for many lithographic generations. However, an increased emphasis needs to be placed on tailoring interfaces because of their increased role in the crystallization process.

The intense efforts and activities are made for the development of PCM, and we can expect that PCM technology will be used either in the consumer market or in embedded systems in the near future. The materials research and understanding of phenomena related to the phase change

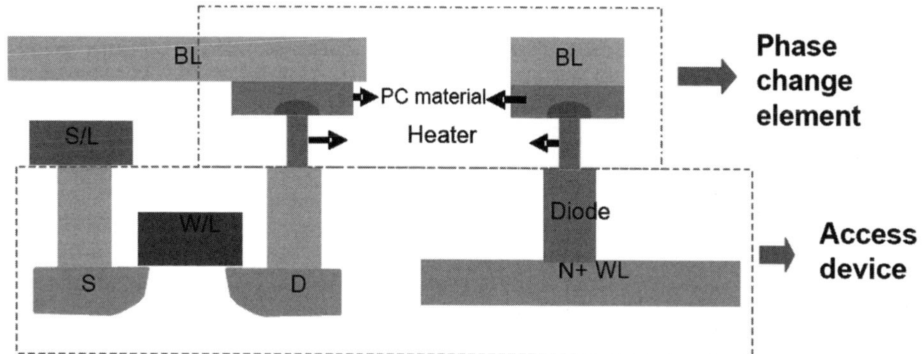

Figure 10. A PCM memory cell = a phase change element + an access device.

materials play a crucial role for the development of this technology.

3. PCM DEVICES

3.1. Basic Device Operation Concepts

PCM cell contains an access device and a phase change memory element. The access device provides programming current to operate the memory element and isolates the leakage current inside a memory array. The PCM element provides an amorphous state and crystalline state to represent "0" and "1" logic states.

Figure 10 shows a typical mushroom-type PCM cell. A PCM cell is a combination of a phase change element (PCE) and an access device. The PCE includes a patterned thin film phase change material and a heater. The access devices are MOSFET, BJT, or diode; it supports the programming current and regulates the array current to minimize the leakage current inside an array. During programming, different electrical pulses are applied to the heater to generate a hot spot on the phase change region of the thin film phase change material. The phase change material can be switched between amorphous and crystalline states by changing the heating/cooling conditions on the hot spot. The amorphous state is generated by heating the PCE above its melting temperature and then following with a rapid quench, while the crystalline state is generated by heating the PCE above its recrystallization temperature and following with a slow quench. The operation of changing the PCE to the amorphous state is called the "RESET" operation, while the operation of changing the PCE to crystalline state is usually called the "SET" operation. Figure 11 shows the SET and RESET operations of GST [52].

The melting temperature of GST is about 620°C and the recrystallization temperature is about 200°C. During reset operation, a tall and short reset pulse generates a high temperature heating and rapid cooling thermal cycle on the memory cell. The strong and sharp pulse melts the PCE and freeze the melting state (amorphous state) after operation. On the other hand, for set operation, a weak and longer set pulse generates a low temperature heating and slow cooling thermal cycle on the memory cell. The weak and long pulse anneals the amorphous phase to become the crystalline phase.

Reset and set operations are critical for PCM applications (Fig. 12). Because reset needs current to heat and melt the PCE, it is a high power operation (or a power limiter). High power operation needs a big access device (i.e., more Si area) to provide more current, so the reset operation is a cost limiter. A chip cannot provide enough current to reset many cells at the same time; as a result, the reset operation is a programming bandwidth limiter.

The set operation needs a longer pulse to anneal the cell to form its crystalline phase. Typically, a set pulse needs hundreds of nanoseconds to crystallize the PCE. Because set operation needs more time, it becomes a performance limiter. The programming speed of a PCM cell is limited by the set speed. Based on the above discussion, it is clear that most of PCM research and development efforts are focused on how to reduce the reset current and increase the set speed.

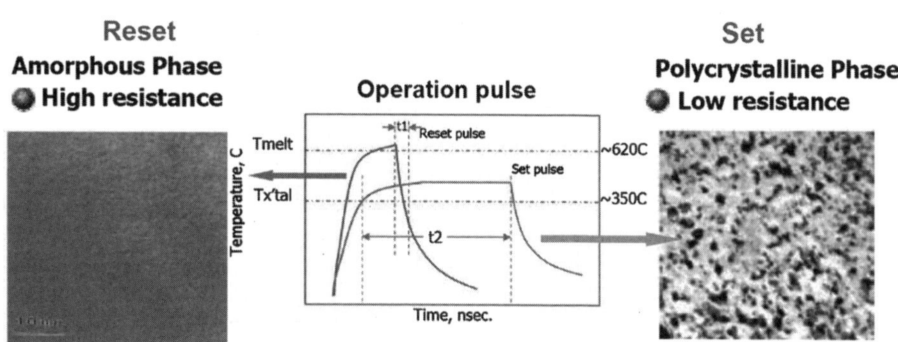

Figure 11. Phase change operations (reset and set) of a PCE. Reprinted with permission from [52], S. Lai, *IEDM* pp. 255–258 (2003). © 2003, IEEE.

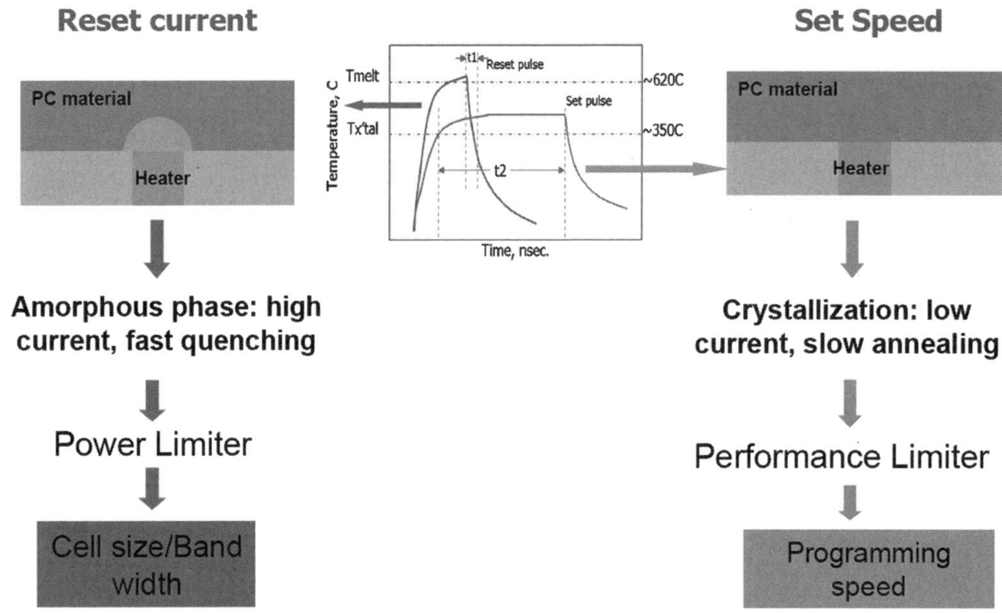

Figure 12. Power limiter and performance limiter of PCM.

3.2. History of PCM Development

The first PCM array was published in September 1970 by Neale and his colleagues [53], and it was the first time that people assembled PCEs and access devices together to make a PCM array. A lateral 200-mA driving current diode was used to drive the PCE. The set speed was about 10 ms, and the operation voltage was about 25 volts (Fig. 13)

The reset current requirement of this device was too big, so it was difficult to make a memory chip using that technology. Eight years later, Shanks and his colleagues [54] inserted a dielectric layer between the electrode and phase change material. A break-down dielectric pinhole device reduced the reset current to 25 mA. The first phase change memory chip in 1978 was a 1024-bit, 15-ms-set speed chip (Fig. 14).

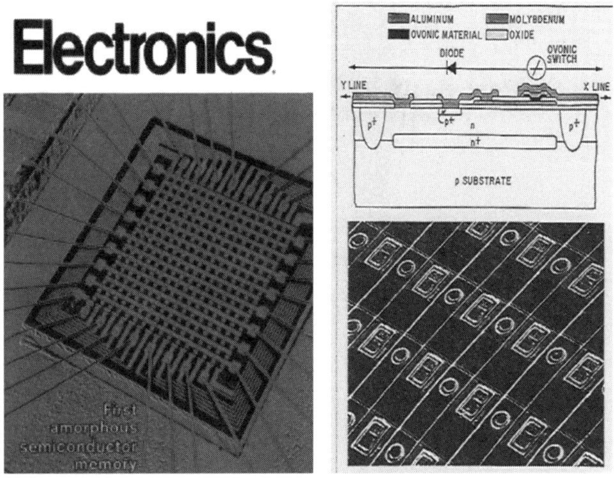

Figure 13. First phase change memory array. Reprinted with permission from [53], R. Neale et al., *Electronics* 56 (1970). © 1970, IEEE.

More than 20 years later, few PCM developing work has been reported. Unstable phase change material and huge reset current are the bottlenecks. One major breakthrough of phase change material development happened in 1987 when Yamada [55] found a reliable phase change material, GST, which has good cycling endurance, fast set speed, and tight resistance distribution. The material paved the road for modern PCM developing. Intel then published the first submicron PCM technology with GST in 2001 [56]. This memory cell owns a sublithographic size bottom heater to decrease the reset current to 1 mA. The fast switching GST improved the set speed to 50 ns. One year later, based on this technology, Intel published a 4-Mb test chip (Fig. 15) [57] that used a 0.18 um-BJT access device to drive the PCE. The reset speed and set speed were 30 ns and 50 ns respectively, and the cycling endurance was improved to 10^{12}.

This result encouraged many other companies with more resources for PCM research and development. In addition, it signaled the beginning of an intensive PCM research and development competition between major companies. Within 3 years (2004–2006), PCM technology migrated from 0.18-um to 90-nm node and increased the density from

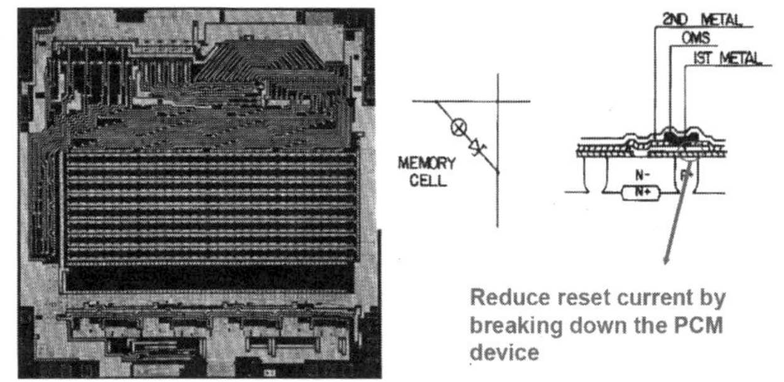

Figure 14. First phase change memory chip. Reprinted with permission from [54], R. Roy et al., *ISSCC* (1978). © 1978, IEEE.

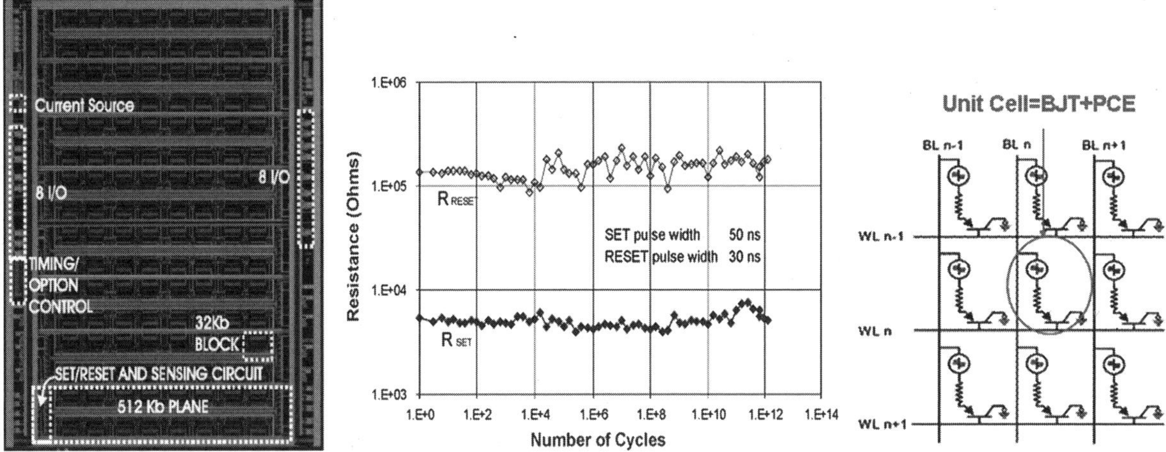

Figure 15. A 0.18 um, 4-Mb, BJT drive PCM chip. Reprinted with permission from [57], M. Gill et al., "Intel, Ovonyx and Azalea," 2002. © 2002, IEEE.

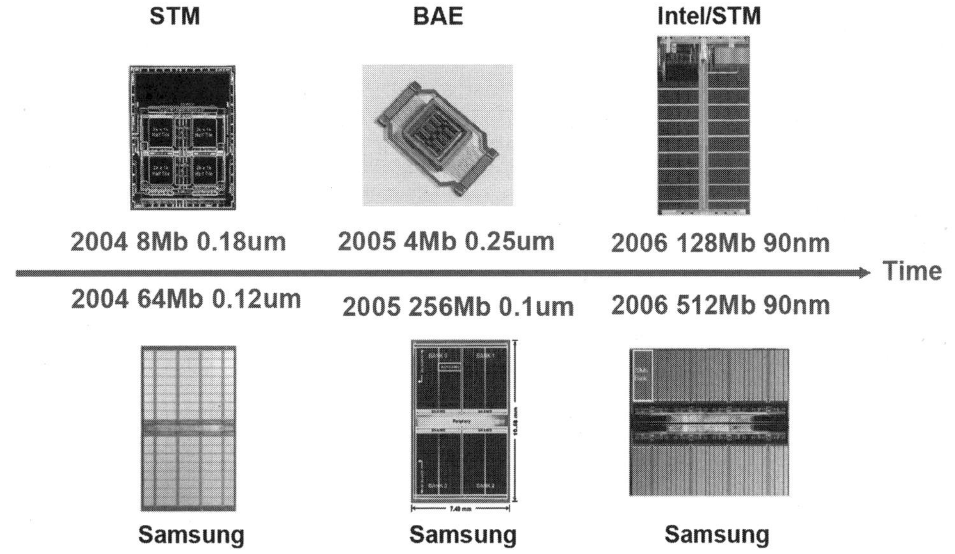

Figure 16. Brief PCM development history (2004–2006).

8 to 512 Mb. This was the first time that a semiconductor memory technology ramped up in such a short period of time. A brief history of PCM developing from 2004 to 2006 appears in Figure 16.

In order to compete with DRAM, NOR flash and cost, PCM needed to be shrunk below 45 nm. A 45-nm, 1-Gb PCM chip [14] presented at the 2009 International Electron Devices Meeting pushed the technology to another milestone.

3.3. Access Devices for PCM

An access device is as important as a PCE for PCM technology because it dominates the cell size of a PCM cell. It also supports the current for reset operation and prevents each cell from read error and writing disturbance. Providing enough reset current and keeping the cell size small were the biggest challenges facing access devices. A good access device needs to satisfy the following requirements: It has to have

(1) a small footprint to keep competitive cell size,
(2) a simple process to limit wafer cost, and

Technology node	45 nm
Cell size	0.0108 μm^2
Bit-Line/Word-Line pitch	104/104 nm
Effective cell size*	0.015 μm^2 (5.5 F^2)
Array selector	Vertical pnp-BJT
Periphery CMOS	Dual gate oxide 8/3 nm
Interconnection	3 Cu + 1 AlCu
Supply voltage	1.8 V

* F = half-pitch

Figure 17. Photographic picture and process features of a 45 nm PCM chip. Reprinted with permission from [14], G. Servalli, "International Electron Devices Meeting," 2009. © 2009, IEEE.

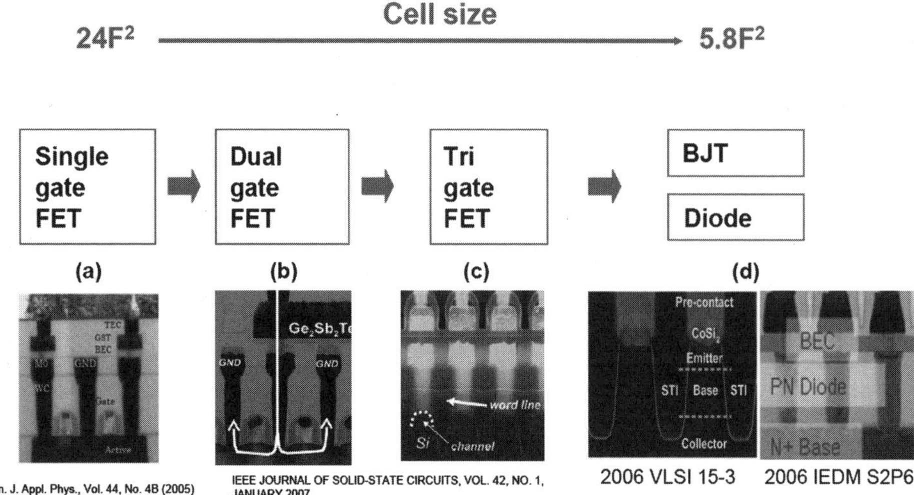

Figure 18. The evolution of PCM access devices (a) single gate MOSFET (b) dual gate MOSFET (c) tri-gate MOSFET (d) BJT.

(3) a high current density ($>10^6$ A/cm^2) for reset operation.

Figure 18 shows the evolution of the development of access devices in the semiconductor industry.

MOSFET is a straightforward access device solution because it comes from the standard complementary metal–oxide–semiconductor process, without any additional process cost (Fig. 18(a)). It is a good solution for embedded memory, but not for high-density memory because of its large cell size. The extra contact that connects the ground line increases the cell size of a MOSFET-driving PCM, and the high reset current requirement adds extra channel width to further increase the footprint of the MOSFET. In order to increase the supporting current and keep small cell size, a dual gate (word line) structure was proposed (Fig. 18(b)). It used two neighboring MOSFETs to drive one PCE, so the minimum channel width design rule can be used in this cell structure. Trigate structure adds two extra sidewall channels to increase the driving current, but it only occupies one MOSFET footprint (Fig. 18(c)). Vertical diode/BJT was the best solution for high-density PCM (Fig. 18(d)). A diode is a two-terminals device without another contact and source line to connect to the ground. Therefore, it has a smaller footprint than MOSFET. Figure 19 shows an example of a P+/N vertical silicon diode array. One bit and one world line decode a PN diode. Forward bias current of a P+/N Si diode provides the reset current of PCE. Reverse biased P+/N diodes isolate the unselected cells. The P+/N diodes sit on N+ diffusion word lines that are above a *P*-well.

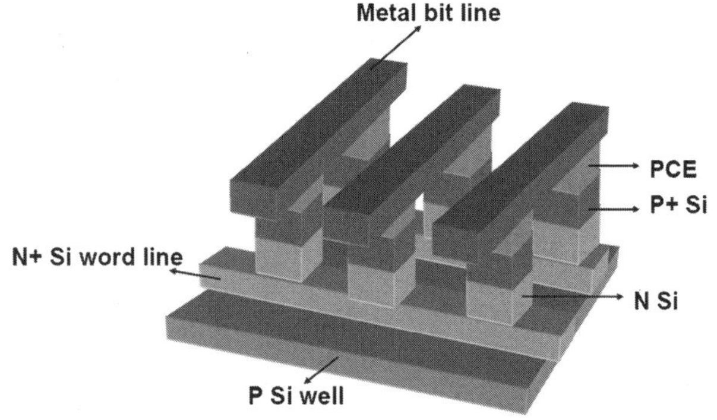

Figure 19. A vertical P+/N diode/BJT PCM array.

An equivalent array circuit is shown in Figure 20. A vertical PN diode connects to *P*-well to form a vertical PNP BJT Q2. A vertical PN diode connecting to the N+ base line and a neighboring vertical PN diode form a horizontal parasitic PNP BJT Q1. Emitter current of Q2 provides the reset current of PCE. The high reset current requirement of Q2 emitter degrades the current gain of Q2, and, as a result, the emitter current mostly comes from the N+ base line rather than the *p*-well collector. High current passing the N+ base line causes two issues: (1) it turns on the neighboring BJT Q1 to generate leakage and disturb current of neighbor cells, and (2) the high loading N+ base line needs to pick up more connections to connect the metal line to reduce the resistance, thus decreasing the array efficiency. An N+ base line needs higher doping does and a better doping profile control to solve those issues. Figure 21 shows a typical current–voltage (I–V) curve of a Si substrate vertical BJT [58]. The emitter current is the same as base current (Fig. 21(a)), which indicates the poor current gain of this BJT device. To provide enough reset current and avoid parasitic BJT turn on, every emitter needs a base contact to connect the base and a metal word line to reduce the resistance (Fig. 21(b)).

The balance between metal word line strapping and the array efficiency needs optimization for the diode array design. More strapping creates a better array performance (higher current, less leakage), but decreases the array efficiency and increases the cost. Figure 22 is a double shallow trench isolation (STI) BJT PCM array [14], using two STI processes to fabricate the word line and the emitter island. Every other four emitters on the N+ base line need a strapping contact to connect to a metal word line. Small cell size and a self-align process are the advantages of this approach, while complex integration flow, more process steps, and hard-control doping profile are the disadvantages. Because

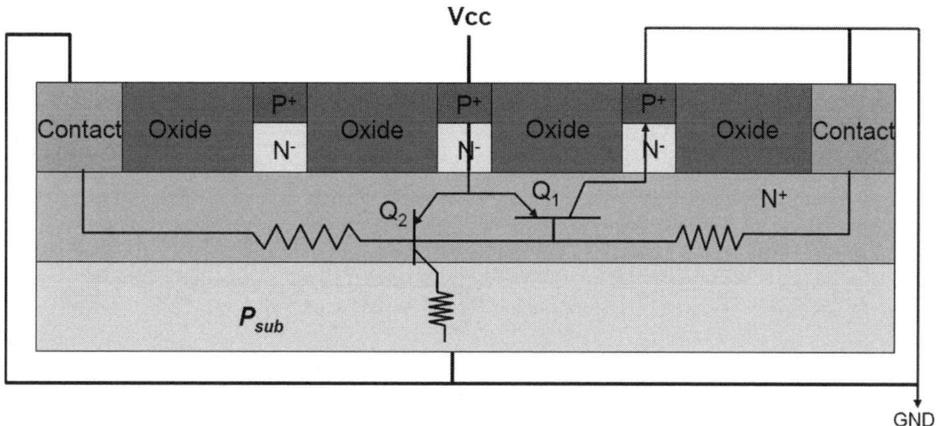

Figure 20. Equivalent circuit of a diode/BJT driving PCM array.

the N+ base line is buried under the substrate, this makes it difficult to have a high doping level. High base line resistance increases the base pick up contact number to decrease the efficiency of the array.

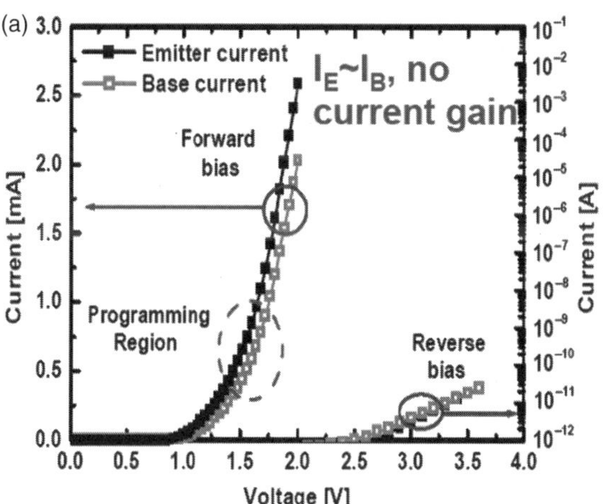

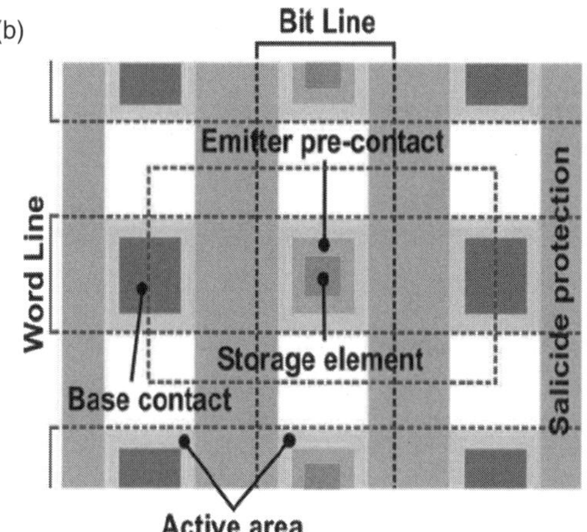

Figure 21. A typical I–V curve of a vertical substrate BJT and a schematic layout of this BJT array. Emitter current is almost the same as base current, indicating no current gain of this BJT device. Each emitter needs one base pickup contact to slow down the base line loading. Reprinted with permission from [58], F. Pellizzer et al., "Intel and STM," 2006. © 2006, IEEE.

A more suitable BJT array solution is shown in Figure 23 [15]. A selective Si epitaxial technique grows a Si diode inside a contact hole. Since the N+ base line and PN diode is fabricated after the MOSFET process, the doping profile and concentration has the better control. This gives the N+ base lines a higher doping concentration and a lower resistance and decreases the base pick up contact number (every other eight emitters) inside the array. The parasitic BJT leakage is also surpassed due to the higher base doping.

3.4. PCM Elements

PCEs use amorphous and crystalline states to represent "0" and "1" logic states. The amorphous state decides the data retention, and the crystalline state decides the operation speed of a PCM cell. Reducing the reset current and improving the reliability are the major goals for PCE development. Generally speaking, PCE includes two parts: (1) bottom heater, and (2) phase change material thin film. The most promising phase change material is GST, which was discovered by Yamada at 1987. This material provides good cycling endurance, fast recrystallization speed, and good resistance distribution for PCM applications. Figure 24 shows that the crystallization temperature of GST is about 172°C [55], and the crystallization speed is about 50 ns. A lower crystallization temperature increases crystallization speed, but it sacrifices data retention.

Different doping improves the properties of GST. Nitrogen doping reduces the reset current and improves the resistance distribution [3], and it also increases the crystallization temperature and activation energy to improve data retention. Figure 25 shows the TEM images of pure GST and nitrogen-doped GST [59]. The doped GST has a smaller grain size and a lower post-annealing effective crystallization ratio. Higher doping levels enhance these effects.

Doping plays an important rule on phase change material. It reduces the reset current and improves the data retention/cycling endurance of PCM. Figure 26 shows a comparison of cycling endurance for doped/undoped GST [60]. Voids are generated after 100 M cycles on the interface between the bottom heater surface and the undoped GST thin film; however, the doped GST sustains 1 G cycles without void formation on the interface. Higher

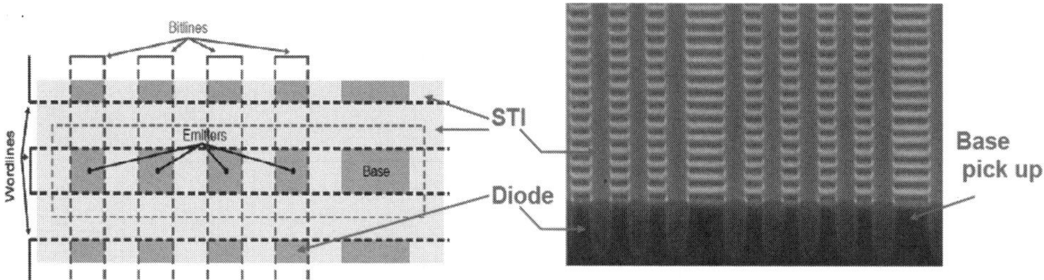

Figure 22. Schematic array layout and SEM cross section of a BJT array. Every four diodes need a pickup contact to reduce the word line resistance. Reprinted with permission from [14], G. Servalli, "International Electron Devices Meeting," 2009. © 2009, IEEE.

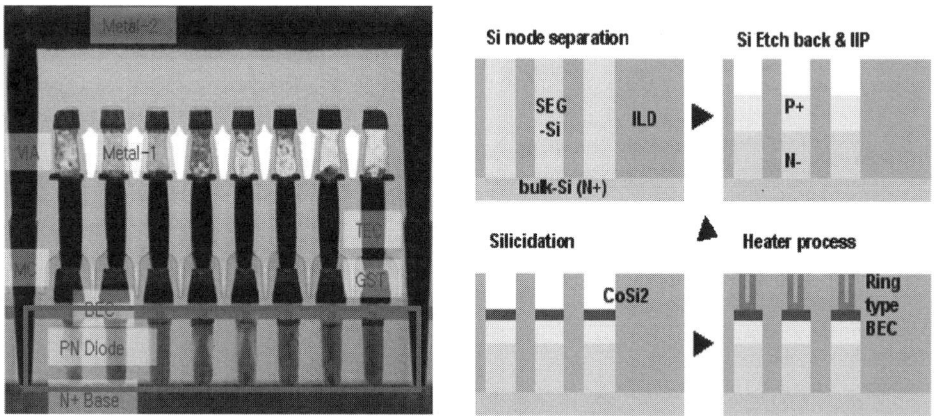

Figure 23. TEM picture and process flow of a selective epitaxial Si contact diode BJT array. Reprinted with permission from [15], J. H. Oh et al., "International Electron Devices Meeting," 2006. © 2006, IEEE.

doping levels suppress the void formation process, thus improving the cycling endurance of a PCM cell.

The bottom heater plays the most important role on reset current reduction and reliability improvement. Mushroom-type PCM cells are the most popular and robust cell structures (Fig. 27). The flat and clean bottom heater top surface provides a good substrate for physical vapor deposition (PVD) and phase change material deposition. The small sublitho-sized bottom heater reduces the reset current.

Figure 28 shows the evolution of a mushroom cell bottom heater. Figure 28(a) is a cylindrical solid bottom heater, while Figure 28(b) is a cylindrical out-ring bottom heater, and Figure 28(c) is a vertical thin film bottom heater. The trend of bottom heater improvement is to shrink the top surface area to reduce the reset current.

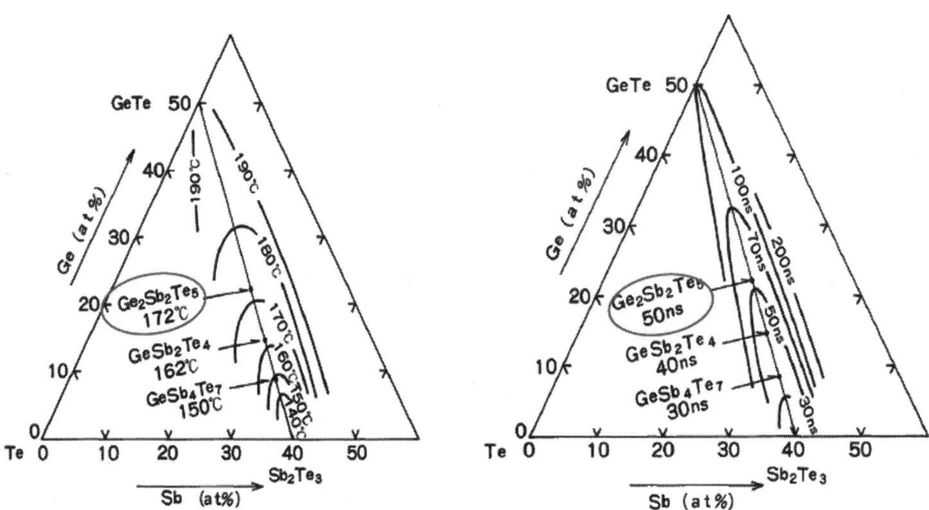

Figure 24. Crystallization temperature and crystallization speed of Ge–Sb–Te alloy. Reprinted with permission from [55], N. Yamada et al., *Jpn. J. Appl. Phys.* 26, 61 (1987). © 1987, JJAP.

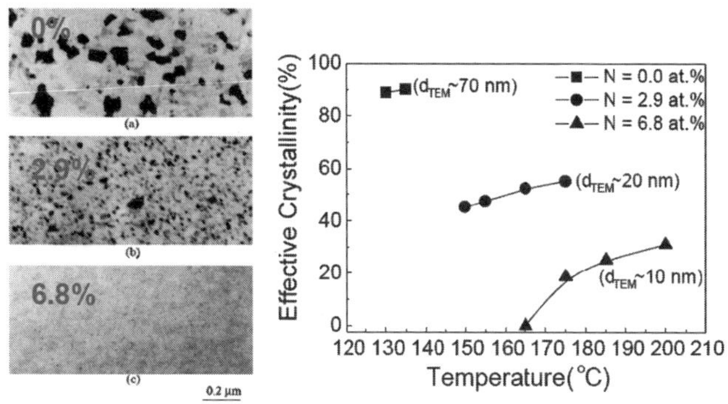

Figure 25. TEM pictures of undoped and different nitrogen doping GST. The doped GST has finer grain and lower postannealing effective crystalline ratio. Reprinted with permission from [59], H. Seo et al., *Jpn. J. Appl. Phys* 39, 745 (2000). © 2000, JJAP.

To reduce the reset current, the size of the bottom heater shrinks to about 30% of the lithographic minimum feature size. Controlling the size variation of the sublitho-sized bottom heater is the most important topic for mushroom cells. The bottom heater size shrinking process enlarges the critical-dimension (CD) variation of the lithographic process.

Figure 29 explains the variation of enlarging effect of a dielectric spacer CD shrinking process. If a 25-nm nitride space is used to shrink the via size to 50 nm, the 10-nm variation becomes a 20% (10 nm/50 nm) CD variation of a 50-nm via. The sublithographic CD of bottom heater has a 20% variation, while the original lithographic CD variation is only 10%. This explains why the shrinking process enlarges the CD variation. A ring-type bottom heater is a straightforward improving of the solid heater (Fig. 28(b)). Figure 30 explains the improvements of a ring-type bottom heater. The top surface area of a solid cylindrical bottom heater is πR^2 (where R is the radius of a bottom heater). The top area size of a ring-bottom heater is $2\pi t(R - t/2)$ (where t is the thickness of the ring-bottom electrode). The top surface area of ring heater is smaller than solid heater due to $t \sim 1/3R$. The CD variation of a solid heater is proportional to the R^2 while the CD variation of the ring heater is proportional to $R \times t$. Because $t < R$, the CD variation of the ring heater is smaller than the solid heater.

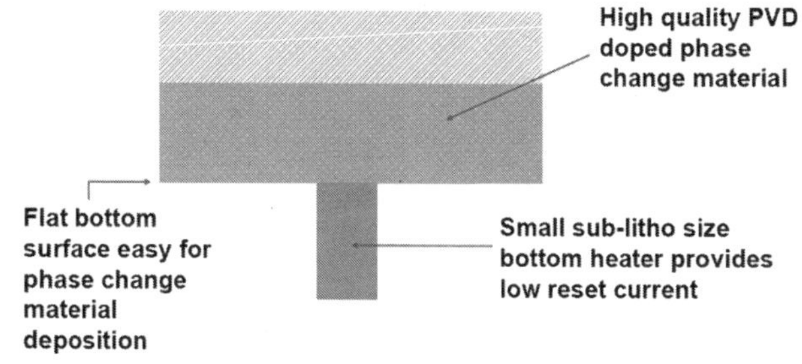

Figure 27. Mushroom-type phase change memory cell.

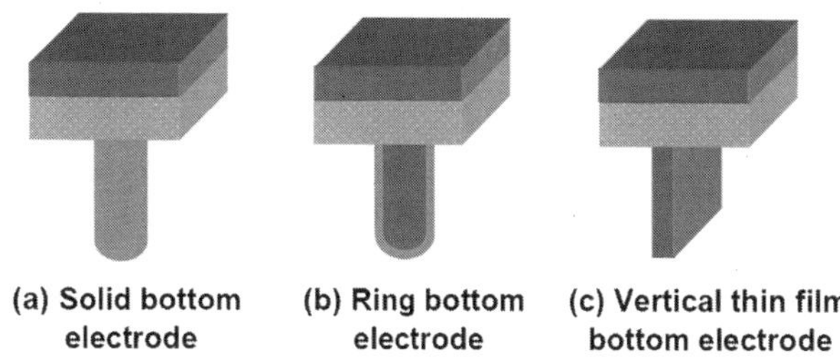

Figure 28. Three types of mushroom cell bottom heaters.

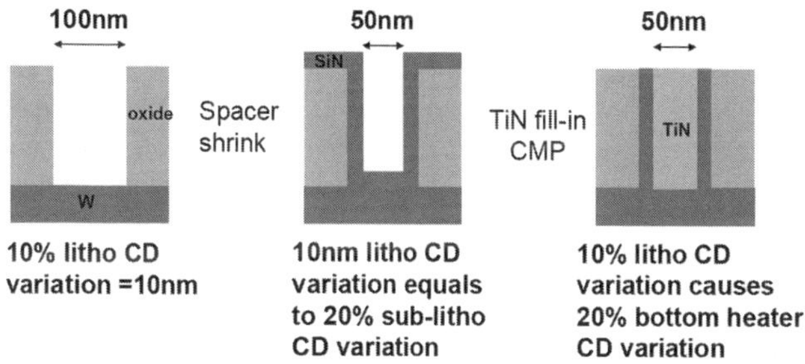

Figure 29. Sublithographic shrinking process enlarges the CD variation.

Another innovative solution to solve the bottom heater sublithographic CD variation issue is the "keyhole transfer" process (Fig. 31) [8]. First, via holes are open on a SiN_x/SiO_2 stacking substrate. The original via size has a CD variation. A wet etching process generates an undercut between the top nitride and oxide layer; the amount of the undercut is independent of the original via CD (Fig. 31(a)). After the undercut process, vias are filled with a conformal CVD polysilicon to generate a keyhole inside the vias. The keyhole

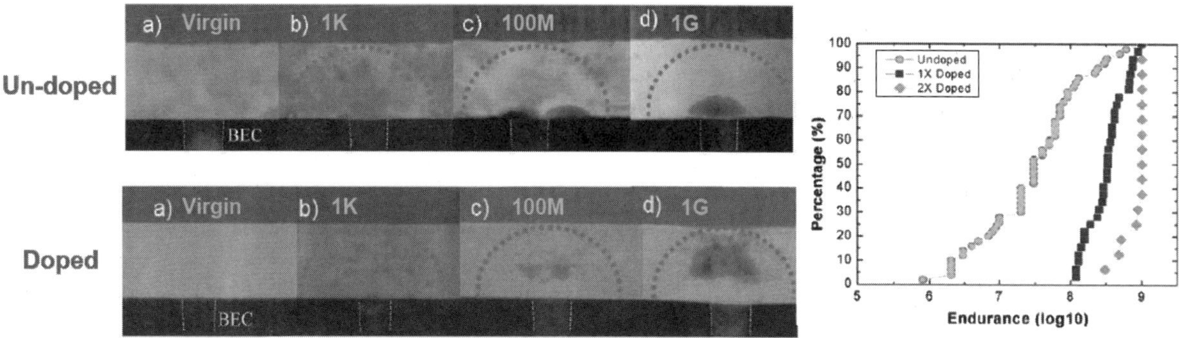

Figure 26. Cycling endurance comparison of doped and undoped $Ge_2Sb_2Te_5$. Reprinted with permission from [60], C.-F. Chen et al., "Macronix/IBM," 2009. © 2009, IEEE.

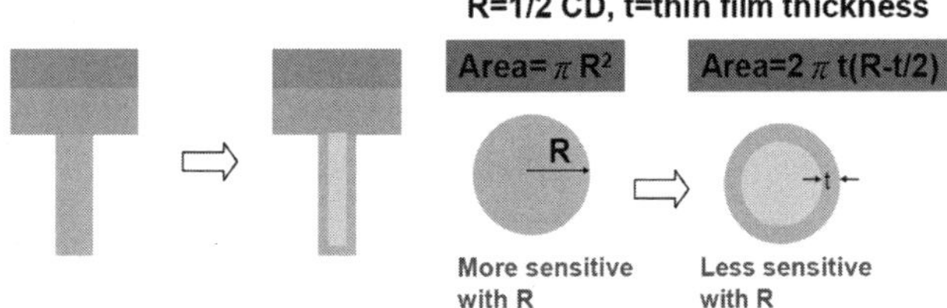

Figure 30. Comparison of solid and ring bottom heaters.

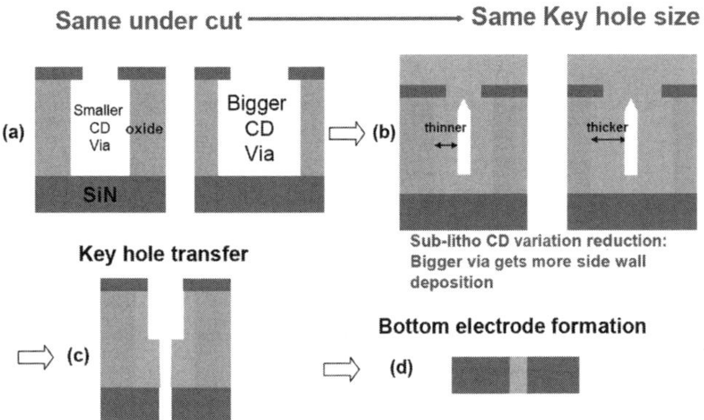

Figure 31. Process flow of a "key hole transfer" technology.

size is independent of the original via size due to bigger via getting thicker Si deposition on the sidewall and small vias getting less deposition on the sidewall (Fig. 31(b)). In the final outcome, the uniform size keyhole is used to pattern the bottom-heater hole (Fig. 31(c)). This method eliminates the CD variation of the lithographic, thus tightens the bottom heater CD variation. Figure 32 shows that two keyholes have same size, even though the original via size is different [8].

The keyhole transfer process also reduces the size of the bottom heater to reduce the reset current. The two methods mention above are related to generate a uniform sublitho-sized hole of a bottom heater. Some companies have proposed a line shape bottom heater to reduce the size and CD variation of the bottom heater. This method deposits a metallic thin film on a sidewall of a dielectric trench. The top cross-section area of the vertical thin film defines the

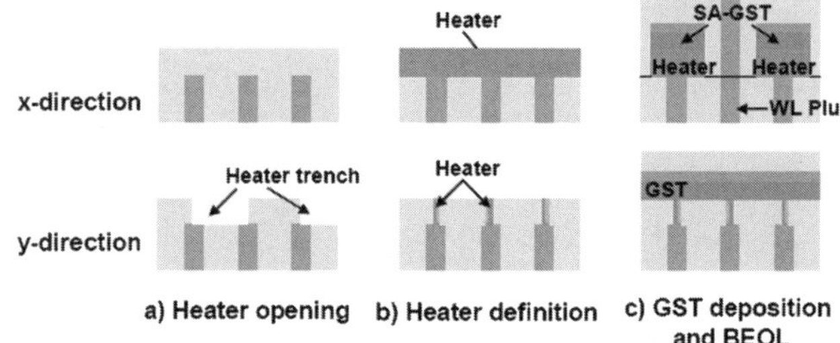

Figure 33. Process flow of a vertical sidewall thin film electrode PCM. Reprinted with permission from [14], G. Servalli, "International Electron Devices Meeting," 2009. © 2009, IEEE.

top surface of a bottom heater. The thickness of the thin film can be well controlled (< 1 nm) to provide a small and uniform bottom heater.

Figure 33 is an example of making a vertical thin film bottom heater [14]. The process flow is shown as following:

(a) trenches are formed above contact layer,
(b) a metallic thin film (usually TiN) deposits on the sidewall. Then, a spacer etching process removes the metallic thin film on the bottom of the trench; the trench is filled with a dielectric layer and plannerized by a chemical mechanical polish process to expose the top surface of the heater, and
(c) a phase change material is deposited on the heaters and patterned together with the bottom heater along the *y*-direction.

Figure 34 shows TEM images of different thicknesses, vertical thin film bottom heaters and the electrical impacts of different heaters dimension [61]. A thicker heater increases the rest current and decreases the set state resistance; nevertheless, thinner electrodes decrease the rest current and increase the set state resistance. Taller heater decreases the reset current and increase both the programming voltage and set state resistance; nevertheless, shorter electrode increases the reset current and decrease both the programming voltage and set state resistance.

Most of the high-density PCM chips use mushroom-type memory cells, because they provide a flat surface for PVD phase change material deposition. Only PVD phase change

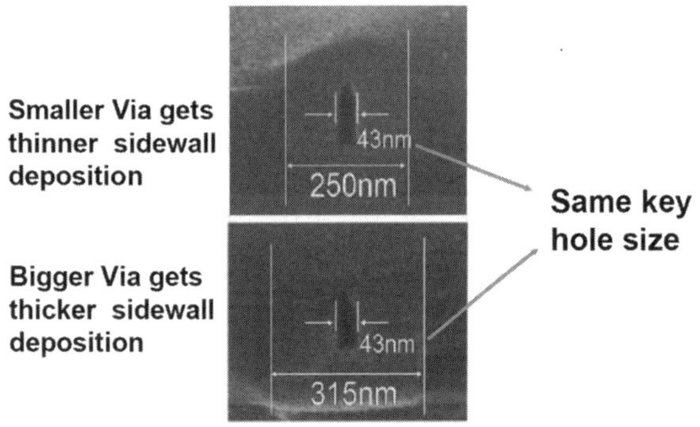

Figure 32. SEM pictures of two vias with the same size of keyhole. Reprinted with permission from [8], M. Breitwisch et al., "Symposium on VLSI Technology," 2007. © 2007, IEEE.

Parameter	Variation	I_{prog}	V_{prog}	R_{set}
Heater thickness	↑	↑	~	↓
	↓	↓	~	↑
Heater height	↑	↓	↑	↑
	↓	↑	↓	↓
GST thickness	↑	↓	↑	↑
	↓	↑	↓	↓

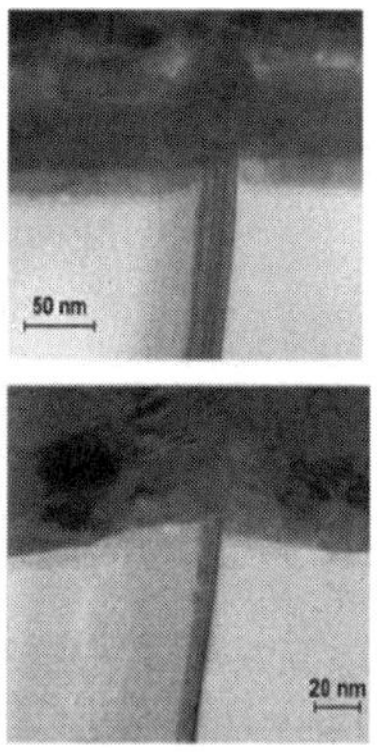

Figure 34. Dimension effects of a vertical thinfilm bottom heater. Reprinted with permission from [61], A. Pirovano et al., "STM," 2005. © 2005, IEEE.

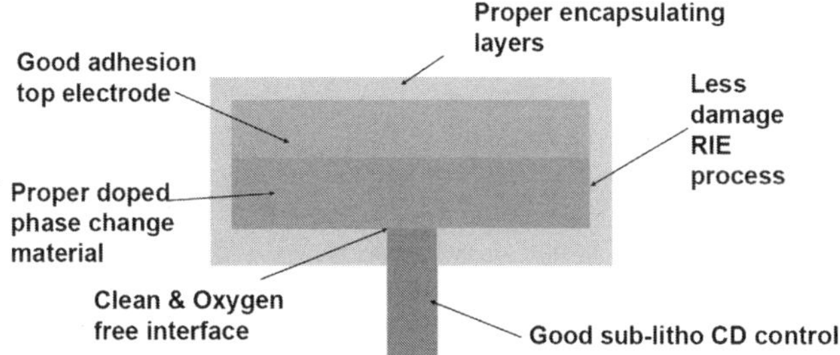

Figure 35. Important process integration concerns of a mushroom-type PCM cell.

materials gives good enough quality (e.g., reliability, yield) for PCM applications. In order to make a good and robust mushroom cell, some important process concerns should be addressed (Fig. 35).

To reduce the reset current and get good distribution, the size of the bottom heater needs to be kept small and uniform. The interface between the bottom electrode and the phase change material need to be kept clean and oxidation free to avoid the cell opening and maintain good reliability. Properly doped phase change material is necessary to get a good yield as well as reliability. Etching damage of phase change material should be avoided. A top electrode needs to have good adhesion with phase change material, and suitable encapsulation layers are required to protect the phase change material to ensure good yield and reliability.

3.5. Advanced PCM Cell Concepts

A lot of advanced cell concepts have been proposed to improve the properties of PCM. The most important topics are reducing the reset current (power) and increasing the memory density. A thermal confine structure is the most discussed structure to reduce the reset current. Figure 36(a) shows a reset current comparison of a mushroom cell and a confined cell [62]. The reset current of a confined cell is about 50% of a mushroom cell. Simulation results show that the heat dissipation of a confined cell is smaller then a mushroom cell. The confined cell has a better power efficiency (confined heat) to lower the reset current requirement. Figure 36(b) shows an example of a confined cell [63], which is made by recessing the vertical sidewall heater (compare to Fig. 28(c)) and filling it with atomic layer deposition (ALD) phase change material.

This confined cell partially or fully replaces the bottom heater with phase change material. During the reset operation, the hottest spot of the confined cell moves away from the bottom heater to decrease the heat dissipation. The chemical vapor deposition (CVD) or the ALD phase change material process is necessary to fill in a small hole/trench, but the poor quality of CVD/ALD phase change material degrades the yield and reliability of memory cell. Exactly how to improve the fill-in phase change material quality is a big challenge for confined cells.

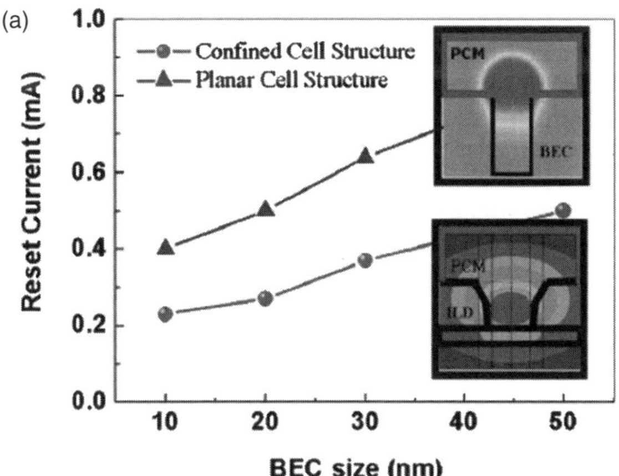

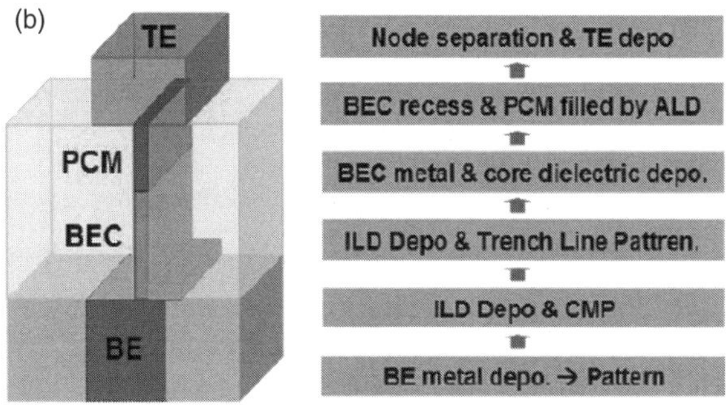

Figure 36. (a) Comparison of reset current between confined and mushroom cell structure. Reprinted with permission from [62], D. H. Im et al., "Samsung IEDM," 2008. © 2008, IEEE; and (b) a recessed vertical sidewall heater confined cell. Reprinted with permission from [63], I. S. Kim et al., "Samsung, VLSIT," p. 203, 2010. © 2010, IEEE.

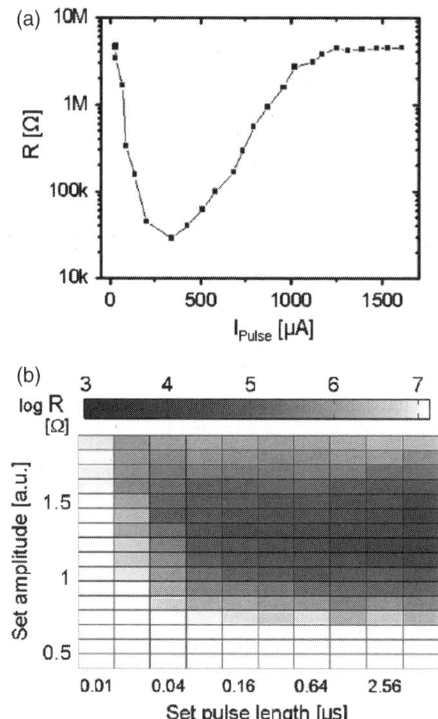

Figure 37. (a) Resistance versus current pulse amplitude of a PCM cell, and (b) memory cell resistance versus pulse duration and amplitude (temperature). Reprinted with permission from [64], T. Nirschl et al., "IBM/Macronix/Qimonda IEDM," p. 461, 2007. © 2007, IEEE.

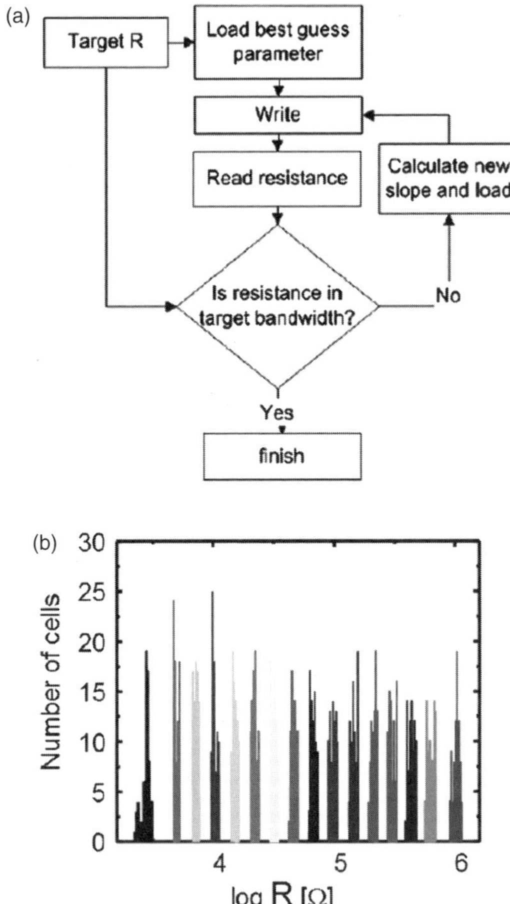

Figure 38. (a) A MLC PCM programming algorithm, and (b) 10 × 10 array test structure programmed into 16 levels to achieve 4bit/cell operation. Reprinted with permission from [64], T. Nirschl et al., "IBM/Macronix/Qimonda IEDM," p. 461, 2007. © 2007, IEEE.

An important method to increase the PCM density is the multiple level cell (MLC) operation. The wide resistance range between the set and reset states of PCE gives enough room for the PCM's MLC operation. How the MLC operation works on PCM operation is shown in Figure 37 [64]. A gradual resistance transition between high and low resistive states (Fig. 37(a)) permits multilevel cells. Different resistance states can be programmed by varying either amplitude or time, or preferably a combination of both (Fig. 37(b)).

Figure 38(a) shows an algorithm of programming MLC PCM cells [64]. For each programming iteration, the applied pulse slope is calculated from the last applied slope and the measured resistance that resulted from the previous iteration. A cell is programmed several times until the designated resistance state is matched. A 10 × 10 PCM array was programmed into 16 levels to represent 4 bit/cell by using the algorithm shown in Figure 38(b). Adjustment of pulse slopes depending on resistance is essential to achieve narrow distributions. One of the challenges of PCM MLC operation is the instability of resistance. The resistance drifts up after programming, and the partial reset state has poor data retention.

Three-dimensional (3D) stackable PCM is an important advanced PCM cell concept that increases memory density. For a conventional PCM cell, the access device is either a Si substrate transistor or a diode, while the 3D stackable approach uses the BEOL access device to replace front end of line access device. Those access devices are made after metal layers formation, such that it is stackable above other memory layers. The 3D multiple stacking layers array is the ultimate solution of making high density PCM. Figure 37 shows an example of a stackable PCM array [65].

This access device is an ovonic threshold switch (OTS) layer (Fig. 39(a)). The OTS has its own threshold voltage; current goes through it when the bias is larger than its threshold voltage. During read operation, the bias is larger than the OTS's threshold voltage but smaller than the set threshold voltage (amorphous layer breakdown voltage) of the PCE. During the write operation, the bias is higher than both threshold voltages of the OTS and the PCE. The threshold voltage differences between the OTS and the PCE is shown in Figure 39(b). Threshold voltage of the memory cell is the sum of the OTS's and the PCE's threshold voltage. The OTS stays at a high resistance state while the bias is smaller than its threshold voltage. Nonaccessing memory cells are isolated from each other by the high resistance state of OTS. Figure 39(c) shows a real memory array SEM picture. The OTS and PCEs are above metals layers, so this approach is capable with 3D stacking. However, there are challenges to the 3D stackable approach, such as read disturbance and reliability of the OTS device.

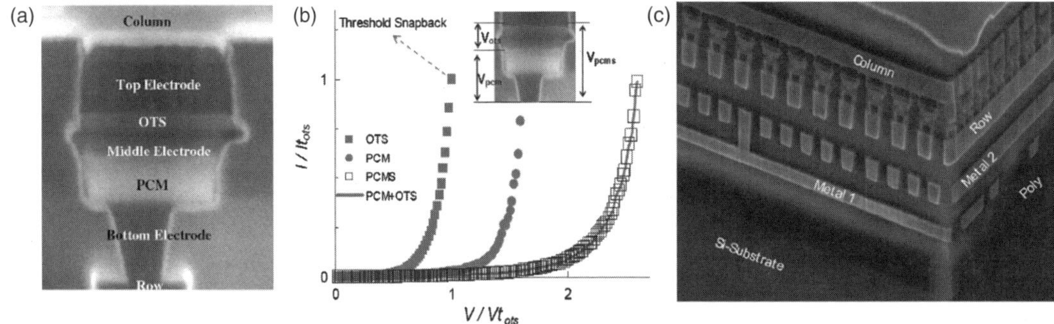

Figure 39. A stackable phase change memory: (a) SEM picture of a unit cell (b) threshold voltages of OTS and phase change element, and (c) SEM picture of a memory array. Reprinted with permission from [65], D. C. Kau et al., "Intel, IEDM," p. 27.1.1, 2009. © 2009, IEEE.

4. PHASE CHANGE MATERIAL FABRICATION

4.1. Introduction of PCM Fabrication

The research and development of phase change material is based on the material that can be fabricated. Phase change material has been discovered and fabricated by a variety of methods. From the earliest discover of phase change material using the metallurgy method to the sputter deposition of GeSbTe on optical storage devices, and, up until recently, the CVD of phase change material has been the focus for phase change memory fabrication. Other novel deposition methods, such as electrodeposition, or solution-phase deposition offer potential advantages in the fabrication of PCM cells or optical discs, yet each method brings its own challenges. In this section, we will review the basics of each strategy, emphasizing the advantages and the difficulties of applying them to phase change materials. To further understand the scaling of phase change material, nanowires and nanoparticles have been synthesized, and these fabrication methods will be reviewed at the end.

4.2. Metallurgy and PVD

One of the earliest types of phase change material was described by Northover and Pearson from Bell Telephone Laboratories in 1961 [66, 67]. They demonstrated that As–Te–I alloys and devices made with these alloys showed two stable resistance states and could be switched between high and low resistance states. The material was made from high purity metallic arsenic and tellurium and resublimed crystalline iodine by heating and cooling the materials in a sealed vial at 600°C for a number of hours. The composition of the final product was controlled by the weight of starting material, and sealed vials avoided a loss of iodine by volatilization.

Most of the resent phase change material deposition is done by PVD or, more specifically, by sputter deposition for both the optical storage and PCM [68, 69]. In a typical sputter process, inert gas ions (Ar^+) are generated by an unusually electric and magnetic field; then, the incident ion collides with target atoms result in one or more atoms, which are ejected or sputtered from the surface of the target [70]. Phase change materials can be deposited by sputtering a single alloy target with the desired composition or by co-sputtering a number of pure elemental targets. Co-sputtering provides more flexible composition control of the product, which is usually a choice for exploring new composition of phase change materials. However, since each target in the co-sputter system is relatively small, film uniformity across the surface is hard to control. So, in the manufacturing process, sputtering a single alloy target is preferred. Additional doping, such as nitrogen, of the phase change material can be achieved by reactive-sputtering.

4.3. CVD

Although PVD of phase change material has been widely used in the optical storage media and in PCM fabrication for blanket film deposition, there are challenges to patterning the blanket film by reactive ion etch (RIE) for the scaling of PCM [71]. To avoid etch damage and to improve the reset current of PCM, pattern phase change material through a Damascene-like process is desired, where filling a small via with phase change material is needed. However, conformality of PVD films is poor and cannot fill in a small via with a high aspect ratio. Therefore, CVD of phase change materials is mainly of interest for its conformal deposition profile and its potential application in PCM.

CVD can be defined as the deposition of a solid on a heated surface from a chemical reaction in the vapor phase. Generally, the precursors and co-reactant vapors are introduced into a deposition chamber under a vacuum, where the substrate can be heated to elevated temperatures. The chemical reaction takes place on the heated surface or in vapor phase above the substrate surface. The advantage of CVD over PVD is its conformal deposition profile, i.e., the film thickness in the field is the same or as close to the thickness on the sidewall in a trench or via structure. CVD can be used to fill deep recesses, holes, and other difficult 3D configurations, but its major disadvantage is the need for a relatively high deposition temperature. In addition, extensive engineering controls can be required due to the high toxicity and volatility of CVD precursors. Most thermal CVD processes are achieved at temperatures of 600°C and above, and many substrate materials are not thermally stable at these temperatures. The deposition temperature can be reduced to below 400°C by introducing plasma in the chamber to enhance the reaction or by using metal-organic precursors (MOCVD), which have lower reaction temperatures than their inorganic counterparts. Currently, CVD has been implemented in many deposition processes for integrated circuit (IC) manufacturing. For instance, the deposition of poly-silicon, silicon dioxide, silicon nitride, metal nitrides, and tungsten are accomplished by CVD processes. The trade off is that CVD is generally a much more complex process than PVD, with more opportunities for the introduction of contaminates that are both beneficial and detrimental [72, 73].

CVD of GST can be achieved using metal-organic precursors. The germanium precursors that have been evaluated for CVD of GST include tetra(allyl)germanium ($Ge(C_3H_5)_4$) [74, 75], tetra(isobutyl)germanium ($Ge(i\text{-}C_4H_9)_4$) [76, 77], isobutylgermane (H3-Ge-(i-C_4H_9) [78], and tetra(dimethylamino)-germanium ($Ge(N(CH_3)_2)_4$ [79–82]. The antimony precursors for CVD of GST include tri(isopropyl)antimony ($Sb(C_3H_7)_3$) [74–78] and tri(dimethylamino)antimony ($Sb(N(CH_3)_2)_3$) [79–82]. Two of the more commonly used tellurium precursors for CVD of GST is di(isopropyl)tellurium ($Te(C_3H_7)_2$) [74, 76–81] and di(tert-butyl)telluride ($Te(C_4H_9)_2$) [75, 82]. The precursors for Ge, Sb, and Te usually share a similar length of the hydrocarbon group, which is desired so all three elements can react or decompose at the same deposition. Some of these precursors have been previously studied for MOCVD for compound semiconductor materials. Generally, the metal organic precursors are less toxic and decompose at lower temperatures in comparison with their hydride or halide counterparts, i.e., the inorganic precursors. This allows the CVD of GST to take place below 400°C. Because of insufficient vapor pressure, carrier gas is used to assist the delivery of the precursor vapor into the deposition chamber. Some metal-organic precursors need be delivered through a vaporizer. The direct liquid source delivery or injection system can allow a wider range of chemicals than the precursors mentioned above for CVD of phase change materials.

The composition of GST films can be altered by the process parameters. For instance, the germanium incorporation into GST films by MOCVD is controlled by the precursor bubbling temperature, the carrier gas flow rate, the deposition temperature, and the pressure. Generally, when the deposition is dominated by surface reactions, film composition is sensitive to the deposition temperature and pressure. When the deposition is dominated by mass transport, film composition is sensitive to the ratio of precursor vapor partial pressures. Different carrier gas flow rates or different precursors bubbling temperatures can be used to adjust the ratio of precursor partial pressures and can, therefore, adjust the GST film composition. When using a liquid precursor injection system, film composition can be altered by changing the opening time and frequency of the injectors as well as the sequence of pulses of different precursors. This is demonstrated as an example in Figure 40, which shows the XRD data on films deposited at the injection condition [80].

In general, all of the deposition parameters mentioned above need to be tuned and simultaneously optimized to achieve GST films with the desired stoichiometry [74]. The choice of precursors is also critical to control the film stoichiometry. For instance, GST films can be deposited using Ge(allyl)$_4$, Sb(iPr)$_3$ and Te(iPr)$_2$ under an optimized deposition condition. When switching the Ge precursor to Ge(iBu)$_4$ and using the same Sb and Te precursors, the Ge amount in the GST film is only 0.4%, despite the 63% partial pressure of Ge precursor during the deposition [77].

It was also noticed that depositions of Ge, Sb, and Te are sensitive to the substrate surface. For instance, Ge can be deposited on TiN surfaces, but nucleation was difficult on

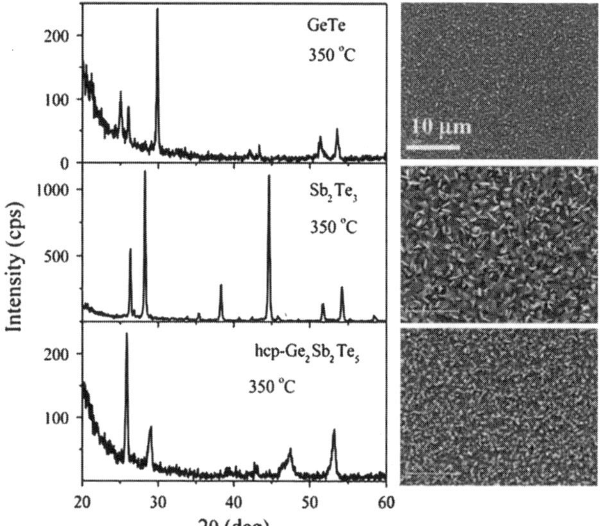

Figure 40. XRD patterns (left) and corresponding SEM images (right) of GeTe, Sb_2Te_3 and $Ge_2Sb_2Te_5$ films grown under the same condition by changing the precursor injection pattern. Reprinted with permission from [80], A. Abrutis et al., *Chem. Mater.* 20, 3557 (2008). © 2008, ACS.

SiO_2 surfaces when using certain precursors. For this reason, the sequence of the precursor pulses must also be optimized for stoichiometric composition [76, 79]. CVD of GST always shows large grains with a rough surface, which could be problematic for filling in small vias. By separating the precursor flow scheme, the ALD or pulsed CVD techniques can interfere with the large grain growth, thus minimizing grain size and surface roughness.

It is known that the resistivity and crystallization behavior of GST can be modified by doping it with nitrogen [83], oxygen [84] or other dielectric materials. For PVD GST films, doping material can be mixed into the sputtering target, co-sputtered from a different target, or introduced by flowing nitrogen or oxygen gas during sputtering. Similarly, doping can be achieved in CVD of GST films. Separate precursors for different dopants can be added during deposition, or dopants can be introduced by flowing nitrogen, ammonia, or oxygen during deposition. Doping can also be done by engineering the precursor. For instance, by attaching amide groups in the precursor, nitrogen can be incorporated in the resulting film. By using tri(hexamethyldisilylamino)-antimony for CVD of GST, Si-doped amorphous GST can be achieved [79].

ALD is an ultimate way to control the phase change material composition and fill in small dimensions with high aspect ratio via. ALD is a chemical gas phase thin film deposition method based on alternate saturated surface reactions [85]. Typically during deposition the precursors and recant gases are separated by inert gas that purges the reactor. Precursors chemisorbed on the surface will not be removed during the purge step. Then, the reactant gas will be introduced into the reactor and react with the monolayer of precursor on the surface. Ideally, monolayers of different elements can be deposited. By altering the number of layers deposited, as well as the sequence, the composition can be well controlled. CVD of GST in an ALD fashion has been reported (Ref. [79]). In this study, single component films of Ge, Sb, and Te were deposited Then by adjusting the number of pulses for each element, $Ge_{23}Sb_{21}Te_{55}$ could be achieved.

Recently, the true atomic layer deposition of $Ge_2Sb_2Te_5$ thin film has been demonstrated [86, 87]. A breakthrough in the development of new ALD precursors contributed to the success of ALD GST. Silyl compounds with a general formula (R3Si)2M (M = Te, Se) has:

(1) sufficient volatility to generate enough vapor pressure that can be delivered to the substrate,
(2) stability that will not thermally decompose on the substrate, and
(3) high reactivity to react with the co-reactant to leave the desired atom on the surface.

Sb_2Te_3, GeTe and GST films were deposited by ALD from $(Et_3\text{–}Si)_2$ Te, $SbCl_3$ and $GeCl_2 \cdot C_4H_8O_2$ at a remarkably low temperature of 90°C. This is well below the crystallization temperature of the film, and this allows the deposition of amorphous film. To verify the true ALD growth behavior, all three precursors show the typical saturative growth (Fig. 41). As is characteristic to ALD, the films showed excellent conformality in a high aspect ratio trench structure (Fig. 42).

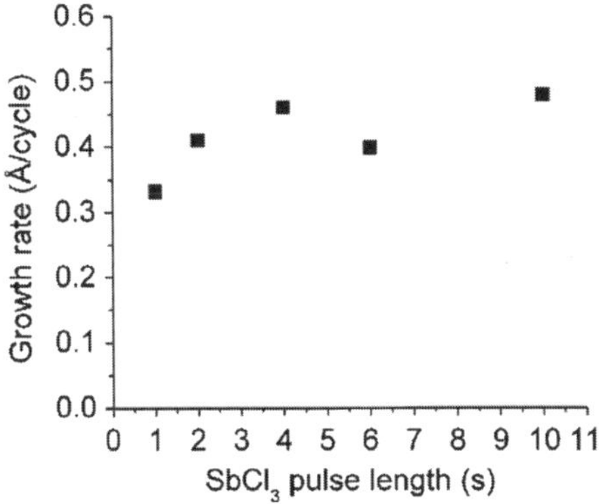

Figure 41. The growth rate does not increase with increasing the Sb precursor pulse length suggesting the true ALD growth. Reprinted with permission from [86], M Ritala et al., *Micro. Eng.* 86, 1946 (2009). © 2009, Elsevier.

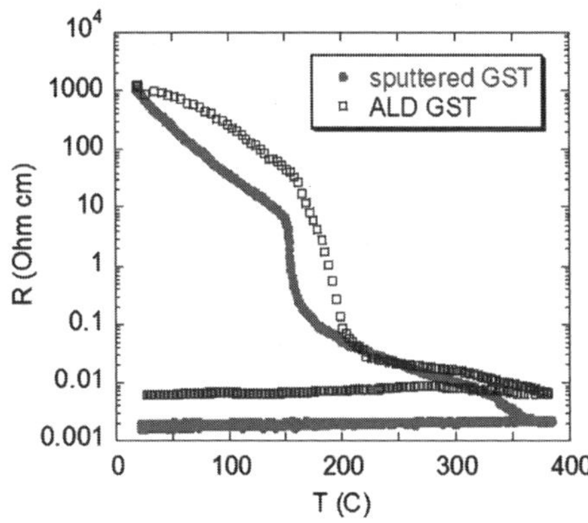

Figure 43. Resistivity versus temperature for GST film made by ALD (hollow) and sputtering (solid). Reprinted with permission from [86], M. Ritala et al., *Micro. Eng.* 86, 1946 (2009). © 2009, Elsevier.

The crystallization behavior of the ALD GST film is determined by high-temperature XRD measurement, resistivity versus temperature (*R*–*T*) measurement (Fig. 43) and laser pulse measurement [86]. The *R*–*T* measurement shows five orders of magnitude upon crystallization. Although ALD film has a relative higher crystallization temperature compared with its sputtered reference film, it could doe to the impurities or the off stoichiometric composition.

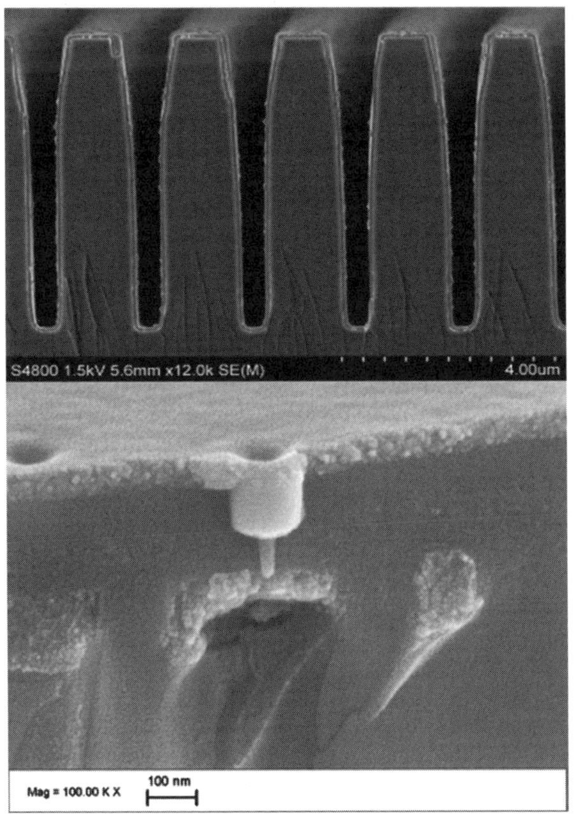

Figure 42. GST film deposited in a deeptrench structure shows excellent step coverage and complete fill in a PCM pore structure. Reprinted with permission from [87], M Ritala et al., "Spring Meeting, Material Research Society," 2010. © 2010, Mater. Res. Soc.

GST is the most popular material for PCRAM, and CVD is compatible with semiconductor process technologies. The combination of PCRAM and CVD is critical for developing high density PCRAM in terms of scaling down the GST volume. A research group from Samsung Electronics [88] demonstrated the first highly scalable phase change memory with CVD GST for sub-50-nm lithography generation. A CVD film with an approximate composition of GST was deposited using metal organic precursors and H_2 at 350°C. Figure 44 shows a TEM image of these GST devices fabricated by CVD with a 50-nm contact diameter to the bottom electrode. One can see the excellent via filling capabilities of CVD that enable the cell design with a confined geometry for the phase change material. The figure also demonstrates the very good control over the materials composition as measured by energy-dispersive X-ray (EDX) spectroscopy.

This cell geometry offers a better confinement of the phase change material compared with a typical mushroom cell and leads to a better thermal isolation of the material and thus to a reduction of the RESET current (about 50% in Ref. [88]). Good data retention (no data loss after 48 hours

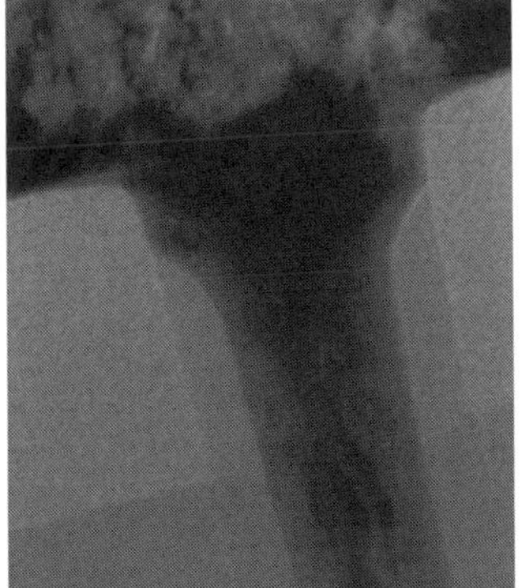

Position	Ge	Sb	Te
T	22.6	22.0	55.3
C	23.5	21.2	55.1
B	24.4	20.0	55.5

Figure 44. TEM image of $Ge_2Sb_2Te_5$ CVD PCRAM device (left) and composition of GST material at different locations within the via determined by EDX in atomic percentage (right). Reprinted with permission from [88], J. I. Lee et al., *VLSI Tech. Dig.* 102, 102 (2007). © 2007, IEEE.

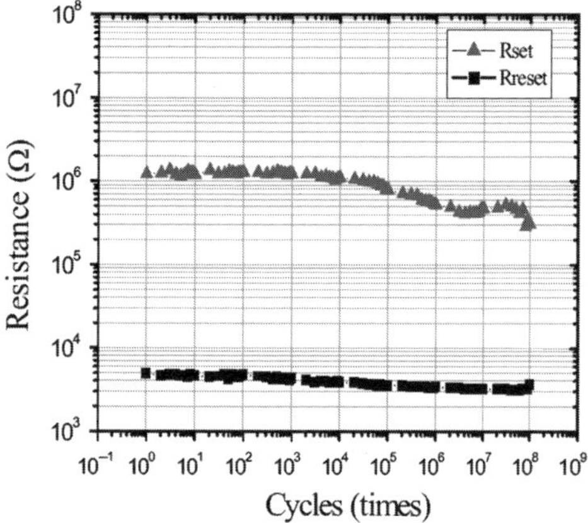

Figure 45. Endurance characteristic of confined cell structure, showing that the memory cell can be operated up to 10^8, cycles and still maintain a good margin between set and reset states. Reprinted with permission from [88], J. I. Lee et al., *VLSI Tech. Dig.* 102, 102 (2007). © 2007, IEEE.

at 140°C) and cyclability (up to 10^8 cycles) was demonstrated (Fig. 45).

To make the implementation of CVD GST successful, various challenges need to be addressed. For instance, the crystallization of the GST during deposition may hinder via fill-in, so minimizing the grain size or depositing amorphous films is desired. Phase change material is sensitive to temperature, so a narrow temperature window for process conditions can be expected. A dependency of the nucleation probability of GST on different surfaces has been observed in a memory cell, so obtaining the same growth rate of GST on dielectric and bottom electrode material may be important. In some cases, the selectivity of GST deposition on bottom electrode material can result in a bottom up fill of GST; however, the yield of complete fill over large memory array could be challenging. Device integration may require surface cleaning, such as wet clean, sputter clean, or plasma treatment, so the difference of the nucleation on different surfaces may be minimized or enhanced by these surface treatments. Precisely controlling the composition within the vias and across the wafer surface is also critical. CVD of phase change material is a relatively new subject when compared with the history of phase change material research, and it will require an extensive understanding of these processes as well as the properties of deposited film in order to implement this technique into devices in the future.

4.4. Solution-Based Depositions

Unlike PVD or CVD that take place in a vacuum, solution-based deposition techniques deposit films into solvents, e.g., it doesn't require an expensive vacuum system and therefore, results in a cheaper cost of ownership compared to PVD or CVD. There are two major approaches for solution-based deposition, electroplating and solution-phase deposition.

Electrodeposition (electrochemical deposition or electroplating) refers to a method where the deposition occurs through an electrochemical reaction in a solution; in most cases, this is a reduction reaction of the dissolved precursor species (ion) in a liquid solution. An electric power source is generally used to provide the electrons and is the driving force for the reaction. Like PVD and CVD, electrodeposition has also been used for I-C interconnect manufacturing [89]. During a typical electrodeposition process, a cationic species in the solution is reduced to its elemental states by externally supplied electrons, forming a thin film or a bulk material on the substrate, i.e., the cathode. The reaction can be written as $M^{n+} + ne^- \rightarrow M$, where e is a free electron, and M^{n+} and M stand for the electrochemical pair in the cationic and elemental form, respectively. The detailed principles for electrodeposition can be found in Refs. [90–92].

Electrochemical deposition of tellurium compounds and other chalcogenides has been studies intensively, e.g., the deposition of CdTe [93–96], Bi_2Te_3 and $Bi_{0.5}Sb_{1.5}Te_3$ [97–103]. The objective of these films has been focused on optoelectronic and thermoelectric applications [104, 105]. Given the superior capabilities of filling small vias, the electrodeposition of PCM has been investigated [106, 107].

Electrodeposition of SbTe phase change material at room temperature has been demonstrated [106]. The linear sweep voltammetry (LSV) of elemental and alloy deposition is shown in Figure 46, where the current density across the cathode and anode is measured as the applied potential. The electrodeposition of Sb in the presence of Te starts at a lower potential than the deposition by itself. However, the Sb deposition rate was found to be independent of the Te concentration in the solution. A mechanism involving a proton-incorporated intermediate was proposed to explain this so-called induced deposition of Sb. While polycrystalline SbTe was electrodeposited at near boiling temperature [107], electrodeposition at room temperature resulted in amorphous states. The amorphous SbTe films show phase transition to crystalline by time resolved XRD (Fig. 47). Plotted is the intensity of diffracted X-rays over a 2θ-range of 15° as a function of temperature, while the sample was heated in a purified He atmosphere at a rate of 1 K/s. The X-ray energy was 6.9 keV. A transition from the amorphous state to crystalline Sb_2Te_3 was observed at about 120°C for SbTe alloys

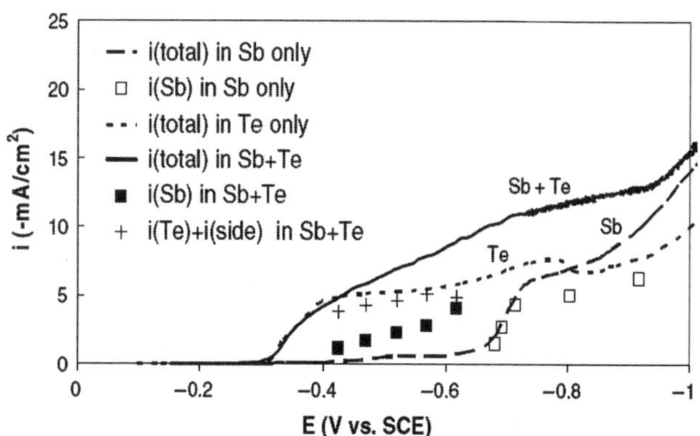

Figure 46. LSV in Sb, Te, and SbTe alloy deposition where a shift of Sb deposition was observed in alloy deposition (solid squares vs. open squares). Reprinted with permission from [106], Q. Huang et al., *J. Electrochem. Soc.* 155, 104 (2008). © 2008, Electrochem. Soc.

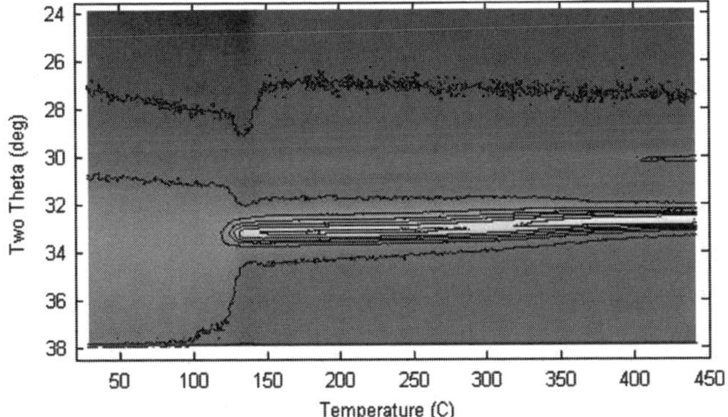

Figure 47. Time resolved X-ray diffraction pattern of the electrodeposited SbTe alloy with temperature ramping, showing crystallization at 120°C. Reprinted with permission from [106], Q. Huang et al., *J. Electrochem. Soc.* 155, 104 (2008). © 2008, Electrochem. Soc.

with 37% to 57% Sb. Additional elements can be incorporated in the SbTe film by electrodeposition to improve the transition temperature [39, 108]; however, the electrodeposited AgSbTe and InSbTe share similar transition temperatures as SbTe.

Electrodeposition of amorphous Ge films was achieved on Si from a nonaqueous solution. A recrystallization into a single crystal was observed upon annealing at 400°C [109]. Despite the fact that Ge deposition has never been achieved from an aqueous solution due to a very high reduction rate of water on Ge surfaces [110], GeSbTe alloys with up to 10% Ge have been electrodeposited from an aqueous solution [111]. However, the compositional uniformity, the incorporation of other elements such as oxygen from the solution, and the phase change properties of the films still remain unknown.

Due to the nature of electrochemical deposition, it requires an electrically conductive surface to carry the electrons for the electrochemical reaction. The seed layer usually causes complications when characterizing the deposited phase change material by providing additional electrons and heat conduction paths. The continuous seed layer across the wafer surface can be addressed by extra steps to remove the seed layer or by isolating individual memory elements in the fabrication flow for PCM. Another challenge for electrodepositing phase change materials is to dope the phase change materials with nonmetallic elements, e.g., N.

High aspect-ratio nanowires of different Te compounds have been demonstrated when deposited through a mask [112–116]. Figure 48 shows SbTe via structures electrodeposited in a patterned SiO_2 layer with an aspect ratio of 8 [117]. The Auger electron spectroscopy analysis shows a uniform $SbTe_2$ composition along the length of a via. This kind of structure is preferred in PCM because it helps reduce the operation current. In addition to the superior filling character, electrodeposition offers another advantage because it uses the electrochemical-ALD method.

Another solution-based deposition technique is solution-phase deposition. This is accomplished by coating the substrate using spin coating, dip coating, spraying, printing, etc. Based on their technological simplicity, such methods offer excellent conformal coating of the substrate features as long as the solution wets the substrate material. In the semiconductor industry, solution-phase deposition has been used to deposit photoresist and some low-k dielectric materials. Solution deposition is most easily accomplished when the material to be deposited is itself soluble so the film is formed directly upon drying. However, inorganic materials such as phase change materials tend not to be directly soluble at concentrations sufficient enough for coating. Even so, some metal chalcogenides are soluble in amine-containing solvents, so this direct approach has been used to coat films of amorphous $As_2S_{3-x}Se_x$, $GeS_{2-x}Se_x$, $GeSe_{2-x}Te_x$, and even As_2Te_3 [118–122].

Generally speaking, a soluble precursor is coated and then thermally decomposed to form the metal chalcogenide film for thin film. For thicker film, thermally decomposition at last can cause the trap of deposition byproducts inside the film. This can be avoided by heating the substrate during the coating, which allows the byproducts to be continuously released [123, 124].

The development of a new class of soluble precursors allows the deposition of metal chalcogenide thin films [125–127]. The precursors consist of salts or neutral complexes of metal chalcogenide clusters with the reducing inorganic solvent, hydrazine. The application of these films deposited

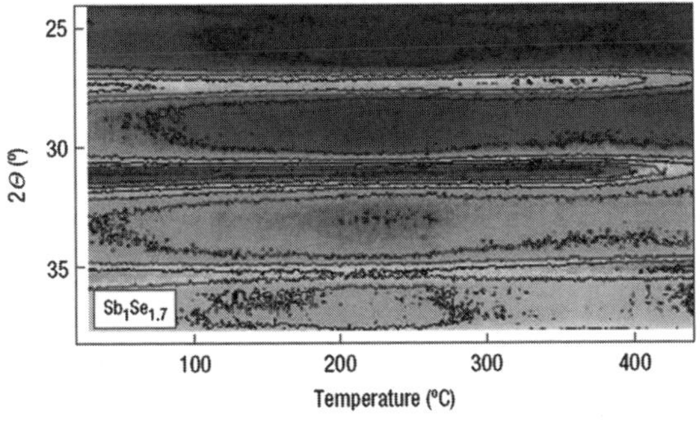

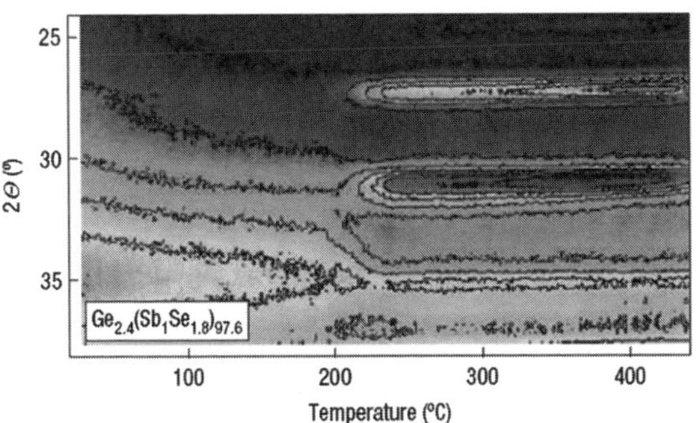

Figure 48. Intensity of diffracted X-ray peaks as a function of temperature for spin-on $Sb_1Se_{1.7}$ (top) and $Ge_{2.4}(Sb_1Se_{1.8})_{97.6}$ (bottom) films. It is apparent that the addition of Ge has a great influence on the crystallization temperature. Although Ge-free films are crystalline after deposition (which includes a bake at 160°C to remove the solvent). Ge-containing films crystallize at temperatures between 200–250°C depending on the composition. The film composition can be fine tuned by adjusting the ratio of the precursors, and good control over the crystallization temperature can be achieved. Reprinted with permission from [129], D. J Milliron et al., *Nature Mater.* 6, 357 (2007). © 2007, NPG.

for thin film transistors has been demonstrated. Recently, KSb_5S_8 [128] and Ge-doped Sb_2Se_3 [129] were synthesized for PCM applications. Since the precursor decomposed at a temperature below the crystallization temperature of $GeSb_2Se_3$, the deposited film is amorphous. The properties of these novel materials are then characterized using XRD when ramping up the sample temperature. Figure 48 shows the crystallization behavior of Ge-doped Sb_2Se_3 film by mixing a Ge–Se and a Sb–Se precursor in a solution, then spin coating and thermally annealing it, then the crystallization temperature could be tuned by adjusting the Ge content so that the films remain amorphous after annealing to decompose the precursors. XRD shows that the crystallization temperature was tuned into the range of 200–250°C by adjusting the Ge content between 2% and 6% (Fig. 48). The Ge Sb_2Se_3 film can also be switched between amorphous and crystalline phases by laser pulse. A melt-quenched spot in a crystalline matrix could be recrystallized in a matter of 100 ns. All of these properties of solution-phase deposited films are similar to the sputtered material, revealing the potential of a solution deposition to yield viable phase change materials.

(a)

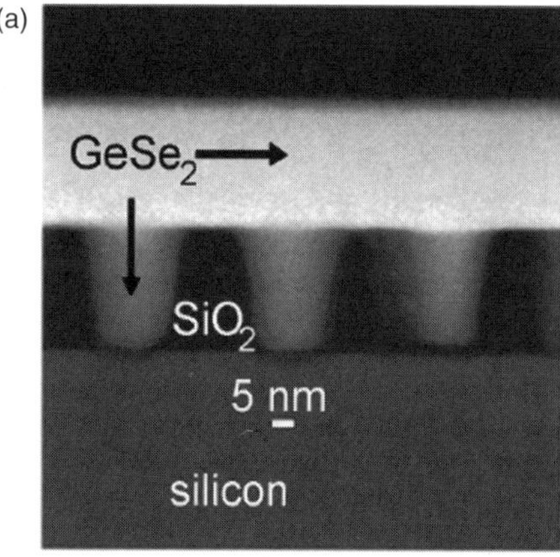

(b)

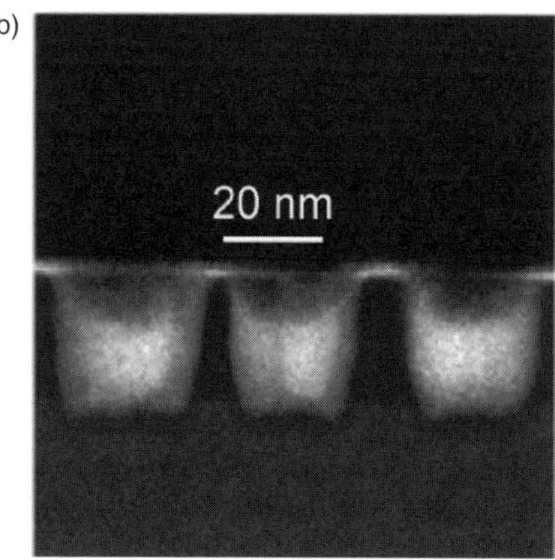

Figure 49. A spin coating process was used to demonstrate filling of nanoscale vias with the metal chalcogenide material $GeSe_2$. By controlling the viscosity and drying time, (a) the vias may be filled completely and the surface planarized, or (b) partially filled from the bottom up. Reprinted with permission from [130], D. J. Milliron et al., *Nano Lett.* 7, 3504 (2007). © 2007, ACS.

The solution phase deposition has the potential advantage of filling small and high aspect ratio structures. It was recently demonstrated that vias approximately 20 nm in diameter could be filled with metal chalcogenide materials using the coating methods described above [130]. When the surface of the material is hydrophilic, it is easily wet by the solution, and capillary forces drive the precursor to fill recessed vias and trenches. By controlling the solution viscosity (i.e., through concentration) and the drying rate (i.e., through the spin coating rate), bottom up filling of vias occurs. Furthermore, these parameters can be adjusted to selectively fill the vias only partially or to planarize the surface above completely filled vias (Fig. 49) Such control is clearly advantageous for the integration of metal chalcogenide materials into PCM devices.

4.5. Nanometer Scale Phase Change Material Synthesis

Phase change materials on a nanometer scale have been synthesized to study their scalability. Semiconductor nanowires have attracted a lot of research interests in the past decade [131–133]. The synthesis of nanowires has been well understood through the vapor–liquid–solid (VLS) mechanism [134]. Very recently, this methodology was applied to synthesis phase change nanowires [51, 135–137]. In the VLS mechanism for nanowire growth, reactants arrive by vapor transport and are dissolved into a metal particle. The particle becomes a liquid as the melting temperature is depressed by the dissolved components.

With the continuous supply from the vapor, the reactants reach supersaturation in the liquid droplet and start to precipitate out and form the nanowire. The diameter of the nanowire is controlled by the metal particle to start with and can be well controlled. In practice, the experiments are often carried out in a tube furnace system, where high purity GeTe and Sb_2Te_3 powers can be heated up at different temperature. Chemically synthesis gold particles with tight size distribution can be used as the metal catalyst so sub-100 nm diameter phase change material can be synthesized and measured. Figure 50 shows the scanning SEM images of GST nanowires with faceted structures [51]. Figure 51 shows the TEM analysis of a core-shell heterostructured phase change nanowire, fabricated by a two-step deposition of GST followed by GeTe [135].

To further decrease the dimension of the phase change material from a wire shape to a dot, different attempts have been demonstrated. One of the approaches is to pattern an ultra-thin blanket of film using electron-beam lithography and RIE [138]. Arrays of nanodots of amorphous GeSb, which had diameters between 20 and 55 nm with spacing between 80 and 100 μm over a field of 2×5 μm^2 were achieved. Size effects were observed for the transition temperature T_x, and T_x decreased with dot size. Using a self-assembled diblock copolymer mask, even smaller nanodots was demonstrated [139].

The reaction between polystyrene-*b*-poly-4-vinylpyridine (PS-*b*-P4VP) and tetraethoxysilance forms a template, which is transferred into a diamond-like carbon (DLC) middle layer by CO_2 RIE. The DLC nanopillar pattern was used as

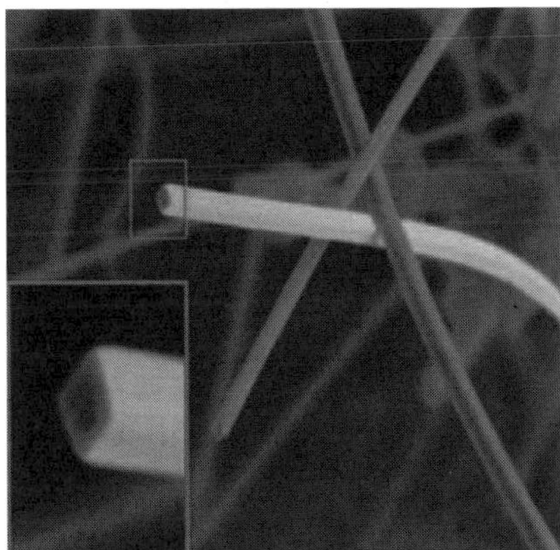

Figure 50. An SEM image of as-grown $Ge_2Sb_2Te_5$ nanowires with a faceted structure Reprinted with permission from [51], S. H. Lee et al., *Nat. Nanotechnol.* 2, 626 (2007). © 2007, NPG.

a hard mask to ion milled into the underlying GeSb layer to form high-density GeSb nanodots.

Recently, a colloidal synthetic route to amorphous germanium telluride nanoparticles with sub-5-nm size was reported [140]. GeTe nanoparticles were synthesized under air-free conditions through a hot injection route. GeI_2 were

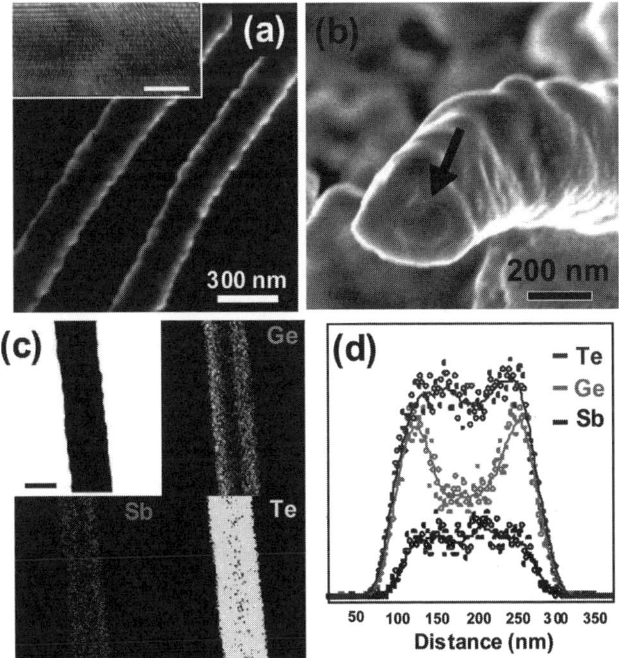

Figure 51. (a) Dark-field TEM image of $Ge_2Sb_2Te_5$ nanowires after GeTe deposition. Inset is a typical HRTEM image of polycrystalline GeTe shell deposited on the surface of $Ge_2Sb_2Te_5$ nanowires. Scale bar; 2 nm (b) SEM image of FIB (Ga^+ ion beam at 30 kV) cross-sectioned $Ge_2Sb_2Te_5$/GeTe-core/shell nanowire. A clear interface between the core and the shell region is visible (arrow). (c) STEM elemental mapping image showing spatial distribution of Ge, Sb, and Te in a $Ge_2Sb_2Te_5$/GeTe-core/shell nanowire. Scale bar; 200 nm (d) cross-sectional EDS line-scan profile of the nanowire in (c) reveals stronger Ge peaks in the shell region. Reprinted with permission from [135], Y. Jung et al., *Nano Lett.* 8, 2056 (2008). © 2008, ACS.

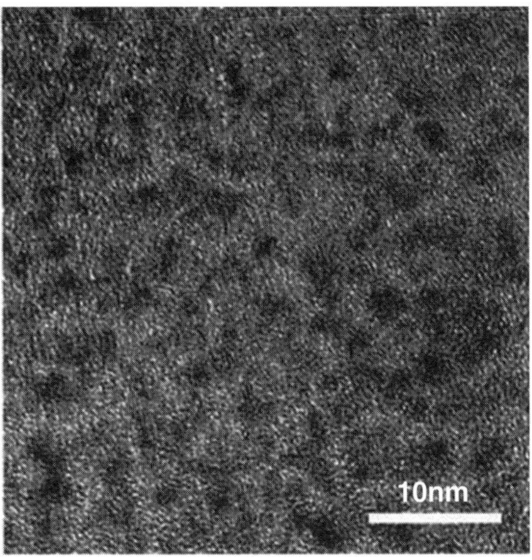

Figure 52. TEM image of GeTe nanoparticles. EDS shows stoichiometric 1:1 Ge:Te. Reprinted with permission from [140], M Caldwell et al., *J. Mater. Chem.* 20, 1285 (2010). © 2010, RSC.

dissolved in trioctylphosphine (TOP) to react with Te–TOP solution at 250°C for 8 min, allowing the nanoparticles to grow. The resulting nanoparticles were readily dispersible in nonpolar solvents such as toluene and chloroform (Fig. 52) [140].

By synthesizing and characterizing the crystallization of small GeTe nanoparticles, a profound size effect on the amorphous–crystalline transition was demonstrated. Nanoparticle films were shown six orders of resistance change between amorphous and crystalline phase. The crystallization temperature was greatly increased than the bulk films. For the 1.8-nm diameter nanoparticles studied, the T_x reached 240°C above that of bulk films. For nanoscale phase change memory devices, these trends in phase transition temperatures predict the improvement of data retention and reduced switching power at small sizes. These predictions give a very positive outlook for scaling PCM to even smaller sizes, and studying nanoparticles may also predict the ultimate scaling limit for phase change devices.

4.6. Summary of PCM Fabrication

The recent surge in phase change material research is inspired by the goal of commercializing the PCM product. Due to the limitation of the conventional deposition method (e.g., PVD) and damage from the patterning technique (e.g., RIE), several nonconventional methods for depositing thin films of phase change materials, such as CVD, electrodeposition, and solution-phase deposition have been explored. These techniques offer greatly improved filling of via structures. This advantage may be critical to reducing the RESET current of phase change memories to an acceptable level. Each method has been previously applied to the deposition of materials related to phase change materials; for example metal chalcogenides with applications in thermoelectrics, photovoltaics, among others. Each has also very recently been applied to phase change materials, although significant challenges remain. Among these techniques, CVD has been demonstrated for GST deposition, and only CVD has been demonstrated on an integrated device chip. Electrodeposition and solution-phase deposition show success mainly on binary material systems. The incorporation of nonmetallic dopants such as N and O, which can strongly modulate phase change properties, can also be difficult to control in electrodeposition and solution phase coating. Deposition morphology is a significant challenge because each of these methods often produces polycrystalline films with a rough surface texture. Early results demonstrating the deposition of homogeneous amorphous films is promising, and the results need to be evaluated further with integrated devices. It is critical that the new deposition method is integrated into the overall processing of the IC. Of the methods discussed here, CVD has the most established position of integration into IC processing, and CVD GST has been demonstrated on a real device. Electrodeposition of metals is also now used in some fabrication processes. Solution-phase deposition is used for photoresist, and there were attempts for spin-on dielectrics, but none have yet been implemented. This could pose additional challenges for the application of this method to PCM

Finally, nanometer scale phase change materials have been synthesized to study phase change properties and predict their scaling limit. Phase change nanowires grown by the VLS mechanism are single crystals with diameters down to 30 nm or so, and devices fabricated from these wires have already begun to elucidate fundamental scaling properties of PCM at small dimensions. Nanopatterned thin films can illuminate the properties of phase change material confined to small volumes, which is a model for the memory devices of the future. Chemically synthesized, sub-5-nm diameter nanoparticles of phase change materials revealed the physics of the amorphous-crystalline phase transformation in these materials in the small-volume limit and enable the prediction of changing device behavior due to scaling.

The phase change materials deposition technique will help improve memory performance, and the technique could be the key to the commercialization of PCM. Novel synthesis approaches of phase change material on a nanometer scale provide opportunities to study the scaling limits of PCM and have provided early evidence of their feasibility for extremely high densities of PCM.

5. CURRENT STATUS

As of today, it is widely expected that the primary application for PCM will be to replace NOR flash [141]. PCM has a number of advantages over NOR flash memory. For example, while NOR flash typically runs 10^5 cycles, PCM can exceed 10^6 cycles. The write speed of PCM is limited only by its GST crystallization time on the order of 100 ns, while NOR flash write speed is on the order of microseconds or longer. Possibly the most serious issue facing NOR flash today is how to scale it beyond 40 nm [142]. PCM, on the other hand, is expected to be able to scale down to about 5 nm [47]. Another limitation for NOR flash is its inability (unlike NAND [143]) to accommodate a 3D architecture on one wafer. Alternatively, it was shown in 2009 by Intel and Numonyx that PCM can be built in a 3D crossbar architecture, using a novel OTS as the array access/driving element (Fig. 39(c)) [65].

Although much progress has been made to increase PCM bit density, some issues have arisen that appear to be fundamental in nature. The most severe and recently discovered issue is the drift of resistance and V_{th} [10], which affects the amorphous state. This issue is a handicap for implementing MLC because the same resistance could have drifted from different initial resistance states over different durations [144]. One workaround has been the use of a reference cell for every write block [145]; however, this will add severe area and power consumption overhead.

Another fundamental issue that becomes more severe with higher density is thermal crosstalk [146]. Since the heat generated during the melting of the crystalline state must diffuse before and during quenching to form the amorphous state, the closer the neighboring cell, the easier for that cell to be converted, at least partially, from the amorphous state to the crystalline state. The diffusion distance is a function of the duration of the heating pulse as well as the energy provided by the pulse and the rate of cooling of its surroundings [147]. Ironically, improving heating uniformity and efficiency actually worsens the risk of thermal crosstalk.

Besides thermal crosstalk, another consequence of improving heating efficiency is the generation of a larger amorphous volume for a given RESET current. This larger amorphous volume results in a larger V_{th} [11]. Hence, there is a tradeoff between reducing RESET current and reducing V_{th}. Commonly, RESET current reduction has higher priority, but, at the same time, care must be taken not to let higher V_{th} result in the breakdown of the interlevel or intercell dielectric.

For the selection of alternative phase change materials, there is also a common tendency to simultaneously seek higher crystallization temperature T_x (for better stability of the amorphous state) and lower melting temperature T_m (for less energy required for RESET). GaTeSb is one such example [148]. Having a narrower temperature range between T_x and T_m also increases the risk of remelting during crystallization. Therefore, maintaining uniform heating throughout the material becomes more important.

Although many recent developments have helped enable competitively high bit densities, cost and a number of fundamental issues have prevented a widespread adoption of PCM in applications that have typically been served by flash memory.

6. OUTLOOK

Looking to the future, PCM faces three challenges:

(1) cost reduction,
(2) resolution of fundamental issues such as drift and thermal crosstalk, and
(3) maintaining competitive performance not only against DRAM and flash memory, but also alternatives such as new nonvolatile memory technologies (e.g., resistive RAM [ReRAM or RRAM] and magneto-resistive [MRAM]).

Cost reduction is driven by the ever-increasing cost competitiveness of NAND flash memory, which allows it to penetrate into markets previously served by NOR flash memory [149]. Although PCM cell size can have the same level of compactness as NAND flash, the key to cost competitiveness would be to simplify the fabrication process. The conventional BJT and diode process flow adds many complex front-end process steps compared with the conventional NAND front-end process flow. However, a 3D crossbar architecture only requires a relatively simple back-end based process flow [65]. Although this is a promising direction for future PCM development, it should be noted that thermal crosstalk would become much more severe due to the stacking of phase change materials, which typically have very low thermal conductivity [150].

The solution of the drift problem is being actively researched. In nearly all cases, the drift saturates after the passing of a temperature-dependent duration [151]. Therefore, it has been proposed to use a brief annealing pulse to effectively accelerate this duration. Of course, care must be taken not to disturb the cell in the amorphous state. Blockwise reference cells [145] are a brute-force, costly approach that may be required until a better solution is found.

The solution to thermal crosstalk is fraught with tradeoffs. In a 3D architecture, the spacing between cells in one plane can be increased and the stand-off distance between planes can also be kept above a safe minimum, thus entailing a maximum bit density (per unit volume). Using brief heating pulses [146] also limits the crosstalk, but they would greatly increase the overall programming time. Less uniform heating, as demonstrated in Refs. [14 and 15], currently appears to be the most widely practiced approach. The increase of V_{th} can also be managed this way, but it becomes harder to deploy phase change materials with a narrower T_x–T_m margin.

As more and more applications shift away from the personal computer-based infrastructure to a mobile-based infrastructure, power consumption and power density become overriding priorities. These have always been particularly difficult challenges for PCM due to the typically high RESET current densities. Two alternative memory technologies have been particularly competitive by offering high performance as well as significant power reduction. The first is spin-torque-transfer MRAM (STT-MRAM). A spin-polarized current can rotate the magnetization of a thin magnetic layer [152]. In turn, this affects the tunnelling current resistance across a magnetic tunnel junction (MTJ). The required programming current density for STT-MRAM is typically several times lower than for PCM at comparable programming speeds (typically 50 ns). Furthermore, the voltage across the MTJ must be kept low enough to prevent the breakdown of the tunnelling barrier, further improving the power consumption. The drawback of STT-MRAM, as with any MRAM, is the sensitivity to magnetic fields [153], particularly DC magnetic fields, which can be emitted by cell phone antennae or built-in compasses. Hence, magnetic shielding would be necessary [153].

Besides STT-MRAM, a more diverse and recent threat to PCM comes from RRAM. RRAM is actively being studied by many groups [154–157]. The sheer diversity of RRAM material systems and mechanisms being studied (reduction-oxidation, electromigration, Joule heating, metal-insulator transition) [158] and deciding which one is the optimum choice are already significant challenges. However, RRAM continues to progress, most notably by achieving operation speeds faster than 1 ns [154] and achieving operation currents down to 10 uA or lower [157]. Therefore, the prospects of PCM could be threatened by a RRAM technology that continues to mature.

Current mainstream memory technologies such as DRAM and flash remain hard to replace, particularly in systems such as servers that call for reliable components based on mature technology. As a result, there have been some proposals to insert PCM as a new class of memory, positioned between DRAM and flash, sometimes known as "storage class memory" [159]. It remains to be seen whether the new level of performance offered by PCM can justify the cost barrier of its entry into the marketplace. If successful, market penetration by PCM will enable the evolution of future memory technologies, possibly even based on MRAM or RRAM, and would be directed toward addressing the performance gaps still left by current memory technologies.

ACKNOWLEDGMENTS

The content of this chapter is based on the summary of efforts on phase change materials from many researchers and institutions, so the authors would like to thank them for their contributions in this field. The authors also appreciate the help they received from Mr. Yu-Chen Hu, Mr. Cheng-Hao Chiang, and Ms. Hsiao-Yu Chen in the collection of useful information for the chapter as well as their help in the organization of this manuscript.

REFERENCES

1. A. V. Kolobov, P. Fons, A. I. Frenkel, A. L. Ankudinov, J. Tominaga, and T. Uruga, *Nat. Mtls.* 3, 703 (2004).
2. S. R. Ovshinsky, US Patent No. 3, 271, 591, 1963.
3. S. J. Ahn, Y. J. Song, C. W. Jeong, J. M. Shin, Y. Fai, Y. N. Hwang, S. H. Lee, K. C. Ryoo, S. Y. Lee, J. H. Park, H. Horii, Y. H. Ha, J. H. Yi, B. J. Kuh, G. H. Koh, G. T. Jeong, H. S. Jeong, K. Kim, and B. I. Ryu, "International Electron Devices Meeting," pp. 907–910, 2004.
4. BAE Systems. http://www.baesystems.com/Newsroom/NewsReleases/2006/autoGen_10703020214.html, [Press release].
5. Y. C. Chen, C. T. Rettner, S. Raoux, G. W. Burr, S. H. Chen, R. M. Shelby, M. Salinga, W. P. Risk, T. D. Happ, G. M. McClelland, M. Breitwisch, A. Schrott, J. B. Phillip, M. H. Lee, R. Cheek, T. Nirschl, M. Lamorey, C. F. Chen, E. Joseph, S. Zaidi, B. Yee, H. L. Lung, R. Bergmann, and C. Lam, "International Electron Devices Meeting," pp. 1–4, 2006.
6. http://numonyx.com/en-US/MemoryProducts/PCM/Pages/PCM.aspx.
7. Samsung. http://www.samsung.com/global/business/semiconductor/products/fusionmemory/Products_NcPRAM. html.
8. M. Breitwisch, T. Nirschl, C. F. Chen, Y. Zhu, M. H. Lee, M. Lamorey, G. W. Burr, E. Joseph, A. Schrott, J. B. Philipp, R. Creek, T. D. Happ, S. H. Chen, S. Zaidi, P. Flaitz, J. Bruley, R. Dasaka, B. Rajendran, S. Rossnagel, M. Yang, Y. C. Chen, R. Bergmann, H. L. Lung, and C. Lam, "Symposium on VLSI Technology," pp. 100–101, 2007.

9. W. S. Chen, C. M. Lee, D. S. Chao, Y. C. Chen, F. Chen, C. W. Chen, P. H. Yen, M. J. Chen, W. H. Wang, T. C. Hsiao, J. T. Yeh, S. H. Chiou, M. Y. Liu, T. C. Wang, L. L. Chein, C. M. Huang, N. T. Shih, L. S. Tu, D. Huang, T. H. Yu, M. J. Kao, and M.-J. Tsai, "International Electron Devices Meeting," pp. 319–322, 2007.
10. A. Pirovano, A. L. Lacaita, F. Pellizzer, S. A. Kostylev, A. Benvenuti, and R. Bez, *IEEE Trans. Elec. Dev.* 51, 714 (2004).
11. D. Yu, S. Brittman, J. S. Lee, A. L. Falk, and H. Park, *Nano Lett.* 8, 3429 (2008).
12. A. Pirovano, A. L. Lacaita, A. Benvenuti, F. Pellizzer, and R. Bez, *IEEE Trans. Elec. Dev.* 51, 452 (2004).
13. A. Pirovano, A. L. Lacaita, A. Benvenuti, F. Pellizzer, S. Hudgens, and R. Bez, "International Electron Devices Meeting," pp. 29.6.1–29.6.4, 2003.
14. G. Servalli, "International Electron Devices Meeting," 2009.
15. J. H. Oh, J. H. Park, Y. S. Lim, H. S. Lim, Y. T. Oh, J. S. Kim, J. M. Shin, J. H. Park, Y. J. Song, K. C. Ryoo, D. W. Lim, S. S. Park, J. I. Kim, J. H. Kim, J. Yu, F. Yeung, C. W. Jeong, J. H. Kong, D. H. Kang, G. H. Koh, G. T. Jeong, H. S. Jeong, and K. Kim, "International Electron Devices Meeting," 2006.
16. C. Lam, "VLSI Technology, Systems and Applications." IEEE, 2008.
17. A. Shah. *PC World.* (2009). http://www.pcworld.com/article/173425/samsung_sees_major_benefits_from_phasechange_memory.html.
18. S. R. Ovshinsky, *Phys. Rev. Lett.* 22, 1450 (1968).
19. S. R. Ovshinsky, US Patent 3, 271, 591, 1966.
20. J. Feinleib, J. deNeufville, S. C. Moss, and S. R. Ovshinsky, *Appl. Phys. Lett.* 18, 254 (1971).
21. M. Chen, K. A. Rubin, and R. W. Barton, *Appl. Phys. Lett.* 49, 502 (1986).
22. N. Yamada, M. Takenaga, and N. Takao, *Proc. SPIE.* 695, 79 (1986).
23. N. Yamada, E. Ohno, K. Nishiuchi, N. Akahira, and M. Takao, *J. Appl. Phys.* 69, 2849 (1991).
24. M. Wuttig and N. Yamada, *Nat. Mater.* 6, 824 (2007).
25. Y. N. Hwang, S. H. Lee, S. J. Ahn, S. Y. Lee, K. C. Ryoo, H. S. Hong, H. C. Koo, F. Yeung, J. H. Oh, H. J. Kim, W. C. Jeong, J. H. Park, H. Horii, Y. H. Ha, J. H. Yi, G. H. Koh, G. T. Jeong, H. S. Jeong, and K. Kim, "International Electron Devices Meeting," p. 893, IEEE, 2003.
26. H. Horii, J. H. Yi, J. H. Park, Y. H. Ha, I. G. Baek, S. O. Park, Y. N. Hwang, S. H. Lee, Y. T. Kim, K. H. Lee, U. I. Chung, and J. T. Moon, "Dig.-VLSI Tech.," p. 177, IEEE, 2003.
27. N. Matsuzaki, K. Kurotsuchi, Y. Matsui, O. Tonomura, N. Yamamoto, Y. Fujisaki, N. Kitai, R. Takemura, K. Osada, S. Hanzawa, H. Moriya, T. Iwasaki, T. Kawahara, N. Takaura, M. Terao, M. Matsuoka, and M. Moniwa, "International Electron Devices Meeting," p. 738, IEEE, 2005.
28. W. D. Song, L. P. Shi, X. S. Miao, and T. C. Chong, *Appl. Phys. Lett.* 90, 091904 (2007).
29. K. Nakayama, K. Kojima, F. Hayakawa, Y. Imai, A. Kitagawa, and M. Suzuki, *Jpn. J. Appl. Phys.* 39, 6157 (2000).
30. K. Nakayama, K. Kojima, Y. Imai, T. Kasai, S. Fukushima, A. Kitagawa, M. Suzuki, Y. Kakimoto, and M. Suzuki, *Jpn. J. Appl. Phys.* 42, 404 (2003).
31. S. M. Yoon, N. Y. Lee, S. O. Ryu, K. J. Choi, Y. S. Park, S. Y. Lee, B. G. Yu, M. J. Kang, S. Y. Choi, and M. Wuttig, *IEEE Electron Device. Lett.* 27, 445 (2006).
32. T. Zhang, Z. Song, F. Wang, B. Liu, S. Feng, and B. Chen, *Appl. Phys. Lett.* 91, 222102 (2007).
33. C. Cabral, K. N. Chen, L. Krusin-Elbaum, and V. Deline, *Appl. Phys. Lett.* 90, 051908 (2007).
34. T. Morikawa, K. Kurotsuchi, M. Kinoshita, N. Matsuzaki, Y. Matsui, Y. Fujisaki, S. Hanzawa, A. Kotabe, M. Terao, H. Moriya, T. Iwasaki, M. Matsuoka, F. Nitta, M. Moniwa, T. Koga and N. Takaura, "International Electron Devices Meeting," p. 307, IEEE, 2007.
35. K. F. Kao, C. M. Lee, M. J. Chen, M. J. Tsai, and T. S. Chin, *Adv. Mater.* 21, 1 (2009).
36. H. Y. Cheng, K. F. Kao, C. M. Lee, and T. S. Chin, *IEEE Trans. Magn.* 43, 927 (2007).
37. C. M. Lee, W. S. Yen, R. P. Chen, and T. S. Chin, *IEEE Trans. Magn.* 41,1022 (2005).
38. P. K. Khulbe, T. Hurst, M. Horie, and M. Mansuripur, *Appl. Opt.* 41, 6220 (2002).
39. L. van Pieterson, M. H. R. Lankhorst, M. van Schijndel, A. E. T. Kuiper, and J. H. J. Roosen, *J. Appl. Phys.* 97, 083520 (2005).
40. M. H. R. Lankhorst, L. van Pieterson, M. van Schijndel, B. A. J. Jacobs, and J. C. N. Rijpers, *Jpn. J. Appl. Phys.* 1, 863 (2003).
41. S. M. Yoon, K. J. Choi, N. Y. Lee, S. Y. Lee, Y. S. Park, and B. G. Yu, *Jpn. J. Appl. Phys.* 46, 99 (2007).
42. S. W. Nam, D. Lee, M. H. Kwon, D. Kang, C. Kim, T. Y. Lee, S. Heo, Y. W. Park, K. Lim, H. S. Lee, J.-S. Wi, K. W. Yi, Y. Khang, and K. B. Kim, *Electrochem. Solid State Lett.* 12, 155 (2009).
43. J. B. Park, G. S. Park, H. S. Baik, J. H. Lee, H. Jeong, and K. Kim, *J. Electrochem. Soc.* 154, 139 (2007).
44. T. Y. Yang, I. M. Park, B. J. Kim, and Y. C. Joo, *Appl. Phys. Lett.* 95, 032104 (2009).
45. S. Raoux, J. L. Jordan-Sweet, and A. J. Kellock, *J. Appl. Phys.* 103, 114310 (2008).
46. S. Raoux, H.-Y. Cheng, J. L. Jordan-Sweet, B. Muñoz, and M. Hitzbleck, *Appl. Phys. Lett.* 94, 183114 (2009).
47. R. E. Simpson, M. Krbal, P. Fons, A. V. Kolobov, J. Tominaga, T. Uruga, and H. Tanida, *Nano Lett.* 10, 414 (2010).
48. G. F. Zhou, *Mater. Sci. Engin. A* 304–306, 73 (2001).
49. H. C. F. Martens, R. Vlutters, and J. C. Prangsma, *J. Appl. Phys.* 95, 3977 (2004).
50. H.-Y. Cheng, S. Raoux, and Y. C. Chen, *J. Appl. Phys.* 107, 074308 (2010).
51. S. H. Lee, Y. Jung, and R. Agarwal, *Nat. Nanotechnol.* 2, 626 (2007).
52. S. Lai, *IEDM* 255 (2003).
53. R. Neale, D. Nelson, and G. Moore, *Electronics* 56 (1970).
54. R. R. Shanks and C. Davi, *ISSCC* (1978).
55. N. Yamada, E. Ohno, K. Nishiuchi, N. Akahira, K. Nagata, and M. Takao, *Jpn. J. Appl. Phys.* 26, 61 (1987).
56. S. Lai and T. Lowery, "Intel and Ovonyx, IEDM," 2001.
57. M. Gill, T. Lowrey, and J. Park, "Intel, Ovonyx and Azalea," ISSCC, 2002.
58. F. Pellizzer, A. Benvenuti, B. Gleixner, Y. Kim, B. Johnson, M. Magistretti, T. Marangon, A. Pirovano, R. Bez, and G. Atwood, "Intel and STM," VLSI, 2006.
59. H. Seo, T.-H. Jeong, J.-W. Park, C. Y., S.-J. Kim, and S.-Y. Kim, *Jpn. J. Appl. Phys.* 39, 745 (2000).
60. C.-F. Chen, A. Schrott, M. H. Lee, S. Raoux, Y. H. Shih, M. Breitwisch, F. H. Baumann, E. K. Lai, T. M. Shaw, P. Flaitz, R. Cheek, E. A. Joseph, S. H. Chen, B. Rajendran, H. L. Lung, and C. Lam, "Macronix/IBM," IMW, 2009.
61. A. Pirovano, F. Pellizzer, A. Redaelli, I. Tortorelli, E. Varesi, F. Ottogalli, M. Tosi, P. Besana, R. Cecchini, R. Piva, M. Magistretti, M. Scaravaggi, G. Mazzone, P. Petruzza, F. Bedeschi, T. Marangon, A. Modelli, D. Ielmini, A. L. Lacaita, and R. Bez, "STM," ESSDERC, 2005.
62. D. H. Im, J. I. Lee, S. L. Cho, H. G. An, D. H. Kim, I. S. Kim, H. Park, D. H. Ahn, H. Horii, S. O. Park, U.-I. Chung, and J. T. Moon, "Samsung IEDM," IEEE, 2008.
63. I. S. Kim, S. L. Cho, D. H. Im, E. H. Cho, D. H. Kim, G. H. Oh, D. H. Ahn, S. O. Park, S. W. Nam, J. T. Moon, and C. H. Chung, "Samsung, VLSIT," p. 203, IEEE, 2010.
64. T. Nirschl, J. B. Philipp, T D. Happ, G. W Burrt, B. Rajendrant, M.-H. Lee A. Schrottt, M. Yang, T. M. Breitwischt, C.-F. Chen, E. Joseph, T. M. Lamorey, R. Chee, S.-H. Chen, S. Zaidi,

S. Raoux, Y. C. Chen, Y. Zhu, R. Bergmann, H.-L. Lunge, and C. Lamf, "IBM/Macronix/Qimonda IEDM," p. 461, IEEE, 2007.
65. D. C. Kau, S. Tang, I. V. Karpov, R. Dodge, B. Klehn, J. A. Kalb, J. Strand, A. Diaz, N. Leung, J. Wu, S. Lee, T. Langtry, K.-W. Chang, C. Papagianni, J. Lee, J. Hirst, S. Erra, E. Flores, N. Righos, H. Castro, and G. Spadini, "Intel, IEDM," p. 27.1.1, IEEE, 2009.
66. W. R. Northover and A. D. Pearson, US Patent No. 3, 117, 013, 1964.
67. J. F. Dewald, W. R. Northover, and A. D. Pearson, US Patent No. 3, 241, 009, 1966.
68. N. Yamada and T. Matsunaga, *J. Appl. Phys.* 88, 7021 (2000).
69. S. Raoux, G. W. Burr, M. J. Breitwisch, C. T. Rettner, Y.-C. Chen, R. M. Shelby, M. Salinga, D. Krebs, S.-H. Chen, H.-L. Lung, and C. H. Lam, *IBM J. Res. Dev.* 52, 465 (2008).
70. S. M. Rossnagel, *J. Vac. Sci. Technol. B* 16, 2585 (1998).
71. E. A. Joseph, T. D. Happ, S. H. Chen, S. Raoux, C. F. Chen, M. Breitwisch, A. G. Schrott, S. Zaidi, R. Dasaka, B. Yee, Y. Zhu, R. Bergmann, H. L. Lung, and C. Lam, "International Symposium on VLSI Technology, Systems and Applications," IEEE, 2008.
72. D. M. Dobkin and M. K. Zuraw, "Principles of Chemical Vapor Deposition." Kluwer, Dordrecht, 2003.
73. H. O. Pierson, "Handbook of Chemical Vapor Phase Deposition (CVD)." Noyes, Park Ridge, 1992.
74. R. Y. Kim, H. G. Kim, and S. G. Yoon, *Appl. Phys. Lett.* 89, 102107 (2006).
75. R. Y. Kim, H. G. Kim, and S. G. Yoon, *J. Electrochem. Soc.* 155, D137 (2008).
76. B. J. Choi, S. Choi, Y. C. Shin, C. S. Hwang, J. W. Lee, J. Jeong, Y. J. Kim, S. Y. Hwang, and S. K. Hong, *J. Electrochem. Soc.* 154, H318 (2007).
77. R. Y. Kim, H. G. Kim, and S. G. Yoon, *Integ. Ferroelectrics* 90, 80 (2007).
78. S. Ovshinsky and S. Kamepalli, U. S. Patent 0172067 A1, 2006.
79. J. Lee, S. Choi, C. Lee, Y. Kang, and D. Kim, *App. Surf. Sci.* 253, 3969 (2007).
80. A. Abrutis, V. Plausinaitiene, M. Skapas, C. Wiemer, O. Salicio, A. Pirovano, E. Varesi, S. Rushworth, W. Gawelda, and J. Siegel, *Chem. Mater.* 20, 3557 (2008).
81. M. Longo, O. Salicio, C. Wiemer, R. Fallica, A. Moole, M. Fanciulli, C. Giesen, B. Seitzinger, P. K. Baumann, M. Heuken, and S. Rushworth, *J. Crystal Growth* 310, 5053 (2008).
82. A. Schrott, C. F. Chen, M. Breitwisch, E. Joseph, R. Dasaka, R. Cheek, Y. Zhu, and C. Lam, *Mater. Res. Soc. Symp. Proc.* 1251E, 1251-H06 (2010).
83. K. Do, H. Sohn, and D.-H. Ko, *J. Electrochem. Soc.* 154, H867 (2007).
84. A. Ebina, M. Hirasaka, and K. Nakatani, *J. Vac. Sci. Technol. A.* 17, 3463 (1999).
85. M. Ritala and M. Leskela, "Handbook of Thin Film Materials." (H. S. Nalwa, Ed.), Elsevier Science & Technology Books, Maryland Heights, MO, USA, 2002.
86. M. Ritala, V. Pore, T. Hatanpaa, M. Heikkila, M. Leskela, K. Mizohata, A. Schrott, S. Raoux, and S. Rossnagel, *Microelectron. Eng.* 86, 1946 (2009).
87. M. Ritala, V. Pore, T. Hatanpää, T. Sarnet, M. Leskelä, A. Schrott, Y. Zhu, and S. Raouxb, "Spring Meeting," Material Research Society, Warrendale, PA, USA, 2010.
88. J. I. Lee, H. Park, S. L. Cho, Y. L. Park, B. J. Bae, J. H. Park, H. G. An, J. S. Bae, D. H. Ahn, Y. T. Kim, H. Horii, S. A. Song, J. C. Shin, S. O. Park, H. S. Kim, U. I. Chung, J. T. Moon, and B. I. Ryu, *Sym. VLSI Tech. Dig.* 102, 102 (2007).
89. P. C. Andricacos, C. Uzoh, J. O. Dukovic, J. Horkans, and H. Deligianni, *IBM J. Res. Dev.* 42, 567 (1998).
90. A. J. Bard and L. R. Faulkner "Electrochemical Methods: Fundamentals and Applications." John Wiley & Sons, New York, 2002.
91. J. S. Newman and K. E. Thomas-Alyea, "Electrochemical Systems." John Wiley & Sons, New York, 2004.
92. M. Schlesinger and M. Paunovic, "Fundamentals of Electrochemical Deposition." John Wiley & Sons, New York, 2006.
93. M. P. Panicker, M. Knaster, and F. A. Kroger, *J. Electrochem. Soc.* 125, 566 (1978).
94. S. Bonilla and E. A. Dalchiele, *Thin Solid Films* 204, 397 (1991).
95. K. Varazo, M. D. Lay, T. A. Sorenson, and J. L. Stickney, *J. Electroanal. Chem.* 522, 104 (2002).
96. V. Venkatasamy, N. Jayaraju, S. M. Cox, C. Thambidurai, U. Happek, and J. L. Stickney, *J. Appl. Electrochem.* 36, 1223 (2006).
97. C. L. Colyer and M. Cocivera, *J. Electrochem. Soc.* 139, 406 (1992).
98. K. Rajeshwar, *Adv. Mater.* 4, 23 (1992).
99. D. Lincot, *Thin Solid Films* 487, 40 (2005).
100. V. Venkatasamy, N. Jayaraju, S. M. Cox, C. Thambidurai, M. Mathe, and J. L. Stickney, *J. Electroanal.Chem.* 589, 195 (2006).
101. V. Venkatasamy, N. Jayaraju, S. M. Cox, and C. Thambidurai, and J. L. Stickney, *J. Electrochem. Soc.* 154, H720 (2007).
102. T. Mahalingam, A. Kathalingam, S. Velumani, S. Lee, H. Moon, and Y. D. Kim, *J. New Mater. Electrochem. Sys.* 10, 21 (2007).
103. J. L. Orts, R. Diaz, P. Herrasti, F. Rueda, and E. Fatas, *Sol. Ener. Mater. Sol. Cell* 91, 621 (2007).
104. K. Tittes, A. Bund, W. Plieth, A. Bentien, S. Paschen, M. Plötner, H. Gräfe, and W. J. Fischer, *J. Solid State Electrochem.* 7, 714 (2003).
105. D. D. Frari, S. Diliberto, N. Stein, C. Boulanger, and J. M. Lecuire, *Thin Solid Films* 483, 44 (2005).
106. Q. Huang, A. J. Kellock, and S. Raoux, *J. Electrochem. Soc.* 155, 104 (2008).
107. G. Leimkühler, I. Kerkamm, and R. Reineke-Koch, *J. Electrochem. Soc.* 149, 474 (2002).
108. S. Privitera, C. Bongiorno, E. Rimini, and R. Zonca, *Appl. Phys. Lett.* 84, 4448 (2004).
109. Q. Huang, S. W. Bedell, K. L. Saenger, M. Copel, H. Deligianni, and L. T. Romankiw, *Solid-State Lett.* 10, D124 (2007).
110. C. G. Fink and V. M. Dokras, *J. Electrochem.* Soc. 95, 80 (1949).
111. Q. Huang, A. Kellock, X. Shao, and V. Venkatasamy, US Patent XX, 2007.
112. S. A. Sapp, B. B. Lakshmi, and C. R. Martin, *Adv. Mater.* 11, 402 (1999).
113. R. Chen, D. Xu, and L. Gui, *J. Mater. Chem.* 12, 2435 (2002).
114. M. S. Sander, A. L. Prieto, R. Gronsky, T. Sands, and A. M. Stacy, *Adv. Mater.* 14, 665 (2002).
115. R. Chen, D. Xu, G. Guo, and Y. Tang, *Chem. Phys. Lett.* 377, 205 (2003).
116. T. Gandhi and K. S. Raja, *Misra, Electrochim. Acta* 51, 5932 (2006).
117. C. Jin, G. Zhang, T. Qian, X. Li, and Z. Yao, *J. Phys. Chem. B* 109, 1430 (2005).
118. G. C. Chern and I. Lauks, *J. Appl. Phys.* 53, 6979 (1982).
119. J. Gutwirth, T. Wagner, T. Kohoutek, M. Vlcek, S. Schroeter, V. Kovanda, M. Vlcek, and M. Frumar, *J. Optoelectron. Adv. Mater.* 5, 1139 (2003).
120. E. Hajto, P. J. S. Ewen, R. Belford, J. Hajto, and A. E. Owen, *J. Non-Crystall. Solids* 97–8, 1191 (1987).
121. T. Kohoutek, T. Wagner, M. Frumar, and M. Vlcek, *J. Glass Sci. Tech. Part B* 47, 250 (2006).
122. T. Kohoutek, T. Wagner, J. Orava, M. Krbal, A. Fejfar, T. Mates, S. O. Kasap, and M. Frumar, *J. Non-Crystall. Solids* 353, 1437 (2007).
123. S. Shirakata, Y. Kannaka, H. Hasegawa, T. Kariya, and S. Isomura, *Jpn. J. Appl. Phys.* 38, 4997 (1999).
124. Y. D. Tembhurkar and J. P. Hirde, *Thin Solid Films* 215, 65 (1992).

125. D. J. Milliron, D. B. Mitzi, M. Copel, and C. E. Murray, *Chem. Mater.* 18, 587 (2006).
126. D. B. Mitzi, M. Copel, and C. E. Murray, *Adv. Mater.* 18, 2448 (2006).
127. D. B. Mitzi, L. L. Kosbar, C. E. Murray, M. Copel, and A. Afzali, *Nature* 428, 299 (2004).
128. D. B. Mitzi, S. Raoux, A. G. Schrott, M. Copel, A. Kellock, and J. Jordan-Sweet, *Chem. Mater.* 18, 6278 (2006).
129. D. J. Milliron, S. Raoux, R. M. Shelby, and J. Jordan-Sweet, *Nature Mater.* 6, 357 (2007).
130. D. J. Milliron, M. A. Caldwell, and H. S. P. Wong, *Nano Lett.* 7, 3504 (2007).
131. Y. Cui and C. M. Leiber, *Science* 291, 851 (2001).
132. M. Law, J. Goldberger, and P. Yang, *Ann. Rev. Mat. Res.* 34, 83 (2004).
133. W. Lu and C. M. Lieber, *J. Phys. D.* 39, 387 (2006).
134. R. S. Wagner and W. C. Ellis, *Appl. Phys. Lett.* 4, 89 (1964).
135. Y. Jung, S. H. Lee, A. Jennings, and R. Agarwal, *Nano Lett.* 8, 2056 (2008).
136. X. Sun, B. Yu, and M. Meyyappan, *Appl. Phys. Lett* 90, 183116 (2007).
137. S. Meister, H. Peng, K. Mcllwrath, K. Jarausch, X. F. Zhang, and Y. Cui, *Nano Lett.* 6, 1514 (2006).
138. S. Raoux, C. Rettner, J. L. Jordan-Sweet, V. Deline, J. Philipp, and H. Lung, "Proceedings of the European Symposium Phase-change and Ovonic Science," Grenoble, France, 2006.
139. Y. Zhang, H. S. P. Wang, S. Raoux, J. N. Cha, C. T. Rettner, L. Krupp, T. Topuria, D. Milliron, P. Rice, and J. L. Jordan-Sweet, *Appl. Phys. Lett.* 91, 012104 (2007).
140. M. Caldwell, S. Raoux, R. Wang, H. S. P. Wang, and D. Milliron, *J. Mater. Chem.* 20, 1285 (2010).
141. S. J. Hudgens, *J. Non-Crystall. Solids* 354, 2748 (2008).
142. C.-Y. Lu, K.-Y. Hsieh, and R. Liu, *Microelectronic Eng.* 8, 283 (2009).
143. H. T. Lue, T. H. Hsu, Y.-H. Hsiao, S. P. Hong, M. T. Wu, F. H. Hsu, N. Z. Lien, S-Y Wang, J.-Y. Hsieh, L.-W. Yang, T. Yang, K.-C. Chen, K.-Y. Hsieh, and C.-Y. Lu, "Symposium on VLSI Technology," 2010.
144. D.-H. Kang, J.-H. Lee, J. H. Kong, D. Ha, J. Yu, C. Y. Um, J. H. Park, F. Yeung, J. H. Kim, W. I. Park, Y. J. Jeon, M. K. Lee, J. H. Park, Y. J. Song, J. H. Oh, G. T. Leong, and H. S. Jeong, "Symposium on VLSI Technology," 2008.
145. G.-T. Jeong, U. S. Patent, 7, 830, 705, 2008.
146. A. Pirovano, A. Redaelli, F. Pellizzer, F. Ottogalli, M. Tosi, D. Ielmini, A. L. Lacaita, and R. Bez, *IEEE Trans. Dev. Mat. Rel.* 4, 422 (2004).
147. F. T. Chen, J. T. Yeh, D. S. Chao, M. J. Chen, P. Yen, C. M. Lee, J. W. Chen, W. S. Chen, M. J. Kao, and M. J. Tsai. "VLSI Technology, Systems and Applications," 2008.
148. K.-F. Kao, Y.-C. Chu, M.-J. Tsai, and T.-S. Chin, "Nanoelectronics Conference," IEEE, 2010.
149. J. In, I. Shin, and H. Kim, "Languages, Compilers, and Tools for Embedded Systems." 2007.
150. F. T. Chen and M.-J. Tsai, U. S. Patent 7, 679, 163, 2010.
151. I. V. Karpov, M. Mitra, D. Kau, G. Spadini, Y. A. Kryukov, and V. G. Karpov, *J. Appl. Phys.* 102, 124503 (2007).
152. Y. Liu, Z. Zhang, P. P. Freitas, and J. L. Martins, *Appl. Phys. Lett.* 82, 2871 (2003).
153. J. Janesky, "Freescale Semiconductor Application Note AN3525, Impact of External Magnetic Fields on MRAM Products." 2007.
154. H. Y. Lee, Y. S. Chen, P. S. Chen, P. Y. Gu, Y. Y. Hsu, S. M. Wang, W. H. Liu, C. H. Tsai, S. S. Sheu, P. C. Chiang, W. P. Lin, C. H. Lin, W. S. Chen, F. T. Chen, C. H. Lien, and M. J. Tsai, "International Electron Devices Meeting," 2010.
155. W. C. Chien, Y. R. Chen, Y. C. Chen, A. T. H. Chuang, F. M. Lee, Y. Y. Lin, E. K. Lai, Y. H. Shih, K. Y. Hsieh, and C. Y. Lu, "International Electron Devices Meeting," 2010.
156. R. Waser, *Microelectronic Eng.* 86, 1925 (2009).
157. M. J. Kim, I. G. Baek, Y. H. Ha, S. J. Baik, J. H. Kim, D. J. Seong, C. R. Lim, Y. J. Shin, S. Choi, and C. Chung, "International Electron Devices Meeting," 2010.
158. F. T. Chen, H. Y. Lee, Y. S. Chen, Y. Y. Hsu, L. Zhang, P. S. Chen, W. S. Chen, P. Y. Gu, W. H. Liu, S. M. Wang, C. H. Tsai, S. S. Sheu, M.J . Tsai, and R. Huang, *Science China* (2011).
159. R. F. Freitas and W. W. Wilcke, *IBM J. Res. Dev.* 52, 439 (2008).

CHAPTER 2

Phase Change Memory

Dae-Hwan Kang[1], Ki-Bum Kim[2], Byung-Ki Cheong[3], Hong-Sik Jeong[1]

[1]*Memory Division, Semiconductor Business, Samsung Electronics Corp. Ltd. Yongin-City, Kyungi-Do, 449-711, South Korea*
[2]*Seoul National University, Department of Materials Science and Engineering, Seoul National University, 599 Gwanak-Ro, Gwanak-Gu, Seoul, 151-744, Korea*
[3]*Electronic Materials Center, Korea Institute of Science and Technology, 39-1 Hawolgok-Dong, Sungbuk-Ku, Seoul, 136-791, Korea*

CONTENTS

1. INTRODUCTION

The practical use of phase transformations in solid state goes back to 1500 to 2000 BC in the vicinity of the Mediterranean Sea. Two so-called representative techniques are quenching and annealing. Air- or water-cooling of heated iron or melted transition metal oxide (quenching) and the following heat treatment at appropriate temperatures (annealing)

ISBN: 1-58883-251-1

Nonvolatile Memories: Materials, Devices and Applications
Edited by Tseung-Yuen Tseng and Simon M. Sze
Volume 2: Pages: 31–55

have been utilized to harden iron-made weapons and agricultural tools or to obtain glass ornaments and vitrified brilliant bowls. The former is to induce the formation of metastable or unstable phase by a rapid cooling process, while the latter is to make a more stable phase via structural changes through thermal energy. It was known that they were accompanied with microstructural changes due to austenite ↔ martensite ↔ ferrite phase transformation in iron alloys and order ↔ disorder transformation in metal glasses, respectively. From the early 1990s, four millenniums past since then, the same techniques have been also applied to cutting-edge, high-density data storage technologies like rewritable optical media such as PD, CD-RW, DVD-RAM, BD-RE [1, 2] and nonvolatile electrical phase change memory [3]. Namely, we are utilizing phase changes between the two different (amorphous and crystalline) solid phases with differing optical properties (reflectivity) and electrical properties (resistance) for writing and reading information.

A nonvolatile electrical phase change memory device encodes binary information into the media of a Ge–Sb–Te-based phase change material through current-driven Joule heating. That is, a higher and shorter pulse melts and quenches the phase change material to produce a high-resistive amorphous state, while a lower and longer pulse makes the material crystallized or annealed and, thus, the material has a low-resistive crystalline state. The former writing operation is called "reset," while the latter operation "set." The stored data are nondestructively sensed by the difference in electrical resistance between the two states. In this chapter, we start with a brief overview on the past and the future of phase change memory technology before reviewing its technological details. Then, we describe the requirements of phase change material for a memory element as well as some important properties of currently used $Ge_2Sb_2Te_5$ material. The fundamental physics, fabrication procedures, and cell reliability characteristics of the device are then successively reviewed.

1.1. Revitalization of Phase Change Memory

It is not surprising that the search for next-generation nonvolatile memory began from the early 2000s with the flash memory "Renaissance age" since it has been expected that NAND- and NOR-type memories have some limitations in terms of programming, read speed, and power consumption, even though they have superior device characteristics of non-volatility and high-density for mobile applications. Phase change memory was being considered by Intelat the International Electron Devices Meeting in 2001 [4] as a candidate for next generation nonvolatile memory, along with ferroelectric random access memory (RAM) and magnetic resistance RAM. Polymer RAM has been particularly appealing to semiconductor chip makers who are seeking to replace conventional flash memories. After almost one decade, Samsung Electronics Corporation Ltd. in South Korea has finally become the first chip maker who has succeeded in the mass production of this nonvolatile memory concept by releasing 512-Mbit phase change RAM (PRAM) in a multichip package for a cellular phone [5], whereas read-only memory of a similar sort failed to survive 40 years ago due to slow programming speed (tens of μs), high power consumption (tens of mA), and poor reliability (degradation in a few of cycles) [6]. The revitalization of phase change memory was enabled by a number of technical innovations. Firstly, phase change materials with low melting temperature and high crystallization speeds have become available since $GeTe–Sb_2Te_3$ pseudobinary alloys were developed for optical recording media by researchers at Matzushita Inc. [7]. Moreover, not only could nano-size patterning techniques significantly reduce the programming current to far below 1 mA, but advanced wet cleaning and/or plasma treatment [8] were also able to produce good-quality interfaces between phase change material and electrodes, realizing more reliable memory switching operations for well above 10^5 cycles.

1.2. Prospect in Terms of Scaling, Performance, and Manufacturability

Multiple advantages of phase change memory are accountable for its emergence as the front-runner in the race for next-generation, nonvolatile memory during the last decade. Firstly, it is readily scalable when compared with other memories. Scalability represents the sustainability of a semiconductor device over generations of scaling-down technology nodes. In the case of a memory device, it should work properly as the physical dimension of a memory cell becomes smaller and the supplied power is significantly reduced in the high-density and low-power mobile applications. Flash memory is hard to be scaled down to sub-20-nm technology nodes because the number of charged electrons in a cell is reduced to below 10 each at these nodes, which are not sufficient to sustain discrete data [9]. On the contrary, theoretical [10] and experimental [11] studies have demonstrated that a phase change memory can be scalable down to below 10 nm. In addition, it is relatively free from the demanding burden of ever-decreasing power consumption with device-scaling since an operation current spontaneously decreases at the same rate of scaling in contact area, sufficing to maintain a required current density (Joule heating) for write operation.

Secondly, intrinsic cell reliability characteristics are superior to and more controllable than conventional flash memory. Indeed, $Ge_2Sb_2Te_5$, which is the most widely accepted material for phase change memory, can provide higher write endurance than flash memory by several orders of magnitude as well as also a higher temperature for 10 years of data retention compared with flash memory [12].

Thirdly, there are a wide compositional spectra of phase change materials, so a person can select an appropriate phase change material according to the application field. For example, doped In–Ge–Te [13] with a high crystallization temperature is appropriate for automotive and aerospace applications, while eutectic Sb_7Te_3-based or Sb-based materials [14] that have high crystallization speeds are better for RAM applications.

Finally, the cell structure of phase change memory is simple and the constituent elements of phase change material are either semiconducting (Ge and Te belong to group IV or VI, respectively) or semimetallic (Sb belongs to group V). Accordingly, it is not exotic to the conventional Si processing technology, so many well-established process techniques and facilities can be directly loaned from a conventional memory device fabrication [15].

2. PHASE CHANGE MATERIALS

2.1. General Requirements

As an active memory material, a phase change material is supposed to satisfy the following performance targets. Firstly, phase transformation time (particularly the crystallization time) of an amorphous phase should be shorter than hundreds of nanoseconds. This is very critical to high-speed mobile applications such as a smart phone or a tablet personal computer (PC), and even shorter crystallization times of fewer than tens of nanoseconds is indeed under growing demands for RAM-like applications. Secondly, crystallization temperature should be high in the range of 150°C to 200°C, which is enough to keep an amorphous phase in the appropriate temperatures, while the melting temperature should be in the range of 500°C to 1000°C so that a phase change material can be melted with a Joule heat at a low voltage of 1.8 V or 3.3 V. (The properties of surrounding dielectrics and electrode materials should not be affected by Joule heating for melting.) Thirdly, phase transformations between crystalline and amorphous phases should be reproducible over 10^5 cycles with no significant change in material composition, which is a requirement for nonvolatile memory.

2.2. Pseudobinary GeTe–Sb_2Te_3 Alloys

A brief review of the material-engineering considerations behind the development of $Ge_2Sb_2Te_5$ phase change material in present use for both commercial electrical memory and optical recording media may be instructive because that compositional modification of $Ge_2Sb_2Te_5$ or the design of a new phase change material for improving memory performances and cell reliability characteristics is very likely to follow similar development lines.

An elementary requirement of a phase change material for the electrical memory is that structural changes between amorphous and crystalline phases are able to take place as a result of Joule heating while involving large changes in electrical resistivity. Insulators are not adequate for Joule heating and metals are improper in light of the latter, leaving semiconductors as candidate materials. Further specifications can be made from the aforementioned performance targets. The requirements for the moderate melting temperature and the high crystallization time can be fulfilled by elements or compounds with relatively weaker covalent bond strength. In this respect, chalcogenide semiconductors based on group VI elements (Se or Te) are quite preferable because they tend to form one-dimensional chain-like bonding from bivalent characteristics, whereas group IV semiconductors (Si or Ge) have a 3-dimensional (3D) network of strong covalent bonding. Moreover, the demand on cycling performance of higher than 10^5 cycles prefers stoichiometric compounds to eutectic or peritectic compositions because there is much less probability of phase separation in the former material group. GeTe was an archetype of phase change material that encompasses the aforementioned required properties and has a particularly fast crystallization time of tens of nanoseconds and the crystallization temperature of 150°C–200°C [16]. Nonetheless, it has a troublesome problem of forming pinholes after repeated phase transformations [17]. This reliability issue was resolved by alloying Sb_2Te_3 compound with GeTe, which led to a broader composition range of useful phase change properties. Actually, the two compounds with the same space group symmetry $(R_{\bar{3}m})$ are readily mixed to form varying crystal structures so that several stoichiometric compounds of different compositions can exist in the pseudobinary GeTe–Sb_2Te_3 system (Fig. 1(a)). $Ge_2Sb_2Te_5$ is a stoichiometric mixture of two-GeTe and one-Sb_2Te_3. It should be noted that Sb_2Te_3 has lower crystallization and melting temperatures due to weaker bond strength (Ge–Te; 18.2 kJ/mol vs. Sb–Te; 11.5 kJ/mol) so that the crystallization of a GeTe–Sb_2Te_3 mixture becomes faster as the content of Sb_2Te_3 is increased, although the stability of the amorphous phase becomes slightly degraded. These are considered important characteristics in an engineering sense because it enables a purposeful control of cell characteristics according to the application fields (Fig. 1(b)).

2.3. Properties of $Ge_2Sb_2Te_5$ Phase Change Material

$Ge_2Sb_2Te_5$ phase change material shows some peculiar characteristics in its electrical, optical, thermal, and structural

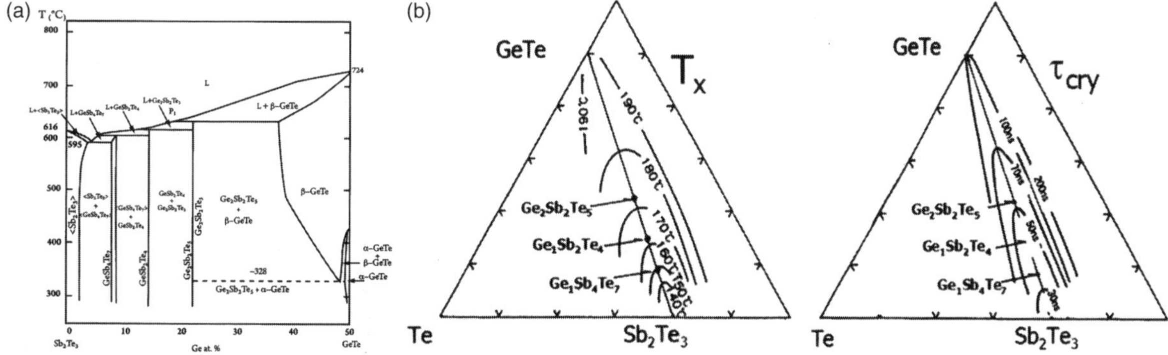

Figure 1. (a) GeTe–Sb_2Te_3 phase diagram. Reprinted with permission from [18], S. Bordas et al., *Thermochim. Acta* 107, 239 (1986). © 1986, Elsevier. (b) Crystallization temperatures and laser heating time for crystallization of pseudo-binary compounds in Ge–Sb–Te ternary phase diagram. Reprinted with permission from [19], N. Yamada et al., *J. Appl. Phys.* 69, 2849 (1991). © 1991, American Institute of Physics.

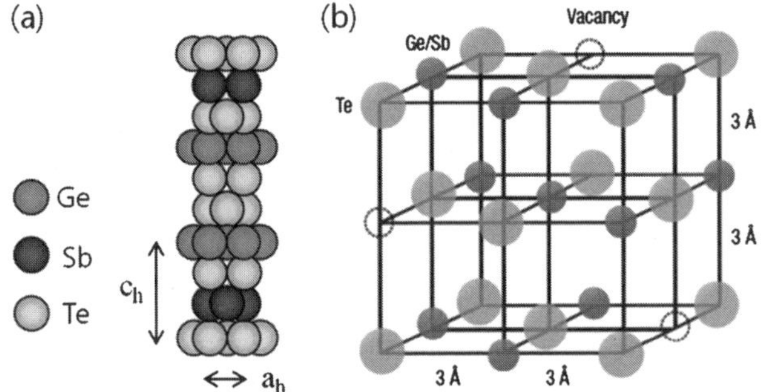

Figure 2. Schematics of (a) hexagonal close-packed (HCP) phase. Redrawn according to the reported stacking sequence by Reprinted with permission from [19], N. Yamada et al., *J. Appl. Phys.* 69, 2849 (1991). © 1991, American Institute of Physics, and (b) face-centered cubic (FCC) phase of $Ge_2Sb_2Te_5$ phase change material. Reprinted with permission from [2], M. Wuttig et al., *Nat. Mater.* 6, 824 (2007). © 2007, Nature Publishing Group.

properties [19–23]. Here, only the structural and electrical resistance changes during phase transformations of $Ge_2Sb_2Te_5$ phase change material are reviewed as a ground work for understanding the operation principles of phase change memory device. This will be considered in the following sections.

$Ge_2Sb_2Te_5$ phase change material has two polymorphic crystalline phases: hexagonal (Fig. 2(a)) and rock-salt type (Fig. 2(b)) phases. The hexagonal phase, which is more stable at high temperature, has the crystal structure of $p_{\bar{3}ml}$ with lattice parameters of $a_h = 4.2$ Å and $c_h = 17.0$ Å, where the stacking sequence of constituent atoms is known as Te–Sb–Te–Ge–Te–Te–Ge–Te–Sb–Te-..., although a slightly different stacking sequence was reported recently [24]. Meanwhile, it is generally known that the rock-salt type phase consists of two face-centered cubic (FCC) lattices; one is occupied by Te atoms, while the other is occupied by Ge, Sb, or a vacancy, and the relative occupancy of each species varies according to the composition of the GeTe–Sb_2Te_3 pseudobinary compounds.

Most models [25–27] on the fast crystallization of $Ge_2Sb_2Te_5$ phase change material are commonly characterized to assume similarity in atomic configurations between the rock-salt type crystalline phase and the amorphous phase. Figure 3 represents a simple but quite plausible account of atomic reconfiguration [2] on an (100) plane consisting of Te, Ge, Sb atoms and vacancy during successive phase changes. When the rock-salt phase is melted into a liquid phase, its long-range order is disrupted, but a short-range order between nearest neighboring atoms is preserved. In other words, types and numbers of neighboring atoms are almost unchanged in the liquid phase and its quenched form (amorphous phase) has a similar atomic configuration as well. Since very small atomic movements of only a few Å are just enough to restore the rock-salt type crystalline phase as depicted in Figure 3, the amorphous-to-crystalline transformation process can be completed very rapidly, i.e., within tens of nanoseconds.

The most attractive property of $Ge_2Sb_2Te_5$ as an active material of phase change memory is its large difference in electrical resistance between its amorphous and crystalline phases (Fig. 4(a)). With the increase of annealing temperature, an initially amorphous $Ge_2Sb_2Te_5$ undergoes abrupt reduction in electrical resistance successively at two different temperatures. The former reduction at near 150°C is due to transformation from amorphous to rock-salt or FCC phase, while the latter one (at about 350°C) resulted from transformation into hexagonal phase. From their slopes of dR/dT in Figure 4(b), it can be also noticed that the rock-salt type $Ge_2Sb_2Te_5$ shows a semiconducting property, whereas the hexagonal $Ge_2Sb_2Te_5$ shows a metallic property. For more information on the electronic, optical, and thermal properties of $Ge_2Sb_2Te_5$ phase change material, Refs. [20, 22, 23] are recommended.

2.4. Application-Specific Alloys

It used to be said that phase change memory had a strong potential for being a universal memory since it could make up the weak points of conventional memories (a low write speed of flash and the volatility of DRAM) with high memory capacities of above 1 Gbit. However, such potential is unlikely to be realized in the near term because known phase change materials are insufficient to provide a comparable performance level to that of DRAM, namely, a write endurance of more than 10^{10} cycles and a write speed of tens of nanoseconds.

Moreover, it is not easy to obtain a fast crystallization speed and long-time data stability at user temperatures at the same time since both require opposing crystallization and material characteristics of an amorphous phase. That is,

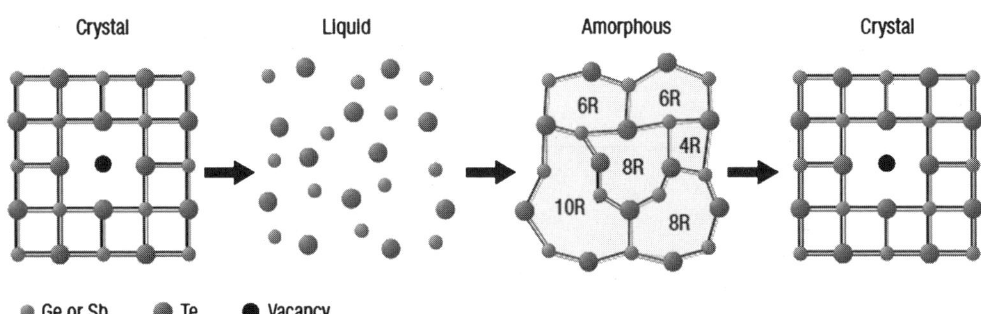

Figure 3. Schematic of arbitrary (100) plane in $Ge_2Sb_2Te_5$ phase change material showing a fast and reversible transformation between rock-salt type crystalline and amorphous phases. Reprinted with permission from [2], M. Wuttig and N. Yamada, *Nat. Mater.* 6, 824 (2007). © 2007, Nature Publishing Group.

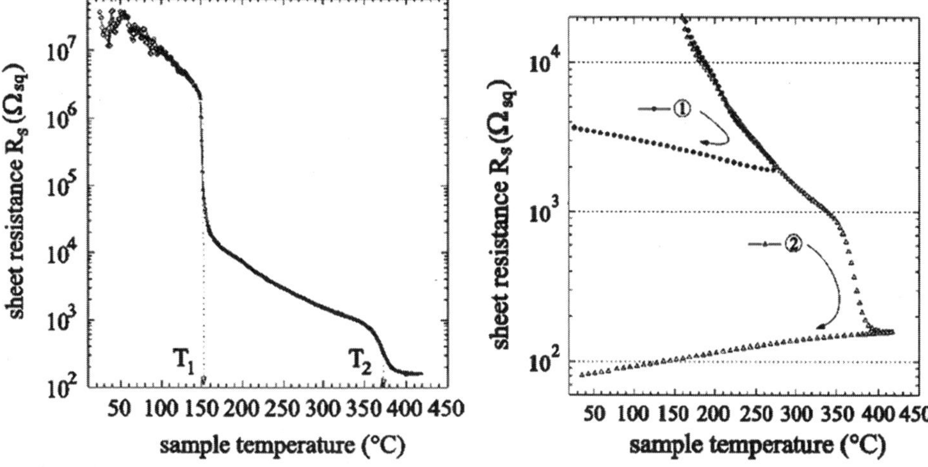

Figure 4. (a) Resistance change of $Ge_2Sb_2Te_5$ thin film as sample temperature is increased, where it is known that amorphous phase is transformed to FCC at T_1 and FCC is transformed to HCP at T_2, and (b) resistance changes as sample temperature is reversely decreased after the respective transformation from amorphous to FCC or from FCC to HCP. Reprinted with permission from [21], I. Friedrich et al., *J. Appl. Phys.* 87, 4130 (2000). ©, 2000, American Institute of Physics.

the former tends to prefer a low crystallization temperature with weaker bonds (e.g., mixture of covalent and metallic bonds) for a faster phase change of an amorphous phase, whereas the latter favors a relatively higher crystallization temperature with stronger bonds (e.g., three- or fourfold coordinated covalent bonds) for higher thermal stability of an amorphous phase. Figure 5 clearly shows a tradeoff relation between crystallization temperature and the time for phase change materials with eutectic Sb_7Te_3-based and Sb-based compositions: higher crystallization temperature (better data stability) tends to yield slower crystallization (lower write speed). Therefore, the development route of phase change materials should be different according to application fields.

2.4.1. High-Speed Crystallization Alloy

There have steadily been approaches to make the best use of the nonvolatility of phase change memory to replace or compensate a DRAM function in low-power mobile applications. For this, use of faster crystallizing materials with eutectic Sb_7Te_3-based [29] or Sb-based compositions [30, 31] has been attempted in electrical phase change memory. Commonly categorized as growth-dominant phase change materials, they are known to have increasingly faster crystallization speed as a data mark size becomes smaller for high-density optical recording. Accordingly, they also received much attention with regard to the potential for high-speed electrical memory applications. For example, Lee and colleagues [29] showed that Ge-doped SbTe alloy with the composition of Ge 5.3 at% Sb 77.7 at%, and Te 17 at% produces a faster set speed by an order of magnitude than mostly used $Ge_2Sb_2Te_5$, along with a guaranteed long-time data retention. However, further investigation and improvement are needed for these materials since there is an apparent drawback of increased reset current that leads to more power consumption.

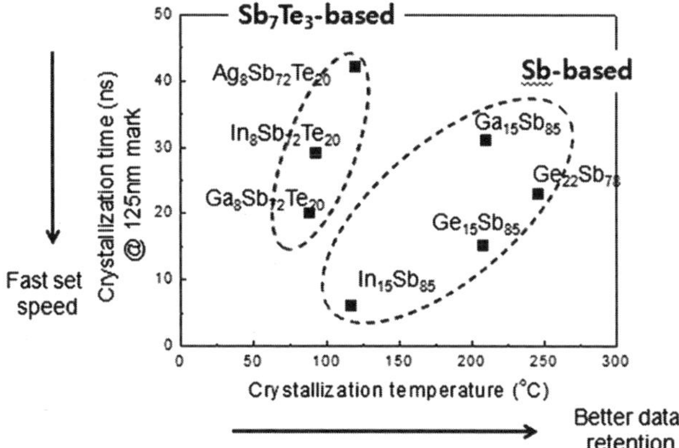

Figure 5. Laser-induced crystallization times at the 125-nm mark and the crystallization temperatures of eutectic Sb_7Te_3-based and Sb-based alloys. Data are extracted and reprinted with permission from [28], L. van Pieterson et al., *J. Appl. Phys.* 97, 083520 (2005). © 2005, American Institute of Physics.

2.4.2. High Data Stability Alloy

Current phase change materials can guarantee a long-time data stability at user temperatures in the range of 70°C to 85°C, which is suitable for mobile information technology (IT) applications. When a usable temperature is extended to higher temperatures than 100–150°C, a phase change memory can find use in other fields, such as automotive or aerospace applications. It has been recently reported that candidate phase change materials are doped In–Ge–Te [32] and Si–Sb–Te [33]. For these materials, 10-year-gurantee temperatures of amorphous phase are known to be 150°C and 100°C, respectively, which are superior to that of conventional $Ge_2Sb_2Te_5$. However, it should be noted that they have produced poor write endurance of at most 10^4 cycles and relatively slow set write speed.

3. DEVICE PHYSICS

3.1. Governing Equations

We introduce governing equations for write operations in a phase change memory cell. According to the first law of thermodynamics (energy conservation law), a 3D heat conduction equation for a volumetric heat source of $\dot{q}$ [W/m^3] is given by [34]

$$\vec{\nabla} \cdot (k \vec{\nabla} T) + \dot{q} = \rho C_p \frac{\partial T}{\partial t} \tag{1}$$

where k is thermal conductivity [W/m · K], ρ mass density [kg/m^3], and C_p heat capacity [J/kg · K]. For an electrical phase change memory cell, two types of heat source can be considered: One is a Joule heat from external current, and the other is a heat from thermoelectric Thompson effect $(-T \vec{\nabla} \cdot (S \vec{J})$ where, S is Seeback coefficient). Since the latter heat source is proven to be trivial in a phase change memory cell, especially with TiN electrode [35], heat generation is essentially due to Joule heat and the volumetric heat source of $\dot{q}$ at a constant voltage condition is given by

$$\dot{q} = \frac{I \cdot V}{v_{\text{heater}}} = \frac{I^2 \cdot R_{\text{heater}}}{v_{\text{heater}}} = J^2 \rho_{\text{heater}} \tag{2}$$

v_{heater} is a heater volume and R_{heater} is a heater resistance $(= \rho_{\text{heater}} \; (L_{\text{heater}}/A_{\text{heater}}))$ J representing a current density, (I/A_{heater}) and ρ_{heater} the electrical resistivity of heater, respectively; heater refers to all of heating elements, that is, phase change material and electrodes. At the same time, the current density J is determined by charge (electron and hole) current density equations and Poisson equation, as given by

$$J_n = qn\mu_n \mathsf{E} + qD_n \nabla_n; \text{ electron} \tag{3}$$

$$J_p = qp\mu_p \mathsf{E} - qD_p \nabla_p; \text{ hole} \tag{4}$$

$$\nabla^2 V = -\nabla \cdot \mathsf{E} = -\frac{q}{\varepsilon}(n - p) \tag{5}$$

where q is an electric charge, μ_n and μ_p electron and hole mobilities, D_n and D_p are electron and hole diffusivities, E electric field, and ε permittivity, respectively.

These governing Eqs. (1), (3)–(5) determine spatial and temporal temperature profiles during write or read operations in a phase change memory cell and may be utilized to characterize device performance for a given cell structure and operation conditions. Except in rare cases, the equations are not solvable by analytical methods and numerical solutions are sought for by computer-aided simulations. As an example, 2-dimensional (2D) temperature profiles are shown in Figure 6 for a reset operation with 0.8-mA and 100-ns pulse in a phase change memory cell with 90-nm technology [36], of which a simulation algorithm and the used material parameters are described elsewhere [37].

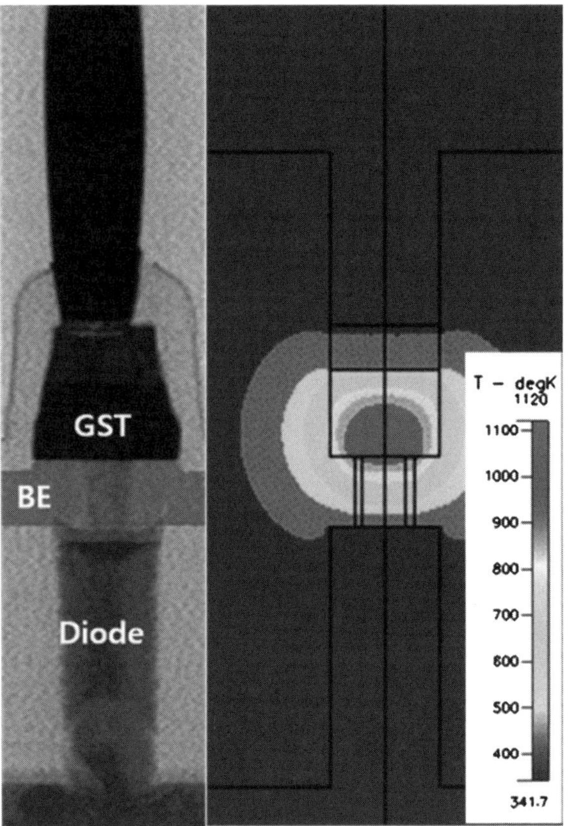

Figure 6. Transmission electron microscopy image of a cell in 512-Mbit PRAM (left) and 2-dimensional temperature profiles during a reset operation with 0.8 m-A and 100-ns pulse (right) from a numerical simulator. Reprinted with permission from [36], D. H. Kang et al., "VLSI Tech. Dig.," p. 96, 2007. © 2007, IEEE.

3.2. Set Write Operation

The write operation of making a low-resistive crystalline state is called "set" operation. Figure 7(a) shows the schematics of a set current pulse and the resulting temperature evolution that lead to the crystallization of an amorphous Ge–Sb–Te. From Figures 7(b and c), the resulting set state of a memory cell can be identified by the crystalline program volume and the corresponding low device resistance, respectively. Here, we first discuss the detailed processes comprising a set operation, i.e., threshold switching, crystallization, and subsequently set pulse engineering for better resistance distributions in a phase change memory array.

3.2.1. Threshold Switching

For amorphous chalcogenides, conducting metal glasses, and *a*-Si alike, an abrupt increase of current takes place without a significant structural change of an amorphous phase when the electric voltage is applied above a critical one. Such a transition from a low-conductive (off) to a high-conductive (on) state is called threshold switching, and the cut-off voltage is a threshold voltage. As representative examples, Figure 8 shows current–voltage characteristics and reproducible current and voltage waveforms as observed for a

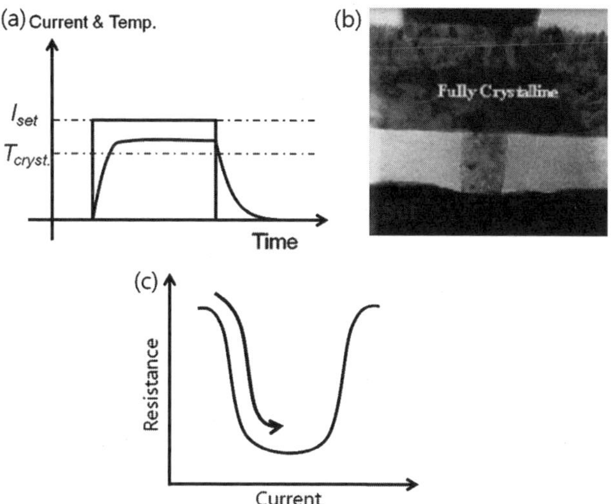

Figure 7. (a) Schematic of a single-square set pulse and the corresponding temperature profile, (b) transmission electron microscopy image of set state, (c) typical resistance change with respect to the current pulse height during set operation (arrow). Reprinted with permission from [38], F. Yeung et al., *Jpn. J. Appl. Phys.* 44, 2691 (2005). © 2005, The Japan Society of Applied Physics.

$Te_{48}As_{30}Si_{12}Ge_{10}$ glass during successive threshold switching phenomena in 60 Hz [39].

There are many models accounting for this switching behavior. Although they are based on different physical backgrounds such as impact ionization [20], the electrothermal effect [40], and the high-field Poole-Fenkel process [41], all of them are common in suggesting that an electrical switching takes place when the balance between charge generation (or injection) and annihilation rates cannot be maintained any longer above a threshold voltage. High current after threshold switching might induce a significant amount of Joule heat to make changes in the atomic arrangement of the high-conductive amorphous phase. In particular, an amorphous chalcogenide material with a relatively low crystallization temperature can transform to a low-resistive crystalline phase, and it remains in a high-conductive state when the electric voltage is off. The widely used $Ge_2Sb_2Te_5$ belongs to this category of memory-type switching material. On the other hand, some chalcogenides return to their original low-conductive states with no structural change when the applied voltage is off and are categorized as threshold-type switching materials. Recently, these materials are also under much attention because they can be applied to cell-selecting switch devices for stackable cross-point phase change memories [42]. Amphibious characteristics are also seen in a certain chalcogenide system depending on the relative amount of constituent elements. For example, in an Al–As–Te system [43], more covalent compositions such as $Al_{20}As_{15}Te_{65}$, $Al_{20}As_{25}Te_{55}$, and $Al_{20}As_{35}Te_{45}$ show a threshold-type switching, whereas a less covalent composition of $Al_{20}As_5Te_{75}$ represents a memory-type switching (Fig. 9).

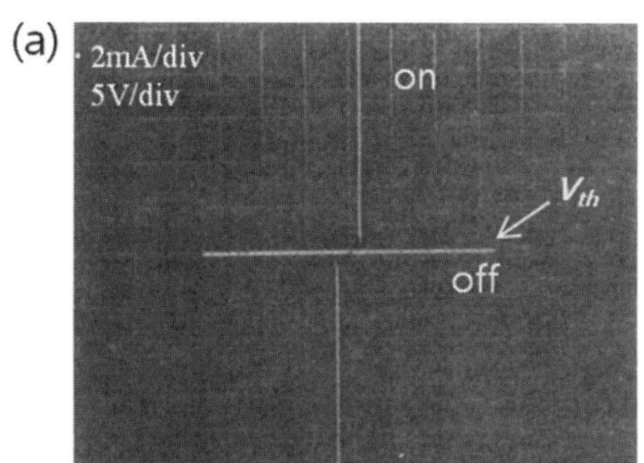

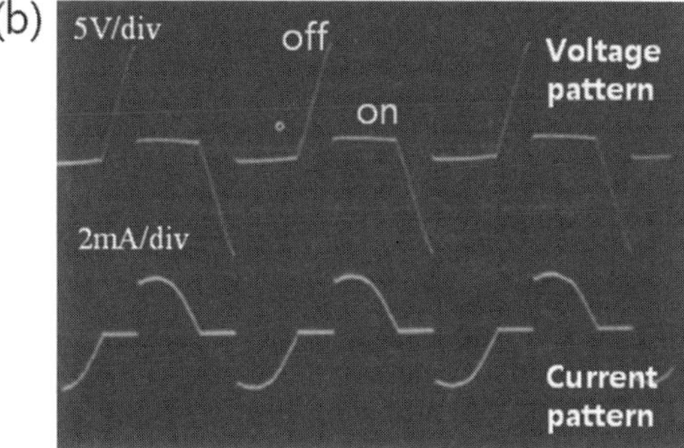

Figure 8. (a) Current–voltage characteristics, and (b) current and voltage pulse patterns in 60 Hz that represents the threshold switching in amorphous $Te_{48}As_{30}Si_{12}Ge_{10}$ film. Reprinted with permission from [39], S. R. Ovshinsky, *Phys. Rev. Lett.* 21, 1450 (1968). © 1968, American Physical Society.

3.2.2. Crystallization

Four decades ago, Ovshinsky [39] interpreted the resistance decrease after the set operation of a memory-type switching device, which was the result of the crystallization

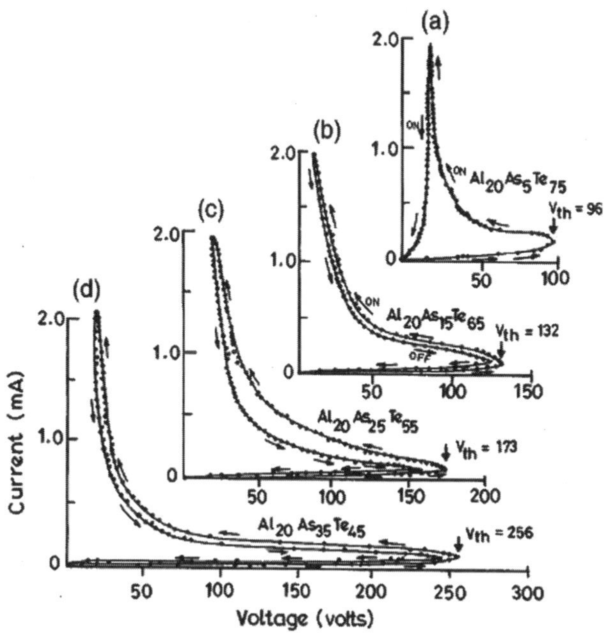

Figure 9. (a) $Al_{20}As_5Te_{75}$ represents a memory-type switching behavior, whereas (b) $Al_{20}As_{15}Te_{65}$, (c) $Al_{20}As_{25}Te_{55}$, (d) $Al_{20}As_{35}Te_{45}$ show threshold-type switching behaviors. Reprinted with permission from [43], S. Murugavel and S. Asokan, *J. Mater. Res.* 13, 2982 (1998). © 1998, Materials Research Society.

of a chalcogenide semiconductor material accompanying threshold switching phenomenon. It is important to understand this current-driven crystallization process because the programming speed of a phase change memory is essentially limited by the crystallization process, which is relatively sluggish compared with the melting and amorphization process for a reset programming operation (see Section 3.3, "Reset Write Operation"). There is still uncertainty on its starting point during a set operation [44, 45], but the current-induced crystallization process is mostly understood as described in the following paragraphs.

When Joule heat generated by the increased current after a threshold switching raises the temperature of an amorphous program volume above its crystallization temperature (T_x), the amorphous volume is thermally activated to undergo nucleation and growth of a more stable crystalline phase. Figure 10(a) shows a cartoon of a program volume in a damascene-type phase change memory cell, where the temperature in the program volume is well above the crystallization temperature of $Ge_2Sb_2Te_5$ material. As in the case of a laser-induced heating in optical recording media [46], crystallization behavior during the set operation can be treated by classical theories of nucleation and growth, since it is believed from experimental results [44] that nucleation of a memory-type switching chalcogenide like $Ge_2Sb_2Te_5$ begins upon electrical threshold switching and requires a power- or temperature-dependent finite time for incubation of the $Ge_2Sb_2Te_5$ nuclei. After an incubation time elapses, nuclei are randomly distributed in the otherwise amorphous volume; in the case of $Ge_2Sb_2Te_5$, it crystallizes in the nucleation-dominant mode (Fig. 10(b)). When a set pulse duration is long enough for nuclei to grow and meet together, a high-conductive path (percolation) [47, 48] can be formed across the program volume (Fig. 10(c)). As a result, the resistance of cell is abruptly decreased to reach a low value of set state.

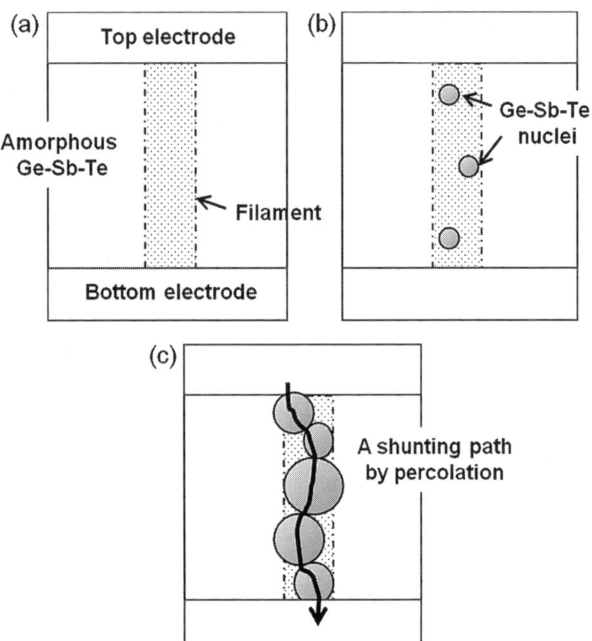

Figure 10. Cartoons of a program volume in damascene-type phase change memory cell. When after threshold switching event takes place, (a) the temperature of a program volume increases above crystallization temperature of $Ge_2Sb_2Te_5$ material, (b) Ge–Sb–Te nuclei sporadically form as a result of nucleation and growth, and successively (c) an electrical shunting path across the program volume between electrodes is made by percolation.

3.2.3. *Write Pulse Engineering*

Compared with a reset write operation, which will be reviewed in the next section, a set write operation is much slower because it involves the most time-consuming crystallization process, resulting in a set pulse width that is longer by an order of magnitude than that of a reset pulse width. Therefore, the write performance of a high-density phase change memory depends on how effectively numerous memory cells can be crystallized at a time. Moreover, due to process-induced variations in contact geometry and material composition and/or subtle variations in the short-range order of the programmed amorphous state over different writes, each cell may have not only different Joule-heating efficiency (different temperature profile), but each cell may also have varying crystallization temperature, thus showing a different crystallization behavior from one another even at the constant-current set operation. (It is worth noting that a constant-current condition is not easy to obtain, so many circuit designers and process engineers are trying to minimize variations of input current in high-density phase change memory devices). Such cell-to-cell or write-to-write inconsistencies in crystallization behavior can be easily understood with the aid of a temperature-time-transformation (*T–T–T*) diagram. Figure 11 shows an example of schematic *T–T–T* diagrams (only five cells are considered for simplicity). According to the aforementioned several variations, five cells have different crystallization temperatures and melting temperatures. The incubation time (t_{inc}) is defined as the intersection of the temperature profile and transformation curves at nucleation. The percolation time (t_{per}) is the intersection of the temperature profile and transformation curve at percolation threshold, respectively, where the percolation threshold is assumed to be 35%. Thus, it can be noticed that

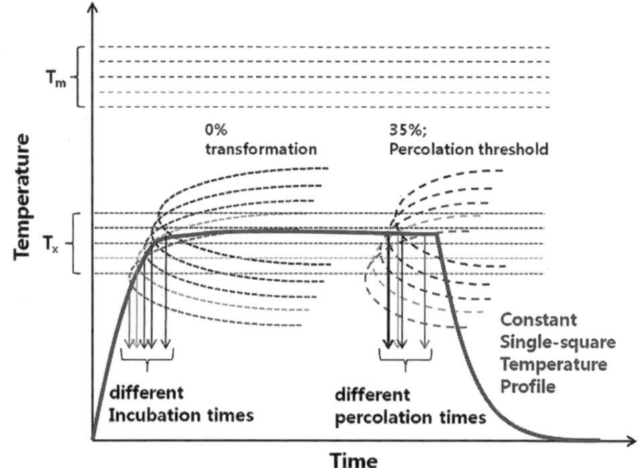

Figure 11. An example of schematic *T–T–T* diagrams of phase change memory cells, where five cells are only considered under the same Joule heating efficiency for simplicity.

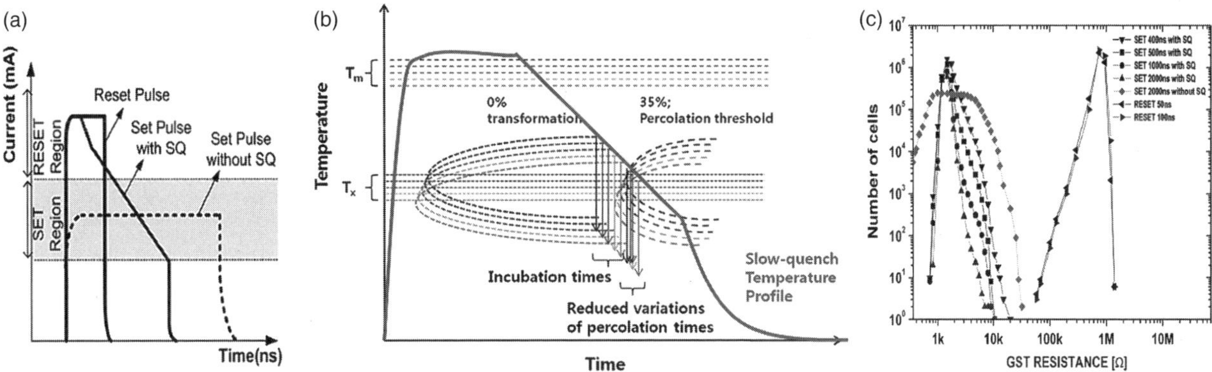

Figure 12. (a) Schematic shapes of conventional single-square pulse and slow-quench pulse, (b) *T–T–T* diagrams in case of slow-quench set operation, where it is noted that the variation of percolation times are significantly reduced compared with the conventional one, (c) comparison of set resistance distribution in 4-Mbit array between conventional single-square pulse and slow-quench pulse. (a and c) are reprinted with permission from [49], K.-J. Lee et al., *IEEE J. Solid-State Circuits* 43, 150 (2008). © 2008, IEEE.

nucleation and percolation times are most likely to spread among different cells or writes.

An effective way of optimizing a set process for a better performance is to use a set pulse of a slow-quench scheme instead of a conventional single-square pulse. A set pulse with a slow-quench trail induces crystallization from a liquid (melt) phase by a slow cooling in contrast to a solid-state crystallization by a single-square pulse (Fig. 12(a)). A slow-quench pulse works in two ways to produce a better distribution in set resistance. In one way, it tends to homogenize the preprogrammed amorphous state by melting so that crystallization in each cell can follow more similar transformation curves. In another way, the pulse works to reduce cell-to-cell variation in the time interval between incubation and percolation stages by driving crystallization to proceed during the cooling process (Fig. 12(b)). It was experimentally proven that a set pulse with a slow-quench trail can make a better distribution in set resistance of a 4-Mbit phase change memory array (Fig. 12(c)) [49].

3.3. Reset Write Operation

When Joule heating by a short current pulse with a duration of tens of nanoseconds raises the temperature in the program volume above the melting temperature (T_m) of a phase change material, as schematically shown in Figure 13(a), the program volume is melted to be a liquid. Subsequently, it is quenched well below its glass transition temperature (T_g), while the accumulated heat is rapidly dissipated into the surrounding electrodes and dielectric materials. As a result, an amorphous phase can be formed in the program volume (Fig. 13(b)). Since this vitrified phase maintains a disordered atomic arrangement of liquid, its resistance is higher than that of the more-ordered crystalline phase [21]. For instance, the resistance of an amorphous $Ge_2Sb_2Te_5$ (reset) is larger by two or three orders of magnitude than that of a crystalline one (Fig. 13(c)).

3.3.1. Reset Current and Dynamic Resistance

Two key parameters affect not only the performance of a phase change memory cell itself but eventually the competitiveness of the memory chip in the mass production stage. They are reset current (I_{reset}) and dynamic resistance (R_{dyn}). Reset current is defined as a minimum current to obtain a cell resistance above a target value corresponding to a reset data state (Fig. 14(a)). Dynamic resistance is the resistance of heating elements (comprising a phase change material and electrodes) during a reset operation, and it determines the amount of Joule heat at a given current. It is generally known [50] that an increased dynamic resistance tends to lower the reset current but it increases the set resistance, as schematically depicted in Figure 14(b). Thus, it is necessary to balance them to optimize the performance of a phase change memory cell.

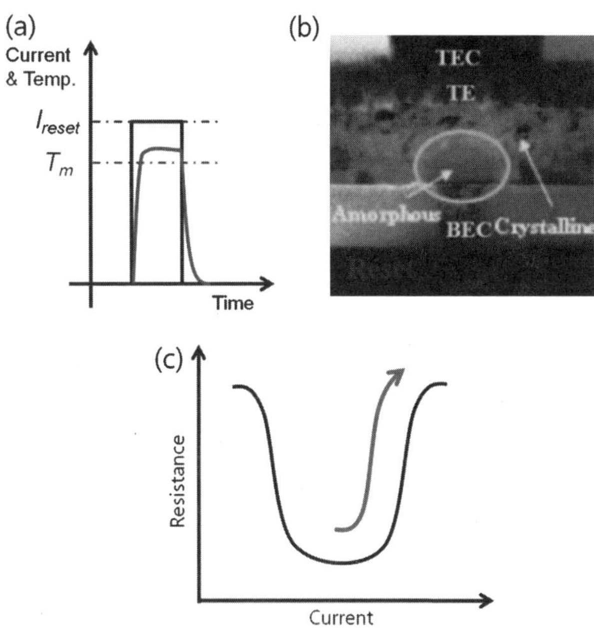

Figure 13. (a) Schematic of a current pulse and the corresponding temperature profile during a reset write operation, (b) transmission electron microscopy image of reset state in a mushroom-type phase change memory cell, (c) typical resistance change during reset operations (arrow). Reprinted with permission from [38], F. Yeung et al., *Jpn. J. Appl. Phys.* 44, 2691 (2005). © 2005, The Japan Society of Applied Physics.

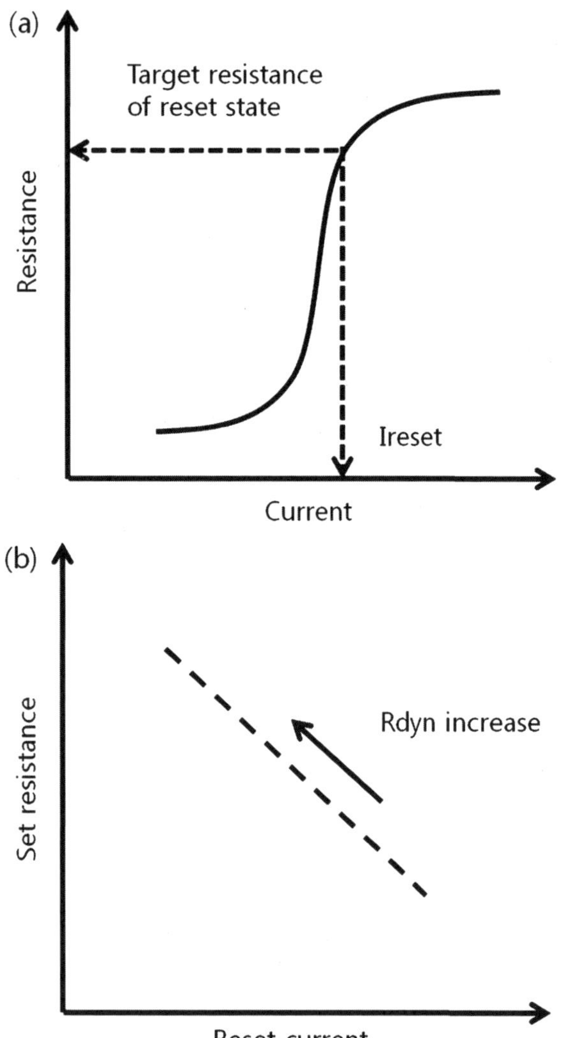

Figure 14. (a) Typical curve of low-field resistance with respect to input current pulse in a phase change memory cell, (b) typical relations of reset current and set resistance.

3.3.2. Power Delivery

The largest power is consumed at a reset write operation or at the beginning of a set write operation with a slow-quench because current-induced heat should be sufficiently large to increase the temperature at a program volume above the melting temperature of a phase change material. Thus, it is critical to deliver the power most effectively on these occasions. In the case of a constant-voltage V operation, a delivered power P can be expressed by,

$$P = VI = I^2 R_{dyn} \tag{6}$$

Since a current I is given by

$$I = V/(R_{dyn} + R_{para}) \tag{7}$$

where R_{para} represents parasitic resistances such as the on-resistance of cell-selecting switch device (metal-oxide-semiconductor field-effect transistor, bipolar junction transistor, or diode) and interconnect resistances. Accordingly, Eq. (6) becomes

$$P = V^2 R_{dyn}/(R_{dyn} + R_{para})^2 \tag{8}$$

The maximum power delivery is achieved at the condition of $R_{dyn} = R_{para}$, where the first derivative of Eq. (8) is zero. To satisfy this condition, careful optimizations are to be exercised in the procedures of cell fabrication process as well as circuit design. The less parasitic resistances becomes, the more power can be delivered (Fig. 15). For this reason, an advanced technique such as Cu back-end metallization is adopted together with high-performance complementary metal-oxide-semiconductor scheme for peripheral circuits in the development line of a phase change memory device.

3.4. Read Operation

3.4.1. Nondestructive Reading

A programmed state is recognized as either a high-resistive reset state or a low-resistive set state depending on the relative magnitude of its measured resistance to a reference value. For a fast read speed, a high-read voltage or current is most favored to reduce a resistive-capacitive time delay. For one thing, a higher voltage or current gives rise to a lower resistance according to nonlinear I–V characteristics of an amorphous phase in the subthreshold region of its I–V curve (Fig. 16(a)). In addition, it can minimize the charging time of the parasitic capacitance as readily noticed from $t = CV/I_{capa}$ where I_{capa} is a charging current of parasitic capacitors. On the contrary, a read voltage should be lower than the threshold voltage of an amorphous phase change material. Otherwise, the increased current by threshold switching may decrease the resistance of an amorphous (reset data) state by partial crystallization process. Thus, it is very critical for a read voltage to be far lower than the threshold voltage. Recently, Lavizzari and others [51] suggested that a maximum read voltage is proper to be approximately 70% of a known threshold voltage when considering read noises such as $1/f$ noises as well as threshold switching variations of numerous cells in a high-density phase change memory device (Fig. 16(b)). Therefore, the read voltage or current should also be carefully chosen for reliable and high-speed read operations. Usually, a read speed is as fast as 10–20 ns for a well-designed phase change memory cell.

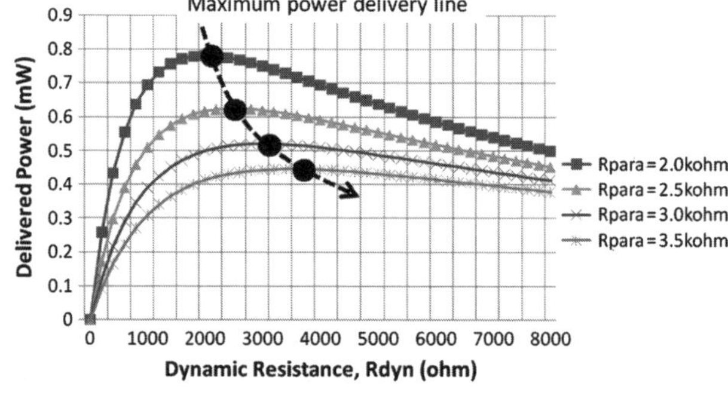

Figure 15. Delivered power as a function of dynamic resistance at various parasitic resistances, where the applied voltage pulse is 2.5 V.

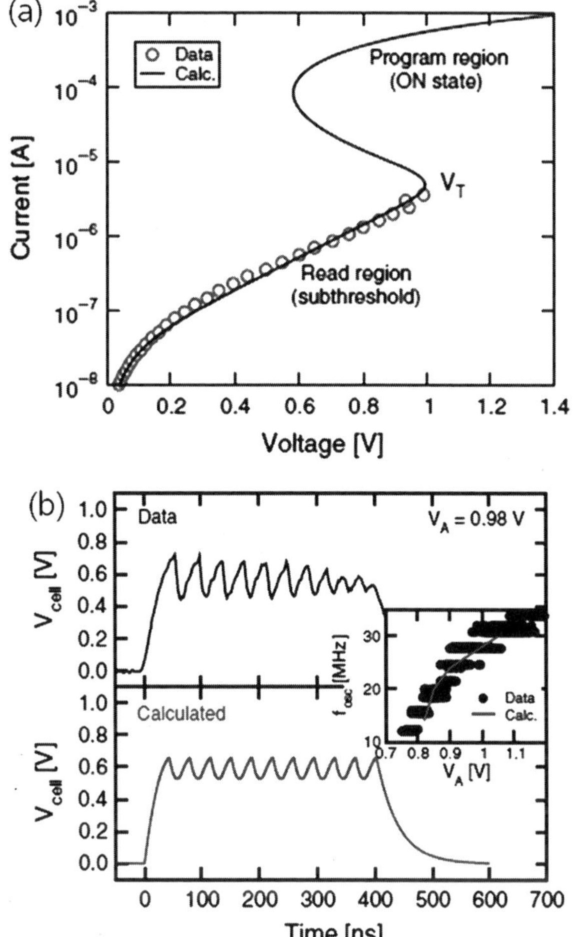

Figure 16. (a) Typical I–V curve in the reset state, (b) voltage fluctuation across cell due to switching and recovery oscillations. (a and b) are reprinted with permission from [51], S. Lavizzari et al., "IEDM Tech. Dig.," p. 1, 2008. © 2008, IEEE.

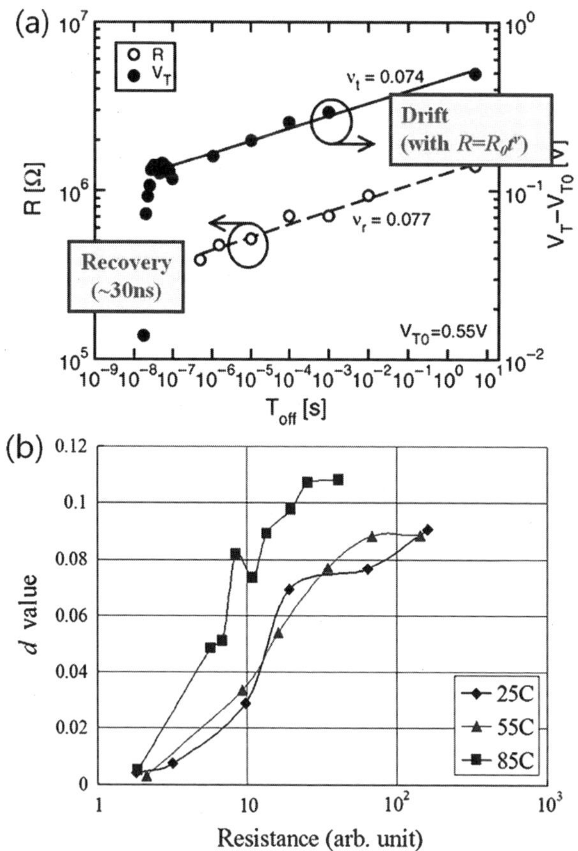

Figure 17. (a) Recovery and resistance drift. Reprinted with permission from [52], D. Ielmini et al., *IEEE Trans. Electron Devices.* 54, 308 (2007). © 2007, IEEE. (b) Drift coefficient changes with respect to initial resistance value and ambient temperature. Reprinted with permission from [54], D. H. Kang et al., "IEDM Tech. Dig.," p. 98, 2008. © 2008, IEEE.

Some due remarks are in order with regard to two characteristic phenomena that involve undesirable changes in the resistance values of data states. One is resistance drift and the other is resistance fluctuation, the former referring to an increase of reset resistance with the lapse of time and inherited from an intrinsic property of an amorphous chalcogenide semiconductor. Meanwhile, the latter refers to the deterioration of set resistance and is supposed to result in part from extrinsic attributes of the interfaces between phase change material and electrodes.

3.4.2. Resistance Drift and Resistance Fluctuation

It has been observed that the resistance of a high-resistive amorphous state (reset data) tends to increase with the lapse of time upon the termination of a reset write pulse. The resistance rises rapidly for the initial tens of nanoseconds and then increases gradually over time with power-law time dependency of $R = R_0 t^d$ where R_0 is an initial resistance at $t = 0$ and d is called a drift coefficient (Fig. 17(a)) [52]. The initial increase is called a recovery, and a recovery time is thought of as an escaping or recombining time of populated charge carriers immediately after the end of a reset pulse. Recovery time is too short to be of importance in practice. Alternatively, the subsequent increase known as resistance drift is to be carefully considered when designing a sensing logic, especially for write-and-verify programming. This is because it may cause some read delay for verifying a previous write operation. Resistance drift has been found to be inherent in an amorphous chalcogenide semiconductor like $Ge_2Sb_2Te_5$ phase change material, and it is due to the relaxation of an amorphous structural accompanied with the reduction of traps, such as dangling and distorted bonds [52, 53]. It has been also reported [54] that the drift coefficient d depends on the composition of a phase change material, the ambient temperature, and the initial resistance (Fig. 17(b)). Since this resistance increment is undesirable and troublesome, there have been approaches to suppress them with a new composition of phase change memory material [55].

Meanwhile, it is inevitable to have some fluctuations in set or reset resistance of a cell at repeated write operations due to several sources. These include Joule heat that varies with irregular programming current from circuit noise and dissimilar atomic structures of the successive programmed states from sporadic nucleation [56], a random behavior of percolation process during crystallization [47, 48], or a diversely disordered nature of amorphous states [57]. In addition, instabilities of the interface between phase change material and electrodes due to improper cleaning or contamination may make resistance fluctuations worse, especially as the relative portion of contact resistance in a device resistance becomes larger with the device size scaled down [58]. Since these resistance fluctuations may be critically large so as not to properly define a low-resistive set state in particular, it should be minimized by process optimization or through designing noise-immune programming circuits.

4. DEVICE FABRICATION

Phase change memory can be made by well-established Si processing technologies except some processes for storage elements, including a phase change material. Here, we first review underlying design concepts of the cell architecture and then describe the key processes that produce the cell select switch, bottom electrode, phase change material, and the top electrode in sequence.

4.1. Cell Design Concept

Most process technologies for semiconductor memories have been developed and well optimized to enable a memory unit cell to have an increasingly smaller dimension, thereby to enhance cost-competitiveness for generating more and more chips per wafer. When it comes to designing the cell architecture of a phase change memory, heat management is a primary concern. This is because a write operation of the memory cell is intrinsically a power-consuming process that comprises current-induced heat generation and dissipation on a time scale of tens or hundreds of nanoseconds. In order to generate Joule heat effectively, designers of the cell architecture have made the best use of the current crowding effect by diminishing the contact area between a phase change material and a bottom electrode using various patterning techniques [59–62], or they have employed electrodes of higher electrical resistivities [63, 64], or a phase change material doped with light elements such as oxygen [65], nitrogen [66], or carbon [67].

However, such device geometry or material designed for a better heating efficiency unfavorably increases the low-field resistance of a set state due to a small contact area or a high resistivity of an electrode material, resulting in diminished write and read speed or a narrower read sensing margin [68]. Thus, it has been critical to keep set resistance unaffected while improving the efficiency of Joule heating. One possible solution is to optimize the dimensions of a phase change material and an electrode. Using computer-aided numerical simulation for a mushroom-type cell with a fixed contact size U. Russo and others [69] have shown that there exists an optimum ratio in the relative height of a phase change material layer to that of an electrode layer that can provide a maximum heat efficiency for reset programming (Fig. 18; left) without affecting the set resistance (Fig. 18; right).

Meanwhile, heat dissipation is another critical factor in thermal design of a memory cell architecture because it greatly influences reset resistance and reset current by way of modulating the quenching rate during a reset operation. Recently, evidence suggested [36] that an immediate heat dissipation right after a pulse-off is most favored to avoid an over-programming (in which programming current is superfluously higher than the required current), which frequently occurs during parallel writing on a few hundreds of megabit cell array. As can be seen from the trace of open-square symbols in Figure 19(a) that refers to the case of a nonoptimized cell, reset writing at an over-programming condition may end in failure due to poor heat dissipation posterior to a reset pulse. As evidenced in Figure 19(b), such reset degradation is due to the fact that a program volume was not fully amorphized but partially crystallized by nondissipated heat in its surrounding. This problem can be significantly suppressed (refer to the trace of solid-square symbols in Fig. 19(a)) by introducing an additional heat-dissipating layer between a bottom electrode and a diode switch (Fig. 19(c)).

4.2. Cell Integration

Like in other memories, a phase change memory is composed of numerous cell blocks. Generally, each block has nearly a million cells that are located at the intersections of word lines and bit lines, and each cell consists of one switch

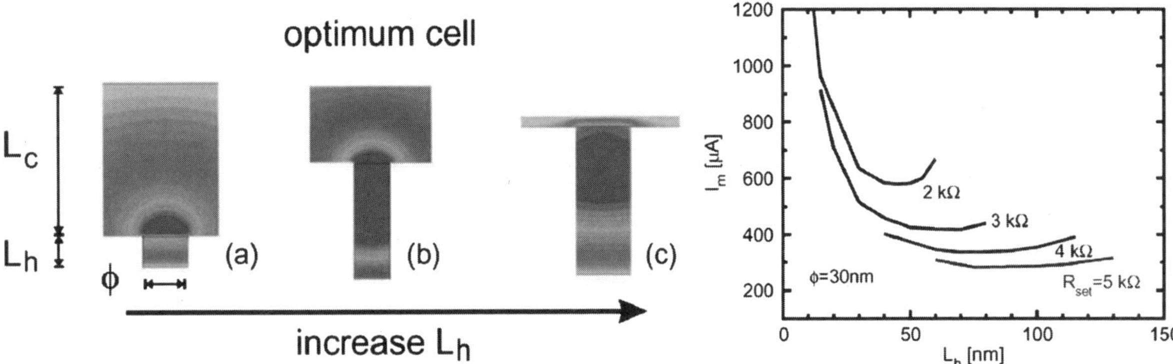

Figure 18. (Left) Heat profiles at three different ratios of phase change material height (L_c) and electrode height (L_h) at a fixed contact size of Φ, (right) I_m (the current at which melt is initially formed) versus electrode height at various set resistances, where there exist minima of I_m at respective set resistance values. Reprinted with permission from [69], U. Russo et al., *IEEE Trans. Electron Devices* 55, 506 (2008). © 2008, IEEE.

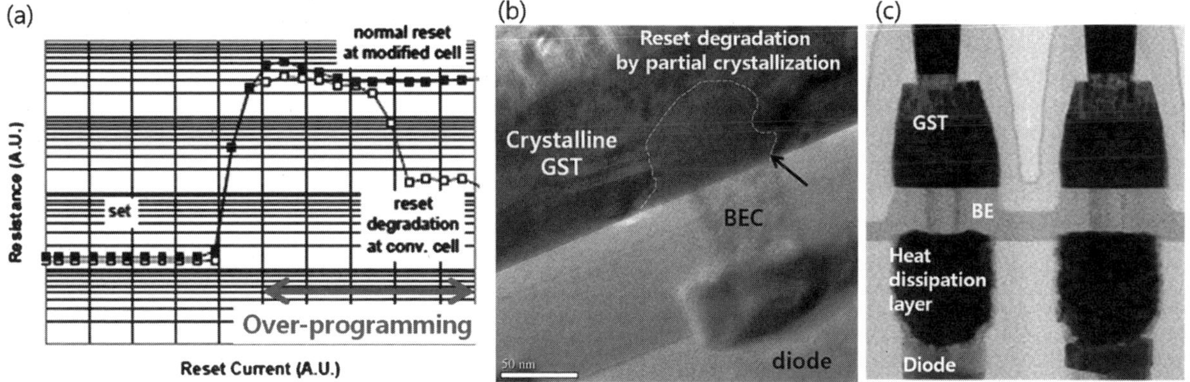

Figure 19. (a) Low-field resistance with respect to programming current, where the reset resistance has failed to reach the target value at over-programming in a thermally non-optimized cell, (b) reset degradation by partial crystallization due to residual heat at over-programming, where it is noted that a high-conductive path is shown between bottom electrode and crystalline Ge–Sb–Te as indicated by an arrow, (c) a thermally modified cell layer without reset degradation in the case of over-programming condition. Reprinted with permission from [36], D. H. Kang et al., "VLSI Tech. Dig.," p. 96, 2007. © 2007, IEEE.

and one resistor. Figure 20 shows a schematic and a cross-section view of a partial cell block, respectively, where a unit cell has a diode-type switch and a resistor of $Ge_2Sb_2Te_5$ phase change material.

4.2.1. Cell-Select Switch

A cell-select switch in a phase change memory device has to meet four requirements:

(1) it should deliver enough current to melt the hot spot of a $Ge_2Sb_2Te_5$ resistor when selected (switch on),
(2) it should deliver as little current as possible when unselected (switch off); otherwise, the resulting off-current may cause malfunctions in write or read operation and significant leakage current may also be produced,
(3) the area of this switch device should be as small as possible for high cell efficiency, and
(4) the switch device should be scalable in successive generations.

In these respects, it is believed that a diode-type switch [70] or a bipolar junction transistor [62] is preferable to the commonly used metal-oxide-semiconductor field-effect-transistor (MOSFET), especially for stand-alone applications. Figure 21(a) compares the current drivability of a p–n diode with that of a MOSFET switch at varying technology nodes. It is worth noting that a p–n diode switch can supply much more current than a MOSFET switch of an active area twice as large at varying technology nodes.

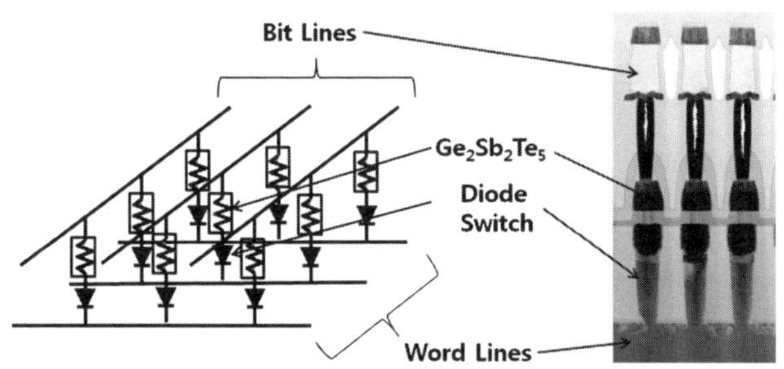

Figure 20. Schematic and transmission electron microscopy image of a partial cell block. A unit cell consisting of a diode-type switch and a $Ge_2Sb_2Te_5$ resistor is located at the cross point of the word line and the bit line.

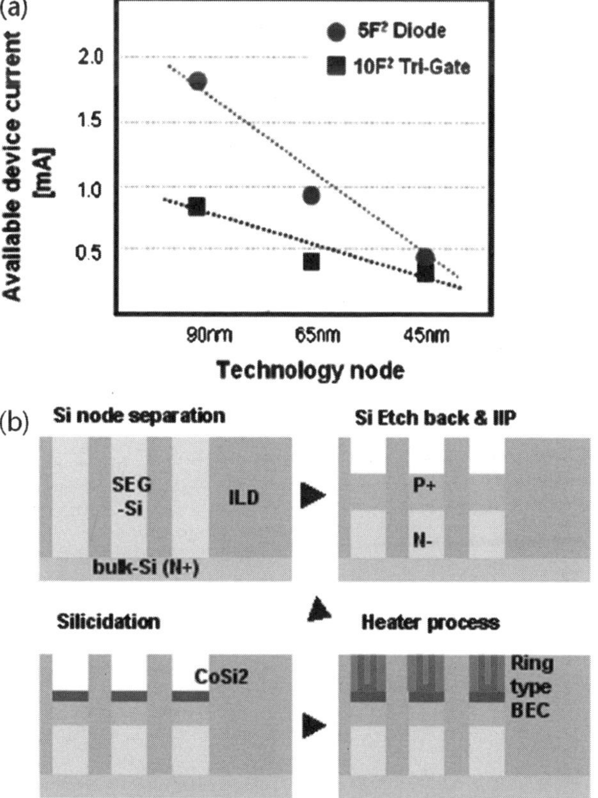

Figure 21. (a) Comparison of on-current drivability of diode switch ($5F^2$) and MOSFET switch ($10F^2$) at varying technology nodes, where F is a minimum feature size, and (b) schematic diagrams show fabrication procedures of p–n diode switches in 512-Mbit phase change memory with 90-nm technology. Reprinted with permission from [70], J. H. Oh et al., "IEDM Tech. Dig.," p. 1, 2006. © 2006, IEEE.

The fabrication procedures of *p–n* diode switches in the 512-Mbit phase change memory of 90-nm technology are schematically described in Figure 21(b). Firstly, a silicon epitaxial layer is vertically grown through the silicon epitaxial growth method in order to fill contact arrays on an n^+ doped Si substrate with shallow trench isolation. Next, ion implantations with phosphor and boron are sequentially performed to make a *p–n* junction in the middle of an epilayer. Subsequently, a cobalt film is deposited and then silicidated by an appropriate heat treatment to form a $CoSi_2$ layer of a low contact resistance. Finally, a bottom electrode, such as a ring-type one in Figure 21(b), is made on the top of a $CoSi_2$/*p–n* vertical diode. (Also see Section 4.2.2, "Bottom Electrode.")

4.2.2. Bottom Electrode

The bottom electrode fabrication has been focused on minimizing the contact area of a physically and chemically reliable electrode material with a phase change material. A common electrode material is titanium nitride (TiN), which has been widely used as a diffusion barrier between silicon and interconnect materials such as aluminum and tungsten due to its low resistivity (20 μohm · cm), good adhesion, superior chemical stability with Al or W metal, high robustness against a high current density of above 20 MA/cm^2, and well-developed physical or chemical deposition techniques to also produce an excellent conformality [71, 72]. In parallel, there have also been pursuits of electrode materials with higher Joule heating efficiencies for low power consumption. Although transition metal oxides [63, 64, 73] and some nitrides, such as silicon tantalum nitride [74] or oxidized titanium nitride [75], were effective to reduce a reset current, their practical use must wait for further qualification as to whether they may cause an undesirable increase of set resistance and also have degrading properties during write operations for above 10^5 cycles. Since the so-called ring-type [61] and line-type electrode [62, 76] schemes show higher manufacturability among several suggested schemes, we have introduced the fabrication procedures of the two in detail.

4.2.2.1 Ring-Type. Figure 22 depicts the key processes of a ring-type electrode scheme. After making contact holes on a doubly stacked dielectric (nitride/oxide) mold by normal photolithography and reactive ion etching (RIE), a dielectric spacer is formed at the sidewall of each contact hole via conformal chemical vapor deposition and the reactive-ion etching (RIE) process to obtain sublithographic size patterns. Then, a heater electrode and a core oxide are sequentially deposited to fill the contact holes (Fig. 22; upper left). Next, chemical-mechanical planarization technology is applied to leave only the core oxide and the heater electrode inside the contact holes to isolate one hole from another (Fig. 22; upper right). Subsequently, the top oxide of the doubly stacked mold is selectively etched back by RIE (Fig. 22; lower right). Finally, the extruded core oxide and heater is removed cleanly by chemical-mechanical polishing (Fig. 22; lower left). Although this scheme requires somewhat complicated processes, it produces highly reliable and uniform contact holes and also provides a good controllability of the contact area with a phase change material by means of varying thickness of the heater metal.

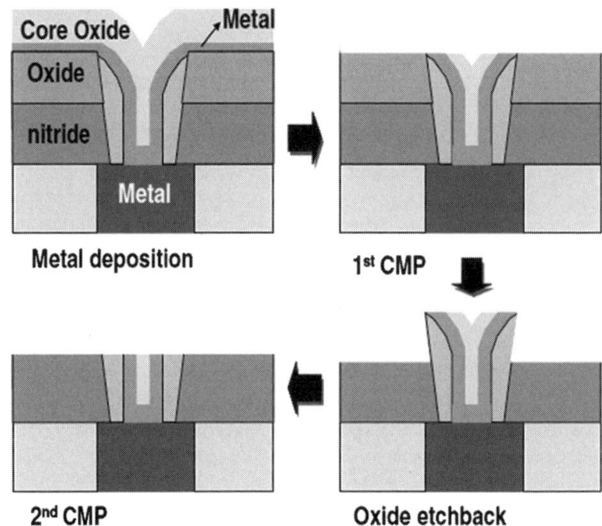

Figure 22. Key process flows of ring-type electrode scheme. Reprinted with permission from [61], K. C. Ryoo et al., *Jpn. J. Appl. Phys.* 46, 2001 (2007). © 2007, The Japan Society of Applied Physics.

4.2.2.2 Line-Type. A line-type electrode scheme has two advantages over the conventional pillar-type or the aforementioned ring-type electrode scheme despite its somewhat

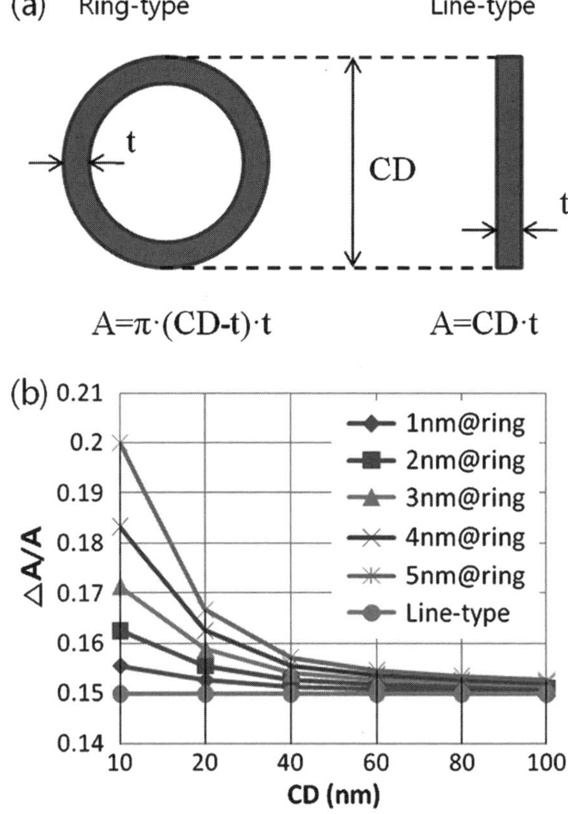

Figure 23. (a) Top schematic views of ring- and line-type contact shape, (b) contact area variations with respect to critical dimension (CD) and bottom electrode thickness when process-induced variations in CD and electrode thickness are 10% and 5%.

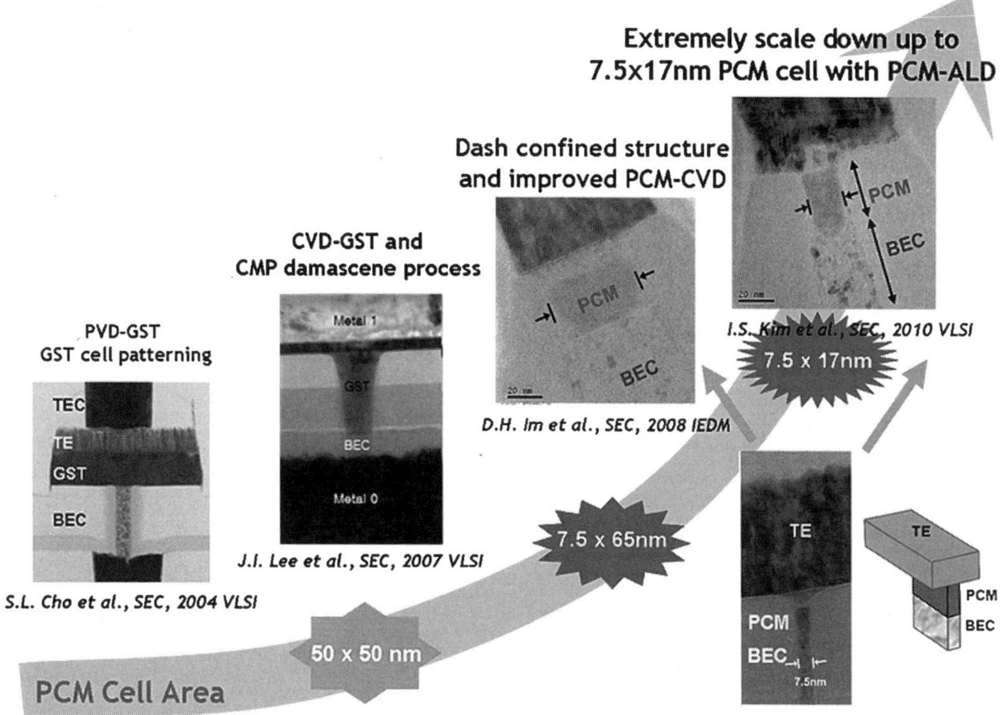

Figure 24. Technology trend of the cell architecture in phase change memory, where it is noted that a bottom electrode scheme is changed from pillar or ring-type to line-type at below tens of nm technology nodes. Reprinted with permission from [77], D. H. Ahn et al., "Proc. Euro. Symp. Phase Change Ovonic Sci.," 2010. © 2010, European\Phase Change and Ovonics Symposium.

complicated fabrication procedures. One advantage is less variation in contact area; the degree of variation in contact area is one of the key factors determining a reset current and it is attributed to process-induced variations in critical dimension (CD) and electrode thickness. Contact area variations ($\Delta A/A$, where A is contact area) in ring-type and line-type electrode schemes are given by Eqs. (9) and (10), respectively. Assuming that process-induced variations in CD and electrode thickness are 10% and 5%, respectively, we find that contact area variation in line-type is not only smaller than in ring-type, but it also remains unchanged with CD (Fig. 23). The other advantage is that the line-type scheme is further scalable down to sub-10 nm because an electrode thickness can be made sufficiently small by an advanced thin film growth technique such as atomic layer deposition. The recent technology trend of the cell architecture of phase change memory is described in Figure 24 where a bottom electrode scheme is shown to change from pillar or ring-type to line-type at below tens of nanometers.

$$\frac{\Delta A}{A} = \frac{\Delta CD}{CD - t} + \frac{\Delta t(CD - 2t)}{t(CD - t)} \tag{9}$$

$$\frac{\Delta A}{A} = \frac{\Delta CD}{CD} + \frac{\Delta t}{t} \tag{10}$$

The so-called μ-trench electrode scheme is an example of line-type bottom electrodes schemes. Here, we introduce step-by-step fabrication procedures of the scheme as schematically described in the upper diagram of Figure 25. At the starting stage, an electrode material is conformally deposited and anisotropically etched back to remain at the sidewalls of trenched patterns. When a dielectric material is filled into trenches and then planarized by CMP, x-directional line patterns of electrode are revealed periodically along the y-direction on the top surface. After deposition of an additional dielectric on this flat surface, μ-trenches are formed along the y-direction by conventional photolithography and dry etch process. Subsequently, a Ge–Sb–Te phase change material layer and a top electrode are sequentially deposited and patterned in parallel with the y-direction. These overlying patterns should be aligned precisely to seal the underlying μ-trench patterns and be separated from each other by anisotropic dry etch process. Shown in Figure 25 are transmission electron microscopy (TEM) images of the resulting μ-trench electrode scheme along the x- and y-directions.

4.2.3. Phase Change Material

Traditional semiconductor fabrication facilities had been unaccustomed to phase change materials such as $Ge_2Sb_2Te_5$ until the early 2000s. However, it was not too long before this phase change material became highly adaptable to most Si-based processes. It has been proven that the material can be uniformly grown on 8″ or 12″ wafer by a conventional physical or chemical vapor deposition method and is easily removed by most acidic chemicals as well as F- or Cl-based plasma etching gases. Here, we describe both the commercialized mushroom-type scheme and more futuristic damascene-type scheme for phase change material integration.

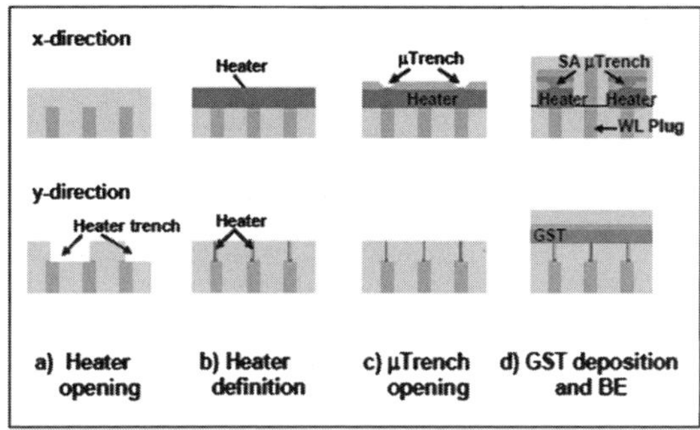

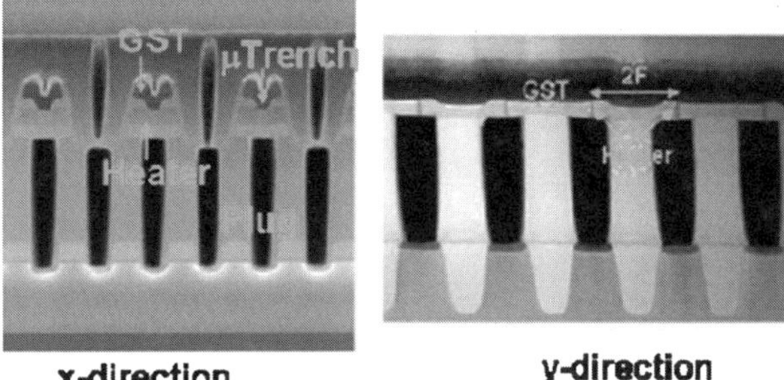

Figure 25. Schematic fabrication processes (upper) and the cross-section TEM images (lower) of μ-trench electrode scheme. Reprinted with permission from [62], A. Pirovano et al., "Proceedings of the European Solid-State Device Research 36th Conference," p. 222, 2007. © 2007, IEEE.

4.2.3.1 Mushroom-Type. Mushroom-type (which is also called planar or T-shaped) structure has been commonly reported [38, 59, 78, 79] as a standard cell architecture for phase change material and has been well adaptable to a mass-producible integration scheme due to its simplicity. Figure 26 shows a schematic view and a TEM image of a mushroom-type cell. It should be noted that a phase change material and a top electrode, clearly patterned with standard patterning processes of photolithography and etching, are stacked flat on the planarized surface with an embedded sub-μm-sized contact. Process-induced damage or degradation of a phase change material may occur and should be minimized for reliable cell operations. It was found out [78] that etch damages from F- or Cl-based reactive ions during the RIE process are too significant to keep set resistance low enough when the cell dimension is scaled down to 300 nm and below (Fig. 27). A precise control of plasma gas chemistry can reduce etching damage remarkably, but a mushroom-type cell can hardly escape from such lateral damages on its phase change material when the device is scaled down in next generations. On the other hand, degradation in phase change material properties may also occur during back-end interconnection processes. Typically, phase change material is easily vaporized when exposed to a thermal environment at above 400°C and it may undergo compositional changes locally or globally by the diffusion of some impurities such as oxygen, fluorine, and titanium. Since these are most likely to degrade cell performances, there have been needs of employing preventive techniques. For instance, it has been demonstrated [79] that double encapsulation of phase change material with thin dielectric materials (Fig. 28) is very effective in preventing oxygen atoms from diffusing and oxidizing the interface of phase change material.

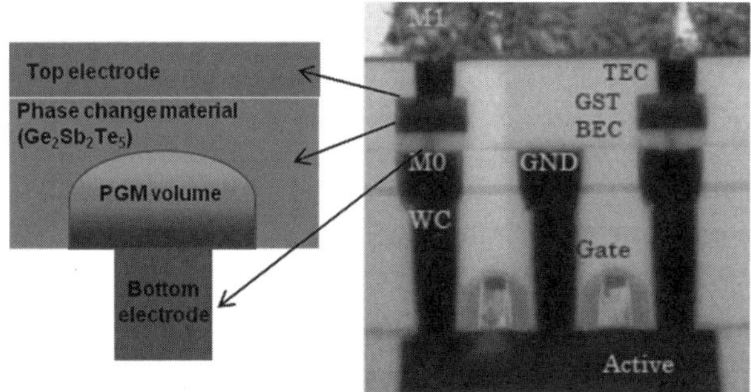

Figure 26. A schematic view (left) and an example (right) of mushroom-type phase change material pattering. Reprinted with permission from [38], F. Yeung et al., *Jpn. J. Appl. Phys.* 44, 2691 (2005). © 2005, The Japan Society of Applied Physics.

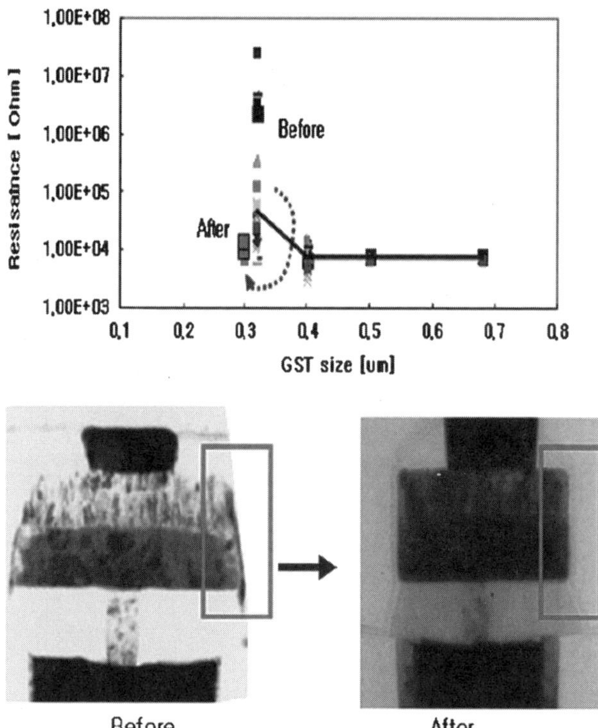

Figure 27. Upper figure shows that the resistance of low-resistive set state becomes higher as the cell size goes down to 300 nm. When etching process is optimized, the set resistance is not only reduced but a better cell morphology is also obtained, as clearly seen from lower TEM images before and after optimization. Reprinted with permission from [78], S. J. Ahn et al., "IEDM Tech. Dig.," p. 907, 2004. © 2004, IEEE.

4.2.3.2 Damascene-Type. This scheme is considered a promising candidate for the next-generation phase change memory cell architecture due to less process-induced damage on its phase change material and higher immunity of an individual cell to thermal disturbance from neighboring cells under writing. Figure 29 shows typical images of damascene-type phase change memory cells [80], which are usually manufactured by the following sequences. Trenches

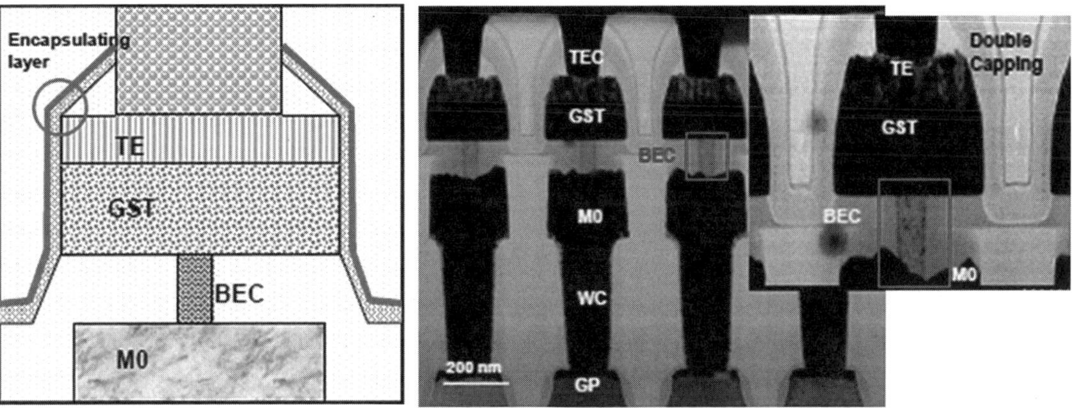

Figure 28. Schematic (left) and TEM image (right) showing a double encapsulation scheme in a mushroom-type phase change memory cell architecture. Reprinted with permission from [79], Y. J. Song et al., "IEDM Tech. Dig.," p. 118, 2006. © 2006, IEEE.

or contact holes are formed in a regular array into a dielectric material by photolithography and RIE process and then filled up with a phase change material by a conformal vapor deposition. Subsequently, they are isolated from each other by CMP technique. Finally, interconnect metal patterning is carried out to complete a damascene-type cell integration. Reasonably, a damascene-type cell is intrinsically free from etch damages since a phase change material is not exposed to plasma etching environment. This attribute will become more and more beneficial for increasingly smaller devices as compared with the case of a mushroom-type cell. This is because, in the latter case, a program volume within a phase change material becomes closer to the lateral interface that is inevitably affected by reactive ions or radicals during etching process. In addition, a damascene-type cell is more resistant to thermal disturbance originating from neighboring cells under write operation. Temperature of a programming region is compared between mushroom (planar)-type and damascene (confined)-type cells as a function of inter-cell distance (Fig. 30). It is evident that the temperature rise due to thermal crosstalk from a neighboring cell at the same distance apart is much smaller in the damascene-type cell scheme. This may be attributed to more effective heat blocking from a thermal boundary resistance effect [81], which might become more significant as technology node is scaled down.

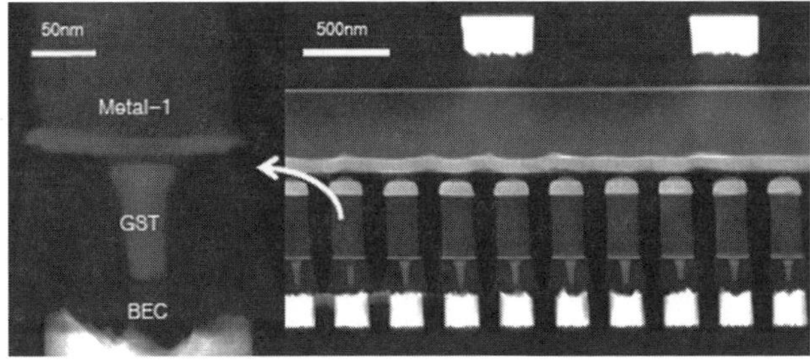

Figure 29. A damascene-type phase change memory cell (left) and full integration image of cell architecture (right). Reprinted with permission from [80], J. I. Lee et al., "IEDM Tech. Dig.," p. 102, 2007. © 2007, IEEE.

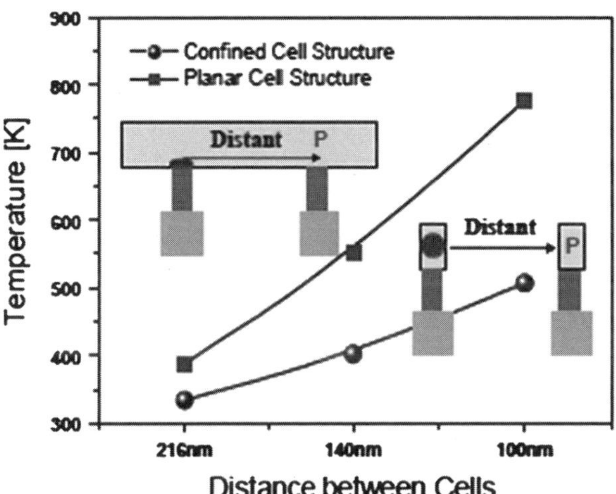

Figure 30. Simulated lateral temperatures when programming a cell in planar (mushroom) and confined (damascene) schemes. Reprinted with permission from [80], J. I. Lee et al., "IEDM Tech. Dig.," p. 102, 2007. © 2007, IEEE.

5. RELIABILITY

Like in other nonvolatile memories, cell reliability characteristics, such as programming repeatability (write endurance), crosstalk between neighboring memory cells on programming (thermal disturbance), and data stability at various thermal environments (data retention), are of great concern in a phase change memory. Since they are directly influenced by intrinsic properties of a phase change material itself, we should evaluate the reliability characteristics of a considered phase change material from the initial stage of development. Here, we consider for each reliability characteristic:

(1) how a phase change material is evaluated to satisfy the respective severe requirements,
(2) what issues are to be resolved, and
(3) what technical solutions are being sought for a more reliable phase change memory device.

5.1. Write Endurance

Phase change memory has been recently commercialized to substitute NOR flash for a code memory in mobile phones, where no significant degradation in the characteristics of phase changes between amorphous (reset) and crystalline (set) states should be guaranteed for at least hundreds of thousands of repeated cycles of write operations. It is known that a phase change memory cell is superior to a flash memory cell in write endurance as long as programming pulse conditions such as pulse height and pulse width are properly optimized [59, 77]. For example, a damascene-type phase change memory cell with the conventional $Ge_2Sb_2Te_5$ material has already demonstrated an excellent write endurance of as many as 10^{11} cycles with no degradation in reset and set resistances (Fig. 31(a)). Furthermore, it has a prospect for the extended write endurance up to 10^{15} cycles at the reduced programming energy of below 10^{-11} Joule (Fig. 31(b)). However, a phase change memory cell does not tend to show a good cycling performance when programming energy is higher than required (i.e., when a cell is over-programmed; see Fig. 31(c)). Typically, two types of poor cycling behaviors of the over-programmed cells appear. As for the first type, which are represented by triangles, resistance of the high-resistive reset state gradually decreases toward a level of the low-resistive set state at above approximately 10^7 cycles and never comes back to a high-resistive level any more. This is called set-stuck failure. As for the second type, which is represented by squares, the cell resistance jumps suddenly to an extremely high level (> 1 Gohm) after initial degradation of reset resistance. This is called reset-stuck failure. These two types of cycling failures are frequently observed in high-density phase change memory devices. Individual cells of a megabit or gigabit cells may have different optimum reset or set programming energy due to process-induced variations in the physical dimension of a cell and in composition of a phase change material as well as also circuitry-induced variations in programming current. As a consequence, it is practically impossible to program numerous cells equally with an optimized energy, and some cells are always liable to undergo over-programming, resulting in the aforementioned cycling failures. Therefore, it is quite necessary to understand the mechanisms of these cycling failures in order to enhance the immunity of phase change memory cell against over-programming.

It has been considered that a set-stuck failure is associated with a compositional change in $Ge_2Sb_2Te_5$ phase change material with the increase of repeated cycles. It turns out that the composition of a programming region tends to become Sb-rich with cycles (Fig. 32(a)) [50, 59]. An Sb-rich programming region tends to yield a lower dynamic resistance (R_{dyn}) and produces less Joule heat under constant programming conditions. Because of an insufficient temperature rise, it would become hard to melt and quench a phase change material and, for this reason, reset resistance becomes diminished with cycles to finally induce a set-stuck failure. It has been suggested that such compositional change into an Sb-rich phase may be attributed to the movement of Sb atoms to the cathode (bottom electrode) region by electromigration [82–84] or thermodynamic propensity for phase separation into GeTe and Sb_2Te_3 by incongruent melting [85], as schematically represented in Figures 32(b and c).

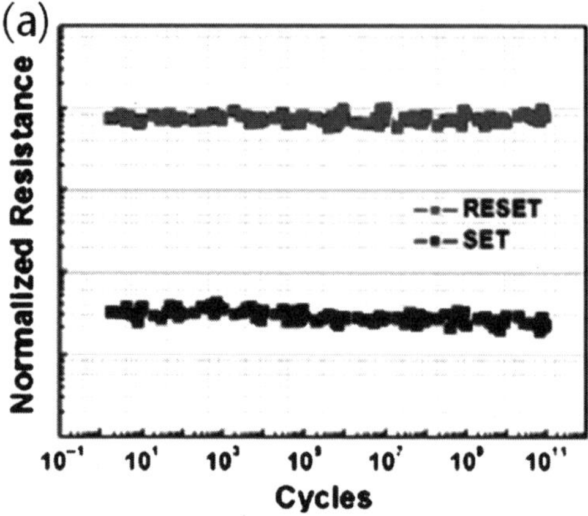

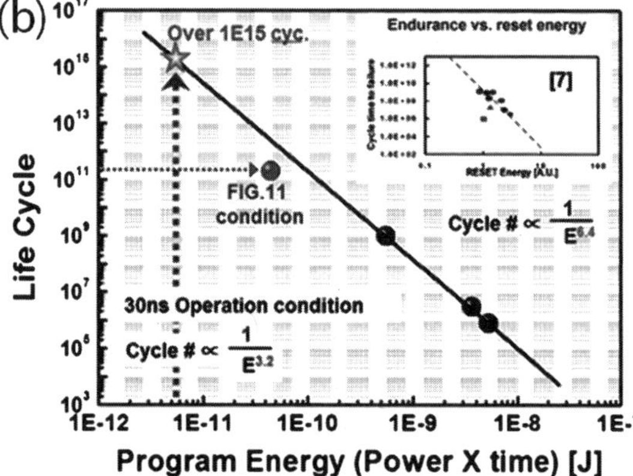

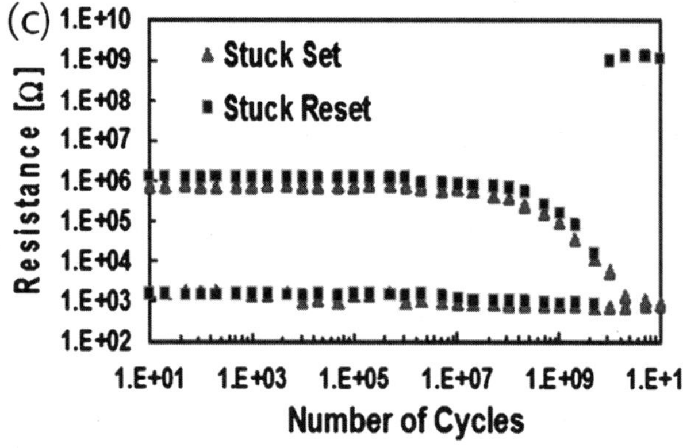

Figure 31. (a) A good reset and set cycling performance at programming energy of 4.5×10^{11} Joule, and (b) life cycles with respect to programming energy in a damascene-type phase change memory. Reprinted with permission from [76], I. S. Kim et al., "VLSI Tech. Dig.," p. 2023, 2010. © 2010, IEEE. (c) Two typical cycling failures when the programming energy is higher than required. Reprinted with permission from [15], K. Kinam et al., "IEEE Annual International Reliability Physics Symposium," p. 157, 2005. © 2005, IEEE.

Meanwhile, it has been revealed that a reset-stuck failure is due to void formation within a program volume or at its interface with electrodes (Fig. 33). In particular, when voids entirely overlay the contact area between the phase

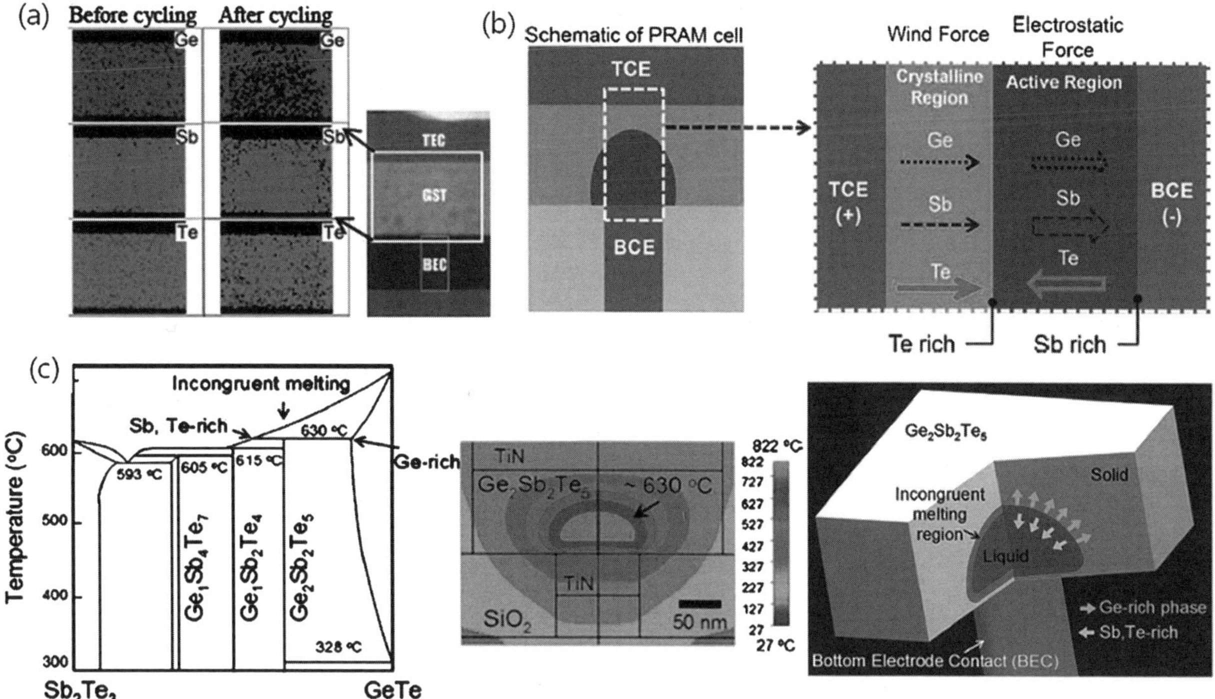

Figure 32. (a) EDS analysis of set failure cell. Reprinted with permission from [50], B. Rajendran et al., "VLSI Tech. Dig.," p. 96, 2008. © 2008, IEEE. (b) Electromigration model. Reprinted with permission from [83], T.-Y. Yang et al., *Appl. Phys. Lett.* 95, 032104 (2009). © 2009, American Physical Society. (c) Incongruent melting model on an Sb-rich phase formation in programming region with repeated cycles. Reprinted with permission from [85], S. W. Nam et al., *Appl. Phys. Lett.* 92, 111913 (2008). © 2008, American Physical Society.

change material and an electrode (Fig. 33(b)), no electrical path is connected so that the resistance rises above a giga-ohm that is higher than a normal reset resistance by two or three orders of magnitude. Since a reset-stuck failure is always observed after a set-stuck failure (Fig. 31(c)), void formation is being modeled as having its root cause in the aforementioned phase separation or electromigration with programming cycles.

Regardless of failure types, it is critical to suppress phase separation or electromigration of the phase change material for improving a write endurance of a phase change memory so that most engineering works have been focused on the compositional modifications such as doping with light element [66, 86] and on the optimization of write programming energy [15].

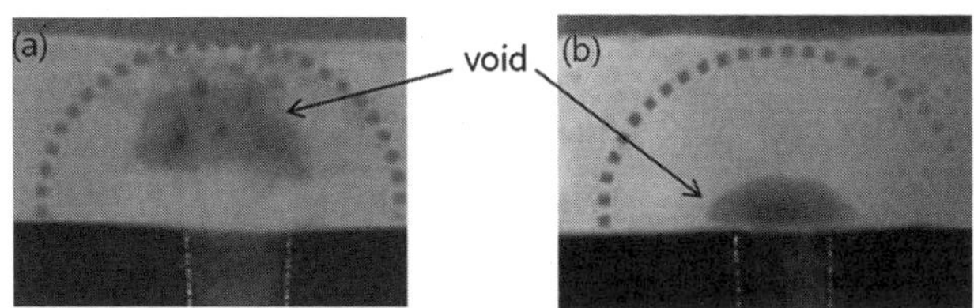

Figure 33. Typical images of voids (a) in the programming volume (dotted semicircle) and (b) at the interface of phase change material and bottom electrode after repeated programming cycles. Reprinted with permission from [86], C.-F. Chen et al., "IMW Tech. Dig.," p. 1, 2009. © 2009, IEEE.

5.2. Thermal Disturbance

Dissipated heat from a programmed cell may unintentionally erase the high-resistive reset data of the nearest cells by partially crystallizing the amorphous phase in a program volume. Such a thermal disturbance, which is also known as write disturbance, becomes detrimental to the reliability of a phase change memory cell, especially when a thermal design of cell architecture is inappropriate or programming energy is excessively larger than required. Temperature around a cell under programming is obliged to increase by heat conduction. In a phase change memory array with the unit cell area of $4F^2$ (F is a minimum feature size; see Fig. 34), neighboring cells nearest (distant by P or $2F$) to a programming cell along the same bit-line or word-line are vulnerable to losing their reset data when temperatures rise above their appropriate crystallization temperatures and then trigger crystallization of the high-resistive amorphous phase. When an over-programming current was applied to a phase change memory cell on 54-nm technology of which an optimum reset current is approximately 200 uA, the reset resistance of its neighboring cell was remarkably decreased (Fig. 35; left) [88]. This was attributed to the partial crystallization of the amorphous phase by dissipated heat from the neighboring programming cells (Fig. 35; right). To achieve cell architecture free from thermal disturbance, it is necessary to place neighboring cells apart as far as possible and to search for adequate materials, including electrodes and dielectrics as well as a phase change material. Besides, it is also important to minimize the height and the width of a programming pulse for it not to become an over-programming pulse past

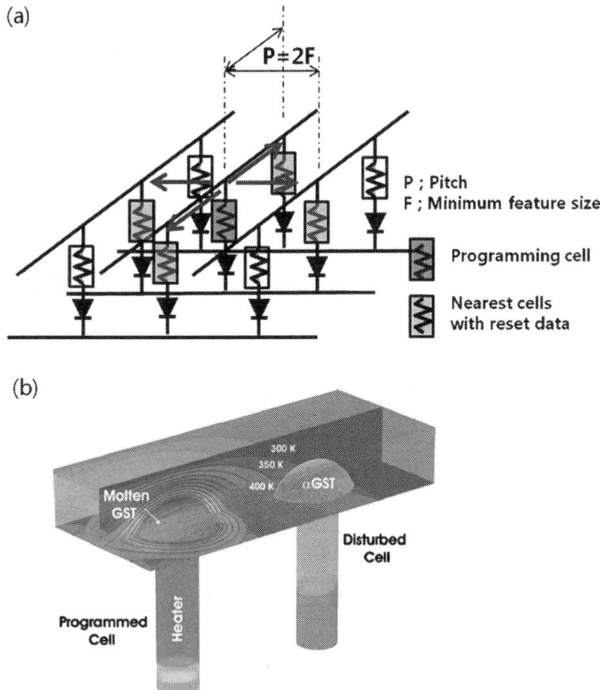

Figure 34. (a) Schematic cell array showing a selected cell under programming and its nearest neighboring cells along same bit-line and word-line, in which they are vulnerable to thermal crosstalk by heat conduction (arrows) when thermal design is not optimized or the selected cell is over-programmed. (b) 3-D temperature profiles of a mushroom-type phase change memory cell. Reprinted with permission from [87], A. Redaelli et al., *J. Appl. Phys.* 103, 111101 (2008). © 2008, American Physical Society.

an optimizing writing circuitry. For a phase change memory to be a true RAM-type memory, this kind of thermal crosstalk should not deteriorate write endurance cycles.

Thermal disturbance has been regarded as a critical factor when scaling down a phase change memory to sub-20-nm technology nodes since the interspacing distance between neighboring cells becomes reduced at the same ratio of scaling. Nonetheless, it is considered [88, 89] that thermal disturbance is not a limiting factor down to 16-nm technology node if the reset current is reduced in accordance with an isotropic scaling scheme and the width of a reset pulse is sufficiently small not to induce a thermal crosstalk (Fig. 36).

5.3. Data Retention

Data retention represents the capability of long-time data storage for a required duration at user temperatures usually ranging from −20°C to 80°C. Phase change memory as a nonvolatile memory device has to keep its data unaltered for 10 years at 80°C. This holds only for a high-resistive reset state since its metastable amorphous phase tends to be crystallized with decreased resistance, whereas a crystalline phase of a low-resistive set state is thermodynamically stable to maintain its resistance under the aforementioned user conditions.

A practical method to estimate the data retention time of phase change memory cells is to experimentally measure the failure times of reset data at elevated temperatures and then to extrapolate them at user temperature. When a high-resistive reset state is left at elevated temperatures, its resistance decreases with the elapse of time and the rate of decrease becomes accelerated at higher temperatures (Fig. 37(a)). This behavior results from crystallization of an amorphous phase in a reset state under an isothermal bake test and its acceleration at higher temperatures is due to Arrhenius-type thermally-activated characteristics given by $t_{\text{fail}} \sim (E_a/kT)$ where t_{fail} is the failure time at which resistance starts to drop below the target value of a reset state (usually 100 kohm) and E_a is the crystallization activation energy of a phase change material (known as 2.6 eV~2.7 eV [48, 91] for $Ge_2Sb_2Te_5$), respectively. Thus, we can project data retention time at user temperatures by extrapolating the measured failure times at elevated temperatures in the plot of t_{fail} versus $1/kT$ as shown in Figure 37(b), where it is noticed that data retention time at 85°C is much longer than 10^5 hours for a single cell and most cells in 512-*k*

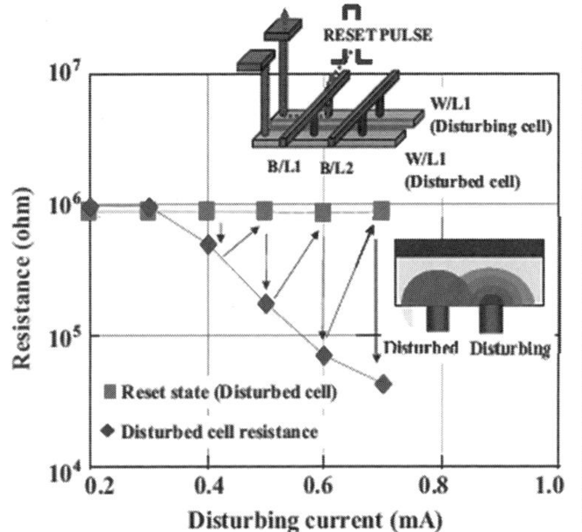

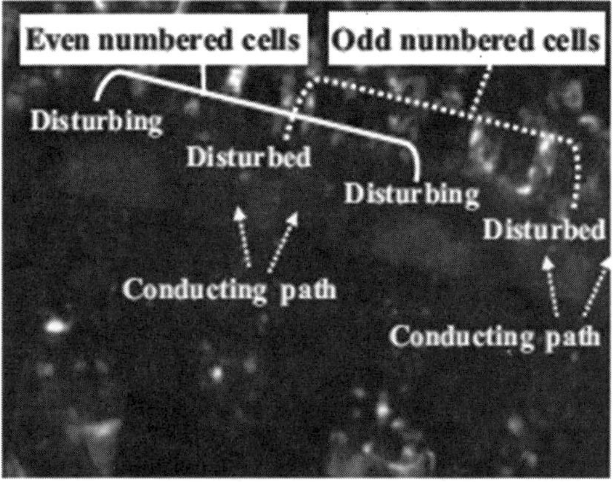

Figure 35. Reset resistance degradation of disturbed cell as a result of over-programming cell (left) and its transmission electron microscopy image (right), where it can be known that the amorphous volume of disturbed cells along the same bit line in phase change memory array with 54-nm technology can significantly shrink. Reprinted with permission from [88], S. H. Lee et al., "VLSI Tech. Dig.," p. 199, 2010. © 2010, IEEE.

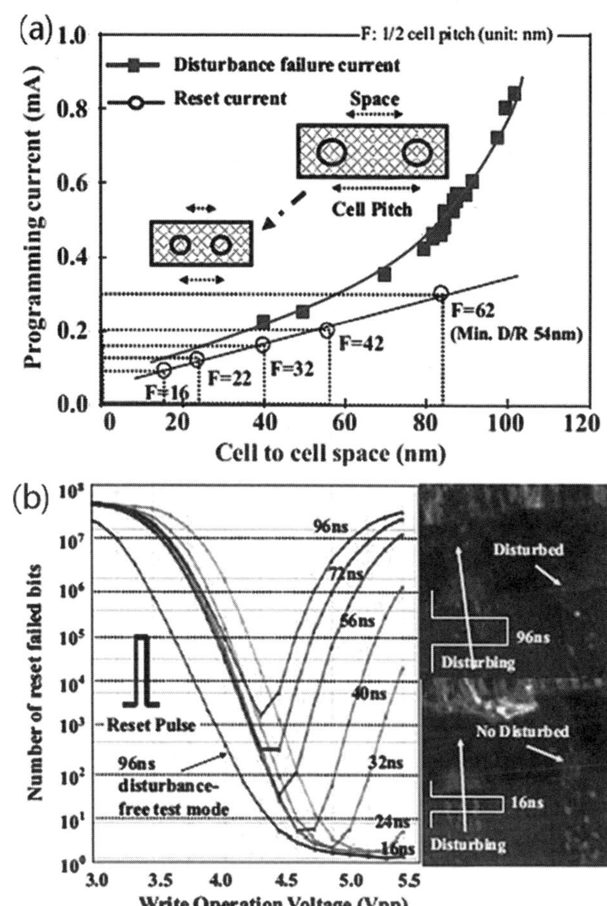

Figure 36. (a) Comparison between reset current scaling and disturbance failure current indicating that thermal disturbance is not issued when if reset current scaling keeps $1/k^2$ ratio where k is scaling factor, and (b) number of reset fail bits with respect to reset pulse width where it is known that there are no failed bits due to thermal disturbance when the width of reset pulse is reduced to 16 ns in a 64-Mbit cell array. Reprinted with permission from [88], S. H. Lee et al., "VLSI Tech. Dig.," p. 199, 2010. © 2010, IEEE.

array of a μ-trench phase change memory device on 90-nm technology [90].

Early failures during isothermal bake tests are frequently observed in some bits of a cell array, and they may significantly degrade data retention properties in ppb-level. Since they are suggested to be closely related with the formation of erratic shunting paths due to process-induced defects or damages [90], or with the existence of spontaneous grains resulting from partial-reset programming (Figs. 38(a and b), respectively) [91], it is quite necessary for cells to have immunity against process damages or to be fully reset by optimizing cell integration processes as well as programming circuit schemes.

Data retention is also one of the aspects of concern when scaling a phase change memory cell down to sub-20-nm technology nodes. According to a Monte Carlo model for crystallization in a nano-scaled phase change memory [92], it is expected that reset data can be maintained for 10 years at 95°C in ppb-level, even if a phase change volume is reduced to 9–10 nm^3, which corresponds to a phase change memory

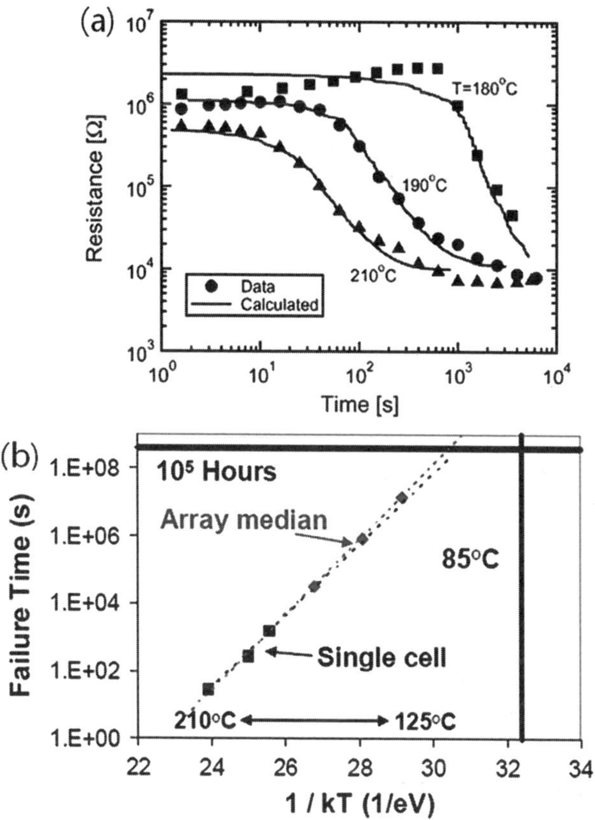

Figure 37. (a) Electrical resistivity changes with respect to the elapsed time at isothermal bake test from 180°C to 210°C for $Ge_2Sb_2Te_5$ films. Reprinted with permission from [48], U. Russo et al., *IEEE Trans. Electron Devices* 53, 3032 (2006). © 2006, IEEE. (b) Typical plot of t_{fail} versus $1/kT$ in μ-trench phase change memory cells with 90-nm technology. Reprinted with permission from [90], B. Gleixner et al., "IEEE Annual International Reliability Physics Symposium," p. 542, 2007. © 2007, IEEE.

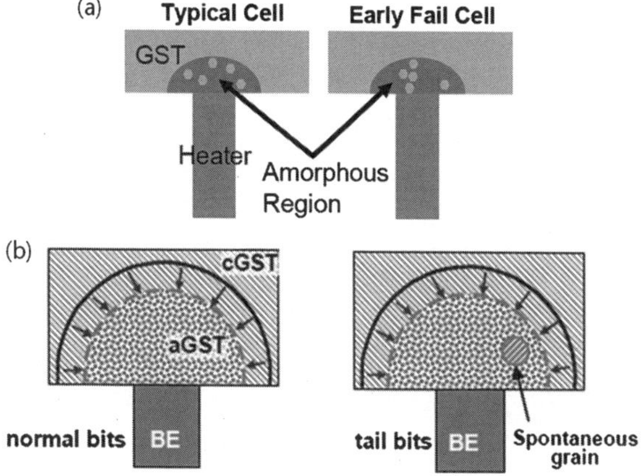

Figure 38. Two possible mechanisms showing early failures in data retention, (a) formation of erratic shunting paths. Reprinted with permission from [90], B. Gleixner et al., "IEEE Annual International Reliability Physics Symposium," p. 542, 2007. © 2007, IEEE. (b) Spontaneous grain growth in programming region. Reprinted with permission from [91], Y. H. Shih et al., "IEDM Tech. Dig.," p. 1, 2008. © 2008, IEEE.

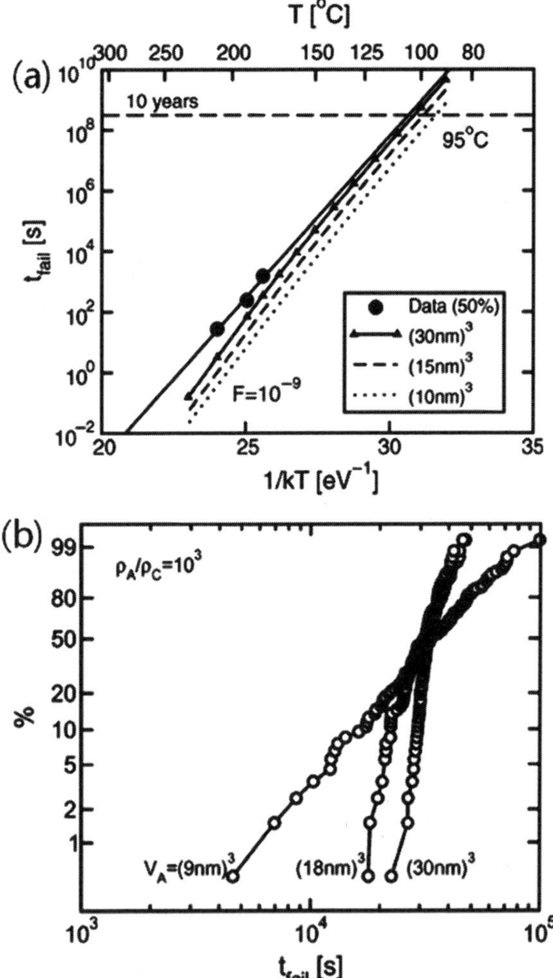

Figure 39. (a) Estimation of data retention failure time when programming volume is scaled down (15 nm)^3 and (10 nm)^3. Reprinted with permission from [92], A. Redaelli et al., *IEEE Trans. Electron Devices* 53, 3040 (2006). © 2006, IEEE. (b) Statistical distributions of failure time at programming volumes of (9 nm)^3, (18 nm)^3, and (30 nm)^3. Reprinted with permission from [48], U. Russo et al., *IEEE Trans. Electron Devices* 53, 3032 (2006). © 2006, IEEE.

cell on 20-nm technology node (Fig. 39(a)). Assuming that an average size of crystalline nuclei is unchanged with scaling down, however, the statistical spread of retention failure time might be larger (Fig. 39(b)). This is because percolation takes place via a smaller number of nuclei, and conducting paths are made with more prominently random characteristics. Accordingly, it becomes important to minimize such statistical variations by properly designing the composition and microstructure of a phase change material. As for a promising phase change memory cell on a sub-20-nm technology, a confined cell with an Sb-rich Ge–Sb–Te phase change material shows good data retention characteristics that guarantee 4.5 years at 85°C (Fig. 40).

6. SUMMARY

We have reviewed fundamental principles of phase change memory device operation based on fast and reliable phase transformations and a large difference in electrical resistance between amorphous and crystalline phases of $Ge_2Sb_2Te_5$ material. Next, we have introduced state-of-the-art fabrication techniques for phase change memory, which are not only well optimized for conventional Si processes, but they also are readily scalable down to sub-20-nm technology nodes compared with other nonvolatile memories. Subsequently, we considered characteristics and issues regarding the reliability of phase change memory such as write endurance, thermal disturbance, and data retention. Currently commercialized for use in mobile handsets, this new concept of electrical memory will certainly enlarge the market volume and application field more and more in coming ubiquitous eras. For this, scaling down of the memory to sub-20-nm technology nodes should be enabled in addition to technical advances in process integration and/or engineering phase change material for gigabit or terabit capacity, combined with low power consumption and high write/read speed. Such advances include:

(1) continuing process optimizations to obtain a damage-free program volume of phase change material and better-quality interfaces with electrodes or surrounding dielectrics,
(2) enhancement in write endurance, either by adopting a new phase change material with a high immunity to phase separation or by designing a circuitry to minimize power delivery to phase change material, and
(3) the development of application-specific phase change materials of diverse compositions.

A recent paradigm for semiconductor devices is the convergence of computing, communication, and consumer

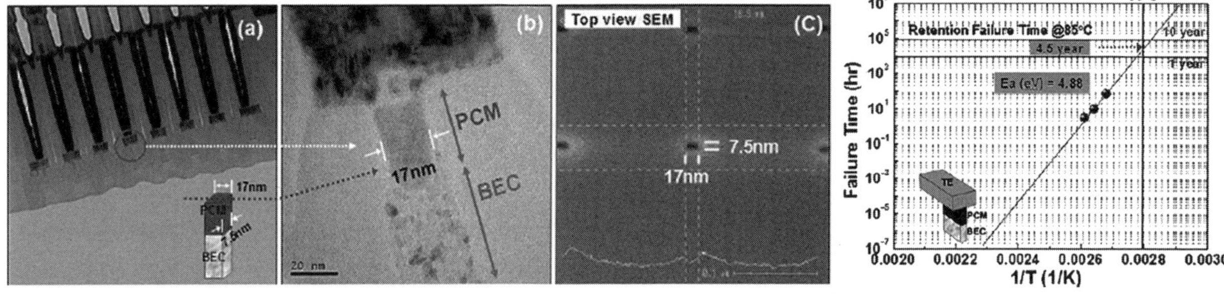

Figure 40. Electron microscopy images showing confined-type cells with 7.5 nm × 17 nm size of an Sb-rich Ge–Sb–Te phase change material (left). Plot of retention failure time versus $1/T$ in this confined phase change memory cell (right). Reprinted with permission from [76], I. S. Kim et al., "VLSI Tech. Dig.," p. 2023, 2010. © 2010, IEEE.

electronics. Representative examples are smart phone, tablet PCs, *e*-Books, and others. The key features of convergence electronics are mutual and seamless connecting, networking, and interfacing. To keep up with this paradigm shift, a memory device should be featured with a large capacity of gigabit or higher, high bandwidth to speed up cross-linking, and low power consumption. In these respects, phase change memory is regarded as one of the most promising memories due to its nonvolatility, high scalability, and random accessibility. Recently, system designers of convergence electronics are paying much more attention to this new memory for high-level systems such as execution in place, storage and download, and hybrid solid-state disk. For phase change memory to fulfill these needs, technical breakthroughs in respect of process architecture and phase change material are clearly required for multilevel cell technology or 3D stackable memory technology, all of which are in the midst of development by major semiconductor chip makers.

ACKNOWLEDGMENTS

K.-B. Kim and B.-K. Cheong would like to acknowledge financial support from the Korean Ministry of Knowledge Economy through the National Research Program for 0.1 terabit nonvolatile memory (NVM) devices.

REFERENCES

1. T. Ohta, *J. Optoelectron. Adv. Mater.* 3, 609 (2001).
2. M. Wuttig and N. Yamada, *Nat. Mater.* 6, 824 (2007).
3. R. Neale, *Electron. Eng.* 73, 67 (2001).
4. S. Lai, "IEDM Tech. Dig.," p. 10, 2003.
5. http://www.samsung.com/global/business/semiconductor/products/fusionmemory/Products_NcPRAM.html.
6. R. G. Neale, D. L. Nelson, and G. E. Moore, *Electronics* 43, 56 (1970).
7. N. Yamada, *MRS Bull. Sep.* 48 (1996).
8. K. P. Lee, Y. S. Park, D. H. Ko, C. S. Hwang, C. J. Kang, K. Y. Lee, J. S. Kim, J. K. Park, B. H. Roh, J. Y. Lee, B. C. Kim, J. H. Lee, K. N. Kim, J. W. Park, and R. J. G. Lee, "IEDM Tech. Dig.," p. 907, 1995.
9. Jim Handy, "Phase-Change Memory Becomes a Reality," A White Paper by Objective Analysis, Semiconductor Market Research http://www.objective-analysis.com.
10. C. D. Wright, M. M. Aziz, M. Armand, S. Senkader, and W. Yu, "Proceeding of the European Symposium on Phase Change and Ovonic Science," Balzers, Liechtenstein, 2004.
11. D. H. Im, J. I. Lee, S. L. Cho, H. G. An, D. H. Kim, I. S. Kim, H. Park, D. H. Ahn, H. Horii, S. O. Park, U. In Chung, and J. T. Moon, "IEDM Tech. Dig.," p. 1, 2008.
12. A. L. Lacaita, *Solid-State Electron.* 50, 24 (2006).
13. T. Morikawa, K. Kurotsuchi, M. Kinoshita, N. Matsuzaki, Y. Matsui, Y. Fuiisaki, S. Hanzawa, A. Kotabe, M. Terao, H. Moriya, T. Iwasaki, M. Matsuoka, F. Nitta, M. Moniwa, T. Koga, and N. Takaura, "IEDM Tech. Dig.," p. 307, 2007.
14. L. van Pieterson, M. H. R. Lankhorst, M. van Schijndel, A. E. T. Kuiper, and J. H. J. Roosen, *J. Appl. Phys.* 97, 083520 (2005).
15. K. Kinam and A. S. Jin, "IEEE Annual International Reliability Physics Symposium," San Jose, CA, USA, 2005, p. 157.
16. M. Chen, K. A. Rubin, and R. W. Barton, *Appl. Phys. Lett.* 49, 502 (1986).
17. Y. Maeda, H. Andoh, I. Ikuta, and H. Minemura, *J. Appl. Phys.* 64, 1715 (1988).
18. S. Bordas, M. T. Clavagueramora, B. Legendre, and C. Hancheng, *Thermochim. Acta* 107, 239 (1986).
19. N. Yamada, E. Ohno, K. Nishiuchi, N. Akahira, and M. Takao, *J. Appl. Phys.* 69, 2849 (1991).
20. A. Pirovano, A. L. Lacaita, A. Benvenuti, F. Pellizzer, and R. Bez, *Electron Devices IEEE Trans.* 51, 452 (2004).
21. I. Friedrich, V. Weidenhof, W. Njoroge, P. Franz, and M. Wuttig, *J. Appl. Phys.* 87, 4130 (2000).
22. B. S. Lee, J. R. Abelson, S. G. Bishop, D. H. Kang, B. K. Cheong, and K. B. Kim, *J. Appl. Phys.* 97, 093509 (2005).
23. H. K. Lyeo, D. G. Cahill, B. S. Lee, J. R. Abelson, M. H. Kwon, K. B. Kim, S. G. Bishop, and B. K. Cheong, *Appl. Phys. Lett.* 89, 151904 (2006).
24. B. J. Kooi and J. T. M. De Hosson, *J. Appl. Phys.* 92, 3584 (2002).
25. A. V. Kolobov, P. Fons, A. I. Frenkel, A. L. Ankudinov, J. Tominaga, and T. Uruga, *Nat. Mater.* 3, 703 (2004).
26. J. Hegedüs and S. R. Elliott, *Nat. Mater.* 7, 399 (2008).
27. N. Yamada, "Phase Change Materials: Science and Applications." (S. Rauox and M. Wuttig, Eds.), pp. 199–226, Springer, New York, 2009.
28. L. van Pieterson, M. H. R. Lankhorst, M. van Schijndel, A. E. T. Kuiper, and J. H. J. Roosen, *J. Appl. Phys.* 97, 083520 (2005).
29. S. Lee, J.-H. Jeong, Z. Wu, Y.-W. Park, W. M. Kim, and B.-K. Cheong, *J. Electrochem. Soc.* 156, H612 (2009).
30. Y. C. Chen, C. T. Rettner, S. Raoux, G. W. Burr, S. H. Chen, R. M. Shelby, M. Salinga, W. P. Risk, T. D. Happ, G. M. McClelland, M. Breitwisch, A. Schrott, J. B. Philipp, M. H. Lee, R. Cheek, T. Nirschl, M. Lamorey, C. F. Chen, E. Joseph, S. Zaidi, B. Yee, H. L. Lung, R. Bergmann, and C. Lam, "IEDM Tech. Dig.," p. 1, 2006.
31. T. Zhang, Z. T. Song, F. Wang, B. Liu, S. L. Feng, and B. Chen, *Appl. Phys. Lett.* 91, 222102 (2007).
32. T. Morikawa, K. Kurotsuchi, M. Kinoshita, N. Matsuzaki, Y. Matsui, Y. Fuiisaki, S. Hanzawa, A. Kotabe, M. Terao, H. Moriya, T. Iwasaki, M. Matsuoka, F. Nitta, M. Moniwa, T. Koga, and N. Takaura, "IEDM Tech. Dig.," p. 307, 2007.
33. Y. Y. Lin, H. B. Lv, P. Zhou, M. Yin, F. F. Liao, Y. F. Cai, T. A. Tang, J. Feng, Y. Zhang, Z. F. Zhang, B. W. Qiao, Y. F. Lai, B. C. Cai, and B. Chen, "IEEE Non-Volatile Semiconductor Memory Workshop," Monterey, CA, USA, 2007, p. 61.
34. H. S. Carslaw and J. C. Jaeger, "Conduction of Heat in Solids." 2nd Edition, Oxford University Press, New York, 1995.
35. D. S. Suh, C. Kim, K. H. P. Kim, Y. S. Kang, T. Y. Lee, Y. Khang, T. S. Park, Y. G. Yoon, J. Im, and J. Ihm, *Appl. Phys. Lett.* 96, 123115 (2010).
36. D. H. Kang, J. S. Kim, Y. R. Kim, Y. T. Kim, M. K. Lee, Y. J. Jun, J. H. Park, F. Yeung, C. W. Jeong, J. Yu, J. H. Kong, D. W. Ha, S. A. Song, J. Park, Y. Park, Y. J. Song, C. Y. Eum, K. C. Ryoo, J. M. Shin, D. W. Lim, S. S. Park, W. I. Park, K. R. Sim, J. H. Cheong, J. H. Oh, J. I. Kim, Y. T. Oh, K. W. Lee, S. P. Koh, S. H. Eun, N. B. Kim, G. H. Koh, G. T. Jeong, H. S. Jeong, and K. Kim, "VLSI Tech. Dig.," p. 96, 2007.
37. Y. T. Kim, Y. N. Hwang, K. H. Lee, K. H. Lee, S. H. Lee, C. W. Jeong, S. J. Ahn, F. Yeung, G. H. Koh, H. S. Jeong, W. Y. Chung, T. K. Kim, Y. K. Park, K. N. Kim, and J. T. Kong, *Jpn. J. Appl. Phys.* 44, 2701 (2005).
38. F. Yeung, S. J. Ahn, Y. N. Hwang, C. W. Jeong, Y. J. Song, S. Y. Lee, S. H. Lee, K. C. Ryoo, J. H. Park, J. M. Shin, W. C. Jeong, Y. T. Kim, G. H. Koh, G. T. Jeong, and K. Kim, *Jpn. J. Appl. Phys.* 44, 2691 (2005).
39. S. R. Ovshinsky, *Phys. Rev. Lett.* 21, 1450 (1968).
40. T. Kaplan and D. Adler, *J. Non-Cryst. Solids* 8–10, 538 (1972).
41. D. Ielmini and Y. G. Zhang, *J. Appl. Phys.* 102, 054517 (2007).
42. D. Kau, S. Tang, I. V. Karpov, R. Dodge, B. Klehn, J. A. Kalb, J. Strand, A. Diaz, N. Leung, J. Wu, S. Lee, T. Langtry,

K.-W. Chang, C. Papagianni, L. Jinwook, J. Hirst, S. Erra, E. Flores, N. Righos, H. Castro, and G. Spadini, "IEDM Tech. Dig.," p. 1, 2009.

43. S. Murugavel and S. Asokan, *J. Mater. Res.* 13, 2982 (1998).
44. D.-H. Kang, B.-K. Cheong, J.-H. Jeong, T. S. Lee, I. H. Kim, W. M. Kim, and J.-Y. Huh, *Appl. Phys. Lett.* 87, 253504 (2005).
45. V. G. Karpov, Y. A. Kryukov, I. V. Karpov, and M. Mitra, *Phys. Rev. B* 78, 052201 (2008).
46. C. Peng, L. Cheng, and M. Mansuripur, *J. Appl. Phys.* 82, 4183 (1997).
47. M. Simon, M. Nardone, V. G. Karpov, and I. V. Karpov, *J. Appl. Phys.* 108, 064514 (2010).
48. U. Russo, A. Redaelli, and A. L. Lacaita, *IEEE Trans. Electron Devices* 53, 3032 (2006).
49. K.-J. Lee, B.-H. Cho, W.-Y. Cho, S. Kang, B.-G. Choi, H.-R. Oh, C.-S. Lee, H.-J. Kim, J.-M. Park, Q. Wang, M.-H. Park, Y.-H. Ro, J.-Y. Choi, K.-S. Kim, Y.-R. Kim, I.-C. Shin, K.-W. Lim, H.-K. Cho, C.-H. Choi, W.-R. Chung, D.-E. Kim, K.-S. Yu, G.-T. Jeong, H.-S. Jeong, C.-K. Kwak, C.-H. Kim, and K. Kim, *IEEE J. Solid-State Circuits* 43, 150 (2008).
50. B. Rajendran, M. H. Lee, M. Breitwisch, G. W. Burr, Y. H. Shih, R. Cheek, A. Schrott, C. F. Chen, M. Lamorey, E. Joseph, Y. Zhu, R. Dasaka, P. L. Flaitz, F. H. Baumann, H. L. Lung, and C. Lam, "VLSI Tech. Dig.," p. 96, 2008.
51. S. Lavizzari, D. Ielmini, D. Sharma, and A. L. Lacaita, "IEDM Tech. Dig.," p. 1, 2008.
52. D. Ielmini, A. L. Lacaita, and D. Mantegazza, *IEEE Trans. Electron Devices* 54, 308 (2007).
53. I. V. Karpov, M. Mitra, D. Kau, G. Spadini, Y. A. Kryukov, and V. G. Karpov, *J. Appl. Phys.* 102, 124503 (2007).
54. D. H. Kang, J. H. Lee, J. H. Kong, D. Ha, J. Yu, C. Y. Um, J. H. Park, F. Yeung, J. H. Kim, W. I. Park, Y. J. Jeon, M. K. Lee, Y. J. Song, J. H. Oh, G. T. Jeong, and H. S. Jeong, "IEDM Tech. Dig.," p. 98, 2008.
55. S. Kostylev and T. Lowrey, "Proceeding of the European Symposium on Phase Change and Ovonic Science," Prague, Czech Republic, 2008.
56. J. H. Coombs, A. Jongenelis, W. Vanesspiekman, and B. A. J. Jacobs, *J. Appl. Phys.* 78, 4906 (1995).
57. M. Naito, M. Ishimaru, Y. Hirotus, and M. Takashima, *J. Appl. Phys.* 95, 8130 (2004).
58. C. W. Jeong, D. H. Kang, D. W. Ha, Y. J. Song, J. H. Oh, J. H. Kong, J. H. Yoo, J. H. Park, K. C. Ryoo, D. W. Lim, S. S. Park, J. I. Kim, Y. T. Oh, J. S. Kim, J. M. Shin, J. Park, Y. Fai, G. H. Koh, G. T. Jeong, H. S. Jeong, and K. Kim, *Solid-State Electron.* 52, 591 (2008).
59. S. Lai and T. Lowrey, "IEDM Tech. Dig.," p. 3651, 2001.
60. Y. H. Ha, J. H. Yi, H. Horii, J. H. Park, S. H. Joo, S. O. Park, U-In Chung, and J. T. Moon, "IEDM Tech. Dig.," p. 175, 2003.
61. K. C. Ryoo, Y. J. Song, J. M. Shin, S. S. Park, D. W. Lim, J. H. Kim, W. I. Park, K. R. Sim, J. H. Jeong, D. H. Kang, J. H. Kong, C. W. Jeong, J. H. Oh, J. H. Park, J. I. Kim, Y. T. Oh, J. S. Kim, S. H. Eun, K. W. Lee, S. P. Koh, Y. Fai, G. H. Koh, G. T. Jeong, H. S. Jeong, and K. Kim, *Jpn. J. Appl. Phys.* 46, 2001 (2007).
62. A. Pirovano, F. Pellizzer, I. Tortorelli, R. Harrigan, M. Magistretti, P. Petruzza, E. Varesi, D. Erbetta, T. Marangon, F. Bedeschi, R. Fackenthal, G. Atwood, and R. Bez, "Proceedings of the European Solid-State Device Research 36th Conference," Munich, Germany, 2007, p. 222.
63. C. Xu, Z. T. Song, B. Liu, S. L. Feng, and B. Chen, *Appl. Phys. Lett.* 92, 062103 (2009).
64. F. Rao, Z. T. Song, Y. F. Gong, L. C. Liangcai, S. L. Feng, and B. M. Chen, *Nanotechnology* 19, 445706 (2008).
65. K. Kurotsuchi, N. Matsuzaki, Y. Matsui, O. Tonomura, N. Yamamoto, Y. Fujisaki, N. Kitai, R. Takemura, K. Osada, S. Hanzawa, H. Moriya, T. Iwasaki, T. Kawahara, N. Takaura, M. Terao, M. Matsuoka, and M. Moniwa, "IEDM Tech. Dig.," p. 1, 2005.
66. H. Horii, J. H. Yi, J. H. Park, Y. H. Ha, I. G. Baek, S. O. Park, Y. N. Hwang, S. H. Lee, Y. T. Kim, K. H. Lee, U. In Chung, and J. T. Moon, "IEDM Tech. Dig.," p. 17, 2003.
67. G. B. Beneventi, E. Gourvest, A. Fantini, L. Perniola, V. Sousa, S. Maitrejean, J. C. Bastien, A. Bastard, A. Fargeix, B. Hyot, C. Jahan, J. F. Nodin, A. Persico, D. Blachier, A. Toffoli, S. Loubriat, A. Roule, S. Lhostis, H. Feldis, G. Reimbold, T. Billon, B. De Salvo, L. Larcher, P. Pavan, D. Bensahel, P. Mazoyer, R. Annunziata, and F. Boulanger, "IMW Tech. Dig.," P. 1, 2010.
68. G. T. Jeong, Y. N. Hwang, S. H. Lee, S. Y. Lee, K. C. Ryoo, J. H. Park, Y. J. Song, S. J. Ahn, C. W. Jeong, Y. T. Kim, H. Horii, Y. H. Ha, G. H. Koh, H. S. Jeong, and K. Kinam, "Proceedings of Integrated Circuit Design and Technology," Austin, TX, USA, 2005, p. 19.
69. U. Russo, D. Ielmini, A. Redaelli, and A. L. Lacaita, *IEEE Trans. Electron Devices* 55, 506 (2008).
70. J. H. Oh, J. H. Park, Y. S. Lim, H. S. Lim, Y. T. Oh, J. S. Kim, J. M. Shin, Y. J. Song, K. C. Ryoo, D. W. Lim, S. S. Park, J. I. Kim, J. H. Kim, J. Yu, F. Yeung, C. W. Jeong, J. H. Kong, D. H. Kang, G. H. Koh, G. T. Jeong, H. S. Jeong, and K. Kinam, "IEDM Tech. Dig.," p. 1, 2006.
71. A. E. Kaloyeros and E. Eisenbraun, *Annu. Rev. Mater. Sci.* 30, 363 (2000).
72. J. Tao, N. W. Cheung, and C. M. Hu, *IEEE Electron Device Lett.* 16, 230 (1985).
73. Y. Matsui, K. Kurotsuchi, O. Tonomura, T. Morikawa, M. Kinoshita, Y. Fujisaki, N. Matsuzaki, S. Hanzawa, M. Terao, N. Takaura, H. Moriya, T. Iwasaki, M. Moniwa, and T. Koga, "IEDM Tech. Dig.," p. 1, 2006.
74. H. Y. Cheng, Y. C. Chen, C. M. Lee, R. J. Chung, and T. S. Chin, *J. Electrochem. Soc.* 153, G685 (2006).
75. D. H. Kang, I. H. Kim, J. H. Jeong, B. K. Cheong, D. H. Ahn, D. Lee, H. M. Kim, K. B. Kim, and S. H. Kim, *J. Appl. Phys.* 100, 054506 (2006).
76. I. S. Kim, S. L. Cho, D. H. Im, E. H. Cho, D. H. Kim, G. H. Oh, D. H. Ahn, S. O. Park, S. W. Nam, J. T. Moon, and C. H. Chung, "VLSI Tech. Dig.," p. 2023, 2010.
77. D. H. Ahn, S. L. Cho, H. Horii, D. H. Im, I.-S. Kim, G. H. Oh, S. O. Park, M. S. Kang, S. W. Nam, and C. H. Chung, "Proceeding of the European Symposium on Phase Change and Ovonic Science," Milano, Italy, 2010.
78. S. J. Ahn, Y. J. Song, C. W. Jeong, J. M. Shin, Y. Fai, Y. N. Hwang, S. H. Lee, K. C. Ryoo, S. Y. Lee, J. H. Park, H. Horii, Y. H. Ha, J. H. Yi, B. J. Kuh, G. H. Koh, G. T. Jeong, H. S. Jeong, K. Kim, and B. I. Ryu, "IEDM Tech. Dig.," p. 907, 2004.
79. Y. J. Song, K. C. Ryoo, Y. N. Hwang, C. W. Jeong, D. W. Lim, S. S. Park, J. I. Kim, J. H. Kim, S. Y. Lee, J. H. Kong, S. J. Ahn, S. H. Lee, J. H. Park, J. H. Oh, Y. T. Oh, J. S. Kim, J. M. Shin, Y. Fai, G. H. Koh, G. T. Jeong, R. H. Kim, H. S. Lim, I. S. Park, H. S. Jeong, and K. Kim, "IEDM Tech. Dig.," p. 118, 2006.
80. J. I. Lee, H. Park, S. L. Cho, Y. L. Park, B. J. Bae, J. H. Park, J. S. Park, H. G. An, J. S. Bae, D. H. Ahn, Y. T. Kim, H. Horii, S. A. Song, J. C. Shin, S. O. Park, H. S. Kim, U. In Chung, J. T. Moon, and B. I. Ryu, "IEDM Tech. Dig.," p. 102, 2007.
81. J. P. Reifenberg, D. L. Kencke, and K. E. Goodson, *IEEE Electron Device Lett.* 29, 1112 (2008).
82. D. Kang, D. Lee, H.-M. Kim, S.-W. Nam, M.-H. Kwon, and K.-B. Kim, *Appl. Phys. Lett.* 95, 011904 (2009).
83. T.-Y. Yang, I.-M. Park, B.-J. Kim, and Y.-C. Joo, *Appl. Phys. Lett.* 95, 032104 (2009).
84. C. Kim, D. Kang, T.-Y. Lee, K. H. P. Kim, Y.-S. Kang, J. Lee, S.-W. Nam, K.-B. Kim, and Y. Khang, *Appl. Phys. Lett.* 94, 193504 (2009).
85. S. W. Nam, C. Kim, M. H. Kwon, H. S. Lee, J. S. Wi, D. Lee, T. Y. Lee, Y. Khang, and K. B. Kim, *Appl. Phys. Lett.* 92, 111913 (2008).

86. C.-F. Chen, A. Schrott, M. H. Lee, S. Raoux, Y. H. Shih, M. Breitwisch, F. H. Baumann, E. K. Lai, T. M. Shaw, P. Flaitz, R. Cheek, E. A. Joseph, S. H. Chen, B. Rajendran, H. L. Lung, and C. Lam, "IMW Tech. Dig.," p. 1, 2009.
87. A. Redaelli, A. Pirovano, A. Benvenuti, and A. L. Lacaita, *J. Appl. Phys.* 103, 111101 (2008).
88. S. H. Lee, M. S. Kim, G. S. Do, S. G. Kim, H. J. Lee, J. S. Sim, N. G. Park, S. B. Hong, Y. H. Jeon, K. S. Choi, H. C. Park, T. H. Kim, J. U. Lee, H. W. Kim, M. R. Choi, S. Y. Lee, Y. S. Kim, H. J. Kang, J. H. Kim, H. J. Kim, Y. S. Son, B. H. Lee, J. H. Choi, S. C. Kim, J. H. Lee, S. J. Hong, and S. W. Park, "VLSI Tech. Dig.," p. 199, 2010.
89. U. Russo, D. Ielmini, A. Redaelli, and A. L. Lacaita, *IEEE Trans. Elect. Dev.* 55, 515 (2008).
90. B. Gleixner, A. Pirovano, J. Sarkar, F. Ottogalli, E. Tortorelli, M. Tosi, and R. Bez, "IEEE Annual International Reliability Physics Symposium," Phoenix, Arizona, USA, 2007, p. 542.
91. Y. H. Shih, J. Y. Wu, B. Rajendran, M. H. Lee, R. Cheek, M. Lamorey, M. Breitwisch, Y. Zhu, E. K. Lai, C. F. Chen, E. Stinzianni, A. Schrott, E. Joseph, R. Dasaka, S. Raoux, H. L. Lung, and C. Lam, "IEDM Tech. Dig.," p. 1, 2008.
92. A. Redaelli, D. Ielmini, U. Russo, and A. L. Lacaita, *IEEE Trans. Electron Devices* 53, 3040 (2006).

CHAPTER 3

Phase Change Random Access Memory

L. P. Shi, R. Zhao

*Data Storage Institute, (A*STAR) Agency for Science Technology and Research, DSI Building, 5 Engineering Drive 1, Singapore 117608*

CONTENTS

1. INTRODUCTION

Nonvolatile memory (NVM) is ubiquitous in the electronics market and is commonly found in consumer goods such as computers, cellular phones, mp3 players etc. Recently, with the rapid growing demand for portable and mobile products, the demand for NVM has greatly increased. NVMs are memories that can retain the stored information even when the power supply is off. Flash memory has dominated the NVM market. Although flash memory is under fast growth, it will be facing technological and physical constraints that make its further scaling more difficult, eventhough the final scaling limits are still under debate. The scaling of flash memory is expected to be slightly below 20 nm. Although advances in flash memory technology have shifted from the floating gate, configuration to charge trapping, charge-based memories at nanoscale dimensions suffer from limited number of stored electrons available and low electron loss threshold for acceptable multilevel cell operation [1–7].

Therefore, this presents an opportunity for researchers to devise disruptive memory technologies, which move away from the practical limits of charge storing. Alternative NVM technologies, such as ferroelectric random access memory (FeRAM), magnetic random access memory (MRAM), phase-change random access memory (PCRAM), organic thin-film memory, molecular memory, nonvolatile silicon memory, have been poised as potential candidates for the next-generation of NVMs [8–18].

Among the various next-generation NVM technologies, PCRAM is believed to be one of the most promising technologies, and it has been stipulated to be the memory technology of choice beyond 10 nm. It has many near ideal memory qualities such as nonvolatility, fast-switching

ISBN: 1-58883-251-1

Nonvolatile Memories: Materials, Devices and Applications
Edited by Tseung-Yuen Tseng and Simon M. Sze
Volume 2: Pages: 57–81

speed, a high endurance of more than 10^{12} read/write cycles, a nondestructive read, direct overwriting, and long data retention time of more than 10 years [19, 20]. Its unique advantage over flash memory and other memory contenders is its high scalability. The programming current of PCRAM decreases as the size of the cell is scaled down [21]. Hence, its theoretical performance actually improves as the dimensions are scaled down.

PCRAM is based on the original invention by Ovshinsky in 1970s that used phase change alloy materials to store information [22–24]. Phase change materials have gone a long way from the works of Ovshinsky to their applications in optical media and to current researches in NVM devices [19, 24]. The early devices had poor operating performances due to the high power consumption, slow speed, and the tendency to degrade, owing to the large currents needed to write and erase data. Most of these technical problems were related to the materials. The success of rewriteable optical disk storage, where most of the problems related to materials were solved, and the discovery of germanium–antimony–tellurium (GeSbTe) alloys were indirectly responsible for PCRAM's second wind. This resulted in the success of the rewriteable optical disk and created renewed interest in PCRAM The new material benefited both electronic and optical memories because it requires much less time and energy to store data, making it possible to program a PCRAM cell with a short current pulse, which is needed to produce a commercially competitive NVM.

PCRAM is based on chalcogenide alloys that contain selenium or tellurium. They generally contain one or more elements from group VI of the periodic table. Phase change materials can change revisable from the amorphous state to crystalline state on a nano time scale.

The critical characteristic of phase change materials is its switching property between amorphous and crystalline states by using electrical pulses. Because the energy needed for operating this memory decreases with cell size, the writing current decreases with cell size scaling and, thus, facilitates memory scaling. This results in the most important advantage of PCRAM—high scalability.

Density, data transfer rate, and performance such as endurance are the most important technological criteria for PCRAM. For PCRAM, density is highly related to the cell size. To achieve high density, minimizing recording bits is one of the most effective approaches. The data transfer rate of PCRAM highly depends on the crystallization speed of the phase change materials.

In this chapter, the principle, key technologies, and recent development of PCRAM, including the technological solutions to achieve high density, high speed, and high performance of PCRAM, will be introduced as well as the main challenges and further key research issues.

2. PCRAM PRINCIPLES

PCRAM is based on revisable phase change switching of phase change materials. The phase change materials, which are mostly chalcogenide-based materials, have two phase structures, amorphous and crystalline phases. The electrical, optical, mechanical, and thermal properties of phase change materials are different for amorphous state and crystalline state. In principle, the phase change can be induced by electric pulse, optical pulse, or thermal method. Figure 1 is the principle of phase change and the feature of phase change materials.

2.1. Electric Current Induced Phase Change

There are two main kinds of electrical induced switching: ovonyx threshold switching (OTS) and memory switching according to whether the high resistance amorphous state can be resuscitated after the low resistance state has been maintained for a given length time. Figure 2 shows the current versus voltage (*I–V*) characteristics of the two switches.

The first type, threshold switching, is memory switching that was first discovered in 1959 by Ovshinsky [25] (Fig. 2(a)). It uses a bistable phase change that allows a change in the conduction state even in the absence of a current or voltage. It is a field-assisted transition that makes an amorphous semiconductor switching from a highly resistive to a conductive state when a threshold voltage is reached. However, because the resistance drop of memory switching is caused by material atomic structure change during the electrical pulses, the curve for memory switching continues through the origin of the graph, which shows that a sustaining current or voltage is not required once in a low resistance state. The difference in atomic structures causes electrical conductivity. The OFF state (or high resistance) is normally the amorphous state with disordered atomic structure; however, the ON state (or low resistance) is normally the crystalline state with ordered atomic structure.

The threshold switching is also a field-assisted transition that makes an amorphous semiconductor switching from a highly resistive to a conductive state when a threshold voltage is reached. The main difference is that the amorphous resistivity drops only once, and the current flowing through the device may heat up the device and lead to a second reversible transformation (called memory switching) that corresponds to the phase change transition from the amorphous to the crystalline state.

More precisely, the basic difference between these two types of electrical switching is whether the atomic structure happens during the switching. This characteristic differentiates the memory switching from threshold switching, in which when the sustaining current is not present, and the device reverts to its high resistance state because the atomic structure did not change. PCRAM is based on memory switching that switches between crystalline and amorphous states. Crystalline state has a lower resistance, whereas amorphous state has high resistance.

2.2. Modeling of Electric Current Induced Phase Change

The reversible phase change between the high resistance amorphous state and the low resistance crystalline state can be achieved by a current or voltage pulse on a nanosecond time scale. The schematic drawing of the common device structure is shown in Figure 3. Phase change materials are sandwiched by two electrodes and are isolated by dielectric materials. The small volume of active phase change material acts as a programmable resistor. The transition from

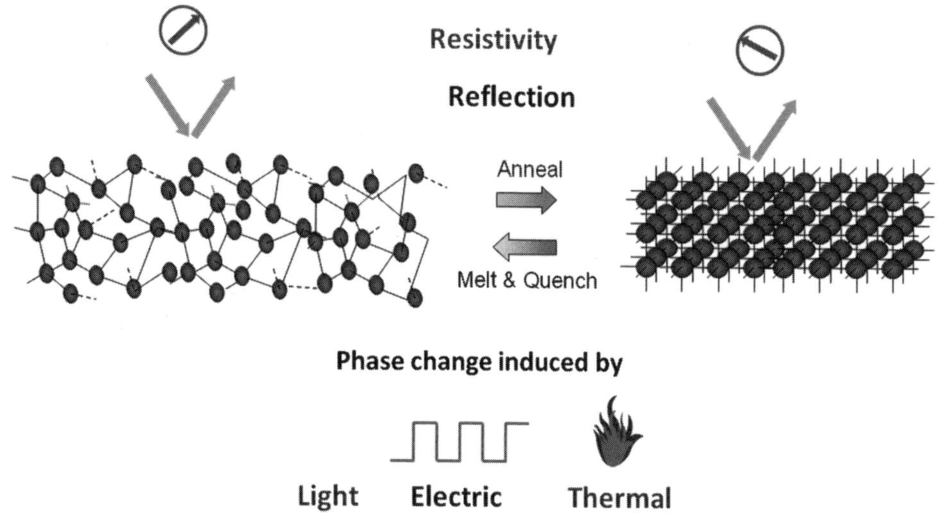

Figure 1. The transformation of the two phases of phase change materials.

the amorphous state to the crystalline state is caused by applying a relative longer pulse with lower amplitude, generally referred to as the SET process. The transition from the crystalline state to the amorphous state is caused by applying a relative short pulse with high amplitude, generally referred to as the RESET process. The resistance difference between the amorphous and crystalline states can be as high as six orders of magnitude. Because of this high difference, there is a high possibility to program PCRAM to intermediate resistance states and achieve multilevel, high-density PCRAM.

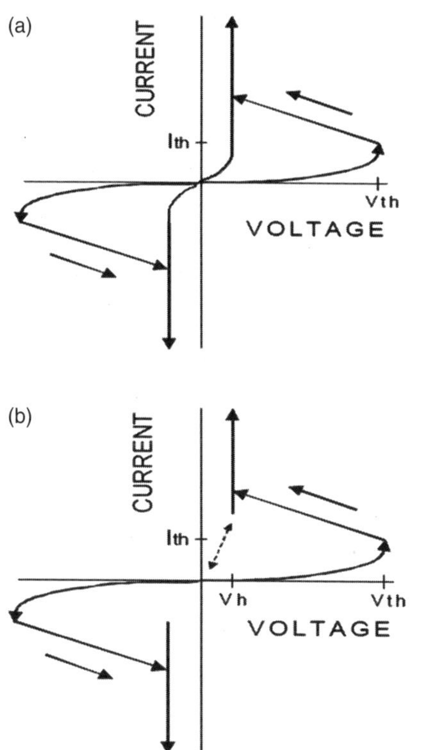

Figure 2. Electrical switching in phase change materials: (a) memory switching, and (b) threshold switching.

Figure 4 shows the temperature against amplitude and pulse width of the SET and RESET electrical pulse in the PCRAM device. When the RESET pulse is applied on the PCRAM cell at crystalline state, the temperature of phase change materials can be heated over the melting point by the Joule's heat. The PCRAM cell structure is designed in such a way that a rapid quenching can be achieved (10^{11} K/s) after the pulse and an amorphous state can be formed. When the SET pulse is applied on the PCRAM cell at the amorphous state, the temperature of phase change materials is heated above crystallization temperature but below melting temperature. The high and low resistances are measured and recorded as data "1" and "0". A much lower current with essentially no Joule heating is used to read the cell. It is easy to see that the energy used for phase transformation decreases with cell size because fewer amounts of phase change materials are involved in the operation. It means the writing current decreases with cell size and, thus, facilitates for PCRAM scaling.

The debate about the mechanism of the threshold switching of phase change materials has been continuing [22, 26, 27]. The phase transformation kinetics can be illustrated on a time-temperature transformation diagram (Fig. 5), which shows two contrasting factors, atom mobility and temperature dependency for reaction. At high temperatures near the melting point, the nucleation driving force is small, but the atom mobility is large. This results in slow crystallization. Similarly at lower temperatures, the nucleation driving force is large but the atom mobility is small, also resulting in slow crystallization. Thus, the highest crystallization rate is seen at an intermediate temperature, termed the "nose temperature," where both driving force and atom mobility are moderately high. Reamorphization can only occur by heating the material to above the melting point and quenching it faster than the material's cooling time, which is typically the line that just touches the C-shaped crystallization region (Fig. 5). Crystallization can be achieved most efficiently by heating the material to the

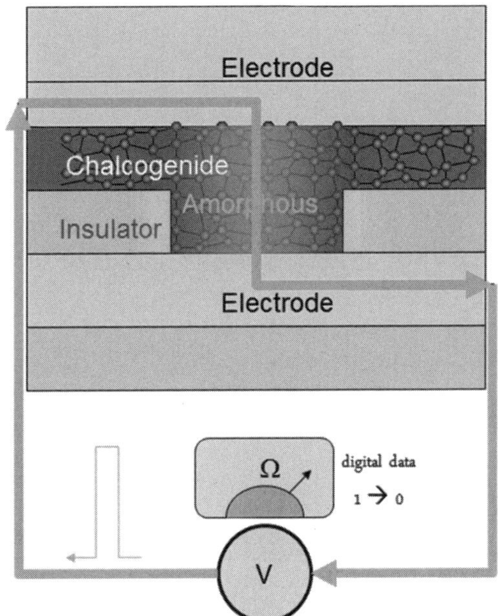

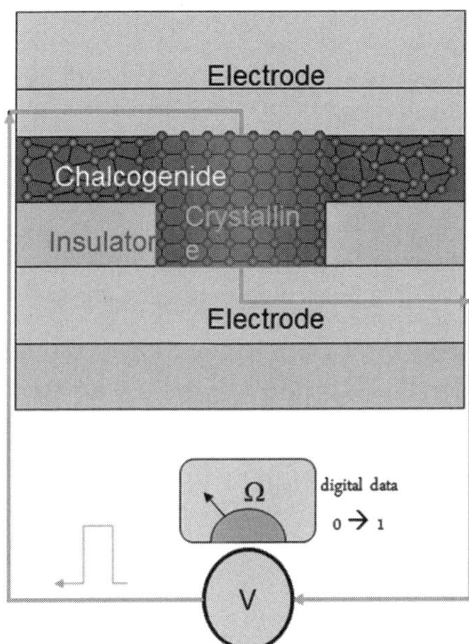

Figure 3. The principle and schematic cross-section of PCRAM cell structure.

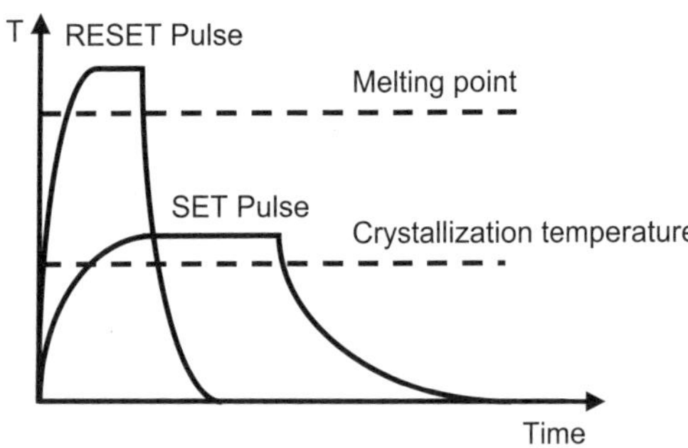

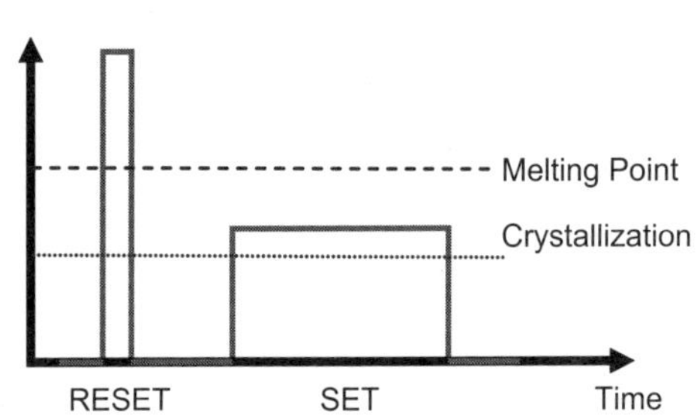

Figure 4. Temperature versus amplitude and pulse width of SET and RESET electrical pulse in PCRAM.

nose temperature for some time so the atoms have enough time to arrange themselves in an orderly manner if the SET process is purely a thermal process. However, the observation of SET speed makes us realize that the SET process is not a purely thermal process.

Since Ovshinsky reported the OTS effect [24], different models have been proposed. Many researchers supported the idea that OTS is essentially a thermal effect and that the current in an amorphous layer rises above due to the creation of a hot filament [28, 29]. Later, Adler [22] showed that, at least in thin chalcogenide films, OTS is not thermal, which was in agreement with Ovshinsky's original picture. He demonstrated that a semiconductor resistor may feature OTS, without any thermal effect, provided that a carrier generation driven by field and carrier concentration competes with a strong Shockley–Hall–Read recombination via localized states [22]. Recently, an original band-gap model consistent with the microscopic structure of both crystalline and amorphous chalcogenide has been proposed as well as a physical picture of the switching mechanism [30, 31]. For the first time, numerical simulations provide a quantitative description of the peculiar current–voltage curve of a $Ge_2Sb_2Te_5$ resistor, which is in good agreement with measurements performed on test devices.

At the very beginning, the quantum theory of semiconductors was completely developed and based on the

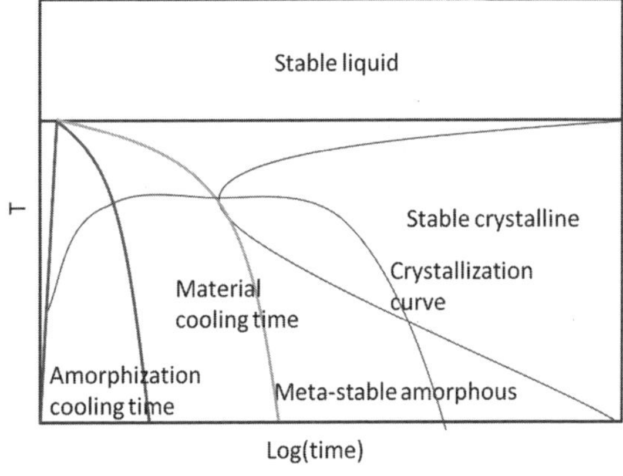

Figure 5. Time-temperature-transformation diagram for crystallization for phase change materials.

presence of long-range order and on the periodicity of the crystalline structures. It used to be believed that amorphous solids could not be described by band structures and could not behave as semiconductors because they did not have long-range periodicity. However, starting from 1955, it because clear that the key to understanding the properties of solids is not their periodic structure but the chemical nature of their constituent atoms. Thus, it was discovered that chalcogenide glasses can also act as semiconductors with an energy gap [23, 32–37]. The covalent interatomic bonds give rise to the usual bonding (valence) and antibonding (conduction) bands. However, since each chalcogenide atom has lone-pairs, a nonbonding density of states appears close to the top of the valence band-edge. These states are quite localized and, correspondingly, their carrier mobility is very low.

In order to correctly compute the temperature effects, the heat transport equation has been included in the solver and coupled self-consistently with a Poisson/drift-diffusion semiconductor device simulator. The resulting coupled set of equations is

$$\nabla \epsilon \cdot \nabla \phi = -q(p - n + N_D^+ - N_A^-) \tag{1}$$

$$\nabla \cdot J_n = qR + q\frac{\partial n}{\partial t} \tag{2}$$

$$\nabla \cdot J_p = -qR - q\frac{\partial p}{\partial t} \tag{3}$$

$$c\frac{\partial T}{\partial t} - \nabla \cdot \kappa \nabla T = -\nabla \cdot (\phi_n J_n + \phi_p J_p) \tag{4}$$

where ϵ is the electrical permittivity, Φ is the electrostatic potential, q is the elementary electronic charge, p and n are the hole and electron-free carrier densities, N_D^+ and N_A^- are the ionized donor and acceptor concentrations, R is the net electron–hole recombination rate, c is the lattice heat capacity, and κ is the lattice thermal conductivity. In the drift-diffusion model, the current density for electrons J_n and J_p holes and are given by

$$J_n = -q\mu_n n \nabla \phi_n \tag{5}$$

$$J_p = -q\mu_p p \nabla \phi_p \tag{6}$$

where μ_n and μ_p are the electron and hole mobility, and ϕ_n and ϕ_p are the electron and hole quasi–Fermi potentials, respectively. In this way, the $Ge_2Sb_2Te_5$ temperature is computed at each mesh point, taking into account the variations of the environment temperature and the local Joule heating, described by Eq. (4). For this it must be noted that $Ge_2Sb_2Te_5$ in amorphous chalcogenide also involves transitions between the conduction and the lone-pair band [34].

This model was used to simulate the *I–V* curve of $Ge_2Sb_2Te_5$. Figure 6 shows the comparison between the *I–V* curves of the test devices in both states and the simulation results. These curves show that the model is able to provide a comprehensive description of the electrical properties of PCRAM cells. It should be noted that the switching effect turns out from the competing role of $Ge_2Sb_2Te_5$ and carrier recombination in the proposed picture, without any need for additional mechanisms, e.g., thermal effects or carrier injection at the contacts.

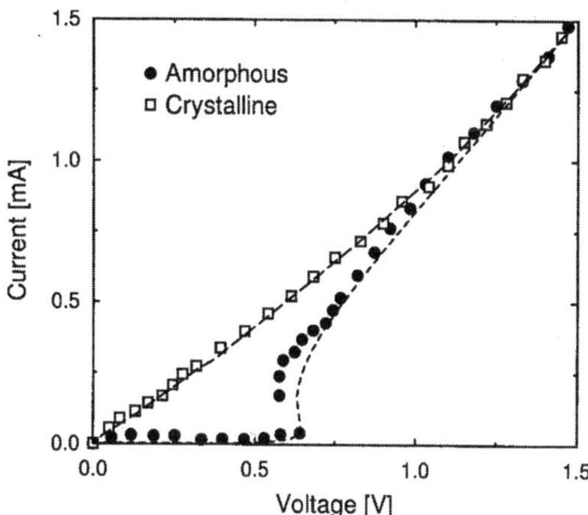

Figure 6. Comparison between experimental (symbols) and simulated (lines) *I–V* curves of crystalline and amorphous $Ge_2Sb_2Te_5$. Reprinted with permission from [30], A. Pirovano et al., *IEEE Trans. Elect. Dev.* 51, 452 (2004). © 2004, IEEE.

Recently, a simple physical model of threshold switching in PCRAM cells based on the field-induced nucleation of conductive cylindrical crystallites has been proposed [38–42]. The model is solved analytically and leads to a number of predictions, including correlations between the threshold voltage V_{th} and material parameters, such as the nucleation barrier and radius, amorphous layer thickness, as well as V_{th} versus temperature and switching delay time. The simulation results are in agreement with experiment results. The theory is more in the spirit of Ovshinsky's nucleation hypothesis [24] and suggests the field-induced nucleation of a shunting crystalline cylinder, which causes voltage to drop. It is considered a flat plate capacitor filled with a uniform (before switching) resistive amorphous $Ge_2Sb_2Te_5$ material of thickness l under bias V and field $E_0 = V/l$. The crystalline particles appear to be highly conductive. Their induced dipole momenta interact with the field, decreasing the system energy and thus facilitating nucleation.

The switching starts with the nucleation of a long ($h \gg R$) conductive cylinder (Fig. 7) that acts as a "lightning rod" and concentrates the electric field. The stronger electric field facilitates nucleation of an additional conductive particle at the cylinder end, which makes it longer, and hence, it further increases the field, and so on.

It is now believed that both thermal and electronic effects may be involved, although the initial models were mostly based on fully thermal or electronic models for the phenomenon. It should be noted that the basic nature of threshold switching is not yet well understood. On the other hand, as PCRAM scales to 10 nm or sub-10 nm, new effects, especially size and interface effects, will play a more important role and may present a variety of mechanisms.

2.3. Phase Change Materials

Phase change materials are the key for PCRAM. Phase change materials need to meet different requirements for the application in PCRAM, and some of those requirements

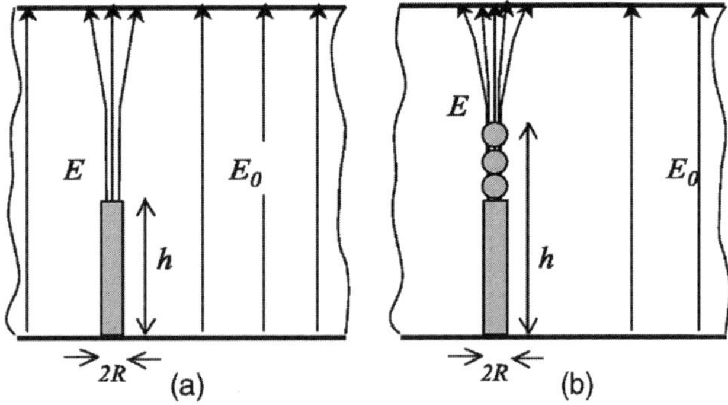

Figure 7. Nucleation of conductive (crystalline) phase in a host of resistive (amorphous) $Ge_2Sb_2Te_5$ material starts with (a) nucleation of a long cylinder embryo, (b) followed by nucleation of spherical particles at the cylinder edge. Reprinted with permission from [38], Y. A. Kryukov, et al., *Appl. Phys. Lett.* 90, 123504 (2007). © 2007, American Institute of Physics.

are contradictory. The first requirement is appropriate crystallization temperature and activation energy so that the device can have a fast switching speed and can keep stability at about 100°C. The second is an appropriate melting point, T_m, so that the device can have good retention and also keep a small program current. The requirements to achieve fast speed as well as stability and those to achieve good endurance, retention, and a small current are opposite. It needs to balance all of these opposite requirements. The important physical parameters for evaluating phase change materials include crystallization temperature, melting temperature, activation energy, thermal conductivity, specific heat, density, and crystal structure.

The nucleation of small crystallites and the subsequent growth are two key distinct processes for crystallization of materials based on the classic crystallization theory. Both the growth rate and nucleation rate are temperature dependent. Phase change materials are classified into nucleation-dominated material and growth-dominated material according to the contribution of nucleation and subsequent growth [43]. The schematic description is shown in Figure 8. If the nucleation rate of a material is higher than its growth rate, this material is called nucleation-dominated material. Alternatively, if the nucleation rate of a material is lower than its growth rate, this material is called

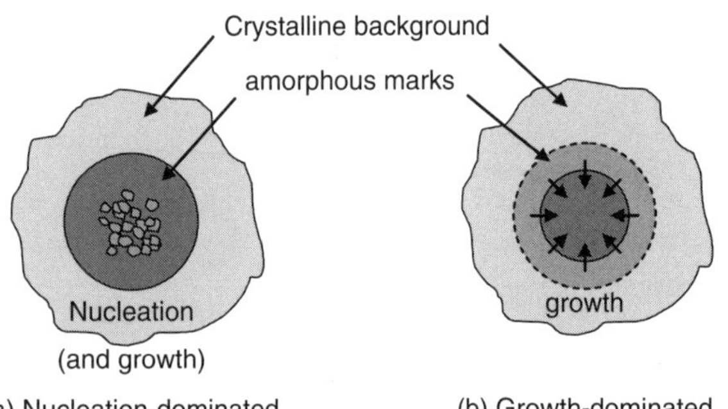

Figure 8. Schematic description of: (a) nucleation dominated phase change and (b) growth dominated phase change material.

growth-dominated material. It has been observed experimentally that nucleation-dominated materials are more suitable for vertical structure PCRAM and growth-dominated materials are more suitable for lateral type structure PCRAM. However, this phenomenon is not yet well understood.

It is always very attractive to utilize molecular engineering to design and model new phase change materials with excellent structure and performance, and some meet those special requirements. Luo and colleagues [44] first used the principle calculation based on density function theory to identify new and possible superior phase change materials. All phase change materials reported by them were characterized by a cubic or near-cubic coordination, which is a dominance of the p-electron bonding. The calculation results showed that the Te-based ternary materials will favor the suitable rock-salt structure if their average number of valence electrons per single atom is larger than 4.1. This criterion facilitated the search for new phase change materials and paved the way to a more fundamental understanding of phase change materials.

Kohary and colleagues [30] studied the structure of amorphous In–Se alloys by a first principles tight-binding molecular dynamics technique. The characteristics of short-range order, such as coordination numbers, radial and bond-angle distribution functions, and electronic structure were analyzed. Similar local bonding environments were found to be present in the amorphous phase as those found in In–Se crystalline alloys, such as In_2Se_3, InSe, and In_4Se_3. There is a large fluctuation in coordination numbers showing that amorphous In–Se alloys cannot be considered as network-forming materials. In the future, the material properties presented in this work can serve as input parameters for continuum models that link crystallization processes to an underlying structure.

Recently, it was shown that resonance bonding in the crystalline state is a unique fingerprint of phase-change materials [45]. The concept of "resonance bonding" addresses the case of covalent bonding with unsaturated bonds, i.e., less than two electrons per bond.

Lencer and colleagues [46] also proposed a method to look for phase change materials by using a so-called "treasure map" based on a fundamental understanding of the bonding characteristics. This map is spanned by two coordinates that can be calculated simply from their composition, and they represent the degree of ionicity and a tendency toward hybridization (or covalence) of the bonding. In this work, two of coordinates that were used were introduced by John, Simons, and Bloch [47, 48]:

$$r'_\sigma = r_p^A - r_p^B, \quad r_\pi^{-1} = [(r_p^A - r_s^A) + (r_p^B - r_s^B)]^{-1} \qquad (7)$$

Here, r_s^X and r_p^X denote the valence radii of the s- and p-orbital of atom X, respectively. The coordinate, r'_σ, provides a quantitative measure for the ionicity of bonds similar to Pauling's electronegativity difference. The second coordinate, r_π^{-1}, describes the degree of "covalence." It can be understood as a measure of the energetic splitting of s- and p-states, which scales with the difference between the radii of s- and p-orbits.

Weighing the corresponding orbital radii with the number of atoms ni of species i per formula unit, stoichiometry-averaged values for r'_σ and coordinate r_π^{-1} are determined as follows:

$$r'_\sigma = \underbrace{\left(\frac{\sum_i n_i r_{p,i}}{\sum_i n_i}\right)}_{\text{Anions}} - \underbrace{\left(\frac{\sum_j n_j r_{p,j}}{\sum_j n_j}\right)}_{\text{Cations}}$$
$$r_\pi^{-1} = \left[\underbrace{\left(\frac{\sum_i n_i (r_{p,i} - r_{s,i})}{\sum_i n_i}\right)}_{\text{Anions}} + \underbrace{\left(\frac{\sum_j n_j (r_{p,j} - r_{s,j})}{\sum_j n_j}\right)}_{\text{Cations}}\right]^{-1} \tag{8}$$

The resulting values for r'_σ and coordinate r_π^{-1} were calculated by using the radii given in Ref. [49], which is shown in Figure 9(a), for a large number of suitable systems. It is worth noting that phase change materials are characterized by a unique range of hybridization and ionicity, which limits the number of materials that can sustain phase change properties. More specifically, phase change materials are found in an area of small ionicity and a limited degree of hybridization, which enables resonance bonding to prevail. Resonance bonding has recently been identified as a crucial property of phase change materials [45]. The finding of resonance bonding in a limited region of the map can be understood

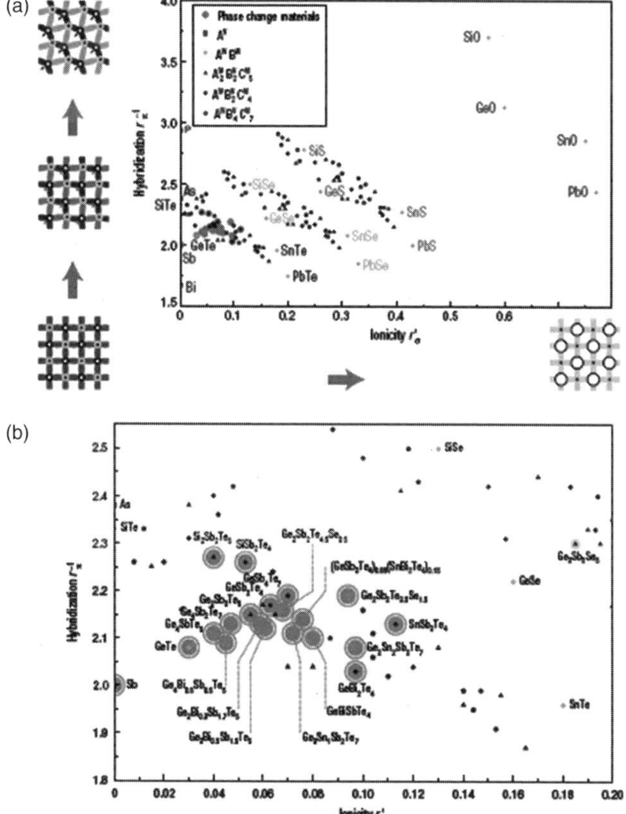

Figure 9. Map for numerous $N_p = 3$ systems: (a) a wide variety of materials is shown that differ in their tendency toward hybridization ('covalence'), r_π^{-1}, and ionicity r'. Reprinted with permission from [46], D. Lencer et al., *Nat. Mater.* 7, 972 (2008). © 2008, Nature Publishing Group.

if we consider the schematic drawings shown in Figure 9(a). These sketches denote how a perfect sixfold-coordinated system that shows resonance bonding would be affected if either of the two coordinates increased. Increasing r_π^{-1} leads to a more pronounced formation of saturated covalent bonds, and it is accompanied by increasing distortions because it invokes a departure from pure p-bonding. The increased charge localization diminishes resonance bonding and, hence, the electronic polarizability. The same happens if r'_σ increases, and the charge is increasingly localized at the ion cores. Therefore, it becomes obvious that resonant bonding can be found only in the region denoted by the filled green circles in Figure 9(b). Therefore, the map enables us to identify suitable candidates on the basis of the material stoichiometry alone.

Three types of system are shown in Figure 9: group V elements (squares), binary $A^{IV}B^{VI}$ compounds (grey circles) and ternary alloys with different compositions including $A_2^{IV}B_2^{V}C^{V}I_5$ (triangles), $A^{IV}B_2^{V}C_4^{VI}$ (diamonds), and $A^{IV}B_4^{V}C_7^{VI}$ (pentagons). Bands of oxides, sulphides, selenides, and tellurides are clearly discernible. The insets on the left illustrate how the bonding mechanism varies with the coordinates. The starting point is a structure with predominant resonance bonding. The resonance character is weakened by increasing hybridization as well as the increasing ionicity. Increasing the former leads to larger distortions that favor a smaller number of more saturated covalent bonds. Increasing ionicity also reduces resonant bonding because the charge is now increasingly localized at the ion cores. Hence, phase change materials, which are marked by green circles, are all localized in a small region of the map (Fig. 9(b)), which is a more detailed view of the small region in which the phase change materials are localized. This region is characterized by the pronounced resonance bonding in the crystalline state.

It has been only recently that many phase change materials are being developed. They are mainly binary, ternary, and quaternary chalcogenide alloys. Table 1 lists some of the materials developed that have been developed. Among them, the most famous is the GeSbTe system, and $Ge_2Sb_2Te_5$ is the most commonly used phase change material because of its excellent performance [50, 51].

It is well known that the GeSbTe system can be seen as pseudobinary GeTe and Sb_2Te_3 alloys with different combinations, such as $Ge_2Sb_2Te_5 \leftrightarrow (GeTe)_2(Sb_2Te_3)$, $Ge_1Sb_2Te_4 \leftrightarrow (GeTe)(Sb_2Te_3)$, and $Ge_1Sb_4Te_7 \leftrightarrow (GeTe)(Sb_2Te_3)_2$. Figure 10 shows the GeTe–Sb_2Te_3 pseudobinary phase diagram from Abrikosov and colleagues [52]

Table 1. Phase change materials.

Binary	Ternary	Quaternary
GaSb	$Ge_2Sb_2Te_5$	AgInSbTe
InSb	InSbTe	(GeSn)SbTe
InSe	GaSeTe	GeSb(SeTe)
Sb_2Te_3	$SnSb_2Te_4$	$Te_{81}Ge_{15}Sb_2S_2$
GeTe	$Ge_1Sb_2Te_4$	$GeSbBiTe_4$
Sb_7Te_3	$Ge_{25}As_{50}Te_{25}$	GeTeSbS
In_2Se_3	$Ge_1Sb_4Te_7$	GeTeInGa

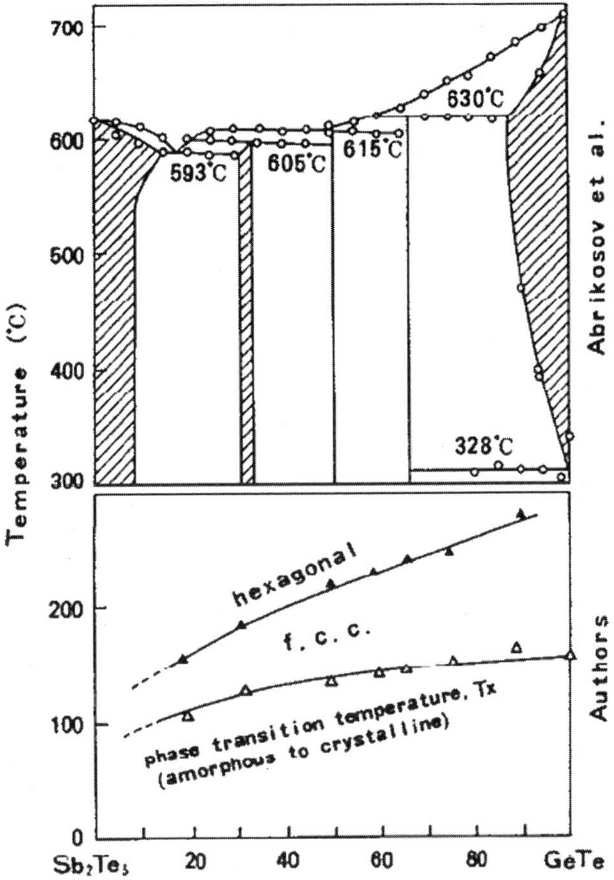

Figure 10. GeTe–Sb_2Te_3 pseudobinary phase diagram from Abrikosov et al. Phase transition temperatures of GeTe–Sb, Te, pseudobinary amorphous alloy films. Reprinted with permission from [50], N. Yamada et al., *J. Appl. Phys.* 69, 2849 (1991). © 1991, American Institute of Physics.

and transition temperatures of GeTe–Sb, Te, which are pseudobinary amorphous alloy films [50].

Sb_2Te_3 has a rhombohedral lattice of the tetradymite (Bi_2Te_2S) type (space group $R3m$) in the hexagonal configuration with the lattice parameters, $a = 0.4264$ nm, $c = 3.0453$ nm [53]; the hexagonal unit cell contains three five-layer packs ($N = 15$). The atomic layers are alternated in the $Te_1SbTe_2SbTe_1$ sequence perpendicular to the c axis. The five-layer packets are bonded to each other by weak Van der Waals force. There are two polymorphic phases in the GeTe compound. The high temperature β phase ($T > 700$ K) has a cubic rock-salt structure (space group $Fm3m$) [54]. The low temperature α phase ($T < 700$ K) has a rhombohedra structure of the α-As type (space group $R3m$) with lattice parameters, $a = 0.5986$ nm and $\alpha = 88.35°$ [54]. The α phase is rhombohedrally distorted along the [111] direction. As a result, the Ge–Te double layer packs of bismuth-type are formed.

Figure 11 shows a ternary alloy phase diagram (Ge, Sb, and Te) with the change tendencies of crystallization speed, melting point, and resistivity difference between the amorphous and crystalline states of GeTe and Sb_2Te_3. It is evident that GeTe has shown a large difference in resistivity between the amorphous and crystalline states, making it suitable for

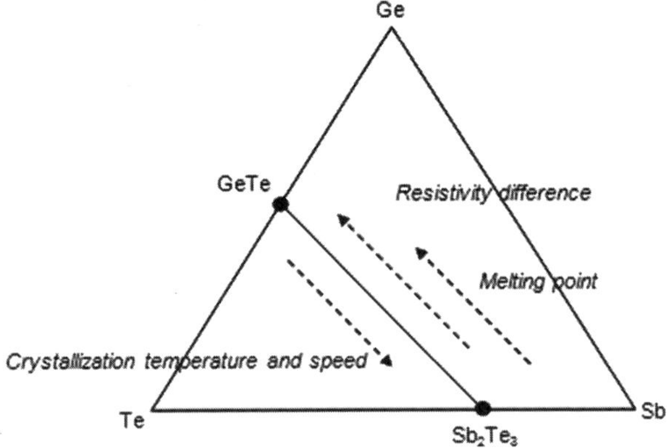

Figure 11. Ternary alloy phase diagram (Ge, Sb, and Te) with the change tendencies of different properties along GeTe and Sb_2Te_3 pseudobinary line.

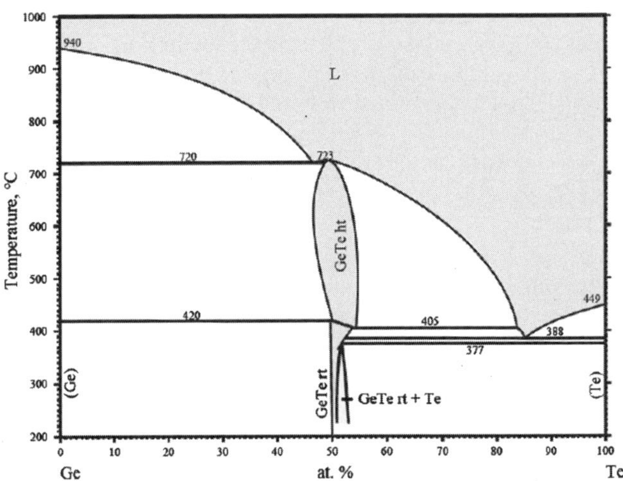

Figure 12. Phase diagram for the binary alloy GeTe. Reprinted with permission from [55], L. Balde et al., *J. Alloys Compd.* 216, 285 (1995). © 1995, Elsevier Ltd.

multilevel applications. Alternatively, GeTe has a high crystallization temperature (189°C) and a high melting point (about 700°C), which makes it attractive for high induction and high retention. As such, GeTe is another frequently studied material. Figure 12 shows the phase diagram of the GeTe system [55].

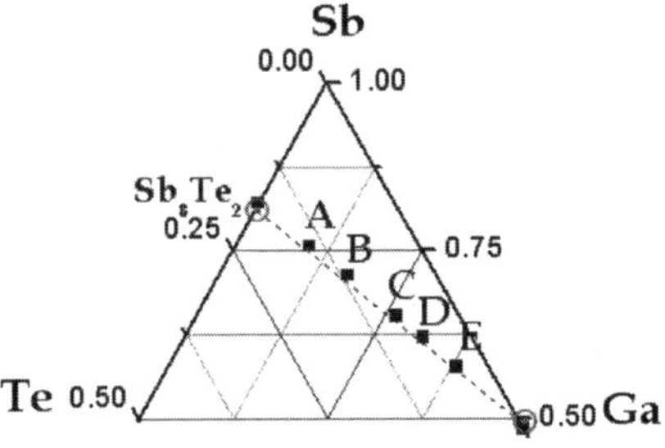

Figure 13. Compositions of studied GaSbTe films in the ternary Ga–Sb–Te phase diagram. Reprinted with permission from [56], H. Y. Cheng et al., *IEEE Trans. Mag.* 43, 927 (2007). © 2007, IEEE.

Table 2. Comparison of T_x and T_m of GaSbTe films.

		Composition (at%)				Specific temperatures (°C)		
Power ratio (W)		Ga	Sb	Te	Sb/Te	T_x	$T_{m,1}$	$T_{m,2}$
0/50	S8T2	0	82.1	17.9	4.59	123	541	–
25/50	A	9.9	75.7	14.4	5.26	195	513.9	559.5
50/50	B	17.1	71.2	11.7	6.08	232	573.6	–
50/25	C	26.4	65.2	8.4	7.76	277	567.5	–
75/25	D	31.6	62.1	6.3	9.86	269	567.3	666.5
75/15	E	38.2	57.7	4.1	14.4	275	564.9	686.8
50/0	GS	51.4	48.6	0	–	275	564.5	687.1

Source: Reprinted with permission from [56], H. Y. Cheng et al., *IEEE Trans. Mag.* 43, 927 (2007). © 2007, IEEE.

Recently, the GaSbTe system was proposed to improve the endurance of PCRAM [56–58]. The compositions of the GaSbTe films, as indicated in the ternary diagram (Fig. 13) analyzed by a field emission electron probe microanalyzer, are listed in Table 2 [56]. The crystallization temperature and melting point of GaSbTe films measured by differential thermal analysis are also depicted therein. The compositions B, C, and D can be denoted as, from simplified atomic ratios, $Ga_{1.5}Sb_6Te_1$, $Ga_3Sb_8Te_1$, and $Ga_5Sb_{10}Te_1$, respectively.

The atomic ratio Sb/Te is rapidly raised by the incorporation of GaSb, and the crystallization speed may be further increased due to its growth-dominated crystallization nature [59]. However, compositions rich in Sb, although they generally show high crystallization rates, have low archival stability. The crystallization temperature and ratio increase with Ga incorporation (Fig. 14), indicating that the amorphization ability and thermal stability will be improved by increasing Ga content and will accompany the sacrifice of crystallization ability. The composition C ($Ga_3Sb_8Te_1$) presents the highest ratio. In principle, a material with low crystallization temperature performs low stability, whereas a material with higher stability based on its higher crystallization temperature exhibits higher melting temperatures and results in higher reset current during amorphization. $Ga_2Sb_3Te_5$ and $Ga_3Sb_8Te_1$ were found to be better candidates.

It is always attractive to look for new phase change materials. But, they are very difficult to find because they need to meet a lot of requirements for various applications. Doping

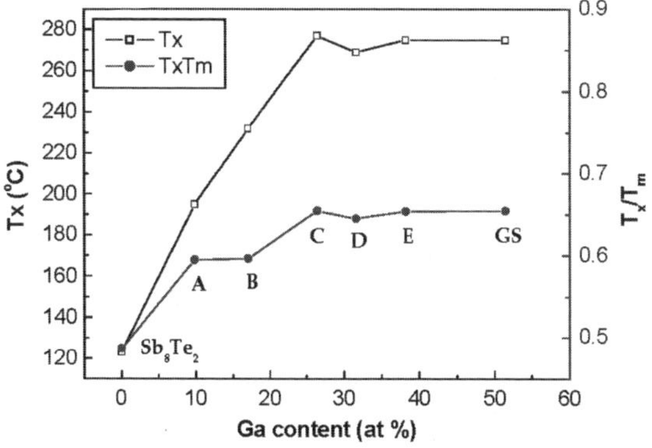

Figure 14. T_x and T_x/T_m ratio of GaSbTe films versus Ga content. Reprinted with permission from [56], H. Y. Cheng et al., *IEEE Trans. Mag.* 43, 927 (2007). © 2007, IEEE.

is a useful way to improve the properties of phase change material. Many works on doping of phase change materials have been carried out. The dopants that have been studied for GeSbTe alloy include N_2, O_2, Bi, Mo, Cu, Ag, Sn, Si, Bi, and In [60–66]. The most commonly used dopant is nitrogen [60, 61, 67–69]. It has been found that the resistivity of the GeSbTe was controllable in a wide range of 0.007 to 0.5 Ω cm by mixing an amount of N_2 gas with Ar during GeSbTe deposition. The fabricated nitrogen-doped GeSbTe had a smaller grain size than undoped GeSbTe; this is because nitrogen suppresses the GeSbTe grain growth and has better thermal stability due to increased crystallization temperature [68]. Doping nitrogen into GeSbTe increases the dynamic resistance at the programming current level and results in lower writing current [67]. Nitrogen doping concentration inside the GeSbTe increases the activation energy, and, as a result, the fabricated memory cell with nitrogen-doped GeSbTe showed a higher SET resistance of 6 k and a lower writing current of 0.6 mA.

2.3.1. Engineering Phase Change Materials

2.3.1.1. Phase Change Materials with Superlattice-Like Structure for PCRAM. Another useful way to modify the properties of phase change materials is to engineer phase change materials by constructing them with artificial structures. One artificial structure is to form superlattice-like (SLL) structure [70] by alternatively depositing two phase change materials. SLL structure can provide flexible approach to control the performance of PCRAM by using a different configuration. For example, we can use one phase change material with a high crystallization speed as one element layer and use another phase change materials with a relatively low crystallization speed but a high stability as another element layer to form the SLL structure. It has been demonstrated that the PCRAM with such structure can operate at a high speed due to the presence of first material while maintain a good stability due to the second material. Because neither of the element material can be used alone for PCRAM; SLL structure paved a way to combine different desirable phase change materials to make particle PCRAM devices that can demonstrate outstanding performance.

Figure 15 shows a basic SLL PCRAM cell structure. As phase change materials can be classified into nucleation-dominated type and growth dominated type, and both types are suitable for vertical and lateral type PCRAM, it is necessary to develop nucleation-dominated type SLL structure

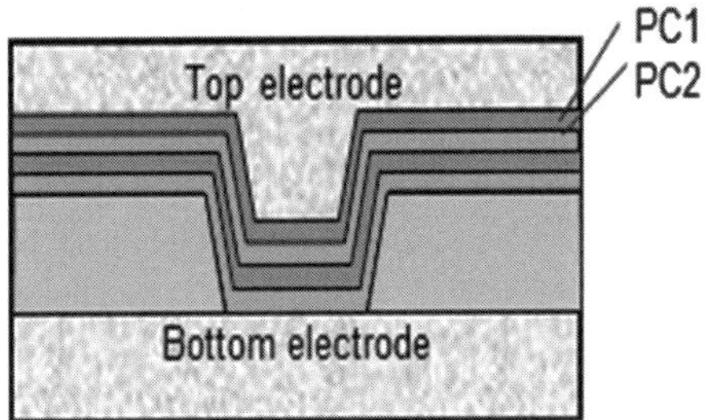

Figure 15. SLL PCRAM cell structure.

and growth-dominated type SLL structure. It was reported that nucleation-dominated type SLL structure can be fabricated by using GeTe and Sb_2Te_3 as element materials and growth-dominated type SLL structure can be made by using GeTe and Sb_7Te_3 as element materials [71–73].

With SLL structure it has been observed that programming current can be significantly reduced. SLL PCRAM cells with size from 1 μm down to 90 nm were fabricated by a system incorporating a near field scanner optical microscope with a femtosecond laser. It was found that the RESET current is about 40% smaller than that of PCRAM with single $Ge_2Sb_2Te_5$ layer. Theoretically, it has been found that the thermal conductivity along both in-plane and cross-plane directions deviates significantly from the corresponding bulk materials due to the interface phonon scattering and phonon confinement effects [74–77]. Significant reductions in both in-plane and cross-plane thermal conductivities of SLL have been observed experimentally [78–86]. These results are also applicable for SLL structure. The reduction of programming current can be attributed to the reduction of thermal conductivity of SLL structure that leads to good thermal confinement and higher heating efficiency.

Program speed is another very important parameter for NVM. For PCRAM the speed is highly dependent on the reversible phase change transition speed of phase change materials that are limited by the nature property of the materials. It was found that SLL structure could not only reduce the programming current, but it also increased the switching speed of PCRAM too [71]. It is reported that SLL PCRAM can function at a much shorter pulse width for both SET and RESET than the device with a single $Ge_2Sb_2Te_5$ layer, although the total composition of active material is both $Ge_2Sb_2Te_5$. It should be noted that the performance of SLL PCRAM is highly dependent on the configuration of SLL structure, especially the layer thicknesses.

Endurance could be one concern for SLL PCRAM. However, it has been demonstrated by TEM that the SLL structure exhibited a good interfacial quality, and although the interface is not sharp after 10,0000 times of overwriting, the ML structure still remained [71].

There are several possible reasons for the good overwrite cycles for SLL structure. Firstly, the electrical pulse applied on PCRAM is very short, only several tens of ns. Within this short period, the phase change material is heated up. The duration for the material above its melting point is even shorter, only a few ns. This will result in a shorter time for molecular exchange and diffusion. This means that working at short pulse width is facilitated for prolonging the overwriting cycle of the SLL structure. Secondly, the viscosity of phase change materials is low. Finally, the active area is localized in a very small area of $< 1\ \mu m^2$, which is tightly surrounded and limited by the solid materials. The diffusion will be mostly realized by atomic exchange. The active area provides a closed environment, which is favorable for diffusion and interchange.

2.3.1.2. Materials by Mixing of Phase Change Materials and Dielectric Materials. Another useful method to engineering phase change materials is mixing phase change materials with dielectric materials [64, 87–93] by co-sputtering. More precisely, phase change materials and dielectric materials form a nano scale region to reduce program current and increase crystallization temperature as well as endurance. A lot of effort has been put into the development of a GeSbTe + SiO_2 system.

The incorporation of nanoscale SiO_2 regions greatly increases the crystallization activation energy. An increase in the crystallization activation energy of the films of composite GeSbTe + SiO_2 has also been reported by Lee and colleagues [94]. The activation energy in this case rose from 2.5 eV for the pure GeSbTe to 6.44 eV for the nominally 10% (8.4 mol%) SiO_2 nanocomposite, although the crystallization temperature of the GeSbTe nanocomposite increased only by ~30°C. The separated domain formation in co-sputtered GeSbTe − SiO_x mixed layer, with SiO_x amount less than 10 mol%, was observed in Figure 16.

Nanometer scale $Ge_2Sb_2Te_5$ domains formed by an immiscible mixture of $Ge_2Sb_2Te_5 - SiO_x$ show remarkable suppression in electrical and thermal conductivity [90]. Thermal boundary resistance with increased $Ge_2Sb_2Te_5 - SiO_x$ interface becomes crucial to the reduction in thermal conductivity. These conductivity reductions concurrently result in the reduction in programming current and power consumption in phase change memory devices. The reset current was reduced by 32% due to the thermal and electrical confinement of the heat and current path and are possibly due to the reduction in the effective volume of the phase-changing region.

The films and PCRAM devices using the co-sputtered $Ge_4Sb_1Te_5$ with SiO_2 nanoscale inclusions were investigated, and both the alloy films and devices exhibited dramatic increases in the crystallization temperature. The presence of the nanoscale SiO_2 inclusions significantly increases the 10-year crystallization temperature for devices to well over 200°C [92].

It is reported that ~20-nm sized $Ge_2Sb_2Te_5$ clusters surrounded by TiO_x phases were formed by co-sputtering using the thermodynamic immiscibility between them [95]. The transformation of $Ge_2Sb_2Te_5$ from the amorphous to the crystalline phase was found to be suppressed by the addition of TiO_x, which was evidenced by the increased crystallization temperature and activation energy for the transformation. In addition, it also confirmed that the electrical resistivity can be tuned in the optimum range by adjusting the amount of TiO_x incorporated, and the reliable repetitive switching behavior of the film was verified by the laser pulse test. The nanocluster of $Ge_2Sb_2Te_5$ with its many interfaces of oxide could reduce the reset current due to their thermally and electrically ineffective transports of heat and

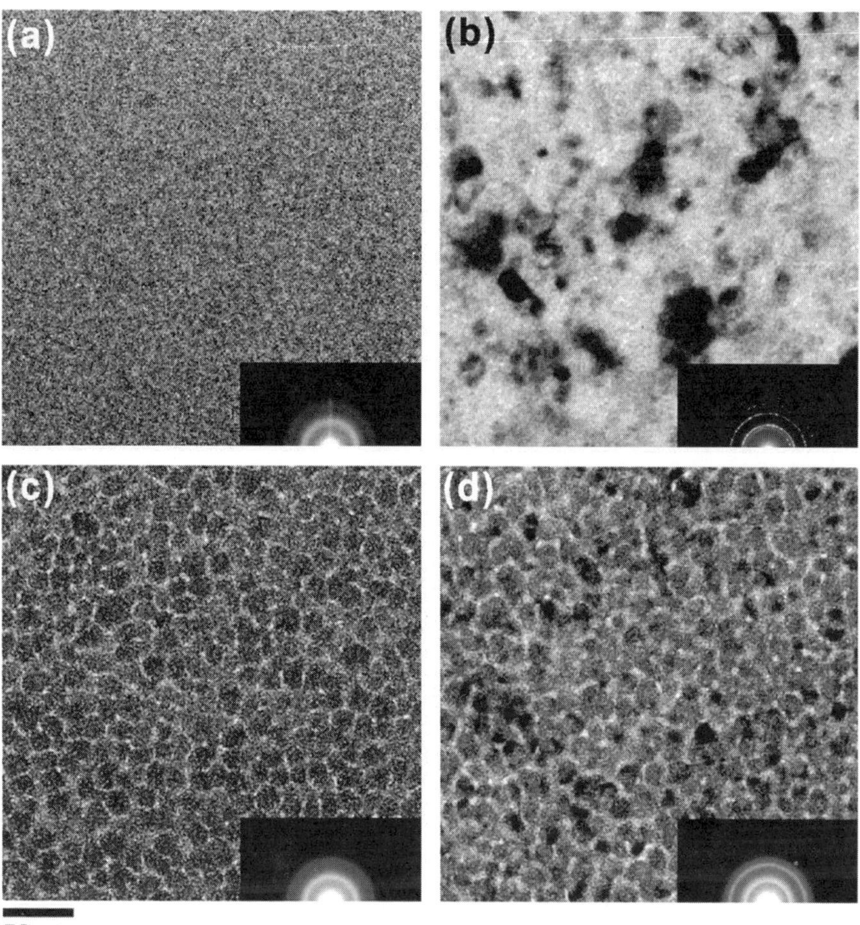

Figure 16. Plan-view bright field TEM images of 500 Å pure $Ge_2Sb_2Te_5$ layer as prepared: (a) and annealed at 200°C, (b) taken at in focus and 500 Å $Ge_2Sb_2Te_5$–SiO_x mixed layer containing 4.6 mol% of SiO_x as prepared, (c) and annealed at 200°C, (d) taken at under focus. Insets show diffraction patterns of each microstructure. Reprinted with permission from [94], T. Y. Lee et al., *Appl. Phys. Lett.* 89, 163503 (2006). © 2006, American Institute of Physics.

current. In addition, the higher activation energy and crystallization temperature of the mixed films contribute to the amorphous stability for data retention.

2.3.2. Deposition of Phase Change Materials

For the scaling of PCRAM with high performance, it is important to maintain a low SET resistance as devices scale to smaller sizes or higher aspect ratio. Both alloy composition and device structure play important roles in these efforts. Structure innovation using a confined cell structure with conformal chemical vapor deposition (CVD)-filled $Ge_2Sb_2Te_5$ leads to improved cell-heating efficiency and, thus, lower RESET current by both minimizing the active $Ge_2Sb_2Te_5$ material volume and reducing heat loss [96, 97]. Reduction of the reset current and improvement of SET speed over planar physical vapor deposition (PVD) $Ge_2Sb_2Te_5$ has been demonstrated in scaled confined devices [97]. A key enablement to scale the confined-cell device architecture is the use of conformal deposition processes for the GeSbTe layer utilizing CVD, metal-organic chemical vapor deposition (MOCVD) or atomic layer deposition (ALD) [98–101].

PCRAM devices were fabricated using MOCVD-deposited 30% Ge, 20% Sb, and 50% Te atomic composition, $Ge_3Sb_2Te_5$ alloy, and then characterized. In 100-nm size test devices, a more than two times reduction of reset current and set resistance were demonstrated compared with equivalent devices using PVD $Ge_2Sb_2Te_5$. The devices show set speeds of 175–260 ns and a 10-year data-retention temperature of 102°C was comparable with devices made using a PVD $Ge_2Sb_2Te_5$ alloy. Cycle endurance of up to 7×10^9 was also demonstrated.

The composition of MOCVD GeSbTe deposited in the test devices was 30% Ge, 20% Sb, and 50% Te with an estimated composition range accuracy of $\pm 3\%$. During deposition, dopants of N and C were incorporated from precursors and co-reactants at atomic concentrations of 7% and 4%, respectively, with an estimated accuracy of $\pm 4\%$ for N and $\pm 2\%$ for C. The as-deposited film is amorphous, smooth, and conformal. Typical film density is equivalent between the as-grown film and annealed films. The doping in this MOCVD $Ge_3Sb_2Te_5$ also increases the crystallization temperature T_x to 220°C compared with a typical T_x of 150°C for $Ge_2Sb_2Te_5$.

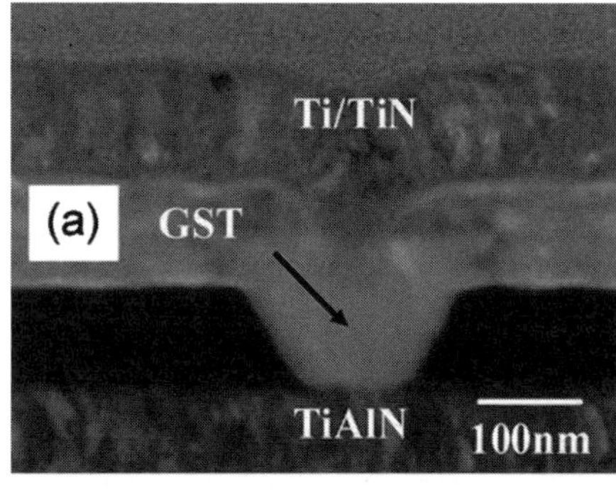

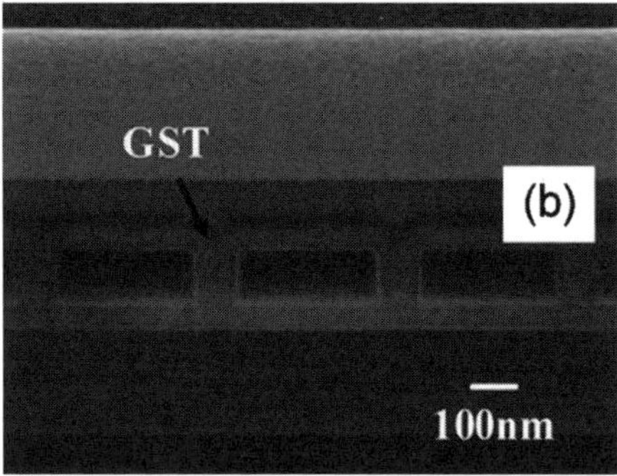

Figure 17. Cross-sectional SEM image of: (a) an MOCVD GeSbTe based PCRAM, and (b) an MOCVD GeSbTe filled 70 nm diameter via with 3:1 aspect ratio. Reprinted with permission from [101], J. F. Zheng et al., *IEEE Elec. Dev. Lett.* 31, 9 (2010). © 2010, IEEE.

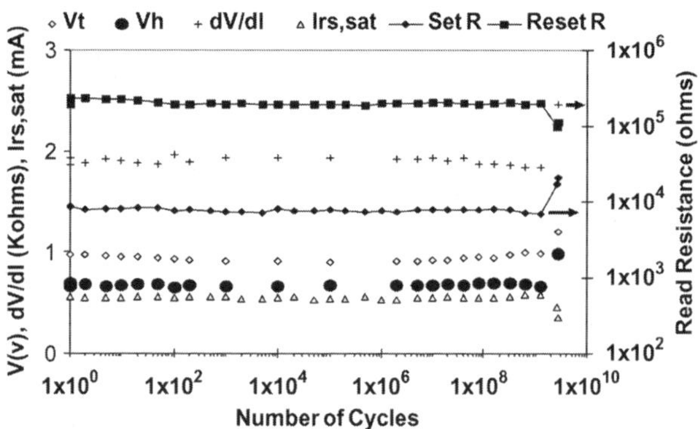

Figure 18. Cycle-endurance measurements. Reprinted with permission from [101], J. F. Zheng et al., *IEEE Elec. Dev. Lett.* 31, 9 (2010). © 2010, IEEE.

Figure 17(a) shows the device structure containing a bottom TiAlN electrode as a heater that is filled GeSbTe in the pore as well as a top TiN electrode. The shallow pore is formed by etching a hole with sloped sidewalls in a 500-Å plasma-enhanced CVD SiO_2 etch stopped on TiAlN. The test structures have nominal design dimensions ranging from 70 to 200 nm. The TiAlN surface inside the pore was cleaned using a dilute HF (50:1) dip prior to a MOCVD deposition of 750 Å GeSbTe. A 620-Å Ti/TiN layer was then deposited over the GeSbTe for the top electrode. The Ti/TiN and GeSbTe were patterned by lithography and a dry etch to isolate the GeSbTe and TiN top electrode in a single PCM device for testing.

Figure 18 shows the cycle-endurance test for a PCRAM device made of MOCVD $Ge_3Sb_2Te_5$. The test used the square-pulse method with a reset pulse time of 100 ns and set pulse time of 500 ns with a cycle period of 1 μsec. There were 1.3×10^9 cycles completed with a stable R_{reset}, R_{set}, V_t, V_h, and dV/dI before the device degraded resulting in a reduced dynamic range. The device shown in Figure 18(a) endured more than 7×10^9 cycles without failure or void formation under similar test conditions in this nonconfined, low-aspect-ratio structure.

One of the keys for the high-cycle endurance is to deposit void-free and high-density amorphous film, which maintains a small density change in the crystalline phase after annealing without void formation [102]. With 3:1 high-aspect-ratio structure devices, it has achieved more than 1×10^{10} cycle endurance with an R_{reset}/R_{set} dynamic range of 100 times from a device made of MOCVD GeSbTe, which was comparable with the best reported cycle endurance of 1×10^{10} in a very narrow 7.5-nm high-aspect-ratio confined-cell structure device made of MOCVD $Ge_2Sb_2Te_5$ [97]. There could be a possible improvement in the cycle endurance if the device were in a high-aspect ratio fully confined structure using a comprehensive metabolic panel to remove excess GST material above the pore, followed by a sealing of the cell with a top electrode, as described in the PCM confined-cell integration processes [96, 97]. The 1.3×10^9 cycle-endurance data presented here are an indication of the device stability, and they demonstrate the promise of this MOCVD $Ge_3Sb_2Te_5$ alloy to enable the continued scaling of PCRAM with increased cycle endurance, also opening up new memory market segments for PCRAM.

Limited electrical data are reported on alloys made by CVD or ALD at compositions other than $Ge_2Sb_2Te_5$ [98]. ALD is a unique modification of the chemical vapor deposition method for highly controlled deposition of thin films. Unique to ALD is that precursor vapors are brought onto the substrates alternately, one at a time, separated by purging periods with inert gas. The film grows via saturating surface reactions between the incoming precursor and the surface species left from the previous precursor. When all the reactions are saturating and no precursor decomposition takes place, the film growth is self-limiting and provides a number of attractive features, such as easy and accurate film thickness control down to an atomic layer level, excellent large area uniformity, and unrivalled conformality on complex-shaped substrates.

ALD is a thin film deposition technique that is based on the sequential use of a gas-phase chemical process. The majority of ALD reactions use two chemicals, which are typically called precursors. These precursors react with a surface one at a time in a sequential manner. The success of ALD depends strongly on appropriate precursor compounds.

Recently, a breakthrough was made in the development of new ALD precursors for tellurium and selenium [99]. Compounds with a general formula, $(R3Si)_2Te$ and $(R3Si)_2Se$, react with various metal halides and then form the corresponding metal tellurides and selenides. It was shown that Sb_2Te_3, GeTe, and GeSbTe films can be deposited by ALD using $(Et3Si)_2Te$, $SbCl_3$, and $GeCl_2 \cdot C_4H_8O_2$ compounds as precursors. All three precursors exhibit a typical saturating ALD growth behavior and GeSbTe films prepared at 90°C show excellent conformality on a high-aspect ratio trench structure.

3. PCRAM TECHNOLOGY

Scaling down the size of PCRAM cells is an important approach to achieve high density and low-cost memory. The more the feature size is scaled down, the higher the density will be. PCRAM shows potential toward high scalability. However, the scaling issues of PCRAM have not been fully understood yet.

3.1. Scalability of PCRAM

It used to be commonly believed that PCRAM technology is only limited by lithography process. Hence, most of the researches in the past have focused their attention on improving the lithography technology. Followed by 180-nm PCRAM fabricated by Intel in 2001, PCRAM was successfully developed at a 90-nm node by Samsung [32]. To keep extending the feature size limitation, various advanced lithography technologies such as electron beam and near-field optical microscopy [33] have been used to fabricate < 50 nm PCRAM cells.

However, with the continuous effect on minimization, it can be foreseen that the physical limitation of phase change materials will become more critical. The scaling limitation of PCRAM can arise from two aspects: (1) the feature size limitation through manufacturing process, and (2) the physical limitation of phase change materials. Because lithography challenges are common for most of the memory techniques, we will discuss the physical limitation of PCRAM materials in detail.

Because PCRAM is currently developed on the order of nano-scale, the interfaces play an important role and strongly cause the deviation of phase change behavior from that of bulk. In fact, the physical limitation of phase change materials is dependent on nano-phase change (NPC). NPC is size-dependent, interface-dominated, and related to the surrounding materials [34]. In order to systemically study the physical limitation of phase change materials for PCRAM application, it is inevitable to take into account the effect of the surrounding materials. From the standard structure of PCRAM cell shown in Figure 3, it can be seen that phase change materials are surrounded by metal/oxides. Considering the surrounding materials, NPC can be classified into three categories:

(1) phase change in free scale,
(2) phase change surrounded by oxides/metals, and
(3) reversible phase change surrounded by oxides/metals.

In the PCRAM application, the physical limitation of phase change materials is determined by the minimum volume of phase change materials that could achieve stable and reversible phase change. This classification can provide useful guidance for scaling research in PCRAM technology.

For PCRAM, the scaling of phase change materials falls into the second and third categories defined above. However, the physical limitation is a three-dimensional (3D) issue and is difficult to be studied with the current technologies. Because the interfaces play a critical role at the nanoscale and the interface conditions are quite similar for both two-dimensional (2D) and 3D cases, the 3D issue could be simplified into a 2D issue. Temperature-dependent electrical resistance was measured to study the NPC in phase change material sandwiched by oxide [35]. For the films $\geq$ 20 nm, the resistance decreased sharply at about 150°C. For the films with thickness < 20 nm but ≥ 3.5 nm, the sharp decrease in resistance became less obvious. Crystallization temperature T_x increased from about 150°C to about 170°C as the film became thinner. An exponential relationship can be plotted on T_x versus film thickness. However, for the films ≤ 3 nm, the sharp decline in resistance was not observed at all. The gradual decrease in this case is due to the temperature dependent ionization in semiconductor material rather than the crystallization process. These results indicate that there is a critical thickness of crystallization at 3 nm. Similar phenomena have been observed in other works. Based on *in situ* X-ray diffraction (XRD) measurement results, it has been reported that 3.6 nm is the thickness limitation of $Ge_2Sb_2Te_5$ thin films capped by Al_2O_3 [36]. Based on current results, it can be expected that the scaling of PCRAM with $Ge_2Sb_2Te_5$ should be carried down to 2–3 nm if only considering the effect of nano phase change.

The scaling behavior of phase change nanostructures has also been investigated [37] as a method to estimate the scaling limits of PCRAM. Nanostructures with a 65-nm diameter and a 100-nm pitch have been fabricated from $Ge_{15}Sb_{85}$ and $Ge_2Sb_2Te_5$ phase change materials over large areas using electron beam lithography. Time-resolved *in situ* XRD was employed to study the structural properties of blanket films and the nanostructures. Blanket films and nanostructures of GeSbTe and GeSb were heated in the *in-situ* XRD setup at a rate of 1°C/sec and the diffracted peak intensity was recorded with the linear detector over a 2θ range of 24 to 40 degrees. This angular range contains strong diffraction peaks for both the $Ge_2Sb_2Te_5$ and GeSb. The measurements show that the nanostructures crystallize at the same temperature as blanket films of the same material. The fcc-hexagonal phase transition that was observed at 360°C for blanket $Ge_2Sb_2Te_5$ film does not occur in the nanostructures. It was also observed that nanopatterning leads to a reduction in grain size, particularly for the $Ge_2Sb_2Te_5$ nanostructures. Both findings are encouraging for the scaling of phase change materials directed toward NVM storage devices. The crystallization behavior studied for blanket films can be extrapolated for nanostructures down to 65 nm size, and data obtained on blanket films are useful for the research regarding devices. The reduction in grain size is also favorable since smaller grains typically lead to a higher resistivity of the materials in the crystalline phase, which, in turn, leads to a desirably smaller required current for switching the devices.

3.2. PCRAM Cell Structure

One of the critical challenges of high density PCRAM is to reduce the programming current, especially the RESET current, because it determines the size of the addressing device that affects the array density. The most effective approach to reduce current is by lithography scaling because programming current scales with the contact area between phase change materials and electrodes. Because the PCRAM cell structure design is also very important on the device performance improving, besides lithography scaling, innovative approaches, including various cell concepts, have been proposed to reduce current. The highlight in this review will be put on three main categories:

(1) improving the thermal confinement,
(2) reduction of contact areas by controlling the electrode thickness, and
(3) other methods such as improving the heating by inserting a heater layer.

3.2.1. Standard PCRAM Structure

The standard PCRAM structures are shown in Figure 19. In general, a phase change layer is vertically sandwiched between two electrodes. In the pore-like structure shown in Figure 19(a), a via was opened in the dielectric layer and then phase change material is deposited into the via. In the pillar-like structure, also called lance structure (Fig. 19(b)), a bottom electrode is first formed by surrounding dielectric materials, and then phase change material is subsequently deposited. Compared with pore-like structures, pillar-like structures require less photomasks for PCRAM element formation and thus have a relatively simple manufacturing process. The key affect parameters for pillar-like PCRAM include dimension of contact area (or size of heater) and resistive heater material. For efficient heating, the heater materials should have high electrical resistivity, low thermal conductivity, and specific heat to generate higher temperature for the same Joule heating rate. The surrounding dielectric material is also critical because it determines the heat lost.

The contact area between phase change material and electrode in these structures is highly determined by lithography technology. To reduce the contact area, various lithography methods (besides the conventional photolithography, such as *e*-beam lithography and near-field scanning optical lithography) have been introduced to create sublithographic features [103, 104].

3.2.2. Structures to Improve Thermal Confinement

PCRAM cell operation relies on Joule heating while the RESET operation requires high current to melt the phase

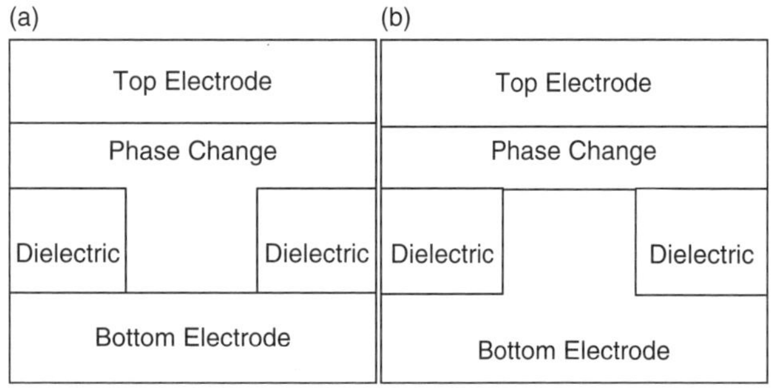

Figure 19. PCRAM device structure: (a) pore-like and (b) pillar-like (or mashroom).

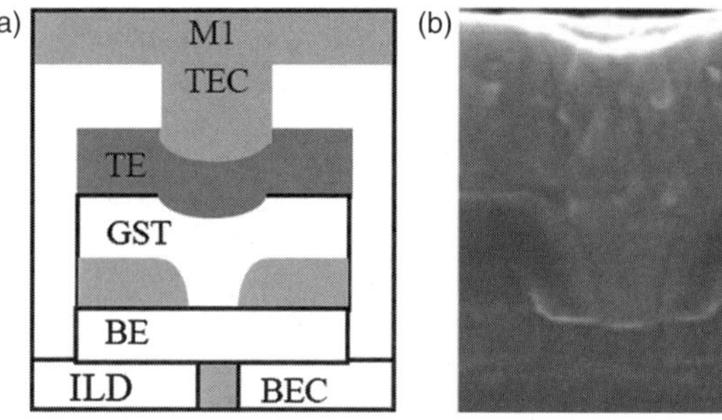

Figure 20. (a) Schematic diagram of on-axis confined cell structure of PCRAM, and (b) novel *in-situ* deposition/etch/deposition sputtering. Reprinted with permission from [105], S. L. Cho et al., "VLSI Symp. Tech. Dig.," 2005. © 2005, IEEE.

change materials. From the above standard cell structures, it can be seen that phase change material is closely sealed with the surrounding dielectric materials with the majority of heat conduction through the top and bottom electrodes. Therefore, the thermal confinement of the heated phase change region has a strong impact on the RESET current because a good thermal insulation reduces the heat lose and the power required for melting. If the volume of phase change material undergoing phase change is the same, the cell structure with good thermal confinement is expected to require less programming current.

The writing current can be effectively reduced by confining phase change materials into a small confined pore because a confined structure results in an increase of current concentration and a decrease of effective transition volume. PCRAM structure with electrically, fully confined self-heating phase change regions has been demonstrated to lead to low RESET currents of 0.4 mA [105]. Figure 20(a) shows a schematic diagram of an on-axis confined structure. Conformal deposition of GeSbTe at the pore is essential for this structure because the top electrode is formed on-axis with pore. The diameter and aspect ratio of the pore are the most important parameters related to the efficiency of the current concentration, the decrease of effective transition volume, and, thus, the writing current reduction. The smaller the pore diameter with higher aspect ratio is, the higher the efficiency is. A novel GeSbTe deposition process base on the *in-situ* deposition/etch/deposition method was developed and had excellent conformal film deposition (Fig. 20(b)).

Another confined pore structure for PCRAM was proposed by Lee and colleagues (Fig. 21(a)) [96]. The process flow of confined cell structure with CVD GeSbTe is shown in Figure 21(b). After metal-0 line, recessed metal bottom electrode contact (BEC) was formed in the contact, in which CVD GeSbTe was filled. For the recessed bottom electrode in the contact, metal plug material was filled in the contact and recessed using the etch back process. Thermally stable CVD $Ge_2Sb_2Te_5$ was uniformly filled within a contact having aspect ratio of three. By adopting confined GeSbTe, the RESET current for PCRAM with a 50-nm design rule was reduced to below ~260 μA, and the endurance characteristic was maintained up to 10^8 cycles without failure.

A contact electrode with higher electrical resistivity and lower thermal conductivity is preferred since it promotes

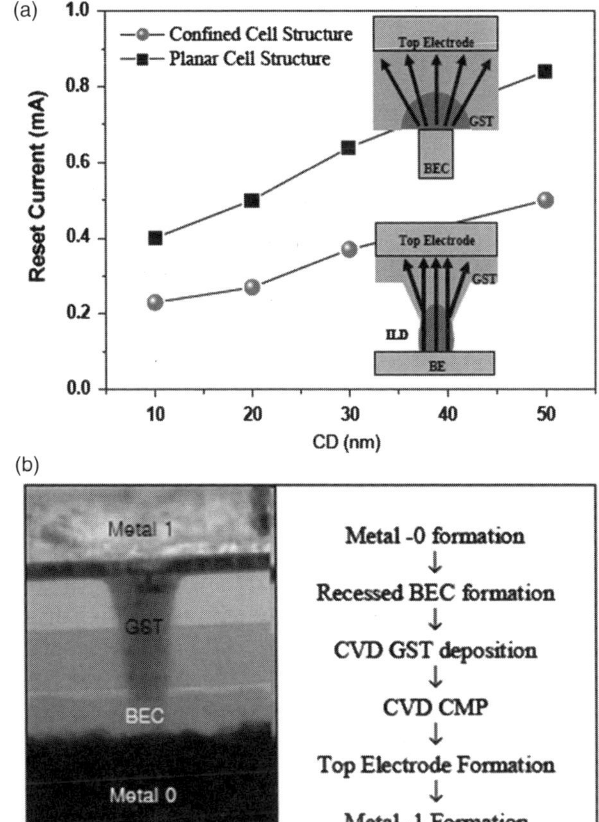

Figure 21. (a) Comparison of reset current between confined and planar cell structure along with contact diameter, (b) process flow of confined cell structure with CVD GeSbTe. Reprinted with permission from [96], J. I. Lee et al., "VLSI Symp. Tech. Dig.," p. 102, 2007. © 2007, IEEE.

heating efficiency in PCRAM, thereby allowing a lower programming power. Tungsten is a commonly used contact material with electrical resistivity and thermal conductivity values of 5.29 $\mu\Omega$ cm and 174 W/mK, respectively. Inserting a dielectric or semiconductor interlayer such as TiO_2, WO_3, Ta_2O_5, SiGe, $SiGeN_x$ between the electrode and the phase change layer has also been reported for improving thermal isolation [89, 106–108]. Ta_2O_5 is particularly useful because it functions as an adhesive layer as well as a thermal insulator. PCRAM structure that enables low-power operation by inserting a very thin buffer layer Ta_2O_5 film between GeSbTe and a *W* plug was also proposed. The Ta_2O_5 layer suppresses the heat diffusion from the GeSbTe film to the *W* plug with high thermal conductivity, and then the GeSbTe temperature increases to more than 600°C. Interestingly, it was noted that the temperature at the Ta_2O_5 layer did not rise. The 3-nm Ta_2O_5 interfacial layer worked not only as a heat insulator by enabling effective heat generation in GeSbTe, but it also worked as an adhesion layer between GeSbTe and undermeath SiO_2. Nonetheless, sufficient current flowed through the interfacial layer due to direct tunneling. A low programming power of 1.5 V/100 μA can therefore be obtained even on a *W* plug with a diameter of 180 nm fabricated using standard 0.13 μm complementary metal–oxide–semiconductor (CMOS) technology. In addition, the uniformity and repeatability of cell resistance are excellent because of the inherently stable Ta_2O_5 film properties [106].

3.2.3. Reduction of Contact Areas by Controlling the Electrode Thickness

One innovative idea was proposed to control the contact area mainly by the thickness of the electrode film (Fig. 22) [109, 110]. Scaling by reducing the film thickness is very efficient because it can be much smaller than the dimension of the lithography and very well controlled. The side-edge contact PCRAM cell with a contact area of 40,000 nm^2 was fabricated and tested. For testing, four key parameters were determined:

(1) holding voltage (V_h),
(2) threshold voltage (V_{th}),
(3) RESET, and
(4) SET current.

The memory cell successfully operated with 30 ns pulses of 0.20 mA for RESET state and 0.13 mA for SET state. The cycling test showed that the resistance ratio between RESET and SET remained larger than 20 after 10^5 cycles.

A novel μTrench structure was proposed to keep the programming current low and maintain a compact vertical integration [110]. Similar to edge contact structure, the contact area between the heater and the phase change material is by the intersection of a thin vertical semimetallic heater and a trench in which the GeSbTe is deposited. Since the μTrench can be defined by sublitho techniques and the heater thickness by film deposition, the cell performance can be optimized by tuning the resulting contact area. By using 0.18 pm CMOS process, the μTrench PCRAM has demonstrated

(a)

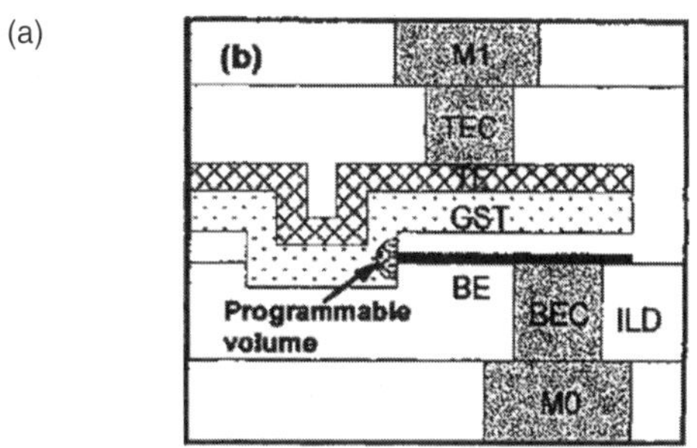

(b)

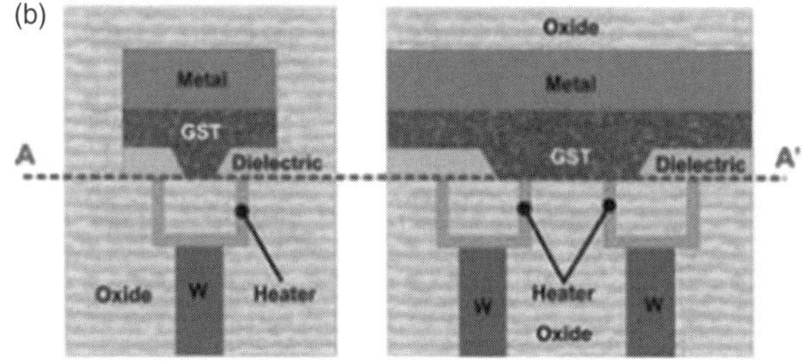

Figure 22. (a) Edge contact PCRAM, (b) μTrench PCRAM. Reprinted with permission from [68], H. Horii et al., "VLSI Symp. Tech. Dig.," 2003. © 2003, IEEE.

programming currents of 600 pA, endurance of 10^{11} programming cycles, and data retention capabilities for 10 years at 110°C.

3.2.4. Line Type and Others

Recently, PCRAM with lateral structures were proposed (Fig. 23) with the most investigated two lateral structures, line-type structure and bridge structure [111, 112]. In lateral structure PCRAM, the phase change material is deposited on the underlying two metal electrodes. There are many advantages of the line type PCRAM. Firstly, it is conceptually simple. Secondly, the requirement for electrode materials is not as high as that for PCRAM vertical contact type because electrode materials should have appropriate resistivity, high temperatures resistive, no reaction with the phase change materials, and good adhesion to the phase change film if using the vertical contract type. Thirdly, lower programming power and current are possible because the phase change materials are surrounded only by dielectric materials, while dielectric materials have much lower thermal conductivity than the electrodes in the vertical type. Lastly, the cross section of line memory can be made very small, leading to further reduction of the programming current.

(a)

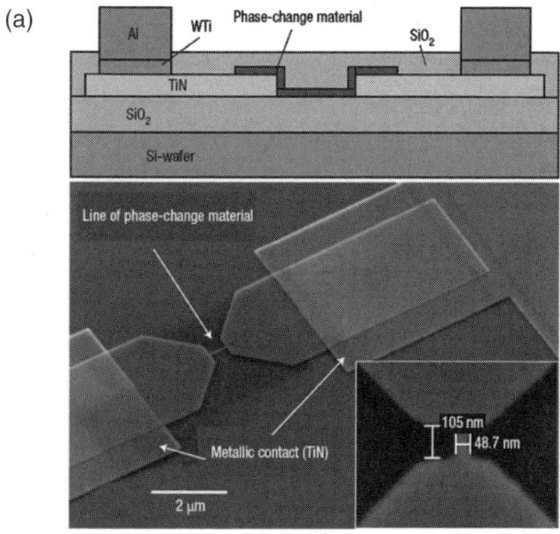

(b)

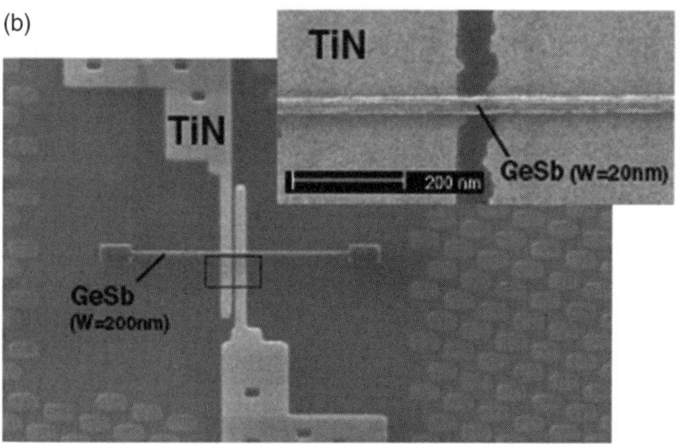

Figure 23. (a) Line-type PCRAM, and (b) bridge PCRAM. Reprinted with permission from [111], M. H. R. Lankhorst et al., *Nat. Mater.* 4, 347 (2005). © 2005, Nature Publishing Group; and from [112], Y. C. Chen et al., "IEDM Tech. Dig.," 2006. © 2006, IEEE.

A phase change between amorphous and crystalline states with 30 ns pulses for both the SET and RESET switch was demonstrated. The speed of the memory increases as the dimensions of the cell are scaled down. This feature can be explained by the growth-dominated crystallization mechanism of the doped SbTe materials, in which crystallization takes place by crystal growth from the crystalline edge of the amorphous volume toward its center. From the various crystal growth speeds measured for many doped SbTe materials, it has be estimated that possible programming time of a line cell ranged from 5 to 100 ns.

The phase-change bridge device consists of a narrow line of ultra-thin phase-change material bridging two underlying electrodes. However, unlike the line-device concept, the electrodes in the bridge PCRAM are formed very close together to obtain a reasonable threshold voltage, and are separated by a small oxide gap that defines the bridge length. The thickness of the phase change material deposited on this planarized surface defines the bridge height, and the width is defined with a subsequent patterning step. Bridge PCRAM with an ultra-thin layer (3 nm) of doped GeSb was fabricated and demonstrated $< 100\ \mu$A RESET current.

So far, nucleation-dominated materials, such as GeSbTe have been used to fabricate vertical type PCRAM. However, it was found that GeSbTe is not suitable for line-type PCRAM. Instead, growth-dominated materials are more suitable for line-type PCRAM. Doped SbTe, doped GeSb, and doped Sb_2Te have been applied in line-type PCRAM. However, these pseudobinary phase-change materials are not good in all aspects. For instance, SbTe has a lower melting point and a shorter crystallization time, but its data stability is poor and the resistivity difference is small. Hence, lateral PCRAM faces the problem of poor lifetime than vertical PCRAM. A growth-dominated superlattice structure incorporating GeTe and Sb_7Te_3 was proposed to engineer the properties of phase change materials to overcome the material limitation [113]. It was found that with the thickness ratio of GeTe to Sb_7Te_3 at 1.6, the RESET current could be as low as 1.5 mA and the endurance could reach as high as 5.3×10^6 cycles. By varying the thickness ratio of GeTe to Sb_7Te_3, the crystallization temperature of superlattice-like (SLL) structures and the performance of lateral phase change memory with these SLL structures can be controlled.

3.3. Fast-Speed PCRAM

Writing speed is another very important parameter for PCRAM. Writing speed is related to many factors, but the most important factor is phase change speed. There are SET and RESET processes in PCRAM; RESET speed is faster than SET speed. It turns out that PCRAM writing speed is mainly dependent on SET speed. However, the phase change speed is mainly dominated and fundamentally limited by the intrinsic nature of the materials. The easy way is to use phase change materials with fast crystallization speed. It was found that resonance bonding plays an important role for fast switching phase change materials [110]. A low degree of iconicity and a low tendency toward hybridization is typical for fast-switching phase change materials [114]. These parameters can guide us to find better materials with improved composition and switching characteristics. However, phase change materials with very fast crystallization speed normally are not stable. We need to balance the requirement from speed and stability.

Recently, the transient current waveform during a crystallization process in a phase change device was measured that revealed two important time parameters, which are termed as delay time and current recovery time [115]. The delay time was found to be the minimum pulse duration time before an onset of resistance change in the device. The current recovery time was the time the device takes to complete its transition from high resistance to low resistance, representing the partial phase change period. The SET speed is related to the crystallization time, the delay time between the applied voltage and the threshold switching event, and the recovery time after switching. The most limiting time constant is the crystallization time. Crystallization times vary greatly with material composition and it is also related to PCRAM cell structure because the thermal confinement effect varies for different structures. In principle, any measurements that can increase heating efficiency facilitate crystallization speed. On the other hand, RESET processing needs a fast quenching, meaning fast cooling, rate that correspondent to slow heating rate.

It has been found that crystallization speed between first crystallization of as-deposited amorphous material and recrystallization of melt-quenched, amorphous material are different [116, 117]. The latter is normally much faster since, in all practical cases, there are small nuclei in amorphous state because of incomplete amorphization; thus, it does not require incubation and nucleation (formation of supercritical nuclei) but only crystal growth from the amorphous/crystalline interface.

In addition, the choice of the phase change materials in the natural world is limited, let alone those that can meet the requirements of the application. SLL structure has demonstrated that it can significantly increase PCRAM speed [71]. The fast recording speed of the SLL structure can be attributed to the following reasons. Firstly, the low thermal conductivity in both in-plane and cross-plane directions of the SLL structure significantly reduces the heat diffusion out of the recording layer and increases the rate of temperature rise. Secondly, the Sb_2Te_3 layer of the SLL structure has small activation energy for crystallization, which is responsible for the fast writing process and the short crystallization time.

Kostylev and others [118] have studied programming speed in PCRAM in terms of the factors affecting programming time and has studied the influence of programming current levels, phase change alloy composition and its thickness, electrode contact materials, device geometry, and temperature. It has been shown that programming speed to SET or to RESET a device is determined mainly by only one electrical contact: SET speed is not as affected by the cathode contact but depends more strongly on the anode contact, and the RESET speed could be changed dramatically with cathode contact (material and geometry), but it is not as sensitive to the anode contact.

Recently, the nano size effects of phase change materials on phase transition speed was studied experimentally on PCRAM with GST and GeTe [119, 120]. When the size

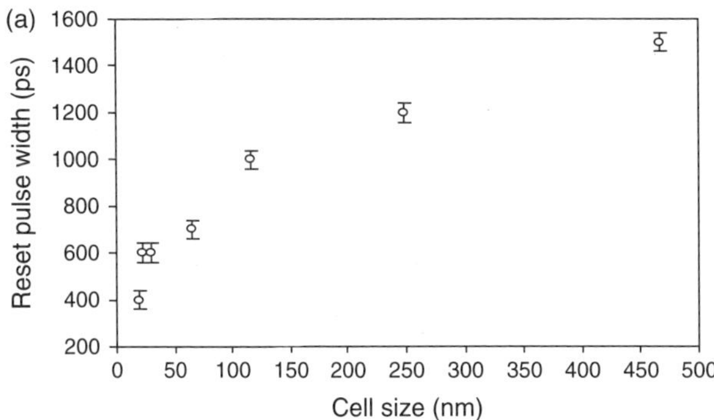

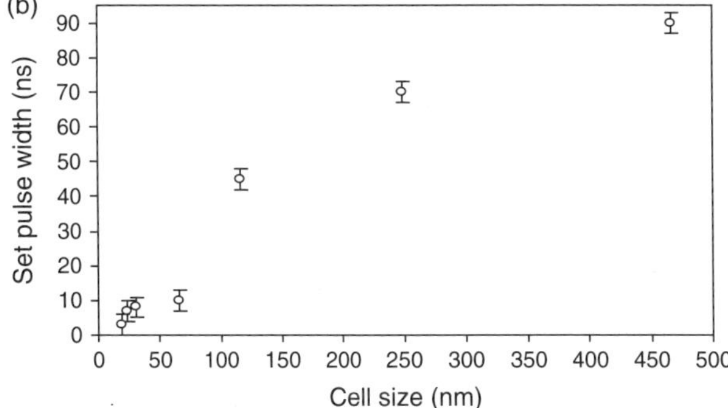

Figure 24. The switching speed as a function of cell size varying from 500 nm to 19 nm for: (a) set, and (b) reset. The pulse amplitudes are 0.8 V for set, and 4.5 V for reset. Reprinted with permission from [119], W. J. Wang et al., *Appl. Phys. Lett.* 93, 043121 (2008). © 2008, American Institute of Physics.

of PCRAM decreases, especially when it shrinks to below 40–50 nm, the material surface or interfaces will play an increasingly important role and may change the dominated mechanism of phase transition. Figure 24 shows the switching speed as a function of cell size varying from 500 nm to 19 nm. Reducing the material dimensions might achieve smaller programming current and the ultra-fast phase transition speed, and this may lead to important applications of PCRAM.

More recently, however, PCRAM cells with $GeTe/Sb_2Te_3$ SLL structure have demonstrated excellent scaling performance of both lower operating power and higher switching speed. The smaller PCRAM cells with SLL have lower switching voltage and faster switching speed compared with cells with larger diameters on $Ge_2Sb_2Te_5$. Forty-nm SLL cells can achieve fast amorphization and crystallization times of 300 ps and 1 ns, respectively, and both are much faster than those obtained on the same size cell with $Ge_2Sb_2Te_5$ [121]. The effects are related the low thermal conductivity, high resistivity, and fast heterogeneous crystallization of small SLL cells. This enables us to achieve high density, highspeed, and high performance PCRAM.

3.4. ML PCRAM

ML PCRAM technologies can be used to increase memory density and, hence, to lower cost per bit for fabrication. On the other hand, it is also a useful tool to increase speed. In the ML PCRAM, a single memory cell can be controlled to any of n different resistance values that means to store

$\log 2(n)$ bits. We can control the intermediate resistance levels between the SET and RESET states. The intermediate resistance levels correspond to different configurations of the crystalline and amorphous phases inside the active phase change materials volume. The cell resistance value depends on the fraction ratio, the volume, and the shape of the two phases. Two levels in bilevel memory are placed at the upper and lower edges of the read window, respectively. ML PCRAM needs higher accuracy writing and reading with respect to the case of two-level memory. More precisely, adjacent programmed levels are closer than the two levels in the bilevel memory. Moreover, for the ML PCRAM, the retention of stored data becomes a critical issue because the signals are affected by the shift of the programmed resistance levels over time.

There are mainly two phenomena that significantly affect the stability of the intermediate resistance levels in ML PCMs. The first one is the crystallization process, which is related to uncompleted crystallization or partially crystallization [122] and results in a decrease in resistance. The second is resistivity drift in the amorphous states, which causes a resistance increase with time. It should be noted that a few solutions have been proposed to reduce the drift effect.

Recently several approaches have been proposed to program the cell resistance to an intermediate level or realize ML in PCRAM, including: (1) control the intermediate resistance levels of partial-SET [123], and (2) control the intermediate resistance levels of partial-RESET programming [124–126] and realize ML by using material and structural engineering [127–129].

In both the first and the second approaches, a common initial state is needed because ML PCRAM needs higher accuracy writing and reading with respect to the case of two-level memory. It is very difficult to achieve direct overwriting. In the first solution, the cell is first to be initialized into the amorphous state, and then a variable programming pulse is applied to partially crystallize the active volume. In the second solution, the cell is first initialized into the SET state, and then a variable programming pulse is applied to partially amorphize the active volume.

It was reported that ML PCRAM using the second approach was studied theoretically and experimentally both at the single cell and at the array level. In particular, aspects such as the programming algorithm, programming speed/accuracy tradeoff, and level placement were studied. In this work, a 180-nm 4-M cell MOS transistor-selected PCM experimental chip was based on the μ-trench cell architecture [110]. The working principle is shown in Figure 25. In each operation, the memory cell is biased by applying an adequate voltage level to the selected bit line through a high-voltage natural n-type MOS transistor YO, which works as a source follower (see Fig. 1). The stored information is read out by sensing the current I_{cell} flowing through the cell, when a suitable read voltage V_{read} is applied to the gate terminal of YO. The addressed word-line select transistor M_{SEL} is turned on by applying a high-voltage level to its gate, and it operates in the triode region.

Figure 26 shows the sequence of program and read pulses that are used to generate ML, which provides the achieved cell resistance as a function of the used programming voltage. The cell is first brought to the SET state by means of a staircase-down (SCD) initializing sequence and then applied to a single partial-RESET voltage pulse that has a predetermined amplitude (V_{RST}) and duration (t_{pulse}). The ML can be realized by controlling V_{RST} and duration t_{pulse}.

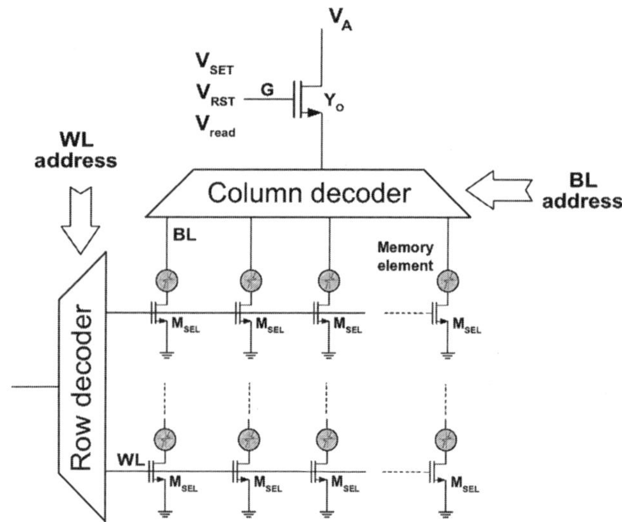

Figure 25. Schematic of the circuit used to program and read memory cells. MSEL and YO are the WL select transistor and the BL bias device, respectively. Reprinted with permission from [126], S. Braga et al., *IEEE Trans. Elect. Dev.* 57 (2010). © 2010, IEEE.

For array because of the cell difference, the programming current to generate ML varies cell to cell. Figure 27 shows R versus V_{RST} obtained by applying the sequence of programming pulses with V_{RST}, start = 3 V, ΔV = 25 mV, and t_{pulse} 50 ns to an array of 1,024 cells. The obtained programming curves greatly vary from cell to cell due to the variability of device parameters. It should be pointed out that a program-and-verify technique [130, 131] can be adopted to compensate for these spreads and improve the accuracy of programmed resistance levels.

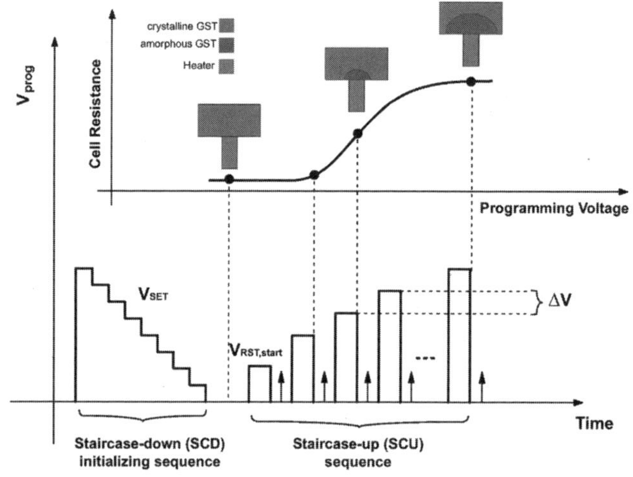

Figure 26. The sequence of program and read pulses that is used to generate ML. Reprinted with permission from [126], S. Braga et al., *IEEE Trans. Elect. Dev.* 57 (2010). © 2010, IEEE.

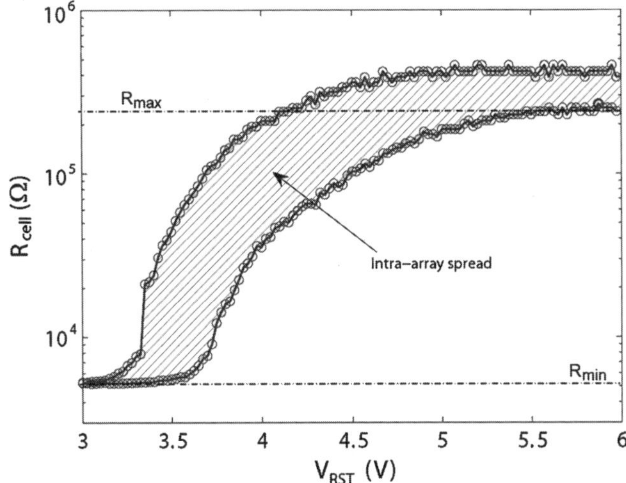

Figure 27. Spread of the measured programming curves over the considered 1024-cell array with V_{RST}, start = 3 V, ΔV = 25 mV, and t_{pulse} 50 ns. Reprinted with permission from [126], S. Braga et al., *IEEE Trans. Elect. Dev.* 57 (2010). © 2010, IEEE.

It is well known that draft will affect the reliability of ML PCRAM. The shift that is due to drift increases with the programmed resistance value (Fig. 28).

It was reported that a phase change memory cell was fabricated by stacking plasma-enhanced cyclic chemical–vapor–deposited $Ge_2Sb_2Te_5$ and ALD deposited TiO_2 thin films [127]. Different pairs of resistance states were obtained by controlling the current flow, which can be used to achieve higher memory density by multilevel operation. A PCRAM cell was fabricated by stacking 100-nm thick GeSbTe and 8-nm thick TiO_2 thin films. The initial cell had robust insulating properties due to the insulating pristine TiO_2 dielectric layer. The electroforming step formed conducting filaments in the TiO_2 layer, which offered a current flow path for the amorphization and recrystallization of GeSbTe.

The larger number of filaments in TiO_2 was accompanied by a larger heat loss to the metal contact that resulted

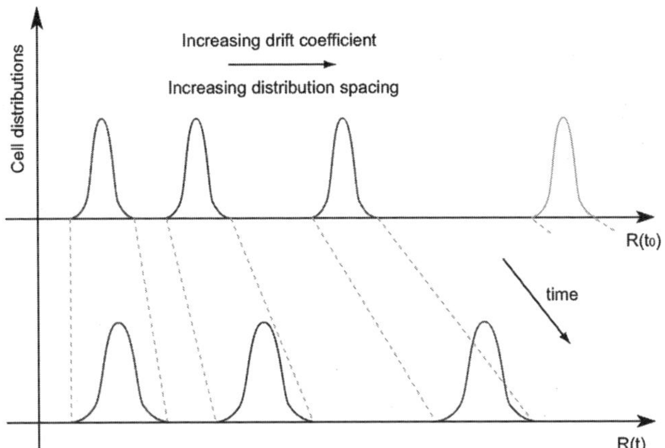

Figure 28. Effect of resistance drift on programmed cell distributions. The shift that is due to drift increases with the programmed resistance value. Reprinted with permission from [126], S. Braga et al., *IEEE Trans. Elect. Dev.* 57 (2010). © 2010, IEEE.

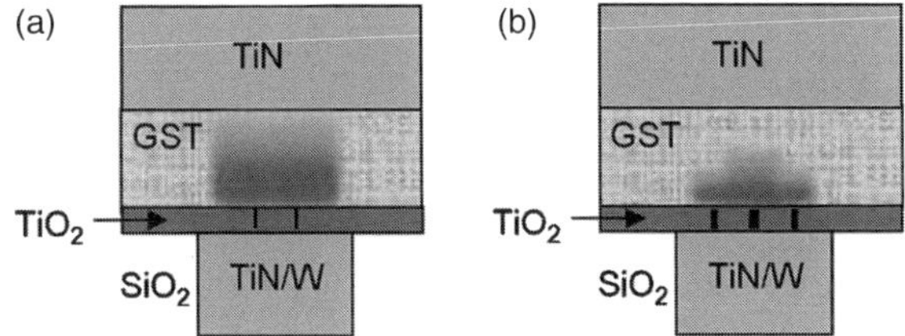

Figure 29. (a) Larger and (b) smaller active GeSbTe volumes by the different filament status in TiO_2. Reprinted with permission from [127], B. J. Choi et al., *Appl. Phys. Lett.* 97, 132107 (2010). © 2010, American Institute of Physics.

in a lower resistance. Four different memory states were achieved by controlling the number of filaments in the TiO_2 layer and by adjusting the maximum current flow. The reset of the filaments in the TiO_2 could be accomplished stably by a bipolar type voltage stress. The multiresistance states of the stacked cell can be explained by the resistance-switching phenomena of TiO_2 and the thermoelectric phase change properties of GeSbTe (Fig. 29). Figures 29(a and b) show schematic diagrams of TiO_2 layers with different filament density and diameters. The phase change characteristics of GeSbTe could be altered by controlling the degree of filament formation in the TiO_2 layer, which eventually changed the phase change volume in the GeSbTe.

3.5. PCRAM Chip

PCRAM memory needs a selecting element to be assembled in an array. If the PCRAM elements are simply integrated together as an array, there would be a large leakage current in other cells in the same column/row when one cell is selected. Normally, a transistor or diode is used as a selecting element to prevent the leakage. When this selecting element is turned off by adding proper voltage, there would be no significant current allowed to pass the selecting element and the memory cell in serial with the selecting element. Therefore, the integration possibility of a new memory technology with the CMOS technology is an important factor to evaluate its commercialization potential. More importantly, the memory density is largely determined by the size of selecting element. The integration of PCRAM memory element is mostly performed after front-end of the line and at the back-end of the line. Figure 30 shows a simplified schematic diagram of PCRAM cell integrating with a selector [132].

To meet the relatively high reset current, the selector must be a good current driver. There are two available selectors, transistor and diode/bipolar junction transistor (BJT). The transistor is more popular in modern integrated circuit design while the diode/BJT is used mostly in high performance circuit design. Either transistor or diode/BJT as the selecting element should meet the requirements of PCRAM element operation. It should provide the required programming current, realize the selection of PCRAM elements, and, most importantly, not affect the reading and programming of PCRAM elements.

The advantages of using diode/BJT as a selector for PCRAM include better current driving capabilities, which

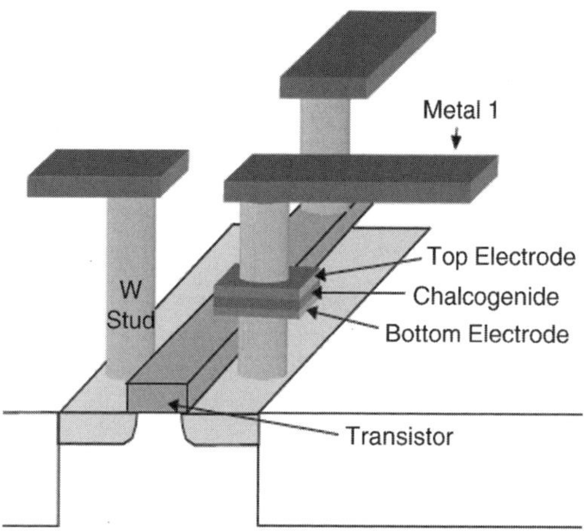

Figure 30. Schematic diagram of PCRAM cell integrating with a selector.

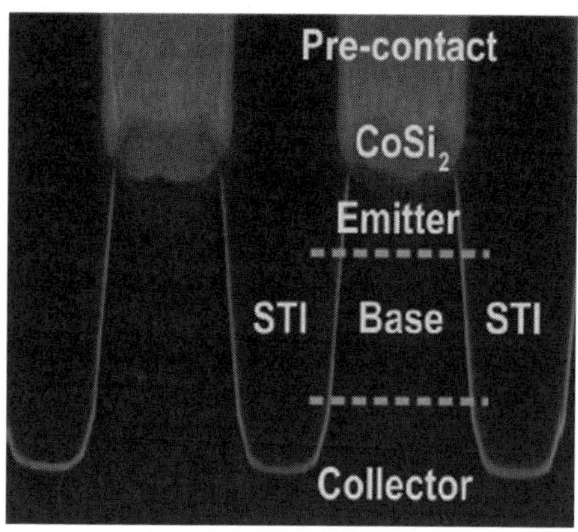

Figure 32. Multi-Mb PCRAM (90 nm) with a 0.0968-μm^2 (12 F^2) cell size was demonstrated using BJT as selection device. 12 F^2 *pnp*-BJT current: ~1.7 mA at 1.8 V. Reprinted with permission from [135], F. Pellizzer et al., "VLSI Symp. Tech. Dig.," 2006. © 2006, IEEE.

will result in small cell size. Hence, it is compact integration that is suitable for high-density applications. The disadvantages include a dedicated process for BJT formation and more complex array design. Different from diode/BJT, the transistor normally has poorer current-driving capability, resulting in larger cell size. However, the use of an MOS transistor device reduces the number of lithographic masks required, thus ensuring lower process cost. This choice also eliminates the problem of cumulative array leakage current due to the reverse-biased base-to-emitter junction of unaddressed BJT selectors. Furthermore, implementing the cell selector with the same transistor device type used in peripheral circuits provides an easier vehicle for PCRAM technology development and characterization [133]. As such, chosen selector device fully depends on the needs and applications. Figures 31 to 33 show the integration of PCRAM with a metal–oxide–semiconductor field-effect transistor (MOSFET), a BJT, and diode, respectively. The demonstrated cell size was reduced from 16.6 F^2 for using MOSFET as a selector to 5.8 F^2 for using diode as a selector by Samsung [134–136].

Oh and colleageus [136] replaced trigate MOSFET with a vertical diode for large I_{on} in a small cell, the precise control of parameters in GST module process, and the adoption of slow quench and write-and-verify schemes. Diode scheme needs higher cell operation voltage than that of MOSFET scheme by about 1.0 V; the adoption of dual gate oxide is inevitable for low external supply voltage less than 3.3 V. The uniformity of RESET current was improved by using the ring-type BEC scheme. Another critical technology of the self-aligned BEC (SABEC) scheme was developed for high manufacturability. The SABEC has several advantages of free-misalign margin, a reduction of critical mask layer, and a favorable correlation effect between the BEC and diode.

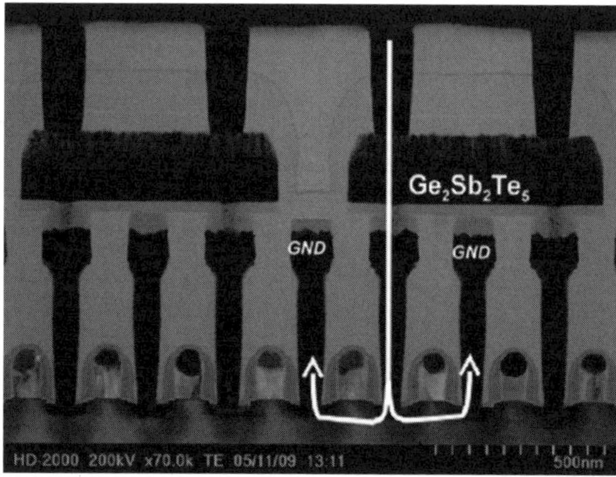

Figure 31. 256 Mb PCRAM (100 nm) with a 0.166 μm^2 (16.6 F^2) cell size was demonstrated using FET as a selection device. Tri-gate *n*MOS current: 1.1 mA at 3 V. The current for each PCRAM is supplied by two FETs in parallel. Reprinted with permission from [134], S. Kang et al., *IEEE J. Solid-State Circuits* 42, 210 (2007). © 2007, IEEE.

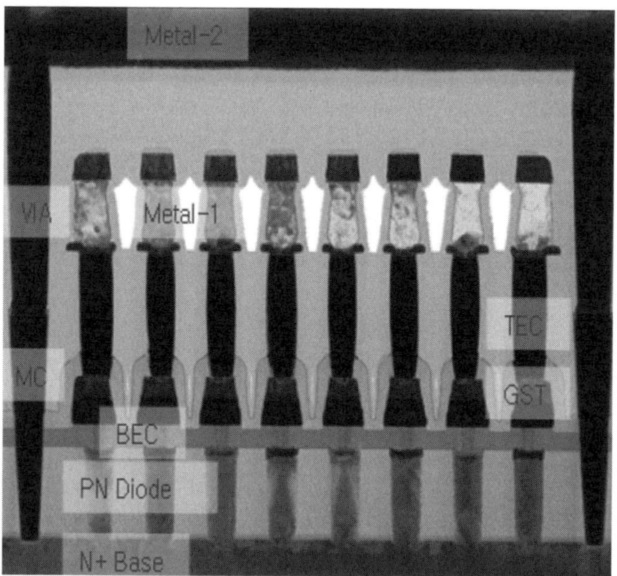

Figure 33. 512-Mb PCRAM (90 nm) with a 0.047-μm^2 (5.8 F^2) cell size was demonstrated using diode as a selection device. 5.8 F^2 *pn*-diode current: 1.8 mA at 1.8 V. Reprinted with permission from [136], J. H. Oh et al., "IEDM Tech. Dig.," 2006. © 2006, IEEE.

In addition, patterning the top-electrode and the GeSbTe under optimal etching condition was proved to improve the write endurance.

1 Gb PCRAM based on a 45-nm technology node was developed in 2009 [137]. The process architecture was developed by considering the small cell size requirements, the process cost, and the high performance characteristics, particularly in terms of achievable high bandwidth and reduced power consumption. Immersion 193-nm lithography, innovative double STI for a vertical BJT selector with thin cobalt salicide, novel fully self-aligned PCRAM storage element architecture ("Wall") and three levels of copper metallization allow the PCRAM memory array integration with a 1.8 V CMOS circuitry. A vertical BJT selector has been chosen to keep compact the cell layout, with one base contact shared by four emitters. The size of the cell is 104 nm × 104 nm and the area for the base contact is 156 nm × 104 nm; the effective area of the cell is 0.015 μm^2. The base contact is shared by four cells and the effective cells size is 5.5 F^2. A larger number of cells per base contact would give a marginal advantage in terms of effective cell size reduction, but would also result in a significant increase of the voltage drop on the base access resistance. A vertical cross-section of the memory array is shown Figure 34 [138].

Besides scaling down the cell size, stackable cross-bar architecture is another efficient approach to increase PCRAM density, which is capable of 4 F^2 cell size. The most significant issue for PCRAM of 4 F^2 cross-point structure is the large reset current [139, 140]. Selection device with an on-current density higher than 8 mA/cm^2 is necessary to fabricate a PCRAM with a cross-point 4 F^2 cell; however, the on-current density of conventional selection devices is too small, and thus the size of the selection device would have to be larger than the PCRAM, resulting in a larger cell size. Thin-film diode technologies have been investigated, such as a selection diode made of poly-Si [141]. Its on- and off-current densities are 8 mA/cm^2 and 100 A/cm^2, respectively. As a result, 4 F^2 cell size was achieved and the cross-sectional view of the cell is shown in Figure 35.

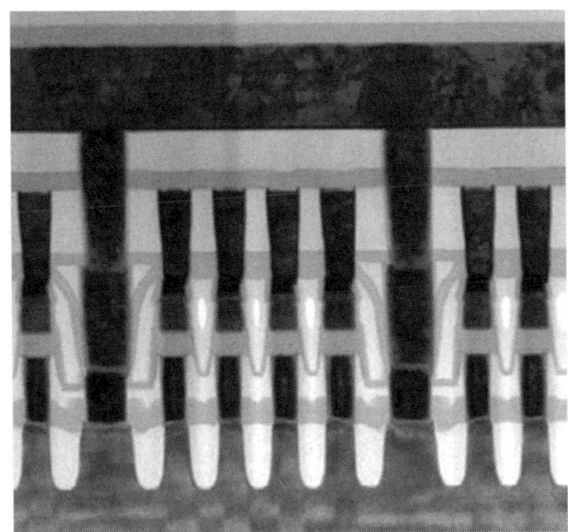

Figure 34. SEM cross-section (along y-direction) of a 1 Gb PCRAM cell array. Reprinted with permission from [137], G. Servalli, "IEDM Tech. Dig.," 2009. © 2009, IEEE.

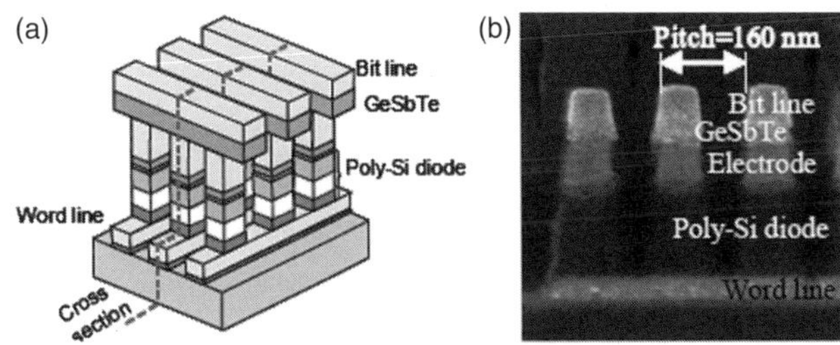

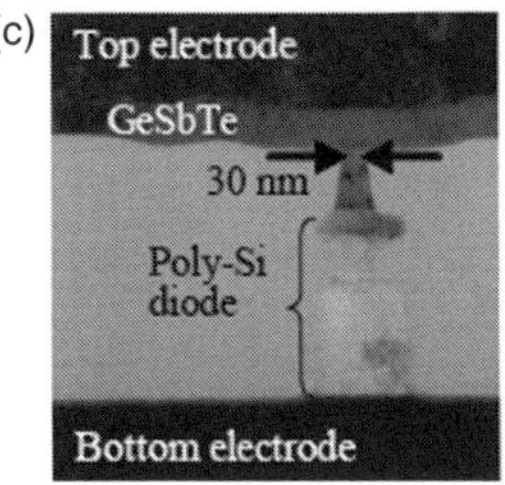

Figure 35. Cross-sectional views of phase change memory array. Reprinted with permission from [141], Y. Sasago et al., "VLSI Symp. Tech. Dig.," 2009. © 2009, IEEE.

3.6. 3-D PCRAM

Recently, a possible solution has been demonstrated by integrating a chalcogenide thin film device, an ovonic threshold switch (OTS), as a selector to build a multi-Mb memory array [142, 143]. The basic structure of the device is shown in Figure 36. OTS is a two-terminal device made of a chalcogenide alloy whose composition is chosen to prevent crystallization during operation. Because the storage element and the selector element are fabricated from thin films, it is possible to stack multiple layers of memory array using the back-end-of-line process, and, therefore, this can potentially be a cost effective NVM technology. To make the OTS work as a selector device, its electrical properties that are crucial to array operation need to be understood.

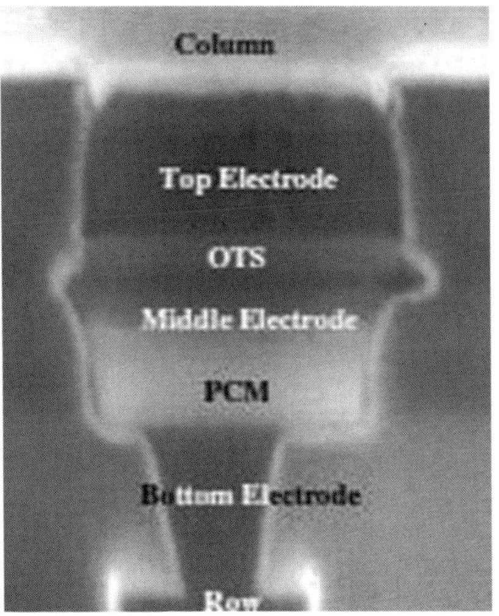

Figure 36. Stackable cross point phase change memory. Reprinted with permission from [142], D. Kau et al., "IEDM Tech. Dig.," p. 617, 2009. © 2009, IEEE.

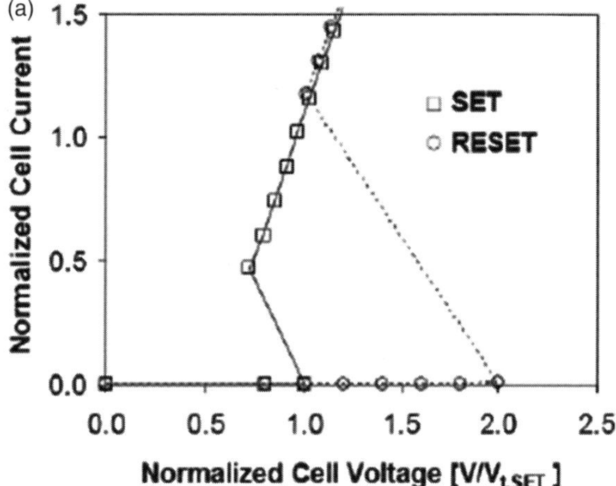

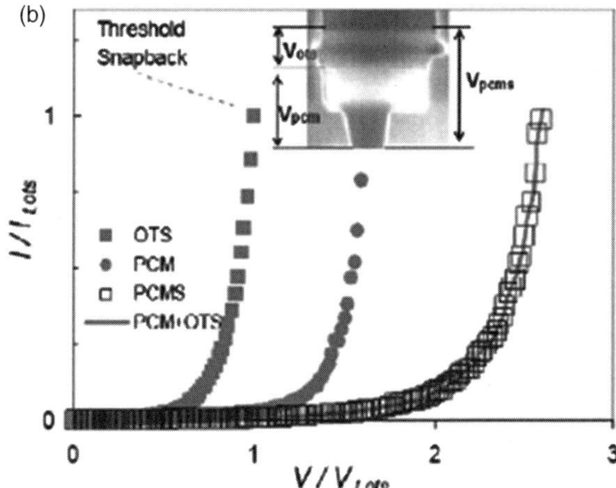

Figure 37. (a) The *I–V* characteristics of a PCMS cell in SET and RESET. Voltage is normalized to the threshold voltage of SET state, V_t, SET, and (b) PCMS + PCM + OTS; the threshold behavior of a RESET PCMS is equal to the additive result of the thresholds of OTS and amorphous PCRAM in series. Reprinted with permission from [143], S. J. W. Lee et al., "Proc. Eur. Phase Change Ovonic Sci. Symp.," p. 21, 2010. © 2010, EPCOS.

The basic electrical behavior of the unit cell in a cross-point PCRAM array with an OTS selector, i.e., a phase change memory switch (PCMS), which is shown in Figure 37. It is a threshold switch with a variable threshold voltage, V_t. In SET state, the chalcogenide in the PCRAM portion of PCMS is in crystalline phase, and therefore V_t, SET is defined by the amorphous chalcogenide in the OTS selector. PCMS cannot be programmed to have V_t lower than $V_{t,\,\mathrm{SET}}$. In RESET state, chalcogenide in the PCM is amorphized to raise $V_{t,\,\mathrm{RESET}}$ of combined PCMS above $V_{t,\,\mathrm{SET}}$.

The principle of read/write is shown in Figure 38. Inset (a) shows part of a cross-point array, where row lines run horizontally and column lines run vertically. PCMS cells are placed at cross points to form the array. Cell 1 (the selected cell) is the subject of the read or write operation. While cell 1 is being manipulated, the rest of the cells (2, 3, and 4, the unselected cells) in the array need to be kept in off-state so that the signal from cell 1 is not masked and cells 2, 3, and 4 are not unintentionally disturbed. This is accomplished by controlling voltages applied to row and column lines. The most important part of cross-point array operation is the selection of one cell out of the array so that it can be operated upon. In one possible addressing scheme, there are two different cases of selection based on what subsequent operation will be. In the first case, the subsequent operation is either read as the state of the selected cell or to program the selected cell from SET to RESET state. Figures 38(b and c) show *I–V* schematics of unselected cells and selected cells, respectively, in this case. Unselected cells are kept off because the voltage applied will not exceed V_t of either SET or RESET phase states. The selected cell will switch on, depending on which phase state it is in. In the second case, the operation following the selection is to program the selected cell from RESET to SET state.

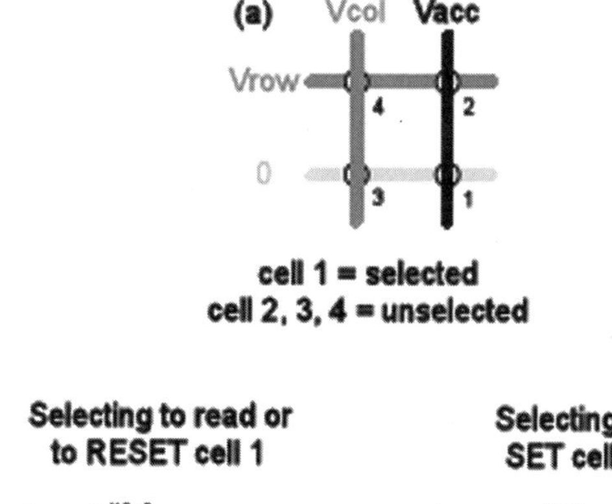

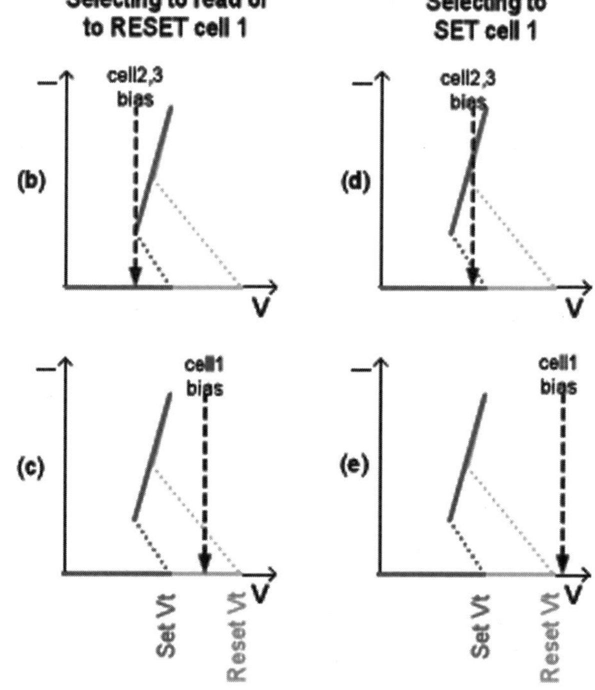

Figure 38. Schematic of cross-point PCMS array operation: (a) voltages on 4 lines are chosen such that only OTS in cell 1 is switched on, while the rest of the bits are kept in off state, (b) schematic *I–V* of unselected cells, (c) and selected cell during selection prior to read or resetting operation, (d) schematic *I–V* of unselected bits, and (e) and selected bit during selection prior to setting operation. In both cases, cells 2, 3, and 4 must be kept off. Reprinted with permission from [143], S. J. W. Lee et al., "Proc. Eur. Phase Change Ovonic Sci. Symp.," p. 21, 2010. © 2010, EPCOS.

Figures 38(d and e) show unselected cells and selected cells, respectively, in this case. Here, V_{acc} is chosen so that the selected cell is switched on in the RESET state, while V_{col} and V_{row} are chosen so that the unselected cells experience only voltages less than $V_{t,\text{SET}}$. $V_{t,\text{SET}}$ and $V_{t,\text{RESET}}$ values need to be engineered so that this row and the column biasing scheme is possible.

4. SUMMARY

PCRAM is one of the most promising NVM technologies. It provides orders of magnitude better-read latency, write latency, and endurance, and it also consumes significantly less read/write energy and idle power than flash memory. It has been demonstrated with a speed level within 10 ns, which shows the possibility of DRAM-like applications. Although the first wave of PCRAM products target mobile handsets, in the near future PCRAM is expected to become a common component of the memory/storage hierarchy for laptops, personal computers, and servers [144]. Currently, PCRAM is at initial production stage. To make PCRAM successful, further reduction of programming current, the demonstration of reliable multilevel, and crossbar technologies are the most critical issues.

REFERENCES

1. W. J. Tsai, N. K. Zous, C. J. Liu, C. C. Liu, C. H. Chen, W. Tahui, S. Pan, C.-Y. Liu, and S. H. Gu, "Int. Elect. Dev. Meet. Tech. Dig.," 32.6.1, p. 719, 2001.
2. *Int. Tech. Road. Semiconduct*. (2009).
3. J. Bu and M. H. White, *Solid State Electron.* 45, 113 (2001).
4. S.-C. Lai, H.-T. Lue, M.-J. Yang, J.-Y. Hsieh, S.-Y. Wang, T.-B. Wu, G.-L. Luo, G.-H. Chien, E.-K. Lai, K.-Y. Hsieh, R. Liu, and C.-Y. Lu, "IEEE Non-Volatile Semiconductor Memory Workshop," p. 88, 2007.
5. A. Shanware, M. R. Visokay, J. J. Chambers, A. L. P. Rotondaro, J. McPherson, and L. Colombo, "Int. Elect. Dev. Meet. Tech. Dig.," 38.6, p. 939, 2003.
6. S. Jeon, J. H. Han, J. Lee, S. Choi, H. Hwang, and C. Kim, *IEEE Electron Dev. Lett.* 27, 486 (2006).
7. K. Kim and J. Choi, "IEEE Non-Volatile Semiconductor Memory Workshop," p. 9, 2006.
8. J. S. Moodera, L. R. Kinder, T. M. Wong, and R. Meservey, *Phys. Rev. Lett*. 74, 3273 (1995).
9. A. Fazio, *MRS Bull.* 29, 814 (2004).
10. S. S. P. Parkin, N. More, and K. P. Roche, *Phys. Rev. Lett*. 64, 2304 (1990).
11. J. C. Scott, *Science* 302, 62 (2004).
12. J. Taylor, M. Brandbyge, and K. Stokbro, *Phys. Rev. B* 68, 121101 (2003).
13. R. F. Service, *Science* 302, 556 (2003).
14. A. A. Yasseri, Z. Liu, J. S. Lindsey, and D. E. Bocian, *Science* 302, 1543 (2003).
15. T. A. Fulton and G. J. Dolan, *Phys. Rev. Lett.* 59, 109 (1987).
16. A. Jujiwara and Y. Takahashi, *Nature* 410, 560 (2001).
17. M. J. Yoo, T. A. Fulton, H. F. Hess, R. L. Willett, L. N. Dunkleberger, R. J. Chichester, L. N. Pfeiffer, and K. W. West, *Science* 276, 579 (1997).
18. Y. Arimoto and H. Ishiwara, *MRS Bull.* 29, 823 (2004).
19. S. Lai, "Int. Elect. Dev. Meet. Tech. Dig.," 10.1.1, p. 255, 2001.
20. Y. N. Hwang, J. S. Hong, S. H. Lee, S. J. Ahn, G. T. Jeong, G. H. Koh, J. H. Oh, H. J. Kim, W. C. Jeong, S. Y. Lee, J. H. Park, K. C. Ryoo, H. Horii, Y. H. Ha, J. H. Yi, W. Y. Cho, Y. T. Kim, K. H. Lee, S. H. Joo, S. O. Park, U. I. Ching, H. S. Jeong, and K. Kim, "Int. Elect. Dev. Meet. Tech. Dig.," 37.1.1, 893, 2003.
21. A. Pirovano, A. L. Lacaita, A. Benvenuti, F. Pellizzer, S. Hudgens, and R. Bez, "Int. Elect. Dev. Meet. Tech. Dig.," 2003.
22. D. Adler, H. K. Henisch, and N. F. Mott, *Rev. Mod. Phys*. 50, 209 (1978).
23. M. H. Cohen, H. Fritzsche, and S. R. Ovshinsky, *Phys. Rev. Lett*. 22, 1065 (1969).
24. S. R. Ovshinsky, *Phys. Rev. Lett*. 21, 1450 (1968).
25. S. R. Ovshinsky, The Physical Base of Intelligence-Model Studies, "Detroit Phys. Soc. Tech. Dig.," p. 17, 1959.
26. M. S. Shur, D. Adler, M. Silver, and S. R. Ovshinsky, *J. Appl. Phys.* 51, 3289 (1980).
27. A. L. Greer, *Proc. EPCOS* [online] 2005, available at http://www.epcos.org.
28. C. Popescu, *Solid State Elect.* 18, 671 (1975).
29. A. E. Owen, J. M. Robertson, and C. Main, *J. Non-Cryst. Solids* 32, 29 (1979).
30. A. Pirovano, A. L. Lacaita, A. Benvenuti, F. Pellizzer, and R. Bez, *IEEE Trans. Elect. Dev.* 51, 452 (2004).
31. A. Redaelli, A. Pirovano, F. Pellizzer, A. L. Lacaita, D. Ielmini, and R. Bez, *IEEE Electron Dev. Lett.* 25, 684 (2004).
32. N. F. Mott and E. A. Davis, "Electronic Processes in Non-Crystalline Materials." Oxford, U.K., Clarendon, 1967.
33. M. Kastner, D. Adler, and H. Fritzsche, *Phys. Rev. Lett*. 37, 1504 (1976).
34. S. R. Ovshinsky, *Phys. Rev. Lett*. 36, 1469 (1976).
35. D. K. Biegelsen and R. A. Street, *Phys. Rev. Lett*. 44, 803 (1980).
36. D. Adler, *J. Non-Cryst. Solids* 35–36, 819 (1980).
37. M. Kastner and H. Fritzsche, *Phyl. Mag. B* 37, 199 (1978).
38. Y. A. Kryukov, V. G. Karpov, S. D. Savransky, and I. V. Karpovlya, *Appl. Phys. Lett.* 90, 123504 (2007).
39. I. V. Karpov, M. Mitra, D. Kau, G. Spadini, V. G. Karpov, and Y. A. Kryukov, *Appl. Phys. Lett.* 92, 173501 (2008).
40. Y. A. Kryukov, V. G. Karpov, I. V. Karpov, and M. Mitra, *Phys. Rev. B* 78, 052201 (2008).
41. Y. A. Kryukov, V. G. Karpov, M. Mitra, and I. V. Karpov, *J. Appl. Phys.* 104, 054507 (2008).
42. M. Simon, M. Nardone, V. G. Karpov, and I. V. Karpov, *J. Appl. Phys*. 108, 064514 (2010).
43. G. F. Zhou, H. J. Borg, J. C. N. Rijpers, and M. Lankhorst, "Tech. Digest of ODS," p. 74, 2000.
44. D. Adler, M. S. Shur, M. Silver, and S. R. Ovshinsky, *J. Appl. Phys*. 51, 3289 (1980)
45. K. Shportko, S. Kremers, M. Woda, D. Lencer, J. Robertson, and M. Wuttig, *Nat. Mater.* 7, 653 (2008).
46. D. Lencer, M. Salinga, B. Grabowski, T. Hickel, J. Neugebauer, and M. Wuttig, *Nat. Mater.* 7, 972 (2008).
47. G. Simons and A. N. Bloch, *Phys. Rev. B* 7, 2754 (1973).
48. J. St. John and A. N. Bloch, *Phys. Rev. Lett*. 33, 1095 (1974).
49. J. R. Chelikowsky and J. C. Phillips, *Phys. Rev. B* 17, 2453 (1978).
50. N. Yamada, E. Ohno, K. Nishiuchi, N. Akahira, and M. Takao, *J. Appl. Phys.* 69, 2849 (1991).
51. S. Raoux, *Annu. Rev. Mater. Res*. 39, 25 (2009).
52. N. Kh. Abrikosov and G. T. Danilova-Dobryakova, *Izv. Akad. Auk. SSSR Neorg. Mater.* 1, 204 (1965).
53. T. L. Anderson and H. B. Krause, *Acta Cryst.* B30, 1307 (1974).
54. O. G. Karpinsky, L. E. Shelimovaa, M. A. Kretova, and J. P. Fleurial, *J. Alloys Compd.* 268, 112 (1998).
55. L. Balde, B. Legendre, and A. Balkhi, *J. Alloys Compd*. 216, 285 (1995).
56. H. Y. Cheng, K. F. Kao, C. M. Lee, and T. S. Chin, *IEEE Trans. Mag*. 43, 927 (2007).
57. K. F. Kao, C. M. Lee, M. J. Chen, M. J. Tsai, and T. S. Chin, *Adv. Mater*. 21, 1695 (2009).
58. K. F. Kao, C. C. Chang, F. T. Chen, M. J. Tsai, and T. S. Chin, *Scripta Mater.* 63, 855 (2010).

59. R. Pandian, B. J. Kooi, J. T. M. De Hosson, and A. Pauza, *Proc. EPCOS* [online] 2005, available at http://www.epcos.org.
60. R. Kojima, S. Okabayashi, T. Kashihara, K. Horai, T. Matsunaga, E. Ohno, N. Yamada, and T. Ohta, *Jpn. J. Appl. Phys.* 37, 2098 (1998).
61. M. C. Jung, Y. M. Lee, H. D. Kim, M. G. Kim, H. J. Shin, K. H. Kim, S. A. Song, H. S. Jeong, C. H. Ko and M. Han, *Appl. Phys. Lett.* 91, 083514 (2007).
62. K. Wang, D. Wamwangi, S. Ziegler, C. Steimer, and M. Wuttig, *J. Appl. Phys.* 96, 5557 (2004).
63. K. Wang, D. Wamwangi, S. Ziegler, C. Steimer, M. J. Kang, S. Y. Choi, and M. Wuttig, *Phys. Stat. Sol.* 201, 3087 (2004).
64. S. W. Ryu, J. H. Oh, J. H. Lee, B. J. Cho, W. Kim, S. K. Hong, C. S. Hwang, and H. J. Kim, *Appl. Phys. Lett.* 92, 142110 (2008).
65. K. Wang, C. Steimer, D. Wamwangi, S. Ziegler, M. Wuttig, J. Tomforde, and W. Bensch, *Microsyst. Techno.* 13, 203 (2007).
66. E. G. Yeo, L. P Shi, R. Zhao, and T. C. Chong, *Mater. Res. Soc. Proc. Online Proceedings* 918, 0918-H05-05-G06-05 (2006).
67. S. J. Ahn, Y. J. Song, C. W. Jeong, J. M. Shin, Y. Fai, Y. N. Hwang, S. H. Lee, K. C. Ryoo, S. Y. Lee, J. H. Park, H. Horii, Y. H. Ha, J. H. Yi, B. J. Kuh, G. H. Koh, G. T. Jeong, H. S. Jeong, K. Ki, and B. I. Ryu, "IEDM Tech. Dig.," 2004.
68. H. Horii, J. H. Yi, J. H. Park, Y. H. Ha, I. G. Baek, S. O. Park, Y. N. Hwang, S. H. Lee, Y. T. Kim, K. H. Lee, U. Chung, and J. T. Moon, "VLSI Symp. Tech. Dig.," 2003.
69. L. W. W. Fang, R. Zhao, M. H. Li, K. G. Lim, L. P. Shi, T. C. Chong, and Y. C. Yeo, *J. Appl. Phys.* 107, 104506 (2010).
70. T. C. Chong, L. P. Shi, W. Qiang, P. K. Tan, X. S. Miao, and X. Hu, *J. Appl. Phys.* 91, 3981 (2002).
71. T. C. Chong, L. P. Shi, R. Zhao, P. K. Tan, J. M. Li, H. K. Lee, X. S. Miao, A. Y. Du, and C. H. Tung, *Appl. Phys. Lett.* 88, 122114 (2006).
72. H. X. Yang, T. C. Chong, R. Zhao, H. K. Lee, J. M. Li, K. G. Lim, and L. P. Shi, *Appl. Phys. Lett.* 94, 203110 (2009).
73. J. Tominaga, R. Simpson, P. Fons, and A. Kolobov, "Int. Elect. Dev. Meet. Tech. Dig.," (2010).
74. S. Y. Ren and J. D. Dow, *Phys. Rev. B* 25, 3750 (1982).
75. G. Chen, *Phys. Rev. B* 57, 14958 (1997).
76. S. Tamura and Y. Tanaka, *Phys. Rev. B* 60, 2627 (1999).
77. J. O. Sofo and G. D. Mahan, *Appl. Phys. Lett.* 65, 2690 (1994).
78. T. Yao, *Appl. Phys. Lett.* 51, 1798 (1987).
79. G. Chen, *J. Heat Trans.* 119, 220 (1996).
80. L. Esaki, *IEEE J. Quantum Electron* QE-22, 1611 (1986).
81. R. Venkatasubramanian, *Phys. Rev. B* 61, 3091 (2000).
82. X. Y. Yu, G. Chen, A. Verma, and J. S. Smith, *Appl. Phys. Lett.* 67, 3554 (1995).
83. S. M. Lee, D. G. Cahill, and R. Venkatasubramanian, *Appl. Phys. Lett.* 70, 2957 (1997).
84. G. Chen and M. Neagu, *Appl. Phys. Lett.* 71, 2761 (1997).
85. W. S. Capinski, H. J. Maris, T. Ruf, M. Cardona, K. Ploog, and D. S. Katzer, *Phys. Rev. B* 59, 8105 (1999).
86. P. Hyldaard and G. D. Maha, *Phys. Rev. B* 56, 10754 (1997).
87. W. Czubatyj, S. R. Ovshinsky, D. A. Strand, P. Klersey, S. Kostylev, and B. Pashmakov, U.S. Patent 5, 825, 046, 1998.
88. S. W. Ryu, J. H. Oh, B. J. Choi, S. Y. Hwang, S. K. Hong, C. S. Hwang, and H. J. Kim, *Electrochem. Solid-State Lett.* 9, G259 (2006).
89. S.-Y. Lee, K.-J. Choi, S.-O. Ryu, S.-M. Yoon, N.-Y. Lee, Y.-S. Park, S.-H. Kim, S.-H. Lee, and B.-G. Yu, *Appl. Phys. Lett.* 89, 053517 (2006).
90. T. Y. Lee, K. H. P. Kim, D.-S. Suh, C. Kim, Y.-S. Kang, D. G. Cahill, D. Lee, M.-H. Lee, M.-H. Kwon, K.-B. Kim, and Y. Khang, *Appl. Phys. Lett.* 94, 243103 (2009).
91. J. S. Noh, D. S. Suh, S. M. Lee, K. H. P. Kim, W. C. Shin, E. Lee, Y. S. Kang, J. C. Park, K. H. Kim, and Y. Khang, *Proc. Mater. Res. Soc. Symp.* 888, 137 (2006).
92. W. Czubatyj, S. J. Hudgens, C. Dennison, C. Schell, and T. Lowrey, *IEEE Electron Dev. Lett.* 31, 869 (2010).
93. W. Czubatyj, T. Lowrey, S. Kostylev, and I. Asano, *Proc. EPCOS* [online] 2006, available at http://www.epcos.org.
94. T. Y. Lee, S. S. Kim, D. Lee, M. H. Lee, D. H. Ahn, and K. B. Kim, *Appl. Phys. Lett.* 89, 163503 (2006).
95. D. Lee, S.-S. Yim, H.-K. Lyeo, M.-H. Kwon, D. Kang, H.-G. Jun, S.-W. Nam, and K.-B. Kima, *Elec. Solid-State Lett.* 13, K8 (2010).
96. J. I. Lee, H. Park, S. L. Cho, Y. L. Park, B. J. Bae, J. H. Park, J. S. Park, H. G. An, J. S. Bae, D. H. Ahn, Y. T. Kim, H. Horii, S. A. Song, J. C. Shin, S. O. Park, H. S. Kim, U.-I. Chung, J. T. Moon, and B. I. Ryu, "VLSI Symp. Tech. Dig.," p. 102, 2007.
97. D. H. Im, J. I. Lee, S. L. Cho, H. G. An, D. H. Kim, I. S. Kim, H. Park, D. H. Ahn, H. Horii, S. O. Park, U.-I. Chung, and J. T. Moon, "Int. Elect. Dev. Meet. Tech. Dig.," 2008.
98. B. J. Choi, S. Choi, Y. C. Shin, C. S. Hwang, J. W. Lee, J. Jeong, Y. J. Kim, S.-Y. Hwang, and S. K. Hong, *J. Electrochem. Soc.* 154, H318 (2007).
99. V. Pore, T. Hatanpaa, M. Ritala, and M. Leskela, *J. Amer. Chem. Soc.* 131, 3478 (2009).
100. P. C. Chen, W. Hunks, M. Stender, T. Chen, G. Stuaf, C. Xu, and J. Roeder, *Mater. Res. Soc. Proc. Online Proceedings* 1071, 1071-F09-10 (2008).
101. J. F. Zheng, J. Reed, C. Schell, W. Czubatyj, R. Sandoval, J. Fournier, W. Li, W. Hunks, C. Dennison, E. S. Hudgens, and T. Lowrey, *IEEE Elec. Dev. Lett.* 31, 999 (2010).
102. J. F. Zheng, P. Chen, W. Hunks, M. Stender, C. Xu, W. Li, J. Roeder, S. Kamepalli, C. Schell, J. Reed, J. Ricker, R. Sandoval, J. Founrnier, W. Czubatyj, G. Wicker, C. Dennison, S. Hudgens, and T. Lowrey, *Mater. Res. Soc. Proc. Online Proceedings* 1160, 1160-H14-11 (2009).
103. D. H. Ahn, D. H. Kang, H. S. Kwon, M. H. Kwon, T. Y. Lee, B. Cheong, K. S. Lee, D. H. Kim, T. S. Lee, W. M. Kim, and K. B. Kim, *Mater. Res. Soc. Proc.* (2003).
104. W. J. Wang, R. Zhao, L. P. Shi, X. S. Miao, P. K. Tan, M. H. Hong, T. C. Chong, Y. H. Wu, and Y. Lin, *J. Appl. Phys.* 98, 124313 (2005).
105. S. L. Cho, J. H. Yi, Y. H. Ha, B. J. Kuh, C. M. Lee, J. H. Park, S. D. Nam, H. Horii, B. O. Cho, K. C. Ryoo, S. O. Park, H. S. Kim, U-In. Chung, J. T. Moon, and B. I. Ryu, "VLSI Symp. Tech. Dig.," 2005.
106. Y. Matsui, K. Kurotsuchi, O. Tonomura, T. Morikawa, M. Kinoshita, Y. Fujisaki, N. Matsuzaki, S. Hanzawa, M. Terao, N. Takaura, H. Moriya, T. Iwasaki, M. Moniwa, and T. Koga, "IEDM Tech. Dig.," 2006.
107. F. Rao, Z. Song, Y. Gong, L. Wu, S. Feng, and B. Chen, *Nano Tech.* 19, 445706 (2008).
108. F. Rao, Z. Song, L. Wu, M. Zhong, S. Feng, and B. Chen, *Appl. Phys. Lett.* 91, 073505 (2007).
109. Y. H. Ha, J. H. Yi, H. Hoe, J. H. Park, S. H. Joo, S. O. Park, U-In. Chung, and J. T. Moon, "VLSI Symp. Tech. Dig.," 2003.
110. F. Pellizzer, A. Pirovano, F. Ottogalli, M. Magistretti, M. Scaravaggi, P. Zuliani, M. Tosi, A. Benvenuti, P. Besana, S. Cadeo, T. Marangon, R. Morandi, R. Piva, A. Spandre, R. Zonca, A. Modelli, E. Varesi, T. Lowrey, A. Lacaita, G. Casagrande, P. Cappelletti, and R. Bez, "Int. Elect. Dev. Meet. Tech. Dig.," 32.6.1, p. 719, 2001.
111. M. H. R. Lankhorst, B. W. S. M. M. Ketelaars, and R. A. M. Wolters, *Nat. Mater.* 4, 347 (2005).
112. Y. C. Chen, C. T. Rettner, S. Raoux, G. W. Burr, S. H. Chen, R. M. Shelby, M. Salinga, W. P. Risk, T. D. Happ, G. M. McClelland, M. Breitwisch, A. Schrott, J. B. Philipp, M. H. Lee, R. Cheek, T. Nirschl, M. Lamorey, C. F. Chen, E. Joseph, S. Zaidi, B. Yee, H. L. Lung, R. Bergmann, and C. Lam, "IEDM Tech. Dig.," 2006.
113. H. X. Yang, T. C. Chong, R. Zhao, H. K. Lee, J. M. Li, K. G. Lim, and L. P. Shi, *Appl. Phys. Lett.* 94, 203110 (2009).

114. M. Salinga, D. Lencer, B. Grabowski, T. Hickel, J. Neugebauer, and M. Wuttig, *Nat. Mater.* 7, 972 (2008).
115. E. G. Yeo, R. Zhao, L. P. Shi, K. G. Lim, T. C. Chong, and I. Adesida, *Appl. Phys. Lett.* 94, 243504 (2009).
116. R. Shelby, S. Raoux, B. Munoz, M. Hitzbleck, D. Krebs, M. Salinga, M. Woda, M. Austgen, K.-M. Chung, and M. Wuttig, *Proc. EPCOS* [online] 2008, available at http://www.epcos.org.
117. D. Krebs, S. Raoux, C. T. Rettner, R. M. Shelby, G. W. Burr, and M. Wuttig, *Mater. Res. Soc. Proc. Online Proceedings* 1072, 1072-G06-07 (2008).
118. S. Kostylev, T. Lowrey, and W. Czubatyj, *Proc. EPCOS* [online] 2009, available at http://www.epcos.org.
119. W. J. Wang, L. P. Shi, R. Zhao, K. G. Lim, H. K. Lee, T. C. Chong, and Y. H. Wu, *Appl. Phys. Lett.* 93, 043121 (2008).
120. G. Bruns, P. Merkelbach, C. Schlockermann, M. Salinga, M. Wuttig, T. D. Happ, J. B. Philipp, and M. Kund, *Appl. Phys. Lett.* 95, 043108 (2009).
121. D. Loke, L. P. Shi, W. J. Wang, R. Zhao, L. T. Ng, K. G. Lim, H. X. Yang, T. C. Chong, and Y. C. Yeo, *Nanotechnology* 22, 254019 (2011).
122. S. Senkader and C. D. Wright, *J. Appl. Phys.* 95, 504 (2004).
123. F. Bedeschi, R. Fackenthal, C. Resta, E. Donze, M. Jagasivamani, E. C. Buda, F. Pellizzer, D. Chow, A. Cabrini, G. M. A. Calvi, R. Faravelli, A. Fantini, G. Torelli, D. Mills, R. Gastaldi, and G. Casagrande, *IEEE J. Solid-State Circuits* 44, 217 (2009).
124. Y. Zhang, J. Feng, Y. Zhang, Z. Zhang, Y. Lin, T. Tang, B. Cai, and B. Chen, *Phys. Stat. Sol.—Rapid Res. Lett.* 1, R28 (2007).
125. A. Pantazi, A. Sebastian, N. Papandreou, M. J. Breitwisch, C. Lam, H. Pozidis, and E. Eleftheriou, *Proc. EPCOS* [online] 2009, available at http://www.epcos.org.
126. S. Braga, A. Sanasi, A. Cabrini, and G. Torelli, *IEEE Trans. Elect. Dev.* 57, 2556 (2010).
127. B. J. Choi, S. Choi, T. Eom, S. H. Rha, K. M. Kim, and C. S. Hwanga, *Appl. Phys. Lett.* 97, 132107 (2010).
128. L. C. Wu, Z. T. Song, F. Rao, Y. F. Gong, and S. L. Feng, *Appl. Phys. Lett.* 94, 243115 (2009).
129. R. Zhao, L. P. Shi, and T. C. Chong, "Proc. Non-Volatile Memory Tech. Symp.," 2009.
130. G. Torelli and P. Lupi, *Alta Freq.* LII, 487 (1983).
131. M. Fandrich V. N. Kynett, J. Anderson, P. Dix, O. Jungroth, J. Kreifels, R. Lodenquai, B. Vajdic, S. Wells, M. Winston, and L. Yang, *IEEE J. Solid-State Circuits* 24, 1259 (1989).
132. J. Maimon, K. Hunt, J. Rodgers, L. Burcin, and K. Knowles, "NVMTS Dig.," (2003).
133. F. Bedeschi, R. Bez, C. Boffino, E. Bonizzoni, E. C. Buda, G. Casagrande, L. Costa, M. Ferraro, R. Gastaldi, O. Khouri, F. Ottogalli, F. Pellizzer, A. Pirovano, C. Resta, G. Torelli, and M. Tosi, *IEEE J. Solid-State Circuits* 40, 1557 (2005).
134. S. Kang, W. Y. Cho, B.-H. Cho, K.-J. Lee, C.-S. Lee, H.-R. Oh, B.-G. Choi, W. Wang, H.-J. Kim, M.-H. Park, Y. H. Ro, S. Kim, C.-D. Ha, K.-S. Kim, Y.-R. Kim, D.-E. Kim, C.-K. Kwak, H.-G. Byun, G. Jeong, H. Jeong, K. Kim, and Y. Shin, *IEEE J. Solid-State Circuits* 42, 210 (2007).
135. F. Pellizzer, A. Benvenuti, B. Gleixner, Y. Kim, B. Johnson, M. Magistretti, T. Marangon, A. Pirovano, R. Bez, and G. Atwood, "VLSI Symp. Tech. Dig.," 2006.
136. J. H. Oh, J. H. Park, Y. S. Lim, H. S. Lim, Y. T. Oh, J. S. Kim, J. M. Shin, J. H. Park, Y. J. Song, K. C. Ryoo, D. W. Lim, S. S. Park, J. I. Kim, J. H. Kim, J. Yu, F. Yeung, C. W. Jeong, J. H. Kong, D. H. Kang, G. H. Koh, G. T. Jeong, H. S. Jeong, and K. Kim, "IEDM Tech. Dig.," 2006.
137. G. Servalli, "IEDM Tech. Dig.," 2009.
138. G. Servalli, A. Pirovano, and R. Bez, "EPCOS Proceeding," 2010.
139. D. H. Kang, J. S. Kim, Y. R. Kim, Y. T. Kim, M. K. Lee, Y. J. Jun, H. Park, F. Yeung, C. W. Jeong, J. Yu, J. H. Kong, D. W. Ha, S. A. Song, J. Park, Y. H. Park, Y. J. Song, C. Y. Eum, K. C. Ryoo, J. M. Shin, D. W. Lim, S. S. Park, J. H. Kim, W. I. Park, K. R. Sim, J. H. Cheong, J. H. Oh, J. H. Park, J. I. Kim, Y. T. Oh, K. W. Lee, S. P. Koh, S. H. Eun, N. B. Kim, G. H. Koh, G. T. Jeong, H. S. Jeong, and K. Kim, "VLSI Symp. Tech. Dig.," 2007.
140. F. Bedeschil, R. Fackenthal, C. Resta, E. M. Donzel, M. Jagasivamanil, E. Buda, F. Pellizzer, D. Chow, A. Cabrini, G. M. A. Calvi, R. Faravellil, A. Fantini, G. Torelli, D. Mills, R. Gastaldil, and G. Casagrandel, "ISSCC Dig. Tech. Papers," 2008.
141. Y. Sasago, M. Kinoshita, T. Morikawa, K. Kurotsuchi, S. Hanzawa, T. Mine, A. Shima, Y. Fujisaki, H. Kume, H. Moriya, N. Takaura, and K. Torii, "VLSI Symp. Tech. Dig.," 2009.
142. D. Kau, S. Tang, I. V. Karpov, R. Dodge, B. Klehn, J. A. Kalb, J. Strand, A. Diaz, N. Leung, J. Wu, S. Lee, T. Langry, K. W. Chang, C. Papagianni, J. W. Lee, J. Hirst, S. Erra, E. Flores, N. Righos, H. Castro, and G. Spadini, "IEDM Tech. Dig.," p. 617, 2009.
143. S. J. W. Lee, I. V. Karpov, and G. Spadini, "Proc. Eur. Phase Change Ovonic Sci. Symp.," p. 21, 2010.
144. S. Chen, P. B. Gibbons, and S. Nath, "5th Biennial Conference on Innovative Data Systems Research (CIDR'11)," 2011.

CHAPTER 4

Phase Change Memory Physics-Based Modeling: Electrical Characteristics, Scaling, and Reliability

Daniele Ielmini

Dipartimento di Elettronica e Informazione and IU.NET, Politecnico di Milano, Piazza L. da Vinci 32, 20133 Milano (MI), Italy

CONTENTS

1. INTRODUCTION

Nonvolatile memory scaling has been one of the key drivers for technology development in the past two decades. The large market expansion of mobile devices, such as smart phones, tablets, *e*-books and media players, has led to a huge demand for nonvolatile memory devices with high capacity and low cost [1]. In this frame, metal-oxide-semiconductor field effect transistor (MOSFET)-based Flash NAND has played a leading role due to its remarkable scaling capability. However, to ensure the further scaling of high-density nonvolatile memories below the 15 nm node, novel processes, materials, and device concepts may need to be introduced [1].

ISBN: 1-58883-251-1

Nonvolatile Memories: Materials, Devices and Applications
Edited by Tseung-Yuen Tseng and Simon M. Sze
Volume 2: Pages: 83–109

Among the emerging memory concepts that are proposed for future scaling of nonvolatile memories, phase change memory (PCM) is one of the most radically new and successful concepts. The memory relies on the phase transition between an amorphous phase and a crystalline phase in a chalcogenide material. The typical chalcogenide material is $Ge_2Sb_2Te_5$ (GST), which has also been used as the storage material in phase-change optical media such as CD-RWs and DVDs [2]. The memory takes advantage of the different electrical resistivity in the two phases, which, thus, can serve as two logic bits. The crystalline and amorphous phase display a relatively low and high electrical resistivity, respectively, resulting in a resistance window of about two decades in the PCM device [3]. The memory cell has a two-terminal structure, with the chalcogenide material sandwiched between two electrical contacts. To transform the chalcogenide material into the amorphous phase, an electrical pulse is applied between the two electrodes of the memory cell. This results in a current flow and in a consequent release of Joule power into the chalcogenide material, causing it to melt. As the pulse is switched off, the liquid chalcogenide volume is suddenly brought to room temperature, and it is frozen into an atomically disordered amorphous phase [2, 4]. This is referred to as the high-resistance reset state of the memory. Only the chalcogenide volume where the temperature exceeds the melting point is transformed into the amorphous phase, and the pulse amplitude can usually control it. To restore the crystalline phase, a similar operation is performed, although the Joule power is kept low enough to anneal the amorphous phase, thus causing crystallization with no melting. As a consequence, a final crystalline phase is obtained, which is also referred to as the low-resistance set state. The electrical operations to program the cell into the reset and the set states are called the reset and the set operations, respectively.

Figure 1 shows the measured current–voltage (I–V) characteristics for the set and the reset states in a PCM cell [5]. The measurement was obtained by the application of a sequence of pulses with increasing voltage V_A to the PCM cell in series with a load resistance R_L, while the voltage drop V_{cell} across the cell was monitored [5]. This allows us to evaluate the current flowing through the cell as:

$$I = \frac{V_A - V_{cell}}{R_L} \tag{1}$$

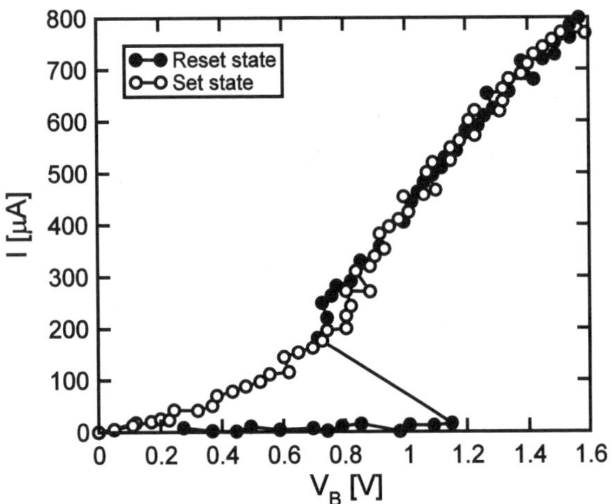

Figure 1. Measured I–V curves for the set and reset states of a PCM cell, corresponding to the crystalline and amorphous phases, respectively. Reprinted with permission from [5], D. Ielmini et al., *IEEE Trans. Electron Devices* 54, 308 (2007). © 2007, IEEE.

The pulsed methodology allowed to measure the I–V characteristics even at relatively large currents close to 1 mA, while minimizing the degradation of the cell active region due to Joule heating and electromigration [6]. The I–V curve for the set state indicates a nonlinear behavior, possibly due to Joule heating and/or the impact ionization at high electric fields. In either cases, the carrier concentration increases at high voltage, thus resulting in a decrease of the electrical resistance [7]. The resistance values at low and high voltages are generally referred to as R and R_{ON}, respectively [8]. Due to the carrier generation at high fields, R_{ON} is believed to reveal the series resistances of the electrodes, with little contribution from the chalcogenide volume itself. In the so-called mushroom-cell structure, for instance, the bottom electrode has a sublithographic size to allow for a relatively good confinement of electrical power and heat, thus the R_{ON} provides an estimate for the bottom electrode (or heater) resistance [8]. On the other hand, the low-voltage set-state resistance can be estimated as $R = R_c + R_{ON}$, where R_c is the 'true' resistance of the crystalline chalcogenide layer.

The nonlinear behavior of the I–V curve becomes even more dramatic in the reset state. The reset state displays a high resistance, generally in the range of a few MΩ. Above a linear (ohmic) regime at low voltages, the current increases with an exponential dependence on voltage [9]. At a specific threshold voltage V_T (about 1.15 V in Fig. 1), the current changes abruptly from a low to a high value, according to a negative differential resistance (NDR) characteristic. This is the typical threshold switching, namely a sudden transition from a high to a low resistance that takes place at threshold voltage V_T and threshold current I_T. Due to threshold switching, the NDR regime can be evidenced by measuring the voltage drop across the cell while applying the voltage across the cell connected in series with a load resistance (Fig. 1). In this case, the slope of the NDR region is equal to $-R_L^{-1}$ according to Eq. (1). Above the threshold point, the cell is in the so-called ON-state of the amorphous phase, namely a high-conductivity state with a large concentration of free carriers as a result of the threshold-switching mechanism. In a practical measurement, the state may also partially crystallize, and the high local temperature may contribute to carrier generation. This explains the similarity between the high-current conduction characteristics for the amorphous ON-state and the crystalline state in Figure 1.

The threshold voltage V_T marks the boundary between the undisturbed read region (the OFF state) and the programming region (the ON state), where the set and reset operation must be performed [10]. This highlights the importance of the prediction of V_T and the understanding of the conduction and switching effects in the amorphous phase. Another key point for memory operation is the understanding and modeling of the set and reset processes and their scaling dependence. In particular, set time statistics is a key issue in the operation of large memory arrays, where each bit must display a sufficiently fast crystallization during set [11]. Reset operation must be thoroughly described to provide schemes for reset current reduction and to predict the impact of scaling on reset parameters [8, 12]. Finally, for nonvolatile memory applications, reliability modeling is essential, and issues such as endurance, data retention, and read disturbs must be carefully characterized and understood for developing high-performance, high-reliability PCM devices.

This chapter will review the switching, operation, and reliability of PCM from the point of view of the physical modeling. Section 2 will cover the conduction and switching mechanisms, mainly addressing conduction modeling in the amorphous phase and the threshold switching mechanism. Section 3 will focus on the set and reset operations, describing the set characteristics and modeling on a statistical level and the reduction/optimization/scaling of the reset current. Section 4 will review reliability issues and modeling for PCM, addressing cycling endurance, noise, resistance drift, and data retention. Finally, the current trends in material engineering of the PCM device aimed at reliability improvement are summarized in the last section.

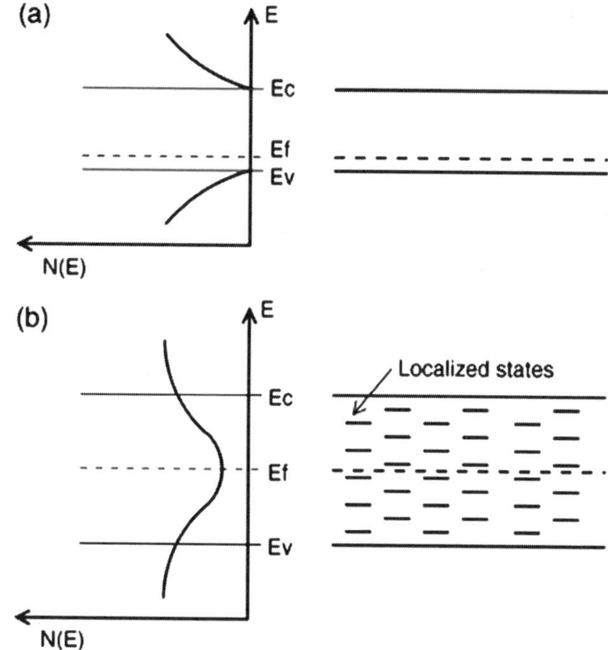

Figure 2. Band structures in the (a) crystalline and (b) amorphous phases of a typical chalcogenide phase change material. Reprinted with permission from [15], D. Ielmini et al., *IEEE Trans. Electron Devices* 56, 1070 (2009). © 2009, IEEE.

2. MODELING CONDUCTION AND SWITCHING

Since the PCM device relies on the difference between the resistances in two chalcogenide phases, studying and understanding the conduction properties of the active material are essential. In fact, the resistance window between the two logic states dictates the read error margin in the memory, therefore the prediction of the resistance window (or ratio) as a function of temperature, annealing conditions, cell dimensions, and active material composition is a key aspect in the design and definition of a PCM technology. In addition, the memory readout is generally carried out by the application of a voltage pulse and the measurement of a current passing through the PCM device. Therefore, one has to ensure that (a) the applied voltage does not disturb or even program the memory cell, and (b) the readout current is sufficient for sensing the memory state in an acceptably short read time, usually in the range of 10–20 ns for PCM devices. To fulfill these conditions, a thorough understanding and modeling of the physical processes for conduction and switching is necessary.

To address the conduction mechanisms in chalcogenide material, one needs to first consider the different band structures in the two phases constituting the logic states, namely the crystalline and the amorphous states [13]. Figure 2 schematically shows the band structures for the (a) crystalline and (b) the amorphous phases of GST [14, 15]. The crystalline phase can be described by a semiconductor model with well-defined conduction and valence band edges, with the Fermi level close to the valence band as a result of *p*-type vacancy doping [16, 17]. The amorphous phase instead features a large concentration of localized states in the *mobility* gap, and the Fermi level is located deep in the band gap as a result of self-compensating donor- and acceptor-like localized states. The origin of these states can be traced back to the Anderson model, where disorder in the structure and chemical composition break the periodical symmetry of the lattice and results in localized states. This is in contrast to the forbidden band gap resulting from the Bloch theory within a periodic lattice [13].

2.1. Thermally Activated Hopping

In the amorphous structure, electrical conduction can be described by thermally activated hopping at localized states [14, 18]. Because the Fermi is located at the middle of the mobility gap and due to the large density of localized states, electrical transport will mostly be due to trapped carriers. This has been evidenced by experiments on amorphous GST, where the current was shown to increase exponentially with the applied voltage, and the activation energy for conduction was found to be about one-half of the energy gap of the amorphous chalcogenide and linearly decreased with applied voltage [19]. These experimental results were interpreted as a consequence of a trap-limited conduction mechanism, i.e., hopping of carriers through localized states by the fundamental mechanisms of tunneling and Poole-Frenkel (PF) effects [14, 19]. It should be noted that thermally activated hopping may include small-polaron effects, where the moving charge (an electron or a hole) also distorts the structure because it is trapped in or emitted from an existing localized state. Therefore, the rearrangement of the structure is needed to accommodate the carrier and also requires thermal excitation. Polaron effects were indeed evidenced by Hall measurements for some chalcogenide glasses, namely As_2Te_3, As_2Se_3, and Sb_2Te_3 [20–22].

The tunneling and PF (or thermal emission) mechanisms are depicted in Figure 3, where the potential energy profile is shown along the direction connecting two positively charged localized states, S1 and S2 [18]. The potential profile is shown for two different values of the applied electric field F, namely (a) $F = 0$ and (b) $F = 0.5$ MV cm^{-1}. The localized states are assumed to be located at an energy $E_T = E_C - 0.3$ eV for zero-applied field, where E_C is the conduction band edge in the middle between the two states. A distance $\Delta z = 5$ nm between the two states is assumed in the figure. Three possible transport mechanisms are considered in the figure, namely:

(1) Tunneling that occurs by direct transmission through the potential barrier from S1 to S2 without any energy excitation of the carrier.
(2) Thermal emission that requires that the electron is first thermally emitted to E_C, i.e., the first available state extending freely from S1 to S2. After the electron accesses the level E_C, recapture by S2 will be possible. This mechanism corresponds to PF in the presence of a relatively high concentration of trap states [14, 23, 24].
(3) A combination of thermal emission and tunneling, namely thermally assisted tunneling. This consists of a thermal excitation of the electron within S1 to an energy level $E < E_C$, followed by tunneling through the remaining potential barrier seen at E. Although the probability of reaching E has exponentially decreased with E, the probability of tunneling through the barrier may be significantly higher than the tunneling probability for a 'cold' electron at E_T, as in mechanism (1). Therefore, we expect the contribution of thermally activated tunneling to be significantly more important than pure tunneling in (1), except for circumstances with exceptionally low temperatures, thereby inhibiting the thermal excitation within the trap potential well.

To assess the nature of the conduction mechanism in chalcogenide glasses, the energy dependence of the average transfer rate from S1 to S2 can be easily calculated [18]. The transfer rate R [s^{-1} eV^{-1}] can be written as:

$$R(E) = \frac{P_{\mathrm{tun}}(E)}{\tau_0}\frac{dP_e}{dE} \tag{2}$$

where τ_0 is the characteristic attempt-to-escape time for electron excitation in the localized state, dP_e is the probability for an electron to be located at an energy between E and $E + dE$, and P_{tun} is the probability for tunneling through the barrier in Figure 3(b) at the energy level E [18]. The attempt-to-escape time can be set to $\tau_0 = 10^{-14}$ s, which is consistent with the typical phonon-induced excitation time (10^{-14}–10^{-13} s) [13]. However, it should be noted that τ_0 may obey the Meyer-Neldel (MN) rule, where τ_0 follows an exponential function of the energy E at which the electron has been excited [25–27]. Evidence for the MN rule in amorphous GST used in PCM devices has been, in fact, provided for conduction [28], crystallization, and structural relaxation at the basis of the resistance drift [29]. Since E is generally quite distant from the Fermi level, the electron distribution dP_e/dE can be obtained according to the Maxwell-Boltzmann law. The tunneling probability $P_{\mathrm{tun}}(E)$ can be calculated according to the Wentzel–Kramers–Brillouin (WKB) approximation, while $P_{\mathrm{tun}} = 1$ for electron energies above the potential barrier top, namely $E > E_C$ in Eq. (2). The energy $E_T = E_C - 0.3$ eV roughly corresponds to typical trap energy levels located close to the Fermi level for materials used in PCM applications, e.g., amorphous GST [19].

Figure 4 shows the electron transfer rate calculated by Eq. (2) as a function of energy for electric fields $F = 0$, 0.1 and 0.2 MV cm^{-1} at room temperature. The proportionality between the transfer rate and the current should be remembered, i.e., the higher the transfer rate, the higher the carrier current contribution. As expected, the obtained results indicate that tunneling at $E = E_T$ (i.e., without excitation) is virtually zero, while thermally assisted tunneling (at energies E between E_T and E_C) and thermal emission (at energies

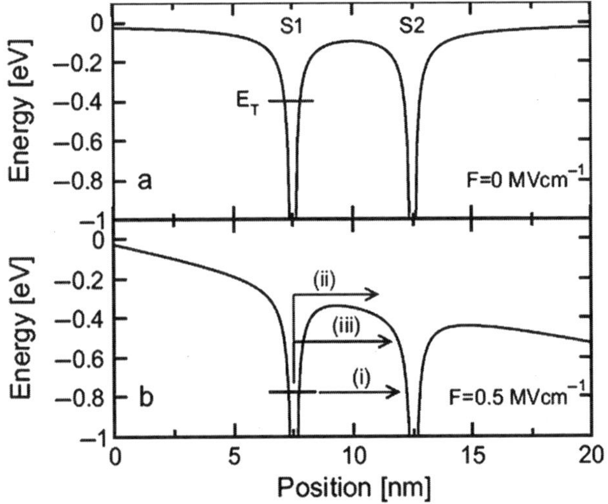

Figure 3. Schematic for the thermally activated hopping mechanism between two Coulombic states, under a (a) zero- and (b) positive-applied voltage. Reprinted with permission from [18], D. Ielmini, *Phys. Rev. B* 78, 035308 (2008). © 2008, APS.

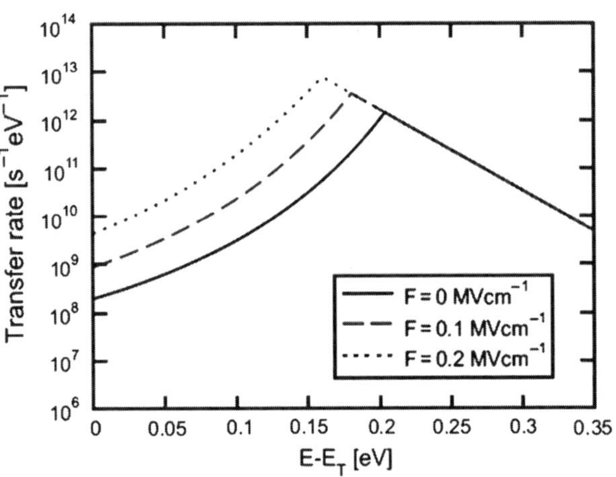

Figure 4. Calculated transfer rate according to Eq. (2) for three different electric field levels. The maximum of the transfer rate corresponds to the electron energy being equal to the top of the potential barrier in Figure 2(b). Reprinted with permission from [18], D. Ielmini, *Phys. Rev. B* 78, 035308 (2008). © 2008, APS.

higher than E_C) are dominant. The maximum of the transfer rate corresponds to the top of the barrier, namely E_C for $F = 0$. This is because, according to Eq. (2), the transfer rate is given by the product of P_e, which decreases for increasing E, and P_{tun}, which strongly increases for the increasing E due to the decreasing potential barrier. The overall contributions of thermally assisted tunneling and thermal emission are, thus, generally comparable for typical trap energies in chalcogenide glasses, namely E_C–E_T between 0.1 and 0.5 eV.

A possible way to discriminate between tunneling and thermal emission contributions in the transport process of chalcogenide glasses is to study the dependence of tunneling time τ_{tun} and the PF time τ_{PF} on the applied electric field F and temperature T. Transfer times τ_{tun} and τ_{PF} represent the average time for an electron to be transferred from S1 to S2 in Figure 3 by thermally assisted tunneling and PF emission, respectively. Figure 5 shows the calculated transfer times as a function of voltage at $T = 300$ K, while Figure 6 shows the calculated times as a function of $1/kT$ at an electric field $F = 0.2$ MV cm^{-1}. The transfer times were calculated as the inverse of the integrated transfer rate in Eq. (2), namely $(\int R(E)dE)^{-1}$, where the integral was evaluated in different energy ranges for τ_{tun} (between E_T and E_C) and for τ_{PF} (above E_C) [18]. The figures also include the total transfer time $\tau_{\text{tot}} = \tau_{\text{tun}}\tau_{\text{PF}}/(\tau_{\text{tun}} + \tau_{\text{PF}})$, namely the 'parallel' contribution of the two equivalent resistances associated with the two transport processes. Both τ_{tun} and τ_{PF} decrease exponentially with F in Figure 5 and increase exponentially with $1/kT$ in Figure 6, thus evidencing an Arrhenius dependence as experimentally verified in Ref. [19]. Note in Figure 5 that τ_{PF} displays an exponential dependence on F, instead of $F^{1/2}$ of the conventional PF mechanism [24]. This is because the potential barrier lowering is proportional to the applied field for relatively short distances among traps, $\Delta z \leq 5$ nm (i.e., Poole behavior [19, 23, 24]). For relatively large $\Delta z > 10$ nm, the conventional PF regime is instead observed [14, 15, 30–32]. Figure 5 also compares calculated times for different trap energies, in the range of 0.2 to 0.4 eV below E_C. The calculations indicate no significant variation in the relative amount of τ_{tun} and τ_{PF} and no significant change in their exponential field dependence. The

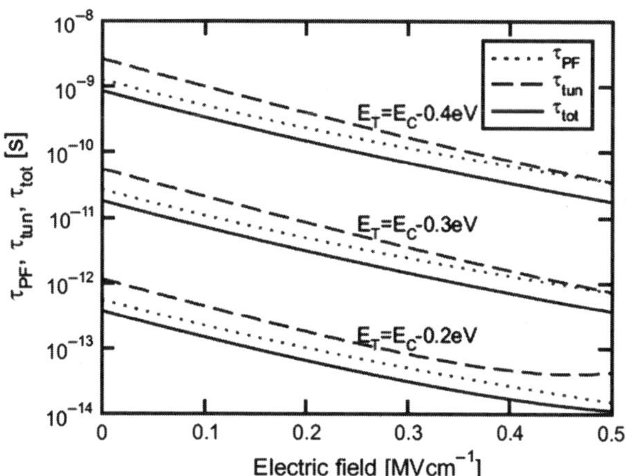

Figure 5. Calculated transfer times τ_{tun}, τ_{PF} and τ_{tot} as a function of the applied electric field. Reprinted with permission from [18], D. Ielmini, *Phys. Rev. B* 78, 035308 (2008). © 2008, APS.

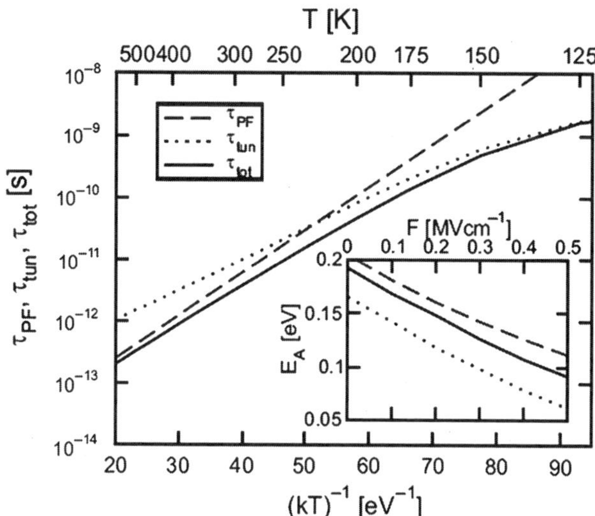

Figure 6. Calculated transfer times τ_{tun}, τ_{PF} and τ_{tot} as a function of $1/kT$. The inset shows the apparent activation energy for the different transfer times as a function of the applied electric field. Reprinted with permission from [18], D. Ielmini, *Phys. Rev. B* 78, 035308 (2008). © 2008, APS.

inset of Figure 6 shows the field dependence of the activation energy for conduction E_A, evaluated from the slope of the calculated transfer times on the Arrhenius plot. E_A decreases linearly with the electric field, which is a signature of the experimentally observed, trap-limited transport in the chalcogenide glasses [19].

Results in Figures 4 to 6 indicate that both the magnitude and the field/temperature dependence of tunneling and the PF contribution to the trap-limited current are comparable, at least in the considered range of temperature, field, energy and trap spacing. These are relevant for typical chalcogenide materials used in memory applications. Most importantly, the two processes share a similar *thermal activation*, in that they need a significant energy excitation (e.g., by electron-phonon interaction) for a successful tunneling or emission across the energy barrier. We will refer to this combined mechanism as a *thermally activated hopping* in the following section. For electrons, hopping can be simply modeled as a purely thermal emission over an *effective* energy barrier, which is obtained by replacing the *band* edge E_C with a conduction-band *mobility* edge E_C'. The latter is slightly smaller than the band edge (namely $E_C' < E_C$) to take into account the significant contribution of electrons tunneling through the energy barrier, which amount to about 50% of the total number of electrons (Fig. 4). A hole-hopping mechanism can be described in a similar way by replacing the valence band edge E_V with the corresponding mobility edge E_V'.

2.2. Thermally Activated Hopping Model

An analytical model for the current due to thermally activated hopping as a function of temperature and applied voltage can be developed as follows: The current density J for electrons can be written by referring to the pictorial energy diagram in Figure 7(a), indicating the mobility edge of the

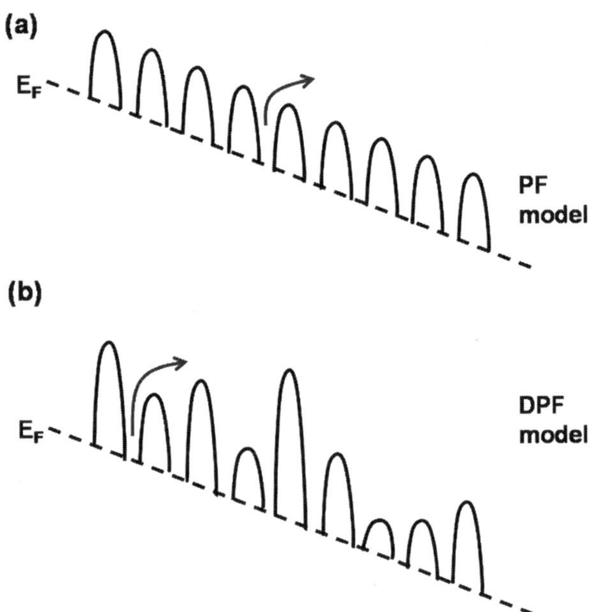

Figure 7. Schematic for the band diagrams responsible for (a) PF and (b) distributed PF conduction in the amorphous chalcogenide. Reprinted with permission from [33], D. Fugazza et al., "IEDM Tech. Dig.," p. 723, 2009. © 2009, IEEE.

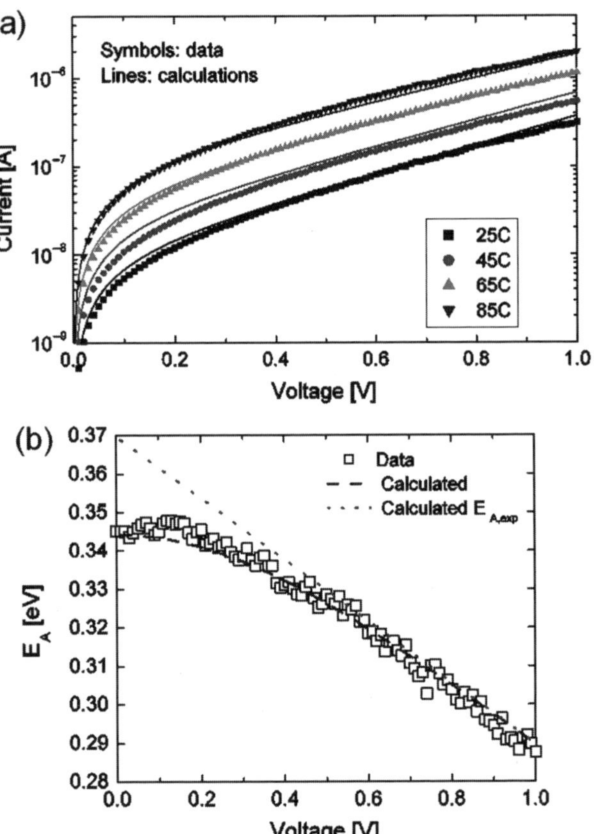

Figure 8. Measured and calculated *I–V* curves for increasing *T* (a) and corresponding activation energy for conduction (b). Reprinted with permission from [14], D. Ielmini and Y. Zhang, *J. Appl. Phys.* 102, 054517 (2007). © 2007, AIP.

conduction band E_C' and the equilibrium Fermi level E_F. For electron hopping, J is given by [14, 18]:

$$J = 2qN_T \frac{\Delta z}{\tau_0} e^{(E_C'-E_F/kT)} \sinh\left(\frac{qF\Delta z}{2kT}\right) \tag{3}$$

where q is the elementary charge, N_T (in units [cm^{-3}]) is the density of localized states between E_F and E_C' (i.e., those contributing to the electron current), and Δz is the average distance between the localized states. The hopping current density in Eq. (3) includes both the PF emission and the thermally assisted tunneling to a neighbor trap. The exponential dependence on $(E_C' - E_F)/kT$ in Eq. (3) represents the probability for thermal excitation from the Fermi energy E_F to the mobility edge E_C' [14, 18]. The sinh function in Eq. (3) instead refers to the competition between the forward and reverse contributions to thermally activated hopping, given by carriers flowing in the same or opposite directions, with respect to the electrostatic force acting on them [14]. At relatively low electric fields, the reverse contribution may be non-negligible thus resulting in a net cancellation of the overall current at zero voltage, as indeed expected from Ohm's law. The sum of the exponential current densities flowing parallel and opposite to the electric field results in a hyperbolic sinusoidal function of the electric field, as shown in Eq. (3) [13, 14, 24].

Figure 8(a) shows the measured and calculated *I–V* characteristics of PCM devices in the amorphous state for increasing temperatures of 25, 45, 65 and 85°C. Calculations by Eq. (3) can account for the observed voltage dependence, which includes linear and exponential regimes at low and high fields, respectively, thanks to the sinh voltage dependence. The temperature dependence of the current is also well captured by the model due to the Arrhenius dependence on temperature in Eq. (3) through an activation energy for conduction $E_C' - E_{F0} = 0.37$ eV [14]. A thickness of 32 nm was assumed in the calculations, which is consistent with the observed thickness of the amorphous cap in mushroom-type PCM devices [34, 35]. Figure 8(b) shows the measured and calculated activation energy for the conduction as a function of voltage. The activation energy decreases with the applied voltage because the activation energy represents the energy barrier for conduction, which is gradually lowered by the applied field. It is useful to recall that it is this lowering barrier that is responsible for the exponential increase of current at sufficiently high voltage in Eq. (3) and Figure 8(a). From Eq. (3), the activation energy can be calculated by differentiating the natural logarithm of the current (or current density) with respect to $1/kT$, namely [14, 36]:

$$\left|\frac{d\log J}{d(1/kT)}\right| = E_C' - E_{F0} - \frac{qV\Delta z}{2u_a}\coth\left(\frac{qV\Delta z}{2kTu_a}\right) \tag{4}$$

which, because the coth function converges to 1 for sufficiently high voltage, tends to the linear function $E_{A,\mathrm{exp}} = E_C' - E_{F0} - qV\Delta z/2u_a$ [14]. Figure 8(b) shows calculations from Eq. (4) and its linear approximation $E_{A,\mathrm{exp}}$, showing an excellent agreement with the measured activation energy. The broad agreement with experimental results shown in

Figure 8 supports the equilibrium-transport model in Eq. (3) as a sound theoretical basis to investigate the threshold-switching mechanism.

2.3. Distributed PF Model

The PF model based on the thermally activated hopping transport has been largely demonstrated in the literature for PCM devices [14, 37]. The model has been used to extract information about the chalcogenide amorphous state, such as the thickness of the amorphous region in multilevel memories [37] and the density of traps [38]. With respect to Eq. (2), predicting an exponential dependence of current on voltage at sufficiently large voltages, some data suggest a conventional PF dependence, i.e., an exponential dependence on the square root of the voltage [2, 15, 31]. The evidence for PF voltage dependence can be explained by relatively large average distance between traps, particularly after elevated-temperature annealing [15, 32]. In fact, it has been shown that the energy-barrier lowering is proportional to the applied voltage only for trap distances less than approximately $\Delta z = 5$ nm, whereas it is proportional to the square root of the voltage for larger values of Δz [14] and particularly at relatively large voltages [32].

One aspect of the thermally activated hopping model, however, deserves a more in-depth analysis. This is the thickness dependence of hopping parameters, such as the activation energy and the resistivity. According to the standard PF transport model in Figure 7(a), the activation energy is a well-defined bulk parameter that refers to the energy difference between the Fermi level and the conduction mobility edge $E_C^{'}$, as shown in Eq. (3). On the other hand, chalcogenide glasses are characterized by a significant disorder at the nanoscale, and they consist of broad distributions of local composition and bond parameters, such as the length and angle. For instance, *ab-initio* simulations of the atomistic structure of amorphous GST have shown that the characteristic rings of atoms can include between 4 and 15 atoms, with an extremely broad distribution [39]. Similarly, the coordination number, i.e., the number of atoms surrounding each Ge, Sb, or Te atom in amorphous GST, was shown to be broadly distributed. This atomistic disorder is expected to result in significant dispersion of the local microscopic parameters for the electronic band structure, including $E_C^{'}$ and $E_V^{'}$, thus resulting in a dispersion of local energy barrier for PF conduction. This is schematically shown in Figure 7(b), which depicts the energy band diagram for a disorder material such as amorphous GST [33]. The resulting transport mechanism was described as a distributed PF model, consisting of a thermally activated hopping transport mechanism with significant percolation effects. In fact, because the carrier transport time depends exponentially on the energy barrier, a significant statistical spread of local conductivity arises in the amorphous material. As a result, the current will follow preferential percolation paths localized at barriers of minimum energies, thus minimizing the transport time or, equivalently, the resistance.

To clarify the percolation effect and its impact on the thickness dependence of conduction in PCM devices, Figure 9 shows calculation results from a numerical Monte Carlo model for two-dimensional (2D) distributed PF [33].

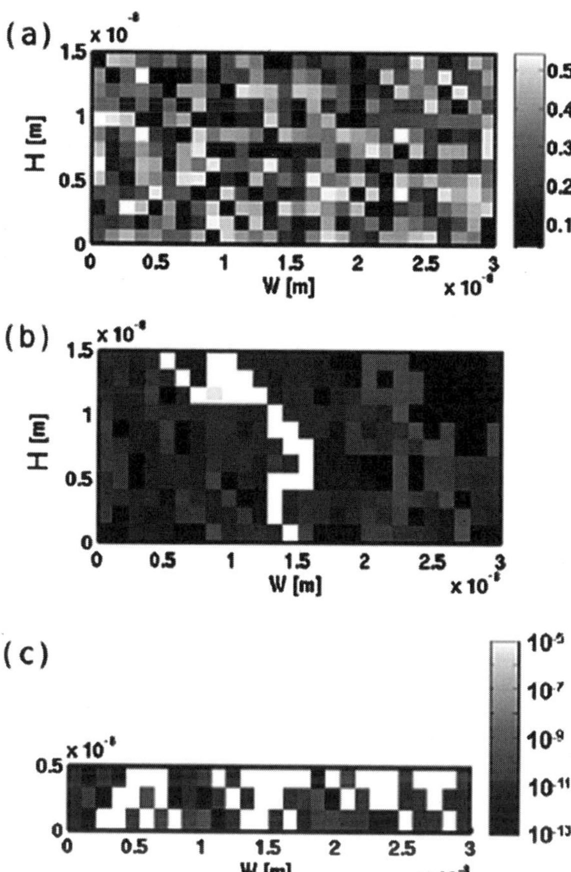

Figure 9. Calculated map of energy barriers (a) and corresponding distribution of current density for a (b) relatively thick and (c) thin amorphous region. Distributed PF calculations were carried out in 2D. Reprinted with permission from [33], D. Fugazza et al., "IEDM Tech. Dig.," p. 723, 2009. © 2009, IEEE.

Following the schematic in Figure 7(b), a random distribution of energy barriers was generated by a Monte Carlo approach within a 2D sample with a thickness of 15 nm and a width of 30 nm (Fig. 9(a)). The simulated volume was discretized by a mesh of square elements, each with a size of 1 nm, and the corresponding energy barriers E_i were randomly extracted according to a uniform distribution between 0 and 0.5 eV. The local resistance R_i of each mesh element was calculated according to [14, 36]:

$$R_i = R_0 e^{(E_i/kT)} \tag{5}$$

where R_0 is a constant. The resulting random resistance network was then solved calculating the voltage and current at each node with the external boundary condition $V = 0$ and $V = V_A$ at the bottom and top electrodes, respectively. Figure 9(b) shows the calculated 2D map of current corresponding to the E_i map in Figure 9(a). The current is highly localized along a percolation path with minimum resistance, which locates at the minimum energy barriers due to the exponential relationship in Eq. (5). The overall resistance of the percolation path is dictated by the highest (or critical) energy barrier in the chain, with all other series resistances being nearly negligible due the exponential relationship between R_i and E_i. For a relatively thin sample, calculations in Figure 9(c) indicate a higher number of percolation paths. This is because the probability to find a conduction path with a relatively low critical barrier is larger in thin samples because of the lower number of mesh elements between the top and bottom electrodes. Therefore, the average activation energy and the number of conduction paths increases for decreasing thickness as a result of the barrier distribution.

The thickness dependence of distributed PF in Figure 9 has a strong impact on the thickness scaling law of PCM resistance. Figure 10(a) shows measured and calculated activation energy E_A for conduction as a function of device resistance [33]. The cell resistance was controlled by changing the amplitude of the voltage pulse applied to the cell for reset. As a result, a different volume of GST was subjected to melting and quenching into the amorphous phase, thus resulting in a variable thickness of the amorphous region. In particular, the amorphous region increased with the applied voltage in the reset pulse. Instead of a constant E_A, which is expected in the PF model (see the dashed line in the figure), the activation energy increases with R, hence with the amorphous region thickness. This can be explained by the simulation results in Figure 9. For increasing amorphous thickness, the probability to find a low-energy percolation path through the disordered barrier distribution decreases, thus the observed E_A increases. Note that E_A tends to zero for low resistance since the active region of the device contains a fully crystalline GST for low resistance values below 10^4 Ω. The figure also shows calculations according to a distributed PF numerical model in good agreement with the experimental E_A. Figure 10(b) shows the measured and calculated R as a function of the amorphous region thickness [33]. The amorphous region thickness was estimated from the measured subthreshold slope (STS) and its theoretical dependence on amorphous region thickness u_a, which can be analytically predicted by Eq. (3) as:

$$\mathrm{STS} = \frac{d \log J}{dV} = \frac{q\Delta z}{2kTu_a} \tag{6}$$

In contrast to the linear increase expected from PF transport with a fixed energy barrier, the resistance increases more than linearly with thickness. The almost exponential increase of R with u_a can be explained based on the increasing E_A in Figure 10(a) and the exponential relationship between R and E_A in Eq. (5). This anomalous scaling of resistance with thickness is in agreement with previously observed thickness-dependence sheet resistance in amorphous semiconductors [40]. More recently, the distributed PF model was shown to account for non-Arrhenius behaviors of resistance as a function of temperature and resistance instability effects, such as noise and drift, in PCM devices [28]. The distributed PF model can be used to predict the dependence of the resistance window in PCM devices as a function of the generation node and the aspect ratio of the amorphous active region [28].

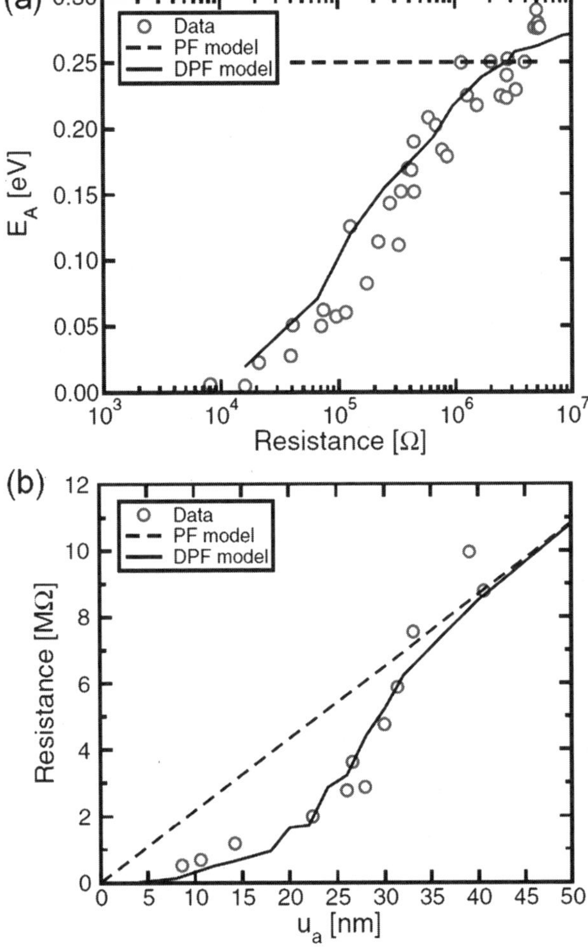

Figure 10. Measured and calculated activation energies for conduction as a function of resistance (top) and measured and calculated resistance as a function of estimated thickness of the amorphous region in PCM devices (bottom). Reprinted with permission from [33], D. Fugazza et al., "IEDM Tech. Dig.," p. 723, 2009. © 2009, IEEE.

2.4. Threshold-Switching Model

Despite the important effects of localized percolation and the thickness-dependent activation energy, Eq. (3) can still provide a satisfactory model for conduction at a given thickness of the amorphous chalcogenide [14, 37]. This conduction scheme allows to develop a model for threshold switching based on the picture of carrier energy increase first introduced by Jonscher (Fig. 11) [18, 41]. Under equilibrium conditions, electrons occupy trap positions below the equilibrium Fermi level E_{F0} (W_f in the figure). The application of a sufficiently high voltage results in a carrier energy increase, thus establishing a nonequilibrium energy distribution of carriers (Fig. 11(b)) [41]. Thus, as a result of the high electric field, the energy distribution of trapped carriers is shifted to higher energies, and the equilibrium Fermi level is replaced by a quasi-Fermi energy E_F, defined as the energy level for which the state-filling probability under nonequilibrium conditions is equal to 50%.

To estimate the carrier energy increase as a function of electric field and material parameters, the following one-dimensional (1D) physical model was proposed [18]. As the carriers move through a differential volume of thickness dz

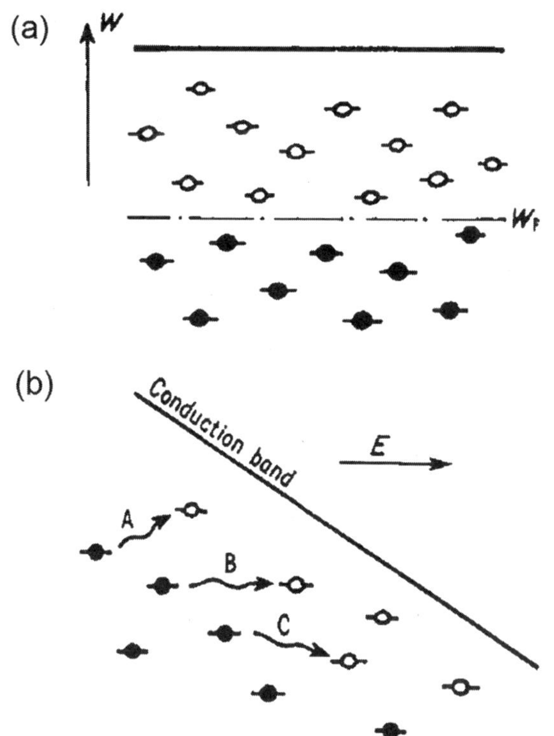

Figure 11. Schematic for the electron energy distribution under (a) equilibrium and (b) high-field conditions. Reprinted with permission from [41], A. K. Jonscher, *J. Phys. C* 4, 1331 (1971). © 1971, IOP.

in an amorphous material, their average energy is dictated by the balance equation:

$$\frac{J(z)\Delta E_F(z)}{q} - \frac{J(z+dz)\Delta E_F(z+dz)}{q} + J(z)F(z)dz - \frac{\Delta E_F}{\tau_{\text{rel}}} n_T(z)dz = 0 \tag{7}$$

where the first and second terms on the left-hand side are the product of J and the average excess energy $\Delta E_F = E_F - E_{F0}$ divided by the unit charge q, and they account for the energy flow into the differential volume in units [J cm^{-2} s^{-1}]. On the other hand, the third and fourth terms on the left-hand side represent energy gain and loss in the differential volume of thickness dz. The energy gain is written as the product between the current density and the absolute value of the electric field F, while the energy relaxation is described by a relaxation term that is proportional to ΔE_F divided by a relaxation time constant τ_{rel} [18]. The latter can be associated to a electron-phonon interaction at localized states [13]. Since current continuity dictates $J(z+dz) = J(z)$, Eq. (7) can be simplified, yielding:

$$\frac{d\Delta E_F}{dz} = qF - \frac{qn_T}{J\tau_{\text{rel}}}\Delta E_F \tag{8}$$

where the energy increase along the transport axis is given by the balance between energy gain and loss, respectively.

Equation (8) can be solved together with Eq. (3), where E_F represents the nonequilibrium Fermi level, for any current bias point, to reproduce the entire I–V curve. Figure 12

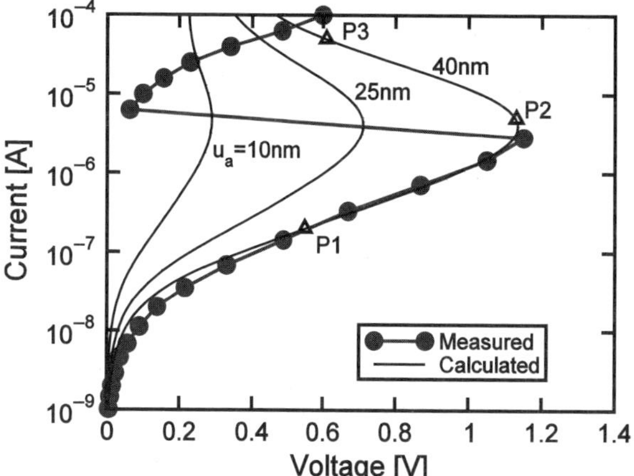

Figure 12. Measured and calculated I–V curves, including the subthreshold regime and threshold switching. Calculations are reported for three different thicknesses, u_a = 10, 25 and 40 nm. Three simulated points, P1, P2 and P3, are shown. Reprinted with permission from [18], D. Ielmini, *Phys. Rev. B* 78, 035308 (2008). © 2008, APS.

shows the measured and calculated I–V curves for a PCM device with GST active material. The main parameters used in the calculations are the activation energy $E_C' - E_{F0} = 0.3$ eV, a trap distance $\Delta z = 7$ nm, and a concentration $N_T = 3 \times 10^{19}$ cm^{-3} of localized states. An energy relaxation time $\tau_{\text{rel}} = 10^{-13}$ s was assumed, consistently with the rate of energy loss in amorphous semiconductors due to electron-phonon interaction [42]. In the figure, different values of the amorphous region thickness u_a were assumed, with the best agreement obtained for $u_a = 40$ nm. Note that the simulation predicts a continuous NDR region above the threshold current I_T, in contrast with the usually observed abrupt snap back, which is experimentally observed. The reason for this disagreement is that the NDR region is unstable; thus, biasing at a point along the NDR necessarily results in oscillations [43, 44]. The large currents and voltages experienced during oscillations just above the onset of the NDR result in fast crystallization and, consequently, in a resistance drop to the low value that is characteristic of the crystalline chalcogenide phase. Therefore, the measured I–V characteristic above switching is largely affected by spurious crystallization and should not be taken as a real evidence of the electrical behavior of the amorphous chalcogenide. The agreement between simulations and data should be thus referred to the subthreshold region and threshold point, i.e., the threshold voltage and current.

To gain more insight about the threshold switching mechanisms according to the model of Eq. (8), Figure 13 shows the calculated E_C', E_F (a) and ΔE_F (b) as a function of the conduction axis z for an amorphous region thickness of $u_a = 40$ nm. The profiles are shown for the three bias points: P1, P2, and P3 (Fig. 12). They describe band diagrams in the subthreshold regime (P1), at the switching point (P2), and above the switching point in the NDR region (P3). In the subthreshold region (P1), E_C' and E_{F0} linearly decrease along z, suggesting a uniform electric field, and the energy increase ΔE_F is negligible. At switching (P2), E_F is significantly higher than E_{F0}, and according to Figure 13(b), ΔE_F increases linearly for very small z close to the cathode,

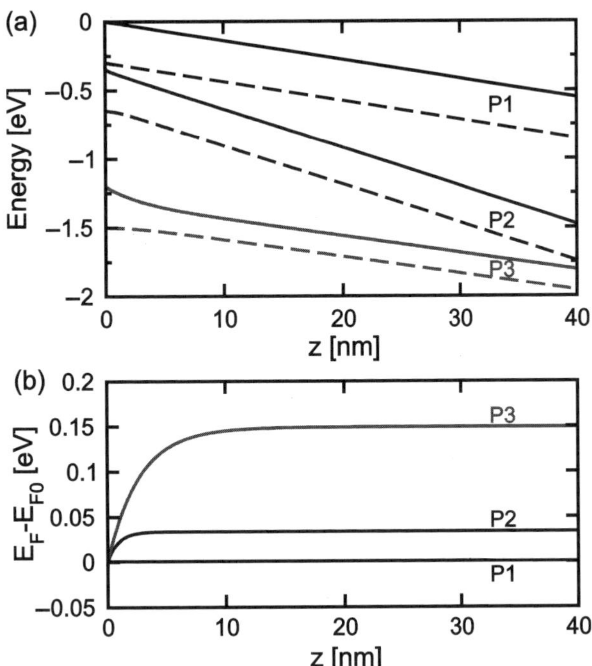

Figure 13. (a) Calculated E_C', E_F and (b) ΔE_F according to the model in Eq. (8). Reprinted with permission from [18], D. Ielmini, *Phys. Rev. B* 78, 035308 (2008). © 2008, APS.

then saturates to $\Delta E_F \approx 30$ meV at sufficiently large Δz. This is due to Eq. (8), where the energy gain dominates for small z close to the electron-injecting electrode (the cathode), yielding a linear increase $\Delta E_F = qFz$. On the other hand, for a sufficiently large z, the energy relaxation starts opposing to further the energy increase, setting a saturated energy level given by:

$$\Delta E_F = \frac{JF\tau_{\text{rel}}}{n_T} \tag{9}$$

From this equation, the excess energy ΔE_F is proportional to the power density $P''' = JF$ in Eq. (9). Thus, ΔE_F can be viewed as the fraction of dissipated Joule power possessed by electrons and not yet converted to lattice heating [18].

In the NDR region (P3), E_C' is markedly nonlinear, thus evidencing a strong localization of the electric field close to the cathode interface. On the other hand, the field collapses to a low value at a sufficient distance from the cathode. This is due to the calculated ΔE_F in Figure 13(b), which increases to a large value (about $\Delta E_F \approx 0.15$ eV) in the saturation region. Due to the exponential relationship between current density and Fermi level in Eq. (3), the large increase of average carrier energy must correspond to a large increase of current density, or, since the current is fixed by continuity, to a drop of the electric field, as shown in the figure. Therefore, it is the field collapse due to the carrier energy increase that is responsible for the NDR and, consequently, leads to threshold switching. Note that the critical energy increase for the onset of the NDR region, thus dictating the condition for threshold switching, is approximately $\Delta E_F = kT$ in Figure 13(b). This is because $J \propto \exp(E_F/kT)$ in Eq. (3), thus an increase of E_F by kT will yield a significant variation of conductivity and trigger the field redistribution and collapse at the basis of the NDR regime.

Figure 14(a) shows calculated I–V curves for increasing temperature. The subthreshold current strongly increases with T due to the thermal activation of the hopping current in Eq. (3), which is in agreement with the experimental results in Figure 8. However, the threshold current I_T only slightly increases. In fact, the threshold voltage V_T and I_T are ruled by Eq. (9) and by the condition $\Delta E_F \approx kT$, i.e., the excess energy at saturation should be at least equal to the thermal energy to trigger the NDR region. This results in a threshold power condition that reads $P = FJ\Omega = n_T kT\Omega/\tau_{\text{rel}} = P_T$, where Omega is the amorphous active volume and P_T is the critical (threshold) power for threshold switching [18]. Curves at constant power $P = P_T(T)$ are shown in Figure 14(a) for different temperatures, showing that the switching points in the simulations indeed obey a constant power condition. Similar T dependences of threshold switching points are reported in the literature [45, 46].

Figure 14(b) shows calculated I–V curves for an increasing mobility gap of the amorphous material. The Fermi level was assumed to be located in the middle of the mobility gap. As a result, an increasing mobility gap dictates an increasing activation energy for thermally activated hopping $E_C' - E_{F0}$, thus resulting in an exponentially decreasing subthreshold current. Similar to the T-dependence in Figure 13(a), the threshold current decreases while the threshold voltage V_T increases for the increasing mobility gap. Because of the increasing mobility gap, the constant-P curve intersects the I–V curve at a larger voltage and lower current. A similar dependence of V_T on the mobility gap was experimentally observed for stable $(GeTe)_x(Sb_2Te_3)_y$ compounds along the pseudobinary line [47].

The model of threshold switching based on the PF conduction allows us to interpret the switching effect as a purely electronic mechanism. However, a possible role of the thermal heating, which is due to the inevitable Joule dissipation in the subthreshold regime, cannot be ruled out. In fact, a local temperature increase would result in both an increase of phonon concentration and in an increase of the density of carriers available for hopping conduction through the thermal activation in Eq. (3). Therefore, due to the presence of

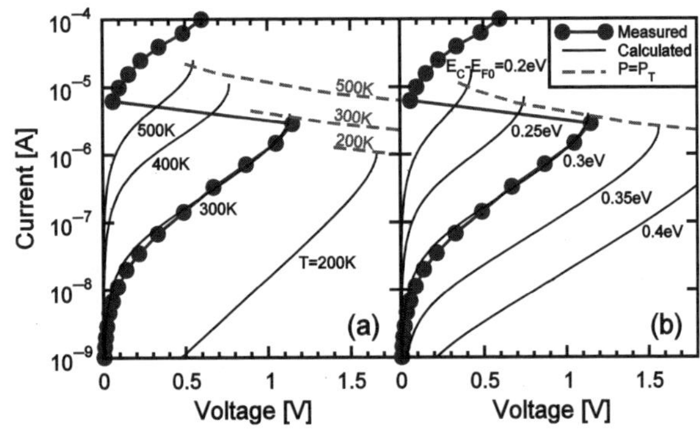

Figure 14. Calculated I–V curves for variable T (a) and E_C'–E_F (b). An I–V curve for a PCM device at room temperature is shown for reference. Reprinted with permission from [18], D. Ielmini, *Phys. Rev. B* 78, 035308 (2008). © 2008, APS.

T in the exponential term in Eq. (3), the local conductivity would also increase along the conduction path, thus possibly contributing to the NDR effect at the basis of threshold switching [48, 49]. Other threshold-switching models have been developed that assume the key role of electronic mechanisms, such as impact ionization and recombination. at deep states [16, 50] and instability of polarons [51]. Finally, threshold switching has also been attributed to the onset of crystallization at high fields [52]. Among all of these interpretations, the PF model described in this section possibly provides the broader generality, since it is solely based on trap-limited conduction and high electric fields, with no specific assumptions on the crystalline/amorphous phase of the material, its composition, or the nature of the localized states that contribute to the conduction and recombination. In fact, it is important to recall that threshold switching is a fairly generalized phenomenon, which is observed not only in chalcogenide glasses [53], but also in amorphous boron [54, 55], amorphous silicon [54, 56], transition metal oxides [57, 58], and amorphous pnictides such as GeSb [59]. Such a large spectrum of materials evidencing the threshold-switching phenomena suggests that a general physical mechanism is involved in all these cases.

3. MODELING SET/RESET TRANSITIONS

Two types of programming operations can be applied to a PCM device, namely set and reset operations. Set is the transition from the amorphous to the crystalline phase, while reset is the reverse transition, usually involving the heating of the crystalline (or, in some cases, amorphous) chalcogenide material above the melting point, followed by the swift cooling to a solidified amorphous phase by switching off the voltage pulse. Set and reset operations are critical for defining the performance, application, and even the density and the architecture of a PCM device. For instance, a very short programming time is usually desired for both set and reset processes to maximize the programming throughput of the memory array. At the same time, the programming energy should be minimum to allow portable applications with low battery consumption. Finally, the programming current should be as low as possible for maximum programming parallelism that again enhances the throughput. Also, the programming current dictates the area of the select device that is needed to access the selected device, e.g., a rectifying diode [60], an ovonic threshold switch (OTS) [61] or a mixed ionic-electronic conductor (MIEC) [62] for crossbar PCM arrays. A low programming current allows for a minimum selector area and for a low current density that needs to be supplied in the select device. For instance, a 100-μA reset current at the $F = 25$ nm node would require a current density of $10^{-4}/(25 \times 10^{-7})^2 = 16$ MA cm^{-2}, which cannot be fulfilled by polysilicon diodes [60] or back-end-of-line (BEOL) oxide-based diodes [63]. Therefore, a minimum reset current allows for a wider availability of select diodes for the integration of crossbar arrays. To optimize the PCM algorithm, materials, and geometry for the best programming performance, physical modeling of set and reset is therefore essential.

3.1. Set Characteristics and Modeling

The set process is the electrically induced transition from the amorphous to the crystalline phase through crystallization. Crystallization generally occurs in a PCM cell through significant Joule heating, which is necessary to increase the local temperature to enhance the probability for nucleation and growth. To this purpose, set must be carried out above the threshold voltage to access the ON-state conduction regime that features a large current flow at relatively low voltages. From this viewpoint, it is important to predict the threshold voltage that plays the role of the voltage boundary between the read and programming operations in the PCM device, e.g., based on the threshold-switching model described in Section 2.4. The read operation must be mandatorily carried out in the subthreshold regime to minimize the thermal disturb and the probability of switching, which may lead to a strong deterioration of the amorphous region.

To study the set characteristics, two different procedures can be followed (Fig. 15) [64]. On the one hand, one can characterize the response of the PCM device to a reset pulse above the melting point with a variable quenching time t_Q along the switching off of the current (Fig. 15(a)). The second procedure consists of applying a rectangular set pulse below the melting point with a variable pulse-width t_{SET} (Fig. 15(b)).

Figure 16(a) shows the measured quench characteristics, i.e., the resistance measured after a variable quench pulse as a function of t_Q [11]. Two cells were characterized, namely an intrinsic (normal) cell and a tail cell, which is a cell that displays a relatively fast crystallization behavior. Also, two different reset currents (800 and 1200 μA) were used in the reset pulse that correspond to two different sizes of the amorphous region. The measured resistance is relatively large at short t_Q, which can be explained by the amorphous volume obtained from the reset process. Above approximately 200 ns for the intrinsic cell (30 ns for the tail cell), R starts decreasing, then it saturates around 500–1000 ns to about 5 kΩ, which is the characteristic value of a fully crystalline PCM device [11]. The R decrease is due to the increasing crystallization for a relatively long quenching time, thus providing sufficient time for the solidification into the ordered crystalline phase from the molten phase. A characteristic quenching time t_Q^* can be defined for each

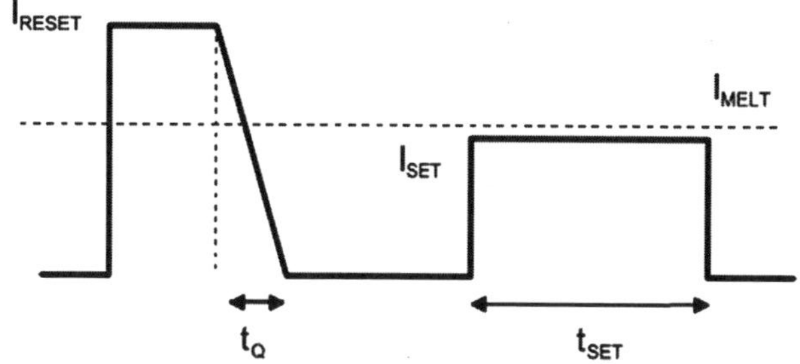

Figure 15. Schematic for the two current pulses to study the set characteristics, namely a reset pulse with variable quench time t_Q and a set pulse with variable pulse width t_{SET}. Reprinted with permission from [64], Mantegazza et al., *Solid-State Electron.* 52, 584 (2008). © 2008, Elsevier.

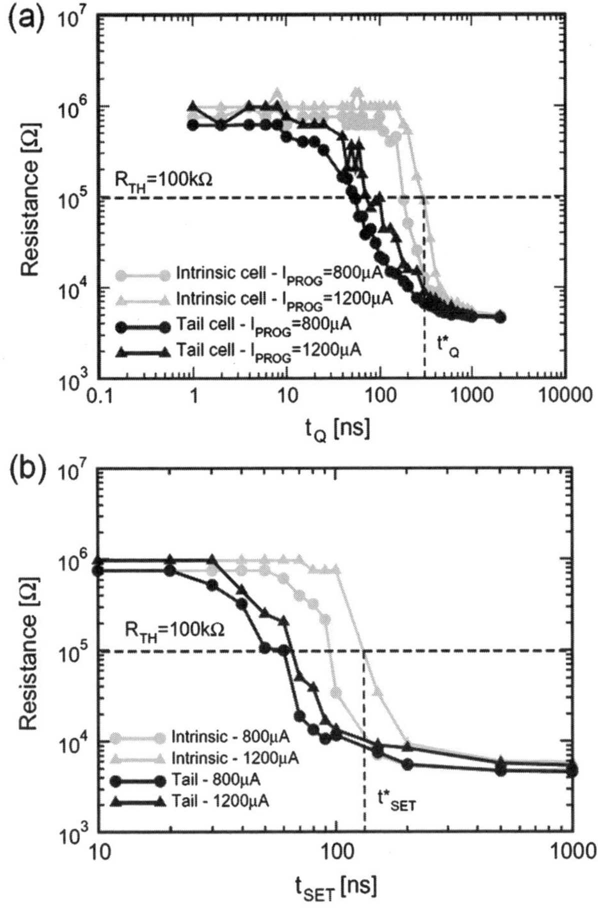

Figure 16. Measured quenching characteristics (top) and set characteristics (bottom) for an intrinsic (normal) cell and tail cell. Reprinted with permission from [64], Mantegazza et al., *Solid-State Electron.* 52 584 (2008). © 2008, Elsevier.

cell as the time needed for R to fall below a threshold resistance value $R_{TH} = 100$ kΩ. Note that the different cells are characterized by different t_Q^*, which is around 200 ns for the intrinsic cell and 50 ns for the tail cell. Also note that t_Q^* slightly increases for increasing I_{PROG} due to the larger amorphous region that needs to be crystallized.

Figure 16(b) shows measured set characteristics, i.e., the resistance measured after a sequence of a reset pulse, to prepare the PCM device in an initial amorphous phase, and a set pulse to crystallize the cell, at least partially, as a function of t_{SET} [11]. Again, the figure compares an intrinsic cell and a tail cell with relatively fast crystallization behavior and two different reset currents (800 and 1200 μA) that correspond to two different sizes of the amorphous region before the applied set pulse. The evolution of the measured resistance for increasing t_{SET} is similar to the quench characteristic in Figure 16(a), namely R first remains constant and equal to the amorphous phase, then it decreases above approximately 150 ns for the intrinsic cell (50 ns for the tail cell), then finally saturating at a set-state resistance of about 5 kΩ [11]. This behavior can be explained by the increasing crystallization effect due to the nucleation and/or growth of the crystalline grains within the amorphous region. A characteristic set time t_{SET}^* can be defined for each cell as the time needed for R to fall below a threshold resistance value $R_{TH} = 100$ kΩ. The tail cell displays a smaller t_{SET}^* than the intrinsic cell, which was already was the case for t_Q^*. Also note that t_{SET}^* slightly increases for increasing I_{PROG} because of the larger amorphous region that needs to be crystallized.

Quench and set characteristics in Figure 16 suggest a correlation between t_Q^* and t_{SET}^*. Tail cells displaying a small t_Q^* also show a small t_{SET}^*, and vice versa. The correlation was studied for a wider statistics of cells within a 2-kb sub-array of PCM devices [11]. Figure 17 shows the scatter plot of measured t_Q^* and t_{SET}^* and the corresponding average t_{SET}^* as a function of t_Q^*. Despite a substantial statistical spread of data, the scatter plot confirms a significant correlation between the crystallization parameters, roughly following a linear law $t_{SET}^* = 0.35t_Q^*$. Note the significant spread of t_Q^* and t_{SET}^*; both cover a factor of about 4 (t_Q^* approximately between 100 and 400 ns; t_{SET}^* approximately between 35 and 140 ns). Further analysis has shown that the statistical distributions of t_Q^* and t_{SET}^* are both lognormal, and there is no dependence of the crystallization times on the electrode size in the PCM cell [11].

The statistical analysis of set transition in Figures 16 and 17 provides the basis for an empirical model of the set and quench transitions, thus allowing us to predict the distributions of resistance after the set and reset pulses in large arrays [11]. In the set model, we assumed an analytical R-t_{SET} characteristic given by:

$$\log\left(\frac{R}{R_m}\right) = -\frac{1}{2}\tan h\left(\frac{\log(t_{SET}) - \log(\gamma t_{SET}^*)}{\beta}\right) \times \log\left(\frac{R_{RESET}}{R_{SET}}\right) \tag{10}$$

where R_{RESET} is the resistance in the reset state, R_{SET} is the resistance in the set state, R_m is the geometrical average between these values, namely $R_m = (R_{RESET}\ R_{SET})^{1/2}$, and β and γ are constants ($\beta = 0.2$, $\gamma = 1.13$). A similar equation can be written to describe the quench characteristics in Figure 16(a). The hyperbolic tangent function in Eq. (10) describes the characteristic behavior of R as a function of

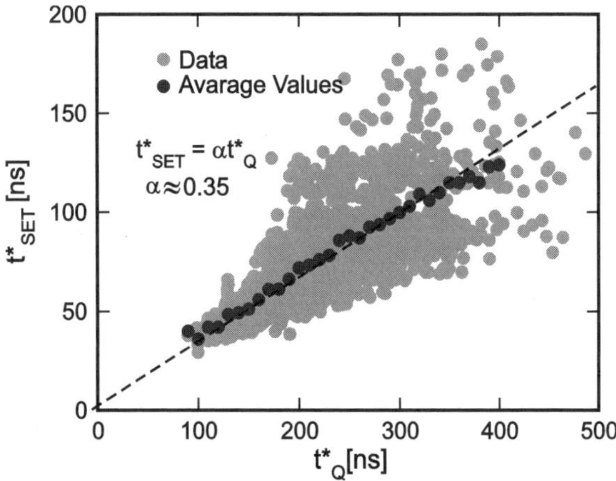

Figure 17. Measured t_{SET}^* as a function of t_Q^* for an array of 2-kb PCM cells, indicating a clear correlation between the two crystallization parameters. Reprinted with permission from [11], D. Mantegazza et al., "IEDM Tech. Dig.," p. 311, 2007. © 2007, IEEE.

time in Figure 16, namely a constant value at short time followed by a typically sudden transition to low resistance in correspondence of the set time t^*_{SET} and by a final saturation at the set resistance. The value of β controls the slope in the transition region. To capture the statistical nature of the characteristic set time t^*_{SET}, we specified its statistical spread according to a log-normal distribution given by:

$$F = \frac{1}{2}\left(1 + erf\left(\frac{\log(t^*_{\mathrm{SET}}) - \log(t^*_{\mathrm{SET0}})}{\sigma\sqrt{2}}\right)\right) \quad (11)$$

where F is the cumulative probability (or percentile), σ is the standard deviation of $\log(t^*_{\mathrm{SET}})$, and t^*_{SET0} is the characteristic quenching time for an average cell in the array, which corresponds to the 50% percentile.

Figure 18 shows the cumulative distributions of measured and calculated R after the reset, with increasing t_Q (a), and after the set with increasing t_{SET} (b). The calculations obtained by the empirical formulas in Eqs. (10) and (11) can describe the time evolution of the resistance distribution. In particular, the model can account for the distribution tail for increasing t_Q and t_{SET}. Note that theanomalous tails were not assumed for crystallization kinetics, where both t_Q and t_{SET} obey lognormal distributions. Therefore, the tails in Figure 18 are due to the highly nonlinear R–t dependence in Eq. (10), where R can change by a large amount in correspondence of the transition time t^*_{SET} and t^*_Q. The spread of crystallization times within the array and the strong R–t dependence due to the large window between the crystalline and amorphous resistivity thus result in the observed tails in R distributions for increasing times. To improve the set/reset distributions, the spread of the crystallization times due to the chemical and structural disorders at the nanoscale should be reduced [11].

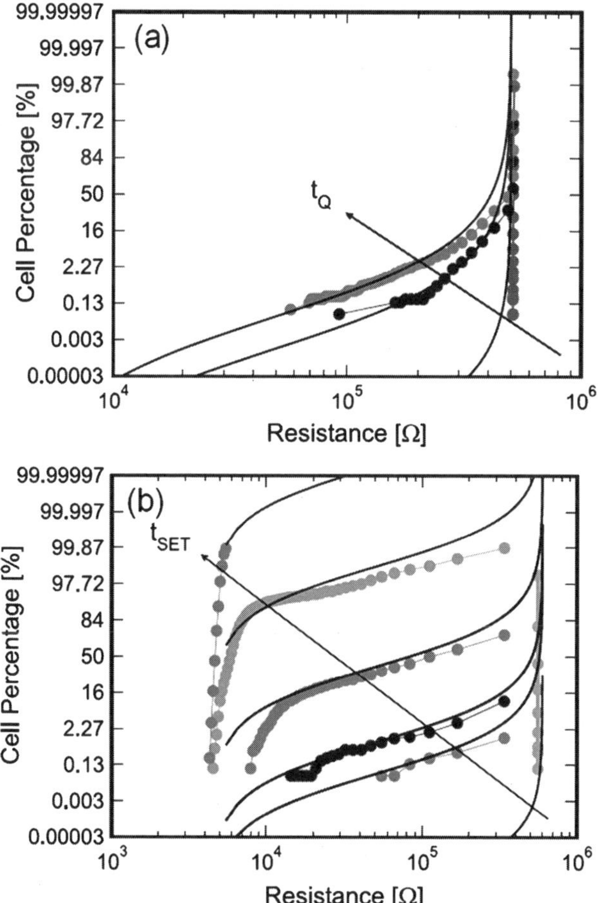

Figure 18. Distributions of measured and calculated resistances after reset pulses with (a) variable t_Q and after set pulses with (b) increasing t_{SET}. Calculations were made by Eqs. (10) and (11) at increasing times. Reprinted with permission from [11], D. Mantegazza et al., "IEDM Tech. Dig.," p. 311, 2007. © 2007, IEEE.

3.2. Reset Characteristics and Modeling

The reset process consists of the melting and fast quenching of a programmed volume within the active chalcogenide layer. Melting occurs as the local temperature and exceeds the melting point of about 888 K in GST, while quenching in the amorphous state is obtained by a rapid switch-off of the voltage pulse that results in a fast decrease in temperature according to the thermal delay time constant $t_{\mathrm{th}} = R_{\mathrm{th}}C_{\mathrm{th}}$. This is usually around a few ns in PCM cells. To provide the Joule heating necessary to reach the melting point, voltages around 1 V and currents in the 50–1000 μA range are usually needed. Figure 19 shows the (a) measured R–I characteristics and the (b) I–V characteristics for PCM devices with increasing size of the bottom contact [66]. The cells were fabricated according to a pore structure, where the active chalcogenide material was confined within a hole through an insulating material that touches the bottom electrode. The pore size dictates the cross-section area and the volume of the active material that must be amorphized to reach the high resistance state of the device. As a result, different conduction and reset characteristics are obtained depending on the pore size, which the results in the figure indicate.

The R–I characteristic displays a typical U shape and describes the relationship between the current in the applied pulse (usually 100 ns–1 μs long) and the resistance measured soon after the pulse application [3]. Starting from an initial amorphous phase with high resistance, the resistance first decreases for the increasing current because of threshold switching, Joule heating, and the consequent crystallization that leads to an increasing crystalline fraction within the amorphous volume. The crystalline phase may grow from the amorphous-crystalline phase boundary at the top of the amorphous dome, or it may nucleate within the amorphous volume or at the interface with the bottom electrode or the surrounding material, or it may do both. After reaching a relatively low resistance, which corresponds to an almost totally crystalline phase within the programmed volume, the resistance starts to increase for increasing I. This indicates the onset of melting combined with a complete crystallization of the pre-existing amorphous phase in the active layer [3]. The minimum R point can be identified as the initiation of melting in a limited chalcogenide region, while the corresponding current can be referred to as the melting current I_m. For $I > I_m$, the increase of R with I is due to the increasing Joule heating in the device, which results in a larger molten and amorphized volume of chalcogenide material, hence a larger resistance [3]. The reset current I_{reset} can be defined as the value of the current for which

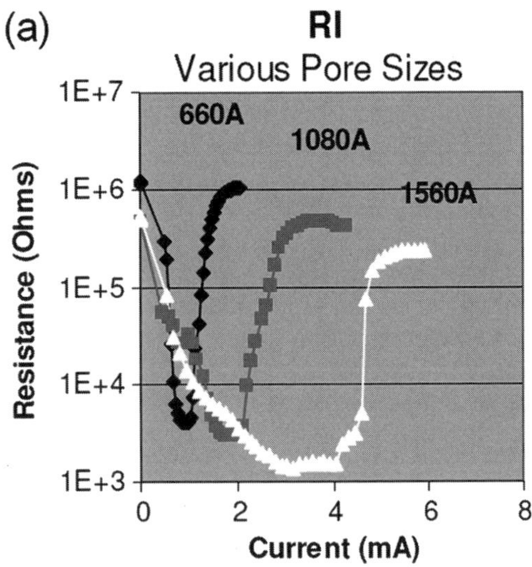

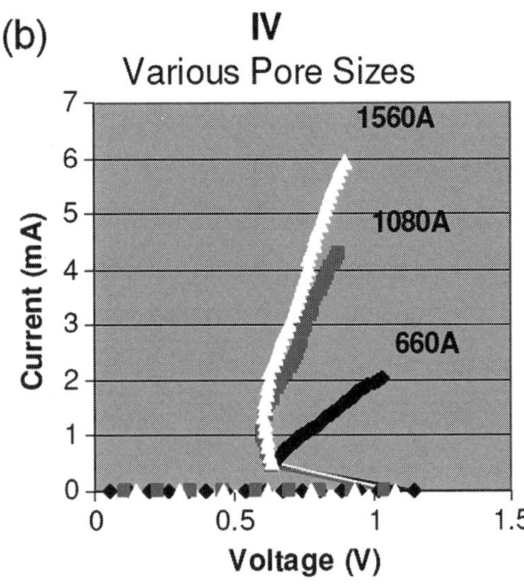

Figure 19. Measured R–I characteristics (top) and I–V characteristics (bottom) of PCM devices with variable pore sizes. Reprinted with permission from [66], W. Czubatyj et al., "European Phase Change and Ovonic Science Symposium," 2006.

the resistance saturates, and it is typically 20%–50% higher than the melting current. The I–V curves in Figure 19(b) show the characteristic threshold switching between 1 and 1.2 V and the ON-state characteristic at the higher currents. Although the threshold voltage V_T does not significantly change with the device size, it is worth noting that the ON-state resistance decreases for increasing pore diameter. This is because V_T is controlled by the thickness of the amorphous region, which depends on the amplitude of the programming voltage. Since all of these curves were obtained for PCM devices in a full reset state, no dependence of amorphous region thickness on pore diameter ϕ should be expected. On the other hand, the pore diameter controls the ON-resistance through:

$$R_{\mathrm{ON}} = \left.\frac{dV}{dI}\right|_{\mathrm{ON}} = \rho_c \frac{u_{\mathrm{chal}}}{A} + \rho_{\mathrm{BE}} \frac{u_{\mathrm{BE}}}{A} \tag{12}$$

where ρ_c and ρ_{BE} are the resistivities of the chalcogenide crystalline phase and of the bottom electrode material, respectively; u_{chal} and u_{BE} are the (effective) thicknesses of the chalcogenide layer and of the bottom electrode, respectivel; and A is the pore area. In Eq. (12), a third term that includes the top electrode should also be added, particularly in the case of a perfectly symmetric pore structure. However, pores are usually more confined at the bottom contact than at the top contact [12, 67, 68], thus the bottom electrode resistance is usually dominant. Eq. (12) also applies to the so-called mushroom structure, which features a thin-film chalcogenide deposited on a confined bottom electrode [69, 70]. From Eq. (12), the ON resistance is inversely proportional to the pore/bottom electrode area $A = \pi\phi^2/4$, which explains the increase of slope and, hence, the decrease of R_{ON}, of the I–V curves in Figure 19 for increasing the pore size.

From Figure 19, it is clear that a straightforward method to reduce the melting and reset currents is the reduction of the active chalcogenide area. To qualitatively understand this point, it is important to remember that, according to a generic Joule heating model for area scaling, the maximum temperature T_{max} within the chalcogenide volume is controlled by the voltage V through:

$$T_{\mathrm{max}} = T_0 + \frac{R_{\mathrm{th}}}{R} V^2 \tag{13}$$

where T_0 is the room temperature, R_{th} is an equivalent thermal resistance controlling heat loss from the heated volume toward the surrounding heat sinks (mainly the top and bottom electrodes), and R is the electrical resistance [8]. In the ON state, the concentration of free carriers is largely enhanced due to the threshold switching, which confines the applied voltage within a very thin ON layer and results in a huge injection of carriers from trapped states below E_{F0} to the high mobility energy levels in the delocalized conduction band [14, 18]. It may be assumed that both the electrical and thermal conductivities in the ON-state chalcogenide region are therefore controlled by free carriers and are similar to the metallic case. As a result, R_{th} and R are proportional and R_{th}/R does not significantly change with the device area. As a result, the maximum temperature increase $\Delta T = T_{\mathrm{max}} - T_0$ is roughly proportional to V^2, thus the melting point is dictated by a constant melting voltage V_m around 0.7 V (Fig. 19), while the melting current is given by the formula:

$$I_m = \frac{V_m - V_{\mathrm{hold}}}{R_{\mathrm{ON}}} \tag{14}$$

where $V_{\mathrm{hold}} \approx 0.5$ V is the so-called holding voltage, i.e., the extrapolated voltage at the zero current from the ON-state characteristics in Figure 19 [3]. Equation (14) indicates $I_m \propto R_{\mathrm{ON}}^{-1} \propto A$, thus the melting/reset current may be reduced by a proper size reduction of the contact electrode. This result should be viewed as a first-order approximation model describing a nonisotropic area scaling of the device, where the active area is reduced without changing the other geometrical dimensions, e.g., the thickness of the chalcogenide layer or of the bottom electrode [8].

3.3. Optimization and Scaling of the Reset Current

Given the strong relevance of reducing the reset current in PCM devices, the scaling properties of the reset current have been addressed by several papers in the literature that provide architecture/material guidelines for I_{reset} reduction [12], analytical studies of the reset current downscaling [71, 72], and detailed numerical simulations of the reset current optimization and scaling [8]. In the latter approach, the conditions for the reset current minimization at a given set-state resistance and minimal feature size were studied by comparison with different geometries of a representative mushroom cell [8]. This optimization approach is described in Figure 20, which schematically shows three different cell geometries, where the length L_h of the bottom electrode (or heater) was increased. The chalcogenide thickness L_c was decreased from (a to c) to maintain a given set-state R. The figure also shows the calculated thermal map computed by a numerical device simulation tool. The hot spot, which corresponds to the molten chalcogenide region during reset, changes position depending on the proportion between L_c and L_h, and it moves from inside the chalcogenide layer, for a relatively thick chalcogenide layer (a), to inside the bottom electrode, for a relatively long bottom electrode (c). The optimum reset condition is (b), where an optimum matching between L_c and L_h results in the hot spot occupying the region of contact between the chalcogenide layer and the bottom electrode. This allows it to dissipate the minimum electrical power, to melt, and to amorphize the chalcogenide region at the bottom electrode interface, thus providing an effective high resistance 'plug' that blocks the current path. Situations (a and c), where the hot spot is not at the bottom electrode interface, need some extra power to amorphize the interface region, and are thus nonoptimized geometries [8]. The optimized geometry should be interpreted by:

$$T_{max} = T_0 + RR_{th}I^2 \tag{15}$$

which is obtained from Eq. (13) by using an ohmic approximation for the I–V curve $V = RI$. A maximum ΔT for a given I requires the maximum product RR_{th}. Assuming a constant product between electrical conductivity and thermal resistivity in the heater and the chalcogenide materials, the optimum condition is obtained in correspondence of equal (i.e., matching) thermal resistances R_{th} in the bottom electrode and the chalcogenide layer [8].

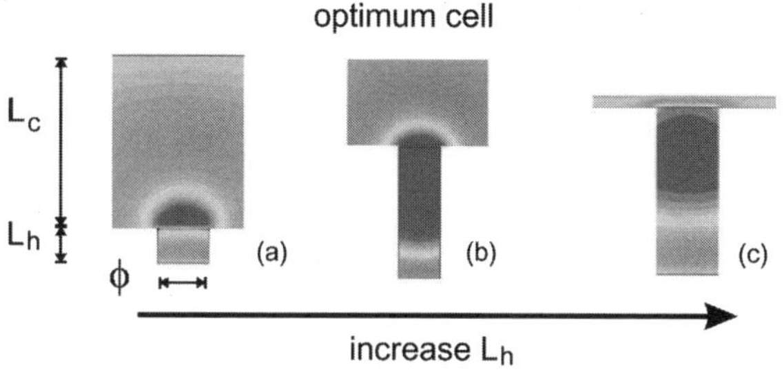

Figure 20. Calculated thermal maps for three geometries of a mushroom cell with fixed resistance R_{set}. For increasing the length of the bottom electrode L_h, the hot spot shifts from the (a) chalcogenide volume to the (c) bottom electrode. The best heating efficiency and minimum reset current occurs for the hot spot located at the interface (b) between the chalcogenide layer and the bottom electrode. Reprinted with permission from [8], U. Russo et al., *IEEE Trans. Electron Devices* 55, 506 (2008). © 2008, IEEE.

Figure 21 shows the calculated melting current I_m as a function of the heater length L_h for increasing set-state resistance R_{set}. Calculations were done within an electrothermal device simulation tool, thus solving the Poisson equation for electrical conduction and the Fourier equation for heat conduction. A cylindrical symmetry was assumed with a bottom electrode diameter of 30 nm. The melting current I_m was calculated as the minimum current value, which provides full amorphization of the chalcogenide-bottom electrode interface region. The calculated I_m as a function of L_h displays a U shape, where the minimum represents the optimum geometry with the least melting current. Given the proportionality between I_{reset} and I_m, also note that the reset current is minimized in correspondence of the optimum point. For increasing R_{set}, the curves shift to a lower I_m given the relationship $I_m \propto R_{set}$ already pointed out in Figure 19. The shift to a higher L_h is due to the increase of the overall stack thickness for increasing R_{set} [8]. These results suggest that an accurate design of the PCM cell with a good matching between the chalcogenide layer thickness and the bottom electrode is needed just to provide a minimum reset current.

Figure 22 shows the calculated (a) melting current and (b) melting voltage for the variable feature size F. An optimized cell geometry was used according to the analysis shown in Figure 21. Two different scaling laws, isotropic and nonisotropic scaling, are considered in Figure 23. In isotropic scaling, all of the cell dimensions are reduced by the same factor for decreasing F. On the other hand, the nonisotropic scaling assumes that only the diameter f of the bottom electrode is reduced, while the heater length and the chalcogenide thickness are constantly maintained. For decreasing F, the melting current decreases, although

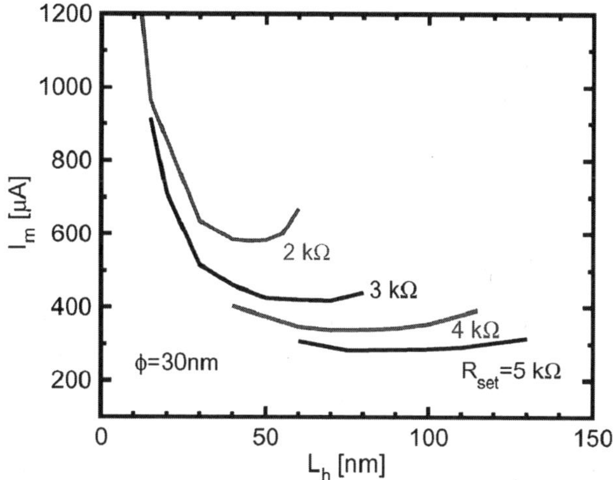

Figure 21. Calculated melting current as a function of L_h, for increasing R_{set} and a fixed feature size ϕ. The minimum I_m indicates the optimized geometry for the best heating efficiency in the PCM device. Reprinted with permission from [8], U. Russo et al., *IEEE Trans. Electron Devices* 55, 506 (2008). © 2008, IEEE.

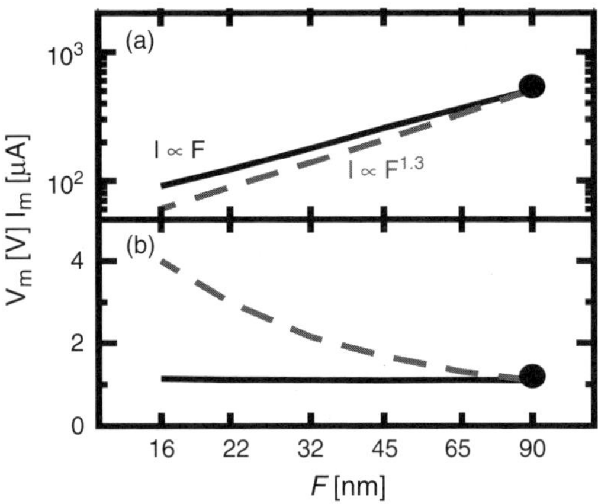

Figure 22. Calculated (a) I_m and (b) V_m as a function of F for isotropic and non-isotropic scaling in a mushroom-type device. The exponents dictating the scaling dependence of I_m are shown. Reprinted with permission from [8], U. Russo et al., *IEEE Trans. Electron Devices* 55, 506 (2008). © 2008, IEEE.

different behaviors are found for isotropic and nonisotropic scaling. To explain the different behaviors in the figure, we extract I_m from Eq. (15), obtaining:

$$I_m = \sqrt{\frac{T_m - T_0}{RR_{\text{th}}}} \tag{16}$$

Since both R and R_{th} are approximately proportional to L/A, where L is the overall thickness of the stack and A is the cross-section of the bottom electrode, the melting current is thus proportional to A/L [73]. In the case of isotropic scaling, A scales as F^2 while L scales as F; thus, $I_m \propto F$ as can be seen in the calculations of Figure 22. On the other hand, only A is decreasing in nonisotropic scaling, therefore Eq. (16) would yield $I_m \propto A \propto F^2$. However, a more detailed analysis by numerical simulations indicates a lower exponent, closer to 1.3, which can be found in the figure for nonisotropic scaling. The different exponent is due to the heat-loss contribution of the region of insulating materials surrounding the cell active area. The size dependence of the melting voltage can be explained, noting that $V_m = RI_m$ and recalling that $R \propto L/A$ from Eq. (12). Therefore,

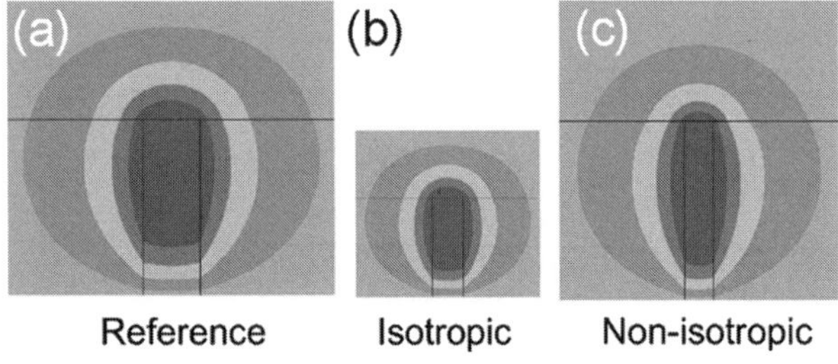

Figure 23. Schematic illustration of the isotropic and non-isotropic scaling of a mushroom PCM device. From an optimized reference device geometry (a), isotropic scaling is obtained by a reduction of all dimensions according to the same factor (b), while reduction of in-plane dimensions only (not the thickness) results in non-isotropic scaling (c). Reprinted with permission from [8], U. Russo et al., *IEEE Trans. Electron Devices* 55, 506 (2008). © 2008, IEEE.

the geometrical dependence cancels out for isotropic scaling in V_m, resulting in a constant melting voltage as shown in Figure 22. On the other hand, the different exponents of R and I_m results in an increasing melting voltage for decreasing F in the case of nonisotropic scaling, namely $V_m = RI_m \propto F^{-2}F^{1.3} \propto F^{-0.7}$. This contradicts with the results in Figure 19, thus suggesting a constant melting voltage for decreasing pore size. However, the difference could be reconciled considering (a) the relatively large size of pores in Figure 19 when compared with the small feature sizes in the calculations of Figure 22, and (b) the pore geometry in Figure 19 as opposed to the mushroom architecture considered in Figure 22.

Figure 24 shows experimental data collected for different PCM device types, namely (a) mushroom [69, 70, 74–80], (b) pore [60, 67, 68, 81, 66, 82–84], and (c) line [59, 85–87], as a function of cell area A. Data were collected from the literature and are compared with two power-law behaviors, namely $I_{\text{reset}} \propto A^{0.5}$, which corresponds to isotropic scaling, and $I_{\text{reset}} \propto A^{0.65}$, which corresponds to nonisotropic scaling (Fig. 22). Values reported in the 2009 International Technology Roadmap for Semiconductors are also shown for Ref. [88]. Note that all of the data approximately follow the scaling trends with an exponent between 0.5 and 0.65, and are thus consistent with the scaling analysis in Figure 22.

The results in Figure 22 suggest that a nonisotropic scaling of the PCM device allows for a more efficient reduction of the reset current. This may be interesting for the integration of high-density crossbar arrays where each PCM element is accompanied by a select device, e.g., a semiconductor diode [60] or an OTS device [61]. An OTS is conceptually identical to a PCM device, except for the lack of any memory switching capability. Therefore, the chalcogenide material in the device is only capable of threshold switching, while Joule heating provided by the electrical pulses is not effective in changing the material structure from amorphous to crystalline [89]. In a memory crossbar array, however, every diode must be capable of delivering the necessary reset current for melting and amorphizing the chalcogenide material, and a proper matching of the scaling properties of the diode and the PCM cell is needed. To this purpose, Figure 25 shows the measured reset current for a typical mushroom cell [69, 70, 74] and the measured forward current of a polysilicon diode used in a PCM crossbar memory array [60] as a function of the technology node F. Data are compared with calculations that correspond to a nonisotropic scaling law for the reset current $I_{\text{reset}} \propto F^{1.3}$ and to a uniform current density model for the forward diode current, thus yielding $I_{\text{fwd}} \propto F^2$. It is clear from Figure 25 that the diode forward current scales faster than the nonisotropic reset current; hence, it is also faster than the isotropic case. As a result, a breakdown of the applicability of the diode-selected PCM crossbar arrays may be expected in correspondence of the crossing between the two extrapolations, which is found around $F = 20$ nm. To improve the scalability of PCM crossbar arrays, a major improvement of select diode materials [62, 63] and operations [90] is needed.

Finally, it should also be noted that the scaling of the reset current is not the only requirement in dictating the cell layout and architecture scaling. Other concerns include

(1) the set-state resistance R_{set},

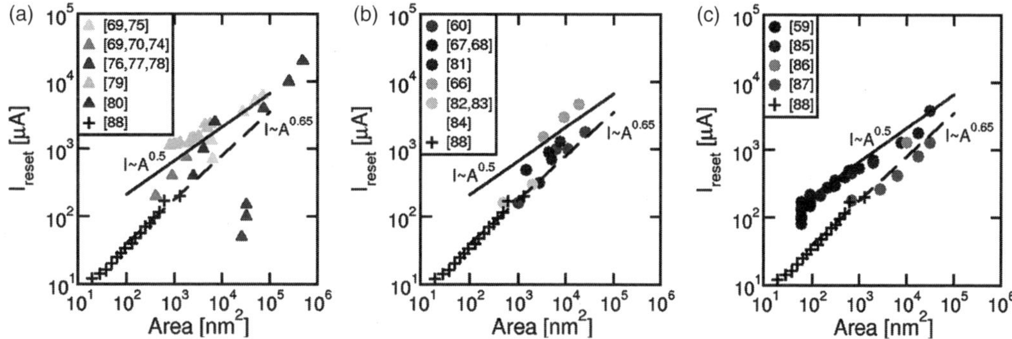

Figure 24. Measured I_{reset} for different PCM device structures in the literature, namely (a) mushroom, (b) pore, and (c) line, as a function of cell area A. The power-laws $I \propto A^{0.5}$ and $I \propto A^{0.65}$, corresponding to isotropic and non-isotropic scaling, respectively, are shown for reference. Reprinted with permission from [73], D. Ielmini, *Mater. Res. Soc. Symp. Proc.* 1251-H05-01 (2010). © 2010, Cambridge University Press.

(2) the programming disturb due to cross-talk [8, 91, 92] and
(3) reliability issues related to electromigration [93].

Since $R \propto L/A$, nonisotropic scaling displays a faster resistance increase with F with respect to isotropic scaling. The increase of the set-state resistance may lead to readout inefficiencies because of the small current available at low voltage in the read regime. This may degrade the performance of PCM in NOR applications, where fast single-bit read is typically necessary. Programming disturbs are also largely impacted by nonisotropic scaling (Fig. 23). Thermal disturb consists of the possible heating of a programmed volume due to the programming in a cell nearby [71, 92, 94]. The resulting Joule heating in the disturbed cell might create a resistance drift or crystallization of the programmed amorphous volume [91]. For isotropic scaling, where all of the dimensions are reduced by an equal factor, all thermal resistances scale down by the same amount from one node to the other, thus resulting in a constant heating induced at the adjacent cell during reset. Correspondingly, the heated volume in Figure 23(b) is reduced according to the cell size in the isotropic scaling. On the other hand, the vertical thermal resistances are reduced less than the lateral thermal resistances in nonisotropic scaling, thus resulting in an increased disturb for decreasing F. This is evident from the relatively wide thermal impact of reset in the non-isotropic case in Figure 23(c). As a result, an increasing thermal disturb is expected for nonisotropic scaling, which is also confirmed by calculations [94].

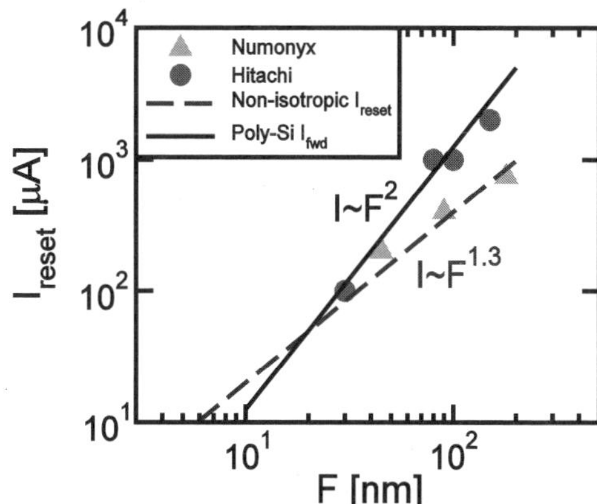

Figure 25. Measured cell I_{reset} [69, 70, 74] and diode I_{fwd} [60] as a function of F. Extrapolations according to $I_{reset} \propto F^{1.3}$ and $I_{fwd} \propto F^2$ are also shown, indicating a possible scaling limit around $F = 20$ nm. Reprinted with permission from [73], D. Ielmini, *Mater. Res. Soc. Symp. Proc.* 1251-H05-01 (2010). © 2010, Cambridge University Press.

4. PCM RELIABILITY

As for any nonvolatile memory, reliability is a key issue for PCM devices. Cycling endurance and the stability of data under repeated read cycles and elevated temperatures are probably the most valuable properties that need to be demonstrated at the statistical level of several Gbit arrays before the PCM can be fully embraced by applications. The main reliability concerns for PCM rely on the specific material and operation modes that characterize the device concept. On the one hand, the reset operation requires a relatively large energy dissipation for reaching temperatures higher than the melting point and obtaining a disordered phase. In an effort to reduce such a high operation power, novel operation schemes and materials have been proposed. These novel concepts take inspiration from metamaterials, where the interface disorder may be established far below the melting point yet inducing the resistance change needed for logic memory [95] and from nonmelting amorphization, which relies on ultrafast electronic excitation to induce a crystalline-amorphous transition [96]. However, such visionary approaches are still too far from practical use, and the melting-based reset still seems unavoidable for PCM technology in the short term. The other potential reliability concern is due to the metastable nature of the disordered atomic phase in the amorphous chalcogenide. In general, the amorphous solid-state structure evolves with time according to a free-energy landscape [97], where several energy minima are possible in correspondence of particular state coordinate. Thermally activated relaxation of the atomic structure can induce a transition among multiple energy minima, with the driving force of energy minimization. Given the strong relationship between local atomic structure and electronic/conduction properties, electrical parameters of the memory cell in the reset state may be affected by a thermally activated change of the atomic structure with time, leading to possible current noise and drift phenomena.

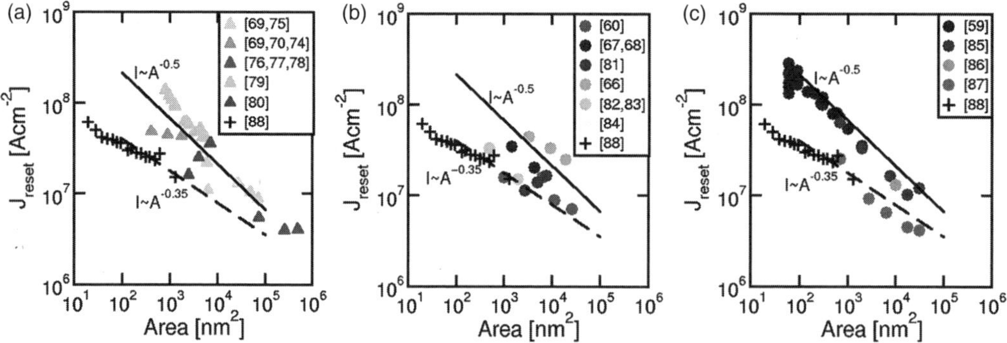

Figure 26. Experimental current density at reset J_{reset}, obtained from data in Figure 24 as I_{reset} divided by the bottom electrode area. Different PCM device structures are considered, namely (a) mushroom, (b) pore, (c) and line. Note the increase of J_{reset} for the decreasing cell area, which is predicted by the isotropic ($J_{reset} \propto A^{-0.5}$) and non-isotropic ($J_{reset} \propto A^{-0.35}$) scaling models.

The transition to the ultimate stable point within the energy landscape, namely the crystalline state, results in the data loss in the memory that must be avoided for the reliable operation of the cell.

The reliability concerns related to the high reset current and the metastable nature of the amorphous state are reviewed in the next section.

4.1. Cycling Endurance

Figure 26 shows the experimental current density at reset J_{reset}, obtained as the reset current I_{reset} in Figure 24 divided by the bottom contact area. The same cell architectures shown in Figure 24 are considered, namely (a) mushroom, (b) pore, and (c) line cells. The current density increases for decreasing cell size according to a slope that is intermediate between those predicted by the isotropic scaling model ($J_{reset} \propto A^{-0.5}$) and the nonisotropic scaling model ($J_{reset} \propto A^{-0.35}$). According to predictions from the International Technology Roadmap for Semiconductors in 2009, the current density at the reset could reach 50 MA cm^{-2} at an electrode diameter of 6 nm and area of 28 nm^2, corresponding to the PCM technology node $F = 9$ nm [88]. This rapid increase of the current density could raise some reliability concern in terms of electromigration within the active chalcogenide volume and the electrodes. After several cycles, in fact, the high programming current may cause voiding within the chalcogenide volume due to the hole electromigration [93]. This was supported by the observation that a programming polarity reversal, where a negative voltage is applied to the top electrode, induces voiding at the chalcogenide-bottom electrode contact in mushroom-type cells [93]. The voids have been explained by the hole current that pushes atoms toward the top electrode under high current density and high temperature [93] and/or by thermal fatigue that has been induced by mismatched expansion coefficients in the active volume [98].

Another key evidence that may contribute to our understanding of the finite endurance of PCM devices is the change in chemical composition within the active chalcogenide region for an increasing number of set/reset cycles. Field- and temperature-induced ion migration that takes place within the chalcogenide during the applied set/reset pulse have been shown to result in Sb accumulation and Te depletion close to the bottom electrode [99, 100]. Figure 27(a) shows the measured R–I characteristics for PCM cells after an increasing number of cycles $N = 1$, 10^5 and 10^6. The R–I displays the resistance R measured after the application of a pulse of current I on a cell in the

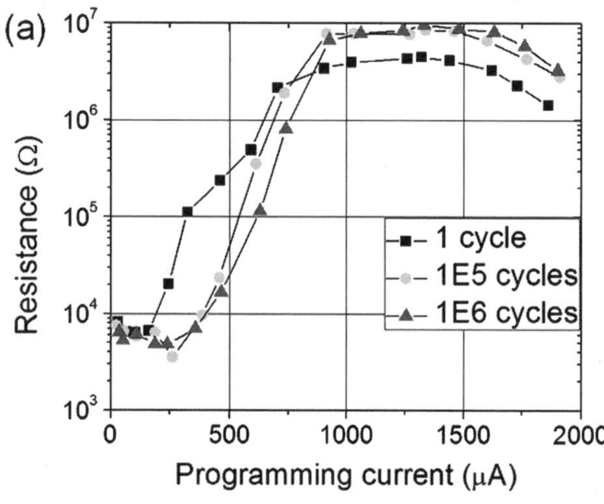

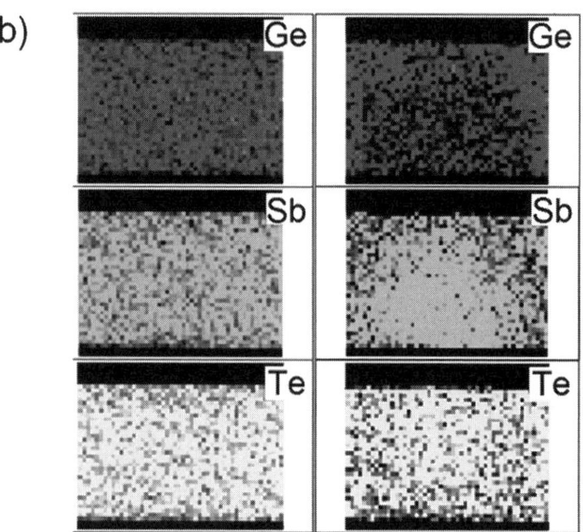

Figure 27. Measured R–I curve for increasing number of set/reset cycles $N = 1$, 10^5 and 10^6 and map of the elemental concentration within the active GST volume for Ge, Sb, and Te, before and after 10^6 cycles. Reprinted with permission from [99], B. Rajendran et al., "IEEE Symp. VLSI Tech. Dig.," p. 96, 2008. © 2008, IEEE.

set state with low resistance. The curve shows a steep rise of R, which indicates the onset of melting and the consequent amorphization in the chalcogenide layer. Note that the melting current increases for increasing cycles, while the maximum resistance increases with the number of cycles. Figure 27(b) shows chemical maps obtained through electron dispersive X-ray spectroscopy (EDX) within the active region, before and after 10^6 set/reset cycles [99]. The chemical maps indicate that Sb is accumulated within the semi-spherical volume and is in direct contact with the bottom electrode, while the same volume appears depleted of Ge and Te after cycling. The accumulation/depletion effects are most probably due to the different electronegativity of the different elements that respond differently to the high electric field during set/reset pulses. These results allow us to interpret the change in the thermal and electrical properties of the cell with cycling as a change in the active material composition induced by electromigration and ionic migration.

4.2. Current Noise

Figure 26 schematically shows the energy landscape picture that describes the structural stability and evolution for the chalcogenide material in the amorphous phase. The figure schematically shows the profile of free energy change DG as a function of a generalized reaction coordinate [97]. Stable/metastable states of the material system can be found in correspondence of the energy minima, and the driving force for the time-evolution of the system is the search for the relative/absolute minimum of energy. As a result, the system dynamically explores different structural configurations through thermally activated many-phonon transitions. These transitions include different types of structural changes between energy states, depending on the energy difference between the initial and final state and on the height of the energy barrier between minima.

The first case is the transition between energy wells with approximately the same energy of the minimum point, with a relatively low energy barrier E'_A. This corresponds to a bistable system, where the two atomic configurations at virtually equal energy are comparably stable, thus leading to a sequence of reversible transitions between the two states. An example of this switching between two structure configurations may be the flipping of a weak bond between two metastable states or the fluctuation of a weakly bonded atom between two positions [102]. Due to the deep relationship between the atomic and electronic structures, the bistable switching between the two structural configurations results in a noise in the measured current. A two-level fluctuation of the current leads to random telegraph noise (RTN), which has been evidenced in PCM devices [28, 103]. However, due to the large number of atoms affecting the conduction path in the active chalcogenide volume, in the most general case the current will display several bistable transitions between metastable states. This will result in a typical $1/f$ noise characteristic, provided that the different transition energy barriers E'_A are broadly distributed. In fact, the latter condition leads to a broad distribution of transition frequencies, according to the Arrhenius relationship between the transition time and energy barrier [102]. The noise spectrum for the PCM current in the reset state usually displays a $1/f$ behavior with the possible appearance of typical bumps, which indicate dominant RTN components. This is shown in Figure 29, where typical power spectral density (PSD) of the current S_I normalized by the square of the current I^2 is plotted as a function of the frequency f [103]. The PSD is shown for different cell states, namely a set state, a reset state, and two intermediate states (A and B). Intermediate states consist of partially reset states where the thickness of the amorphous region in the cell is relatively small, thus leading to a smaller value of the resistance with respect to the full reset state. All states display a $1/f$ behavior, where S_I/I^2 increases with resistance. The larger noise for increasing R supports the metastable nature of the amorphous phase according to the energy landscape picture in Figure 28. It has also been pointed out that the noise is intimately related to the activation energy of conduction in Eq. (3) [28]. This is because the atomic structural fluctuation results in a change in the electronic structure and in the corresponding potential barrier for hopping transport. Since the energy barrier exponentially affects the current in the amorphous phase, even small changes in the atomic structure may lead to huge current fluctuations. The fluctuation may be enhanced by the localization of the current path due to the random distribution of energy barriers discussed in Section 2. When the fluctuating defect is within the interaction range of the main percolation path, the impact on the measured resistance might be significant. On the other hand, bistable fluctuations of defects far from the localized current may play a negligible role in the current noise.

While the set and reset states in Figure 29(a) display almost ideal $1/f$ behaviors, the PSD for intermediate states include bumps that indicate RTN components, showing a typical $1/f^2$ Lorentzian shape. Figure 29(b) shows the measured current for state B in the time domain, indicating a two-level RTN fluctuation [103]. Times τ_{21} and τ_{12} represent the times for the transitions over the energy barrier E'_A in Figure 28. The transition times are statistically distributed according to the Poisson model, indicating uncorrelated transition events between the two states [103]. A detailed analysis of the temperature and voltage dependence τ_{12} and τ_{21} allows us to gain insight into the energy difference and the barrier between the two states [103].

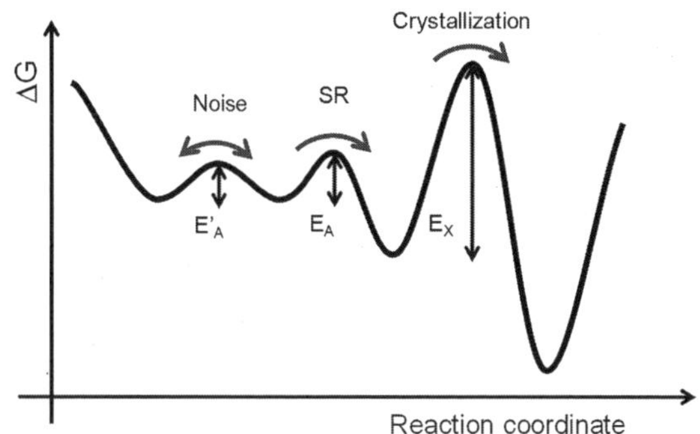

Figure 28. Energy landscape picture for the metastable amorphous phase in a PCM cell. Three different transitions, corresponding to noise, SR, and crystallization are shown. Reprinted with permission from [101], D. Ielmini, *Cur. App. Phys.* 11, e85 (2011). © 2011, Elsevier.

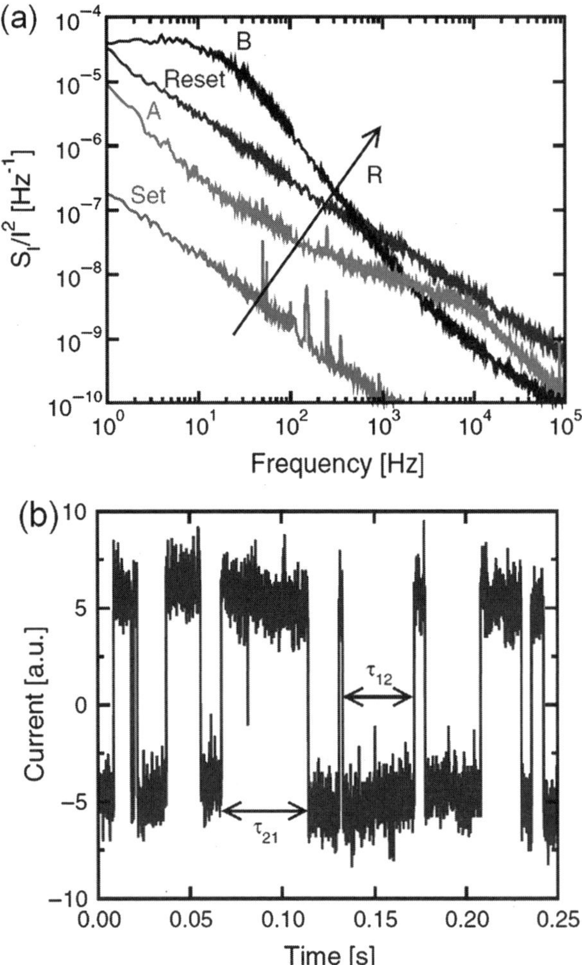

Figure 29. (a) Measured normalized PSD for set, reset, and intermediate states, and (b) time-domain analysis of the RTN responsible for the $1/f^2$ bump in the PSD of cell *B*. Reprinted with permission from [103], D. Fugazza et al., *IEEE IRPS* 743 (2010). © 2010, IEEE.

4.3. Structural Relaxation

The second type of transition in Figure 28 is similar to the one leading to current fluctuation, although with a larger energy difference between the two states. As a result, only one transition occurs from the higher energy state to the lower energy state across a barrier of energy E_A. In fact, the reverse transition would require the system to hop over a significantly higher energy barrier, and is thus inhibited. This transition is known as structural relaxation (SR), a common phenomenon observed in all amorphous materials, including (i) amorphous semiconductors such as *a*-Si [105, 106], *a*-Se [107] and other amorphous chalcogenides [108], and (ii) metallic glasses [109, 110]. In amorphous semiconductors like *a*-Si and *a*-Se, SR was interpreted as an annihilation of defects [106] that resulted in a reduction of the density of localized states within the mobility gap [107]. SR in metallic glasses has been explained by viscous flow at microvoids and relaxation of distorted bonds, leading to a change in the material properties [109]. In all cases, SR was shown to result in a significant increase in the electrical resistivity with time and/or temperature. For instance, temperature-accelerated SR was shown to lead to an increase of resistance in amorphous silicon (*a*Si), between 300–450°C, due to the decrease of dangling bond concentration [111]. Similarly, the room-temperature resistance increased in amorphous silicon carbide (*a*SiC) by almost 3 decades after annealing up to 885°C, which was explained by the relaxation of defects such as dangling bonds, distorted bonds, and vacancies [112]. Annealing-induced resistance drift effects were also demonstrated in tetrahedral amorphous carbon ($ta - C$), where annealing also led to a decrease in the defect density and an increase of the activation energy [113]. Finally, it was shown that electrical resistance increases with time in bulk metallic glasses, possibly as a result of short range ordering and reduced carrier scattering [110].

Similar to these material systems, SR in PCM devices gives rise to a resistance 'drift,' i.e., an increase of resistance with time starting from the reset event [5, 114]. Figure 30 shows the typical resistance drift characteristic at room temperature for a PCM cell [104]. The resistance drift is characterized by a power law dependence on time according to:

$$R = R_0\left(\frac{t}{t_0}\right)^{\nu} \tag{17}$$

where R_0 is the resistance measured at time t_0 and ν is a characteristic exponent, usually in the range from about 0 for the set state to about 0.1 for the reset state at ambient temperature. In view of the previous interpretations of SR in amorphous semiconductors and metallic glasses, SR at the basis of resistance drift has been explained by annihilation of defects, like dangling bonds, vacancies and wrong bonds, leading to a change in the band structure [15]. The change of the electronic band structure might result from a decrease in the concentration of localized states associated to defects and disorder, and/or to an increase in the connectivity of the amorphous network, leading to a larger energy barrier required for self-trapping within the polaron hopping description [15]. Other interpretations attribute resistance drift and SR to the relaxation of a compressive stress in the amorphous chalcogenide region soon after quenching because of the specific volume in the amorphous phase being

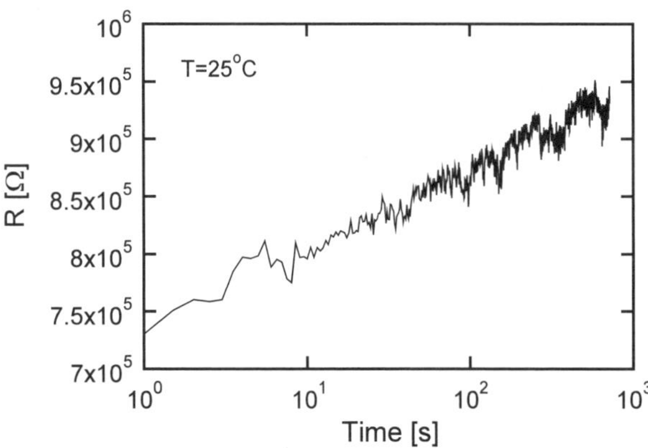

Figure 30. Measured resistance as a function of time after reset. The resistance increases with time due to SR in the amorphous phase. Reprinted with permission from [104], S. Lavizzari et al., *IEEE Trans. Electron Devices* 56, 1078 (2009). © 2009, IEEE.

larger by 7% than the one in the crystalline phase [115, 116]. This picture seems to be supported by resistance drift experiments in nanowire PCM that show a relatively low drift exponent in free-standing nanowires [117]. However, these experiments might be affected by surface oxidation, thereby leading to a lower activation energy of conduction for small nanowires and result in a smaller drift exponent.

Although the fundamental mechanism behind resistance drift is still not clarified, the basic kinetic features are well understood. The power law dependence of resistance drift has been explained by the energy barrier E_A in Figure 28, which is being distributed over a broad spectrum and has resulted in a distribution of transition times spanning several decades. This is because the transition time for a single SR event in Figure 28 follows the Arrhenius formula:

$$\tau_{\mathrm{SR}} = \tau_{\mathrm{SR0}} e^{(E_A/kT)} \tag{18}$$

where τ_{SR0} is a pre-exponential time. Based on this equation, a single value of E_A would yield a single transition time, convoluted by the statistical spread associated with the stochastic thermal excitation over the energy barrier [101]. On the other hand, a distributed E_A results instead in a stretched evolution over several decades of time. It has been experimentally observed that the resistance drift at room temperature extends from about 30 ns [5] to several months [114]. To gain more insight into the distribution of activation energies, Figure 31(a) shows the measured R as a function of time for annealing temperature in the temperature range 90–180°C [29]. The annealing was done at elevated temperature to accelerate the resistance drift phenomenon, while the cell resistance was measured at room temperature to avoid changes in the measured resistance due to the temperature acceleration of conduction in Eq. (3). In the figure, all data display a power-law increase of R, where the exponent ν increases with the annealing temperature. This can be understood by the temperature acceleration of SR [30]: In fact, the activation energy from Eq. (18) reads:

$$E_A = kT \log \frac{t}{\tau_{\mathrm{SR0}}} \tag{19}$$

where $t = \tau_{\mathrm{SR}}$ was used. Equation (19) indicates that, as time increases, SR involves defects with increasing activation energy E_A. The rate at which these barriers are affected by SR can be written as $dE_A/d\log t \propto kT$, which shows that the defect annihilation rate on the logarithmic scale of time increases with temperature [30].

The activation energies of SR can be extracted from the Arrhenius plot of τ_{SR}, where the SR time τ_{SR} can be evaluated as the time to achieve a given resistance R^* in Figure 31(a). A resistance R^* can be viewed as a particular state of the system, marking a given amount of annihilated defects within the amorphous structure, hence a given maximum energy barrier E_A affected by SR. Figure 32 shows the Arrhenius plot of τ_{SR} for increasing R^* [29]. As expected, data indicate an Arrhenius behavior of τ_{SR} according to Eq. (18), with an increase of the activation energy for increasing R^*. Most importantly, the crossing of the Arrhenius extrapolation lines for different R^* is not found at $1/kT = 0$, i.e., the infinite temperature axis, as one might expect for a constant τ_{SR0} in Eq. (18). This can be understood by the pre-exponential time τ_{SR0}, which is an exponential function of E_A. This is confirmed by Figure 33, which shows the correlation plot of τ_{SR0} as a function of E_A: τ_{SR0} exponentially decreases for increasing E_A, according to the MN rule:

$$\tau_{\mathrm{SR0}} = \tau_{00} e^{(-E_A/kT_{\mathrm{MN}})} \tag{20}$$

where τ_{SR00} is a constant and T_{MN} is the isokinetic temperature, i.e., the temperature value marking the point of crossing of all extrapolations in the Arrhenius plot. Data in Figure 32 yield $T_{\mathrm{MN}} = 760$ K and τ_{SR00} of a few μs [29]. The MN rule, which controls the SR in amorphous chalcogenides, is generally demonstrated in several solid-state processes, including thermally accelerated hopping [25, 28, 121], diffusion [122, 123], and SR [29]. Yelon and colleauges [26] have demonstrated the most widely accepted interpretation

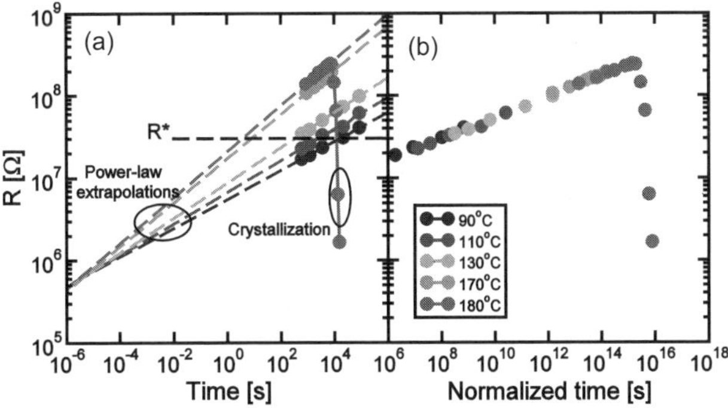

Figure 31. Measured resistance after reset for increasing temperature (a) as a function of time and (b) as a function of renormalized time. The latter was obtained by Eq. (22) through the MN rule. Reprinted with permission from [29], D. Ielmini and M. Boniardi, *Appl. Phys. Lett.* 94, 091906 (2009). © 2009, AIP.

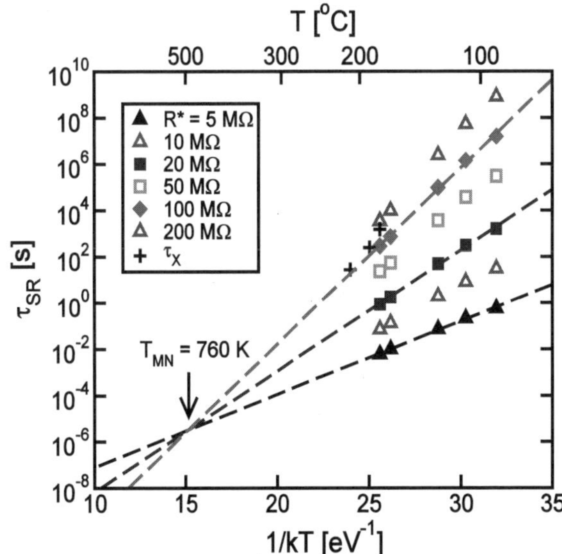

Figure 32. Arrhenius plot namely for τ_{SR}, the relaxation time needed to achieve a resistance R^* in the drift experiment in Figure 31(a). Data and extrapolations are shown for increasing values of R^* and for the crystallization time τ_x. Reprinted with permission from [29], D. Ielmini and M. Boniardi, *Appl. Phys. Lett.* 94, 091906 (2009). © 2009, AIP.

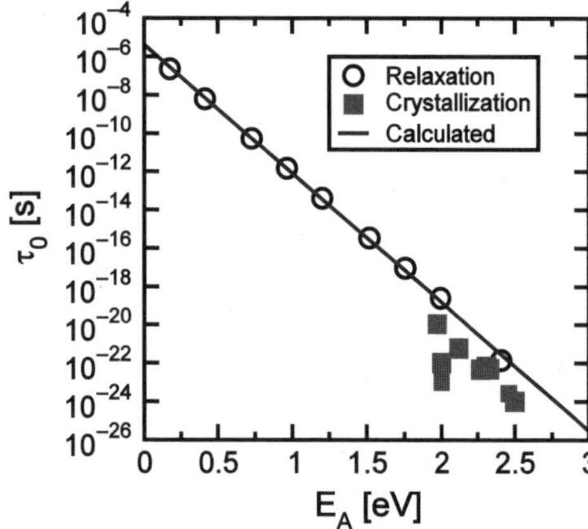

Figure 33. Pre-exponential time in the Arrhenius law for SR (open circles) and crystallization (filled squares) as a function of the activation energy E_A. Crystallization data were obtained from various sources. Reprinted with permission from [87], Both SR and crystallization obey the same MN rule. Reprinted with permission from [29], D. Ielmini and M. Boniardi, *Appl. Phys. Lett.* 94, 091906 (2009). © 2009, AIP.

of the MN rule in terms of the multiexcitation entropy effect. Solid-state transitions that involve large activation energy require several phonons for a successful thermal excitation, thus the configurational entropy associated to the large number of phonons cannot be neglected in such cases. As a result, the transition time must include both the enthalpy and entropy terms through the free-energy change $\Delta G = \Delta H - T\Delta S$, thus leading to:

$$\tau = \tau_{00} e^{(\Delta G/kT)} = \tau_{00} e^{(\Delta H/kT)} e^{(-\Delta S/k)} \tag{21}$$

In Eq. (21), ΔH should be viewed as the energy barrier $E_A = n\Delta$, where n is the minimum number of phonons needed for the transition and Δ is the individual phonon energy. An analytical study indicates that $\Delta S \approx kn$, thus the exponent in the second exponential term in Eq. (21) is given by $\Delta S/k = E_A/\Delta$, where T_{MN} appears to have the physical meaning of Δ/k by comparison between Eqs. (20) and (21). In support of this theory, the isokinetic temperatures are experimentally found to correlate with the phonon energy in a given material [124, 125]. In amorphous GST, the MN rule was verified for SR and hopping conduction, yielding $T_{MN} =$ 760 K and 500 K, respectively, which correspond to $\Delta =$ 65 meV [29] and 43 meV [28], respectively. This is in qualitative agreement with the optical phonon energy in amorphous GST, namely $\Delta = 25$ meV [126]. Note, finally, that the MN rule has a key practical consequence for the kinetics of thermally activated processes, namely the apparent pre-exponential constant for the Arrhenius law that exponentially decreases with the activation energy (Fig. 32). This is generally referred to as the *compensation* effect because the increase of the energy barrier leads to a decreased transition probability since more phonons need to be collected; however, the number of successful configurations increases for increasing n, hence with E_A. As a result, the entropy term partially compensates the enthalpy term in Eq. (21).

Based on the MN rule in Eqs. (18) and (20), analytical models for the temperature acceleration of SR and resistance drift can be developed. In particular, it is important to relate data obtained at a specific high temperature to operation conditions, such as 85°C or room temperature, where the observation time would be too long. A time-renormalization law can be developed based on the relationship between the SR time and temperature in Eqs. (18) and (20), leading to:

$$\tau_{SR,norm} = \tau_{00}^{1-\eta(T/T_{norm})} \tau_{SR}^{\eta(T/T_{norm})} \tag{22}$$

where $\tau_{SR,norm}$ is the re-normalized SR time referred to temperature T_{norm} and τ_{SR} is the experimental SR time at the annealing temperature T. The parameter η is given by:

$$\eta = \frac{T_{MN} - T_{norm}}{T_{MN} - T} \tag{23}$$

Figure 31(b) shows the measured resistance from Figure 31(a), plotted as a function of time normalized to 25°C according to Eq. (22). Times corresponding to high temperatures are shifted to exponentially longer times, resulting in a universal evolution of resistance versus time irrespective of the experimental conditions. This demonstrates the validity of the renormalization formula and of the MN rule for data analysis and reliability prediction.

4.4. Crystallization

The third type of transition in Figure 28 occurs across a relatively large energy barrier E_x of about 2.5 eV, and it results in the transition from the amorphous to the crystalline phase. This is evidenced in Figure 31(a) by the sudden drop of resistance at 180°C after about 10^4 s. Crystallization generally proceeds through nucleation and growth at the solid state. As the crystalline fraction increases in the active volume, resistance decreases due to the buildup of a percolation channel through low-resistivity crystalline grains [120, 127]. Since both the SR and crystallization rely on the same energy landscape model shown in Figure 28, the crystallization time τ_x obeys MN rule, namely:

$$\tau_x = \tau_{00} e^{(E_x/kT)} e^{(-E_x/kT_{MN})} \tag{24}$$

with the same pre-exponential time τ_{00} and iso-kinetic temperature used for SR. This is demonstrated in Figure 32 by the crystallization time τ_x, which is defined as the time for the resistance to match 10^5 Ω, i.e., a resistance intermediate between the amorphous and the crystalline values [120, 127]. In Figure 31, data for crystallization and SR at $R^* = 200$ MΩ overlap almost perfectly, confirming that the crystallization shares the same kinetic parameters of SR. Note that the crystallization can be described by a single value of the activation energy E_x, as evidenced by the distinct drop of resistance at a given τ_x as opposed to the stretched time dependence of SR.

Figure 33 shows the apparent pre-exponential time τ_{x0} of crystallization, which is given by Eq. (24) to be $\tau_{x0} = \tau_{00}\exp(E_x/kT_{MN})$ as a function of the observed activation energy. Data were obtained from a wide literature for GST crystallization [6, 87, 118–120]. Note the extremely short pre-exponential time $\tau_{x0} = 10^{-23}$ s, which clearly cannot have the meaning of a physical frequency. The origin of such a short pre-exponential factor is again due to the entropy-related compensation in the MN rule [29].

From a reliability point of view, a key aspect is the statistics of crystallization time at a given temperature. This was addressed by repeated measurements of single-cell crystallization to understand the intrinsic spread of crystallization time [120, 127] and by the analysis of the crystallization statistics within large arrays [11]. Figure 34(a) shows the cumulative distribution of crystallization time in a 2 kb subarray of PCM cells within a larger array of 4 Mb [11]. The distributions were collected for two annealing temperatures, 160 and 180°C, and τ_x was measured as the time for a decrease of resistance below 100 kΩ, measured at room temperature after interrupting the elevated-temperature annealing stage. The crystallization time decreases for increasing temperature with average activation energy of about 3.12 eV. The crystallization time displays a log-normal distribution, where the relative spread increases for decreasing annealing temperature. The analysis of crystallization times τ_x at two temperatures in Figure 34(a) showed a strong correlation, thus indicating that cells systematically displayed a 'fast' or 'slow' crystallization as a result of different activation energies E_x. The activation energies can be estimated from the relative change of τ_x in the distribution at high and low percentile in Figure 34(a), corresponding to relatively slow and fast crystallization respectively. Activation energies of 3.3 and 2.7 eV are found for slow and fast crystallization, respectively. Note that these values are slightly higher than the typical E_x for GST in Figure 33, possibly due to a different chemical composition in the cell within the array [11]. Despite this disagreement, it is interesting to note that statistical data obey the MN rule for SR and crystallization. In fact, Figure 34(b) shows the Arrhenius plot of τ_x for the median, fast and slow crystallization cells, corresponding to the 50%, 0.13%, and 99.87% percentiles in Figure 34(a). All extrapolations approximately cross at $T_{MN} = 600$ K and $\tau_{x0} = 5 \times 10^{-6}$ s, which are comparable with the isokinetic temperature and pre-exponential time already observed for SR and crystallization for single cells in Figure 32. This suggests that the MN rule also regulates the change of crystallization kinetics among different cells in the array, corresponding to amorphous GST regions with infinitesimal changes in the composition at the nanoscale [11]. Also note that the MN rule is at the basis of the observed increase of the statistical spread in the lognormal distributions of τ_x for decreasing temperature in Figure 34(a). In fact, the MN rule predicts that all crystallization times approach τ_{x0} as the temperature is increased toward T_{MN}. On the other hand, relative differences in crystallization speed become stronger as the temperature decreases (Fig. 34(b)).

The statistical spread of crystallization times in Figure 34 can be explained by the composition-variability model (Fig. 35) [11]. The model assumes that the crystallization time is a local property within the amorphous volume, and it changes depending on the position as a result of the chemical and structural disorders. It was proposed that the nanometer fluctuations of atomic concentration of Ge, Sb, and Te in GST-based PCM cells might result in a local fluctuation of the crystallization time [11]. As a result, the overall cell crystallization kinetics is dictated by (a) the distribution of local crystallization times within the amorphous volume, and (b) the spatial configuration of fast/slow crystallization domains. For instance, Figure 35 compares the crystallization kinetics in two cells. Each cell is divided into subdomains with a local crystallization time. Cell 1 is characterized by a vertical 'string' of subdomains with a relatively short crystallization time, thus resulting in the fast growth of a percolation channel connecting the bottom electrode and the top conductive area, which consists of the crystalline chalcogenide layer. On the other hand, cell 2 is characterized by the presence of a horizontal 'barrier' of subdomains with long crystallization time, thus inhibiting the development of a percolation channel from top to bottom electrodes. These examples highlight that the 'global' crystallization time for the cell is dictated not only by the distribution of local crystallization times, but it is also dictated by the spatial location of the fast and slow crystallizing domains within the amorphous volume [11].

4.5. Material Engineering

Since the alloy composition has a strong impact on the crystallization properties of chalcogenide materials, material engineering to improve reliability has been largely investigated in the literature. It was shown that materials along the pseudobinary line $(GeTe)_x(Sb_2Te_3)_y$ in the ternary diagram

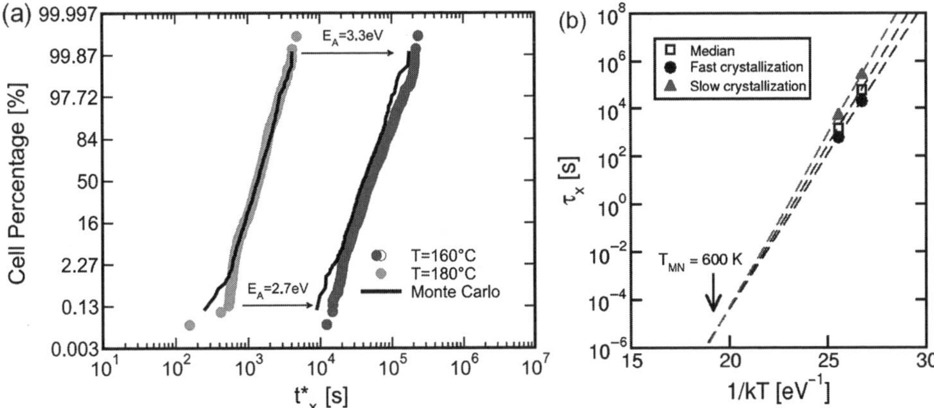

Figure 34. Distributions of measured and calculated crystallization times for annealing at 160 and 180°C for a 2 kb subarray of cells within a 4-Mb PCM array (a), an Arrhenius plot of τ_x for the median cell (50%), and (b) fast crystallization cell at low percentile and slow crystallization cell at high percentile. Reprinted with permission from [11], D. Mantegazza et al., "IEDM Tech. Dig.," p. 311, 2007. © 2007, IEEE.

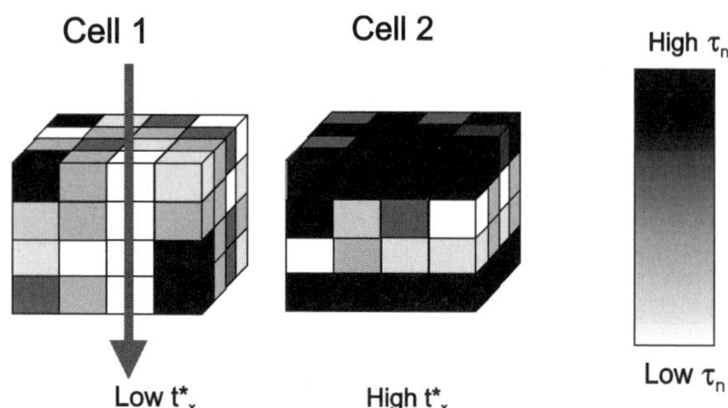

Figure 35. Model for the statistical spread of crystallization times in a PCM device memory array. Cells for annealing at 160 and 180°C for 2*k* cells within a 4 Mb PCM array are also shown. Reprinted with permission from [11], D. Mantegazza et al., "IEDM Tech. Dig.," p. 311, (2007). © 2007, IEEE.

of Ge–Sb–Te display an increasing crystallization temperature, going from Sb_2Te_3 to GeTe [47, 128]. Although fast crystallization is generally required for high-speed programming, it also conflicts with the stability of the amorphous phase. Therefore, fast crystallizing materials such as Sb_2Te_3 are generally not suitable for PCM applications due to insufficient retention time. To solve this issue, doped GeSb was proposed as a material with relatively fast crystallization, thanks to its growth-driven crystallization dynamics. But, it still shows a higher crystallization temperature than GST [59]. The crystallization temperature in GeSb spanned from 130–450°C as the Ge content was increased from 7.3%–81.1% [129]. The composition $Ge_3Sb_2Te_5$ was shown to provide a good high-temperature retention (i.e., 10 years at 102°C), while reducing the reset current with respect to GST [130]. For the purpose of achieving high temperature retention, which is desired in embedded and automotive applications, the composition InGeTe was shown to yield a remarkably high crystallization temperature of around 275°C without compromising the set/reset programming characteristics [130].

Similar studies explored the impact of doping on PCM reliability and programming characteristics. Oxygen-doping of GST was shown to result in a stronger stability at high temperature, with an activation energy for crystallization as high as 4.4 eV and an extrapolated retention of 10 years at 100°C [77]. Nitrogen doping of GST was shown to lead to higher crystallization temperatures [132] and higher resistance in the crystalline state, thus allowing a reduction in the reset current [12]. Most recently, GeTe doping with carbon and nitrogen was investigated to extend the high-temperature retention range of GeTe [133, 134]. In both cases, the crystallization temperature and the activation energy for crystallization were improved, although with a significant degradation of the set speed in the programming characteristics in C-doped GeTe [133]. Doping was shown to play a negligible role in the resistance drift, again suggesting a universal role of SR in all chalcogenide material [133, 134].

Figure 36 shows the correlation plot of pre-exponential time τ_{x0} and activation energy E_x of crystallization from reported experiments as a function of PCM active material [6, 29, 87, 118–120, 130–134]. Data for SR in GST and the corresponding MN rule are also shown for comparison [29]. With respect to GST, InGeTe and doped GeTe

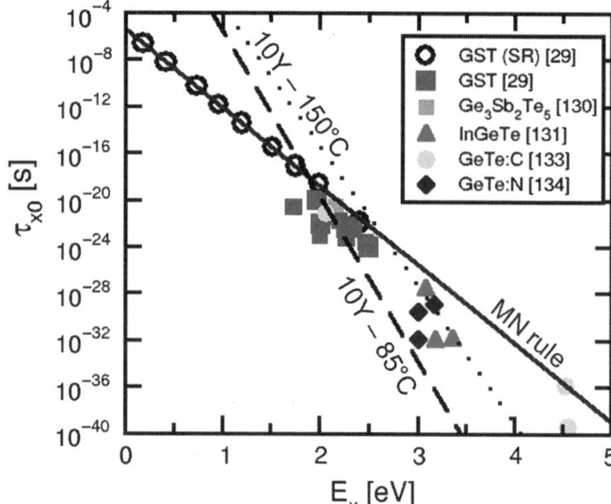

Figure 36. MN plot of the pre-exponential crystallization time τ_{x0} as a function of the activation energy for crystallization E_x. Data were collected from the literature for GST [Refs. 6, 29, 87 118, 119, 120] and other chalcogenide materials for variable composition [Refs. 130, 131] and doping [Refs. 133, 134]. The figure also shows SR data and the corresponding MN rule for comparison [Ref. 29]. For the purpose of reliability prediction, the minimum τ_{x0} guaranteeing 10 years crystallization at 85°C (dashed line) and 150°C (short dashed line) is shown. Reprinted with permission from [29], D. Ielmini and M. Boniardi, *Appl. Phys. Lett.* 94, 091906 (2009). © 2009, AIP.

display a higher E_x and a correspondingly lower τ_{x0}, which is predicted by the MN rule. All data are approximately consistent with the MN rule describing SR and crystallization for GST [29]. For the purpose of evaluating the data retention of different materials, lines corresponding to equation:

$$\tau_{x0} = t_{\text{ret}} e^{(-E_A/kT_{\text{ret}})} \tag{25}$$

were obtained from Eq. (24), where $t_{\text{ret}} = 10$ years and T_{ret} is either 85°C (solid line) and 150°C (dashed line). Equation (25) indicates the minimum τ_{x0} ensuring 10 years reliability at T_{ret}, as a function of E_x and assumes an Arrhenius behavior of the retention time. From the comparison between the data and retention lines, GST appears to match the 85°, 10 years requirement, although the data present some scattering. N-doped GeTe and InGeTe fulfill the 85°C criterion, while carbon-doped GeTe may also withstand 150°C for more than 10 years. Note that data retention is only one aspect of the overall PCM properties, which also include programming characteristics, array variability, endurance, multilevel capability, and several other functional parameters.

5. CONCLUSIONS AND OUTLOOK

This chapter provides a review of the PCM operation and reliability from a physical modeling point of view. The most relevant aspects concerning material, device, and array behaviors have been addressed, from the electrical conduction to the threshold switching, from the programming characteristics to the rules and predictions for device scaling, and from the reliability physics to the impact of the active material composition and doping. In most cases, the community has achieved a sufficient understanding, which is the necessary basis for the development of numerical models and for the predictability and feasibility of device scaling. Clearly several gaps and challenges still need to be overcome to clarify the ultimate scaling limits of PCM. In particular, cycling degradation is one of the key issues that should be understood and solved to take full advantage of the high programming speed and bit granularity of PCM devices. Although materials are being investigated mostly on an empirical basis, first-principle modeling of phase transition and SR properties as a function of material composition should be extensively addressed. The fundamental mechanisms of crystallization, amorphization, and SR require a deeper insight, which may allow the development of engineered materials and operation schemes to improve programming characteristics and better stability, particularly for the case of multilevel operation mode. Finally, more efforts are needed in the identification of high-density architectures, such as crossbar arrays, and of high-performance, stackable diodes for PCM selection. Improvement in all these fields will ensure the extended scaling of PCM devices and novel applications in memory and logic.

REFERENCES

1. K. Kim, "IEDM Tech. Dig.," p. 1, 2011.
2. M. Wuttig and N. Yamada, *Nat. Mater.* 6, 824 (2007).
3. D. Ielmini, A. L. Lacaita, A. Pirovano, F. Pellizzer, and R. Bez, *IEEE Electron Device Lett.* 25, 507 (2004).
4. H.-S. P. Wong, S. Raoux, S. Kim, J. Liang, J. P. Reifenberg, B. Rajendran, M. Asheghi, and K. E. Goodson, *Proc. IEEE* 98, 2201 (2010).
5. D. Ielmini, A. L. Lacaita, and D. Mantegazza, *IEEE Trans. Electron Devices* 54, 308 (2007).
6. A. Pirovano, A. Redaelli, F. Pellizzer, F. Ottogalli, M. Tosi, D. Ielmini, A. L. Lacaita, and R. Bez, *IEEE Trans. Device Material Reliability* 4, 422 (2004).
7. D. Ielmini, "Phase Change Memory Device Modeling," (S. Raoux and M. Wuttig, Eds.), p. 209, Springer, New York, 2009.
8. U. Russo, D. Ielmini, A. Redaelli, and A. L. Lacaita, *IEEE Trans. Electron Devices* 55, 506 (2008).
9. D. Ielmini and Y. Zhang, "IEDM Tech. Dig.," p. 401, 2006.
10. S. Lavizzari, D. Sharma, and D. Ielmini, *IEEE Trans. Electron Devices* 57, 1047 (2010).
11. D. Mantegazza, D. Ielmini, E. Varesi, A. Pirovano, and A. L. Lacaita, "IEDM Tech. Dig.," p. 311, 2007.
12. Y. N. Hwang, S. H. Lee, S. J. Ahn, S. Y. Lee, K. C. Ryoo, H. S. Hong, H. C. Koo, F. Yeung, J. H. Oh, H. J. Kim, W. C. Jeong, J. H. Park, H. Horii, Y. H. Ha, J. H. Yi, G. H. Koh, G. T. Jeong, H. S. Jeong, and K. Kim, "IEDM Tech. Dig.," p. 893, 2003.
13. N. F. Mott and E. A. Davis, "Electronic Processes in Non-Crystalline Materials." Oxford, Clarendon, 1979.
14. D. Ielmini and Y. Zhang, *J. Appl. Phys.* 102, 054517 (2007).
15. D. Ielmini, D. Sharma, S. Lavizzari, and A. L. Lacaita, *IEEE Trans. Electron Devices* 56, 1070 (2009).
16. A. Pirovano, A. L. Lacaita, A. Benvenuti, F. Pellizzer, and R. Bez, *IEEE Trans. Electron Devices* 51, 452 (2004).
17. B.-S. Lee, J. R. Abelson, S. G. Bishop, D.-H. Kang, B.-K. Cheong, and K.-B. Kim, *J. Appl. Phys.* 97, 093509 (2005).
18. D. Ielmini, *Phys. Rev. B* 78, 035308 (2008).
19. D. Ielmini and Y. Zhang, *Appl. Phys. Lett.* 90, 192102 (2007).
20. D. Emin, C. H. Seager, and R. K. Quinn, *Phys. Rev. Lett.* 28, 813 (1972).
21. C. H. Seager, D. Emin, and R. K. Quinn, *Phys. Rev. B* 8, 4746 (1973).
22. D. Emin, *Philos. Mag.* 35, 1189 (1977).
23. R. M. Hill, *Thin Solid Films* 8, R21 (1971).
24. A. K. Jonscher and R. M. Hill, "Electrical Conduction in Disordered Nonmetallic Films, Physics of Thin Films," (G. Hass, M. H. Francombe and R. W. Hoffman, Eds.), Vol. 8, Academic, New York, 1975.
25. R. S. Crandall, *Phys. Rev. B* 43, 4057 (1991).
26. A. Yelon, B. Movaghar, and H. M. Branz, *Phys. Rev. B* 46, 12244 (1992).
27. A. Yelon and B. Movaghar, *Phys. Rev. Lett.* 65, 618 (1990).
28. D. Fugazza, D. Ielmini, G. Montemurro, and A. L. Lacaita, "IEDM Tech. Dig.," p. 652, 2010.
29. D. Ielmini and M. Boniardi, *Appl. Phys. Lett.* 94, 091906 (2009).
30. D. Ielmini, S. Lavizzari, D. Sharma, and A. L. Lacaita, *Appl. Phys. Lett.* 92, 193511 (2008).
31. Y. H. Shih, M. H. Lee, M. Breitwisch, R. Cheek, J. Y. Wu, B. Rajendran, Y. Zhu, E. K. Lai, C. F. Chen, H. Y. Cheng, A. Schrott, E. Joseph, R. Dasaka, S. Raoux, H. L. Lung, and C. Lam, "IEDM Tech. Dig.," 2009.
32. A. Calderoni, M. Ferro, D. Ielmini, and P. Fantini, *IEEE Electron Device Lett.* 31, 1023 (2010).
33. D. Fugazza, D. Ielmini, S. Lavizzari, and A. L. Lacaita, "IEDM Tech. Dig.," p. 723, 2009.
34. K. Kim and S. J. Ahn, *Proc. IEEE IRPS* 157 (2005).
35. D. H. Kang, J. S. Kim, Y. R. Kim, Y. T. Kim, M. K. Lee, Y. J. Jun, J. H. Park, F. Yeung, C. W. Jeong, J. Yu, J. H. Kong, D. W. Ha, S. A. Song, J. Park, Y. Park, Y. J. Song, C. Y. Eum, K. C. Ryoo, J. M. Shin, D. W. Lim, S. S. Park, W. I. Park, K. R. Sim, J. H. Cheong, J. H. Oh, J. I. Kim, Y. T. Oh, K. W. Lee, S. P. Koh, S. H. Eun, N. B. Kim, G. H. Koh, G. T. Jeong, H. S. Jeong, and K. Kim, "IEEE Symp. VLSI Tech. Dig.," p. 96, (2007).
36. S. Raoux, W. Welnic, and D. Ielmini, *Chemical Rev.* 110, 240 (2010).
37. N. Papandreou, A. Pantazi, A. Sebastian, E. Eleftheriou, M. Breitwisch, C. Lam, and H. Pozidis, *Solid-State Electron.* 54, 991 (2010).
38. S. W. Ryu, J. H. Lee, Y. B. Ahn, C. H. Kim, B. J. Choi, C. S. Hwang, and H. J. Kim, *Appl. Phys. Lett.* 93, 172114 (2008).
39. S. Caravati, M. Bernasconi, T. D. Kühne, M. Krack, and M. Parrinello, *Appl. Phys. Lett.* 91, 171906 (2007).
40. P. Thomas, *Phys. Stat. Sol. B* 71, 763 (1975).
41. A. K. Jonscher, *J. Phys. C* 4, 1331 (1971).
42. N. K. Hindley, *J. Non-Cryst. Solids* 5, 31 (1970).
43. D. Ielmini, D. Mantegazza, and A. L. Lacaita, *IEEE Electron Device Lett.* 30, 568 (2008).
44. S. Lavizzari, D. Ielmini, and A. L. Lacaita, *IEEE Trans. Electron Device* 57, 1838 (2010).
45. P. J. Walsh, R. Vogel, and E. J. Evans, *Phys. Rev.* 178, 1274 (1969).
46. S. Lee, D. S. Jeong, J.-H. Jeong, W. Zhe, Y.-W. Park, H.-W. Ahn, and B.-K. Cheong, *Appl. Phys. Lett.* 96, 023501 (2010).
47. X. S. Miao, L. P. Shi, H. K. Lee, J. M. Li, R. Zhao, P. K. Tan, K. G. Lim, H. X. Yang, and T. C. Chong, *Jpn. J. Appl. Phys. Part 1* 45, 3955 (2007).
48. A. C. Warren, *IEEE Trans. Electron Device* 20, 123 (1973).
49. Bogoslovskij and K. D. Tentsin, *J. Non-Cryst. Sol.* 357, 992 (2011).
50. D. Adler, M. S. Shur, M. Silver, and S. R. Ovshinsky, *J. Appl. Phys.* 51, 3289 (1980).
51. D. Emin, *Phys. Rev. B* 74, 035206 (2006).
52. V. G. Karpov, Y. A. Kryukov, S. D. Savransky, and I. V. Karpov, *Appl. Phys. Lett.* 90, 123504 (2007).
53. S. R. Ovshinsky, *Phys. Rev. Lett.* 21, 1450 (1968).
54. Feldman and K. Moorjani, *J. Non-Cryst. Solids* 2, 82 (1970).
55. G. W. Turner, H. K. Charles, and C. Feldman, *J. Appl. Phys.* 47, 3618 (1976).
56. W. den Boer, *Appl. Phys. Lett.* 40, 812, (1982).

57. S. Seo, M. J. Lee, D. H. Seo, E. J. Jeoung, D.-S. Suh, Y. S. Joung, I. K. Yoo, I. R. Hwang, S. H. Kim, I. S. Byun, J. S. Kim, J. S. Choi, and B. H. Park, *Appl. Phys. Lett.* 85, 5655 (2004).
58. S. H. Chang, S. C. Chae, S. B. Lee, C. Liu, T. W. Noh, J. S. Lee, B. Kahng, J. H. Jang, M. Y. Kim, D.-W. Kim, and C. U. Jung, *Appl. Phys. Lett.* 92, 183507 (2008).
59. Y. C. Chen, C. T. Rettner, S. Raoux, G. W. Burr, S. H. Chen, R. M. Shelby, M. Salinga, W. P. Risk, T. D. Happ, G. M. McClelland, M. Breitwisch, A. Schrott, J. B. Philipp, M. H. Lee, R. Cheek, T. Nirschl, M. Lamorey, C. F. Chen, E. Joseph, S. Zaidi, B. Yee, H. L. Lung, R. Bergmann, and C. Lam, "IEDM Tech. Dig.," 2006.
60. Y. Sasago, M. Kinoshita, T. Morikawa, K. Kurotsuchi, S. Hanzawa, T. Mine, A. Shima, Y. Fujisaki, H. Kume, H. Moriya, N. Takaura, and K. Torii, "IEEE Symp. VLSI Tech. Dig.," p. 24, 2009.
61. Kau, S. Tang, I. V. Karpov, R. Dodge, B. Klehn, J. A. Kalb, J. Strand, A. Diaz, N. Leung, J. Wu, S. Lee, T. Langtry, K.-W. Chang, C. Papagianni, J. Lee, J. Hirst, S. Erra, E. Flores, N. Righos, H. Castro, and G. Spadini, "IEDM Tech. Dig.," 2009.
62. K. Gopalakrishnan, R. S. Shenoy, C. T. Rettner, K. Virwani, D. S. Bethune, R. M. Shelby, G. W. Burr, A. Kellock, R. S. King, K. Nguyen, A. N. Bowers, M. Jurich, B. Jackson, A. M. Friz, T. Topuria, P. M. Rice, and B. N. Kurdi, "IEEE Symp. VLSI Tech. Dig.," p. 205, 2010.
63. M.-J. Lee, S. Seo, D.-C. Kim, S.-E. Ahn, D. H. Seo, I.-K. Yoo, I.-G. Baek, D.-S. Kim, I.-S. Byun, S.-H. Kim, I.-R. Hwang, J.-S. Kim, S.-H. Jeon, and B. H. Park, *Adv. Mater.* 19, 73 (2007).
64. D. Mantegazza, D. Ielmini, A. Pirovano, A. L. Lacaita, E. Varesi, F. Pellizzer, and R. Bez, *Solid-State Electron.* 52, 584 (2008).
65. D. Mantegazza, D. Ielmini, and A. L. Lacaita, *IEEE Electron Device Lett.* 31, 341 (2010).
66. W. Czubatyj, T. Lowrey, S. Kostylev, and I. Asano, "European Phase Change and Ovonic Science Symposium," 2006.
67. T. D. Happ, M. Breitwisch, A. Schrott, J. B. Philipp, M. H. Lee, R. Cheek, T. Nirschl, M. Lamorey, C. H. Ho, S. H. Chen, C. F. Chen, E. Joseph, S. Zaidi, G. W. Burr, B. Yee, Y. C. Chen, S. Raoux, H. L. Lung, R. Bergmann, and C. Lam, "IEEE Symp. VLSI Tech. Dig.," p. 121, 2006.
68. M. Breitwisch, T. Nirschl, C. F. Chen, Y. Zhu, M. H. Lee, M. Lamorey, G. W. Burr, E. Joseph, A. Schrott, J. B. Philipp, R. Cheek, T. D. Happ, S. H. Chen, S. Zaidi, P. Flaitz, J. Bruley, R. Dasaka, B. Rajendran, S. Rossnagel, M. Yang, Y. C. Chen, R. Bergmann, H. L. Lung, and C. Lam, "IEEE Symp. VLSI Tech. Dig.," p. 100, 2007.
69. F. Pellizzer, A. Pirovano, F. Ottogalli, M. Magistretti, M. Scaravaggi, P. Zuliani, M. Tosi, A. Benvenuti, P. Besana, S. Cadeo, T. Marangon, R. Morandi, R. Piva, A. Spandre, R. Zonca, A. Modelli, E. Varesi, T. Lowrey, A. Lacaita, G. Casagrande, P. Cappelletti, and R. Bez, *IEEE Symp. VLSI. Tech. Dig.* 18 (2004).
70. F. Pellizzer, A. Benvenuti, B. Gleixner, Y. Kim, B. Johnson, M. Magistretti, T. Marangon, A. Pirovano, R. Bez, and G. Atwood, "IEEE Symp. VLSI Tech. Dig.," p. 122, 2006.
71. A. Pirovano, A. L. Lacaita, A. Benvenuti, F. Pellizzer, S. Hudgens, and R. Bez, "IEDM Tech. Dig.," p. 699, 2003.
72. S. Kim, H.-S. P. Wong, *IEEE Electron Device Lett.* 28, 697 (2007).
73. D. Ielmini, *Mater. Res. Soc. Symp. Proc.* 1251-H05-01 (2010).
74. G. Servalli, "IEDM Tech. Dig.," p. 113, 2009.
75. S. Lai and T. Lowrey, "IEDM Tech. Dig.," p. 803, 2001.
76. N. Takaura, M. Terao, K. Kurotsuchi, T. Yamauchi, O. Tonomura, Y. Hanaoka, R. Takemura, K. Osada, T. Kawahara, and H. Matsuoka, "IEDM Tech. Dig.," p. 897, 2003.
77. N. Matsuzaki, K. Kurotsuchi, Y. Matsui, O. Tonomura, N. Yamamoto, Y. Fujisaki, N. Kitai, R. Takemura, K. Osada, S. Hanzawa, H. Moriya, T. Iwasaki, T. Kawahara, N. Takaura, M. Terao, M. Matsuoka, and M. Moniwa, "IEDM Tech. Dig.," p. 758, 2006.
78. Y. Matsui, K. Kurotsuchi, O. Tonomura, T. Morikawa, M. Kinoshita, Y. Fujisaki, N. Matsuzaki, S. Hanzawa, M. Terao, N. Takaura, H. Moriya, T. Iwasaki, M. Moniwa, and T. Koga, "IEDM Tech. Dig.," p. 769, 2007.
79. W. Jeong, D. H. Kang, D. W. Ha, Y. J. Song, J. H. Oh, J. H. Kong, J. H. Yoo, J. H. Park, K. C. Ryoo, D. W. Lim, S. S. Park, J. I. Kim, Y. T. Oh, J. S. Kim, J. M. Shin, J. Park, Y. Fai, G. H. Koh, G. T. Jeong, H. S. Jeong, and K. Kim, *Solid-State Electron.* 52, 591 (2008).
80. S. L. Cho, J. H. Yi, Y. H. Ha, B. J. Kuh, C. M. Lee, J. H. Park, S. D. Nam, H. Horii, B. O. Cho, K. C. Ryoo, S. O. Park, H. S. Kim, U.-I. Chung, J. T. Moon, and B. I. Ryu, "Symp. VLSI Tech Dig.," p. 96, 2005.
81. D.-S. Chao, Y.-C. Chen, F. Chen, M.-J. Chen, P. H. Yen, C.-M. Lee, W.-S. Chen, C. L. M.-J. Kao, and M.-J. Tsai, *IEEE Electron Device Lett.* 28, 871 (2007).
82. I. Lee, H. Park, S. L. Cho, Y. L. Park, B. J. Bae, J. H. Park, J. S. Park, H. G. An, J. S. Bae, D. H. Ahn, Y. T. Kim, H. Horii, S. A. Song, J. C. Shin, S. O. Park, H. S. Kim, U-In. Chung, J. T. Moon, and B. I. Ryu, "IEEE Symp. VLSI Tech. Dig.," p. 102, 2007.
83. H. Im, J. I. Lee, S. L. Cho, H. G. An, D. H. Kim, I. S. Kim, H. Park, D. H. Ahn, H. Horii, S. O. Park, U-In. Chung, and J. T. Moon, "IEDM Tech. Dig.," p. 211, 2008.
84. W. S. Chen, C. M. Lee, D. S. Chao, Y. C. Chen, F. Chen, C. W. Chen, P. H. Yen, M. J. Chen, W. H. Wang, T. C. Hsiao, J. T. Yeh, S. H. Chiou, M. Y. Liu, T. C. Wang, L. L. Chein, C. M. Huang, N. T. Shih, L. S. Tu, D. Huang, T. H. Yu, M. J. Kao, and M.-J. Tsai, "IEDM Tech. Dig.," p. 319, 2007.
85. S.-H. Lee, D.-K. Ko, Y. Jung, and R. Agarwal, *Appl. Phys. Lett.* 89, 223116 (2006).
86. Kim, D. Kang, T.-Y. Lee, K. H. P. Kim, Y.-S. Kang, J. Lee, S.-W. Nam, K.-B. Kim, and Y. Khang, *Appl. Phys. Lett.* 94, 193504 (2009).
87. S. H. Lee, Y. Jung, and R. Agarwal, *Nat. Nanotech.* 2, 626 (2007).
88. International Technology Roadmap for Semiconductors (2009). Available at: http://www.itrs.net.
89. E. Van Landingham, *IEEE Trans. Electron Devices* 20, 178 (1973).
90. A. Redaelli, A. Pirovano, I. Tortorelli, F. Ottogalli, A. Ghetti, L. Laurin, and A. Beneventi, *IEEE IRPS* 615 (2010).
91. S. B. Kim, B. Lee, M. Asheghi, G. A. M. Hurkx, J. Reifenberg, K. Goodson, and H.-S. P. Wong, *Proc. IEEE IRPS* 99 (2010).
92. S. H. Lee, M. S. Kim, G. S. Do, S. G. Kim, H. J. Lee, J. S. Sim, N. G. Park, S. B. Hong, Y. H. Jeon, K. S. Choi, H. C. Park, T. H. Kim, J. U. Lee, H. W. Kim, M. R. Choi, S. Y. Lee, Y. S. Kim, H. J. Kang, J. H. Kim, H. J. Kim, Y. S. Son, B. H. Lee, J. H. Choi, S. C. Kim, J. H. Lee, S. J. Hong, and S. W. Park, "IEEE Symp. VLSI Tech. Dig.," p. 199, 2010.
93. M. H. Lee, R. Cheek, C. F. Chen, Y. Zhu, J. Bruley, F. H. Baumann, Y. H. Shih, E. K. Lai, M. Breitwish, A. Schrott, S. Raoux, E. A. Joseph, H. Y. Cheng, J. Y. Wu, H. L. Lung, and C. Lam, "IEDM Tech. Dig.," p. 978, 2010.
94. U. Russo, D. Ielmini, A. Redaelli, and A. L. Lacaita, *IEEE Trans. Electron Devices* 55, 515 (2008).
95. J. Tominaga, R. Simpson, P. Fons, and A. Kolobov, "IEDM Tech. Dig.," p. 978, 2010.
96. P. Fons, H. Osawa, A. V. Kolobov, T. Fukaya, M. Suzuki, T. Uruga, N. Kawamura, H. Tanida, and J. Tominaga, *Phys. Rev. B* 82, 041203(R) (2010).
97. P. G. Debenedetti and F. H. Stillinger, *Nature* 410, 259 (2001).
98. C.-F. Chen, A. Schrott, M. H. Lee, S. Raoux, Y. H. Shih, M. Breitwisch, F. H. Baumann, E. K. Lai, T. M. Shaw, P. Flaitz, R. Cheek, E. A. Joseph, S. H. Chen, B. Rajendran, H. L. Lung, and C. Lam, "IEEE International Memory Workshop," p. 10, 2009.

99. B. Rajendran, M.-H. Lee, M. Breitwisch, G. W. Burr, Y-H. Shih, R. Cheek, A. Schrott, C.-F. Chen, M. Lamorey, E. Joseph, Y. Zhu, R. Dasaka, P. L. Flaitz, F. H. Baumann, H-L. Lung, and C. Lam, "IEEE Symp. VLSI Tech. Dig.," p. 96, 2008.
100. A. Padilla, G. W. Burr, K. Virwani, A. Debunne, C. T. Rettner, T. Topuria, P. M. Rice, B. Jackson, D. Dupouy, A. J. Kellock, R. M. Shelby, K. Gopalakrishnan, R. S. Shenoy, and B. N. Kurdi, "IEDM Tech. Dig.," p. 656, 2010.
101. D. Ielmini, *Current Applied Phys.* 11, e85 (2011).
102. P. Dutta and P. M. Horn, *Rev. Mod. Phys.* 53, 497 (1981).
103. D. Fugazza, D. Ielmini, S. Lavizzari, and A. L. Lacaita, *IEEE IRPS* 743 (2010).
104. S. Lavizzari, D. Ielmini, D. Sharma, and A. L. Lacaita, *IEEE Trans. Electron Devices* 56, 1078 (2009).
105. P. Donovan, F. Spaepen, D. Turnbull, J. M. Poate, and D. C. Jacobson, *J. Appl. Phys.* 57, 1795 (1985).
106. S. Roorda, W. C. Sinke, J. M. Poate, D. C. Jacobson, S. Dierker, B. S. Dennis, D. J. Eaglesham, F. Spaepen, and P. Fuoss, *Phys. Rev. B* 44, 3702 (1991).
107. K. Koughia, Z. Shakoor, S. O. Kasap, and J. M. Marshall, *J. Appl. Phys.* 97, 33706 (2005).
108. J. A. Kalb, M. Wuttig, and F. Spaepen, *J. Mater. Res.* 22, 748 (2007).
109. D. B. Miracle, T. Egami, K. M. Flores, and K. F. Kelton, *MRS Bull.* 32, 629 (2007).
110. P. Tiwari, R. V. Ramanujan, M. R. Gonal, R. Prasad, P. Raj, B. P. Badguzar, and G. L. Goswami, *Mater. Sci. Eng.* A304, 499 (2001).
111. K. P. Chik, S. Y. Feng, and S. K. Poon, *Solid State Comm.* 33, 1019 (1980).
112. L. Snead and S. J. Zinkle, *Nucl. Instr. Method Phys. Res. B* 191, 497 (2002).
113. M. J. Conway, A. Ilie, J. Robertson, W. I. Milne, and A. Tagliaferro, *Appl. Phys. Lett.* 73, 2456 (1998).
114. A. Pirovano, A. L. Lacaita, F. Pellizzer, S. A. Kostylev, A. Benvenuti, and R. Bez, *IEEE Trans. Electron Devices* 51, 714 (2004).
115. V. Karpov, M. Mitra, D. Kau, G. Spadini, Y. A. Kryukov, and V. G. Karpov, *J. Appl. Phys.* 102, 124503, (2007).
116. Im, E. Cho, D. Kim, H. Horii, J. Ihm, and S. Han, *Phys. Rev. B* 81, 245211 (2010).
117. M. Mitra, Y. Jung, D. S. Gianola, and R. Agarwal, *Appl. Phys. Lett.* 96, 222111 (2010).
118. V. Weidenhof, I. Friedrich, S. Ziegler, and M. Wuttig, *J. Appl. Phys.* 89, 3168 (2001).
119. G. Ruitenberg, A. K. Petford-Long, and R. C. Doole, *J. Appl. Phys.* 92, 3116 (2002).
120. A. Redaelli, D. Ielmini, U. Russo, and A. L. Lacaita, *IEEE Trans. Electron Devices* 53, 3040 (2006).
121. H. Overhof and P. Thomas, "Electronic Transport in Hydrogenated Amorphous Semiconductors." Springer, New York, 1989.
122. D. J. Fisher, *Def. Diffus. Forum.* 192 (2001).
123. G. Boisvert, L. J. Lewis, and A. Yelon, *Phys. Rev. Lett.* 75, 469 (1995).
124. W. Linert and R. F. Jameson, *Chem. Soc. Rev.* 18, 477 (1989).
125. A. Yelon, B. Movaghar, and R. S. Crandall, *Rep. Prog. Phys.* 69, 1145 (2006).
126. M. Forst, T. Dekorsy, C. Trappe, M. Laurenzis, H. Kurz, and B. Bechevet, *Appl. Phys. Lett.* 77, 1964 (2000).
127. U. Russo, D. Ielmini, A. Redaelli, and A. L. Lacaita, *IEEE Trans. Electron Devices* 53, 3032 (2006).
128. N. Yamada, E. Ohno, K. Nishiushi, N. Akahira, and M. Takao, *J. Appl. Phys.* 69, 2849 (1991).
129. S. Raoux, C. Cabral, L. Krusin-Elbaum, J. L. Jordan-Sweet, K. Virwani, M. Hitzbleck, M. Salinga, A. Madan, and T. L. Pinto, *J. Appl. Phys.* 105, 064918 (2009).
130. F. Zheng, J. Reed, C. Schell, W. Czubatyj, R. Sandoval, J. Fournier, W. Li, W. Hunks, C. Dennison, S. Hudgens, and T. Lowrey, *IEEE Electron Device Lett.* 31, 999 (2010).
131. T. Morikawa, K. Kurotsuchi, M. Kinoshita, N. Matsuzaki, Y. Matsui, Y. Fuiisaki, S. Hanzawa, A. Kotabe, M. Terao, H. Moriya, T. Iwasaki, M. Matsuoka, F. Nitta, M. Moniwa, T. Koga, and N. Takaura, "IEDM Tech. Dig.," p. 307, 2007.
132. Y. Ling, Y. Lin, L. Lai, B. Iao, Y. Lai, J. Feng, T. Tang, B. Cai, and B. Chen, *Proc. Solid-State Integr. Cir. Tec.* 707 (2004).
133. G. Betti Beneventi, E. Gourvest, A. Fantini, L. Perniola, V. Sousa, S. Maitrejean, J. C. Bastien, A. Bastard, A. Fargeix, B. Hyot, C. Jahan, J. F. Nodin, A. Persico, D. Blachier, A. Toffoli, S. Loubriat, A. Roule, S. Lhostis, H. Felds, G. Reimbold, T. Billon, B. De Salvo, L. Larcher, P. Pavan, D. Benshael, P. Mazoyer, R. Annunziata, and F. Boulanger, "International Memory Workshop," p. 21, 2010.
134. A. Fantini, V. Sousa, L. Perniola, E. Gourvest, J. C. Bastien, S. Maitrejean, S. Braga, N. Pashkov, A. Bastard, B. Hyot, A. Roule, A. Persico, H. Fedis, C. Jahan, J. F. Nodin, D. Blachier, A. Toffoli, G. Reimbold, F. Fillot, F. Pierre, R. Annunziata, D. Benshael, P. Mazoyer, C. Vallee, T. Billon, J. Hazart, B. De Salvo, and F. Boulanger, "IEDM Tech. Dig.," p. 644, 2010.

CHAPTER 5

Metal-Oxide-Based Resistive-Switching Memory: Materials, Device Scaling, and Technology Design

Jinfeng Kang[1], Bin Gao[1], Bin Yu[2]
[1] *Institute of Microelectronics, Peking University, Beijing 100871, China*
[2] *College of Nanoscale Science and Engineering, State University of New York, Albany, New York 12203, USA*

CONTENTS

ISBN: 1-58883-251-1

Nonvolatile Memories: Materials, Devices and Applications
Edited by Tseung-Yuen Tseng and Simon M. Sze
Volume 2: Pages: 111–137

1. INTRODUCTION: TREND OF SEMICONDUCTOR MEMORY TECHNOLOGY

Success of research in semiconductor-based data storage, especially nonvolatile memory (NVM), has been one of the main driving forces for information technology. The vast market demands for NVM, including those from consumer electronics (e.g., television, stereo-audio, MP3, digital camera), network communication (e.g., cell phone, global positioning system), computer (e.g., solid state disk, desktop/laptop, display, printer), and military applications, drive the rapid technology development of NVM. Cost reduction per bit is one of the most crucial targets in the growth of memory industry and has been achieved through continuous scaling of memory cell devices. This is coupled with the highly demanded large-capacity memory with low power dissipation. However, conventional floating-gate (FG)-based flash memory technology faces serious limits on both device design and process development when scaling down to sub-30-nm nodes. The challenges include cost-intensive lithography, coupling ratio, crosstalk between neighboring cells, short channel effect (SCE), tunneling dielectrics scaling, and data retention [1–3].

Emerging memories based on new mechanisms and/or new materials are in eminent demand, along with a rapid evolution of the technology to roll out alternatives to overcome the problems of the traditional FG-based NVM [4, 5]. The candidates of emerging memory technologies include charge trapping memory (CTM) in which the charges are trapped in thin dielectric materials rather than floating gate, ferroelectric random access memory (FeRAM) with data storage in polarization states of ferroelectric material with reversibly changed atomic structure, magnetic RAM (MRAM) that stores data using magnetic tunnel junctions with magnetoresistive change, phase-change RAM (PRAM) based on the thermally induced reversible phase change between crystalline and amorphous states in a chalcogenide compound material such as $Ge_2Sb_2Te_5$ (GST), as well as resistive RAM (RRAM) based on electrically induced reversible resistance change in an insulator. Among a spectrum of candidates, transition-metal oxide-based RRAM has emerged as one of the most promising candidates due to its excellent memory performance and potential applications in new areas such as memristor or neuron cell systems.

The concept of RRAM is based on the reversible resistance switching observed in various dielectric materials such as oxides, selenides, sulfides, and organic compounds [5, 6]. The resistance switching behavior is usually defined as the resistance change between at least two resistance states, namely low resistance state (LRS) and high resistance state (HRS), respectively. A large number of materials have been explored for RRAM. Among which, superior resistive switching characteristics has been demonstrated in transition-metal oxides. RRAM is expected to become the "universal memory" technology replacing both dynanic RAM (DRAM) and flash.

Historically, the first report on resistive switching in metal oxides was in the 1960s. Hickmott published his paper on electric fields induced hysteretic current–voltage (I–V) characteristics in metal-insulator-metal (MIM) structures such as $Al/Al_2O_3/Al$ [7]. Later, resistive switching phenomenon was subsequently reported in a wide variety of metal oxides, especially transition metal oxides such as NiO [8, 9], SiO [10], Pr–Ca–Mn–O [11, 12], Cr–Sr–Zr–O [13], $SrTiO_3$ [14, 15], TiO [16], and Cu–O [17]. Up to the late 1990s, the research activity on resistive switching memory technology pasted its inflection point [11, 17–20].

As a new member of the NVM family, RRAM has demonstrated its superior capability and rapid advancement in research and development. The excellent memory performance as observed in transition metal oxide-based RRAM [21–23] offers advantages possessed by both DRAM and flash, e.g., low operating voltage (< 2 V), fast program/erase P/E) speed (< 5 ns), a large window of high/low resistance ratio (> 100), excellent cycling endurance ($> 10^6$), and long data retention (> 10 years). Meanwhile, RRAM technology also shows superior scalability and three-dimensional (3D) integration capability. Being possible in crossbar architecture, the memory cell may be scaled to $4F^2$ dimensions—the best possible scaling so far in memory. Further scaling is possible by vertical 3D stacking of crossbars. For instance, n times scaling will make the cell area $4F^2/n$ when we use a 3D integration approach of crossbars with n stacking storage layers.

Despite of the fact that rapid progresses in RRAM technology have been made recently, several key challenges still need to be addressed toward mass manufacturing. Currently, the major roadblock is the unclear physical switching mechanism. Meanwhile, other challenges exist such as optimization of material/cell structure/storage array architecture, process technology, characterization methods, and reliability.

There are two classes of physical mechanisms that have been proposed to explain resistive switching observed in transition metal oxides (TMO)-based RRAM [5, 6]. One is the filament conduction mechanism, in which resistive switching could be attributed to the formation and rupture of conducting filaments consisted of defects such as oxygen vacancies or other metallic defects in an insulating matrix. The other is the interface mechanism, the resistive switching related to various interface effects such as electrochemical migration of oxygen vacancies, trapping of charge carriers, and a Mott transition induced by carriers doped at the interface. The filament and interface types of resistive switching can be distinguished by the area dependence of cell resistance. Currently, the filament conduction mechanism has been widely adopted to elucidate the resistive switching behavior of TMO-based RRAM. In the filament conduction mechanism, the formation of filamentary conducting paths is similar to soft breakdown induced by electric field, resulting in device switching from high resistance state to low resistance state during forming (or SET) process. Meanwhile, the rupture of filaments takes place during the RESET process. Various chemical/physical processes such as Joule heating, redox reaction, and electrochemical migration of oxygen ions have been proposed to explain the resistive switching behavior [5, 6]. However, the physical origins have still not been clarified. Meanwhile, direct observation of conducting filaments in insulating oxides has not been achieved [25]. Basic knowledge about conducting filaments with respect to their composition, size, and distribution density has only been indirectly inferred.

For TMO-based RRAM technology, significantly advancement has been subsequently reported. In 2005, the research groups from Spansion and Samsung firstly reported the excellent scaling behavior of one transistor-one resistor (1T-1R) and one diode-one resistor (1D-1R) cells in TMO-based RRAM [17, 26]. Spansion's group reported that improved switching behaviors could be achieved in a 1T-1R cell of RRAM [17]. Samsung group reported multilayer crosspoint-structured RRAM [26]. Novel plug-contact-type bottom electrode (plug-BE) was applied to achieve 50-nm memory cell size, smaller operational current, and improved switching distribution. These results demonstrated the application potential of TMO-based RRAM technology integrated with complementary metal–oxide–semiconductor (CMOS) circuits. In 2007, Fujitsu and Samsung groups further reported improved switching behavior in scaled 1T-1R and 1D-1R cells such as small RESET current, fast RESET time, stable device performance, and better controllability/scalability [27, 28]. It was also demonstrated that proper doing is effective to improve the resistive switching behavior [21, 27, 28]. Besides, the impact of new storage materials [29, 30], the electrode effect [31–34], and the switching mode effect [27, 32] were addressed. In 2009, Taiwan Industrial Technology Research Institute's group demonstrated a 30×30 nm^2 HfO_x-RRAM device with excellent electrical performance and scalability. The 1 Kb 1T-1R array exhibits high device yield (~100%) and robust cycling endurance ($> 10^6$) measured by a pulse width of 40 ns [22].

As mentioned above, critical memory performance such as fast switching speed (< 10 ns), low operating voltage (< 1.5 V), low RESET current (< 10 μA), high endurance ($> 10^6$) cycles, long retention time (> 10 years at 150°C), excellent uniformity of cycle-to-cycle and device-to-device, and process compatibility with CMOS have been demonstrated by different research groups. However, the community still faces a great challenge for RRAM to meet all critical technical requirements. It is deserved to seek out solutions from the fundamentally technical levels. To achieve this goal, an understanding of the deep materials on the microscopic nature of resistance switching and development of effective solutions to control the switching process is critical.

In this chapter, we will review the latest advancements in TMO-based RRAM. Firstly, the resistive switching characteristics of TMO-based RRAM are discussed in Section 2. Then, a unified physical mechanism of bipolar switching behavior is presented in Section 3. In Section 4, quantified models for RESET and retention behavior in TMO-based RRAM are introduced based on the unified physical mechanism. The technical solutions based on material- and operation-oriented methodology are addressed and discussed in Section 5. Finally, the prospect of future technological trend of TMO-based RRAM is highlighted in Section 6.

2. RESISTIVE SWITCHING CHARACTERISTICS OF TMO-BASED RRAM

In this section, the typical resistive switching phenomena and the concept of RRAM is introduced. Then, the typical resistive switching characteristics, including scalability, switching speed and voltage/power, RESET current, uniformity, endurance, and retention are discussed. In addition, the correlated effects such as material system, doping, electrode, and operation mode, are addressed. Systematic investigation on these characteristics and effects helps to understand the physical mechanisms of resistive switching behavior and to find out the effective technical solutions to overcome the challenges of RRAM technology.

2.1. Concept of RRAM

The electric-induced resistance-switching phenomenon between the two bistable resistance states (LRS and HRS) has been observed in many dielectric materials including transition metal oxides. This resistance switching (RS) behavior can be applied to construct RS-based memory device using a typical sandwiched structure between two electrodes (TE and BE; Fig. 1), namely RRAM. Figure 2 shows the typical resistance switching of a RRAM device. Generally, the *ex-situ* fabricated RRAM devices are in HRSs. An electric *forming* process is required to achieve the RS behavior. After the forming process, the RRAM device is electrically switched between at least two different resistance states of LRS and HRS by SET and RESET processes. The SET and RESET indicate the switching processes from HRS (off state) to LRS (on state) and from LRS to HRS, respectively. The critical voltages and currents corresponding to the resistance transitions during the forming, SET, and RESET processes are named as the forming voltage (V_{Forming}), SET voltage and current (V_{SET} and I_{SET}), and RESET voltage and current ($V_{\text{RESET}}/I_{\text{RESET}}$), respectively. A current compliance (CC) is usually used to prevent the device from damage during forming and SET processes. Actually, using current compliance is also an effective approach to control the resistance in LRS.

Two types of resistive switching modes are observed in the TMO-based RRAM, namely as unipolar and bipolar respectively. For the unipolar operation scheme, the typical I–V curves are schematically shown in Figure 3(a), and the switching procedure does not depend on the

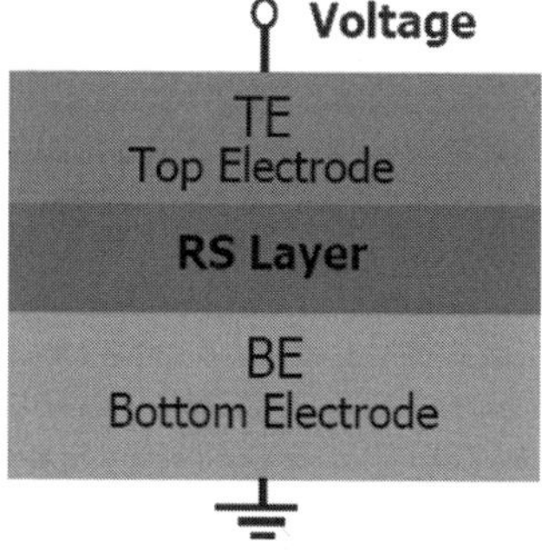

Figure 1. Typical structure of RRAM.

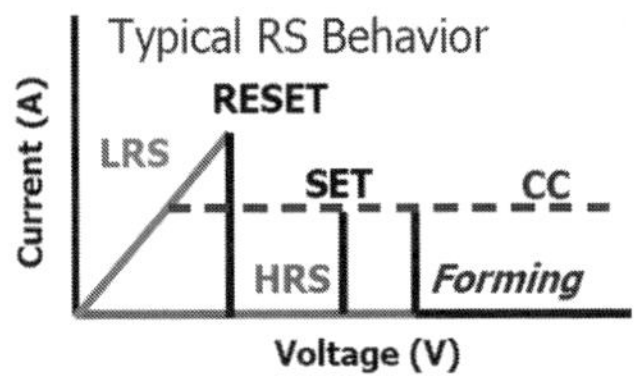

Figure 2. Typical resistance switching behavior of RRAM.

polarity of applied voltage on the RRAM device, or the RRAM can be SET and RESET by using the same polarity of voltage, respectively. For the bipolar operation scheme, the typical *I–V* curves are schematically shown in Figure 3(b); a reversed polarity of RESET voltage is required to switch the RRAM with respect to the SET voltage. In brief, the unipolar operation involves programming/erasing using the same voltage polarity. In contrast to this, the bipolar operation needs the opposite polarity of SET and RESET voltages.

For the RRAM, the typical array architecture is designed as matrix consisting of the rows and columns and storage nodes or cells located at the crosspoints of the rows and columns. Generally, a selector device is needed in addition to memory element for a memory cell of RRAM memory array in order to correctly access each cell without read/write disturbance. Various RRAM cell architectures,

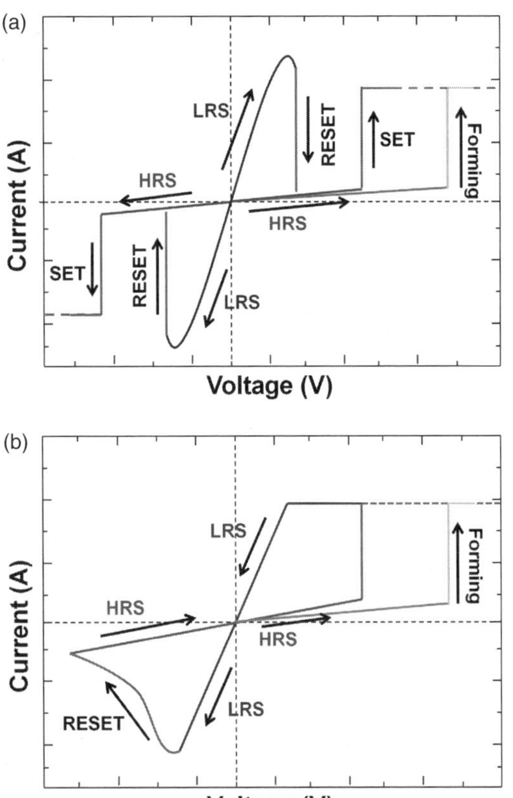

Figure 3. The typical *I–V* curves of the two different operation schemes in TMO-based RRAM devices: (a) unpolar operation scheme, (b) bipolar operation scheme.

such as 1T-1R, 1D-1R, or 1R, have been proposed and demonstrated [26, 34, 36].

For the 1T-1R cell [35], a transistor as the selector device is connected to a RRAM element to access the selected memory cell during the write/read operations without read/write disturbance. This is a typical architecture of RRAM cell that is available for both unipolar and bipolar operation schemes. Since the transistor can effectively screen the crosstalk between the selected cell and the unselected cell, no special specifications on the switching behavior of RRAM device are needed. However, the typical unit cell size of a 1T-1R structure is about 6~8 F^2, where F refers to minimum lithographic feature for a particular technology node and the 1T-1R structure is not suitable for the 3D stacked structures. Therefore, the 1T-1R cell is not available for high the density of memory application.

In the 1D-1R cell [26], a diode is used as the selector to access the selected cell and to eliminate crosstalk between the selected and the unselected (or semi-selected) cells based on the rectifying characteristic of the diode to prevent "sneak" currents from passing through non-selected cells. Based on the 1D-1R cell, the simple $4F^2$ cross-point array structure and 3D stacked integration for high density memory application can be achieved. However, since a diode could not fully screen the crosstalk between the selected cell and the unselected or semi-selected cells, the operation modes need to be optimized in order to effectively eliminate the crosstalk. In this case, some special requirements on the switching behavior of memory device, i.e., uniploar switching mode, are usually needed.

Recently, the 1R cell architecture consisting of only an individually RRAM device without an additional selector was proposed and experimentally explored [36]. For the 1R cell, the self-rectifying characteristic of the RRAM device is needed in order to effectively eliminate the crosstalk between the selected cell and unselected or semi-selected cells. Generally, a Schottky barrier exists at the interface of the electrode with the resistive switching layer. Up until now, the high SET or RESET current of RRAM devices is a critical issue to limit the scalability of RRAM technology, which causes the excess requirements for the current driving ability of the selector devices such as transistor or diode. Therefore, the 1R cell may also effectively overcome the scaling limit of RRAM technology that originated from the high SET/RESET current, but the research exploration on the optimized device structure with the self-rectifying characteristic is still a great challenge.

2.2. Characteristics of TMO-Based RRAM

As one of the most promising next-generation memory technologies, TMO-based RRAM shows excellent memory performance. In this section, we will address the major characteristics of TMO-based RRAM.

2.2.1. Material Systems

The resistive switching characteristics of various TMO material systems, such as NiO [8, 9], TiO_x [16], CuO_x [17], TaO_x [37], WO_x [29], FeO_x [30], ZnO [31], CeO_x [38], ZrO_x [32, 39], and HfO_x [22, 40], have been explored. Generally, RRAM devices based on various material systems

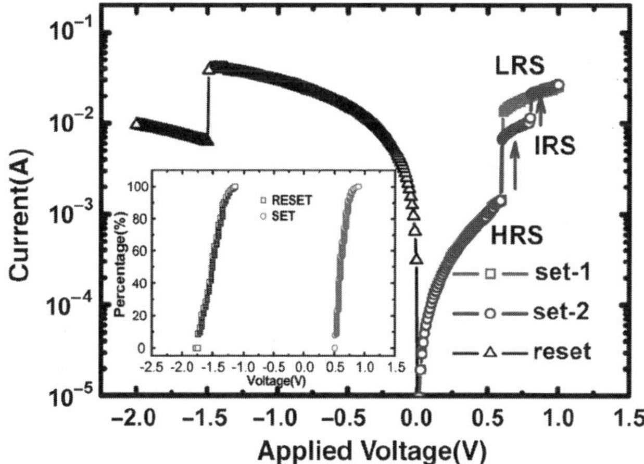

Figure 4. The typical I–V curves of an Al/CeO_x/Pt device. The inset shows the statistics for the distribution of Set and Reset voltages. Reprinted with permission from [38], X. Sun et al., *IEEE Electron Device Lett.* 30, 334 (2009). © 2009, IEEE.

often show the unique resistive switching characteristics, which may relate to the intrinsic material properties. Our researches indicate that, based on the TiO_x and ZnO material systems, the RRAM devices occasionally present excellent switching behavior, as demonstrated in Refs. [31, 41]. However, these devices usually behave with the worst performance repeatability and fabrication process controllability. Different lots with the same fabrication process often produce significantly different device performances. In contrast to this, the ZrO_x and HfO_x devices [32, 40] show stable and repeatable device performances with the controlled fabrication process.

Unique switching behavior was observed in the CeO_x devices (Fig. 4) [38]. In the devices, no forming process was needed and a multistep set process with a self-current compliance was observed (Fig. 5).

These observed resistive switching characteristics in various TMO systems imply that deep explorations for the fundamental physical mechanisms on the resistive switching behavior in various TMO material systems are needed.

2.2.2. Scalability

As a candidate of next-generation memory technologies, a scalability of the device is one of the most critical components. For the RRAM, excellent scaling behavior has been demonstrated, which is also one of the most predominant advantages of RRAM. At the 2005 International Electronic Devices Meeting, the Spansion group first reported an important characteristic of oxide-based RRAM, i.e., that the improved memory performances could be achieved in the scaled 1T-1R device [17]. After that, the fast research advances in oxide-based RRAM were achieved. In 2007, Fujitsu and Sony [29, 35] successively demonstrated that the improved memory performances could be achieved in the scaled 1T-1R cell, respectively. Recently, a 30 × 30 nm HfO_x-based RRAM with good memory performance was demonstrated [22], indicating the excellent scalability of TMO-based RRAM. This is superior to the conventional NVM and other candidates of novel NVM technologies.

2.2.3. Speed

High speed read/write (SET/RESET) capacity is another performance metrics demonstrated in the TMO-RRAM. Nanoseconds switching speed can be easily achieved in the devices (Fig. 6).

Recently, sub-ns switching speed in the HfO_x-based RRAM devices was reported [42], demonstrating the high-speed operation capacity in the TMO-based RRAM.

2.2.4. Voltage and Power

The performance of low operation voltage and power is required for the next generation of memory devices. In this aspect, RRAM also demonstrated the excellent behavior.

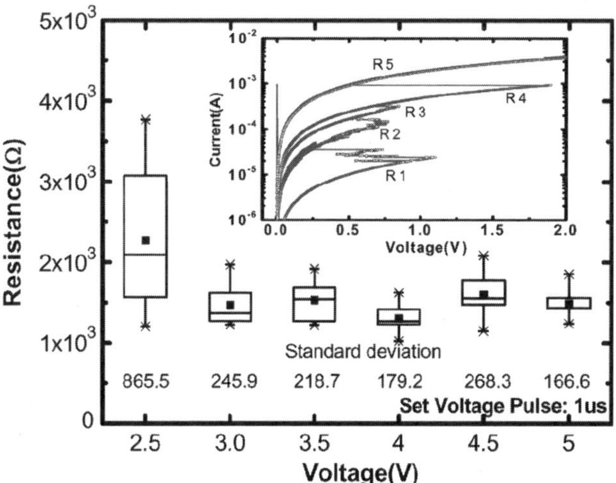

Figure 5. The statistics for the distribution of resistance as a function of set voltage. The inset shows the multiple reset process of under DC sweeping current mode. Reprinted with permission from [38], X. Sun et al., *IEEE Electron Device Lett.* 30, 334 (2009). © 2009, IEEE.

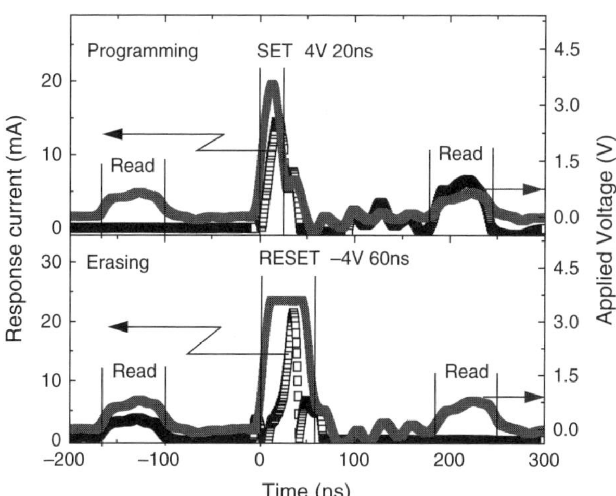

Figure 6. Measured respondent current under an applied switching voltage on TE (TiN). (a) 4 V/20 ns Set pulse, and ∗ (b) −4 V/60 ns RESET pulse. Reprinted with permission from [49], N. Xu et al., "Symp. VLSI Technology Dig.," p. 100, 2008. © 2008, IEEE.

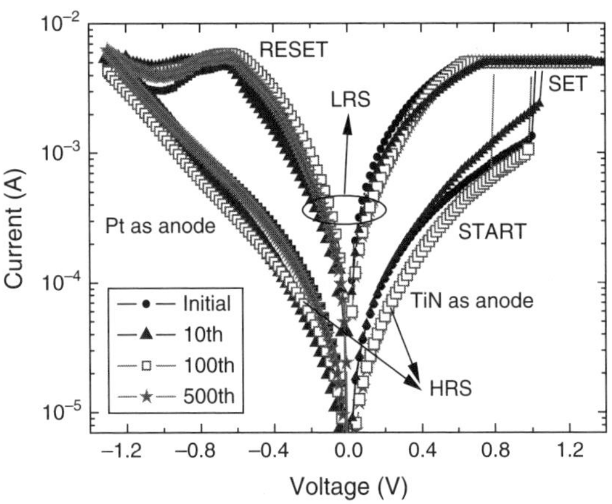

Figure 7. *I–V* curves of TiN/ZnO/Pt device for initial and 10th, 100th and 500th DC cycles. Reprinted with permission from [49], N. Xu et al., "Symp. VLSI Technology Dig.," p. 100, 2008. © 2008, IEEE.

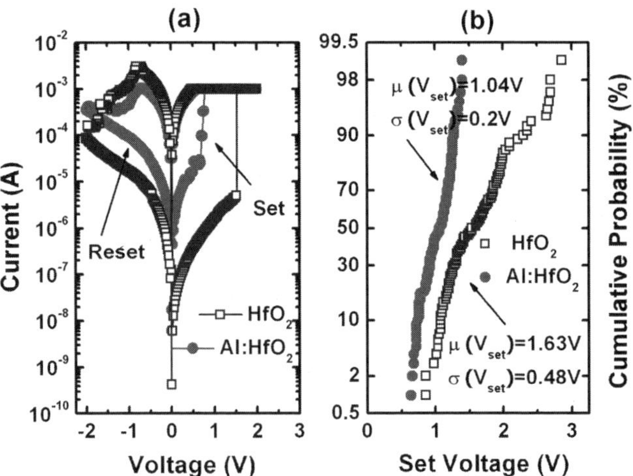

Figure 9. Typical DC sweep *I–V* curves of cycle-to-cycle for the Al-doped and undoped HfO_2 devices. (a) SET/RESET behavior, and (b) statistical distribution of set voltages (V_{set}).

Generally, lower SET/RESET voltage less than 1 V is easily obtained in the TMO-based RRAM devices (Fig. 7).

Recently, the ultra-low operation power less than 4 μW was reported in the GeO/$SrTiO_x$ RRAM devices [43]. These observed behaviors indicate the great potential of TMO RRAM devices in low voltage and low power circuit applications.

2.2.5. Uniformity

The uniformity of switching parameters of cycle-to-cycle and device-to-device, such as the forming/SET and RESET voltages, resistances in LRS and HRS, are important parameters for RRAM devices. It has been widely accepted that formation and rupture of conductive filaments (CFs) are responsible for the RS. Due to the randomness of the local filament formation, large variations of RS parameters were usually observed. Therefore, the fluctuation of the switching parameters cycle-to-cycle and device-to-device are still a great challenge for RRAM technology. We have demonstrated that the proper doping in the RS matrix materials and proper electrode selection could effectively improve the uniformity [40, 44]. Figures 8 and 9 show the uniformity comparisons of switching parameters between the Al-doped and undoped HfO_2 devices [40]. The significantly uniformity improvement could be attributed to the Al-doping effect on the local filament formation.

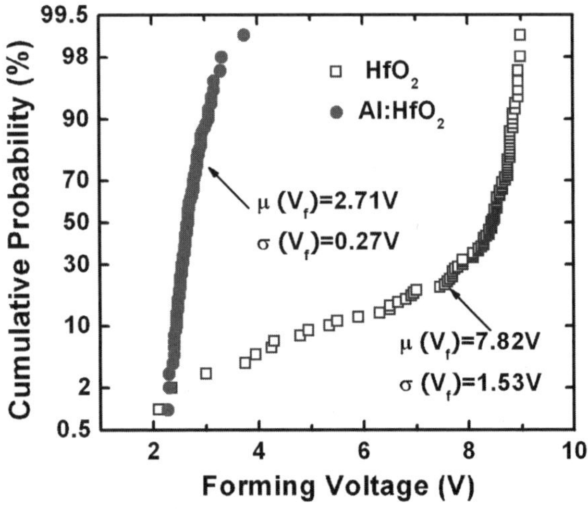

Figure 8. Statistical distribution of forming voltages of device-to-device for 100 samples. μ is the mean value and σ is the standard deviation. Reprinted with permission from [40], B. Gao et al., "Symp. VLSI Technology Dig. Tech.," p. 30, 2009. © 2009, IEEE.

2.2.6. Endurance

Frequently *P*/*E* (switching) operations are needed for NVM. The degradation and failure of the memory cell normally occurs during the switching cycling. The number of switching cycles that the memory can withstand is called "endurance." The endurance as a function of the number of switching cycles is one of the critical parameters for NVM devices. The endurance target is usually set as 10^6 switching cycles for the commercial NVM products. For the TMO-based RRAM, endurance characteristics are usually associated with the switching speed, polarity of the switching signals, and electrode or its interface with the RS layer. The TiN electrode has been demonstrated to be beneficial for the improved endurance of RRAM devices due to the high oxygen ions storage capacity of TiN [31, 40]. It is not difficult for the updated RRAM device to reach the endurance target of *r* the commercial NVM products. However, as one of the major candidates for universal memory, the robust endurance up to more than 10^{12} cycles is needed. Recently, the endurance of 10^{10} cycles was reported in the TiN/Ti/HfO_x/TiN devices [42], indicating the great potential of implementing RRAM into the universal memory.

2.2.7. RESET Current

Low operational current is required for nano-scaled memory technology. However, the RESET current of several mA was usually observed in the TMO-based RRAM devices (Fig. 9(a)). Importantly, the RESET current usually could not be scaled with the reduced device size. Even though the

RESET current of μA has been reported [45], high RESET current is still a great challenge for TMO-based RRAM devices. For memory array, high operation current requires great current driving ability of the selectors (transistor or diode). This also becomes the major limiting factor on the scalability of RRAM and has seriously blocked the advance of RRAM technology. How to reduce the RESET current is still one of the major concerns and technology challenges for RRAM. Finding an effectively and fundamentally technical solution is required for RRAM technology.

RRAM provides a potential solution for down scaling beyond NVM, but the very high RESET current is the limit for low-power high-density operation.

2.2.8. Retention

Retention is the measured time that an NVM cell can retain the stored data, whether it is powered or unpowered. For the RRAM devices, the retention usually shows the unique characteristics (Fig. 10). A sharp transition and large variations were often observed, which is obviously different from that observed in the conventional NVM. This indicates that the conventional reliability evaluation method on retention could not be applied to predict the lifetime of the RRAM devices. Therefore, new evaluation methods are needed.

However, the determined physical mechanism on the retention failure is still debatable [46]. To determine the physical origins of retention failure and to set up the available evaluation methods are still challenges for TMO-based RRAM technology. Good data retention may be obtained when we implement the resistance switching materials with high activation energy of oxygen vacancy [46].

2.2.9. Doping Effect

Proper doping is effective for performance improvement. Improved memory characteristics were demonstrated in the Cu-doped MoO_x devices [21] and Ti doped NiO devices [27]. In the TiO_2-based unipolar devices, the significantly improved uniformity was achieved in the Gd-doped devices rather than with undoped devices (Fig. 11) [41].

Meanwhile, the doping effect on the uniformity improvement was also observed in Al-doped HfO_2 bipolar devices [40]. These performance improvements could be attributed to the doping-induced modification of the trapping states characteristics [41, 46].

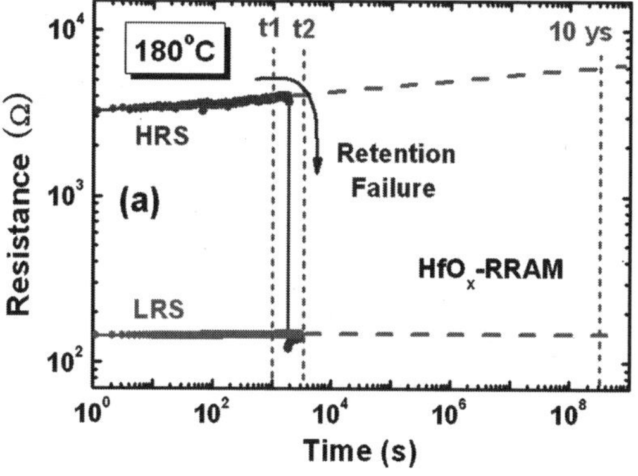

Figure 10. The typical retention behavior measured in a HfO_x-based RRAM device and the projected lifetime by the traditional retention evaluation method.

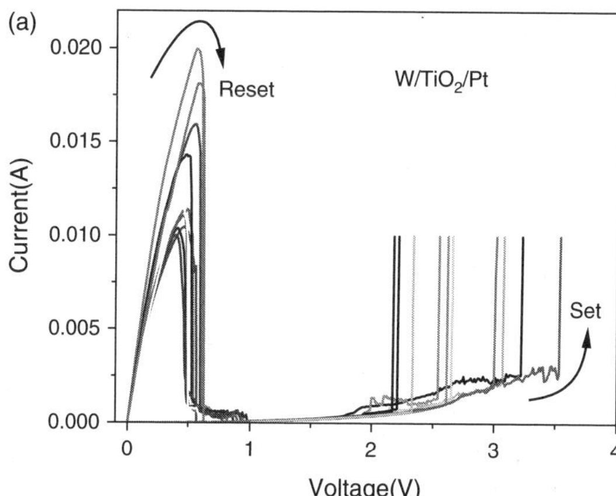

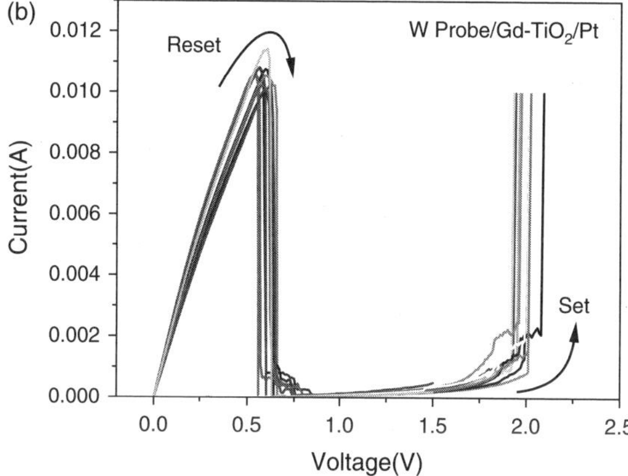

Figure 11. *I–V* characteristics of TiO_2-based RRAM devices. (a) Pure TiO_2 devices, and (b) Gd-doped TiO_2 devices. Reprinted with permission from [41], L. F. Liu et al., *Jap. J. Appl. Phys.* 47, 2701 (2008). © 2008, Japan Society of Applied Physics.

2.2.10. Electrode Effect

The electrode is a key impact factor of the switching behavior of RRAM devices. The systematic study for the electrode effects on the RS behavior were reported by Spansion in 2006. Significant dependence on the oxide/top electrode interface were observed in the Cu_2O RRAM devices with different top electrodes such as Ti, Ta, Ni and Co, suggesting different switching mechanisms [34].

In our studies, the bipolar and unipolar switching behaviors were observed in TiN/ZnO/Pt devices and W/ZnO/Pt, respectively (Figs. 12 and 13) [31]. Meanwhile, the improved RS characteristics were also achieved by using TiN electrode in the ZnO and ZrO_2 devices rather than devices using the W electrode (Figs. 12, 14, and 15) [31, 32]. This suggests that the optimization of the electrode, including material and structure as well as the understanding on the related mechanisms, is required.

2.2.11. Operation Effect

For RRAM, operation mode has been demonstrated to be critical for the RS behavior. Significantly operation

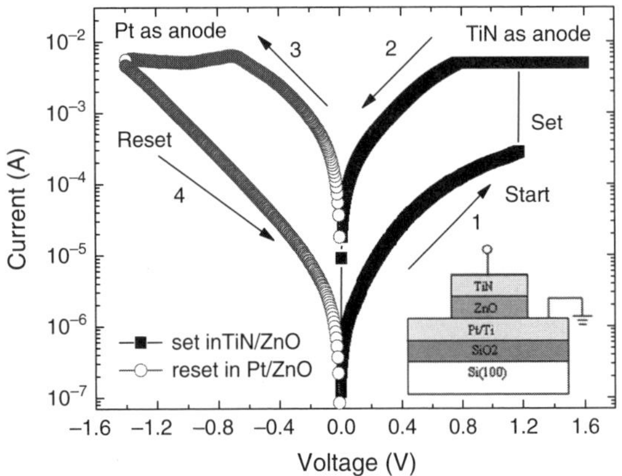

Figure 12. The typical bipolar current versus voltage curve of the fabricated memory cell.

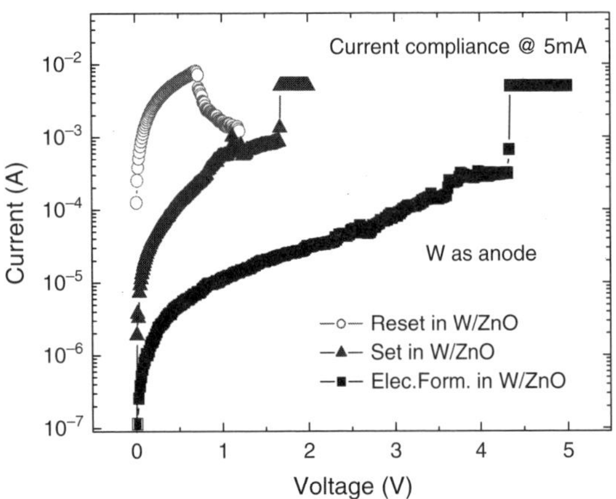

Figure 13. The typical unipolar current versus voltage curve of the fabricated memory cell.

mode dependence of switching behavior was observed in both uniplar and bipolar devices. In 2007, Fujitsu reported the improved uniformity in the Ti-doped NiO unipolar devices by using a pulse switching mode compared

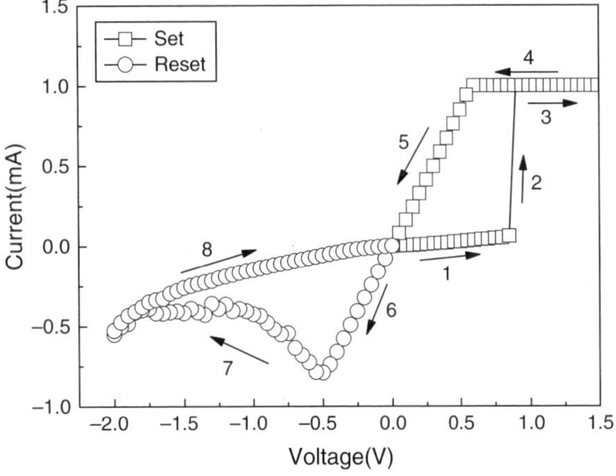

Figure 14. The typical bipolar current versus voltage curve of the fabricated memory cell. Reprinted with permission from [32], B. Sun et al., *J. Appl. Phys.* 105, 061630 (2009). © 2009, American Institute of Physics.

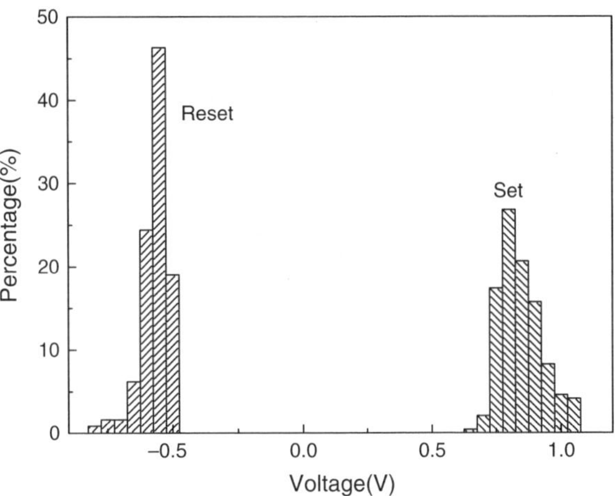

Figure 15. Distribution of the SET and RESET voltages in the case of the DC sweep. Reprinted with permission from [32], B. Sun et al., *J. Appl. Phys.* 105, 061630 (2009). © 2009, American Institute of Physics.

with a direct current (DC) switching mode [34]. In our fabricated ZrO_2-based bipolar devices, significantly improved cycle-to-cycle uniformity was also observed (Figs. 16 and 17).

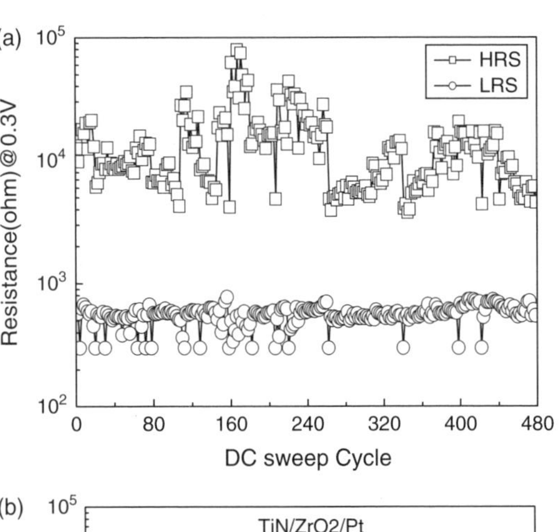

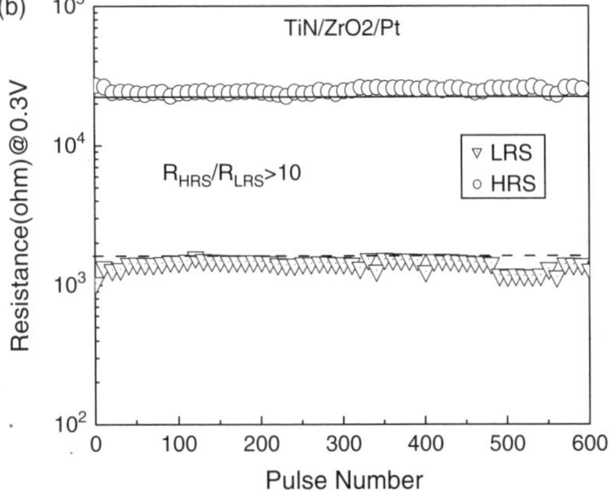

Figure 16. The cycling endurance of the cell in DC and pulse sweep modes, respectively. (a) DC sweep mode, and (b) pulse sweep mode. The applied pulse is 1.5 V/1 us for the set process and −2 V/1 us for the reset process. The resistance measured at 0.3 V read voltage is dispersion. Reprinted with permission from [32], B. Sun et al., *J. Appl. Phys.* 105, 061630 (2009). © 2009, American Institute of Physics.

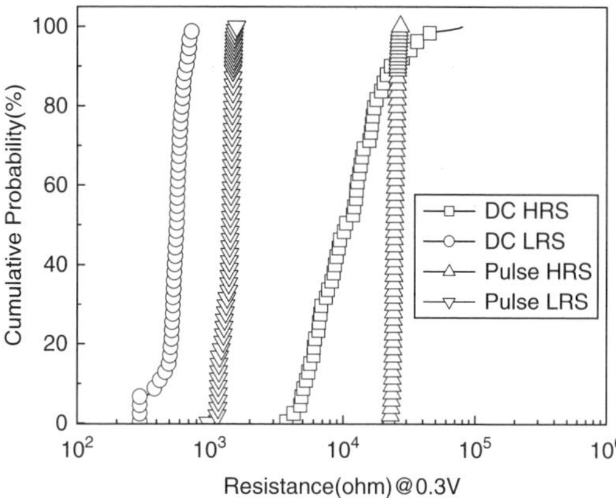

Figure 17. The cumulative probability of R_{HRS} and R_{LRS} of the memory devices under the DC and pulse sweep modes. Reprinted with permission from [32], B. Sun et al., *J. Appl. Phys.* 105, 061630 (2009). © 2009, American Institute of Physics.

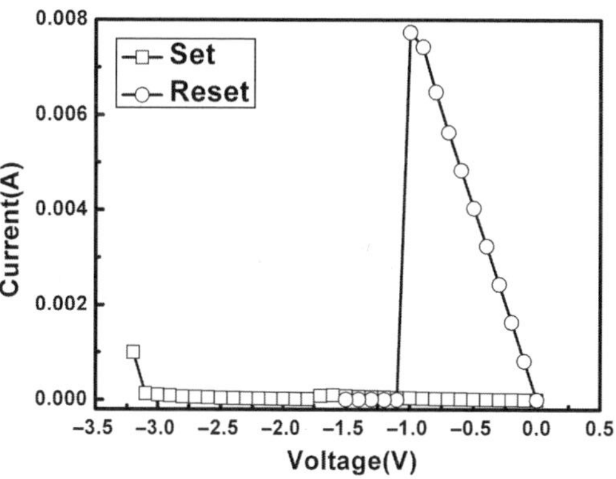

Figure 19. Current–voltage curve of the unipolar resistive behavior of the memory device under negative voltage sweep with high current compliance of > 10 mA. Reprinted with permission from [33], B. Sun et al., *Jpn. Appl. Phys.* 48, 04C061 (2009). © 2009, Japan Society of Applied Physics.

High uniformity of R_{HRS} and R_{LRS} was measured in the pulse sweep. Comparison of the cumulative probability distributions of R_{HRS} and R_{LRS} of the memory cell between the DC sweep and pulse sweep is shown in Figure 16. It is clear that the uniformity characteristic of R_{HRS} and R_{LRS} under the pulse sweep is much better than that under the DC sweep. This phenomenon could be attributed to the dispersive SET and RESET voltages in the multiple oxygen vacancy CFs (MOCFs) [34]. In DC sweep operations, the MOCFS are not formed or ruptured at a same time; the number of CFs is increased with the applied voltage, and the formed CFs have a large influence on the formation of other CFs in the SET process. Meanwhile, the ruptured CFs have a large influence on the rupture of other CFs in the RESET process, which results in various resistance states in both the LRS and HRS. On the contrary, in pulse sweep operations, the formation and rupture of the MOCFs occur at almost at the same time, and they have negligible influence on each other, achieving better uniform distribution of R_{LRS} and R_{LRS}.

Current compliance during the SET process could be used to control the RS behavior. In our fabricated ZrO_2 devices, bipolar RS behavior with nearly linear dependence of R_{HRS}/R_{LRS} was demonstrated in the low current compliance less than 10 mA (Fig. 18) [33]. In contrast to this, when the current compliance was sufficiently high, such as more than 10 mA, unipolar RS behavior could be observed in the same ZrO_2 devices (Fig. 19) [33]. This implies that the correlated physical origin on the RS behavior needs to be well investigated.

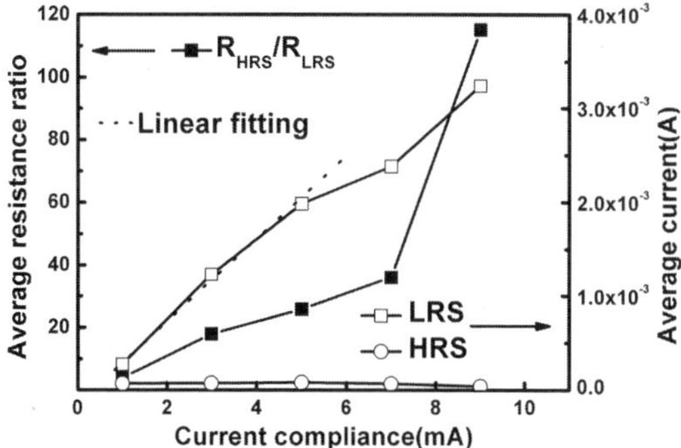

Figure 18. The measured resistance ratio and average read current versus current compliance curves at low current compliance of < 10 mA. All the data were measured at −0.5 V. Reprinted with permission from [33], B. Sun et al., *Jpn. Appl. Phys.* 48, 04C061 (2009). © 2009, Japan Society of Applied Physics.

In summary, excellent memory performance superior to the conventional NVM is achieved in TMO-based RRAM. Various interesting effects and behaviors have been demonstrated. However, the correlated physical mechanisms with the observed effects and behaviors have not been made clear. Deep understanding on the observed physical effects or behavior is required.

3. PHYSICAL MECHANISM OF RESISTIVE SWITCHING

3.1. Survey of Resistive Switching Mechanisms

Investigating the mechanism of RRAM is crucial to the evaluation and enhancement of device performance, scalability, and other significant perspectives in potential applications. However, due to the complexity of the material system and the experimental instrument limit, it is quite difficult to elucidate its physical mechanism. In the early years of RRAM research, the proposed physical origins of RS are surprisingly diverse, including the thermal effect, Schottky barrier effect, metal-insulator transition, ferroelectricity, magnetism, and so on [25]. Lacking efficient experimental support, these mechanisms were not widely accepted. Presently, we have known that RS is mainly due to the generation, transport, and recovery of point defects in the dielectric layer or the valence change of metal oxide. There are three main types of RS based on different mechanism: valence change, oxygen vacancy, and electrochemical metallization.

The first type of RS is mainly observed in material in which metal ions are easy to change the chemical valence, such as TiO_x, FeO_x, TaO_x, CeO_x and so on [25, 38]. For example, titanium oxide can change its phase between TiO_2 (insulating) and Ti_4O_7 (conductive). Only a few metal oxides have this property. The second type is universally observed. For these materials, the lattice structures do not change in the SET and RESET process. Instead, some oxygen vacancies are generated or recovered in the metal-oxide layer [25]. Therefore, these two types can both be seen as oxidation and deoxidization processes, associating with the movement of oxygen ions in the oxide layer or between oxide and electrode interface.

The third type is also called a conductive bridge (CB). In a CB, the intermedium layer is not limited to metal oxide, so this type of RS is quite special. Under the SET voltage, the metal atoms in one of the electrodes ionizes into positive ions, and then it moves into the intermedium layer to form a CB. While under the RESET voltage, these metal ions move back to electrode and the CB is ruptured. This kind of RRAM requires an active electrode with the material easy to ionize and diffusion, e.g., Cu and Ag. At the same time, another electrode should be indolent; thus, Pt is often used [25].

3.2. Filamentary Conduction in RRAM

Experimental evidence has demonstrated that current through an RS layer is not uniform when the RRAM device is in LRS. Conductive-AFM (C-AFM) images have shown that only some point on the surface is highly conductive, indicating that there are filamentary conductive paths through the RS layer. The current of the RS layer under applied voltage is formed mainly from the electrons going through these paths. Generally, this current path is called the CF. However, in HRS conduction, CF is rarely observed. The current density is more uniform rather than localized. Therefore, it is concluded that the current conduction in HRS is mainly due to the bulk leakage current, which is quite small.

Based on the above understanding, a CF model is proposed to interpret the RS phenomenon. When a RRAM device changes from HRS to LRS, some CFs are formed, supporting large current through them. Whereas in the transition from LRS to HRS, these CFs are ruptured, causing the reduction of current [25]. The CF model is widely accepted now. The debate is mainly focused on why and how the CFs are formed and ruptured. To clarify this question, investigating the mechanisms of RRAM beyond the basic of physics is required.

3.3. Physical Mechanisms of Metal-Oxide-Based RRAM

3.3.1. Oxygen Vacancy Filament and Conduction Transport in RRAM

The required formation energy of oxygen vacancy (V_o) in many metal oxides, especially transitional metal oxides, is much lower than other point defects. Therefore, V_o easily forms in these metal oxides [25]. V_o supplies a new electron state in the band gap of oxide [48]. The electron state of V_o supplies a possible way for current conduction.

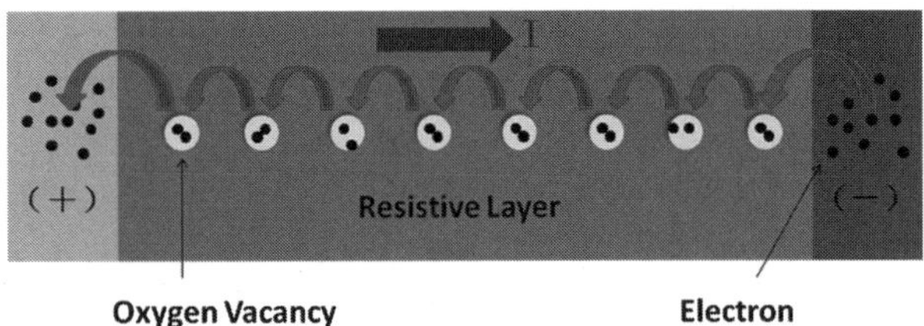

Figure 20. Schematic view of electron hopping through oxygen vacancy based conductive filament in the metal oxide layer.

It can be concluded that the CF in metal oxide is formed by V_o with the CF model. The current conduction is due to the electron hopping transport among these V_o (Fig. 20). The hopping occurs due to a quantum transition when electrons are highly localized and the energy difference can be compensated by phonons [50].

3.3.2. Resistive Switching Mechanism

Since the filament is formed by V_o in most of the metal-oxide based RRAM, the formation and rupture of CF is due to the generation and recovery of V_o in the oxide layer, respectively. The SET process is similar as dielectric soft breakdown, which generates V_o to form CF. As illustrated in Figure 21, under the applied SET voltage, some of the lattice oxygen atoms are ionizing from their original position due to the large local electric field, resulting in the generation of new V_o in these position. These ionized oxygen atoms become interstitial ions in the oxide layer, and they transport under the electric field until they accumulate at the interface between metal-oxide layer and electrode [49].

The forming process is similar to the SET process. The only difference is when the device is in its original state, usually a few V_o exist in the oxide layer. After the forming process, there is already a certain amount of V_o, even if the device is in its HRS state. For this reason, the forming process requires a larger voltage and a longer time than the SET process. It is easy to conclude that if the device has a defect-rich oxide layer in its original state, forming-free phenomenon can be observed.

The RESET process is due to the recovery of V_o with interstitial oxygen ions, causing the rupture of CF (Fig. 21). For bipolar-type RRAM, the oxygen ions are mainly accumulated at the interface between the electrode and oxide layers due to the localization effect of the electrode. Under the RESET voltage, these ions transport from the interface to the oxide layers and recombine with V_o, recovering to a lattice oxygen atom. Alternatively, clarification is still needed to determine where the interstitial oxygen ions come from in unipolar-type RRAM.

3.3.3. RESET Mechanism: Recombination Process

Interstitial oxygen ion is negatively charged. Under an applied electric field, it transports to the anode. Therefore, to finish the recombination process between interstitial oxygen ions and V_o, V_o must be positively charged. Normally, V_o is electric neutral under zero or less than the RESET voltage because it is full of electrons. The capture section

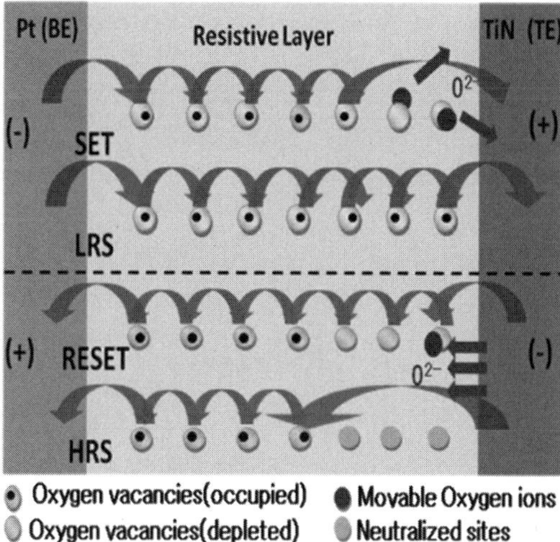

Figure 21. Schematic view of the SET and RESET process in RRAM. Reprinted with permission from [49], N. Xu et al., "Symp. VLSI Technology Dig.," p. 100, 2008. © 2008, IEEE.

of the fully occupied electron V_o to interstitial oxygen ion is very small due to the electron shielding effect on V_o (Fig. 22(a)). When the applied voltage reaches the RESET voltage, some V_o are electron-depleted, and a low-electron occupied (LEO) region along the filament is formed. The V_o in LEO region become positively charged, which causes a significant increase in the capture section to interstitial oxygen ion by more than 100 times (Fig. 22(b)) [53]. The oxygen ions accumulate at the electrode interface transport to the positively charged vacancies and recombine with them.

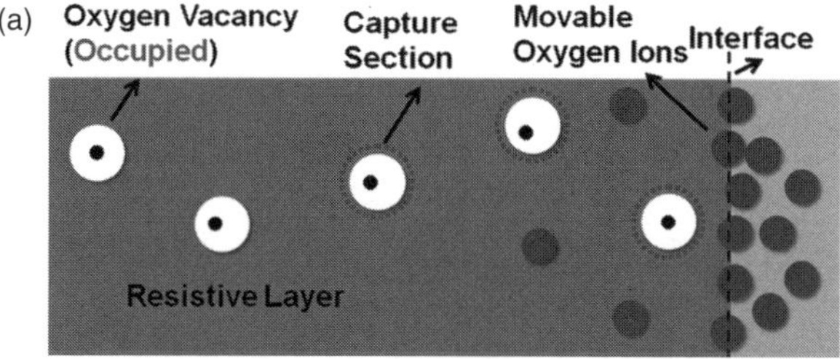

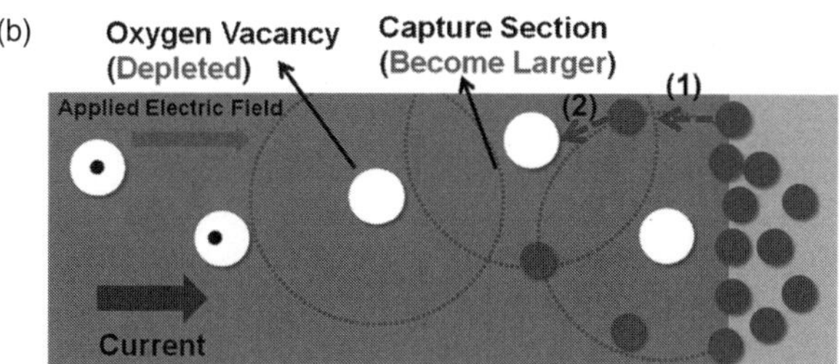

Figure 22. Schematic view of RESET process in RRAM. (a) When applied voltage is below RESET voltage, capture section is very small, and (b) when voltage is larger than RESET voltage, capture section become much larger due to the electron depletion. Reprinted with permission from [53], B. Gao et al., "IEDM Tech. Dig.," p. 563, 2008. © 2008, IEEE.

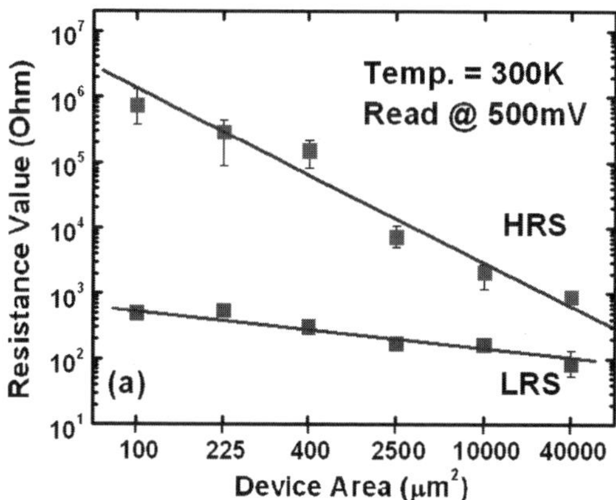

Figure 23. Area dependence of the resistance value in HRS and LRS. Reprinted with permission from [49], N. Xu et al., "Symp. VLSI Technology Dig.," p. 100, 2008. © 2008, IEEE.

3.4. Verification of Resistive Switching Mechanisms

Many experiments have been performed to verify the RS mechanisms [49]. Figure 23 shows cell area dependence of resistance by using a RRAM device with a TiN/ZnO/Pt structure. The result shows a weak dependence of the resistance in LRS on the cell's geometrical size, demonstrating the current distribution through the device as locally confined, filament paths, rather than a homogeneously distributed one, which supports the filamentary conducting mechanism. The linearly dependence of the resistance in the HRS on the size area also demonstrates that the current distribution is uniform, supporting that all of the CFs are ruptured in HRS.

Figure 24 shows the dependence of LRS resistance values on the previous SET current compliance. The decreased resistance with the increased current compliance demonstrates that the LRS current is influenced by the amount of CFs. Under a larger SET current compliance, more CFs are formed, resulting in larger LRS current. This is also evidence to support CF model.

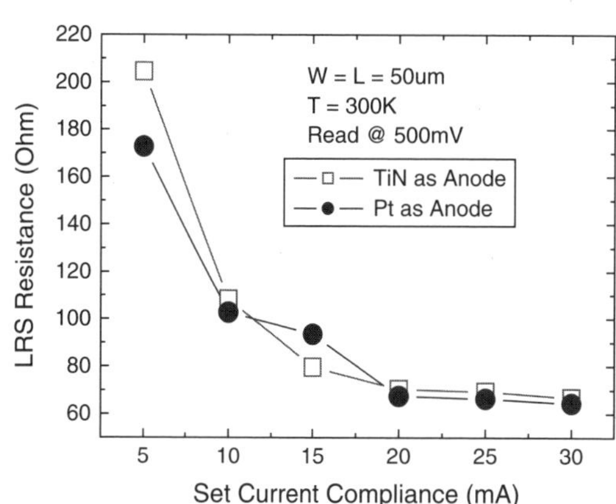

Figure 24. SET current compliance dependence of LRS resistance. Reprinted with permission from [49], N. Xu et al., "Symp. VLSI Technology Dig.," p. 100, 2008. © 2008, IEEE.

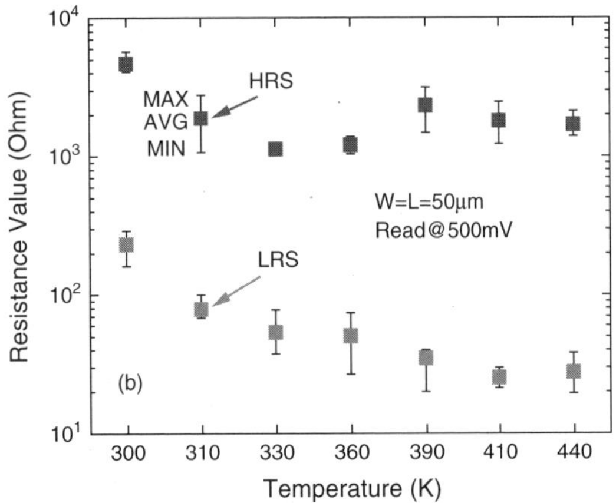

Figure 25. Temperature dependence of the resistance value in HRS and LRS. Reprinted with permission from [49], N. Xu et al., "Symp. VLSI Technology Dig.," p. 100, 2008. © 2008, IEEE.

To verify the conduction mechanism, electrical measurements are performed under different conditions. Figure 25 and show a temperature dependence of DC resistances and frequency dependence of alternating current (AC) conductance in the LRS for the TiN/ZnO/Pt RRAM device. In Figure 24, the decreased resistance in the LRS with increased temperature demonstrates that the electrons transport in the LRS is attributed to the electrons hopping among the localized V_o as the increased number of phonons help the electrons hop through the V_o. At the same time, the measured AC conductance in Figure 26 can be well fitted to Mott's theories for hopping conduction, which also demonstrate this mechanism [50].

To investigate the SET mechanisms, a constant voltage stress less than the SET voltage was applied on the TiN top electrode when the device was in the HRS. A multilevel breakdown phenomenon was observed (Fig. 27). After the multilevel breakdown, the devices can be reset to the HRS from the LRS without any degradation in

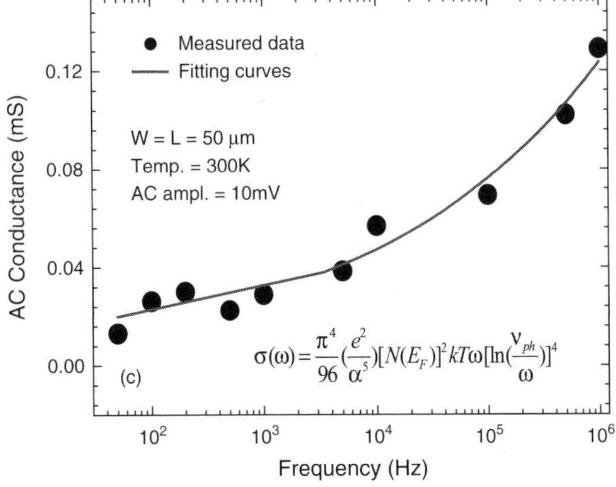

Figure 26. Frequency dependence of the AC conductance in LRS. The insert shows the fitted curves using Mott's hopping theories. Reprinted with permission from [49], N. Xu et al., "Symp. VLSI Technology Dig.," p. 100, 2008. © 2008, IEEE.

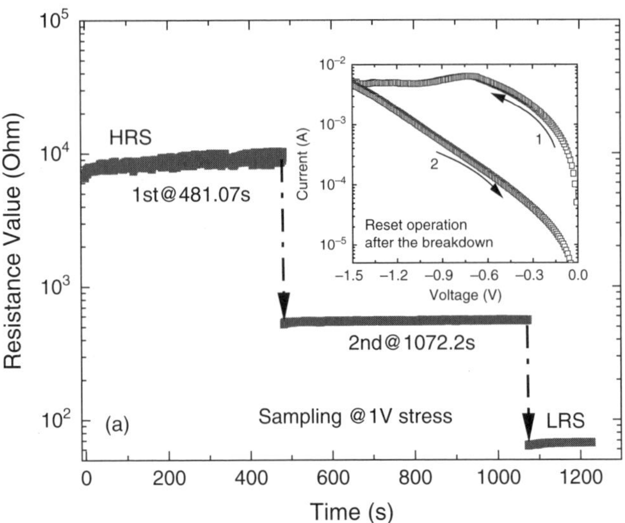

Figure 27. Multilevel breakdown phenomenon in the RRAM device; the insert shows the RESET operation after the thoroughly breakdown. Reprinted with permission from [49], N. Xu et al., "Symp. VLSI Technology Dig.," p. 100, 2008. © 2008, IEEE.

switching performances. This means that both the fast-pulse-controlled SET process and the slow soft dielectric breakdown process under a lower voltage stress than the SET voltage can switch the device to the LRS from the HRS. In order to further understand these processes, the respondent current as a function of the stress time was measured under a 500 mV constant stress, as shown in Figure 28. A relaxation process well fitted by the Pillai model [51] was observed, suggesting that the space-charge polarization effect due to the migration of oxygen vacancies (ions) occurred under a voltage stress.

Figure 29 shows the XPS spectra of oxygen 1-s core levels spectra of ZnO film, indicating that the high content

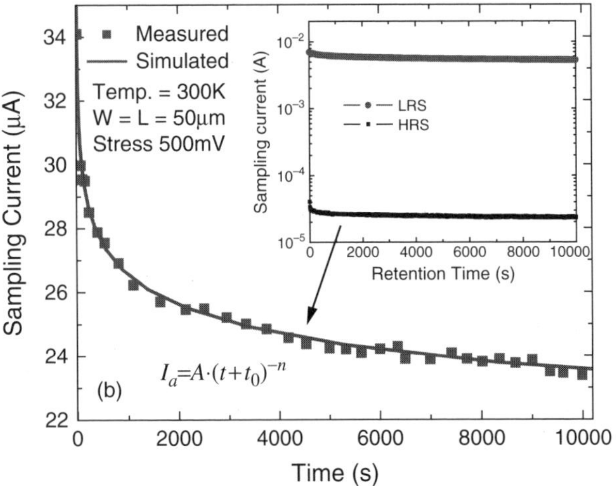

Figure 28. Relaxation process. Respondent current values under 500 mV durable stress for 10,000 s using the sampling mode and the simulated current curve in HRS. Reprinted with permission from [49], N. Xu et al., "Symp. VLSI Technology Dig.," p. 100, 2008. © 2008, IEEE.

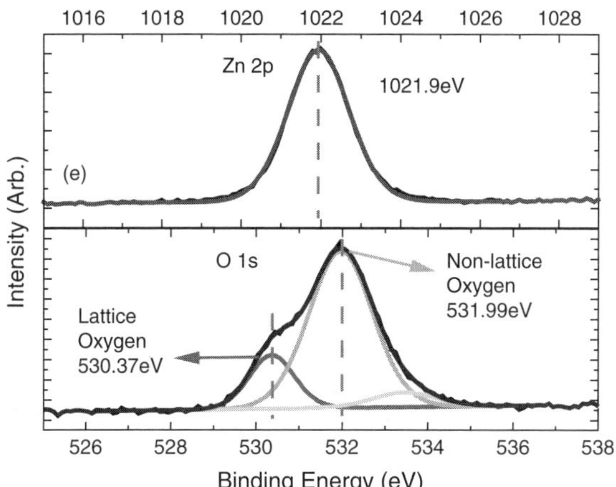

Figure 29. XPS spectra of zinc 2 p and oxygen 1 s core levels in a ZnO film. Reprinted with permission from [49], N. Xu et al., "Symp. VLSI Technology Dig.," p. 100, 2008. © 2008, IEEE.

non-lattice oxygen ions exist on the surface of the ZnO film. However, it is difficult to directly observe the movement of these interstitial oxygen ions in the RESET process. Therefore, the verification of the RESET mechanisms must be discussed after constructing the RESET model.

4. MODELING OF RESISTIVE SWITCHING BEHAVIOR

Based on the understanding of the RS mechanism, a physical model is proposed to quantify the behavior of the RRAM. The model helps to analyze and predict RS characteristics, which are critical to optimizing the performances of RRAM devices.

4.1. Conduction Model

The electron conduction in RRAM includes three processes:

(1) electron transports through V_o in the metal-oxide layer,
(2) electron transports from electrode to V_o state or from V_o state to electrode, and
(3) electron transports in the oxide without the assistant of V_o (only exists in the HRS).

To calculate the I–V curve of RRAM, a unified model is proposed to quantify the electron transport process [52]. This model is called the tunneling-assisted electron-hopping model (TAEP). It is different from the traditional electron-hopping model because it considers the electron tunneling between the oxide and the electrode.

As illustrated in Figure 21, there are three kinds of hopping that correspond to the associated electron transport processes discussed above. To simplify the calculation, we combine the last two transport processes into one hopping. We do this by changing the value of a parameter in the calculation. In this case, we can determine both the LRS and the HRS by using the same expression.

Based on the model, the electron transport characteristics along the filament can be mathematically calculated. The time evolution of electron-occupied probability (EOP) for a V_o contains the rate for the electron

(1) hopping into this V_o from other V_o,
(2) escaping to another V_o from this V_o,
(3) hopping into this V_o from an electrode, and
(4) escaping to an electrode from this V_o.

The rate is proportional to the electron-occupied probability in the mth V_o and unoccupied probability in the nth V_o, but only if the electron hops from the mth V_o to the nth V_o. However, if the electron hops from (to) the electrode, only the unoccupied (occupied) probability in the V_o should be considered. So, the equation is expressed as:

$$\dot{f}_n = (1 - f_n)\sum_m W_{nm} f_m - f_n \sum_m (1 - f_m) W_{mn} + W_n^i (1 - f_n) - W_n^o f_n$$

where f_n indicates the EOP of the nth V_o along the filament. W_{mn} denotes the electron hopping rate from the nth V_o to the mth V_o, and it can be described as:

$$W_{mn} = W_0 \exp(-2\alpha R_{mn} - E_{mn}/k_B T)$$

where α^{-1} is the localization length, R_{mn} is the distance between two V_o, and E_{mn} is the energy difference of the two V_o. W_n^i and W_n^o denote the electron-hopping rate from electrode to V_o and from V_o to electrode, respectively, and can be given as $W_n^x = W_n^{xA} + W_n^{xC}$, (with x referring i or o, and "A" and "C" denoting the anode and cathode, respectively). For the LRS condition, these rates can be calculated by the Fermi Golden Rule, e.g.,:

$$W_n^{iC} = g\frac{2\pi}{\hbar}|H'_{k_c k_n}|^2 \int \rho(E) f(E) dE$$

where $f(E)$ is the Fermi function of the cathode, ρ(E) is the energy density of states, g is the degeneration factor, and H' is the transition Hamilton matrix. Similarly, W_n^{iA}, W_n^{oA} and W_n^{oC} can be evaluated. Both types of hopping will be influenced by the biasing voltage.

When the system reaches stabilization, it is easy to conclude that:

$$\dot{f}_n = 0$$

so EOP could be calculated.

Current generated by hopping could be calculated by:

$$I = -e\sum_n [(1 - f_n) W_n^{iC} - W_n^{oC} f_n]$$

after obtaining all of the EOP. Figure 30 shows a simulated I–V curve of RRAM based on the above model.

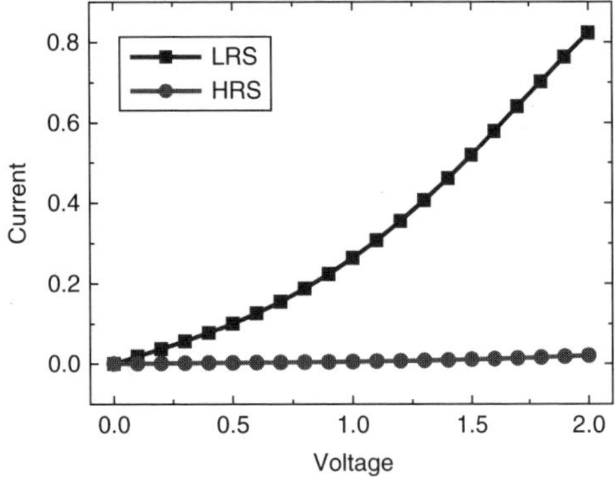

Figure 30. Simulated I–V curve of LRS and HRS.

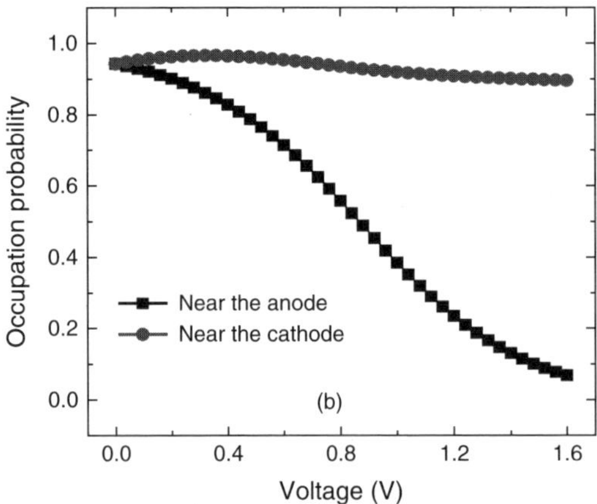

Figure 32. Voltage dependence of electron occupied probability near the anode and cathode. Reprinted with permission from [52], B. Gao et al., *IEEE Electron Device Lett.* 30, 1326 (2009). © 2009, IEEE.

4.2. RESET Model

Based on the physical mechanism, the RESET process can be separated into two processes [52, 53]: (1) electron depletion in some of V_o in the CFs, and (2) a recombination between positively charged V_o and interstitial oxygen ions.

To prove the existence of the LEO region, calculations were made to achieve the EOP based on the conduction model. To simplify the calculation, we assume that the CF is formed by several V_o located in line with the same spacing between the adjacent V_o. All the V_o are in the same energy level when there is no voltage applied; thus, the energy difference between V_o only comes from the applied electric field. We also consider only one electron for each V_o.

Figure 31 shows the EOP of the V_o distribution along the filament under varying voltage. Although the two electrodes are in the same condition, the EOP is not the same when the applied voltage is not zero, and the ones near the anode are lower than the other part along the CFs. The EOP decreases with the applied voltage (Fig. 32). When the applied voltage reaches a critical value, the EOP near the anode drops fast to zero. Figure 33 shows the EOP distribution when the LEO region is near the cathode. The location of the LEO region and related critical voltage are mainly dependent on the W_{mn}, W_n^i, and W_n^o. In a device, W_{mn} depends on the oxide material, while W_n^i and W_n^o depend on the electrode materials depicted by the Fermi functions $f(E)$ and the coupling between the electrode and the V_o depicted by the transition Hamilton matrix H'.

To quantify the RESET behavior of RRAM, it is important to exactly describe the transport and recombination process of oxygen ions. An ion-transport-recombination model is established to achieve this [53]. The model attributes the RESET process to the transportation of O^{2-} from the interface to oxide layer and the recombination of low-electron-occupied V_o^+ with mobile O^{2-}. These ions are mainly accumulated at the interface between the electrode and oxide layers due to the localization effect of the electrode. The mobile oxygen ions can jump over the interface barrier into the oxide layer under an applied electric field (Fig. 34). The interface barrier height is electrode dependent and is slightly different for each oxygen ion.

To describe the transport process of oxygen ions, local concentration approximation is introduced, in which the local oxygen ions concentration ($C_O(\boldsymbol{r})$) is constant in a small region. For the simplicity of calculation, we assume that the oxygen ion concentration is uniform in a plane parallel to

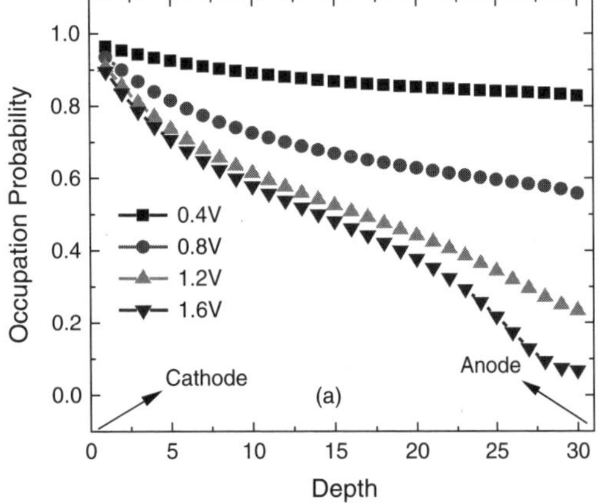

Figure 31. Calculated distribution of electron occupied probability along CF under various biasing voltages. The number of V_O was set as 30. Reprinted with permission from [52], B. Gao et al., *IEEE Electron Device Lett.* 30, 1326 (2009). © 2009, IEEE.

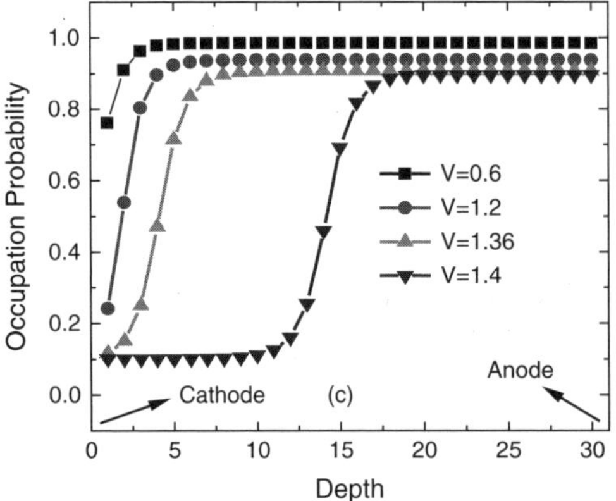

Figure 33. The calculated electron occupied probability distribution with different voltage. Reprinted with permission from [52], B. Gao et al., *IEEE Electron Device Lett.* 30, 1326 (2009). © 2009, IEEE.

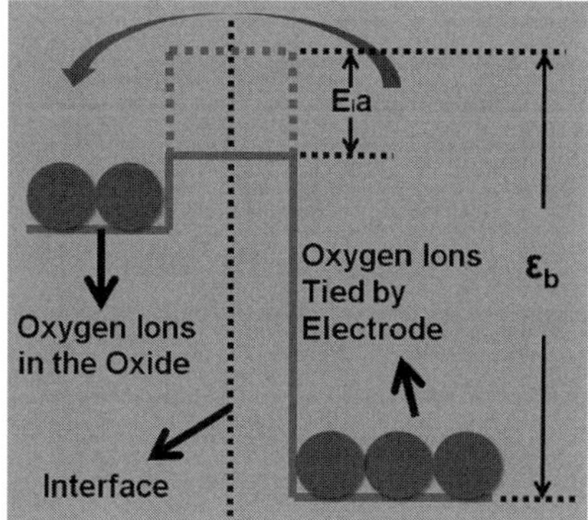

Figure 34. Schematic view of the accumulation and transport of oxygen ions at the interface between electrode and oxide layer. Reprinted with permission from [53], B. Gao et al., "IEDM Tech. Dig.," p. 563, 2008. © 2008, IEEE.

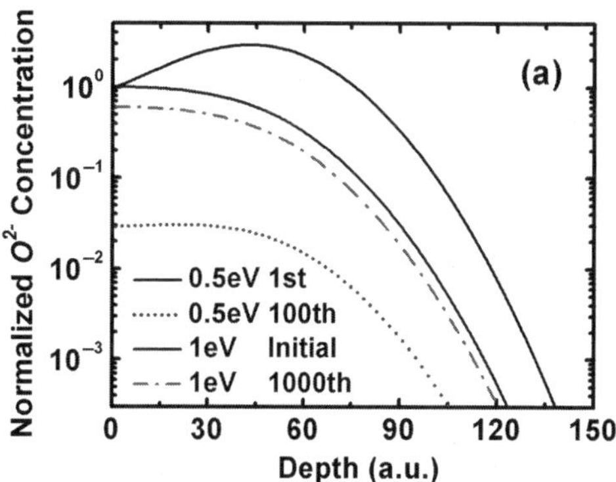

Figure 35. Calculated O^{2-} concentration distribution as a function of depth from the interface with different interface barrier.

the interface. Based on the diffusion and drift effect, the local oxygen ion concentration $C_O(r)$ obeys the following equation:

$$\frac{\partial C_O(x)}{\partial t} = D\left(Ze\frac{\partial \phi}{\partial x}\frac{\partial C_O(x)}{\partial x} + k_B T\frac{\partial^2 C_O(x)}{\partial x^2}\right)$$

The corresponding boundary conditions are expressed as:

$$C_O(x \geq 0, t = 0) = 0$$
$$C_O(x = 0, t) = C_O^b(t)$$
$$\frac{\partial}{\partial x}C_O(x = l, t) = 0$$

where ϕ, D, T, k_B, Ze, and l are electric potential in the oxide layer, diffusion coefficient, temperature, Boltzmann constant, electric quantity of oxygen ions, and oxide layer thickness, respectively. C_O^b is the oxygen ion concentration near the interface, which can be expressed as:

$$C_O^b(t) = \gamma N(t)\exp\left(-\frac{\varepsilon_b - ZeE_i a}{k_B T}\right) \quad (1)$$

$$N(t) = N(0) - \int_0^l C_O(x, t)\,dx \quad (2)$$

where N is the amount of oxygen ions accumulated in the electrode, ε_b is the height of interface barrier at zero electric field, E_i is the interface electric field, a is the length of barrier region, and γ is a constant value. The height of interface barrier ε_b is given by $\varepsilon_b = \bar{\varepsilon} + \Delta\varepsilon$, where $\bar{\varepsilon}$ is associated with the electrode and $\Delta\varepsilon$ is the variation for the different oxygen ions.

For the purpose of investigating the RESET behavior, the O^{2-} concentration distributions in the oxide layer are calculated. Figure 35 shows the calculated normalized concentration distribution along the perpendicular direction to the interface plane when a RESET voltage pulse is applied after several switching cycles. In the calculation, we assume that $\Delta\varepsilon$ is 20%. When $\bar{\varepsilon}$ is small (e.g., 0.5 eV), a significant reduction of concentration in the oxide layer is observed after several switching cycles, which is due to the depletion of O^{2-} with a smaller barrier at the interface. The reduction of O^{2-} concentration triggers the RESET failure and impacts the device endurance. When $\bar{\varepsilon}$ is large enough (e.g., 1 eV), no obvious concentration decay is observed. These simulations indicate that the RRAM endurance can be improved if an electrode with a large ε_b is used. It should be noted that the total amount of O^{2-} accumulated at the interface ($N(0)$) is also a crucial factor for the RESET process.

Based on the proposed model, RESET time (t_{RESET}) is dependent on two factors: (1) the transport time (t_{tran}) for O^{2-} to move from interface to V_o, and (2) the recombination time (t_{rec}) for V_o to react with nearby O^{2-}. The latter is inversely proportional to the O^{2-} concentration near where V_o is located, which is dependent on the transport time. Figure 36 shows the calculated dependency of the transport time on the O^{2-} concentration at a different position. As the transport time increases, more O^{2-} transferred from the interface to the oxide layers, reducing the required recombination time. Therefore, there is a minimal value for the sum of t_{tran} and t_{rec}, which is t_{RESET}. In addition, we also found that there is a critical time t_0 for the different position (Fig. 36), which is the minimal time for O^{2-} to transport to one place from the interface. Because t_0 is inversely proportional to the applied voltage and diffusion coefficient, the RESET speed can be improved by choosing resistive materials with large diffusion coefficients.

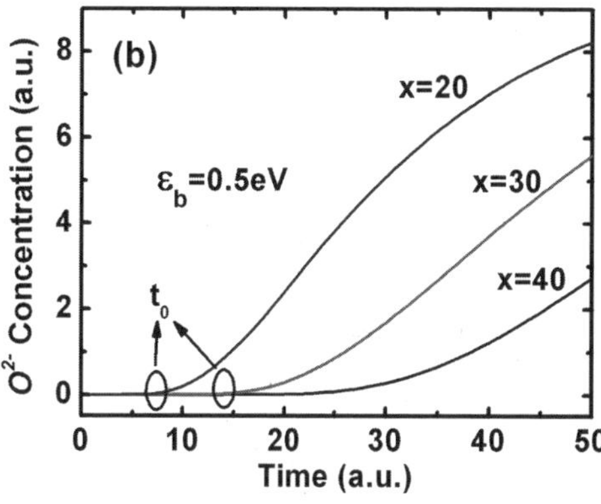

Figure 36. Calculated time evolution of O^{2-} concentration at different point.

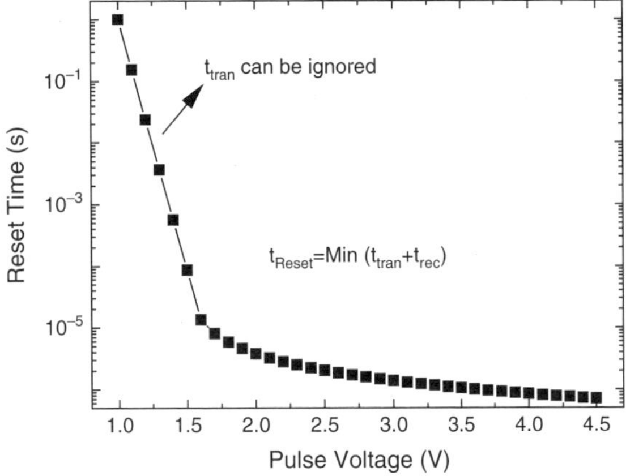

Figure 37. Calculated voltage dependence of RESET time. Reprinted with permission from [53], B. Gao et al., "IEDM Tech. Dig.," p. 563, 2008. © 2008, IEEE.

Based on this model, we can calculate the RESET speed. As shown in Figure 37, the RESET time (t_{RESET}) is exponentially dependent on the pulse voltage (V_p) with an approximately linear behavior after a turning point. It should be noted that, based on the model, t_{rec} is exponentially dependent on the applied voltage, but t_{tran} approximately linearly depends on the voltage. When the voltage is low, t_{tran} is much smaller than t_{rec}, and it can be ignored. Therefore, with voltage increasing, t_{RESET} appears to drop exponentially until t_{rec} is close to t_{tran}. Then t_{RESET} is mainly dependent on t_{tran} when the voltage is higher than that point. At this time, t_{RESET} is approximately equal to t_0, which is the minimal time for O^{2-} to transport from interface to V_o, as discussed above.

4.3. RESET Model Verification

To verify the SET and RESET model, many experiments have been performed using RRAM devices with various types of materials [52–54]. Figure 38 shows the measured temperature dependence of the RESET time (t_{RESET}) using a TiN/ZnO/Pt RRAM device, where t_{RESET} refers to the minimal width of pulse voltage to switch the device from the LRS to the HRS. With increased temperature, t_{RESET} is shortened due to the faster transport of O^{2-}, and log(t_{RESET}) is fitted well linearly with $1/T$, agreeing with the RESET model prediction.

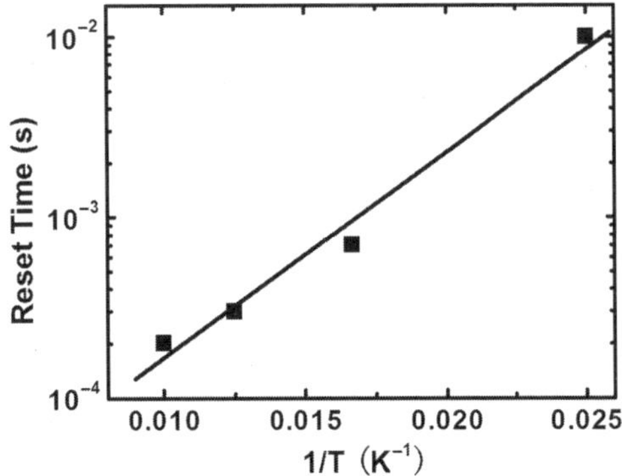

Figure 38. Temperature dependence of reset time under pulse voltage. Reprinted with permission from [53], B. Gao et al., "IEDM Tech. Dig.," p. 563, 2008. © 2008, IEEE.

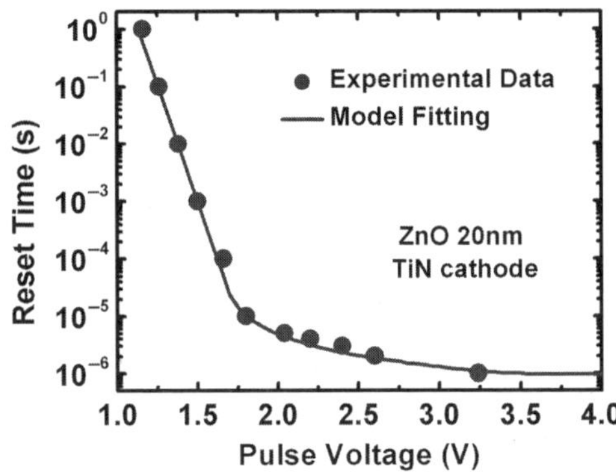

Figure 39. Measured pulse voltage dependency of RESET time and the fitting curve based on the model.

Figure 39 shows the dependency of t_{RESET} on the pulse voltage (V_p). It is found that t_{RESET} is exponentially dependent on V_p with approximately linear behavior after a turning point. The measured data agree well with the simulation, indicating the validity of the model. Figure 40 shows that the thickness of the resistive layer does not affect the slope, but the cathode materials does. This supports the prediction that the RESET time mainly depends on the interface barrier when the applied bias is low.

Based on the calculation result shown in Figures 31 and 33, when the applied RESET voltage is larger, more V_o are electron depleted and recovered, resulting in a larger HRS resistance. This prediction is verified in Figures 41 and 42 by using a TiN/HfO_2/Pt RRAM device for measurement. By using a voltage sweep with a different stop voltage and a voltage pulse with a different amplitude, respectively, different HRS resistance is achieved. The increased HRS resistance with increased the RESET voltage demonstrates the above conclusion. Furthermore, by using the current sweep RESET with a different voltage compliance, HRS resistance can also be

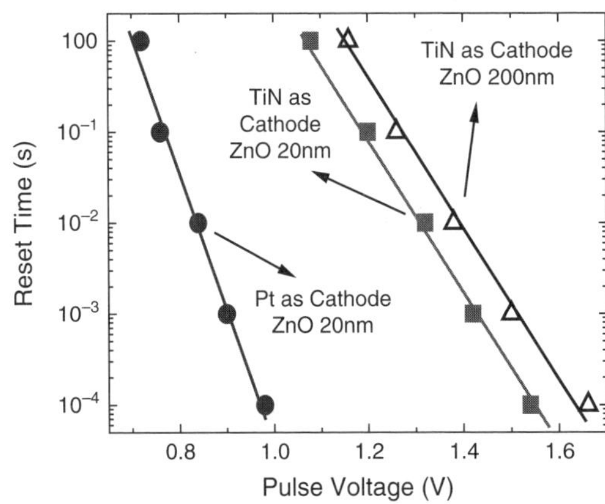

Figure 40. Measured voltage dependence of reset time for the ZnO RRAM with different thickness and electrode. Reprinted with permission from [53], B. Gao et al., "IEDM Tech. Dig.," p. 563, 2008. © 2008, IEEE.

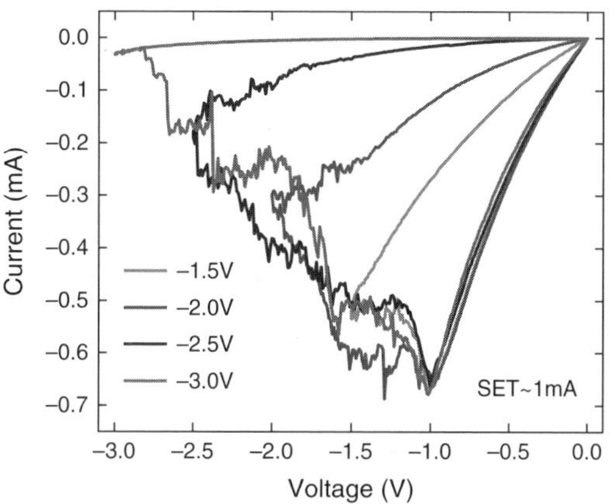

Figure 41. I–V curves of the TiN/HfO_2/Pt RRAM device during RESET process by using 1 mA SET current and different stop voltages (−1.5, −2.0, −2.5, −3.0 V). Reprinted with permission from [54], B. Gao et al., "ICSICT," p. 978, 2010. © 2010, IEEE.

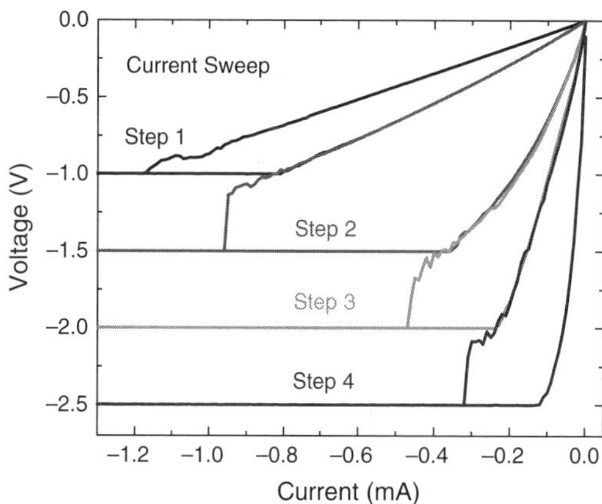

Figure 43. Different RESET steps controlled by voltage compliance using current sweep to switch the TiN/HfO_2/Pt device.

controlled (Fig. 43). We found that larger HRS resistance corresponds to a larger compliance voltage but smaller RESET current. This indicates that the current cannot be the critical parameter to control the RESET process. Therefore, the evidence shows that the RESET process is voltage controlled instead of current controlled, which is consistent with the model prediction.

4.4. SET Model

The SET process is due to the ionizing of oxygen atoms from their original position to form V_o and interstitial oxygen ions under an applied electric field. V_o is generated randomly in the oxide layer, with the generation probability at each place expressed as:

$$p = \exp[(eEL - \varepsilon_V)/kT]$$

where e, L, ε_V, and E are electrical quantity of electron, lattice constant, formation energy of V_o and the applied electric field, respectively (Fig. 44) [46]. The total amount of V_o generated in a period of t is expressed as:

$$N_V = N_O \int \exp\{[eLE(t) - \varepsilon_V]/kT\}\, dt$$

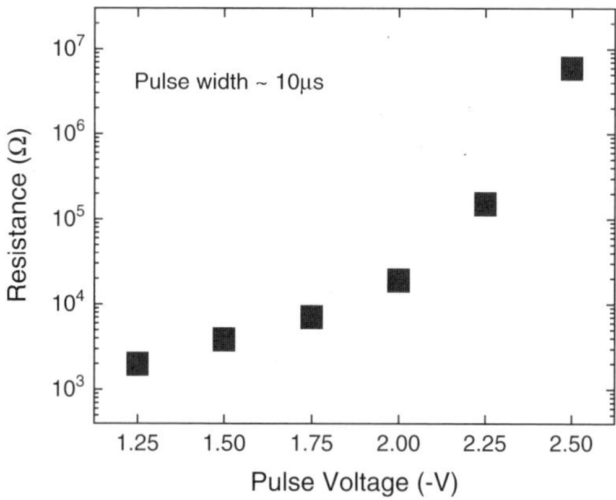

Figure 42. Voltage dependence of resistance on the pulse voltage during RESET process.

where N_O is the total amount of lattice oxygen atoms. If the applied voltage is constant, this equation can be simplified as:

$$N_V = ptN_O$$

Based on the percolation theory, the resistance of the RS layer is a function of N_V, as expressed below:

$$R = 1/f(N_V)$$

Therefore, the model shows that larger or longer SET voltages applied on the device could result in low LRS resistance. To achieve the same LRS resistance, the SET speed is also exponentially dependent on the SET voltage, which is similar with RESET behavior.

4.5. SET Model Verification

The SET model is also verified by experiments [46, 54]. Figure 45 shows the typical I–V curve of the SET process using the current sweep. Gradual resistance transition is observed, indicating that the SET process is an accumulation process, just as the model predicts. Under applied voltage,

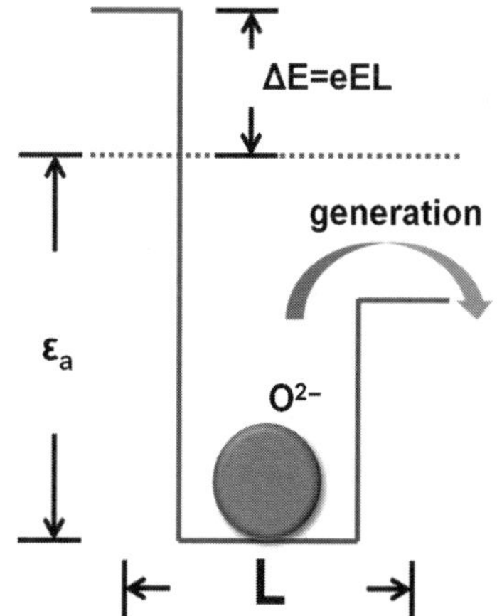

Figure 44. Schematic view of oxygen ions ionizing from lattice under applied electric field.

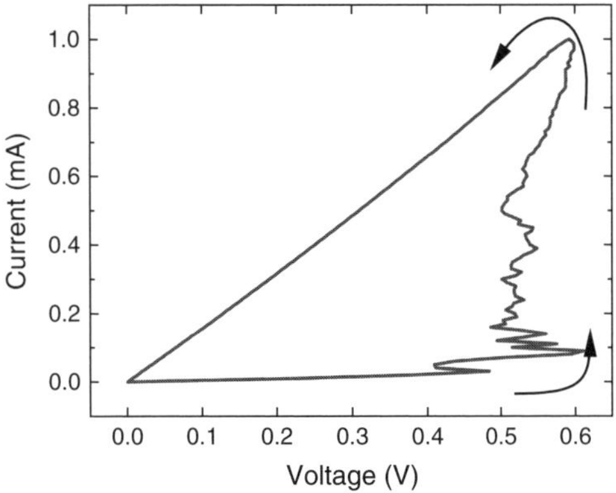

Figure 45. I–V curve of the current sweep SET process. TiN/HfO_2/Pt device is used for the measurement.

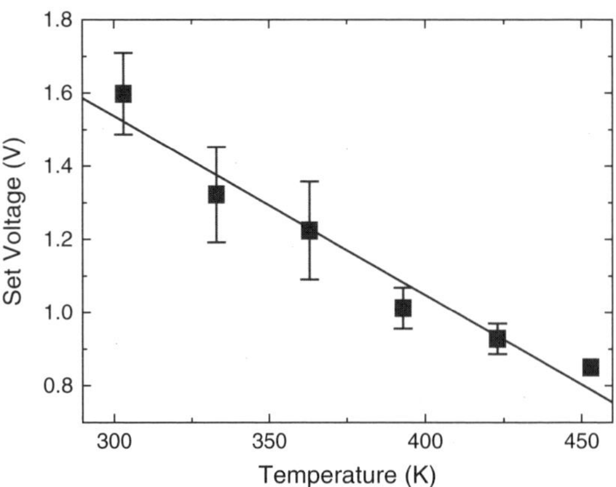

Figure 47. Temperature dependence of the SET voltage. Reprinted with permission from [46], B. Gao et al., *IEEE ESSDERC* 392 (2010). © 2010, IEEE.

V_o generates randomly. The LRS resistance is decreasing when the V_o is generating; this results in the gradual resistance change. However, why is a sudden resistance change observed when using the voltage sweep? It is easily to clarify that the sharp current transition for the SET by the voltage sweep is not essential. In fact, this observed sharp transition results from the measurement effect due to monotonically increasing of sweep parameters (voltage). If we suppose that the SET process includes multisteps of RS behavior, then the sharp transition from the LRS to the HRS is due to the SET voltage of the first step will be larger than that of the sequential steps. In this case, the applied sweep voltage is maintained at a higher voltage point after the first SET step during the voltage sweep process, even though a lower SET voltage is required for the sequential SET steps. A sudden jump of current is observed at a critical voltage, corresponding to the set voltage of the first step. Therefore, it can be concluded that the SET process is gradual due to the V_o accumulation, which is just as the model predicted.

Similar pulse measurement experiments have also been done for the SET and RESET processes. However, due to the large variation of SET voltage, it is difficult to fit the similar lines for SET voltage and SET time exactly as is seen in the RESET process. Only the LRS resistance can be measured under different DC or pulse conditions to verify the SET model. Figure 46 shows that the LRS resistance by the pulse SET is amplitude and duration dependent. Longer duration or larger amplitude of pulse results in a smaller LRS resistance, which is consistent with the SET model.

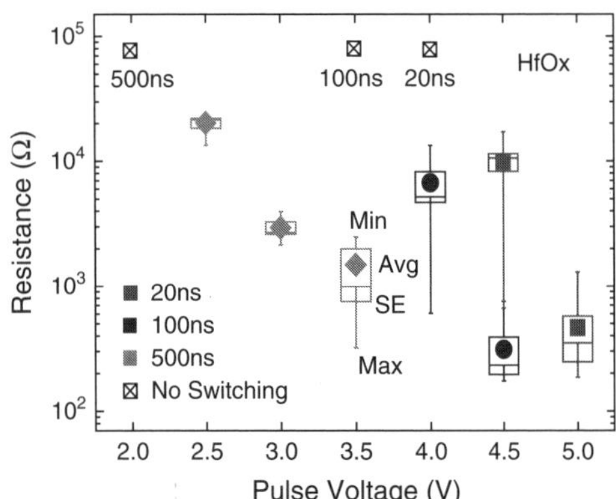

Figure 46. Voltage dependence of resistance after voltage pulse SET process under different pulse duration. TiN/HfO_2/Pt devices are used for the measurement.

Figure 47 shows the temperature dependence of the SET voltage using the voltage sweep. The decreased SET voltage with an increased temperature is due to the easier generation of oxygen atoms from the lattice. Based on the model, to get the same LRS resistance, the below relationship should be satisfied:

$$(eEL - \varepsilon_V)/kT = \text{const}$$

Since the formation energy of V_o is a constant value, the SET voltage should be directly proportional to temperature (Fig. 47).

4.6. Retention Model

Generally, data retention of traditional memories is often evaluated by extending the resistance evolvement to the target time. However, for RRAM, there is limited theory to demonstrate the validity of this method. In fact, sudden resistance transition usually occurs during a typical retention process in RRAM. This retention failure behavior is quite different from that observed in the traditional memories [46]. Therefore, new models and retention evaluation methods for RRAM are required.

To investigate the RRAM retention behavior, TiN/HfO_x/Pt RRAM devices are used for measurement. Figure 48 shows the resistance distribution using the pulse voltage to SET and RESET the device. Excellent uniformity of resistance is observed, which is beneficial for the investigation of the reliability and related mechanisms of the RRAM devices.

Figure 49 shows the measured retention behavior. Positive-negative read pulses are alternately applied on the device to avoid the dielectric polarization effect or read disturbance. Based on the traditional evaluation method, if the measurement is stopped at the time of t_1, the projected device lifetime of 10 years could be anticipated. However, when extending the measuring time to t_2, the HRS retention

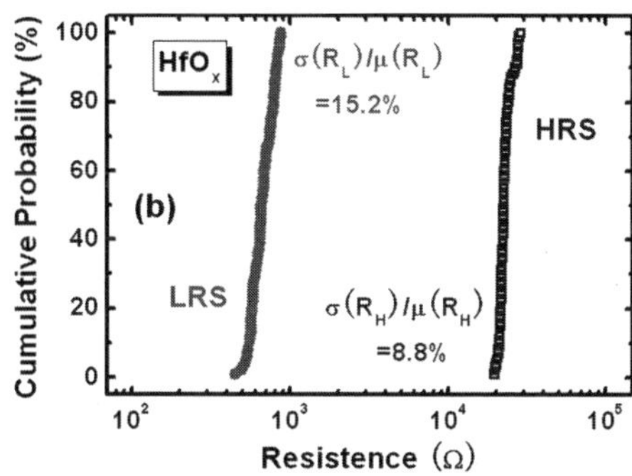

Figure 48. Measured distribution of the R_{LRS} and R_{HRS} of the HfO_x-based devices under pulse voltage switching for 100 cycles. Pulse voltage of +1.5 V/1 μs and −1.5 V/100 μs is used for SET and RESET, respectively. Reprinted with permission from [46], B. Gao et al., *IEEE ESSDERC* 392 (2010). © 2010, IEEE.

failure with a sudden resistance transition is observed. This typical and unique retention failure phenomenon of RRAM implies the infeasibility of the traditional evaluation method on the lifetime of RRAM devices.

To evaluate the RRAM retention correctly, a new model should be established [46]. Based on the crystal defect and probability theories, the failure probability $F(t)$ as a function of time can be expressed as:

$$F(t) = 1 - (1 - p)^{\alpha t}$$

where t refers to the retention time, α is a constant value, p is the activation probability (generation probability for the HRS and recombination probability for the LRS) of V_0. Based on the SET and RESET models, this probability can be expressed as:

$$p = \exp[(eEl - \varepsilon_a)/kT]$$

where ε_a is the activation (generation or recombination) energy according to the SET and RESET model. Considering $p < 1$, the targeted retention time and failure probability can be approximately expressed as below:

$$t_E(V, T) \approx \alpha^{-1} \exp[(\varepsilon_a - qEl)/kT]$$

and

$$F(t; V, T) \approx F(t; 0, T) \exp(qEl/kT)$$

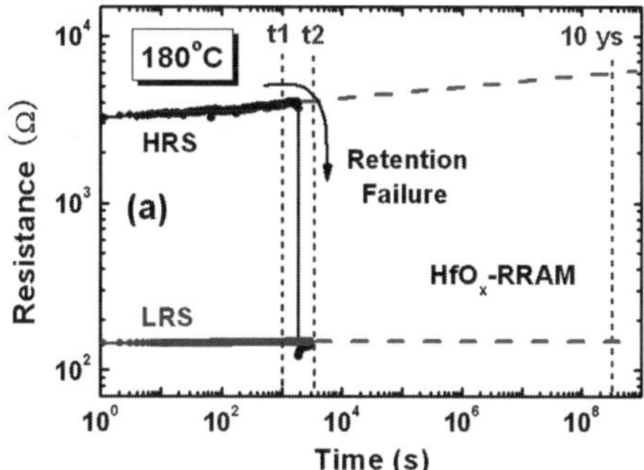

Figure 49. The typical retention behavior of a RRAM device measured at 180°C and the projected lifetime by the traditional retention evaluation method.

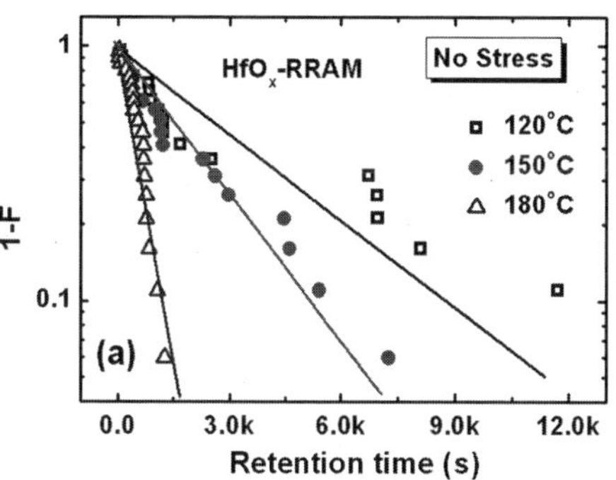

Figure 50. Measured HRS failure probability as a function of time at various temperatures.

The exponentially dependence of the targeted retention time and failure probability on the applied voltage and the inverse of temperature can be found from these equations.

To verify this model, retention behavior of TiN/HfO_2/Pt RRAM devices are measured. Taking the HRS retention as an example, Figure 50 shows the measured retention failure probability distributions for one device in different switching cycles. In contrast to the excellent uniformity of resistance (Fig. 48), a large variation of retention failure time is observed. The data can be approximately fitted using exponential distributions, which is just as the model predicts. The decreased average retention failure time with the condition temperature is also observed.

Meanwhile, a measurement method by applying constant voltage stress on the RRAM device is also used to verify the model (Fig. 51).

The retention failure time can be exponentially fitted. At the same time, the reduced average retention failure time with the stress voltage is also measured. The measured failure probability at a critical time and the extracted targeted retention time as a function of voltage stress are shown in Figure 52. The measured data are fitted well by the proposed model.

In the model, the activation energy ε_a is a key factor in helping to determine RRAM retention behavior. Increasing ε_a is an effective way to enhance the device retention performance. Figure 53 shows the calculated temperature dependence of retention time at different ε_a. Based on such dependence, if ε_a is determined for the selected storage

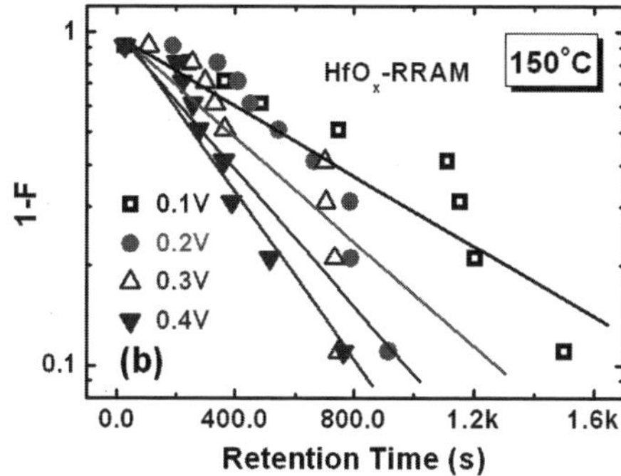

Figure 51. Measured retention failure probability as a function of time under different stress voltages. All data are measured at 150°C for a device.

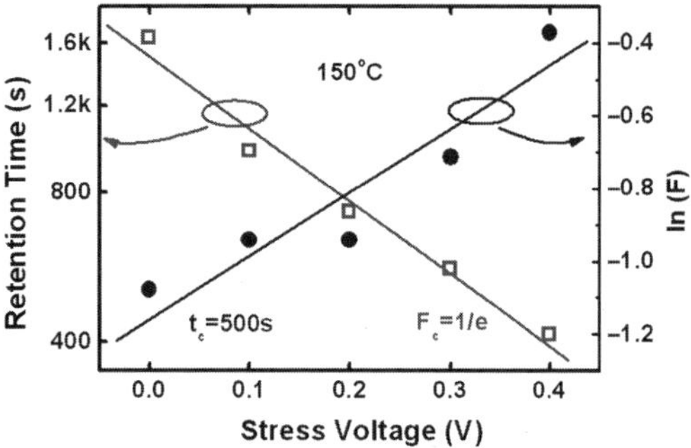

Figure 52. Measured targeted retention time and failure probability as a function of voltage stress. The targeted retention time refers to the time when $1/e$ of the total devices is failed. The failure probabilities are measured at a fixed time of 500 s.

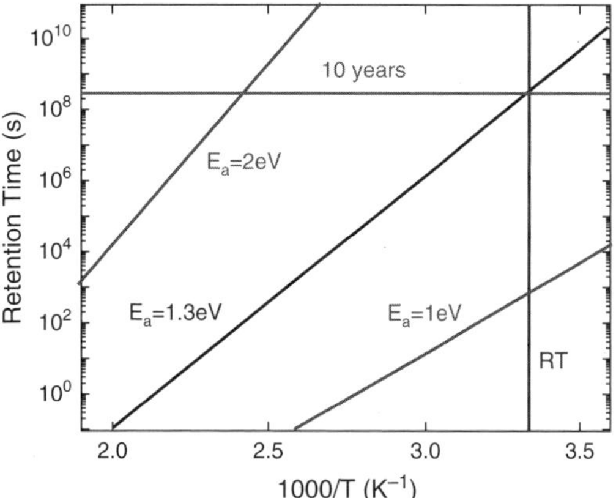

Figure 53. Retention time as a function of temperature for different activation energy. Once activation energy is measured, the retention time can be estimated easily at 150°C for a device. Reprinted with permission from [46], B. Gao et al., *IEEE ESSDERC* 392 (2010). © 2010, IEEE.

layer, the retention of RRAM can be easily extracted. The expected retention time is longer than 10 years if ε_a is larger than 1.3 eV.

The proposed model quantifies the dependence of the failure probability and targeted retention time on temperature and applied bias. Based on the model, the temperature- and voltage-accelerating measurement methods are developed. After measuring the distribution of retention failure time under different elevated temperatures and voltages, the targeted retention time and the failure probability at a specified temperature can be evaluated by extrapolating the measured curves to zero voltage stress and the specified temperature.

5. ENGINEERING OF RRAM CELL

5.1. Performance Challenges of RRAM Cell

Although great progresses have been made on RRAM to enhance performance, several key issues still need to be solved. These issues include how to reduce parameter variation, improve endurance and data retention, control RESET current, and so on.

Reducing the fluctuation of key RS parameters is one of the major problems for RRAM's application [55]. The key parameters include resistance of HRS and LRS, and SET and RESET voltage. Resistance uniformity is of great important since it decides the complexity of the peripheral circuits for reading. However, larger variations over one order of magnitude dispersion are often observed for RRAM with different materials. Furthermore, large switching voltage variation may lead to mis-operation, especially for unipolar type RRAM device. Unfortunately, up to now, how to improve SET voltage uniformity is still a question. Besides, uniformity of RRAM is divided into different types such as cycle to cycle (CTC), device to device (DTD), and wafer to wafer (WTW). Among them, CTC and DTD uniformities are most important, which have to be improved by using different method as discussed later.

The limited data retention and endurance also affect the application of RRAM. As discussed in Section 4.6, the retention failure in RRAM is a random process rather than an accumulate process. Therefore, RS material with relative large activation energy of V_0 should be selected; otherwise, the devices may be influenced by a retention issue. Similarly, endurance failure is also observed in RRAM. Up to now, RRAM devices with endurance of 10^6 to 10^7 cycles are often reported, which is still far from the required value of 10^{10} to 10^{11}, because endurance failure always occurs during continuously switching. However, few model have addressed this issue. In other words, it is still difficult to evaluate and find effective ways to improve the endurance of RRAM.

Large current results in large power consumption. In addition, the series transistors in RRAM cannot afford too large of a current; otherwise, the transistors take up too much area to increase the maximum current. Normally, the RESET current is the largest current in the whole switching process, so we usually use this parameter to represent RRAM performance. The ideal RESET current is about 1–0 μA. However, most of the RRAM devices reported now have a RESET current larger than 100 μA, which is mainly due to the uncontrollability of forming and the SET process. This is especially true under pulse switching without current compliance. So, fighting with large current is still a major roadblock for RRAM research.

Apart from the major issues, other memory parameters should be improved to satisfy different types of special applications. For example, to use RRAM as a field-programmable gate array (FPGA), a large resistance ratio is needed. For multilevel memory usage, multiple resistance states should be steady and easy to approach; to use RRAM instead of DRAM, very quick switching and read speeds are required. To fulfill these, special attention to the design of RRAM is needed to achieve an ultra-high performance in some selected memory parameters.

As a result, the performance of RRAM still needs to be improved. This improvement relies on carefully chosen material and the use of effective operation methods to control the switching behavior.

5.2. Material-Oriented Methodology for RRAM Cells

To engineer RRAM performance, a material design platform should be established. The materials for RRAM include the RS layer material and electrode material. For the RS layer material, the formation and recombination energies of V_o are most importantly based on the model discussed above. To achieve these energy barriers, both experiments and theoretical calculations need to be performed. The calculations are mainly based on first principle calculations. For example, to get the formation energy of $V_o(E_f^O)$, the density functional theory (DFT) calculations were carried out by using a generalized gradient approximation (GGA) for the exchange-correlation potential and Vanderbilt-type ultrasoft pseudopotentials as implemented in the CASTEP code. E_f^O is defined as $E_f^O = E_{vac} - E_{free} + E_{O_2}/2$, where E_{vac}, E_{free}, and E_{O_2} represent the total energies of the vacancy and vacancy-free system and the energy of the O_2 molecule, respectively. To calculate the first two parameters, a super cell with 96 atoms was constructed (Fig. 54). The energy of the vacancy system is calculated by removing one oxygen atom from the super cell [40].

The calculations show that the trivalent elements, such as Al or La, doping in the host materials with high E_f^O, such as HfO_2 or ZrO_2, causes the lower E_f^O near the doping sites (Table 1). It is almost unaffected at locations several atoms away from the impurities, which implies that V_o can be easily formed and located near the doping sites. Therefore, more stable CFs are expected to be formed during different switching processes, which could account for the remarkable uniformity improvement of the switching parameters such as the SET voltages and the resistances in two states under continuous switching cycles.

To verify this method of uniformity improvement, experiments have been performed that fabricated undoped and Al- or Gd-doped HfO_2-based RRAM devices. Figure 55 compares the forming voltage distribution of the control and Al-doped HfO_2 devices, and it shows a much narrower dispersion in the Al-doped devices than in the control devices. The standard deviation of forming voltage is reduced from 1.53 to 0.27 V. This more uniform distribution of forming voltages from different devices characterizes an improvement of the DTD variations. In addition, a significant reduction in the forming voltage is observed in the Al-doped device. The mean value of the forming voltage decreases from 7.82 to 2.71 V. This is desirable in the application of RRAM devices because they do not initially need a high voltage to be triggered. The reduced forming voltage is also attributed to the lower formation energy of V_o near the Al atom in the HfO_2 layer.

Table 1. Summary of the calculated E_f^O in selected materials.

	Undoped (eV)	Ti (eV)	Al (eV)	La (eV)
HfO_2	6.53	6.48	4.09	3.42
ZrO_2	6.37	6.11	3.66	3.74

Source: Reprinted with permission from [40], B. Gao et al., "Symp. VLSI Technology Dig. Tech.," p. 30, 2009. © 2009, IEEE.

Figure 56 compares the SET voltage distribution obtained by 100 DC sweep cycles, which shows a less dispersive distribution in the Al-doped device. The standard deviation of the SET voltage is reduced from 0.48 to 0.2 V. Figure 57 compares the distribution of resistances in the HRS and the LRS during the continuous pulse sweep cycles. The SET and RESET pulse are set to be ± 2 V for 100 us. The resistances in the two states are read out by a 100 mV read voltage. Significantly reduced dispersions of both the HRS and the LRS are observed in the Al-doped device. The relative fluctuation (defined by the standard deviation divided by the mean value) decreased from 70.7% to 39.7% in the HRS resistance and from 76.2% to 10.4% in the LRS resistance. The above results indicate that the CTC uniformities by both the DC and the pulse sweep modes are improved by Al doping.

Similar results are also demonstrated in Gd-doped HfO_2-based RRAM devices. The SET and RESET voltage distribution of controlled and Gd-doped devices for 100 cycles is shown in Figure 58. For the undoped HfO_2 device, the SET voltage varies from 0.7 V to 2.7 V, and the mean value and standard deviation of the set voltage are 1.16 V and 0.32 V, respectively. For the Gd-doped HfO_2 device, it is clear that the distribution of SET voltage is reduced, with a mean

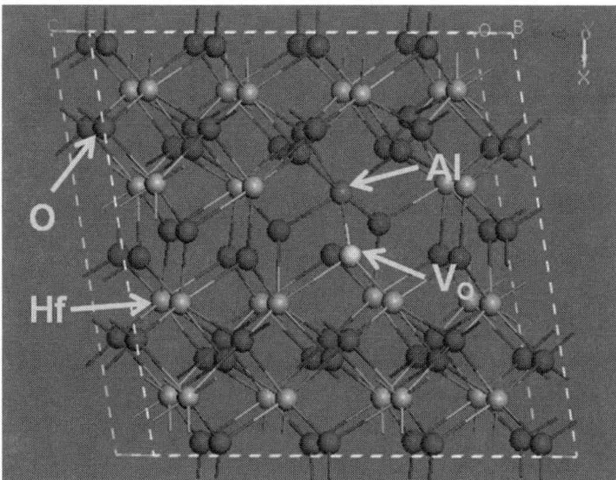

Figure 54. Schematic view of 96 atoms in a HfO_2 supercell with one oxygen vacancy and one Al doping atom. Reprinted with permission from [40], B. Gao et al., "Symp. VLSI Technology Dig. Tech.," p. 30, 2009. © 2009, IEEE.

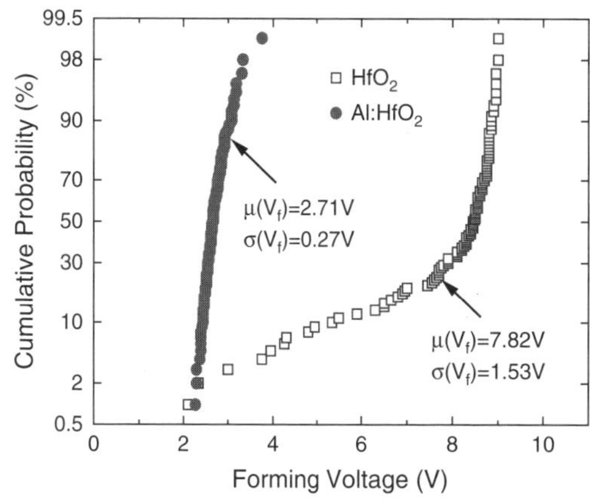

Figure 55. Distribution of forming voltage for control and Al-doped HfO_2 devices. Reprinted with permission from [40], B. Gao et al., "Symp. VLSI Technology Dig. Tech.," p. 30, 2009. © 2009, IEEE.

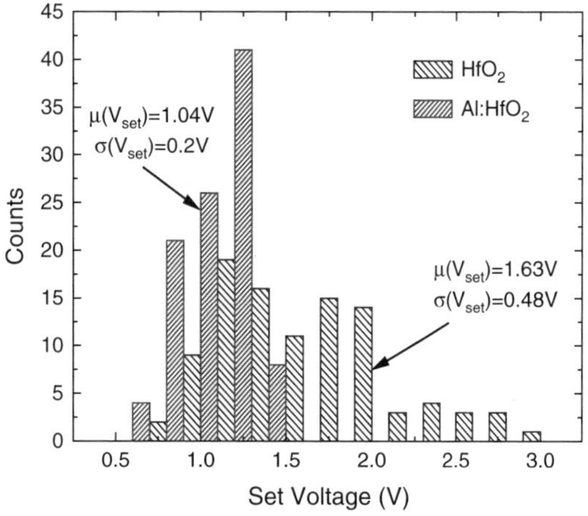

Figure 56. SET voltage distribution of control and Al-doped HfO_2 devices under DC sweeping mode. Reprinted with permission from [40], B. Gao et al., "Symp. VLSI Technology Dig. Tech.," p. 30, 2009. © 2009, IEEE.

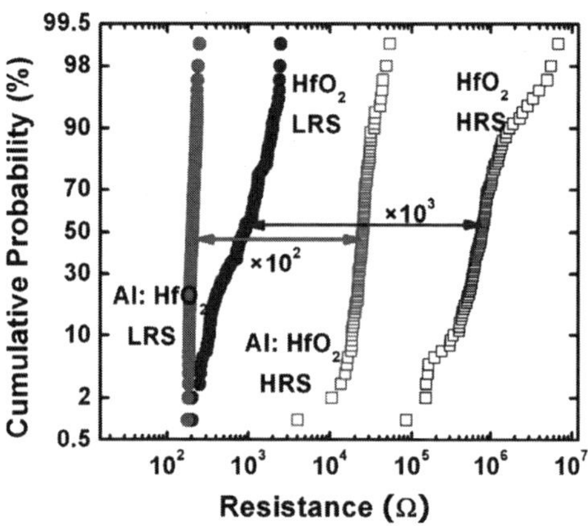

Figure 57. Statistical distribution of resistances in the HRS and LRS for 100 pulse sweep cycles.

value of 0.89 V and a standard deviation of 0.03 V. In addition, the uniformity of the RESET voltage distribution in the Gd-doped HfO_2 is also improved. The HRS and LRS distribution in the sweeping cycles is exhibited in Figure 59.

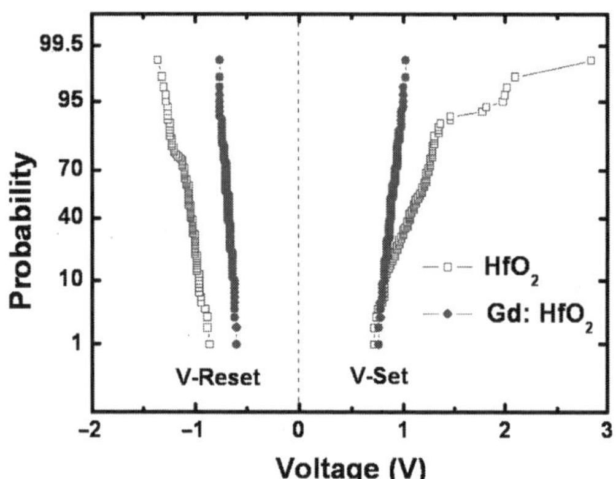

Figure 58. SET and RESET voltage distribution of control and Gd-doped HfO_2 devices under DC sweeping mode.

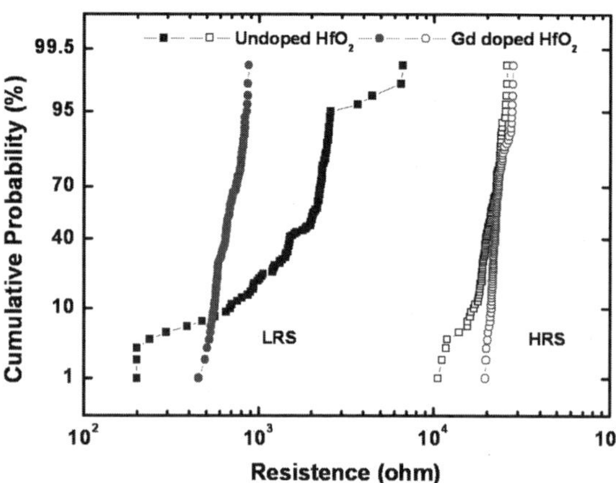

Figure 59. Statistical distribution of resistances in HRS and LRS for 100 pulse sweep cycles.

The resistance is read at 100 mV. Both the uniformity of the HRS and LRS in Gd-doped HfO_2 devices have been improved compared with the undoped devices. The relative fluctuation of the HRS resistance of the Gd-doped HfO_2 is 9% compared with the undoped one at 16%, and the relative fluctuation of LRS resistance was 15% compared with undoped one at 62%.

The HRS and LRS distribution between the different devices are also statistically measured in the pulse mode (Fig. 60). Each of Gd-doped and undoped HfO_2 devices are switched for more than 20 cycles, with a 1.5-V height and a 1-μs width pulse for the SET process, and a −1.5-V height and a 100-μs width pulse for the RESET process. The resistance is read at 100 mV. Compared with the undoped HfO_2 devices, the Gd-doped HfO_2 devices showed improved uniformity of the HRS resistance and LRS resistance distribution. Furthermore, it is also noticed that the R_{HRS}/R_{LRS} ratio (window margin for RRAM) is also increased 10 times. The improved margin is also resulted from better control of the conductive filament.

As discussed in Section 4.6, choosing material with a high formation energy of V_o is an effective way to enhance the device's HRS retention performance. Therefore, the tradeoff between data uniformity and retention needs to

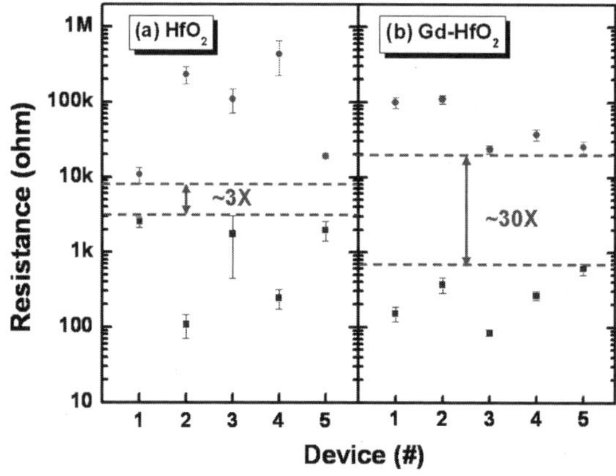

Figure 60. Statistical measurement of different Gd-doped and undoped HfO_2 RRAM devices using pulse mode.

be considered when selecting the storage material for RRAM devices. Similarly, other device parameters can also be improved by engineering required energy barriers for RS material, which are also calculated by first principle calculations.

Furthermore, selecting proper material for the electrode is also crucial. Figure 61 shows the measured endurance of the ZnO-based RRAM devices using Pt and TiN as the cathodes, respectively. The negative voltage was applied on the cathode during the RESET process. Excellent endurance was measured using TiN as the cathode. In contrast to this, degraded endurance was measured using Pt as the cathode. The degradation could be attributed to the lower barrier height at Pt interface based on the model prediction discussed in Section 4.3. The results indicated that a lower barrier against oxygen ion diffusion exists at the Pt interface rather than at the TiN interface. Because the oxygen ion is negatively charged, only the cathode influences the oxygen ion transport. Therefore, choosing a proper cathode material is important to enhance its endurance. Materials with a high barrier and a sufficient supply of oxygen ions, such as TiN, are the ideal cathode selections [53].

As a result, based on the first principle calculations, technical solutions to significantly improve the uniformity and other key device parameters in oxide-based RRAM are demonstrated. The results indicate that fundamental improvement of the RS behavior in oxide-based RRAM devices can be achieved by using optimized material systems.

Apart from the performance improvement, special device parameter requirements can be also achieved based on a material-design methodology. For example, we can use material with an ultra-low diffusion barrier of oxygen to achieve very fast switching by trading off other device parameters. We can also select a special electrode material to realize a large resistance ratio to use the RRAM as an FPGA. As shown in Figure 62, using Ti as an electrode instead of TiN can achieve a very sharp resistance transition, thus resulting in the large HRS to LRS resistance ratio (Fig. 63). This is because the transition layer is not easily formed between Ti and HfO_2 layers. Therefore, only a main CF is formed in a Ti electrode device. For a TiN electrode device, a V_o rich interface layer exists between TiN and HfO_2, and it can be seen because multiple CFs exist in the layer. The formation and rupture of each CF results in a change of resistance. A very large resistance ratio of 10^5 is observed in Ti electrode device (Fig. 63), which is attributed to the significant change of the main CF in the RS layer [56].

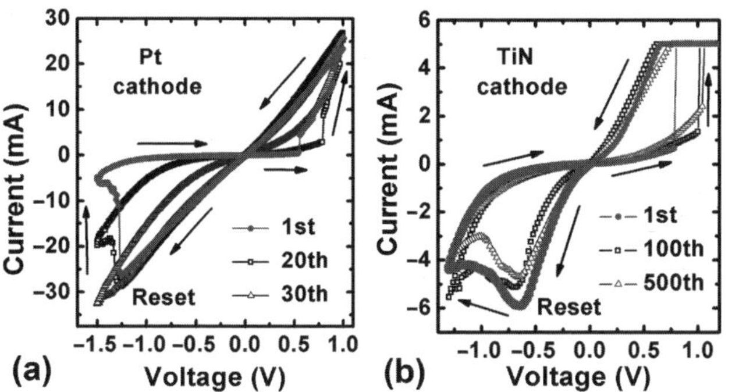

Figure 61. Switching curves of ZnO device: (a) with Pt as cathode, and (b) with TiN as cathode. Reprinted with permission from [53], B. Gao et al., "IEDM Tech. Dig.," p. 563, 2008. © 2008, IEEE.

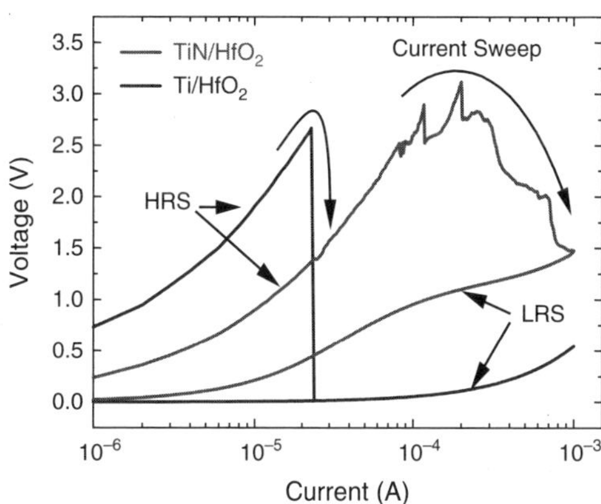

Figure 62. Typical IV relation of Ti/HfO_2 and TiN/HfO_2 in set process by using current sweep. Reprinted with permission from [56], B. Gao et al., "VLSI-TSA," p. 144, 2010. © 2010, IEEE.

Therefore, material selection is the most important task for engineering the performance of RRAM. To find the proper material, a design platform should be established to meet various requirements. This platform is based on the basic understanding of the physical mechanisms of RRAM. By modeling RS behavior, material-oriented methodology is proposed to help to establish this platform.

5.3. Operation-Oriented Methodology for RRAM Cells

Other than material selection, proper operation applied on the device after the fabrication process is also important for performance improvement. First of all, using current-controlled forming and SET processes and voltage-controlled RESET processes, instead of an all voltage-controlled process, can achieve better uniformity and reduce the current.

Figure 64 compares the measured distribution of resistance in the LRS and HRS by using different operation

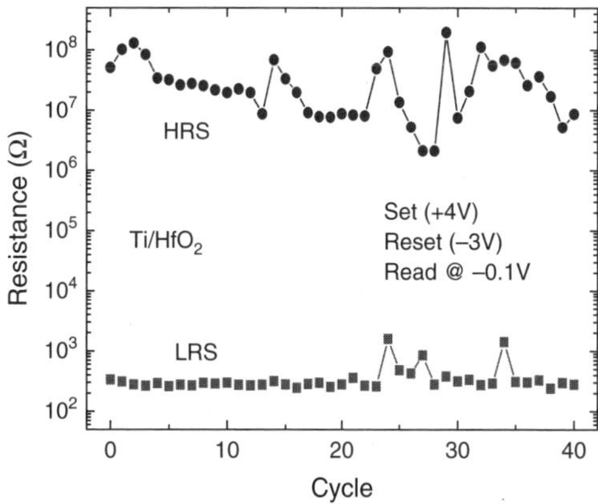

Figure 63. Resistance distribution of Ti/HfO_2 during continuous switching cycle. Reprinted with permission from [56], B. Gao et al., "VLSI-TSA," p. 144, 2010. © 2010, IEEE.

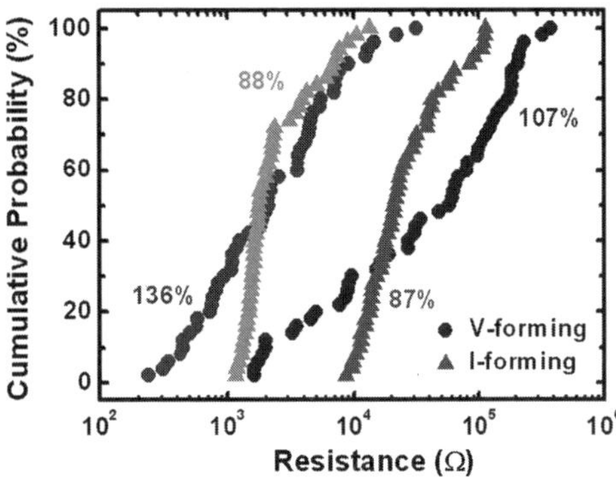

Figure 64. Distributions of mean value of 50 devices' LRS and HRS resistance using the voltage and current sweep mode.

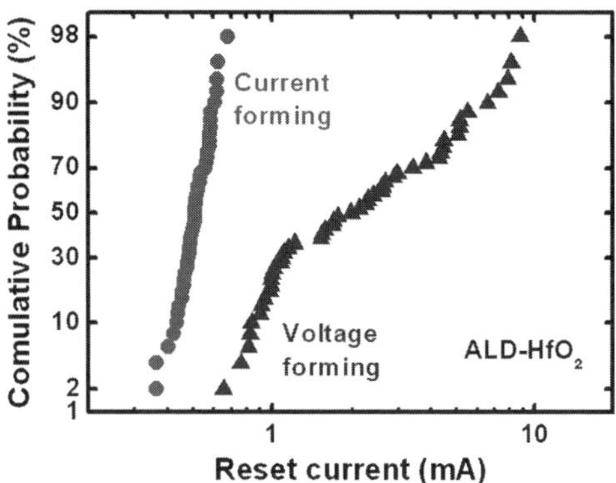

Figure 66. Distributions of mean value of 50 devices' maximum RESET current using the voltage and current sweep mode.

modes for the SET and forming processes. Fifty TiN/HfO_2/Pt-based RRAM devices are statistically measured, with each device switching 20 cycles and showing the mean value of these twenty cycles. Better uniformity of the DTD is observed using the current sweep compared with the voltage sweep. The DTD fluctuation of the HRS resistance using the current sweep mode is 87% compared with 107% for the voltage sweep mode, and the DTD fluctuation of the LRS resistance using the current sweep is 88% compared with 136% for the voltage sweep. Figure 65 compares the CTC variation distribution using these two modes, and the variations of 20 cycles for the 50 devices are statistically shown. It is found that CTC uniformity is also improved by using the current sweep mode.

Apart from the uniformity improvement, the maximum RESET current is also reduced using current forming and the SET process instead of voltage forming in combination with the SET process (Fig. 66).

The origin of such an improvement is attributed to the well-controlled overshoot current and the reduced local electric field caused by the additional voltage. Due to the large parasitical capacitance of the oxide layer, an overshoot current is produced in the forming and SET process when using a voltage sweep mode with a current compliance. This overshoot current results in the larger LRS current and a more unsteady resistance. When using the current-controlled forming and SET mode, the overshoot current can be eliminated. Besides, when using voltage controlled mode, the local electric field in the rupture region of CF is increasing accompanying with the growing of CF, due to the decreasing of effective length of voltage-influenced region. Based on the model, V_0 is easily generated under a large electric field. Therefore, the uncontrolled generation of V_0 occurs rapidly. However, when using the current-controlled mode, the local electric field remains almost constant in the whole switching process. This is because the electric field is directly proportional to the current, which is controlled in this mode, whereas the RESET process is absolutely voltage controlled as discussed in Sections 3 and 4. Therefore, the ideal operation mode includes the current-controlled forming/SET and the voltage-controlled RESET.

Secondly, using pulse switching instead of DC voltage sweep switching can also improve uniformity. As shown in Figure 67, significant improvement of uniformity is observed in both the HRS and LRS resistance under pulse switching. The origin of this phenomenon is similar to the comparison between voltage and current-controlled switching as discussed above. But, it should be noted that this result is much more promising, since the practical application of RRAM is almost under pulse switching [53]. Further experimental results show that using a current pulse instead of a voltage pulse in the SET process can achieve a more uniform

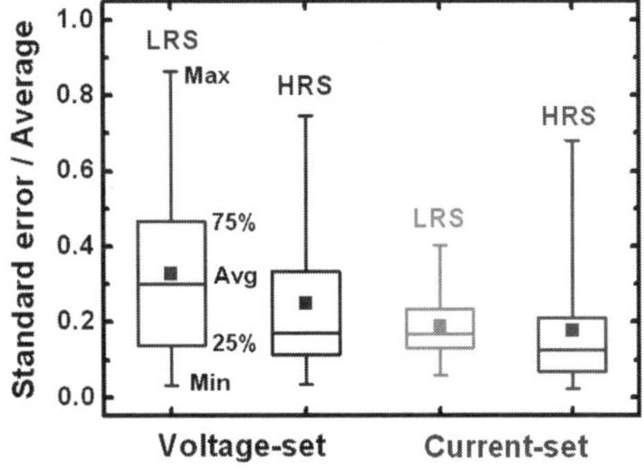

Figure 65. Distributions of cycle to cycle variation of 50 devices' LRS and HRS resistance using the voltage and current sweep mode.

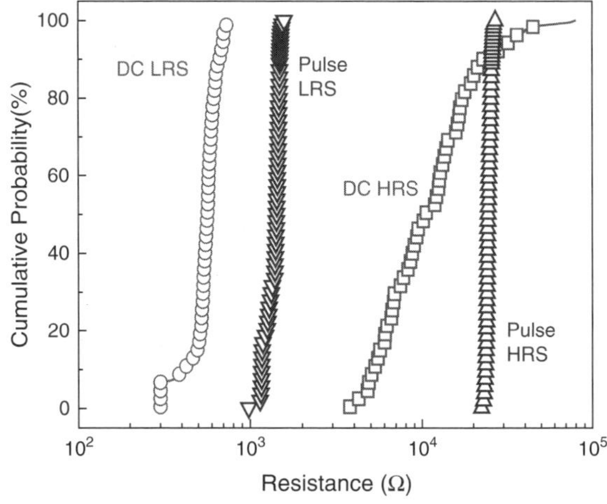

Figure 67. Statistical distribution of resistances in HRS and LRS of TiN/ZrO_2/Pt-based RRAM device using DC voltage sweep switching and voltage pulse switching.

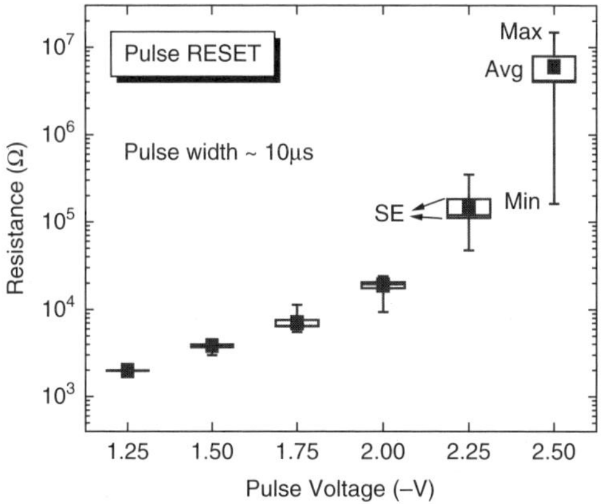

Figure 68. Voltage dependence of resistance after pulse RESET process. Reprinted with permission from [54], B. Gao et al., "ICSICT," p. 978, 2010. © 2010, IEEE.

resistance. The current pulse can be realized by adding a series resistor, diode, or transistor [54].

Another important issue is how to control the window between the different resistance states. As discussed in Section 4, changing the RESET voltage can adjust the HRS resistance. However, the relative variation increases with the increasing resistance (Fig. 68). This is because, in the HRS, very few V_o exists in the rupture region of RS layer, so the recombination or diffusion of one V_o may induce a large resistance change. Therefore, for multilevel usage, it is not advisable to operate at a HRS, and we should leave a large window of margin for the HRS to achieve better reliability [54].

In contrast to the RESET process, it is difficult to control the LRS resistance simply by changing the SET voltage. Because the SET process is current controlled, changing the current compliance in the voltage-controlled model or the SET current in the current-controlled mode are the most effective ways to achieve a multiple resistance state. In this way, the resistance window is easy to adjust. It should also be noted that, similar to RESET process, a relatively large variation exists when resistance is high (Fig. 69).

To control the resistance by the pulse SET, a series resistor is needed. As shown in Figure 70, a change in the resistance can be controlled with good uniformity and is

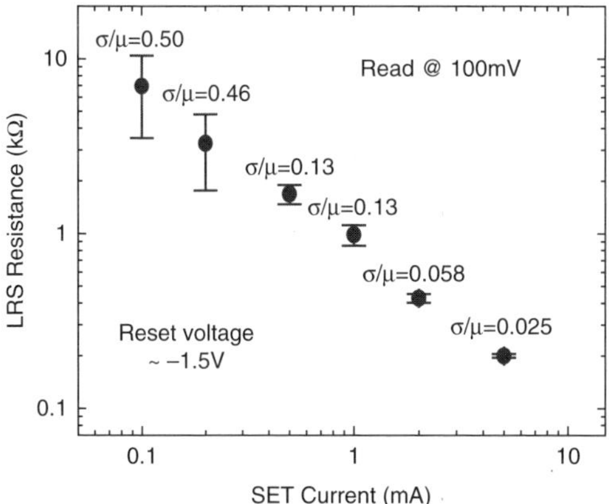

Figure 69. Dependence of LRS resistance on the SET current.

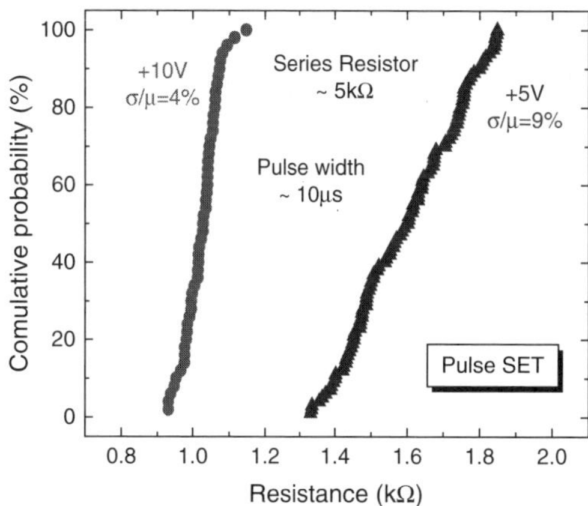

Figure 70. Resistance distribution under pulse SET process. A 5 kΩ resistor is put in series with RRAM device. Different SET voltages are used. Reprinted with permission from [54], B. Gao et al., "ICSICT," p. 978, 2010. © 2010, IEEE.

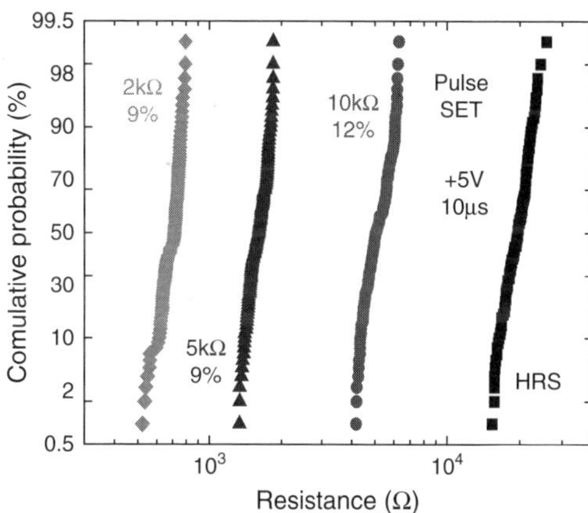

Figure 71. Resistance distribution under the pulse SET process. Different series resistors are used.

achieved by changing the pulse voltage after adding a series resistor. Larger voltage accounts for a lower LRS resistance. The value of the series resistance should be carefully selected, since it can influence the RRAM's resistance after the pulse SET. As shown in Figure 71, the RRAM's resistance can also be controlled after changing the resistance value of the series resistor. Therefore, in the practical application of RRAM, the 1T-1R structure is good for a multilevel resistance state operation. By controlling V_{ds} and V_g, different resistance of the LRS and HRS can be easily achieved, even though the applied signal is only a voltage pulse.

In summary, proper electrical operation after the devices have been fabricated is also crucial, except in material selection. To achieve better performance, an operation-oriented methodology is also needed that is based on a deep understanding of the mechanism of RRAM.

6. SUMMARY AND PROSPECTS

The resistive switching characteristics of various transitional metal oxides have been widely explored. As a new member in the NVM family, TMO-based RRAM has demonstrated its superior capability and rapid advancement in research and development. An excellent memory performance, such as low operating voltage, a fast P/E speed, a large window of high/low resistance ratio, an excellent cycling endurance ($> 10^6$), long data retention, superior scalability, and 3D integration capability, has been demonstrated and have indicated the great application potential of TMO-based RRAM as the next generation of universal memory technologies. However, unclear physical origins of RS behavior are still the bottleneck for developing new RRAM technologies. Understanding the microscopic nature of resistive switching and seeking an effective way to control the switching process are critical.

Firstly, the resistive switching characteristics and important impact factors of TMO-based RRAM devices were addressed and reviewed. Two types of resistive switching modes, including unipolar and bipolar, were presented. The systematic investigation on both unipolar and bipopar resistive switching characteristics was performed. The studies demonstrate that superior memory performances such as faster switching speed, lower operational voltage/current and power, and better uniformity and endurance, can be achieved in the bipolar devices compared with the unipolar counterparts. However, unipolar devices possess unique advantages that realize the high density of the $4F^2$ cross-point array structure based on an 1D-1R cell, as compared with the bipolar devices.

Then, we presented the naturally physical origins of the switching behavior and the related effects, material- and operation-oriented methodologies, in TMO-based bipolar RRAM devices. Studies show that among the various TMO material systems, an HfO_x-based material system emerges as the most promising candidate for resistive switching materials in TMO-based RRAM devices with the large and controllable process window. However, the uniformity of DTD and CTC is still a great challenge for the HfO_x system. This material-related switching performance of TMO-based RRAM devices could be due to the natural material properties, but a more deep understanding of such properties is needed.

A unified physical mechanism on the natural properties of the TMO-based bipolar RRAM devices proposed has been presented and discussed, and it clarifies that the formation and rupture of filaments responsible for the resistive switching is mainly due to the generation and recombination of oxygen vacancies controlled by the local electric field. Based on the new unified physical mechanism, the resistive switching characteristics and the related physical effects such as electrode and doping effects can be understood. Furthermore, the quantified models on the critical switching behavior such as resistive switching and retention are developed and demonstrated. Aimed at the requirements of technology optimization, the material- and operation-oriented methodologies were also developed based on the unified physical mechanism for the TMO-based RRAM devices, structure, and materials to achieve targeted performances. Proper doping in the matrix materials such as the stable HfO_x is demonstrated as a good solution to improve and control the switching behavior by both the theory calculations and experimental data.

For the integration of memory array, the design and optimization of memory cells for the storage nodes of RRAM memory array is critical. The memory cell based on 1T-1R, 1D-1R, and 1R has been proposed and identified. The 1T-1R is the typical architecture available for both unipolar and bipolar RRAM devices. The 1D-1R architecture is available for the high-density crossbar, but unipolar devices are usually required. The best choice for the cell architecture is the 1R architecture with a reduced number of selectors, which can effectively overcome the scaling limit due to the high operation current usually required in 1T-1R and 1D-1R architectures. The additional selected function with RRAM devices such as self-rectifying characteristics is needed. This is a great challenge for the selection of materials and structures of RRAM devices.

Despite the fact that rapid progresses in RRAM technology have been made, key challenges still exist. First, the argued physical mechanisms need to be further clarified. Even though the unified physical mechanism is successful at explaining the bipolar switching behavior of TMO-based RRAM devices, a deep understanding and experiment verifications are needed. Furthermore, material- and operation-oriented technical solutions to optimize material/cell structure/storage array architecture, process technology, characterization methods, and reliability need to be further developed and improved. With deep understanding on the fundamental physical properties of both materials and switching behavior, technical solutions should tackle various technical challenges in the development and applications, which may help to advance the research and development of RRAM as well as the and mass-production of TMO-based RRAM technology.

REFERENCES

1. International Technology Roadmap for Semiconductors. http://www.itrs.net/.Accessed October 10, 2011.
2. M. A. A. Sanvido, F. R. Chu, A. Kulkarni, and R. Selinger, *Proceedings of the IEEE* 96, 1864 (2008).
3. K. Prall and K. Parat, "IEDM Tech. Dig.," p. 102, 2010.
4. A. Chung, J. Deen, J.-S. Lee, and M. Meyyappan, *Nanotechnology* 21, 412001 (2010).
5. A. Sawa, *Mater. Today* 11, 28 (2008).
6. R. Waser, R. Dittmann, G. Staikov, and K. Szot, *Adv. Mat.* 21, 2632 (2009).
7. T. W. Hickmott, *J. Appl. Phys.* 33, 2669 (1962).
8. J. F. Gibbons and W. E. Beadle, *Solid-State Electron.* 7, 785 (1964).
9. J. C. Bruyere and B. K. Chakraverty, *Appl. Phys. Lett.* 16, 40 (1970).
10. J. G. Simmons and R. R. Verderber, "Proceedings of the Royal Society of London, Series A, Mathematical and Physical Sciences," The Royal Society, Vol. 31, p. 77, 1967.
11. A. Asamits, Y. Tomioka, H. Kuwahara, and Y. Tokura, *Nature* 388, 50 (1997).
12. S. Q. Liu, N. J. Wu, and A. Ignatiev, *Appl. Phys. Lett.* 76, 2749 (2000).
13. A. Beck, J. G. Bednorz, Ch. Gerber, C. Rossel, and D. Widmer, *Appl. Phys. Lett.* 77, 139 (2000).
14. Y. Watanabe, J. G. Bednorz, A. Bietsch, Ch. Gerber, D. Widmer, and A. Beck, *Appl. Phys. Lett.* 78, 3738 (2001).
15. K. Szot, W. Speier, G. Bihlmayer, and R. Waser, *Nat. Mat.* 5, 312 (2006).
16. B. J. Choi, D. S. Jeong, S. K. Kim, C. Rohde, S. Choi, J. H. Oh, H. J. Kim, C. S. Hwang, K. Szot, R. Waser, B. Reichenberg, and S. Tiedke, *J. Appl. Phys.* 98, 033715 (2005).

17. A. Chen, S. Haddad, Y. C. Wu, T.-N. Fang, Z. L. S. Avanzino, S. Pangrle, M. Buynoski, M. Rather, W. Cai, N. Tripsa, C. Bill, M. VanBuskirk, and M. Taguchi, "IEDM Tech. Dig.," p. 746, 2005.
18. M. N. Kozicki, M. Yun, L. Hilt, and A. Singh, *J. Electrochem. Soc.* 146, 298 (1999).
19. W. W. Zhuang, W. Pan, B. D. Ulrich, J. J. Lee, A. Burmaster, D. R. Evans, S. T. Hsu, M. Tajiri, K. Inoue, T. Naka, N. Awaya, A. Sakiyama, Y. Wang, S. Q. Liu, N. J. Wu, and A. Ignatiev, "IEDM Tech. Dig.," p. 193, 2002.
20. I. G. Baek, M. S. Lee, S. Seo, M. J. Lee, D. H. Seo, D.-S. Suh, J. C. Park, S. O. Park, H. S. Kim, I. K. Yoo, U.-In Chung, and J. T. Moon, "IEDM Tech. Dig.," p. 587, 2004.
21. D. Lee, D.-J. Seong, H. J. Choi, I. Jo, R. Dong, W. Xiang, S. Oh, M. Pyun, S.-O. Seo, S. Heo, M. Jo, D.-K. Hwang, H. K. Park, M. Hasan, and H. Hwang, "IEDM Tech. Dig.," 2006.
22. Y. S. Chen, H. Y. Lee, P. S. Chen, P. Y. Gu, C. W. Chen, W. P. Lin, W. H. Liu, Y. Y. Hsu, S. S. Sheu, P. C. Chiang, W. S. Chen, F. T. Chen, C. H. Lien, and M.-J. Tsai, "IEDM Tech. Dig.," p. 105, 2009.
23. B. Lee and H.-S. P. Wong, "Symp. VLSI Technology Dig.," p. 28, 2009.
24. D.-H. Kwon, K. M. Kim, J. H. Jang, J. M. Jeon, M. H. Lee, G. H. Kim, X.-S. Li, G.-S. Park, B. Lee, S. Han, M. Kim, and C. S. Hwang, *Nat. Nanotech.* 5, 148 (2010).
25. R. Waser and M. Aono, *Nat. Mat.* 6, 833 (2007).
26. I. G. Baek, D. C. Kim, M. J. Lee, H.-J. Kim, E. K. Yim, M. S. Lee, J. E. Lee, S. E. Ahn, S. Seo, J. H. Lee, J. C. Park, Y. K. Cha, S. O. Park, H. S. Kim, I. K. Yoo, U.-In Chung, J. T. Moon, and B. I. Ryu, "IEDM Tech. Dig.," p. 769, 2005.
27. K. Tsunoda, K. Kinoshita, H. Noshiro, Y. Yamazaki, T. Iizuka, Y. Ito, A. Takahashi, A. Okano, Y. Sato, T. Fukano, M. Aoki, and Y. Sugiyama, "IEDM Tech. Dig.," p. 767, 2007.
28. M. J. Lee, Y. Park, B. S. Kang, S. E. Ahn, C. Lee, K. Kim, W. Xianyu, G. Stefanovich, J. H. Lee, S. J. Chung, Y. H. Kim, C. S. Lee, J. B. Park, I. G. Baek, and I. K. Yoo, "IEDM Tech. Dig.," p. 771, 2007.
29. C.-H. Ho, E. K. Lai, M. D. Lee, C. L. Pan, Y. D. Yao, K. Y. Hsieh, R. Liu, and C. Y. Lu, "Symp. VLSI Technology Dig.," p. 228, 2007.
30. S. Muraoka, K. Osano, Y. Kanzawa, S. Mitani, S. Fujii, K. Katayama, Y. Katoh, Z. Wei, T. Mikawa, K. Arita, Y. Kawashima, R. Azuma, K. Kawai, K. Shimakawa, A. Odagawa, and T. Takagi, "IEDM Tech. Dig.," p. 779, 2007.
31. N. Xu, L. F. Liu, X. Sun, C. Chen, Y. Wang, D. D. Han, X. Y. Liu, R. Q. Han, J. F. Kang, and B. Yu, *Semicond. Sci. Technol.* 23, 075019 (2008).
32. B. Sun, Y. X. Liu, L. F. Liu, N. Xu, Y. Wang, X. Y. Liu, R. Q. Han, and J. F. Kang, *J. Appl. Phys.* 105, 061630 (2009).
33. B. Sun, L. F. Liu, N. Xu, B. Gao, Y. Wang, D. D. Han, X. Y. Liu, R. Q. Han, J. F. Kang, *Jpn. Appl. Phys.* 48, Part 2, 04C061 (2009).
34. T.-N. Fang, S. Kaza, S. Haddad, A. Chen, Y.-C. Wu, Z. Lan, S. Avanzino, D. Liao, C. Gopalan, S. Choi, S. Mahdavi, M. Buynoski, Y. Lin, C. Marrian, C. Bill, M. VanBuskirk, and M. Taguchi, "IEDM Tech. Dig.," p. 543, 2006.
35. K. Aratani, K. Ohba, T. Mizuguchi, S. Yasuda, T. Shiimoto, T. Tsushima, T. Sone, K. Endo, A. Kouchiyama, S. Sasaki, A. Maesaka, N. Yamada, and H. Narisawa, "IEDM Tech. Dig.," p. 783, 2007.
36. M. Jo, D. Seong, S. Kim, J. Lee, W. Lee, J.-B. Park, S. Park, S. Jung, J. Shin, D. Lee, and H. Hwang, "Symp. VLSI Technology Dig. Tech.," p. 53, 2010.
37. Z. Wei, Y. Kanzawa, K. Arita, Y. Katoh, K. Kawai, S. Muraoka, S. Mitani, S. Fujii, K. Katayama, M. Iijima, T. Mikawa, T. Ninomiya, R. Miyanaga, Y. Kawashima, K. Tsuji, A. Himeno, T. Okada, R. Azuma, K. Shimakawa, H. Sugaya, T. Takagi, R. Yasuhara, K. Horiba, H. Kumigashira, and M. Oshima, "IEDM Tech. Dig.," p. 293, 2008.
38. X. Sun, B. Sun, L. F. Liu, N. Xu, X. Y. Liu, R. Q. Han, J. F. Kang, G. C. Xiong, and T. P. Ma, *IEEE Electron Device Lett.* 30, 334 (2009).
39. C. Y. Lin, C.-Y. Wu, C.-Y. Wu, T. C. Lee, F.-L. Yang, C. Hu, and T.-Y. Tseng, *IEEE Electron Device Lett.* 28, 366 (2007).
40. B. Gao, H. W. Zhang, S. Yu, B. Sun, L. F. Liu, X. Y. Liu, Y. Wang, R. Q. Han, J. F. Kang, B. Yu, and Y. Y. Wang, "Symp. VLSI Technology Dig. Tech.," p. 30, 2009.
41. L. F. Liu, J. F. Kang, N. Xu, X. Sun, C. Chen, B. Sun, Y. Wang, X. Y. Liu, X. Zhang, and R. Q. Han, *Jap. J. Appl. Phys.* 47, 2701 (2008).
42. H. Y. Lee, Y. S. Chen, P. S. Chen, P. Y. Gu, Y. Y. Hsu, S. M. Wang, W. H. Liu, C. H. Tsai, S. S. Sheu, P. C. Chiang, W. P. Lin, C. H. Lin, W. S. Chen, F. T. Chen, C. H. Lien, and M.-J. Tsai, "IEDM Tech. Dig.," p. 460, 2010.
43. C. H. Cheng, A. Chin, and F. S. Yeh, "Symp. VLSI Technology Dig. Tech.," p. 85, 2010.
44. H. W. Zhang, B. Gao, B. Sun, G. P. Chen, L. Zeng, L. F. Liu, X. Y. Liu, J. Lu, R. Q. Han, J. F. Kang, and B. Yu, *Appl. Phys. Lett.* 96, 123502 (2010).
45. C. H. Ho, C.-L. Hsu, C.-C. Chen, J.-T. Liu, C.-S. Wu, C.-C. Huang, C. Hu, and F.-L. Yang, "IEDM Tech. Dig.," p. 436, 2010.
46. B. Gao, J. F. Kang, H. W. Zhang, B. Sun, B. Chen, L. F. Liu, X. Y. Liu, R. Q. Han, Y. Y. Wang, Z. Fang, H. Y. Yu, B. Yu, and D.-L. Kwong, "40th European Solid-State Device Research Conference IEEE ESSDERC 2010," 392, 2010.
47. S. M. Yu, B. Gao, H. B. Dai, B. Sun, L. F. Liu, X. Y. Liu, R. Q. Han, J. F. Kang, and B. Yu, *Electrochemical Solid-State Lett.* 13, H36 (2010).
48. H. W. Zhang, B. Gao, S. M. Yu, L. Lai, L. Zeng, B. Sun, L. F. Liu, X. Y. Liu, J. Lu, R. Q. Han, and J. F. Kang, 2009 International Conference on Simulation of Semiconductor Process and Devices IEEE SISPAD 2009, 155, 2009.
49. N. Xu, B. Gao, L. F. Liu, X. Y. Liu, R. Q. Han, J. F. Kang, and B. Yu, "Symp. VLSI Technology Dig.," p. 100, 2008.
50. N. F. Mott and E. A. Davis, "Electronic Processes in Non-Crystalline Materials," 2nd Edition, Oxford University Press, Oxford, 1979.
51. P. K. C. Pillai and Rashmi, *Euro. Poly. J.* 17, 611 (1981).
52. B. Gao, B. Sun, H. W. Zhang, L. F. Liu, X. Y. Liu, R. Q. Han, J. F. Kang, and B. Yu, *IEEE Electron Device Lett.* 30, 1326 (2009).
53. B. Gao, S. Yu, N. Xu, L. F. Liu, B. Sun, X. Y. Liu, R. Q. Han, J. F. Kang, B. Yu, and Y. Y. Wang, "IEDM Tech. Dig.," p. 563, 2008.
54. B. Gao, B. Chen, Y. S. Chen, L. F. Liu, X. Y. Liu, R. Q. Han, and J. F. Kang, "The 10th International Conference on Solid-State and Integrated-Circuit Technology," p. 978, 2010.
55. G. I. Meijer, *Science* 319, 1625 (2008).
56. B. Gao, W. Y. Chang, B. Sun, H. W. Zhang, L. F. Liu, X. Y. Liu, R. Q. Han, T .B. Wu, and J. F. Kang, "2010-International Symposium on VLSI Technology, Systems and Applications," p. 144, 2010.
57. B. Chen, B. Gao, S. W. Sheng, L. F. Liu, X. Y. Liu, Y. S. Chen, Y. Wang, J. F. Kang, and B. Yu, "2010 IEEE Silicon Nanoelectronics Workshop," p. 55, 2010.

CHAPTER 6

Resistance Switching Effects in Transition Metal Oxide Thin Films for Nonvolatile Memory Applications

Dinghua Bao

State Key Laboratory of Optoelectronic Materials and Technologies, School of Physics and Engineering, Sun Yat-Sen University, Guangzhou 510275, People's Republic of China

CONTENTS

1. INTRODUCTION

A variety of transition metal oxide thin films exhibit important resistance switching effects that can be used for resistive random access memory (RRAM) applications [1–3]. In recent years, due to the increasing request for better properties of the transition metal oxide thin films for RRAM device applications and the importance of fundamental research, these kinds of transition metal oxide thin films have received much attention. Many transition metal oxide thin films have been prepared to obtain better resistance switching properties, as well as to explore the physical mechanism of resistance switching [4–6].

Several important growth methods have been used to prepare these kinds of transition metal oxide thin films, including sputtering, pulsed laser deposition, metalorganic chemical vapor deposition, chemical solution deposition, and atomic layer deposition. Each method has its own advantages and disadvantages for preparing the transition metal oxide thin films. In addition, selection of electrode materials is also important because electrode material and the interface between the electrode and the film play an important role on resistance switching properties.

Up until now, there have been more and more studies on transition metal oxide thin films for RRAM applications, and several review papers on transition metal oxide

ISBN: 1-58883-251-1

Nonvolatile Memories: Materials, Devices and Applications
Edited by Tseung-Yuen Tseng and Simon M. Sze
Volume 2: Pages: 139–159

thin films and perovskite oxide thin films have been published that can provide some understanding in the research area [7–10]. In this chapter, we briefly review the research status and new progress on several typical transition metal oxide thin films such as NiO, TiO_2, ZrO_2, ZnO, their combinations, and gold/silver-doped transition metal oxide nanocomposite thin films for RRAM applications as well as some of our own work in this research field.

2. RESISTANCE SWITCHING EFFECTS

So-called resistance switching effects simply mean a large change in resistance has taken place within several nanoseconds on applying pulsed voltages or currents. Usually they can be classified into two types: (1) one is unipolar or nonpolar, and (2) the other is bipolar, depending on difference of material systems. Typical current–voltage (I–V) characteristics that correspond to unipolar and bipolar switching effects are shown in Figures 1(a and b), respectively [3].

For bipolar resistance switching, its switching direction is dependent on the polarity of the applied voltage. This type of resistance switching phenomenon usually appears in perovskite structure metal oxides.

Different from bipolar resistance switching, unipolar resistance switching depends on the amplitude of the applied voltage but not on the polarity. This type of resistance switching phenomenon usually occurs in binary metal oxides. Note that the coexistence of the bipolar and unipolar resistive-switching modes can also be observed in the same cells, but the bipolar and unipolar switching modes possibly have different driving mechanisms [11, 12].

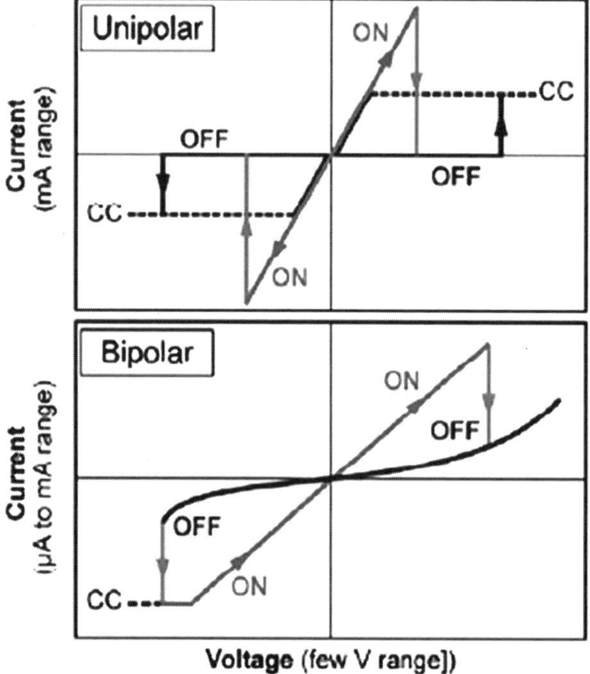

Figure 1. Unpolar and bipolar switching schemes. Reprinted with permission from [3], R. Waser and M. Aono, *Nat. Mater.* 6, 833 (2007). © 2007, Nature Publishing Group.

3. SEVERAL IMPORTANT TRANSITION METAL OXIDE THIN FILMS

3.1. NiO Thin Films

NiO is one of the most promising transition metal oxide materials for RRAM applications. It is a *p*-type oxide with a typical three-dimensional (3D) electron structure. Due to its simple composition and structure, studies of NiO thin films have been interesting. Studies of NiO have mainly focused on enhancing resistance ratio of high resistance state to low resistance state and improving resistance-switching properties. For RRAM applications based on NiO thin films, understanding of the physical mechanism of conductive filament formation and rapture and obtaining direct experimental evidence for resistance switching of NiO thin films are major research topics. Park and coworkers [13] observed electric-field induced Ni filament channels in polycrystalline NiO_x films and found that the irreversible low resistance state facilitates further increase of Ni filament channels and Ni filament density. To visualize nano-sized conducting filamentary paths in the surface of NiO thin films during repetitive resistance switching, a current sensing-atomic force microscopy was used to observe random and localized resistive switching in Pt/NiO/Pt [14]. Some areas (or spots), which were assumed to be the beginning of the conducting filaments, appeared (formation) and disappeared (rupture) in a localized and random fashion during the switching and are thought to contribute to resistive memory switching. The formation and rupture of conducting filaments of NiO thin films with Hg/NiO/Pt structure were also directly observed for a high resistive state and a low resistive state by a conducting atomic force microscope (CAFM) [15]. Figure 2 shows the CAFM images of the NiO thin film, (a) for the R_{off} state, and (b) for the R_{on} state corresponding to 100 switching cycles. Recently, Ye et al. [16] fabricated regular nanoelectrode arrays on NiO thin films via a nanosphere lithography method and directly measure the nanoscale resistive switching properties using a CAFM. Their results suggested that the unipolar resistive switching process be consistent with the mechanism of conducting filament formation and rupture.

Hwang et al. [17] also investigated conducting nanofilaments in single-crystalline Ni/NiO core/shell nanodisk arrays

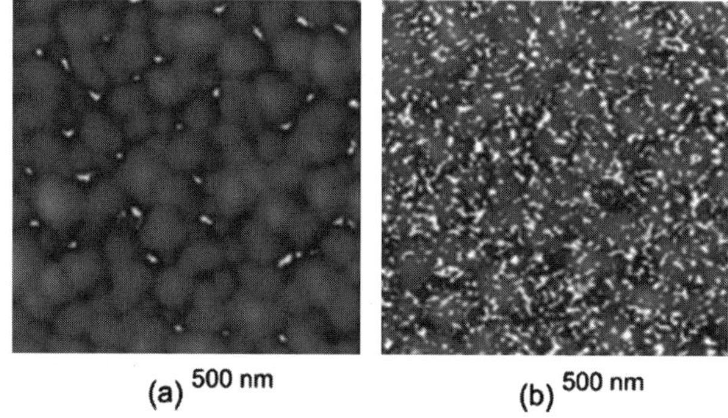

Figure 2. CAFM images of the NiO thin film: (a) for the R_{off} state, and (b) for the R_{on} state corresponding to 100 switching cycles. Reprinted with permission from [15], J. Y. Son and Y. H. Shin, *Appl. Phys. Lett.* 92, 222106 (2008). © 2008, American Institute of Physics.

using CAFM. It was found that the conducting filaments are highly localized on the surface of nanostructure. The local current distributions observed in such a single-grained nanodisk demonstrate that the contact area and the contact time between the conductive tip of CAFM and the surface of nanodisk have a critical influence on the electroforming behaviors of nanofilaments in NiO switching nanoblocks. The contact parameters, such as the contact area and the contact time, are interpreted to the electrode size and the voltage-stress time for the formation of filaments in metal oxides.

Considering that the conductive filament controls the localized current flow in the low resistive state of NiO-based RRAM devices, it is significant to evaluate the conductive filament temperature during operation. Recently, Russo et al. [18] performed a statistical characterization of the critical filament temperature for the transition of switching from low resistance state to the high resistance state by the thermal dissolution of the conductive filament. In addition, the temperature dependence of high- and low-resistance states in NiO films is a concern for NiO-based RRAM. Studies of the temperature dependence of the resistance switching of NiO thin films in the temperature range of 10°K < T < 300°K indicated that metallic Ni defects might play a key role in the formation of a metallic channel [19]. These studies are helpful to further understand the resistance-switching mechanism of NiO thin films.

Son et al. [20] studied the ferromagnetism of conducting filaments formed in a NiO thin film that exhibited a typical bistable resistive-switching characteristic. The NiO thin film showed an antiferromagnetic hysteresis loop for a high resistive state; whereas for a low resistive state, the conducting filaments exhibited a ferromagnetic hysteresis loop for the field cooling. The ferromagnetic hysteresis behavior of the low resistive state indicates a switchable exchange coupling between the ferromagnetic Ni conducting filaments and the antiferromagnetic NiO layer.

Structural defects such as Ni vacancies or oxygen vacancies or grain boundaries might have an important influence on resistance-switching properties of NiO films. This has been confirmed by Park et al. [21, 22]. Park et al. [21] prepared NiO thin films on Pt/Ti/SiO_2/Si substrates by rf reactive sputtering and found that the resistive-switching behavior has a strong dependence on oxygen content, which might relate to Ni vacancies and compensating holes inside the NiO film. Park et al. [22] investigated the resistive-switching characteristics of two types of Pt/NiO/Pt structures with epitaxial and polycrystalline NiO layers. Results indicated that Pt/polycrystalline-NiO/Pt showed very reproducible switching behavior, much better than Pt/epitaxial-NiO/Pt (see Fig. 3). This meant that microstructural defects may play a crucial role in the reliability of the resistive switching behavior.

The electrode is another important factor possibly affecting resistance-switching properties of NiO thin films. Lee and coworkers [23, 24] studied the effects of various metal electrodes, including Ni, $Ni_{0.83}Pt_{0.17}$ alloy, Ta, Al, Ag, and Cu electrodes, on the resistance switching of polycrystalline NiO thin films. Despite the popular belief that Pt enables Ohmic contact to *p*-type NiO due to its high work function, their results showed that resistive switching was observed in

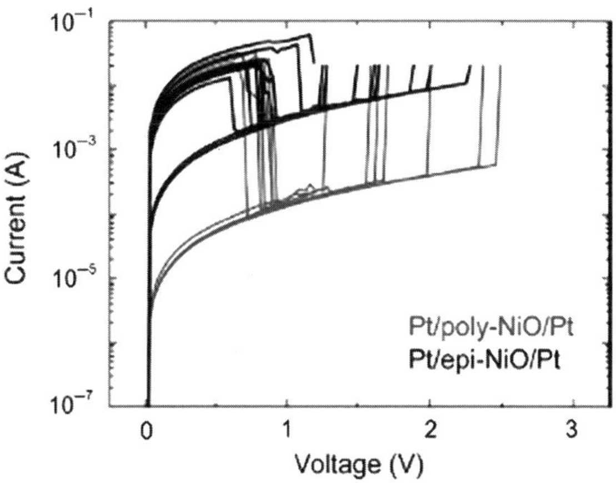

Figure 3. Typical I–V characteristics of Pt/Poly-NiO/Pt/TiO_x/SiO_2/Si and Pt/Epi-NiO/Pt/Al_2O_3. Reprinted with permission from [22], C. Park et al., *Appl. Phys. Lett.* 93, 042102 (2008). © 2008, American Institute of Physics.

NiO thin films using Ta or Al electrodes with a low work function. The resistive switching of films using an Ag or Cu top electrode with a low work function and high free energy of oxidation shows the importance of the formation of an oxide layer at the metal/NiO interface.

The effect of different electrode materials on resistive switching characteristics of NiO-based resistive-switching memory devices has been studied [25]. The use of noble metal electrodes, instead of Si contacts, results in a lowering of the set/reset voltage. This is ascribed to a different chemical composition of the conductive filament in the set state for varying electrodes, suggesting that atomic diffusion from the electrodes takes place during the formation of the conductive filaments at the set process.

Interfacial reactions between electrode and transition oxide thin film were found to affect resistive switching behaviors of metal/NiO/metal structures. Characterization of the interfacial reactions between the NiO and the electrode can provide insights on the switching mechanism. Studies [26] have indicated that when a positive bias was applied to the Pt electrode, Ag/NiO/Pt structures exhibited reproducible resistive switching. However, if a positive bias was applied to the Ag electrode, the Ag/NiO/Pt structures did not exhibit resistive switching behavior. Further analysis by X-ray photoemission spectroscopy (XPS) revealed that different interfacial chemical interactions for the two cases may affect filament formation and rupture processes near the electrode and, hence, alter the resistive switching behaviors. Figure 4 shows a schematic of interfacial microstructure changes based on XPS analysis.

The effect of doping on resistance switching properties of NiO thin films is worth studying. Jung et al. [27] studied the effects of Li-doping on bistable resistance switching in polycrystalline NiO film in the temperature range of 10°K < T < 300°K. It was believed that Li-doping could improve retention properties of NiO thin films as well as the stability of switching between the low resistance state and high resistance state.

Resistive switching dispersion of NiO_x thin film can also be improved by Cu-Doping. Liu et al. [28] prepared

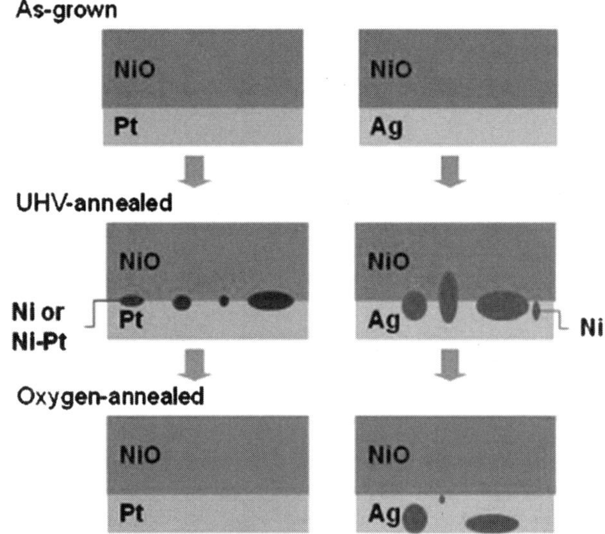

Figure 4. Schematic of the reduction/oxidation processes in NiO/Pt and NiO/Ag samples. Reprinted with permission from [26], S. H. Phark et al., *Appl. Phys. Lett.* 94, 022906 (2009). © 2009, American Institute of Physics.

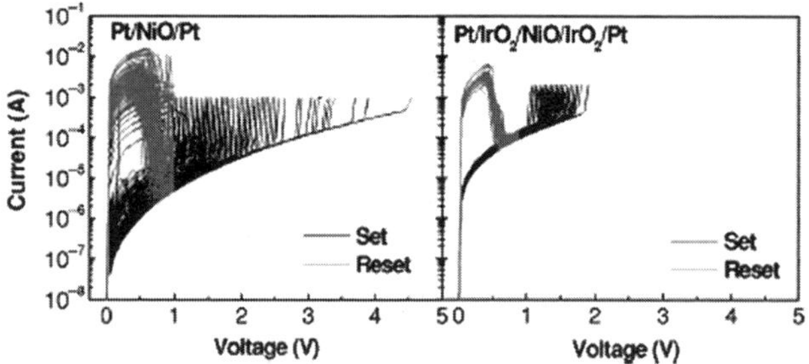

Figure 5. I–V curves of memory switching in Pt/NiO/Pt and Pr/IrO_2/NiO/IrO_2/Pt memory cells. The data are from continuous memory switchings of 200 times. Reprinted with permission from [31], D. C. Kim et al., *Appl. Phys. Lett.* 88, 232106 (2006). © 2006, American Institute of Physics.

Cu/NiO_x/Pt and Cu/Cu:NiO_x/Pt devices using thermally grown NiO_x and Cu-doped NiO_x (Cu:NiO_x) thin films as resistive switching layers. Both the devices exhibited reversible resistive-switching properties with a nondestructive readout and long retention. However, the Cu-doping NiO_x thin films exhibited obviously improved voltage dispersions of the resistive-switching operation and smaller operating voltages than the Cu/NiO_x/Pt device.

Considering that Nb has a valence different from that of Ni, Nb doping of up to 3.5% in polycrystalline NiO_x films with Pt/Nb–NiO_x/Pt structures resulted in a higher endurance for the Set/Reset processes with a narrower distribution of V_{SET} as compared with the undoped NiO_x films [29]. XPS indicated that the Nb–NiO_x films had a higher metallic Ni–O density than the undoped NiO_x films deposited at the same temperature.

Besides the doping method, other attempts to improve the resistive switching characteristics of NiO thin films have been made. Lee et al. [30] studied an alternative approach of improving bistable resistance switching of NiO by fabricating a multilayer structure of three NiO_x layers with varying oxygen contents. By adjusting the oxygen partial pressure during NiO_x layer deposition, improved resistance and switching voltage distribution from cycle to cycle was achieved.

Inserting thin IrO_2 layers between NiO and electrodes can also improve the resistive switching properties of NiO such as minimizing the dispersions of all memory switching parameters [31]. Figure 5 shows I–V curves of memory switching in Pt/NiO/Pt and Pr/IrO_2/NiO/IrO_2/Pt memory cells. The data are from continuous memory switchings of 200 times. Note that in NiO thin films with noble metal electrodes, broad dispersions of switching parameters are generally observed during continuous switching cycles. The IrO_2 thin layer was thought to help stabilize the local oxygen migrations for the filament formation and rupture, therefore, leading to more stable memory switching parameters.

The resistance-switching behavior of NiO can be controlled through forming NiO/SiO_2 double-layer structures and adjusting the thickness of SiO_2 layer [32]. A repeatable resistance-switching behavior was observed with the ON/OFF ratio of 10^5. The operation voltage of the device depended on the thickness of the SiO_2 layer and it increased with increasing SiO_2 thickness. High-resolution transmission electron microscopy (TEM) analyses revealed that the formation/rapture of Ni filaments like the percolation path inside the SiO_2 layer was responsible for the current transport mechanism.

Recently, Sato et al. [33] reported on fabrication of a RRAM consisting of NiO resistive memories and control transistors with 0.18 μm complementary metal–oxide–semiconductor (CMOS) technology. The initial forming voltage is as low as 2 V for NiO thin film, and the reset current is lower than 100 μA due to control of the filamentary conductance by the current limit of the metal–oxide–semiconductor field-effect transistor (MOSFET) and by using the current limit of a selected cell transistor in the set process ($1T$-$1R$). The current level was determined by its gate voltage, resulting in the control of electrical resistance of the filamentary conductive paths in the low resistive state. In addition, a large voltage increase in the Reset operation, which may cause an undesirable Set operation, was also suppressed by a voltage-clamp transistor connected to the $1T$-$1R$ cell in series. On the basis of these proposed switching schemes, the stable pulse operation was demonstrated successfully, which indicated good potential for this device design.

In most cases, the electroforming process is needed for NiO resistive-switching devices. It is confirmed to be a time-dependent process by analyzing the different I–V characteristics between direct current (DC) sweep mode and pulse mode [34]. Statistical time-dependent dielectric breakdown measurements indicated that the electroforming time exponentially depended on applied voltage, suggesting that the forming process is not a spontaneous process at some critical voltage, but it is instead an upsurge process resulting from stress-induced defects.

Retention properties of the device are also important for practical RRAM applications. Ielmini et al. [35] found that the retention time in NiO-based resistive-switching memories is size dependent. They studied temperature-accelerated data retention in RRAM cells and addressed the size/nature of the conductive filament and clarified the tradeoff between data retention and reset current.

In addition, a NiO RRAM nanocapacitor array was prepared on a graphene sheet on an Nb-doped $SrTiO_3$ substrate that had terraces with a regular interval of about 100 nm and an atomically smooth surface [36]. The NiO RRAM nanocapacitor array on graphene exhibited typical unipolar switching characteristics with lower Set and Reset voltages than those on a bare surface of Nb-doped $SrTiO_3$.

Oka et al. [37] demonstrated the nonvolatile bipolar resistive memory switching in single crystalline NiO heterostructured nanowires. The self-assembled NiO nanowires are expected to open up opportunities to explore not only the detailed nanoscate mechanisms in NiO resistive memory switching but also next-generation nanoscate nonvolatile memory devices with the potential for high-density device integration and improved memory characteristics. They also reported on the resistive switching effects of NiO nanowire/metal junctions [38]. By constructing highly stable resistive switching junctions with a metal/NiO nanowire/metal structure, they used the junctions to elucidate the crucial role of redox events in the nanoscale bipolar resistive switching. The presented approach utilizing oxide nanowire/metal junctions offers an important system and platform for investigating nanoscale resistive switching mechanisms for various oxide materials.

3.2. TiO_2 Thin Films

Usually, TiO_2 thin films exhibit anatase or rutile phase structures depending on difference of deposition temperatures or preparation methods. Studies have confirmed that both phase structures showed bipolar resistive-switching behavior [39, 40]. In addition, the influence of crystalline constituent on resistive-switching properties of $Pt/TiO_2/Pt$ was also studied [41]. It was observed that the leakage current in the high-resistance state depended on the crystal phase composition of TiO_2 thin films; however, the current of the thin films in the low-resistance state was hardly affected. The high-resolution scanning transmission electron microscopy (STEM) characterization of the TiO_2 anatase nanolayer of about 2.5 nm thick on the TiN thin film suggested that the resistive change was due to the Mott transition in the TiO_2 anatase nanolayer, which could relate to the formation of the filament paths [40].

Based on the different switching behaviors of $Pt/TiO_2/Pt$ and $Ir(O)/TiO_2/Pt$, the mechanism of resistance switching of TiO_2 thin films was thought to be due to local rupture and recovery of conducting filaments near the anode interface [42]. Further research indicated that only small part of the conducting filaments in the thin films near the anode contributed to the resistance switching. Another study on the influence of electron injection on the resistive switching of $Pt/TiO_2/Pt$ structure indicated that when the carrier injection by Schottky emission or space-charge-limited conduction was excessive, the resistance switching from the high resistance state to the low resistance state by a filamentary mechanism was suppressed [43].

Resistive-switching properties of polycrystalline TiO_2 thin film sandwiched between the Pt electrodes could be enhanced using a tungsten nitride barrier layer [44]. This enhancement can be attributed to the decrease in the number of oxygen vacancies at the interfaces between the Pt electrode and the TiO_2 layer due to the inserted tungsten nitride buffer layer. Gd doping of TiO_2 films was also found to improve resistive switching characteristics of TiO_2-based resistive memory devices such as decreasing dispersions of resistive switching parameters due to continuous resistive switching [45].

Using X-ray absorption spectromicroscopy and TEM, the chemistry and structure of the conducting channels responsible for the bipolar resistance switching in these devices in titanium dioxide memristive devices have been directly identified [46]. The formation of a Ti_4O_7 Magneli phase possessing metallic properties and ordered planes of oxygen vacancies has been observed within the TiO_2 matrix.

Jung et al. [47] prepared transparent TiO_x-based resistive switching films on an indium tin oxide-coated glass layer. The fabricated TiO_x-based ReRAM device exhibits distinct resistive switching under consecutive DC voltage sweeps of ± 2 V. The device also exhibits good memory performance, including fast switching speed with a pulse width of 1 μs, stable pulse endurance over 1000 cycles, and excellent retention characteristics at up to 125°C. The reversible formation/rupture of the conducting filaments in the oxygen-deficient TiO_x layer was suggested to be the switching mechanism, based on the I–V curves and XPS analysis of the thin films.

Kim et al. [48] studied the reversible resistive-switching effect of the $Al/TiO_x/TiO_2/Al$ heterostructure. It was suggested that the resistive switching was ascribed to space-charge-limited conduction as controlled by localized traps in the TiO_x layer. Then, they extended space-charge-limited conduction theory to analyze the abrupt resistance transition considering the ratio of free and trapped carrier density. The proposed model can be applicable to resistance-switching phenomena induced by interface-type traps in other material system.

Nauenheim et al. [49] investigated the electroforming process in resistively switching TiO_2 nanocrosspoint junction devices with a reactive-sputtered TiO_2 thin film between Pt and Ti/Pt electrodes. The TiO_2 needs an electroforming process before it can be switched. The results indicated that a current-driven electroforming with negative polarities leads into the switchable high resistive state without the need of a current compliance. These devices show an improved stability and reliability in bipolar resistive switching performance.

Biju et al. [50] studied the improved resistive-switching properties of solution processed TiO_2 thin films. The $Pt/TiO_2/Pt$ device exhibited bipolar switching with a uniform high resistance state compared with the low resistance state. By choosing a proper compliance current in the first set operation, reliability and stability of the device was significantly improved. The switching properties were explained by a physical model based on localized generation/recovery of oxygen vacancy defects near the bottom electrode interface.

Atomic structure study of conducting nanofilaments in TiO_2 is very crucial for understanding of the resistive switching mechanism. Kwon et al. [51] used a high-resolution TEM to directly probe the nanofilaments in a $Pt/TiO_2/Pt$ system during resistive switching. *In situ* I–V and low-temperature (about 130°K) conductivity measurements confirm that switching occurs by the formation and disruption of TiO_{2n-1} filaments. Understanding the composition, structure, and dimension changes of these filaments will be beneficial to finally unraveling the fully resistance-switching mechanism of oxide thin films.

By combining the delamination technique with the conductive AFM after electroforming and switching, spatially resolved morphology and electrical conductance changes in TiO_2 memristive devices induced by electroforming and switching have been studied [52]. The electroforming leads to the creation of localized conductance channels induced by oxygen evolution, while subsequent resistive switching results in an additional conducting structure next to the forming spot. It was observed that the lateral extent of this structure depends on the number of switching cycles, indicating an ongoing breaking of existing and newly created neighboring current channels during subsequent switching.

To clarify the resistive switching and failure mechanisms in Al/amorphous-TiO_2/Al devices, Jeong et al. [53] studied the microscopic change in amorphous titanium oxide films and interface layers after the set process. For low temperature (< 150°C) samples, the thickness of the top interface layer decreased after the set process due to the dissociation of a top interface layer by uniform migration of oxygen vacancies. But, for high temperature samples, crystalline TiO_x phases emerged in the failed state, meaning the formation of conducting paths from the local clustering of oxygen vacancies in nonhomogeneous titanium oxide film (see Fig. 6).

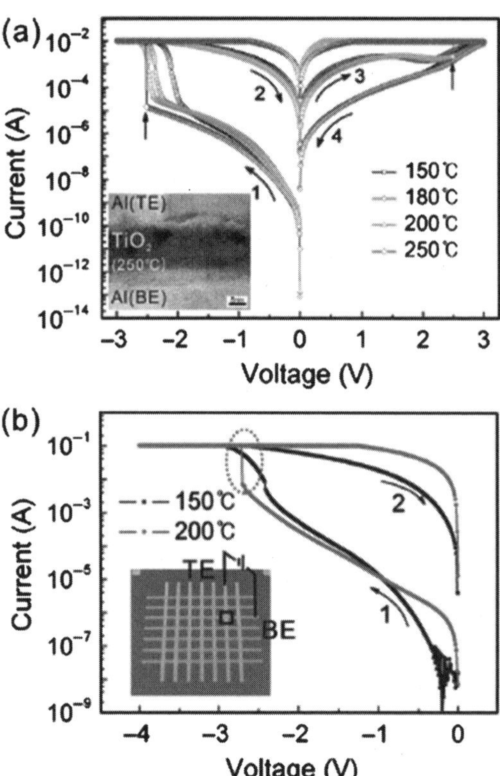

Figure 6. (a) I–V characteristics of Al/TiO_2/Al devices deposited at various temperatures (150, 180, 200, and 250°C). The HRTEM image of Al/TiO_2 (25°C)/Al stacked structure is shown in the left inset. (b) I–V characteristics of Al/TiO_2/Al devices deposited at 150 and 200°C measured during negative sweeps. The left inset shows the real photograph of our memory device. Reprinted with permission from [53], H. Y. Jeong et al., *Appl. Phys. Lett.* 97, 042109 (2010). © 2010, American Institute of Physics.

Xia et al. [54] fabricated cross-point arrays of TiO_2-based memristive devices using a self-aligned, one-step nanoimprint lithography process that simultaneously patterns the bottom electrode, resistive switching film, and the top electrode. The major advantages of this process are greatly reduced fabrication complexity and significantly increased throughput, since the process does not require overlay alignment. In addition, the critical interfaces are exposed to much less contamination and, thus, under better chemical control. The junction area is 100 nm × 100 nm. No electrical forming is required and the device can be operated with nA-level currents.

The effect of the top electrode (TE) metal on the resistive switching of (TE)/TiO_2/Pt structure should be investigated because the potential barrier height between the metal and TiO_2 is an important factor on the resistive switching characteristics [55]. When the high Schottky barrier was formed with the TiO_2 film, using Pt or Au as a top electrode, both stable unipolar and bipolar resistive-switching characteristics were observed depending on the current compliance level. In the case of Ag, which forms a relatively low Schottky barrier, only bipolar resistive switching characteristics were observed, regardless of the current compliance level. In the case of Ni and Al, which have a similar work function as Ag, unstable unipolar and bipolar resistive-switching properties at very low current compliance levels were observed due to a chemical reaction at the interface. For the Ti electrode, resistive switching was not observed because the work function of Ti is lower than that of TiO_2 and the TiO phase was formed at the interface (Ti/TiO_x contact is ohmic).

By changing the position of the TiN electrode, with regard to TiO_2 thin films, to form two structures of top TiN/TiO_2/Pt and Pt/TiO_2/TiN bottom, it was observed that TiN electrode could induce bipolar resistive switching of TiO_2 thin films [56]. The bipolar resistive-switching characteristics in polycrystalline TiO_2 thin films after regular forming process were studied using the two different top or bottom TiN electrodes. Two different switching directions of counterclockwise and clockwise bipolar switching behaviors were observed, depending on the relative position of the TiN electrode. These two switching characteristics could be understood by considering the forming and rupture of the conducting path due to the migration of oxygen ions between the TiO_2 layer and the TiN electrode, which acts like the oxygen reservoir. In addition, both samples clearly display high reliable memory switching characteristics, such as stable switching speed (μs), endurance behaviors (> 10^4), and long retention times (> 10^4 s).

Kwak et al. [57] studied the roles of interfacial TiO_xN_{1-x} layer and TiN electrode in bipolar resistive-switching properties of TiN/TiO_2/TiN structures. Reversible counterclockwise and clockwise resistive switching in a TiN/TiO_2/TiN structure was studied by different polarities of bias voltage (Fig. 7). The nature of the bipolar switching phenomenon is related to the creation and annihilation of filament paths caused by redox reactions at locally confined interfaces between the TiO_2 layer and TiN electrode. The analysis of

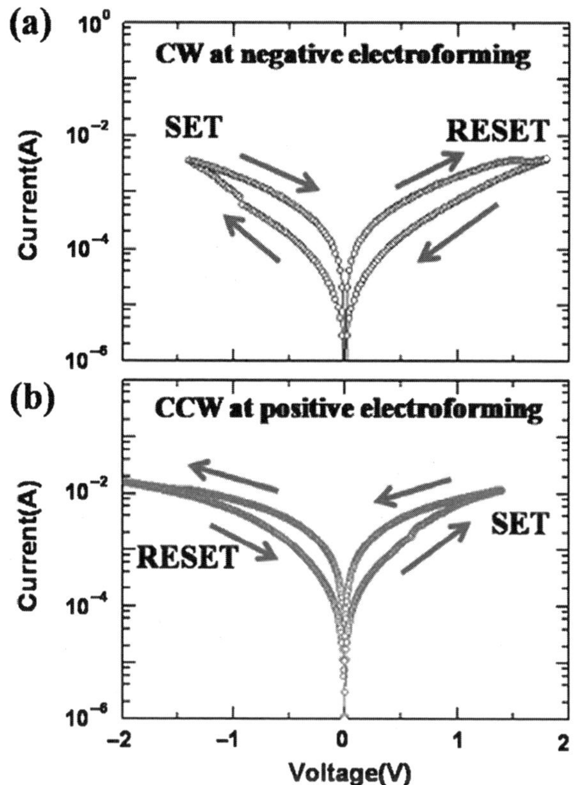

Figure 7. Bipolar switching behaviors for samples A and B. Two different switching modes, clockwise (CW) and counter-clockwise (CCW). Reprinted with permission from [57], J. S. Kwak et al., *Appl. Phys. Lett.* 96, 223502 (2010). © 2010, American Institute of Physics.

electron energy loss spectroscopy confirmed the formation of interfacial TiO_xN_{1-x} layer between the TiO_2 and TiN bottom electrode. The TiO_xN_{1-x} layer reduces current levels of ON and OFF states by partially blocking oxygen ion drift to the TiN bottom electrode.

The influence of copper-top electrodes on the resistive switching effect in TiO_2 thin films was also studied by conductive atomic force microscopy [58]. The 30-nm thick TiO_2 thin films on platinized substrates showed repetitive bipolar resistive switching confirmed by CAFM (Fig. 8). Experiments using macroscopic copper-top electrodes, which are electroformed, bipolar switched, and removed again from the TiO_2-Pt stack, prove the formation of local conductive filaments with bipolar-switching properties. The localized filaments can be switched repetitively with a resistance ratio of 30. It is believed that Cu diffusion and the formation of filaments are the major mechanisms for the resistive switching in Cu/TiO_2/Pt cells.

In addition, Al electrode-dependent transition to bipolar resistive switching characteristics in pure TiO_2 films was reported (Ref. [59]). It was demonstrated that polycrystalline TiO_2 films in two different structures (Al/TiO_2/Pt and Pt/TiO_2/Al) with two different top and bottom Al electrodes exhibited stable bipolar resistive switching after a forming process. With an Al electrode, the transition to bipolar resistive switching was clearly observed, together with counterclockwise and clockwise switching directions, which depended on the position of the Al electrode. The transition from unipolar to bipolar resistive switching seems to be attributable to the redox reaction and trap/detrap at the interfaces between the Al electrode and TiO_2 layer due to the migration of oxygen ions and electrons. However, the current level analysis of the devices reveals that the forming process method basically leads to the formation of conducting paths inside the TiO_2 layers.

Yarmarkin et al. [60] studied the mechanisms of the forming process and subsequent resistive switching in Au/TiO_2/Pt on silicon substrates. They believed that the physical mechanism underlying the forming consists in a sharp increase of the density of surface states in TiO_2 films initiated by electric breakdown of the Schottky barrier at the contact with the platinum electrode, while the resistive switching of the structures is governed by the variation of the occupation of surface states in the TiO_2 band gap and/or of defect concentration in the barrier region under the action of electric field.

Cao et al. [61] also studied the effects of the compliance current on the resistive switching behavior of TiO_2 thin films. The nanocrystalline TiO_2 thin films were prepared on Pt(111)/Ti/SiO_2/Si substrates by thermally oxidizing Ti films. The Reset current increased when the compliance current increased from 10 mA to 20 mA. When the compliance current exceeded 20 mA, no switching behavior was observed. This was attributed to the change of the conducting behavior in the low-resistance state.

Jeong et al. [62] studied the electroforming effects on the composition, structure, and electrical resistance of Pt/TiO_2/Pt switching structures. They discussed the correlation between the electroforming procedure and the resulting bipolar switching behavior. It was observed that the symmetry of electroforming is a key factor in determining the resulting bipolar switching characteristics. An explanation in terms of the formation of oxygen gas and the vacancies in the vicinity of the anode was given to the mechanism of electroforming in Pt/TiO_2/Pt.

Spatially resolved near-edge X-ray absorption fine structure spectroscopy coupled with microscopy has been used to characterize the electronic, structural, and chemical properties of bipolar resistive switching metal/TiO_2/metal devices [63]. The metal/TiO_2/metal devices were electroformed with both bias polarities and then physically opened to study the material changes before and after resistive switching. The morphology and structural changes indicated that a localized polarity-independent heating occurred in these devices initiated by and subsequently accelerating the polarity-dependent electrochemical reduction/oxidation processes.

Jeong et al. [64] reported a direct observation of the microscopic origin of the bipolar resistive switching behavior of titanium oxide films through an analytical TEM technique using energy-filtering TEM (see Fig. 9) and an *in situ* XPS. It was demonstrated that the oxygen ions accumulated at the top interface by an oxidation-reduction between the titanium oxide layer and the top Al metal electrode. The drift of oxygen ions during the ON/OFF switching was the reason for the bipolar resistive switching in the titanium oxide thin films.

If the transition metal oxide thin films deposited directly on Si substrates exhibit resistive switching properties, this

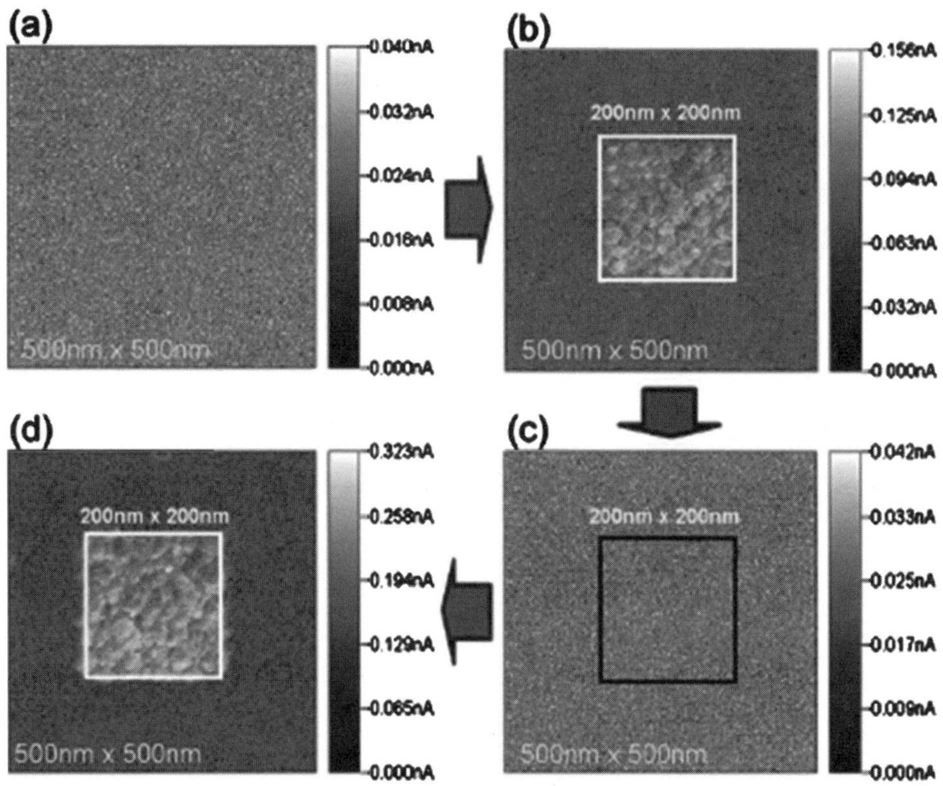

Figure 8. CAFM measurement on an as-deposited ALD TiO_2 film. The current images with $V_{read} = +1$ V are always in the same area ($500 * 500$ nm^2) after subsequent Set and Reset operations in the center area ($200 * 200$ nm^2). (a–d) indicate subsequent OFF–ON–OFF–ON states after the Set or Reset operation. Reprinted with permission from [58], L. Yang et al., *Appl. Phys. Lett.* 95, 013109 (2009). © 2009, American Institute of Physics.

would be of significance because of their compatibility with conventional semiconductor process. Won et al. [65] fabricated sputter-Pt/atomic layer deposition TiO_2/n^+-Si structures for RRAM. As a result, after annealing Pt (100 nm)/TiO_2 (38 nm)/n^+-Si structures in an O_2 ambient at a temperature range of 100–500°C, the resistive switching behavior was observed.

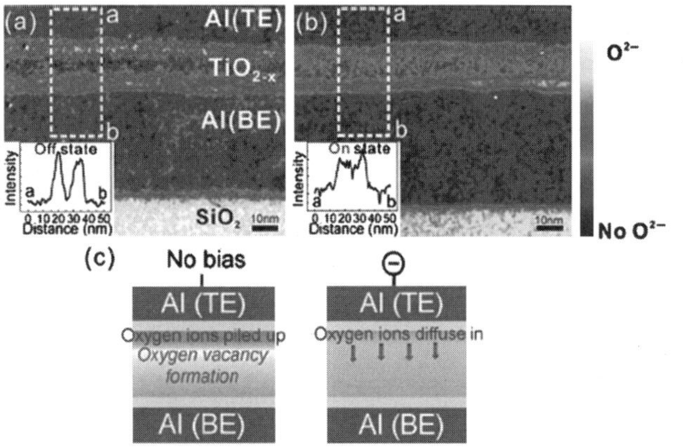

Figure 9. Energy filtered-TEM elemental (oxygen) maps of two different samples (the OFF and ON states): (a) EELS-based oxygen elemental map of as-grown Al/TiO_2/Al structure, corresponding to the OFF state, (b) oxygen elemental map of the sample applied negative set bias (−3 V) on the top Al electrode, corresponding to the ON state. The left insets are the corresponding average intensity profiles obtained from the white rectangular areas, (c) schematics of the proposed model for bipolar resistive switching of Al/TiO_2/Al device. Reprinted with permission from [64], H. Y. Jeong et al., *Appl. Phys. Lett.* 95, 162108 (2009). © 2009, American Institute of Physics.

3.3. ZrO_2 and HfO_2 Thin Films

ZrO_2 thin films sandwiched by top and bottom electrodes also exhibited promising resistive-switching properties.

The effect of TE materials on resistive-switching characteristics of ZrO_2 films has been studied [66]. Compared with Pt/ZrO_2/Pt and Al/ZrO_2/Pt devices, the Ti/ZrO_2/Pt device exhibits better resistive-switching properties. For example, the resistive-switching parameters of the Pt/ZrO_2/Pt and Al/ZrO_2/Pt devices exhibited a broad dispersion during continuous resistive switching cycles, but those dispersions are suppressed by using Ti as a TE for a Ti/ZrO_2/Pt device.

The interface engineering of the RRAM device should be very crucial to improve its performance for future commercial applications. Thickness of Ti TE was found to have an influence on the resistive-switching behaviors of rf-sputtered ZrO_2 memory films by the Tseng research group [67]. With increasing Ti thickness, the induced interface thickness also increases, thus the dielectric strength of the ZrO_2 degraded and results in lower-forming voltage. However, when the interface layer is thick enough, it will trap sufficient charges to build up an opposite electric field to increase the forming voltage. The induced interface thickness is found to obviously affect the bias polarity of the resistive-switching behavior and the device reliability. More recently, a Ti-induced recovery phenomenon of resistive switching in ZrO_2 thin films was found [68]. Tseng research group used W-probe directly contacted with the as-deposited ZrO_2 films to perform the resistive switching, and the ZrO_2-based device finally broke down (defined as BD-ZrO_2/Pt device). It was observed that the resistive-switching phenomenon appeared again in a BD-ZrO_2-based device after Ti TE deposition (i.e., recovery). Whereas, when using the Pt and Al TEs on the BD-ZrO_2/Pt devices, no such phenomenon happened. The Ti-induced recovery phenomenon has been explained by the effects of the interface layer formation. The interface layers, TiO_z and ZrO_y, served as the oxygen reservoir and the series resistance, respectively, to provide sufficient oxygen ions for inducing the redox reaction of the conducting filament near the ZrO_y layer.

Implanting Ti ions into ZrO_2-based thin films can improve the resistive switching properties. Liu et al. [69] demonstrated that doping Ti in ZrO_2 can remove the electroforming process and reduce the variations of switching parameters such as Set voltage and resistance in OFF state. Furthermore, the Ti-doped ZrO_2 resistive switching memory also exhibits high device yield (nearly 100%), low operating voltage, fast speed, large ON/OFF ratio ($> 10^4$), and long retention time ($> 10^7$ s). The formation and rupture of conducting filaments are suggested to be responsible for the resistive switching phenomenon.

TiN can be used as the TE of ZrO_2 films for high performance resistive switching memory devices. TiN/ZrO_2/Pt structures were reported to exhibit good bipolar resistive switching characteristics, including high switching cycles and uniform switching parameters, as well as long retention time [70]. The improved switching behavior of TiN/ZrO_2/Pt could be attributed to the oxygen reservoir effect of TiN electrodes on the formation and rupture of the filamentary conducting paths by modifying the concentration distributions of the oxygen ions and vacancies in ZrO_2 thin films.

Using a metal nanocrystal to cover the bottom electrode (BE) can realize controllable growth of nanoscale conductive filaments in the Ag/ZrO_2/Cu-NC/Pt structure [71]. The Cu-NC covered Pt-BE can control nucleation and growth of conductive filaments, leading to superior uniformity of resistive switching properties. The controllable growth of nanoscale conductive filament bridges between Cu-NC and Ag TE has been observed by TEM. On the basis of energy-dispersive X-ray spectroscopy and elemental mapping analyses, it was further confirmed that the chemical contents of the conductive filaments are mainly Ag atoms.

Wang et al. [72] reported on controllable oxygen vacancies to enhance resistive switching performance in a ZrO_2-based RRAM with an embedded Mo layer. Their experimental results show that the forming process can be removed by inserting an embedded Mo metal layer within ZrO_2 via a postannealing process. The excellent memory performance includes lower operation voltage (< 1.5 V), good endurance ($> 10^3$ cycles), a stubborn nondestructive readout property ($> 10^4$ s), and long retention time ($> 10^7$ s). Moreover, high-speed operation (10 ns) can be successively maintained over 10^3 cycles without any operational errors observed in this memory device. Due to the interface layer induced by the Ti top electrode, the formation and rupture of conducting filaments are suggested to occur near the Ti/ZrO_2 interface. The oxygen vacancies induced by the embedded Mo can enhance the formation of conducting filaments and further improve the switching characteristics in ZrO_2-based devices.

Lee et al. [73] prepared ZrO_x thin films on p^+-Si substrates with a Pt/ZrO_x/p^+-Si sandwich structure by reactive sputtering and observed two stable resistance states. The resistance switching of this Pt/ZrO_x/p^+-Si sandwich structure was explained by electron trapping and detrapping of excess Zr^+ ions in the transition layer. This could affect the distribution of electric field inside the oxide and, hence, the current flow.

It is well known that HfO_2 is a promising high-k dielectric material. Recently, HfO_2 has been reported to exhibit resistive-switching behavior. The polycrystalline HfO_2 films with graded compositions of Hf and O atoms grown by metal organic chemical vapor deposition at 400°C had high resistance ratios of about 10^4–10^9 and low operation voltage below 2 V [74]. The resistance ratio was higher than those of other comparable materials, such as TiO_2 and ZrO_2. Nonstoichiometric hafnium oxide thin films with Pt/HfO_x/TiN/Si structure were also reported to show stable resistance-switching behavior with low-power operation [75].

The Cu/HfO_2:Cu/Pt sandwiched structure has been investigated for nonvolatile memory applications [76]. The device shows excellent resistive switching characteristics, including good endurance, long retention time, fast operation speed and a large resistance ratio of 10^7. Based on the temperature-dependent test results, the formation of Cu conducting filaments is believed to be the reason for the resistance switching from the OFF state to the ON state.

Chen et al. [77] studied the impact of Ti layer at the interface of HfO_x/TiN on the performance of a HfO_x resistive memory. Microstructures of 5-nm thick HfO_x films seem insensitive to the bottom layer (BL) with/without Ti. The switching behavior of the HfO_x resistive memory depends on the position and the thickness of the Ti layer. More oxygen atoms in HfO_x films are captured during the deposition of a Ti overlayer; this result leads to a Ti/HfO_x device with lower-forming voltage and initial resistance. A thick Ti BL (> 30 nm) results in a HfO_x/Ti device with yield of 100% and superior endurance ($> 10^6$ cycles).

In an TiN/Ti/HfO_x/TiN stacked structure, the addition of a thin Ti cap layer can greatly improve the memory performance of hafnium oxide (HfO_x)-based resistive memory [78]. Due to the excellent ability of Ti to absorb oxygen atoms from the HfO_x film after postmetal annealing, a large amount of oxygen vacancies are left in the HfO_x layer of the TiN/Ti/HfO_x/TiN stacked layer. These oxygen vacancies are crucial to make a memory device with a stable bipolar resistive switching behavior. Aside from the benefits of low operation power and the large ON/OFF ratio (> 100), this memory also exhibits reliable switching endurance ($> 10^6$ cycles), robust resistance states (200°C), high device yield (similar to 100%), and fast switching speed (< 10 ns).

Inserting thin Al layers between HfO_2 and electrode layers can also improve the uniformity of switching parameters such as forming voltages, set voltages, and resistances in high/low states in HfO_2-based resistive switching memory [79]. Al atoms are assumed to diffuse into HfO_2 thin films and are intended to localize oxygen vacancies due to reduced oxygen vacancy formation energy, thus stabilizing the generation of conductive filaments. This helps improve the resistive switching uniformity.

A Cu electrode was reported to improve the switching performance of Cu/HfO_2/Pt structure due to Cu ion diffusion [80]. No forming process in the Cu/HfO_2/Pt structure is needed. The current step difference from one state to the other one was in the order of 10^3–10^4, giving a sufficient ON/OFF ratio. Voltage sweep polarity suggested that filamentary Cu paths were formed due to Cu ion diffusion and annihilated at the HfO_2/Pt interface at reversed bias. This filament path formation and annihilation was the origin of the switching device performance.

Atomic-layer-deposited HfLaO-based devices are reported to have excellent resistive-switching characteristics for nonvolatile memory applications [81]. With the help of nonlattice oxygen ions, which are designed to incorporate into the film by decomposing the H_2O_2 during the process, highly uniform and reproducible resistance switching cycles could be observed with the resistive ratio as high as 10^6 for more than 10,000 cycles. In addition, a fast operation speed (10 ns) has been demonstrated. Conduction of the OFF state is dominated by the space-charge-limited hopping, while the ohmic behavior dictates the ON state, suggesting a filamentary conduction mechanism. Moreover, the estimated readout characteristics under different read voltages from 0.3 to 1 V were sufficiently stable to fulfill the requirement for memory application.

In addition, the Pt/CeO_2/Pt structure also had a repeatable resistive switching behavior with a resistance ratio between two memory states of about five orders of magnitude [82]. Al/CeO_x/Pt devices with nonstoichiometric CeO_x thin films were confirmed to exhibit resistive switching behaviors [83].

3.4. ZnO Thin Films

Villafuerte et al. [84] firstly reported on nonvolatile resistance switching of S- and Co-doped ZnO thin films deposited on different substrates using magnetron sputtering and pulsed laser deposition. In the Co-doped ZnO samples, the two resistance states were remarkably stable and uniform. Later, highly (002)-oriented ZnO thin films with Pt/ZnO/Pt configuration were prepared by radio frequency magnetron sputtering at room temperature [85]. The Pt/ZnO/Pt devices also exhibited reversible and steady bistable resistance switching behaviors with a narrow dispersion of the resistance states and switching voltage. The resistance ratios of high resistance state to low resistance state were in the range of 3–4 orders of magnitude within 100 cycles of testing. The conduction mechanisms dominating the low and high resistance states were thought to exhibit Ohmic behavior and Poole–Frenkel emission, respectively.

TiN/ZnO/Pt sandwich structures were also observed highly stable bipolar resistive switching behavior with fast switching speed (< 20 ns for Set and < 60 ns for Reset), long retention (in the order of 10^5 s), and no need of the electroforming process [86, 87]. The bipolar switching behaviors were explained by the formation and rupture of the filamentary conductive path consisting of oxygen vacancies. The generation/recovery of oxygen vacancies and nonlattice oxygen ions were suggested to play a critical role in resistance switching.

Considering that Mg-doped ZnO is a very important multifunctional material, the Bao research group firstly studied the resistance switching properties of the Mg-doped ZnO thin films [88, 89]. They prepared highly *c*-axis-oriented $Mg_{0.2}Zn_{0.8}O$ thin films with hexagonal structure on Pt/TiO_2/SiO_2/Si substrates by sol–gel spin coating technique. The Pt/$Mg_{0.2}Zn_{0.8}O$/Pt devices showed a reversible and stable resistance-switching characteristic. The dominant conduction mechanisms of LRS and HRS were explained by Ohmic behavior and trap-controlled space charge limited current, respectively. Further study showed that when increasing Mg contents in MgZnO thin films, the thin films formed a *spinel-like* structure; thus, a colossal resistance switching effect was discovered in the polycrystalline *spinel-like* structure MgZnO thin films with high Mg contents sandwiched by Pt electrodes. Figure 10 shows *I–V* behavior of a memory cell in semilog scale based on Pt/*spinel*-$Mg_{0.8}Zn_{0.2}O$/Pt devices. The ultrahigh resistance ratio of the high resistancestate to the low resistance state of about 7–9 orders of magnitude with a low reset voltage of less than 1 V was obtained in this thin film system. Obviously, this colossal resistance switching effect will greatly improve the signal-to-noise ratio and simplify the process of reading memory state for nonvolatile memory applications. This study also provides a material base for studying the origin of resistance switching phenomenon.

Shi et al. [90] fabricated fully transparent ZnO:Mg-based devices exhibiting bipolar resistance switching effect. The devices have the structure of ITO/ZnO:Mg/F-doped SnO_2. In addition to the transmittance above 80% for visible light, the devices showed an endurance of more than 10^5 cycles and a retention of longer than 5000 s, even at the temperature of 110°C (although high-to-low resistance ratio was small). The field-induced resistance change can be explained based on the formation/rupture of conduction

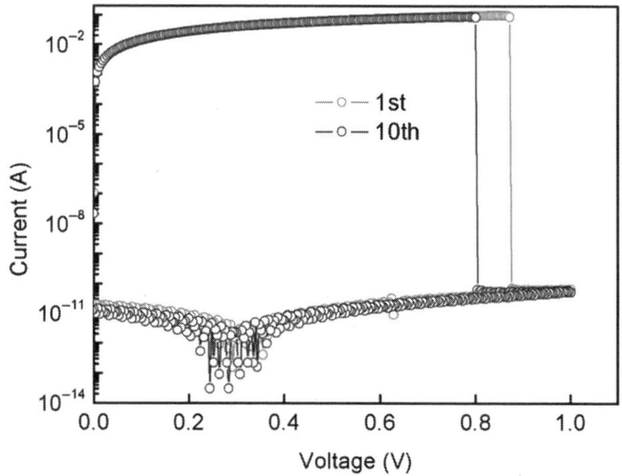

Figure 10. *I–V* behavior of memory cell in a semilog scale based on Pt/spinel-$Mg_{0.8}Zn_{0.2}O$/Pt devices. Reprinted with permission from [89], X. M. Chen et al., *Appl. Phys. Lett.* 94, 033501 (2009). © 2009, American Institute of Physics.

filaments due to the migration of the structural defects in the electric field.

Besides Mg doping in ZnO thin films, more recently Mn doped ZnO thin films have been prepared for RRAM applications [91]. The Ag/ZnO:Mn/Pt structures exhibited excellent resistance-switching properties, such as an ultrafast programming speed of 5 ns, ultrahigh resistance ratio of 10^7, long retention time of more than 10^7 s, good endurance, and high reliability at elevated temperatures. Furthermore, the realization of visualizing nanoscale Ag bridges penetrating through the memory film could account for the high conductivity in the low resistance state. Therefore, the formation and rupture of the Ag bridges has been suggested to explain the switching effect. These results indicated that the Ag/ZnO:Mn/Pt device represents an ultrafast and highly scalable (down to sub-100-nm range) resistive memory element for next generation nonvolatile memories.

Using conductive TiN as the TE on the ZnO:Mn film to form TiN/ZnO:Mn/Pt devices, the devices can be reproducibly switched between the two resistance states by applying bidirectional voltage biases [92]. Moreover, both resistance states can maintain more than 10^4 s without electrical power. The mechanism of resistance switching effects in TiN/ZnO:Mn/Pt is interpreted in terms of the drift of oxygen vacancies and the resultant formation/annihilation of local conductive channels through ZnO:Mn/Pt Schottky barrier.

Similarly, the Cu/ZnO:Mn/Pt also exhibits bipolar resistance switching property with a large ON/OFF ratio (similar to 10^3), suitable threshold voltages (1.4 and −0.7 V for Set and Reset, respectively), long retention ($> 10^4$ s at 85°C) and low write current (10 μA) [93]. The study of dependence of threshold voltages on ZnO:Mn thickness reveals that resistive switching should be an interfacial effect rather than bulk behavior. By elevating the current compliance during the Set process, an anomalous transition from bistable memory switching to a monostable threshold switching was observed, which was attributed to the instability of conductive filaments induced by Joule heating effects. Apart from this, fast voltage sweep cycles without efficient heat dissipation were also found to accelerate the hard dielectric breakdown of the device, reflecting the impact of accumulative Joule heating. These results reveal the possible influences of Joule heating effects on bipolar resistance switching and, thus, the necessity of avoiding them in future high-density memory applications.

Peng et al. [94] also studied the electrode dependence of resistive switching in Mn-doped ZnO grown on Pt and Si substrates. The Mn-doped ZnO thin films on different substrates showed unipolar and bipolar switching behaviors, respectively (Fig. 11). Fittings of the I–V curves and the area dependence of the device resistance reveal the filamentary conduction in Pt/Mn:ZnO/Pt. On the other hand, the interfacial effect dominates in Pt/Mn:ZnO/Si, and its low resistance state exponentially relaxes toward the high resistance state in contrast to the good data retention in Pt/Mn:ZnO/Pt. These results suggest that selecting the electrodes dictates the resistive switching mechanism presumably by affecting the migration dynamics of oxygen vacancies.

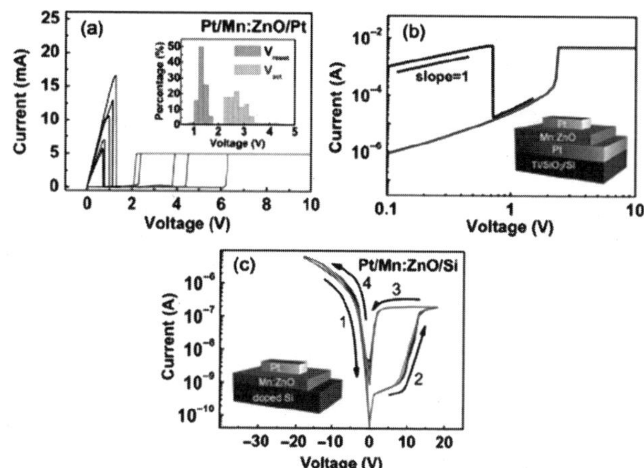

Figure 11. (a) I–V characteristics of the Pt/Mn:ZnO/Pt device. The inset shows the distribution of the set and reset voltages, (b) log–log plot showing the Ohmic behavior in LRS. Inset is the device configuration, (c) I–V characteristics of the Pt/Mn:ZnO/Si device in semilog scale showing 20 consecutive sweepings. Inset is the device configuration. Reprinted with permission from [94], H. Y. Peng et al., *Appl. Phys. Lett.* 96, 192113 (2010). © 2010, American Institute of Physics.

InGaZnO was also used as a switching layer in resistive nonvolatile memory [95]. The memory cells composed of Ti/InGaZnO/TiN exhibited the bipolar switching behavior, including stable resistance ratio of 10^2 and switching responses over 100 cycles (Fig. 12). The resistance switching was ascribed to the formation/disruption of conducting filaments on electrochemical reaction near/at the bias-applied electrode. Using Pt to replace Ti as the TE to form Pt/InGaZnO/TiN structure, the influence of electrode material on resistive switching was investigated. It was observed to show the unipolar and bipolar behavior as applying bias on Pt and TiN electrode, respectively. This demonstrated that the switching behavior was selective by the electrode. They also studied the resistive-switching characteristics of transparent InGaZnO (IGZO) RRAM by forming an indium tin oxide (ITO)/IGZO/ITO structure by sputtering [96]. The device exhibits a repeatable bipolar resistance switching behavior without an electroforming process and an excellent transmittance in the visible region. The conduction mechanisms for low and high resistance states are dominated by Ohm's law and space-charge-limited current behavior, respectively. In retention and endurance tests, a resistance ratio of more than one order remains after 10^4 s at 90°C and after 100 sweeping cycles.

A highly transparent RRAM device is of much interest for future see-through devices. Seo et al. [97] fabricated an ITO/ZnO/ITO structure and studied its resistive switching characteristics [97]. The ITO/ZnO/ITO structure including the substrate had a transmittance of 81% in the visible region and an excellent switching behavior under 3 V. The retention study suggests that the ITO/ZnO/ITO device could maintain its memory property for more than 10 years (Fig. 13).

Chang et al. [98] prepared vertically aligned ZnO nanorod layers (NRLs) on ITO electrodes using a hydrothermal process. The Pt/ZnO-NRL/ITO capacitor exhibited

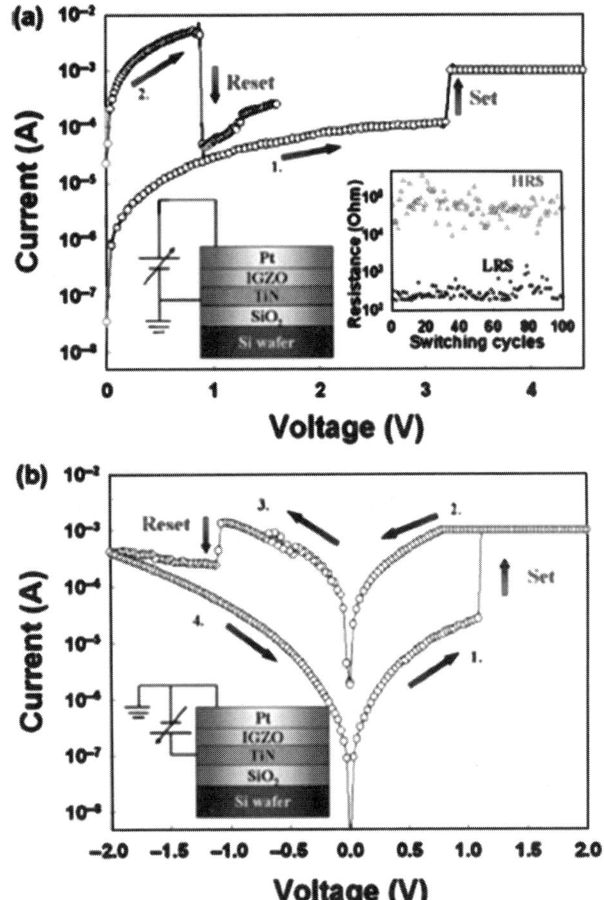

Figure 12. (a) Unipolar behavior in Pt/IGZO/TiN cell, measured by applying bias on Pt electrode. Lower right inset plots the resistance switching characteristics detected at a reading voltage of 0.1 V during continuous I–V sweep of 100 cycles, (b) bipolar behavior in Pt/IGZO/TiN cell, measured by applying bias on TiN electrode. Reprinted with permission from [95], M. C. Chen et al., *Appl. Phys. Lett.* 96, 262110 (2010). © 2010, American Institute of Physics.

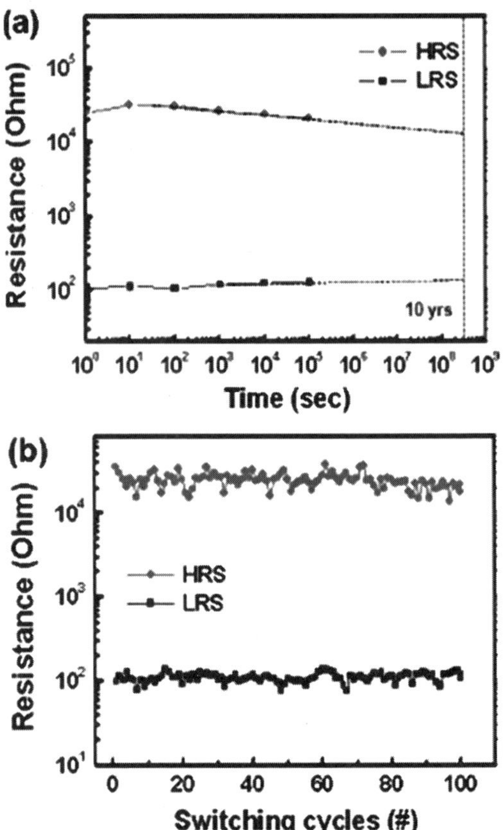

Figure 13. (a) Retention and (b) switching cycling characteristics for the HRS and LRS at room temperature as measured at 0.5 V. Reprinted with permission from [97], J. W. Seo et al., *Appl. Phys. Lett.* 93, 223505 (2008). © 2008, American Institute of Physics.

bipolar resistive-switching behaviors. The resistive-switching behavior may be related to the oxygen vacancies and/or zinc interstitials confined on the surface of the ZnO NRLs, giving rise to the formation of straight and extensible conducting filaments along each vertically aligned ZnO NRLs. Superior stability in resistive-switching characteristics was also observed, demonstrating that ZnO NRLs have the potential for next-generation nonvolatile memory applications.

Ji et al. [99] prepared ZnO thin films on heavily doped silicon substrates using DC reactive magnetron sputtering and studied the resistive-switching characteristics of Cu/ZnO/n^+-Si structures. The metallic Cu TE layer was prepared by thermal evaporation. Reproducible resistive-switching characteristics were observed in Cu/ZnO/n^+-Si structures. The conduction mechanisms in the high and low resistance states are dominated by space-charge-limited conduction and ohmic behavior, respectively, which suggests that resistive-switching behaviors in such structures are related to filament formation and rupture. It was also found that the Reset current decreases as oxygen partial pressure increases due to the variation of oxygen vacancy concentration in the ZnO thin films. As the ZnO thickness was reduced from 100 to 25 nm in Cu/ZnO/n^+-Si structures, the forming process became unnecessary. The forming-free cells showed more stable resistive-switching characteristics. The oxygen vacancies pre-existing in the ZnO films played an important role in the realization of forming-free cells [100].

ZnO thin films were also prepared on flexible plastic substrates by the sol–gel method for flexible resistance-switching memory applications [101]. Fast programming (less than 50 ns) and a high resistance ratio (higher than 10^4) was demonstrated. The devices fabricated on flexible plastic substrates exhibited excellent durability after repetitive bending tests, demonstrating their potential as flexible low-cost memory devices.

The resistive-switching characteristics of ZnO thin film grown on stainless steel for flexible nonvolatile memory devices were reported by Lee and coworkers [102]. The device consists of Au/ZnO/stainless steel (SS) structure fabricated by radio frequency sputtering ZnO thin film on the SS substrate. The fabricated device showed stable unipolar and bipolar resistive-switching behaviors with reliable switching responses over 100 cycles (Fig. 14). The device performance was not degraded on bending, indicating a high potential for flexible RRAM applications.

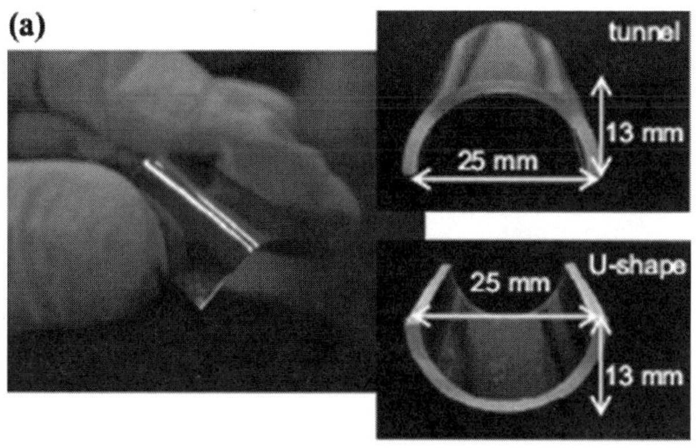

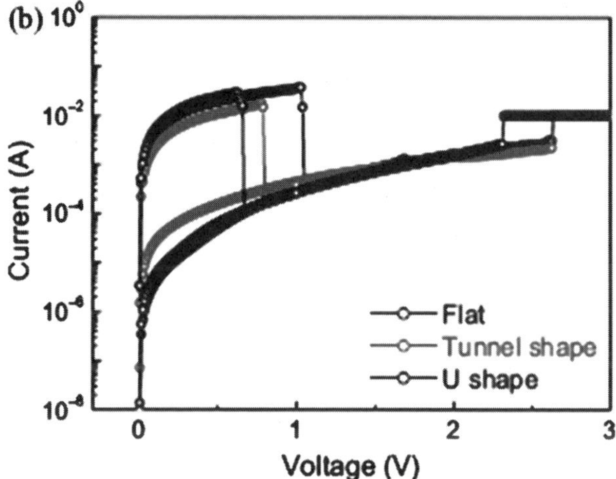

Figure 14. (a) Typical unipolar resistive switching characteristics of flat and bent Au/ZnO/SS device, and the (b) image of the bent device and the templates used for the bending. Reprinted with permission from [102], S. Lee et al., *Appl. Phys. Lett.* 95, 262113 (2009). © 2009, American Institute of Physics.

3.5. Al_2O_3, CuO, and MnO_x Thin Films

Unipolar resistive switching of aluminum oxide thin films with an $Al/Al_xO_y/Al$ structure was recently studied for flexible nonvolatile memory applications [103]. The Al_xO_y thin films were prepared by plasma oxidation, and a high resistance ratio (higher than 10^4) was achieved. Due to the good ductility of aluminum, the performance of resistive switching on a flexible substrate was not degraded by severe substrate bending. Note that the low process temperature of the plasma oxidation process is also advantageous for the fabrication of flexible electronic devices and modern interconnection processes (Fig. 15).

Radio-frequency-sputtered Al_xO_y thin films also showed resistive-switching behavior, with a resistance ratio of high resistance state and low resistance state of over 10^3 [104]. It was observed that both high resistance states and low resistance states were stable and reproducible during successive resistive switching by DC voltage sweeping.

It has been reported that using an ultrathin Al inserting layer to form Al–AlO_x multilayered junctions with an amorphous aluminum oxide as active layer can considerably improve resistive-switching performance [105]. The mechanism of the resistance switching basically reflects the filament model. The temperature dependence of the transport

Figure 15. (a) A photograph of flexible RRAM, (b) the structure and process flow of the fabricated flexible RRAM. Reprinted with permission from [103], S. Kim and Y. K. Choi, *Appl. Phys. Lett.* 92, 223508 (2008). © 2008, American Institute of Physics.

in each resistance state revealed additional features, i.e., a well-defined thermal activation behavior in the high-resistance state is not observed in the layered device and the metallic conduction in the low-resistance state is not affected. The improved endurance properties are discussed in terms of the increased effective number of active regions, where the Reset and Set processes probably occur before a permanent dielectric breakdown.

Ventura et al. [106] studied the time evolution of the electrical resistance of $Ta/AlO_x/Ta$ nanostructures that display resistive switching. At low temperature and in the early switching stages the resistance rapidly varied. However, as time proceeded, resistance jumped between terraces through different processes, such as discontinuous steps, two levels, or dumped fluctuations. Furthermore, a wealth of active fluctuators was visible even after the current led to no net resistance variations. This was reinforced at high temperatures, where the fluctuating rate and number of active fluctuators led to complex signals.

Aluminum/anodized aluminum film structure with metal-insulator-metal structure was reported to show resistive switching without the need of forming process [107]. Unipolar resistive switching between a high-resistance state and a low-resistance state with a high resistance ratio (> similar to 10^4) was observed from the structure. The pre-existing conductive filaments in the Al-rich Al_xO_y layer formed by the anodization were responsible for the switching occurrence with no forming process. Each resistance state exhibited ohmic behavior, which could be explained by the metallic conduction and the electron hopping from one isolated state to the next in the Al-rich Al_xO_y layer.

Another recent study showed that CuO_x thin film with gradual oxygen concentration distribution enhanced resistive-switching characteristics for RRAM applications [108]. By using an $Al/CuO_x/Cu$ structure with gradual oxygen concentration, forming was not needed and the endurance of the switching was greatly enhanced.

$Ni/Cu_xO/Cu$ structure using thermally grown Cu_xO thin film as an active layer also exhibited resistive switching properties [109]. The resistance of the device can be reversibly switched between the high-resistance-state and the low-resistance-state by DC voltages. The device with the unipolar switching behavior can be either operated by DC voltages in the same direction (unipolar operation method) or in the opposite directions (bipolar operation method). When using the bipolar operation method, the switching dispersions were smaller than when using the unipolar operation method. This may be attributed to the compensation of the defect migration during the switching cycles. The switching behaviors of the bipolar operation method and the unipolar operation method were similar. The conducting filament model with the thermochemical effect may explain the resistive switching behaviors.

In TaN/Cu_xO/Cu structures, the role of TaON interface for Cu_xO resistive switching memory was studied based on a combined model [110]. Stable bipolar switching behavior was observed for the TaN/Cu_xO/Cu device. TaON was observed at the anode interface by XPS and TEM, which is believed to play a key role in the resistance transition. A filament/charges trapped combined model was proposed to clarify the electrical characteristics of the TE/oxide reactions (Fig. 16). This observation presented a unique opportunity to elucidate a universal mechanism for the resistive switching of transitional metal oxides.

Furthermore, the compliance current (CC) dependence of the resistive-switching behaviors has been investigated in TaN/Cu_xO/Cu memory devices with 1-*R* architecture and 1*T*-1*R* architecture, respectively [111]. The correlation of the Reset current *I*–*R* and the ON-state resistance, *R*-on, can be verified by adjusting the compliance current *I*-comp. Meanwhile, *I*-Reset and *R*-on become independent on *I*-comp in the 1-*R* architecture when *I*-comp is below 1 mA. A serious CC overshoot phenomenon is *in situ* observed in a 1-R-architecture device, and it remarkably affects the resistive-switching characteristics because the CC dominates the memory behaviors. Therefore, resistive-switching investigation based on 1T-1R architecture is much more reliable.

The flat-surfaced and (111)-oriented Cu_2O films grown through an electrochemical approach were reported to exhibit unipolar resistive-switching properties with a high resistance ratio (*R*-off/*R*-on) over three orders of magnitude [112].

In addition, the endurance enhancement of Cu-oxide-based resistive switching memory with an Al TE was reported (Ref. [113]). Compared with the Pt electrode, the Al electrode showed better stability, preferable endurance, and larger resistance ratio. An interface AlO_x layer was detected by TEM and Auger electron spectroscopy. This layer can strongly affect the movement of oxygen vacancies. However, the sample with the pure Ti electrode had almost no switching characteristics. The Ti/TiN electrode with thin Ti exhibited good switching behavior. The thickness control of the Ti layer was quite critical. So, it was suggested that the oxygen diffusion in the electrode was another important factor for switching performance.

The Pt/MnO_x/Al structure was found to exhibit reversible resistive-switching behavior [114]. When Al was used as TE instead of Pt, the device had a better endurance performance. Additionally, the Pt/MnO_x/Al device showed fast switching speed and long retention ability.

The Ti/MnO_2/Pt structure also showed stable and reproducible bipolar resistive switching behaviors (Fig. 17) [115]. The dependency of the memory behavior on the cell area and the operating temperature suggested that the conducting mechanism in the low resistance states was due to the locally conducting filaments formed. XPS showed that nonlattice oxygen ions formed at the MnO_2 surface. The mechanism of resistance switching in the system examined involved the generation and recovery of oxygen vacancies with the nonlattice oxygen ions.

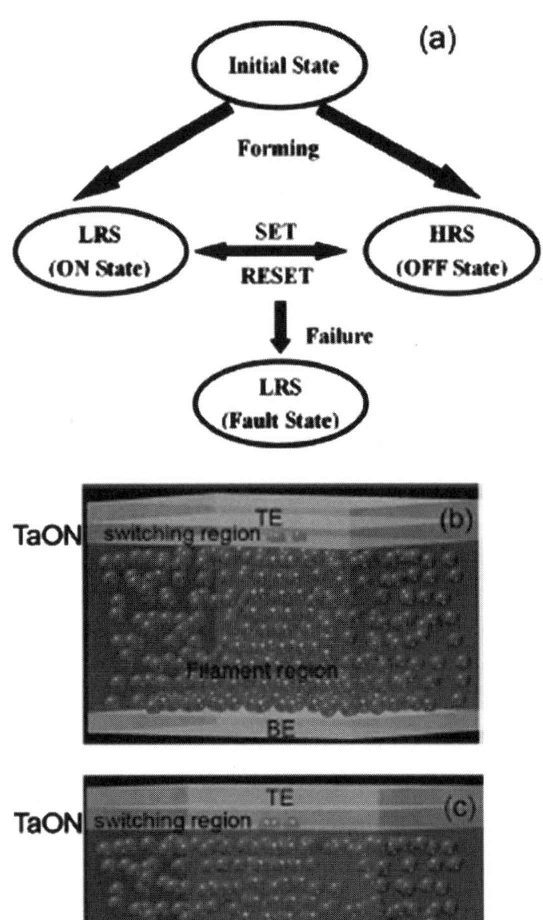

Figure 16. Schematic views for the filament/charges trapped combined model. (a) The four states of a normal RRAM device and the relative transition processes, (b) schematic diagram of the TaN/Cu_xO/Cu structure. It is composed of the switching region and filament region (positively charged oxygen vacancies). Here, the trap centers in the TaON interface are empty so that the system is in the OFF state. The trap centers in TaON interface are filled by holes. The larger balls represent trap centers (local states, oxygen vacancies, and defects); the small white dots with cross represent the holes, and the small white dot in the larger balls represent positively charged trap centers. Reprinted with permission from [110], P. Zhou et al., *Appl. Phys. Lett.* 94, 053510 (2009). © 2009, American Institute of Physics.

Using TiN to replace the Ti TE to form the TiN/MnO_2/Pt device structure, bipolar resistive-switching characteristics were demonstrated in a low power operation (250 μA/$\pm$0.6 V) [116]. The devices showed good endurance of 10^5 cycles at a 1-us pulse and reliable data retention at both RT and 125°C. Moreover, the benefits of a high device yield and potential multilevel storage make them promising devices in next generation nonvolatile memory applications.

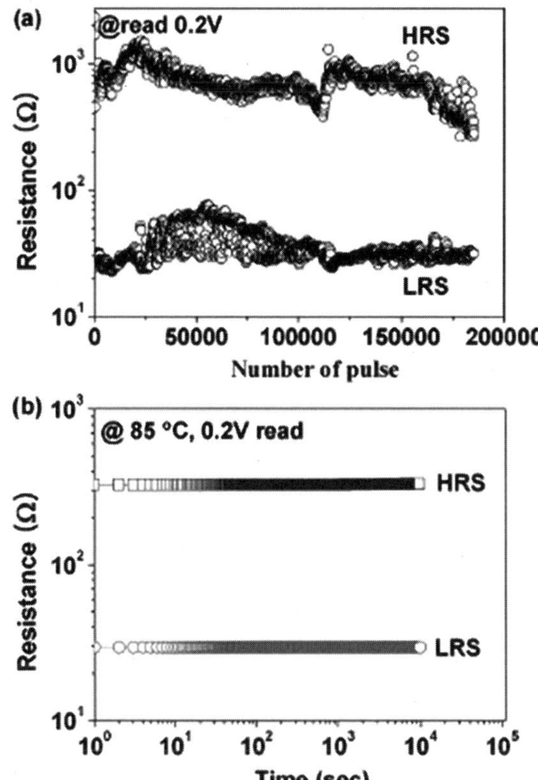

Figure 17. (a) Resistance measurements of the Ti/MnO_2/Pt device after voltage pulses. The set and reset voltage was ±1.5 V and the resistance was measured at 0.2 V. The pulse width was 10 ms, (b) retention behaviors of the HRS and LRS, showing no degradation for up to 10^4 s at 85°C. Reprinted with permission from [115], M. K. Yang et al., *Appl. Phys. Lett.* 95, 042105 (2009). © 2009, American Institute of Physics.

The cell area dependency suggested that the conducting mechanism in the low-resistance states was due to the formation of locally conducting filaments. The results demonstrated the feasibility of high performance resistive-switching memory devices based on transition metal oxides by using TiN as the TE.

The Liu research group [117] studied resistive switching characteristics of Pt/MnO_x/Al structures. The devices exhibited reversible resistive-switching behavior under both sweeping voltages and voltage pulses. The formation and rupture of conductive filaments were used to explain the resistive switching behaviors. The Pt/MnO_x/Al device showed fast switching speed and long retention ability. The experiment results suggested that the Pt/MnO_x/Al device had potential for practical memory applications.

3.6. Other Transition Metal Oxide Thin Films

Zhang et al. [118] prepared TaO_x-based unipolar resistive switching thin film combined with an electrode design. The fabricated unipolar film devices exhibited lower switching voltages, fast switching speed of less than 80 ns, excellent retention capabilities, and stable cycling behaviors.

Tsuruoka et al. [119] studied the forming process and switching mechanisms of Cu/Ta_2O_5/Pt structures. The Cu/Ta_2O_5/Pt can be initialized (Set operation from the OFF state to the ON state) through a low positive bias voltage applied to the Cu electrode. This first Set operation corresponded to the first formation of a metal filament by inhomogeneous nucleation and subsequent growth of Cu on the Pt electrode based on the migration of Cu ions in the stable Ta_2O_5 matrix. After the forming, the device exhibited bipolar switching behavior (Set at positive bias and Reset [from the ON state to the OFF state] at negative bias) with increasing the ON resistance from a few hundred Omega to a few k Omega. From the measurements of the temperature stability of the ON states, it can be concluded that the Reset process consists of the Joule-heating-assisted oxidation of Cu atoms at the thinnest part of the metal filament followed by diffusion and drift of the Cu ions under their own concentration gradient and the applied electric field, disconnecting the metal filament. With ON resistances on the order of a few k Omega, the Set and Reset operations were repeated by the inhomogeneous nucleation and the Joule-heating-assisted dissolution of a small filament on a remaining filament.

Pt/Co_3O_4/Pt structures were also reported to show unipolar resistive switching behavior [120]. The resistance ratio of the high- and low-resistance states was over 5×10^3. The resistance of the two states can be kept for more than 16 hours without degradation. The temperature dependence of the resistance shows a metallic behavior at the low-resistance state but a semiconductor behavior at the high-resistance state.

Similarly, Pt/CoO_x/Pt stacks with metal-deficient CoO_x exhibited reproducible and stable unipolar switching under a DC sweeping voltage [121]. In order to investigate the role of oxygen reduction in the metal-deficient CoO_x layer, resistive switching of the postannealed CoO_x thin film was compared with those of the as-deposited CoO thin film. Results showed a larger reproducible resistance switching and decreasing of current level in the postannealed CoO thin film. This may be explained by a reduction in oxygen stoichiometry without phase transformation of the CoO_x. In addition, stable switching in the postannealed CoO_x layer is considered to originate from the decrease of the Co vacancies in the local Co_3O_4 region and partially distributed in the whole CoO_x layer, not in the dominant CoO.

Wang et al. [122] studied the effects of compliance currents on the formation and rupture of conducting filaments in unipolar resistive switching of CoO film. The compliance current strongly affected the local structure of conducting filaments. Lower compliance currents produced conducting filaments with simple connectivity and good controllability, resulting in a narrow distribution of switching voltages and a high ratio of high-to-low resistance states. In contrast, the stronger net-like conducting filaments were formed at higher compliance currents, and their complete rupture was difficult. Thus, the lower high-resistance states and a wide distribution of switching voltages appeared in the reversible switching processes.

Lai et al. [123, 124] fabricated a complementary metal oxide semiconductor-compatible WO_x-based resistive memory. The WO_x resistive layer was obtained through the rapid thermal oxidation of W plugs. The CAFM characterization indicated that the nanoscale-conducting channels existed in the WO_x layer and resulted in a low initial resistance. The

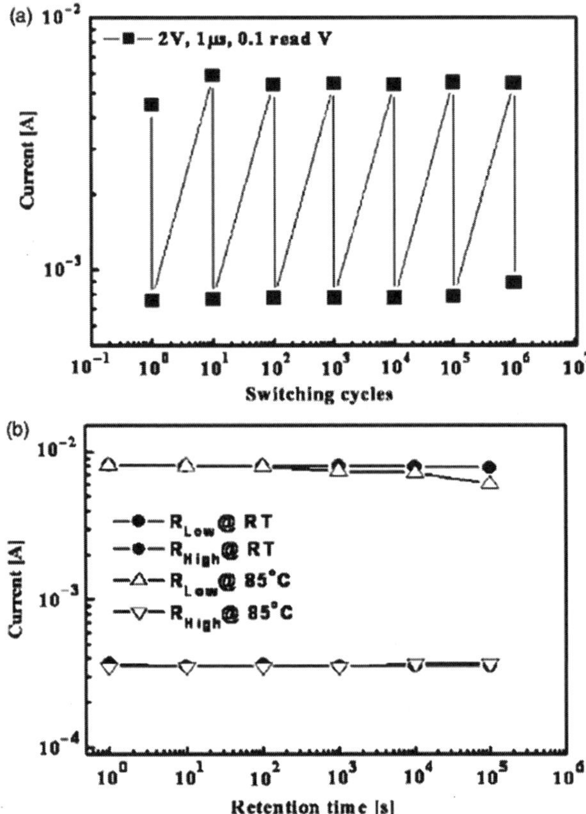

Figure 18. Endurance of Cu:MoO_x by voltage pulses and retention properties of R_{on} and R_{off} at *RT* and 85°C. Reprinted with permission from [125], D. Lee et al., *Appl. Phys. Lett.* 90, 122104 (2007). © 2007, American Institute of Physics.

good electrical properties of the devices included fast switching speed (similar to 2 ns) and low programming voltage (< 1.4 V). For a single-level cell operation, the device shows a large resistance window and a 10^8-cycle endurance. For a multilevel cell operation, it demonstrates a 2-bit/cell storage with an endurance of up to 10,000 times.

Nonvolatile and reversible resistance switching of Cu-doped MoO_x film was studied [125]. Figure 18 shows endurance of Cu:MoO_x by voltage pulses and retention properties of R_{on} and R_{off} at *RT* and 85°C. The resistance switching might be strongly related to the rupture and the generation of multifilaments, which can be confirmed by spreading resistance images of a conducting atomic force microscope as well as filamentary conduction by double logarithmic plots. Based on the XPS analysis, it was thought that local conducting filaments could be formed by thermally diffused Cu into MoO_x film from the bottom electrode.

4. SEVERAL MULTILAYERED TRANSITION METAL OXIDE THIN FILMS

Multilayered structures can be used to improve and adjust the resistive-switching properties.

Resistive-switching characteristics of Al_2O_3/TiO_2 and $Al_2O_3/TiO_2/Al_2O_3$ multilayered thin films with a Pt/ insulator/Ru structure were studied [126]. For comparison, TiO_2 and Al_2O_3 thin films were prepared with the same Pt/insulator/Ru structure. Both TiO_2 films and Al_2O_3 films show resistive switching by a filamentary switching mechanism with linear conduction behavior in the low *V* region. The multilayered thin films showed a bias polarity-dependent switching behavior. This suggested that the nucleation of the conducting filaments could occur at the interface where the electrons were injected.

Both lowering the "Reset" current and raising the resistance in the low resistance state are crucial for practical use of RRAM. Kinoshita et al. [127] prepared a heterojunction structure consisting of transition metal oxides and NiO_y/TiO_x/Pt and combined them with direct contact to the NiO_y using a *W*-probe. The *W*-probe/NiO_y/TiO_x/Pt structure could lead to extreme downsizing of the effective area of both the top and bottom electrodes for NiO_y and, thus, decreased the number of filaments formed in the "forming" process. Reducing the number of filaments is essential to the issues of lowering the "Reset" current and raising the resistance.

Considering that both NiO and MgZnO on Pt electrodes exhibit the resistive switching effect, Bao et al. [128] proposed a heterojunction structure composed of *p*-NiO and *n*-MgZnO with high Mg contents with an aim to tuning or improving the resistive-switching properties. The *p*-NiO/*n*-MgZnO heterojunction was fabricated on $Pt/TiO_2/SiO_2/Si$ substrates by the sol–gel spin coating technique. It has been confirmed that the *p–n* heterojunction device exhibited typical *I–V* behaviors with rectifying characteristics. After an electroforming process, the Pt/NiO/MgZnO/Pt heterojunction device showed good reproducible resistance switching properties, such as a reduced threshold current of 1 μA for device initiation, a small dispersion of reset voltage ranging from 0.55 to 0.62 V, and a high resistance ratio of high resistance state to low resistance state about six orders of magnitude.

Yang et al. [129] prepared Cu/ZnO/Cu/ZnO/Pt structures. The structures showed resistance switching under electrical bias both before and after a rapid thermal annealing (RTA) treatment. The memory cell after the RTA exhibited remarkable device parameter improvements, including lower threshold voltages, lower write current, and higher *R*-off/*R*-on ratio. A high-voltage forming process is avoided in the annealed device as well. Scanning electron microscopy observations and Auger electron spectroscopy depth profiles revealed that the Cu-charge trapping layer in the ZnO/Cu/ZnO dispersed uniformly into the storage medium after RTA, while X-ray diffraction and XPS analyses demonstrated that the Cu atoms had become Cu^{2+} ions after dispersion. Therefore, the altered status of the Cu in the ZnO/Cu/ZnO trilayer films during RTA treatment should be responsible for the switching transition mechanism.

TiO_2/TiO_{2-x} multilayer homojunctions were also studied as alternative resistive switching structures for both high- and low-resistance transitions [130]. The structures possessed stable bipolar resistive switching characteristics, including stable switching speeds and endurance behaviors, and long retention times (> 10^4 s). The nature of the resistive-switching phenomenon in multilayer structures seems to be a combination of the conduction path and the redox reaction, resulting from the oxygen ions drifting

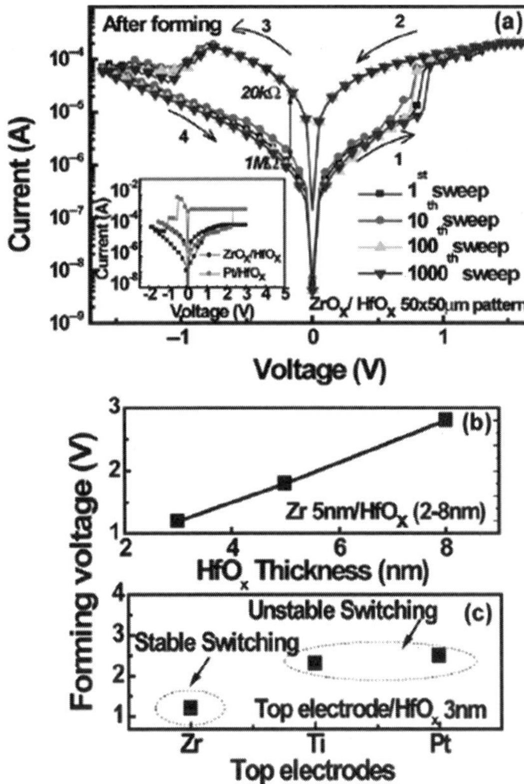

Figure 19. (a) Typical *I–V* curve of ZrO_xHfO_x bilayer structure. The inset shows a comparison of the bilayer structure with a HfO_x monolayer structure. (b) The HfO_x thickness dependence. The switching properties of metal (5 nm) HfO_x (3 nm)/TiN stacks with Zr, Ti, and Pt top electrodes. Reprinted with permission from [131], J. Lee et al., *Appl. Phys. Lett.* 97, 172105 (2010). © 2010, American Institute of Physics.

between the oxygen rich and poor regions of the multilayer structures.

The ZrO_x/HfO_x bilayer structure was reported to show a lower reset current and operating voltage than the HfO_x monolayer under DC sweep voltage (Fig. 19) [131]. Furthermore, the bilayer structure exhibited a tight distribution of switching parameters, good switching endurance up to 10^5 cycles, and good data retention at 85°C. The resistive switching mechanism of memory devices incorporating the ZrO_x/HfO_x bilayer structure can be attributed to the control of multiple conducting filaments through the occurrence of redox reactions at the tip of the localized filament.

Whereas, the Al_2O_3/SiO_2 gate stack with Ru metal nanocrystals embedded in the Al_2O_3 layer exhibited a trilevel resistive-switching behavior with a resistance ratio of the high-resistance state to the low-resistance state of more than 10^3 [132]. The insulator-to-conductor (and vice versa) transition of the Al_2O_3 and SiO_2 dielectric layers was elucidated by a model, which invokes the O^{2-} trapping/detrapping at the metal-oxide interfaces, as well as O^{2-} transport and annihilation with the oxygen vacancies in the breakdown percolation path. The switching transition of each individual dielectric layer was found to depend on the polarity of the gate bias.

Park et al. [133] studied the state stability of the low-resistance state in a resistive switching memory having a Pt/Cu:MoO_x/GdO_x/Pt structure. Various resistance values of low-resistance state were accurately controlled using an external load resistor connected in a series with the resistive memory device. It was found that the retention time decreased with an increase in the resistance of low-resistance state.

Bilayered thin films combining eicosanoic acid (EA) and ZrO_2 with a sandwich structure of Al/EA/ZrO_2/Au also showed resistance switching characteristics [134]. The Al/EA/ZrO_2/Au devices exhibited asymmetric electrical bistable behavior with a rectifying effect. The asymmetry and rectifying bistable behavior was thought to result from the Schottky barrier due to the ZrO_2 layer/Au interface. Reversible and reproducible bistable switching properties were observed.

5. SEVERAL METAL-NANOCOMPOSITE TRANSITION METAL OXIDE THIN FILMS

Besides multilayered structure transition metal oxide thin films for RRAM applications, metal Au or Ag or Cu metal-nanocomposite transition metal oxide thin films were prepared for the same aims.

Guan et al. [135, 136] studied resistive switching characteristics of Au–ZrO_2 thin films with TE/Au–ZrO_2/n^+ Si sandwich structure. Figure 20 shows typical *I–V* characteristics of Au–ZrO_2 in a semilog scale. The voltage is swept in the direction as follows: 0 V → 4 V → 0 V → −4 V → 0 V. By applying proper voltage, reproducible resistive switching between the high-resistance state and the low-resistance state can be achieved with a resistance ratio of the high-resistance state and the low-resistance state of about two orders. In the voltage pulse test, the "write" and "erase" speeds can be as fast as 50 and 100 ns, respectively. No data loss is observed for more than 10^6 s. The formation and rupture of conducting filamentary paths related to the implanted Au ions were suggested to be responsible for the resistive-switching phenomenon. The dependence

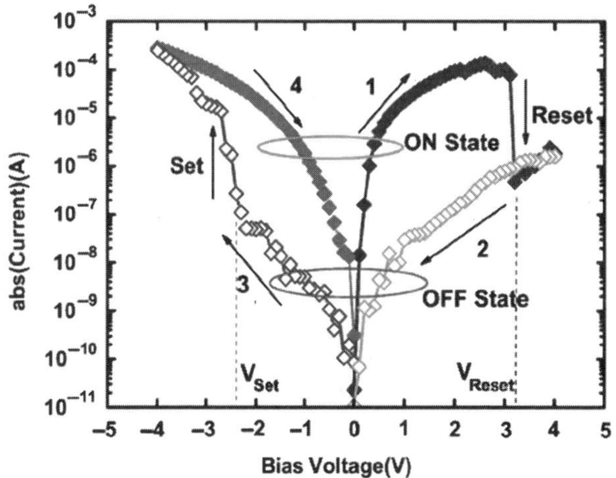

Figure 20. Typical *I–V* characteristics of a sample Au-800 in semilog scale. The voltage is swept in the direction as follows: 0 V → 4 V → 0 V → −4 V → 0 V. Reprinted with permission from [135], W. H. Guan et al., *Appl. Phys. Lett.* 91, 062111 (2007). © 2007, American Institute of Physics.

of resistance on temperature indicated that the variable-range hopping conduction mechanism was dominated in the low-resistance state, while the current characteristics were governed by the trap-controlled space limited conduction mechanism in the high-resistance state.

In comparison, the Cu/ZrO_2:Cu/Pt sandwiched structure also showed resistive switching behavior with a resistance ratio of the order of 10^6 [137]. The switching mechanism is believed to be related to the formation and rupture of conducting filamentary paths. Liu et al. [138] inserted a Cu nanocrystal layer between the Pt electrode and ZrO_2 film to improve resistive switching properties in the ZrO_2-based resistive switching memory. The Cu/ZrO_2:Cu/Cu NC/Pt structure exhibited asymmetric nonpolar resistive switching behavior, low operating voltage (< 1.2 V), low Reset current (< 50 μA), and high uniformity of resistance switching. The nanocrystal-induced electrical field enhancement was beneficial to accelerate and control the conductive filament formation process, thus leading to low-switching threshold voltage and high uniformity.

In addition, Au/Cr/Zr^+-implanted-ZrO_2/n^+-Si sandwiched structure exhibited reversible bipolar resistive switching behavior under DC sweeping voltage with a resistance ratio as high as five orders of magnitude at a 0.5-V readout bias [139].

Sol–gel derived Ag-doped ZrO_2 thin films on Pt/Ti/SiO_2/Si substrates were reported to show improved resistive-switching characteristics [140]. The improved resistive-switching behavior in the Ag-doped ZrO_2 thin films could be attributed to the Ag doping effect on the formation of the stable filamentary conducting paths.

Chang et al. [141] reported the improved resistive switching characteristics of TiO_2 thin films with embedded Pt nanocrystals (Pt-NCs). Reversible and steady bistable resistance switching behavior was observed for the Pt/TiO_2/Pt capacitors with Pt-NCs embedded in the TiO_2 films (Fig. 21). Moreover, an improvement in the stability of resistance switching and retention properties was also achieved from the embedding of uniform and fine Pt-NCs. Ru nanodots embedded in a Pt/TiO_2/Pt resistive switching cell were also found to improve the uniformity of the switching parameters [142].

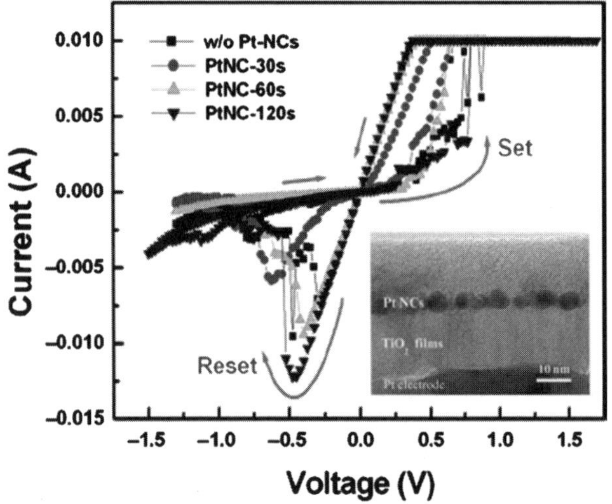

Figure 21. Typical I–V characteristics of the TiO_2 thin film capacitors with or without Pt-NCs embedded. The inset shows the crosssectional TEM image of the Pt-NCs self-assembled in the TiO_2 matrix for the PtNC-30 s sample. Reprinted with permission from [141], W. Y. Chang et al., *Appl. Phys. Lett.* 95, 042104 (2009). © 2009, American Institute of Physics.

Pt nanoparticle (NP)-embedded TiO_2 nanocomposite films can be obtained by thermal annealing Pt-NP-embedded TiO_2 nanocomposite multilayers. These multilayers were prepared by an electrostatic layer-by-layer assembly on Pt-coated Si substrates. The Pt-NP-embedded TiO_2 nanocomposite films also exhibited good nonvolatile bipolar resistive switching properties [143]. The bipolar switching properties were observed at low operating voltages with the high ON/OFF ratio ($> 10^4$) as well as good device stability.

Verbakel et al. [144] made an attempt to fabricate diodes based on spin-coated layers of nanoparticles of Al_2O_3, CeO_2, TiO_2, ZrO_2, Y_2O_3, or ZnO and a semiconducting polymer sandwiched between two electrodes. It was found that the inclusion of the metal oxide nanoparticles results in similar nonvolatile resistance switching properties to those observed for the corresponding "bulk" oxides. Furthermore, the nanoparticle-containing polymer layers do not require an electroforming process. This research is also of interest for flexible RRAM applications.

Silva et al. [145] fabricated the planar capacitor structures based on granular films composed of nanometric ferromagnetic grains embedded in an Al_2O_3 matrix. The structures can be resistively switched between a high-conductance and a low-conductance state. The switching properties were induced by a forming process. The ON/OFF resistance ratio was as high as 10^4. This resistive switching was accompanied by a capacitive switching between two well-defined, voltage-independent states. The behavior was not readily explained by the filamentary type of conduction.

6. CONCLUSIONS

Transition metal oxide thin films that have reversible, bistable resistance switching behaviors exhibit good potential for nonvolatile RRAM applications. Although there have been some physical mechanisms proposed to explain the resistive-switching behaviors of transition metal oxide thin films, more efforts should still be made to better understand the switching mechanisms, including effects of the interface between electrode and oxide film and defects (e.g., oxygen vacancies and grain boundaries). *In situ* characterization of physical and chemical changes of the materials during drastic resistance changes induced by applied voltage pulse or current pulse will be helpful. There is no doubt that study on transition metal oxide thin films for RRAM applications will be a topic of great interest in the forthcoming years, and it is expected that a better understanding of the physical mechanisms for the bistable resistance switching of the transition metal oxide thin films sandwiched between two metal electrodes will speed up RRAM applications of the transition metal oxide thin films.

ACKNOWLEDGMENTS

The authors received financial support from the National Natural Science Foundation of China, (Nos. 50872156 and

U0634006), the Natural Science Foundation of Guangdong Province, China (Grant No. 10251027501000007), and the Specialized Research Fund for the Doctoral Program of Higher Education of China (Grant No. 20090171110007).

REFERENCES

1. D. B. Strukov, G. S. Snider, D. R. Stewart, and R. S. Williams, *Nature* 453, 80 (2008).
2. M. J. Lee, S. Seo, D. C. Kim, S. E. Ahn, D. H. Seo, I. G. Baek, D. S. Kim, I. S. Byun, S. H. Kim, I. R. Huang, J. S. Kim, S. H. Jeon, and B. H. Park, *Adv. Mater.* 19, 73 (2007).
3. R. Waser and M. Aono, *Nat. Mater.* 6, 833 (2007).
4. Y. B. Nian, J. Strozier, N. J. Wu, X. Chen, and A. Ignatiev, *Phys. Rev. Lett.* 98, 146403 (2007).
5. J. J. Yang, M. D. Pickett, X. Li, D. A. A. Ohlberg, D. R. Stewart, and R. S. Williams, *Nature Nanotechnol.* 3, 429 (2008).
6. S. H. Chang, J. S. Lee, S. C. Chae, S. B. Lee, C. Liu, B. Kahng, D. W. Kim, and T. W. Noh, *Phys. Rev. Lett.* 102, 026801 (2009).
7. A. Sawa, *Mater. Today* 11, 28 (2008).
8. A. Ignatiev, N. J. Wu, X. Chen, S. Q. Liu, C. Papagianni, and J. Strozier, *Phys. Stat. Sol. B* 243, 2089 (2006).
9. A. Ignatiev, N. J. Wu, X. Chen, Y. B. Nian, C. Papagianni, S. Q. Liu, and J. Strozier, *Phase Transit.* 81, 791 (2008).
10. C. Y. Lin, C. Y. Liu, C. C. Lin, and T. Y. Tseng, *J. Electroceram.* 21, 61 (2008).
11. L. Goux, J. G. Lisoni, M. Jurczak, D. J. Wouters, L. Courtade, and C. Muller, *J. Appl. Phys.* 107, 024512 (2010).
12. S. Lee, H. Kim, J. Park, and K. Yong, *J. Appl. Phys.* 108, 076101 (2010).
13. G. S. Park, X. S. Li, D. C. Kim, R. J. Jung, M. J. Lee, and S. Seo, *Appl. Phys. Lett.* 91, 222103 (2007).
14. J. B. Yun, S. Kim, S. Seo, M. J. Lee, D. C. Kim, S. E. Ahn, Y. Park, J. Kim, and H. Shin, *Phys. Stat. Sol.-Rapid. Res. Lett.* 1, 280 (2007).
15. J. Y. Son and Y. H. Shin, *Appl. Phys. Lett.* 92, 222106 (2008).
16. J. Y. Ye, Y. Q. Li, J. Gao, H. Y. Peng, S. X. Wu, and T. Wu, *Appl. Phys. Lett.* 97, 132108 (2010).
17. I. Hwang, J. Choi, S. Hong, J. S. Kim, I. S. Byun, J. H. Bahng, J. Y. Koo, S. O. Kang, and B. H. Park, *Appl. Phys. Lett.* 96, 053112 (2010).
18. U. Russo, D. Ielmini, C. Cagli, and A. L. Lacaita, *IEEE Trans. Electron Dev.* 56, 186 (2009).
19. K. Jung, H. Seo, Y. Kim, H. Im, J. Hong, J. W. Park, and J. K. Lee, *Appl. Phys. Lett.* 90, 052104 (2007).
20. J. Y. Son, C. H. Kim, J. H. Cho, Y. H. Shin, and H. M. Jang, *ACS Nano* 4, 3288 (2010).
21. J. W. Park, J. W. Park, K. Jung, M. K. Yang, and J. K. Lee, *J. Vac. Sci. Technol. B* 24, 2205 (2006).
22. C. Park, S. H. Jeon, S. C. Chae, S. Han, B. H. Park, S. Seo, and D. W. Kim, *Appl. Phys. Lett.* 93, 042102 (2008).
23. C. B. Lee, B. S. Kang, M. J. Lee, S. E. Ahn, G. Stefanovich, W. X. Xianyu, K. H. Kim, J. H. Hur, H. X. Yin, Y. Park, I. K. Yoo, J. B. Park, and B. H. Park, *Appl. Phys. Lett.* 91, 082104 (2007).
24. C. B. Lee, B. S. Kang, A. Benayad, M. J. Lee, S. E. Ahn, K. H. Kim, G. Stefanovich, Y. Park, and I. K. Yoo, *Appl. Phys. Lett.* 93, 042115 (2008).
25. U. Russo, C. Cagli, S. Spiga, E. Cianci, and D. Ielmini, *IEEE Electron Dev. Lett.* 30, 817 (2009).
26. S. H. Phark, R. Jung, Y. J. Chang, T. W. Noh, and D. W. Kim, *Appl. Phys. Lett.* 94, 022906 (2009).
27. K. Jung, J. Choi, Y. Kim, H. Im, S. Seo, R. Jung, D. Kim, J. S. Kim, B. H. Park, and J. P. Hong, *J. Appl. Phys.* 103, 034504 (2008).
28. C. Y. Liu, X. J. Lin, H. Y. Wang, and C. H. Lai, *Jpn. J. Appl. Phys.* 49, 056507 (2010).
29. J. Kim, K. Lee, and H. Sohn, *J. Electrochem. Soc.* 156, H881 (2009).
30. M. J. Lee, C. B. Lee, D. Lee, S. R. Lee, J. Hur, S. E. Ahn, M. Chang, Y. B. Kim, U. I. Chung, C. J. Kim, D. S. Kim, and H. Lee, *IEEE Electron Dev. Lett.* 31, 725 (2010).
31. D. C. Kim, M. J. Lee, S. E. Ahn, S. Seo, J. C. Park, I. K. Yoo, I. G. Baek, H. J. Kim, E. K. Yim, J. E. Lee, S. O. Park, H. S. Kim, U. I. Chung, J. T. Moon, and B. I. Ryu, *Appl. Phys. Lett.* 88, 232106 (2006).
32. J. H. Choi, S. N. Das, and J. M. Myoung, *Appl. Phys. Lett.* 95, 062105 (2009).
33. Y. Sato, K. Tsunoda, K. Kinoshita, H. Noshiro, M. Aoki, and Y. Sugiyama, *IEEE Trans. Electron Dev.* 55, 1185 (2008).
34. G. H. Buh, I. Hwang, and B. H. Park, *Appl. Phys. Lett.* 95, 142101 (2009).
35. D. Ielmini, F. Nardi, C. Cagli, and A. L. Lacaita, *IEEE Electron Dev. Lett.* 31, 353 (2010).
36. J. Y. Son, Y. H. Shin, H. Kim, and H. M. Jang, *ACS Nano* 4, 2655 (2010).
37. K. Oka, T. Yanagida, K. Nagashima, H. Tanaka, and T. Kawai, *J. Am. Chem. Soc.* 131, 3434 (2009).
38. K. Oka, T. Yanagida, K. Nagashima, T. Kawai, J. S. Kim, and B. H. Park, *J. Am. Chem. Soc.* 132, 6634 (2010).
39. C. Yoshida, K. Tsunoda, H. Noshiro, and Y. Sugiyama, *Appl. Phys. Lett.* 91, 223510 (2007).
40. M. Fujimoto, H. Koyama, M. Konagai, Y. Hosoi, K. Ishihara, S. Ohnishi, and N. Awaya, *Appl. Phys. Lett.* 89, 223509 (2006).
41. W. Y. Chang, Y. T. Ho, T. C. Hsu, F. Chen, M. J. Tsai, and T. B. Wu, *Electrochem. Sol. Stat. Lett.* 12, H135 (2009).
42. K. M. Kim, B. J. Choi, D. S. Jeong, C. S. Hwang, and S. Han, *Appl. Phys. Lett.* 89, 162912 (2006).
43. K. M. Kim, B. J. Choi, and C. S. Hwang, *Appl. Phys. Lett.* 90, 242906 (2007).
44. J. S. Kwak, Y. H. Do, J. H. Lee, J. P. Hong, B. H. Park, H. S. Im, and S. J. Woo, *J. Korean Phys. Soc.* 53, 3685 (2008).
45. L. F. Liu, J. F. Kang, N. Xu, X. Sun, C. Chen, B. Sun, Y. Wang, X. Y. Liu, X. Zhang, and R. Q. Han, *Jpn. J. Appl. Phys.* 47, 2701 (2008).
46. J. P. Strachan, M. D. Pickett, J. J. Yang, S. Aloni, A. L. D. Kilcoyne, G. Medeiros-Ribeiro, and R. S. Williams, *Adv. Mater.* 22, 3573 (2010).
47. S. Jung, J. Kong, S. Song, K. Lee, T. Lee, H. Hwang, and S. Jeon, *J. Electrochem. Soc.* 157, H1042 (2010).
48. S. Kim, H. Y. Jeong, S. Y. Choi, and Y. K. Choi, *Appl. Phys. Lett.* 97, 033508 (2010).
49. C. Nauenheim, C. Kuegeler, A. Ruediger, and R. Waser, *Appl. Phys. Lett.* 96, 122902 (2010).
50. K. P. Biju, X. Liu, E. Bourim, I. Kim, S. Jung, J. Park, and H. Hwang, *Electrochem. Solid State Lett.* 13, H443 (2010).
51. D. H. Kwon, K. M. Kim, J. H. Jang, J. M. Jeon, M. H. Lee, G. H. Kim, X. S. Li, G. S. Park, B. Lee, S. Han, M. Kim, and C. S. Hwang, *Nature Nanotechnol.* 5, 148 (2010).
52. R. Munstermann, J. J. Yang, J. P. Strachan, G. Medeiros-Ribeiro, R. Dittmann, and R. Waser, *Phys. Stat. Sol.(R)* 4, 16 (2010).
53. H. Y. Jeong, J. Y. Lee, and S. Y. Choi, *Appl. Phys. Lett.* 97, 042109 (2010).
54. Q. F. Xia, J. J. Yang, W. Wu, X. M. Li, and R. S. Williams, *Nano Lett.* 10, 2909 (2010).
55. W. G. Kim and S. W. Rhee, *Microelectron. Eng.* 87, 98 (2010).
56. Y. H. Do, J. S. Kwak, Y. C. Bae, J. H. Lee, Y. Kim, H. Im, and J. P. Hong, *Curr. Appl. Phys.* 10, e71 (2010).
57. J. S. Kwak, Y. H. Do, Y. C. Bae, H. S. Im, J. H. Yoo, M. G. Sung, Y. T. Hwang, and J. P. Hong, *Appl. Phys. Lett.* 96, 223502 (2010).
58. L. Yang, C. Kuegeler, K. Szot, A. Ruediger, and R. Waser, *Appl. Phys. Lett.* 95, 013109 (2009).
59. Y. H. Do, J. S. Kwak, J. P. Hong, K. Jung, and H. Im, *J. Appl. Phys.* 104, 114512 (2008).
60. V. K. Yarmarkin, S. G. Shul'man, and V. V. Lemanov, *Ferroelectr.* 391, 139 (2009).

61. X. Cao, X. M. Li, X. D. Gao, Y. W. Zhang, X. J. Liu, Q. Wang, and L. D. Chen, *Appl. Phys. A* 97, 883 (2009).
62. D. S. Jeong, H. Schroeder, U. Breuer, and R. Waser, *J. Appl. Phys.* 104, 123716 (2008).
63. J. P. Strachan, J. J. Yang, R. Munstermann, A. Scholl, G. Medeiros-Ribeiro, D. R. Stewart, and R. S. Williams, *Nanotechnol.* 20, 485701 (2009).
64. H. Y. Jeong, J. Y. Lee, S. Y. Choi, and J. W. Kim, *Appl. Phys. Lett.* 95, 162108 (2009).
65. S. Won, S. Go, K. Lee, and J. Lee, *Electron. Mater. Lett.* 4, 29 (2008).
66. C. Y. Lin, C. Y. Wu, C. Y. Wu, T. C. Lee, F. L. Yang, C. Hu, and T. Y. Tseng, *IEEE Electron Dev. Lett.* 28, 366 (2007).
67. S. Y. Wang, D. Y. Lee, T. Y. Tseng, and C. Y. Lin, *Appl. Phys. Lett.* 95, 112904 (2009).
68. D. Y. Lee, S. Y. Wang, and T. Y. Tseng, *J. Electrochem. Soc.* 157, G166 (2010).
69. Q. Liu, S. B. Long, W. Wang, Q. Y. Zuo, S. Zhang, J. N. Chen, and M. Liu, *IEEE Electron Dev. Lett.* 30, 1335 (2009).
70. B. Sun, Y. X. Liu, L. F. Liu, N. Xu, Y. Wang, X. Y. Liu, R. Q. Han, and J. F. Kang, *J. Appl. Phys.* 105, 061630 (2009).
71. Q. Liu, S. B. Long, H. B. Lv, W. Wang, J. B. Niu, Z. L. Huo, J. N. Chen, and M. Liu, *ACS Nano* 4, 6162 (2010).
72. S. Y. Wang, D. Y. Lee, T. Y. Huang, J. W. Wu, and T. Y. Tseng, *Nanotechnol.* 21, 495201 (2010).
73. D. Lee, H. Choi, H. Sim, D. Choi, H. Hwang, M. J. Lee, S. A. Seo, and I. K. Yoo, *IEEE Electron Dev. Lett.* 26, 719 (2005).
74. S. Lee, W. G. Kim, S. W. Rhee, and K. Yong, *J. Electrochem. Soc.* 155, H92 (2008).
75. H. Y. Lee, P. S. Chen, C. C. Wang, S. Maikap, P. J. Tzeng, C. H. Lin, L. S. Lee, and M. J. Tsai, *Jpn. J. Appl. Phys.* 46, 2175 (2007).
76. Y. Wang, Q. Liu, S. B. Long, W. Wang, Q. Wang, M. H. Zhang, S. Zhang, Y. T. Li, Q. Y. Zuo, J. H. Yang, and M. Liu, *Nanotechnol.* 21, 045202 (2010).
77. P. S. Chen, H. Y. Lee, Y. S. Chen, P. Y. Gu, F. Chen, and M. J. Tsai, *Electrochem. Solid State Lett.* 13, H423 (2010).
78. H. Y. Lee, Y. S. Chen, P. S. Chen, T. Y. Wu, F. Chen, C. C. Wang, P. J. Tzeng, M. J. Tsai, and C. Lien, *IEEE Electron Dev. Lett.* 31, 44 (2010).
79. S. M. Yu, B. Gao, H. B. Dai, B. Sun, L. F. Liu, X. Y. Liu, R. Q. Han, J. F. Kang, and B. Yu, *Electrochem. Solid State Lett.* 13, H36 (2010).
80. M. Haemori, T. Nagata, and T. Chikyow, *Appl. Phys. Express* 2, 061401 (2009).
81. L. Chen, Y. Xu, Q. Q. Sun, P. Zhou, P. F. Wang, S. J. Ding, and D. W. Zhang, *IEEE Electron Dev. Lett.* 31, 1296 (2010).
82. C. Y. Lin, D. Y. Lee, S. Y. Wang, C. C. Lin, and T. Y. Tseng, *Surf. Coat. Technol.* 203, 480 (2008).
83. X. Sun, B. Sun, L. F. Liu, N. Xu, X. Y. Liu, R. Q. Han, J. F. Kang, G. C. Xiong, and T. P. Ma, *IEEE Electron Dev. Lett.* 30, 334 (2009).
84. M. Villafuerte, S. P. Heluani, G. Juarez, G. Simonelli, G. Braunstein, and S. Duhalde, *Appl. Phys. Lett.* 90, 052105 (2007).
85. W. Y. Chang, Y. C. Lai, T. B. Wu, S. F. Wang, F. Chen, and M. J. Tsai, *Appl. Phys. Lett.* 92, 022110 (2008).
86. N. Xu, L. F. Liu, X. Sun, C. Chen, Y. Wang, D. D. Han, X. Y. Liu, R. Q. Han, J. F. Kang, and B. Yu, *Semicond. Sci. Technol.* 23, 075019 (2008).
87. N. Xu, L. F. Liu, X. Sun, X. Y. Liu, D. D. Han, Y. Wang, R. Q. Han, J. F. Kang, and B. Yu, *Appl. Phys. Lett.* 92, 232112 (2008).
88. X. M. Chen, G. H. Wu, and D. H. Bao, *Appl. Phys. Lett.* 93, 093501 (2008).
89. X. M. Chen, G. H. Wu, P. Jiang, W. F. Liu, and D. H. Bao, *Appl. Phys. Lett.* 94, 033501 (2009).
90. L. Shi, D. S. Shang, J. R. Sun, and B. G. Shen, *Appl. Phys. Express* 2, 101602 (2009).
91. Y. C. Yang, F. Pan, Q. Liu, M. Liu, and F. Zeng, *Nano Lett.* 9, 1636 (2009).
92. Y. C. Yang, B. Fan, F. Zeng, and F. Pan, *J. Nanosci. Nanotechnol.* 10, 7370 (2010).
93. Y. C. Yang, F. Pan, and F. Zeng, *New J. Phys.* 12, 023008 (2010).
94. H. Y. Peng, G. P. Li, J. Y. Ye, Z. P. Wei, Z. Zhang, D. D. Wang, G. Z. Xing, and T. Wu, *Appl. Phys. Lett.* 96, 192113 (2010).
95. M. C. Chen, T. C. Chang, C. T. Tsai, S. Y. Huang, S. C. Chen, C. W. Hu, S. M. Sze, and M. J. Tsai, *Appl. Phys. Lett.* 96, 262110 (2010).
96. M. C. Chen, T. C. Chang, S. Y. Huang, S. C. Chen, C. W. Hu, C. T. Tsai, and S. M. Sze, *Electrochem. Solid State Lett.* 13, II191 (2010).
97. J. W. Seo, J. W. Park, K. S. Lim, J. H. Yang, and S. J. Kang, *Appl. Phys. Lett.* 93, 223505 (2008).
98. W. Y. Chang, C. A. Lin, J. H. He, and T. B. Wu, *Appl. Phys. Lett.* 96, 242109 (2010).
99. Z. G. Ji, Q. N. Mao, and W. Q. Ke, *Solid Stat. Commun.* 150, 1919 (2010).
100. Q. N. Mao, Z. G. Ji, and J. H. Xi, *J. Phys. D* 43, 395104 (2010).
101. S. Kim, H. Moon, D. Gupta, S. Yoo, and Y. K. Choi, *IEEE Trans. Electron Dev.* 56, 696 (2009).
102. S. Lee, H. Kim, D. J. Yun, S. W. Rhee, and K. Yong, *Appl. Phys. Lett.* 95, 262113 (2009).
103. S. Kim and Y. K. Choi, *Appl. Phys. Lett.* 92, 223508 (2008).
104. C. Y. Lin, C. Y. Wu, C. Y. Wu, C. Hu, and T. Y. Tseng, *J. Electrochem. Soc.* 154, G189 (2007).
105. J. Song, A. I. Inamdar, B. Jang, K. Jeon, Y. Kim, K. Jung, Y. Kim, H. Im, W. Jung, H. Kim, and J. P. Hong, *Appl. Phys. Express* 3, 091101 (2010).
106. J. Ventura, J. P. Araujo, J. B. Sousa, Y. Liu, Z. Zhang, and P. P. Freitas, *Appl. Phys. Lett.* 96, 043505 (2010).
107. W. Zhu, T. P. Chen, Z. Liu, M. Yang, Y. Liu, and S. Fung, *J. Appl. Phys.* 106, 093706 (2009).
108. P. Zhou, H. B. Lv, M. Yin, L. Tang, Y. L. Song, T. A. Tang, Y. Y. Lin, A. Bao, A. Wu, S. Cai, H. Wu, C. Liang, and M. H. Chi, *J. Vac. Sci. Technol. B* 26, 1030 (2008).
109. C. Y. Liu and J. M. Hsu, *Microelectron. Eng.* 87, 2504 (2010).
110. P. Zhou, M. Yin, H. J. Wan, H. B. Lu, T. A. Tang, and Y. Y. Lin, *Appl. Phys. Lett.* 94, 053510 (2009).
111. H. J. Wan, P. Zhou, L. Ye, Y. Y. Lin, T. A. Tang, H. M. Wu, and M. H. Chi, *IEEE Electron Dev. Lett.* 31, 246 (2010).
112. S. O. Kang, S. Hong, J. Choi, J. S. Kim, I. Hwang, I. S. Byun, K. S. Yun, and B. H. Park, *Appl. Phys. Lett.* 95, 092108 (2009).
113. H. B. Lv, M. Wang, H. J. Wan, Y. L. Song, W. J. Luo, P. Zhou, T. A. Tang, Y. Y. Lin, R. Huang, S. Song, J. G. Wu, H. M. Wu, and M. H. Chi, *Appl. Phys. Lett.* 94, 213502 (2009).
114. S. Zhang, S. B. Long, W. H. Guan, Q. Liu, Q. Wang, and M. Liu, *J. Phys. D* 42, 055112 (2009).
115. M. K. Yang, J. W. Park, T. K. Ko, and J. K. Lee, *Appl. Phys. Lett.* 95, 042105 (2009).
116. M. K. Yang, J. W. Park, T. K. Ko, and J. K. Lee, *Phys. Stat. Sol. (R)* 4, 233 (2010).
117. S. Zhang, S. B. Long, W. H. Guan, Q. Liu, Q. Wang, and M. Liu *J. Phys. D* 42, 055112 (2009).
118. L. J. Zhang, R. Huang, M. H. Zhu, S. Q. Qin, Y. B. Kuang, D. J. Gao, C. Y. Shi, and Y. Y. Wang, *IEEE Electron Dev. Lett.* 31, 966 (2010).
119. T. Tsuruoka, K. Terabe, T. Hasegawa, and M. Aono, *Nanotechnol.* 21, 425205 (2010).
120. X. Gao, H. X. Guo, Y. D. Xia, J. Yin, and Z. G. Liu, *Thin Solid Films* 519, 450 (2010).
121. J. S. Kwak, Y. H. Do, Y. C. Bae, H. Im, and J. P. Hong, *Thin Solid Films* 518, 6437 (2010).
122. Z. Q. Wang, X. H. Li, H. Y. Xu, W. Wang, H. Yu, X. T. Zhang, Y. X. Liu, and Y. C. Liu, *J. Phys. D* 43, 385105 (2010).
123. E. K. Lai, W. C. Chien, Y. C. Chen, T. J. Hong, Y. Y. Lin, K. P. Chang, Y. D. Yao, P. Lin, S. F. Horng, J. Gong, S. C. Tsai, C. H.

Lee, S. H. Hsieh, C. F. Chen, Y. H. Shih, K. Y. Hsieh, R. Liu, and C. Y. Lu, *Jpn. J. Appl. Phys.* 49, 04DD17 (2010).

124. W. C. Chien, Y. C. Chen, E. K. Lai, Y. D. Yao, P. Lin, S. F. Horng, J. Gong, T. H. Chou, H. M. Lin, M. N. Chang, Y. H. Shih, K. Y. Hsieh, R. Liu, and C. Y. Lu, *IEEE Electron Dev. Lett.* 31, 126 (2010).

125. D. Lee, D. J. Seong, I. Jo, F. Xiang, R. Dong, S. Oh, and H. Hwang, *Appl. Phys. Lett.* 90, 122104 (2007).

126. K. M. Kim, B. J. Choi, B. W. Koo, S. Choi, D. S. Jeong, and C. S. Hwang, *Electrochem. Sol. Stat. Lett.* 9, G343 (2006).

127. K. Kinoshita, T. Tamura, M. Aoki, Y. Sugiyama, and H. Tanaka, *Jpn. J. Appl. Phys.* 45, L991 (2006).

128. X. M. Chen, H. Zhou, G. H. Wu, and D. H. Bao, *Appl. Phys. A* 100, 987 (2011).

129. Y. C. Yang, F. Pan, F. Zeng, and M. Liu, *J. Appl. Phys.* 106, 123705 (2009).

130. Y. H. Do, J. S. Kwak, Y. C. Bae, K. Jung, H. Im, and J. P. Hong, *Appl. Phys. Lett.* 95, 093507 (2009).

131. J. Lee, E. Bourim, W. Lee, J. Park, M. Jo, S. Jung, J. Shin, and H. Hwang, *Appl. Phys. Lett.* 97, 172105 (2010).

132. Y. N. Chen, K. L. Pey, K. E. J. Goh, Z. Z. Lwin, P. K. Singh, and S. Mahapatra, *IEEE Trans. Electron Dev.* 57, 3001 (2010).

133. J. Park, M. Jo, E. Bourim, J. Yoon, D. J. Seong, J. Lee, W. Lee, and H. Hwang, *IEEE Electron Dev. Lett.* 31, 485 (2010).

134. D. Tu, M. Liu, L. W. Shang, X. H. Liu, and C. Q. Xie, *Appl. Phys. Lett.* 92, 123302 (2008).

135. W. H. Guan, S. B. Long, R. Jia, and M. Liu, *Appl. Phys. Lett.* 91, 062111 (2007).

136. Q. Liu, W. H. Guan, S. B. Long, M. Liu, S. Zhang, Q. Wang, and J. N. Chen, *J. Appl. Phys.* 104, 114514 (2008).

137. W. H. Guan, S. B. Long, Q. Liu, M. Liu, and W. Wang, *IEEE Electron Dev. Lett.* 29, 434 (2008).

138. Q. Liu, S. B. Long, W. Wang, S. Tanachutiwat, Y. T. Li, Q. Wang, M. H. Zhang, Z. L. Huo, J. N. Chen, and M. Liu, *IEEE Electron Dev. Lett.* 31, 1299 (2010).

139. Q. Liu, W. H. Guan, S. B. Long, R. Jia, M. Liu, and J. N. Chen, *Appl. Phys. Lett.* 92, 012117 (2008).

140. B. Sun, L. F. Liu, D. D. Han, Y. Wang, X. Y. Liu, R. Q. Han, and J. F. Kang, *Chin. Phys. Lett.* 25, 2187 (2008).

141. W. Y. Chang, K. J. Cheng, J. M. Tsai, H. J. Chen, F. Chen, M. J. Tsai, and T. B. Wu, *Appl. Phys. Lett.* 95, 042104 (2009).

142. J. H. Yoon, K. M. Kim, M. H. Lee, S. K. Kim, G. H. Kim, S. J. Song, J. Y. Seok, and C. S. Hwang, *Appl. Phys. Lett.* 97, 232904 (2010).

143. C. Lee, I. Kim, H. Shin, S. Kim, and J. Cho, *Nanotechnol.* 21, 185704 (2010).

144. F. Verbakel, S. C. J. Meskers, D. M. de Leeuw, and R. A. J. Janssen, *J. Phys. Chem. C* 112, 5254 (2008).

145. H. Silva, H. L. Gomes, Y. G. Pogorelov, P. Stallinga, D. M. de Leeuw, J. P. Araujo, J. B. Sousa, S. C. J. Meskers, G. Kakazei, S. Cardoso, and P. P. Freitas, *Appl. Phys. Lett.* 94, 202107 (2009).

CHAPTER 7

Resistive-Random Access Memory Based on Amorphous Films

Yuchao Yang, Wei Lu
Department of Electrical Engineering and Computer Science, The University of Michigan, Ann Arbor, Michigan 48109, USA

CONTENTS

1. INTRODUCTION

The semiconductor industry has been persistently seeking for an ideal nonvolatile memory that could simultaneously possess favorable attributes, such as high density, high speed, low power consumption, and low cost [1]. Charge-based flash memory represents the state-of-the-art nonvolatile memory technology at present, and it is widely adopted in applications from embedded systems to portable electronics and mass storage because of its large capacity and inexpensive manufacturing [1–3]. However, circumventing the problems associated with flash memory, such as limited endurance, slow write speed, and complicated data management schemes, has become more challenging as the storage density increases. Moreover, density scaling through continued complementary metal–oxide–semiconductor (CMOS) scaling also faces several fundamental and technological challenges that will likely present a limit below 20 nm. Several alternative nonvolatile random access memory (RAM) concepts, including ferroelectric random access memory (FRAM) [4–8], magnetoresistive random access memory (MRAM) [9–12], phase change random access memory [13–16] and resistive random access memory (RRAM) [17–19] have been actively pursued to replace flash and if possible, to ultimately serve as a universal memory

ISBN: 1-58883-251-1

Nonvolatile Memories: Materials, Devices and Applications
Edited by Tseung-Yuen Tseng and Simon M. Sze
Volume 2: Pages: 161–184

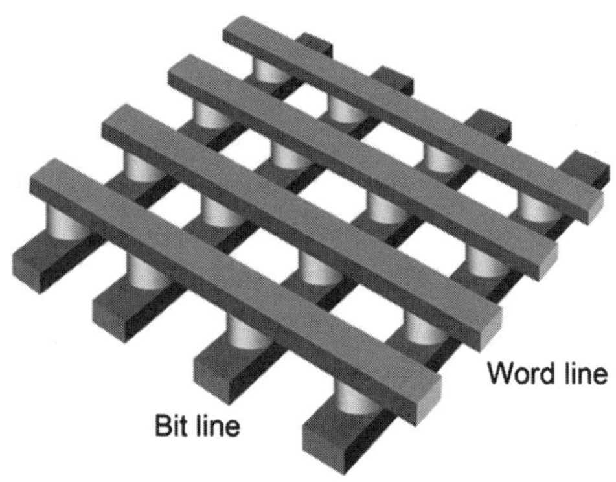

Figure 1. Schematic of a crossbar array formed by two-terminal resistive devices at each crosspoint with a M-I-M structure.

technology. Increasing efforts have been devoted to this rapidly growing area, making it one of the fastest growing areas in electronics, materials science, and physics.

Among the emerging memory technologies, RRAM, also known as resistive memory, has become a promising candidate due to its simple structure, fast programming, high stacking density, and facile fabrication [17–19]. In principle, RRAM is based on the resistive-switching effect observed in two-terminal devices. That is, the memory devices possess two or more nonvolatile resistance states, a high-resistance state (HRS; or OFF) and a low-resistance state (LRS; or ON), and the cells could be reversibly switched between different resistance states by utilizing external electrical stimuli. Once a resistance state is programmed, it could stably retain its resistance unless another programming operation is performed. Besides the nonvolatile nature, RRAM devices have shown fast switching speed on the level of nanoseconds [20–23], which is comparable with the main memory in present computers, hence combining key advantages of flash and dynamic random access memory (DRAM).

The resistive memory devices are usually fabricated with a metal-insulator-metal (MIM) configuration, in which "M" could be any electrode materials showing high conductivity, including various metals and conducting compounds, and "I" denotes a dielectric layer sandwiched by the two electrodes and serving as the storage medium (sometimes the I-layer can also consist of conductive materials, such as $Pr_{0.7}Ca_{0.3}MnO_3$ [24, 25], depending on the initial resistance state of the devices). The two-terminal structure of RRAM allows it to be integrated in a crossbar structure formed by connecting two sets of parallel electrode wires crossing over each other with a device formed at each crosspoint (Fig. 1). The crossbar structures offers the smallest theoretical cell area of $4F^2$ (F represents the feature size used for pattering the cells), a simple, straightforward interconnect configuration, and the potential for three-dimensional (3D) stacking with an even higher density [26]. Besides its simplicity and high density, memory cells in a RRAM crossbar array can be randomly accessed (read, written, and erased), making this approach extremely attractive for low-power nonvolatile memory integration.

Since the first report of resistive switching in metal oxides by Hickmott in 1962 [27], extensive research activities on resistive-switching materials and their applications in nonvolatile memories and related areas have been performed. As a result, a large variety of material systems have been found to exhibit resistive-switching characteristics, such as Ag–Ge–Se [28–30], Ag-Ge–S [31–33], Ag-Ge–Te [34, 35], Cu-Ge–S [31], Cu-Ge–Se [36, 37], Ag-As–S [38], Ag_2S [39, 40], Cu_2S [41–43], Ag_2Se [44], Cu–Te [20], AlO_x [27, 45, 46], SiO_x [27, 47, 48], TiO_x [27, 49–52], NiO [53–56], Nb_2O_5 [57], ZnO [23, 58–60], ZrO_2 [27, 61–64], HfO_2 [65–67], CuO_x [68–70], MoO_x [71], CeO_x [72, 73], MnO_x [74, 75], TaO_x [27, 76, 77], WO_x [78–80], CoO [81–83], Fe_2O_3 [81], Lu_2O_3 [84], $Cd_{1-x}Zn_xS$ [85], $SrZrO_3$ [86–88], $SrTiO_3$ [89–92], Sr_2TiO_4 [93], $Pr_{0.7}Ca_{0.3}MnO_3$ [24, 25, 94], $La_{0.67}Ca_{0.33}MnO_3$ [95, 96], amorphous Si [21, 97–99], carbon [100–102], and even organics [103, 104], including both crystalline and amorphous materials. In this review, we mainly focus on presenting the recent progress of RRAM devices based on amorphous materials (Section 3) and the current understanding of the underlying mechanism of resistive-switching effects (Section 4). Besides size scaling, multivalue data storage is expected to provide an equivalent method to increase the memory density. Multilevel resistive-switching effects in amorphous materials will be discussed in Section 5. Section 6 summarizes the expanded applications of resistive-switching devices in different fields, such as nonvolatile static random access memory (SRAM), analog circuits, and neuromorphic systems. Finally, the scaling potential of RRAM devices and their integration and reliability issues will be discussed in Section 7, together with a brief summary and outlook in Section 8.

2. GENERAL FEATURES OF RESISTIVE SWITCHING

A prerequisite for resistive switching is that the memory device has at least two stable resistance states, namely, HRS and LRS, both of which could retain their resistance without electric power. As a result of electrical programming, the switching from HRS to LRS is termed the "Set" process, while the reverse switching from LRS to HRS is defined as the "Reset" process. In many RRAM devices, an electrical initiation process is required before reversible resistive switching could be observed. This kind of initiation process is called "forming" or "electroforming" in the literature. Depending on the electrical polarities that are used in the Set and Reset processes, resistive-switching effects in RRAM devices could be generally categorized into two types: (1) unipolar switching and (2) bipolar switching. Resistive switching that could be accomplished without changing the programming voltage/current polarity is called unipolar switching, as depicted in the schematic current–voltage (I–V) curve in Figure 2(a). One can see that when the applied voltage (positive or negative) exceeds a threshold, the resistance of the device rapidly decreases. As a result, the cell is Set to its ON state. A current compliance (CC) is usually adopted herein to prevent the devices from permanent dielectric breakdown. In practice the CC could also be realized by attaching a series resistor to the memory device. Subsequently, another applied voltage (with the same or opposite polarity) is able to Reset the device back to the OFF state. It seems that the controlling factor in unipolar switching process is the magnitude of the

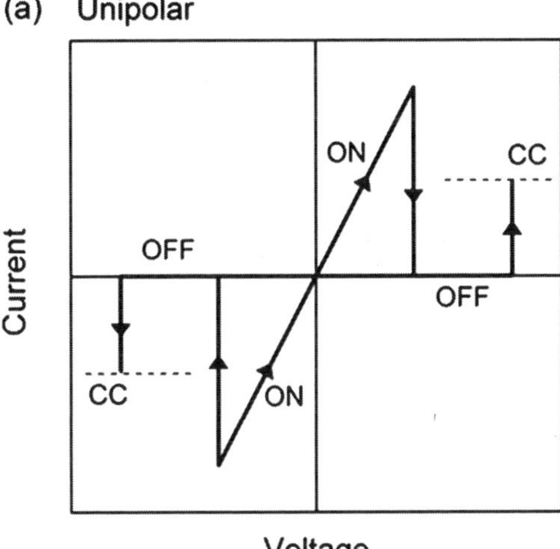

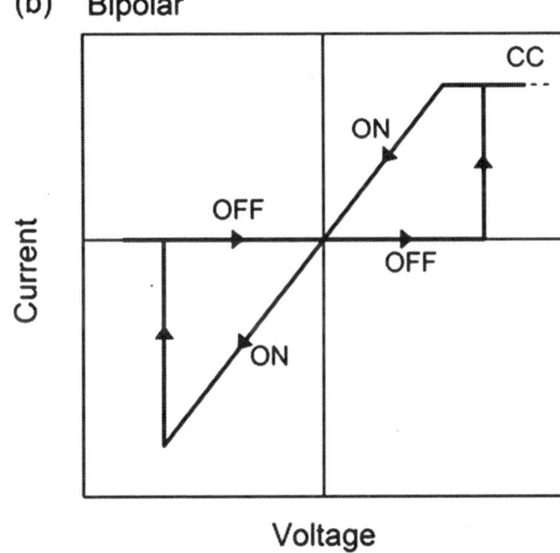

Figure 2. Classification of resistive-switching effects by *I–V* characteristics. (a) Unipolar switching and (b) bipolar switching. ACC is normally applied during the Set process to protect the device.

electric signal instead of the polarity. As a result, it is usually suggested that the mechanism of unipolar switching is related to Joule heating effects [54, 105]. Unipolar resistive switching has been observed in many amorphous materials especially metal oxides, such as SiO_x [47, 106], AlO_x [27, 107–109], Nb_2O_5 [57], and Lu_2O_3 [84]. Since switching only involves one polarity, in principle unipolar devices are easier to implement in a circuit. However, it should be noted that a general request for repetitive unipolar switching is that there should be no overlap between the Set and Reset threshold voltages. Otherwise, a programming error would take place. Much effort has been undertaken to address this uniformity issue [55, 110–112] but reliability still remains a concern. On the contrary, for bipolar switching devices programming voltage/current signals with opposite polarities are required during the Set and Reset processes, as sketched in the *I–V* curve in Figure 2(b). RRAM devices based on various solid electrolytes [28, 33, 113], amorphous silicon [21, 99], and many oxides [46, 76] have been found to exhibit bipolar switching. Since the polarity of the programming signals is important here, bipolar switching is normally believed to be caused by electric field-driven effects. Sometimes, both unipolar and bipolar resistive switching could coexist in the same memory devices, and the roles of the thermal and electric field effects could be reversed by either controlling the fabrication details or modulating the electrical operations such as altering the value of current compliance [114–116].

Besides the usual classification of unipolar and bipolar switching, resistive-switching effects can also be classified according to the underlying physical mechanisms or the width of the voltage window during which the ON–OFF switching takes place. These categories will be described in detail in Sections 4 and 6, respectively.

It is worthwhile to point out that the bipolar resistive-switching effects in MIM structures can be explained and predicted by the theory of memristor (memory + resistor; i.e., a resistor with inherent memory). The concept of a memristor was proposed by Chua in 1971 based on symmetry arguments in order to complement the set of previously known passive devices [117]. The resistance of a memristor (memristance) is determined by charge or flux (i.e., the time integral of the current or voltage, instead of the present values of current or voltage) and thus, is a function of the device history and can exhibit hysteresis behavior. Chua recognized memristor as the fourth passive circuit element besides the resistor, the capacitor, and the inductor. The definition has since been generalized to memristive devices and systems [118] that satisfy these two general equations:

$$i = G(w, v)v \tag{1}$$

and

$$\dot{w} = f(w, v) \tag{2}$$

Here Eq. (1) is the normal *I–V* equation for a resistive device, where w is an (or a group of) internal state variable(s). Equation (2) is a rate equation that states that (dw/dt), i.e., only the rate of the state variable change/time derivative is determined by the external signals (e.g., voltage here for a so-called flux-controlled memristor), unlike normal devices where the internal state variable w itself is specifically determined by the present control signals. By choosing different internal state variables and modifying the rate equation, a broad range of devices and behaviors can be shown to fall in the general category of memristive devices/effects. For example, in the simplest case where both expressions are linear functions, regularly spaced, pinched-hysteresis loops can be observed in the device *I–V* characteristics [119].

The first connection between memristors and resistive-switching devices was made by Strukov et al. [119, 120], who used the memristor theory to explain the resistive-switching effects observed in $Pt/TiO_2/Pt$ devices. Many groups have since followed this approach because Eqs. (1) and (2) provide a simple and elegant means to explain the device characteristics and allow the development of simulation packages to predict and simulate the device behaviors ranging from steady-state to transient effects [121].

3. AMORPHOUS RESISTIVE-SWITCHING MATERIALS AND MEMORY DEVICES

On the whole, three types of amorphous materials have been found to exhibit resistive-switching effects:

(1) higher chalcogenide-based solid electrolytes, including sulfides, selenides, and tellurides, such as Ag–Ge–Se [28–30], Ag–Ge–S [31–33], Ag–Ge–Te [34, 35],
(2) amorphous silicon [21, 97–99] and carbon [100–102] and
(3) various amorphous oxides, such as SiO_x [27, 47, 48], TiO_x [122], AlO_x [46, 107, 108], and TaO_x [76].

We will summarize the main research activities in these three kinds of resistive-switching materials separately in Sections 3.1–3.3 and compare their performance with crystalline material-based RRAM devices in Section 3.4.

3.1. Chalcogenide Glasses

RRAM devices based on solid electrolytes such as chalcogenide glasses are sometimes called electrochemical metallization (ECM) cells, conductive bridge random access memory (CBRAM) or programmable metallization cells (PMC). In general, this type of device is based on an electrochemical redox process and the subsequent formation of conducting metallic filaments. The ECM cells are composed of a solid electrolyte layer that is a solid-state fast ion conductor material, an electrochemically active metal electrode serving as the anode (such as Ag and Cu) as well as an inert metal electrode acting as the cathode (such as Pt, Au, and W). Most chalcogenide solid electrolytes have a glass-like structure. Figure 3 shows the transmission electron microscopy (TEM) image and selected area electron diffraction (SAED) pattern of Ag–Ge–Se films deposited by pulsed laser deposition (PLD), which apparently demonstrates an amorphous structure. In ECM cells based on chalcogenide glasses, bipolar resistive-switching effects are usually observed.

Ag–Ge–Se might be the most widely studied chalcogenide glass as a solid electrolyte material in ECM memory cells [28–30, 123–128]. There are mainly two kinds of methods to prepare the Ag–Ge–Se glass that give birth to Ag–Ge–Se films with different microstructures. The first one is to deposit a germanium-selenide layer followed by a successive deposition of a thin Ag film, and then the Ag dopants are incorporated into the Ge–Se layer by ultraviolet photodiffusion [28, 126, 129] or thermal diffusion [28]. In this way, a phase separation can take place at Ag saturation [28]. At this time, the solid electrolyte layer is actually a combination of separate crystalline Ag_2Se phase and glassy Ge_2Se_3 phase. The Ag_2Se clusters are dispersed in the insulating Ge_2Se_3 phase, therefore the films exhibit high resistivity but also have good superionic characteristics [28]. A GeO_2 layer is sometimes introduced to prevent the diffusion of excess Ag into chalcogenide films in case the percolation limit is reached [30]. The second approach is to directly deposit the Ag–Ge–Se ternary compound films using techniques such as PLD, which is good at maintaining the stoichiometry of the target materials in deposited films. In this way, Ag–Ge–Se films with uniform amorphous structures are prepared (Fig. 3) [29, 128]. The Ag–Ge–Se films deposited

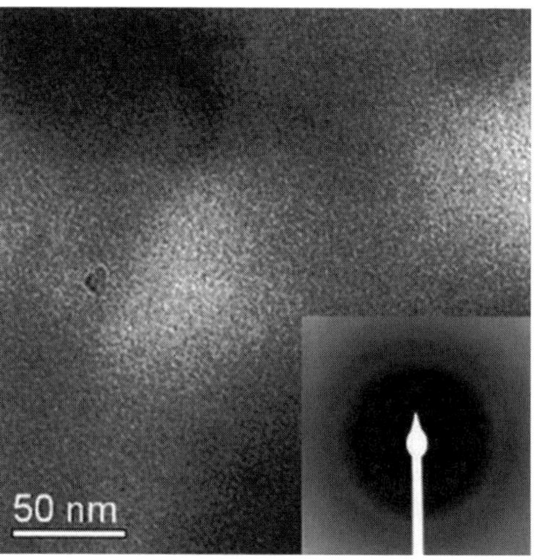

Figure 3. Typical TEM image of the as-prepared $Ag_{30}Ge_{17}Se_{53}$ films by pulsed laser deposition. The inset shows the corresponding SAED pattern. The results apparently show the amorphous structure of $Ag_{30}Ge_{17}Se_{53}$. Reprinted with permission from [127], L. Chen et al., *Appl. Phys. Lett.* 95, 242106 (2009). © 2009, American Institute of Physics.

below 300°C have a uniform amorphous structure, whereas a crystalline Ag_8GeSe_6 phase begins to appear with increasing temperature above 300°C [128]. Since it is difficult to induce resistive-switching behavior in highly conductive crystalline phases, the crystalline temperature effectively sets a thermal stability limit of the resistive-switching effects in chalcogenides.

The operation of these chalcogenide based devices depends on the drift and redox processes of Ag^+ ions inside the storage matrix. It is well known that Se-rich Ge–Se glass is a good Ag ion conductor with high Ag ion mobility and solubility [28], and well-defined resistive-switching characteristics have been observed in this system. Figure 4 shows *I–V* characteristics of Ag–Ge–Se-based ECM cells measured at room temperature with typical bipolar resistive-switching behavior. Prior to the repetitive switching events, a forming process is usually needed to initiate the cells, whose effect is to change the nanomorphology and create the conducting paths for the first time [18, 124] or modify (incorporate or extract) the oxidizable metal content in the as-prepared chalcogenide layers [30]. In Ag–Ge–Se-based ECM cells, resistive switching with a high ON/OFF ratio of $\sim 10^6$ [129, 130], a switching speed faster than 100 ns [28] a long data retention (months), an excellent endurance of $> 10^{10}$ cycles [28], and a multilevel storage capability [130, 131] are demonstrated. The threshold voltages required for programming operations are usually in the range of several hundreds of millivolts, and the write current could be scaled down to ~1 nA [30], which are highly desirable for the low power operation of RRAM devices.

The Ag–Ge–Se-based ECM cells have also shown excellent scaling potential. Figure 5 displays a cross-sectional scanning electron microscopy (SEM) image of a 20-nm ECM device based on Ag–Ge–Se and its corresponding *I–V* curve. Successful resistive switching can be observed in the nanoscale device, demonstrating a potential memory density of $> 10^{10}$ bit/cm^2 [130]. Beyond the high performance

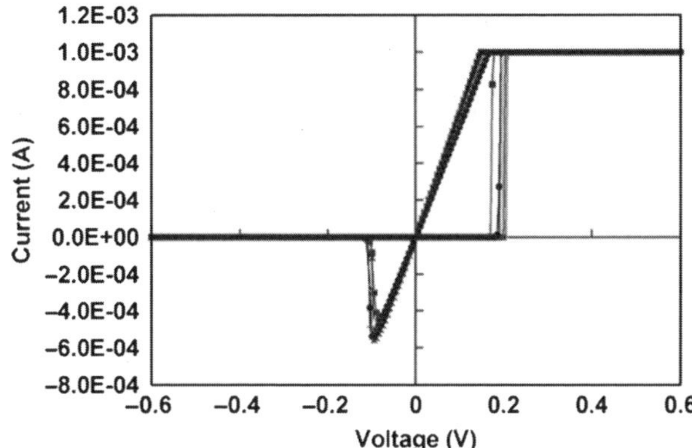

Figure 4. Typical *I–V* characteristics for Ag–Ge–Se-based ECM cells measured at room temperature. Reprinted with permission from [28], M. N. Kozicki et al., *IEEE Trans. Nanotechnol.* 4, 331 (2005). © 2005, IEEE.

obtained in single Ag–Ge–Se ECM cells, a 2-Mbit CBRAM core has been integrated using 90 nm CMOS technology with a one transistor-one resistor (1*T*-1*R*) structure [131]. However, a main drawback of the Ag–Ge–Se solid electrolyte is that it will not survive a processing temperature above 200°C, making its integration with the standard back-end-of-the-line CMOS processes very challenging. Thus, this has stimulated research interests in other ternary chalcogenide solid electrolytes, such as Ag–Ge–Te and Ag–Ge–S, with possibly better thermal stabilities.

ECM cells comprised of Ge–Te and Ge–S show similar bipolar memory characteristics with those of Ge–Se films. Ge–Te amorphous alloys are thought to be important and interesting materials from both a scientific and industrial point of view due to their previous applications in phase change memory and phase change optical disks. Similar to Ag–Ge–Se, the sputtered Ag–Ge–Te films crystallize at about 250°C, as reflected by a sudden decrease of sheet resistance when the temperature increases (see Fig. 6(a)) [34]. Therefore, Ag–Ge–Te would still fail to conform to the back-end-of-the-line CMOS processes. In order

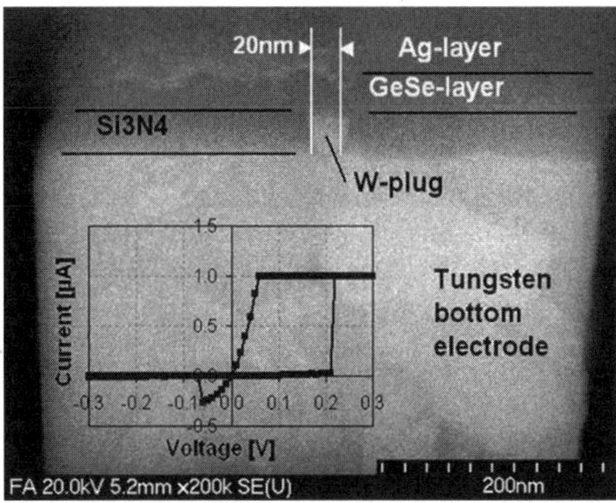

Figure 5. Cross sectional SEM image of a 20nm ECM device based on Ag–Ge–Se and the corresponding *I–V* curve. Reprinted with permission from [130], M. Kund et al., "International Electron Devices Meeting," p. 773, 2005. © 2005, IEEE.

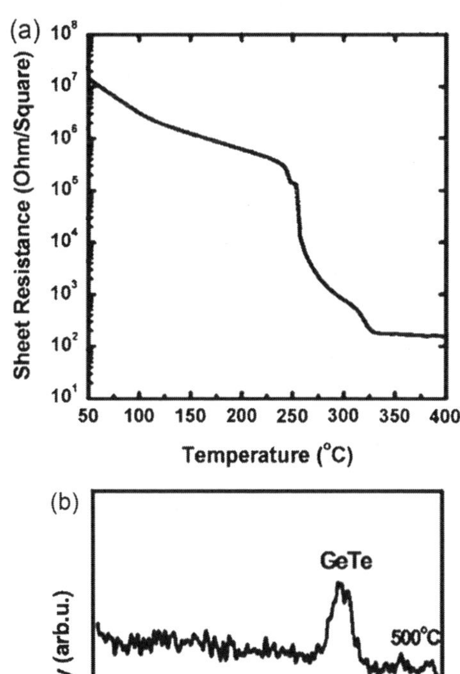

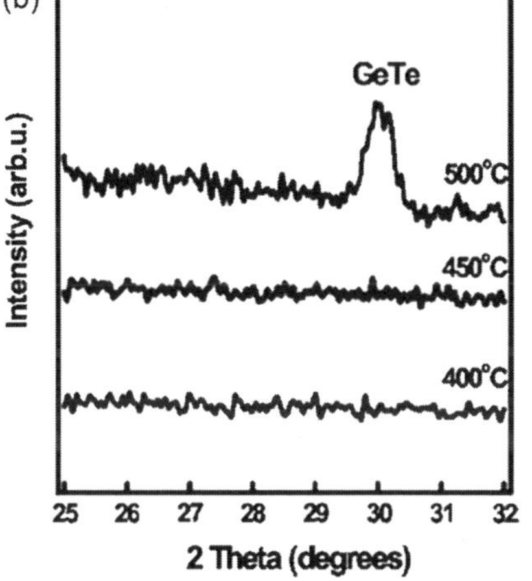

Figure 6. Crystalline temperatures of Ge–Te films before and after nitrogen doping. (a) Variation in sheet resistance as a function of temperature in Ge–Te films without nitrogen doping, showing that the crystalline temperature is around 250°C. Reprinted with permission from [34], S.-J. Lee et al., *J. Vac. Sci. Technol. B* 24, 2312 (2006). © 2006, American Vacuum Society. (b) XRD pattern evolution as a function of annealing temperature in Ge–Te films doped by N_2/Ar ratio of 30%, indicating that the crystalline temperature is above 400°C. Reprinted with permission from [132], S.-J. Lee et al., *Electrochem. Solid-State Lett.* 9, G364 (2006). © 2006, The Electrochemical Society.

to overcome this problem, researchers have tried doping the Ag–Ge–Te films with nitrogen and have obtained a crystalline temperature of > 400°C, as demonstrated by the X-ray diffraction (XRD) pattern evolution in Figure 6(b). This indicates a significantly improved thermal stability of *N*-doped Ag–Ge–Te films [132]. The Ag–Ge–S glass has also been shown to be able to withstand higher processing temperature than Ag–Ge–Se [31, 133]. Figure 7 displays a representative resistance–voltage (*R–V*) plot of a nanoscale Ag–Ge–S-based ECM cell with a diameter of 350 nm that has underwent annealing treatment at 430°C [31]. The evident resistive switching in Figure 7 indicates a good thermal stability of the Ag–Ge–S films. In addition, it was reported that the OFF resistance of the ECM cells based on Ag–Ge–S is more than one order of magnitude higher than its selenide counterpart, and the write and erase threshold voltages are also much higher, possibly because of the larger band gap

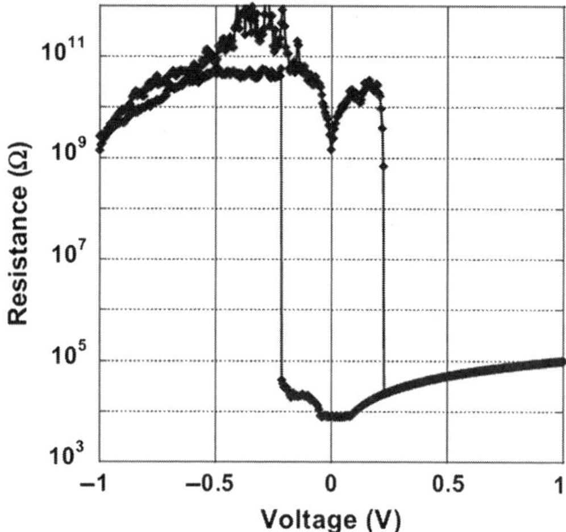

Figure 7. Representative *R–V* characteristics of Ag–Ge–S-based ECM cells with a diameter of 350 nm, which had underwent annealing treatment at 430°C. Reprinted with permission from [31], M. N. Kozicki et al., "Proceeding of Non-Volatile Memory Technology Symposium," p. 83, 2005. © 2005, IEEE.

of sulfides [31]. These are expected to provide extra noise margins and avoid read disturb effects with an acceptable compromise in power consumption. Using Ag–Ge–S glass as the solid electrolyte, a 4-Mbit ECM memory array has been successfully fabricated using 90-nm CMOS technology with a 1*T*-1*R* structure [134]. Like devices based on Ag–Ge–Se, a major concern for Ag–Ge–Te, Ag–Ge–S, or other chalcogenide systems is their material compatibility and reliability and the robustness of their conducting filaments, particularly for applications that require fast switching speed, long endurance, or retention.

In general, chalcogenide glass-based ECM cells show similar resistive-switching behaviors when Cu is adopted as the oxidizable material to replace Ag, such as in Cu–Ge–S [31], Cu–Ge–Se [36, 37], and Cu–Te [20] systems. In some respects, Cu is a more desirable electrode material for RRAM than Ag because of its wider applications in the semiconductor industry. However, it is also more active and hence more susceptible to unwanted reactions. The thermal stability of the chalcogenide glasses would be influenced by the incorporation of Cu. For example, Sakurai et al. [135] reported that the introduction of Cu into Ge–Te would increase its glass-forming tendency due to the ionic nature of Cu–Te bonding. Nevertheless, the introduction of a large amount of Cu dopants would destroy the glass network and in turn, decrease the glass-forming ability [135]. Therefore, it is critical to control the concentration of Cu in chalcogenides in order to obtain optimized thermal stability. In addition, the write/erase thresholds in Cu–Ge–S cells are much lower than those in Ag–Ge–S cells with an erasing threshold of < 100 mV [31]. This is apparently too low for stable memory applications. In this regard, it is worthwhile to mention the encouraging performance reported in RRAM devices that comprise a dual-layered active medium, in which a Cu–Te electrolyte serves as the ion conductive layer and a GdO_x layer is introduced between Cu–Te and the inert electrode for the purpose of controlling and maintaining the shape of the conducting filaments. The dual-layered memory cells were integrated in a 4-kb array organized with a 1*T*-1*R* structure and exhibited good retention (100 hours at 130°C), nanosecond programming speed (Set: 5 ns, Reset: 1 ns), scalability down to 20 nm, endurance up to 10^7 cycles and multilevel data storage [20].

Among the various resistive memories with different switching materials and device configurations, ECM cells based on chalcogenide electrolytes are the earliest studied and possibly best understood RRAM devices. The most significant aspect of these devices, in our view, is their extremely low power consumption in terms of programming voltage, current, and speed. Other attractive performance metrics in terms of endurance [28, 133], retention, and scaling potential [20, 130] have also been demonstrated. In order to prompt the applications of chalcogenide-based resistive memories, however, special efforts must be paid to evaluate the reliability of the cells and improve the compatibility of chalcogenide glasses with conventional CMOS processes.

3.2. Amorphous Silicon and Carbon

Resistive switching in amorphous silicon (*a*-Si) has been observed and studied since the 1980s [99, 136–141]. One of the reasons for the special interest in this system is its full compatibility with conventional CMOS technology in terms of materials and required processes. The first period of research enthusiasm was generated by hydrogenated amorphous silicon (*a*-Si:H) because of its threshold switching behavior in the 1970s and 1980s [136, 137, 142], and then the investigations on *a*-Si:H were further extended to nonvolatile resistive memory switching effects [99, 139–141]. As a representative work by Jafar et al. [99], bipolar resistive switching was observed in *p*-type *a*-Si:H films in a M/*a*-Si:H/Cr device structure, before which the cells needed to go through a high-voltage forming process. The top electrode material M could be one of V, W, Ni, Co, Cr, and Ag, and different top contacts could result in analog- or digital-type switching behaviors possibly because of the different homogeneities of conducting filament profiles. The switching time in these systems was verified to be in the level of tens of nanoseconds [99]. Similar to chalcogenide-based devices, resistive switching in *a*-Si was believed to be due to the drift and redox of metal ions (e.g., Ag^+) and the formation of metallic filaments inside the *a*-Si matrix. However, the interest essentially died out in the 1990s due mainly to the low yield associated with the high-voltage forming process.

The research on *a*-Si-based RRAM devices was recently reinvigorated after the observation of resistive-switching effects with high yield in nanoscale devices after device structure optimizations [21]. Applications of such devices in high-density memory arrays, logic switches, and neuromorphic circuits have also been demonstrated [21, 98, 143]. The device structure consists of a top metal electrode M, an *a*-Si layer as the active medium, and a heavily doped *p*-type silicon (*p*-Si) layer as the bottom electrode (Fig. 8(a)). The use of *p*-Si instead of metals as the bottom electrode allows better control of the electrode/*a*-Si interface quality and the filament formation process (which presumably takes place at the *a*-Si grain boundaries/defect sites). The *p*-Si electrode also introduces a reverse-biased Schottky junction under

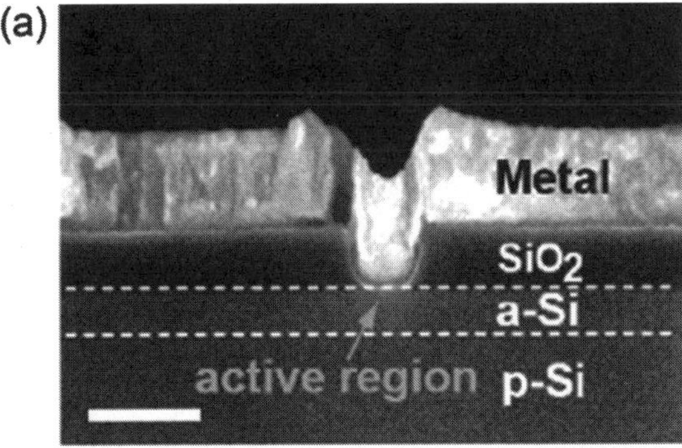

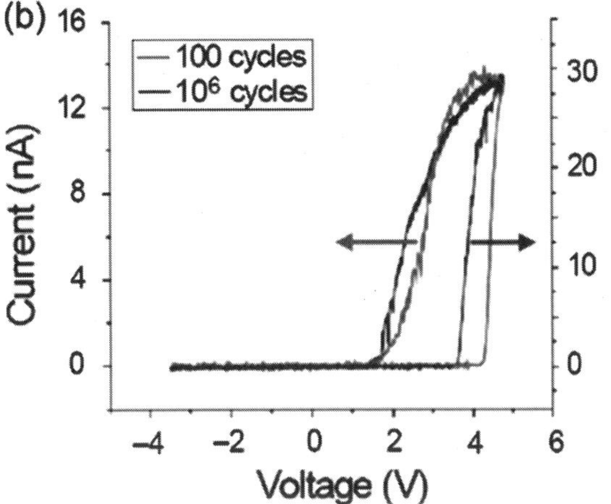

Figure 8. a-Si-based RRAM devices. (a) Cross-sectional SEM image of a device with M/a-Si/p-Si structure. The scale bar represents 100 nm (b) resistive-switching I–V curve of the device with an active area of 50 nm × 50 nm. The I–V curves were measured after 10^2 and 10^6 write/erase cycles. Reprinted with permission from [21], S. H. Jo and W. Lu, *Nano Lett.* 8, 392 (2008). © 2008, American Chemical Society.

positive bias, which reduces the forming voltage and helps limit damages to the devices during the forming and Set processes, therefore improving the device yield. The a-Si dielectric layer could be prepared by either plasma-enhanced chemical vapor deposition (PECVD) or low-pressure chemical vapor deposition (LPCVD) techniques, and the growth conditions can be used to effectively control the device behaviors including the initial resistance, the ON/OFF ratio, and the rectifying effect [21]. In these devices, typical bipolar resistive switching was observed (Fig. 8(b)) that were measured from a Ag/a-Si/p-Si cell with an active area of 50 nm × 50 nm [21]. Significantly, the devices can exhibit an intrinsic current rectifying behavior in the ON state, which is of crucial importance in suppressing crosstalk when integrated in passive crossbar arrays. Resistive switching has been obtained in M/a-Si/p-Si cells with M being Ag, Ni, and Au among others. However, devices with Ag top electrodes yield superior performance to other cells, especially in terms of lower operation voltages and longer endurance, thus making Ag a preferential choice for top contacts [21]. The a-Si-based RRAM cells have demonstrated very encouraging performance metrics, including a high device yield of 99%, scaling potential of < 50 nm, fast programming speed of 5 ns, high endurance of 10^8, a long retention of ~7 years, and multilevel storage capability [21, 97, 144].

It is interesting to note that the M/a-Si/p-Si devices could be controlled to show either rectifying or nonrectifying behaviors in the ON state by choosing suitable a-Si deposition techniques (PECVD or LPCVD), changing the medium thickness (Figs. 9(a and b)) or modulating the series resistance the cell sees (e.g., changing the programming current; Figs. 9(c and d)). This flexibility provides multiple choices of memory devices to suit different requirements [21]. For example, the rectifying cells offer the capability to suppress sneak current when integrated in passive arrays and ultralow write current (~10 nA in Fig. 8(b)), while the nonrectifying cells offer even faster switching speed and normally better data retention [21]. On the basis of the high performance obtained in single cells, 1 kb high-density crossbar array of a-Si RRAM cells has been successfully fabricated (Fig. 10). Excellent device yield and performance uniformity have been obtained [98], which suggests that a-Si-based RRAM can be a promising candidate for high-density and CMOS compatible memory applications.

Similar with a-Si, RRAM devices built from amorphous carbon (a-C) were also reported including both experimental [100, 102] and simulative [100, 145] studies. Amorphous carbon is thought to be a potential solid electrolyte material because of its high Cu diffusivity with a low activation energy of 0.76 eV [146, 147]. This indicates the possibility of fabricating ECM cells based on a-C films with oxidizable electrodes such as Cu. The resistive-switching effects in hydrogenated amorphous carbon (a-C:H)-based RRAM cells with Cu anodes were investigated [102], and the devices showed essentially analogous switching characteristics and operation principles with other ECM cells. Similar carbon-based resistive-switching materials also include copper–carbon-mixed (Cu–C) amorphous films [101, 148], in which the concentration of carbon could

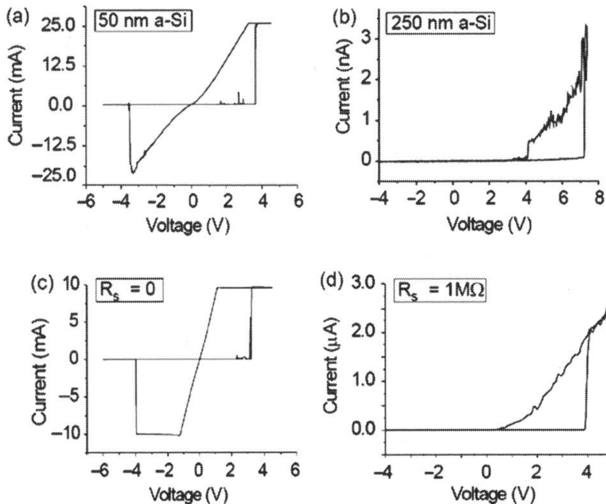

Figure 9. Control of the rectifying and nonrectifying behaviors in M/a-Si/p-Si cells. Switching characteristics of devices deposited by LPCVD are (a) nonrectifying with 50-nm thick a-Si and (b) rectifying with 250 nm thick a-Si. Switching characteristics of another device with 40-nm thick a-Si deposited by LPCVD are: (c) nonrectifying without series resistor and (d) rectifying with a 1-MΩ series resistor. Reprinted with permission from [21], S. H. Jo and W. Lu, *Nano Lett.* 8, 392 (2008). © 2008, American Chemical Society.

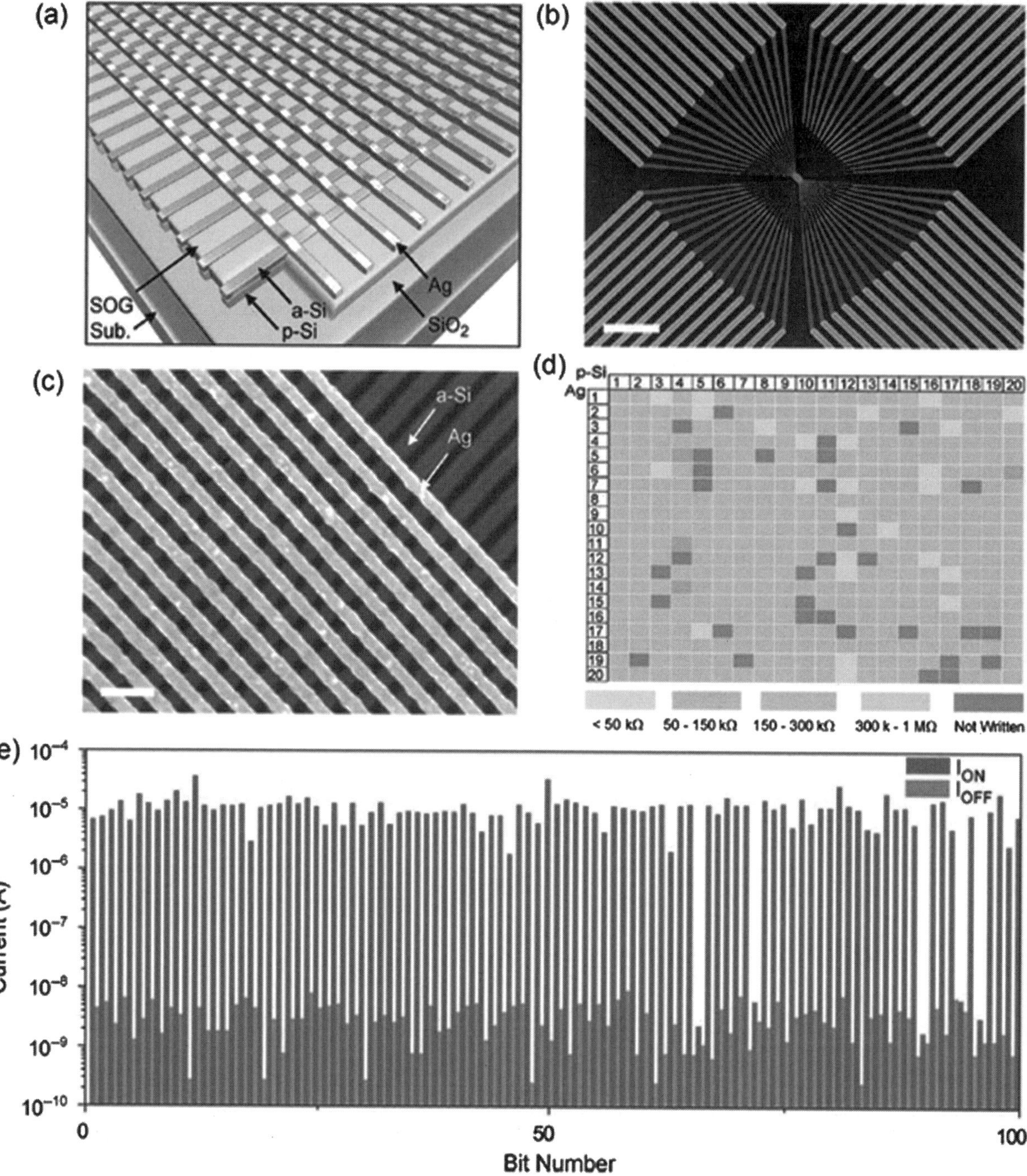

Figure 10. Crossbar RRAM array based on *a*-Si. (a) A crossbar memory array formed with Ag and *p*-Si nanowire electrodes and *a*-Si as the active layer. (b) SEM image of the array. Scale bar: 40 μm. (c) zoomed-in SEM image of the memory array. Scale bar: 200 nm, (d) yield map of 400 cross-point cells in the array, (e) the ON and OFF currents of the first 100 bits in the array, showing high uniformity. Reprinted with permission from [98], S. H. Jo et al., *Nano Lett.* 9, 870 (2009). © 2009, American Chemical Society.

be used to effectively modulate the film resistance [146]. Hwang et al. [101, 148] fabricated RRAM devices employing amorphous Cu–C films (Cu:C $\approx$ 1.5) as the solid electrolyte layer, and the obtained Cu/Cu–C/Pt [101] or Pt/Cu–C/Pt [148] devices presenting bipolar memory characteristics with endurance of $> 10^3$ cycles, switching stability at 175°C, tight distribution of resistance values, and good cell-to-cell uniformity [148].

Another type of RRAM cell based on phase change has also been explored in amorphous-carbon devices. It is well known that several allotropes of carbon exist that have different conductivity, such as the sp^2-dominated graphitic form with high conductivity and the sp^3-dominated diamond form with low conductivity [100]. By applying the appropriate current pulses, it was reported that one could switch carbon between an ordered sp^2-rich state and a

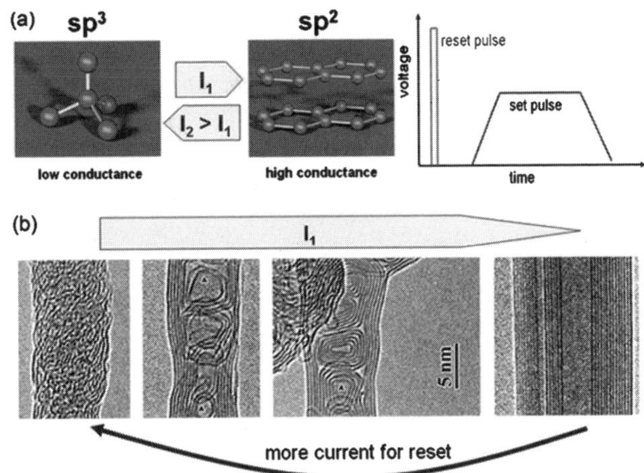

Figure 11. (a) One possible operation principle of carbon-based RRAM devices. Reprinted with permission from [100], F. Kreupl et al., "International Electron Devices Meeting," p. 521, 2008. © 2008, IEEE. (b) Visualization of the memory switching between an ordered state and a disordered state under TEM. Reprinted with permission from [149], J. Y. Huang et al., *Nano Lett.* 6, 1699 (2006). © 2006, American Chemical Society.

disordered sp^3-rich state reversibly, therefore resulting in nonvolatile unipolar switching (Figs. 11(a and b)) [100, 149]. The *a*-C based resistive memory shows fast switching speed in the order of tens of nanoseconds, and it indicates high scaling potential because of the monoatomic nature of carbon. As a supplement to the experimental achievements, the above switching processes of carbon-based RRAM devices have been simulated on a fully atomistic level by Guan et al. [145] using the molecular dynamics method and Extended-Hückel-Theory based Non-equilibrium Green's Function method.

3.3. Oxides

A large set of oxide materials have been shown to exhibit resistive-switching effects [19, 49, 50, 53, 55, 150, 151], in which oxygen vacancies are usually suggested to be the active species in the switching processes [17, 89, 90, 151, 152]. Amorphous oxide materials including SiO_x [27, 47, 48, 106, 153], TiO_x [122, 154, 155], AlO_x [46, 107–109, 156], Nb_2O_5 [57], TaO_x [76, 157], WO_x [133, 158], Ti-Ni-O [159], Lu_2O_3 [84], and $Pr_{0.7}Ca_{0.3}MnO_3$ [160] thin films, have been investigated and reported for their resistive-switching effects and possible applications in nonvolatile memories. It is worthwhile to note that some oxides, e.g., TiO_x and $Pr_{0.7}Ca_{0.3}MnO_3$, are found to exhibit resistive-switching behavior in both amorphous [122, 154, 155, 160] and crystalline [49, 50, 52, 94, 152, 161, 162] structures.

The resistive-switching characteristics in amorphous oxide films seem to vary from case to case, showing strong dependence on stoichiometry of the oxide film, fabrication techniques, electrode materials, and measurement setups. For example, both unipolar and bipolar resistive-switching behaviors have been reported in amorphous oxides. The AlO_x films exhibited unipolar switching in Al/AlO_x/Pt [107] and Al/AlO_x/Al [108, 109, 163] cell structures but bipolar switching in Ti/AlO_x/Pt cells [46, 156], suggesting different switching mechanisms in these cases. In Cu/Cu-doped SiO_2/W memory devices, it was reported that both unipolar and bipolar resistive-switching effects can be observed in the same cells if different levels of erase currents were used [47]. The complexity of the switching phenomena adds difficulties to the interpretation of the switching mechanisms in oxides.

In the situation that oxidizable electrodes are used in the cells, some amorphous oxides also fall into the category of solid-state electrolytes, e.g., Cu–SiO_2 [47, 48, 164], Cu–TaO_x [77, 113], Cu–WO_3 [80, 133] and these cells exhibit essentially similar electrical characteristics as those observed in chalcogenide-based ECM cells and involve redox processes. Compared with higher chalcogenides, oxides usually have higher thermal stability and better compatibility with the entrenched CMOS processes. However, as a tradeoff, the oxide-based ECM cells may be slower in programming speed because of the relatively lower mobility of copper or silver ions in oxide electrolytes [47]. The oxide-based ECM cells can also offer relatively low power consumption. In a study conducted by Schindler et al. [48], the Ir/Cu-doped SiO_2/Cu cells have demonstrated extremely low write current of 10 pA (Fig. 12).

As an essential part of the MIM structure, the role of the electrode materials on resistive-switching properties can have significant impacts. An in-depth understanding of the relationship between the electrode materials and the resistive-switching effects is helpful not only for the improvement of device performance but also for the understanding of the switching mechanism. Such a study was performed for cells based on amorphous TaO_x films [76]. It was found that only devices composed of electrodes with higher electrode potentials than Ta have a possibility to show resistive switching. Therefore, it is likely that the resistive-switching effect in TaO_x films [76] does not involve the electrode material in redox reactions. Furthermore, the stability of the resistive-switching effects in TaO_x shows dependence on the work function of electrode materials. TaO_x memory cells comprising metal electrodes with high work function, such as Ir and Pt, show stable resistive switching; in contrast, TaO_x

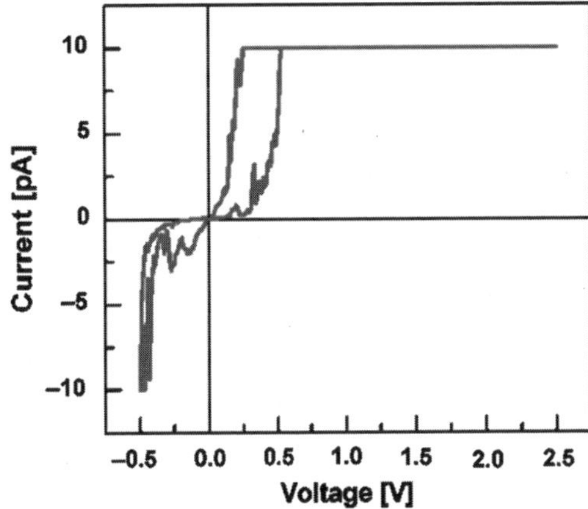

Figure 12. *I–V* characteristics of an Ir/Cu–SiO_2/Cu memory cell with a write current of 10 pA. The ON/OFF ratio is ~10 at 80 mV. Reprinted with permission from [48], C. Schindler et al., *Appl. Phys. Lett.* 92, 122910 (2008). © 2008, American Institute of Physics.

memory devices consisting of metal electrodes with relatively lower work function, such as Ag and W, exhibit unstable resistive-switching behavior [76], once again highlighting the role of the electrode materials and thus, the importance of metal/dielectric interface in switching processes.

The effect of metal/dielectric interface was also studied in AlO_x-based cells by creating more metal/dielectric interfaces through the insertion of one or multiple Al layers into the AlO_x films [107]. Figure 13(a) depicts the schematic structure of the memory devices with different numbers of metal/dielectric interfaces, where S_1, S_2, and S_3 denote single-, double-, and triple-stacked AlO_x memory devices, respectively [107]. Figure 13(b) presents the corresponding resistive-switching *I–V* characteristics of the devices with different numbers of insertion layers. It is evident that all the cells show unipolar resistive-switching behavior. However, as the stack number increases, the endurance property and threshold uniformity are significantly improved. This was explained by the increased effective number of active regions where Set/Reset switching occurs [107], therefore allowing the device not to fail even after part of the film breaks down.

To summarize, RRAM built on amorphous oxides can show promising performance including switching speed of ~10 ns [46, 165], high endurance over 10^{10} cycles [165], extrapolated data retention exceeding 10 years at 85°C [76], and low write current of 10 pA [48]. Beyond the above achievements in single memory cells, an 8-kbit memory array based on TaO_x films was fabricated with a 1*T*-1*R* structure using standard 180-nm CMOS technology [76]. By fabricating $Al/Al_xO_y/Al$ RRAM devices with ductile Al as the electrodes and flexible polyethersulfone as the substrates, flexible resistive memory devices have also been developed [108] that might be interesting for future flexible electronics.

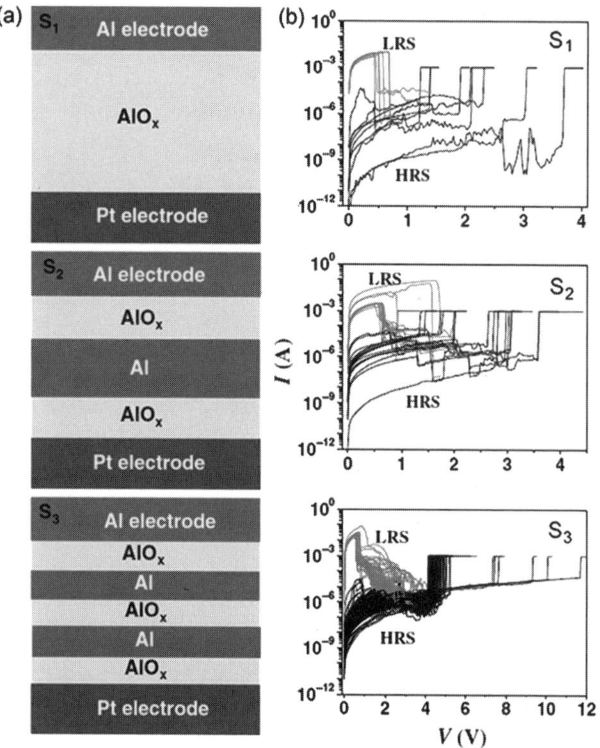

Figure 13. (a) Schematics of AlO_x multijunction devices with Al insertion layers (b) resistive-switching *I–V* curves in for devices with different structures. Reprinted with permission from [107], J. Song et al., *Appl. Phys. Express* 3, 091101 (2010). © 2010, The Japan Society of Applied Physics.

3.4. Comparison of Resistive Switching Devices Based on Amorphous and Crystalline Materials

Since the first report of resistive switching by Hickmott in 1962 [27], a large number of crystalline and amorphous materials have been found to show resistive-switching behavior. As already noted in Section 3.3, some materials such as TiO_x and $Pr_{0.7}Ca_{0.3}MnO_3$ were reported to show resistive switching in both amorphous [122, 154, 155, 160] and crystalline [49, 50, 52, 94, 152, 161, 162] structures. Nevertheless, limited efforts have been dedicated to reveal the relationship between the crystallinity of the materials and their resistive-switching effects. In the study of Fujimoto et al. [160], it was found that the $Pr_{0.7}Ca_{0.3}MnO_3$ films only exhibited resistive switching in amorphous structure, and this behavior disappeared after film crystallization through high temperature annealing. Similarly, Jeong et al. [122] found that the amorphous TiO_2 films deposited at 150 and 180°C showed reversible resistive switching, whereas the crystalline TiO_2 films deposited at 200 and 250°C tended to fail very quickly. However, it is important to point out that the phenomena observed in specific cases/materials do not suffice to yield general conclusions, e.g., both $Pr_{0.7}Ca_{0.3}MnO_3$ and TiO_2 have been reported to show resistive switching in other studies.

Because of the lack of sufficient data on device performance such as programming speed, endurance, and retention in many publications, it is difficult to directly compare the RRAM performance of amorphous and crystalline materials in the same material system. As an alternative, we summarize the properties of some well-characterized RRAM devices in the literature and make an indirect comparison between amorphous- and crystalline-material-based devices to shed some light on this issue. As can be seen from the representative results in Table 1, promising performance metrics such as low threshold voltages, large ON/OFF ratio, fast programming speed, long data retention, and multivalue storage have all been achieved in RRAM devices based on either amorphous or crystalline films. However, it seems that RRAM devices comprised of amorphous mediums have apparently better endurance than their crystalline counterparts judging from the data reported to date. Until now, the endurance record of $> 10^{10}$ cycles was obtained in two amorphous systems, Ag–Ge–Se [28] and TaO_x films [165]. Besides this difference in cycling ability, generally speaking amorphous thin films should have higher resistivity than crystalline films for the same material system because of the absence of long-range lattice periodicity and hence, stronger scattering effects and better compliance to low-temperature deposition and material compatibility requirements [166]. Based on these advantages, it is our opinion that devices based on amorphous thin films should be more desirable

Table 1. Summary of well-characterized resistive memory devices based on amorphous and crystalline films.

Device structure	V_{Set}/V_{Reset} (V)	ON/OFF	Speed (ns)	Endurance	Retention	Multilevel storage	References
Amorphous							
Ag/Ag–Ge–Se/Ni	0.2/−0.5	$\sim 10^3$	< 100	$> 10^{10}$	> 10 yr^e	Yes	[28, 130, 133]
Ag/*a*-Si/*p*-Si	~3.5/−3.5	10^4–10^7	5	$> 10^8$	~6.8 yr^e	Yes	[21, 97, 98, 144]
Pt/TaO_x/Pt	−0.9/2.0	~20	10	$> 10^9$	> 10 yr^e	No	[76]
Cu/Cu–Te/GdO_x/W	~1.1/−0.7	$> 10^2$	< 5	$> 10^7$	$> 10^3$ s	Yes	[20]
Pt/TaO_x/Ta	1.9/−2.2	< 10	< 10	$> 10^{10}$	>3 m	No	[165]
Crystalline							
Pt/TiO_2/TiN	−1.8/0.7	10^3	5	2×10^6	256 h	Yes	[22]
TiN/TiO_x/HfO_2/TiN	~1/−0.7	$> 10^2$	5	$> 10^6$	10 yr*	Yes	[65]
Ag/ZnO:Mn/Pt	1.9/−2.2	$> 10^7$	5	$> 10^2$	$> 10^7$ s	No	[23]
Ti/MnO_2/Pt	0.7/−1.1	~10	10^7	$> 10^5$	$> 10^4$ s	No	[75]
Cu/ZrO_2:Ti/Pt	1.4/−0.7	$> 10^4$	100	> 250	$> 10^7$ s	No	[61]
TiN/WO_x/W	1.4/−1.2	5	< 300	$> 10^7$	$> 10^4$ s	Yes	[78]

Note: *Denotes that retention time was obtained by extrapolating experimental data.

in high-density and low-power memory architectures than devices based on crystalline films.

4. RESISTIVE-SWITCHING MECHANISMS AND OPERATION PRINCIPLES

A broad range of materials have so far been explored for their possible applications in RRAM devices. The underlying resistive-switching mechanism in many of the devices, however, is still a matter of heated debate. Different physical models, such as charge trapping/detrapping [167], metal-insulator transition [168–170], formation/dissolution of conducting filaments [164, 171, 172], valence change [76], have been proposed to interpret the experimental results. Here we summarize the prevailing theories on resistive-switching mechanism in amorphous thin films, which represent our current understanding on these deceivingly simple two-terminal devices.

4.1. Formation of Conducting Filaments

The filamentary mechanism is the most popular model used to interpret resistive-switching behavior, which has been adopted in many RRAM devices. The basic idea of the filamentary mechanism is that one or multiple local conducting paths are formed in the active medium of RRAM devices (the I layer in the MIM structure), therefore strongly affecting the resistance of the device. The conducting paths are constructed/ruptured under the effects of Set/Reset electric signals; hence, they give rise to repetitive resistive switching between high-conductance ON and low-conductance OFF states. As an important characteristic of the locally formed filamentary mechanism, the ON-state resistance of the cells usually shows weak dependence on the cell area [21, 61, 75, 152]. Furthermore, according to the chemical compositions of the filaments, this model can be further classified into three main types of filamentary mechanisms:

(1) conducting filaments formed by migration and redox reactions of metal ions, which are usually imported from the electrode materials,
(2) conducting filaments formed by drift and accumulation of oxygen vacancies, which is applicable to many oxides, and
(3) conducting filaments formed by the precipitation and percolation of secondary phases, whose conductivity significantly differs from the original phases.

We will discuss the basic operation principles of the above three types of filamentary mechanisms hereinafter.

4.1.1. Drift of Metal Ions and Formation of Conducting Filaments Through Redox

4.1.1.1. Physical Processes. The resistive-switching mechanism based on the formation/dissolution of metal filaments is usually used to explain the resistive-switching effects in RRAM devices based on chalcogenide solid electrolytes [17, 28, 36, 124], *a*-Si [21, 97, 98], *a*-C [102], and many other amorphous oxides [113, 133, 164], especially when oxidizable electrodes are adopted in the cells. A typical example is the ECM cell, which is built from ion conductive solid electrolytes such as chalcogenide glasses [31, 33, 124], amorphous carbon [102], and oxides [47, 48, 113, 164]. The physical process of the filament formation/dissolution in ECM cells is schematically depicted in Figure 14, which could be interpreted as follows: The as-fabricated devices are usually in OFF state (Fig. 14(a)). When a positive voltage is applied on the oxidizable electrode, oxidation of this electrochemically active material occurs, generating metal cations through the electrochemical reaction in Eq. (3):

$$M \rightarrow M^{n+} + ne^- \tag{3}$$

where M denotes the active metal atoms, such as Ag or Cu, M^{n+}, represents the metal cation, and n is the charge number. The mobile cations migrate toward the inert electrode through the solid electrolytes (Fig. 14(b)) with the assistance of the applied electric field. When they arrive at the inert counter electrode (cathode), the M^{n+} cations are reduced by electrons from the cathode, and this could be described by the reaction in Eq. (4):

$$M^{n+} + ne^- \rightarrow M \tag{4}$$

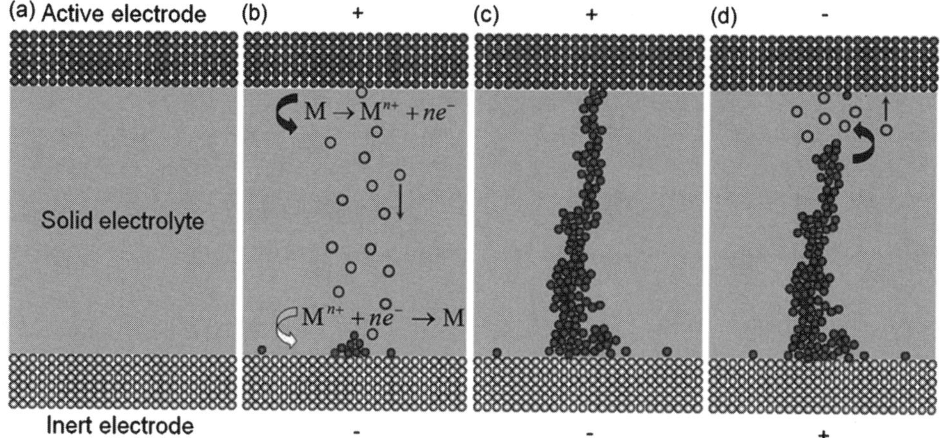

Figure 14. Schematic diagram for the electrochemical metallization mechanism. (a) The initial state of the device, (b) generation and migration of the mobile cations in the solid electrolyte layer and metal particle precipitation due to cation reduction at the cathode, (c) growth of the metal protrusion leading to the formation of a highly conductive bridge in the cell, (d) electrochemical dissolution of the filament when the polarity of the applied voltage is reversed, corresponding to the Reset process.

As a result, metal particles are precipitated on the surface of the inert electrode. The successive precipitations of metal particles at the cathode will lead to a growth of metal protrusion, which, when finally reaching the anode, will form a highly conductive path in the solid electrolyte matrix (Fig. 14(c)). This process corresponds to the OFF–ON Set process. When the polarity of the applied voltage is reversed, the dissolution of the metal filament is initiated through a reverse electrochemical process driven by the reaction in Eq. (3) (Fig. 14(d)). The high resistance of the device is recovered when the conducting filaments are broken and the ON–OFF Reset process is completed.

If the solid electrolyte layer contains no Ag or Cu ions to start with (such as the case for oxide electrolytes, or cases when the chalcogenide glasses such as Ge–Se and Ge–S are not previously doped by the active electrode elements), a forming procedure will be required to incorporate the metal ions into the electrolytes. Forming produces large amounts of intrusions of the electrode material inside the electrolyte, providing nearby reservoirs for subsequent filament creation/destruction processes.

The redox-based filament formation processes are likely behind a majority of RRAM devices studied to date. For instance, the resistive switching in *a*-Si is also attributed to metal filament formation [21, 99, 173], and it is explained by the migration process of metal ions such as Ag^+ between adjacent trapping sites inside *a*-Si (Fig. 15(d)). In the case of a single-filament formation, the step-by-step hopping of metal ions would manifest as a stepwise switching feature in the *I–V* curve, which has been observed in Ag/*a*-Si/*p*-Si memory devices [97, 98]. One could also imagine that a direct consequence of this filament formation model is that the switching rate would be bias-dependent [174]. In essence, the ion migration is a field-assisted and thermally activated process [175]. Therefore, the hopping rate Γ is determined by the bias-dependent activation energy E_a' [97]:

$$\Gamma = 1/\tau = \nu e^{-E_a'(V)/k_B T} \tag{5}$$

where τ denotes the characteristic wait time (average time-to-switch), υ is the attempt frequency, T is the absolute temperature, and k_B is the Boltzmann constant. Since E_a' can be reduced by the applied electric field and is thus a function of the bias voltage, the switching rate would strongly (e.g., exponentially) depend on the external bias.

Figure 15(e) plots the measured average time-to-switch τ values at five different bias voltages that could be fitted using an exponential Equation [97]:

$$\tau(V) = \tau_0 e^{-V/V_0} \tag{6}$$

The good agreement between the experimental and fitting results proves the bias-dependent nature of resistive switching, and it indicates that the switching speed could be dramatically improved by increasing the amplitude of bias voltage [174]. As shown in Figure 15(e), as the bias is increased by only 1 V, and the time-to-switch is decreased by about 10^3. This effect plays favorably in addressing the so-called voltage-time dilemma: by increasing the programming voltage slightly, the switching speed (hence the power consumption) can be exponentially improved.

The other consequence of the thermally activated switching process is that the process is stochastic; we can only predict the average switching time in the statistical sense but not the exact time for each switching event. In fact, the wait time follows a Poisson distribution if assuming no correlation is formed between subsequent switching events (a reasonable assumption), and the probability of switching to occur within a period of Δt could be described by [97]:

$$P(t) = \frac{\Delta t}{t} e^{-t/\tau} \tag{7}$$

Figures 15(a–c) displays the histograms of the measured switching time at different voltages of 2.6, 3.2, and 3.6 V, with the fitting curves based on Eq. (7). The stochastic and time-dependent switching nature suggests that: (1) Essentially there is not a definite threshold voltage that guarantees 100% switching; however, we can define a threshold voltage that garantees a percantage of switching, e.g., >99%, and (b)

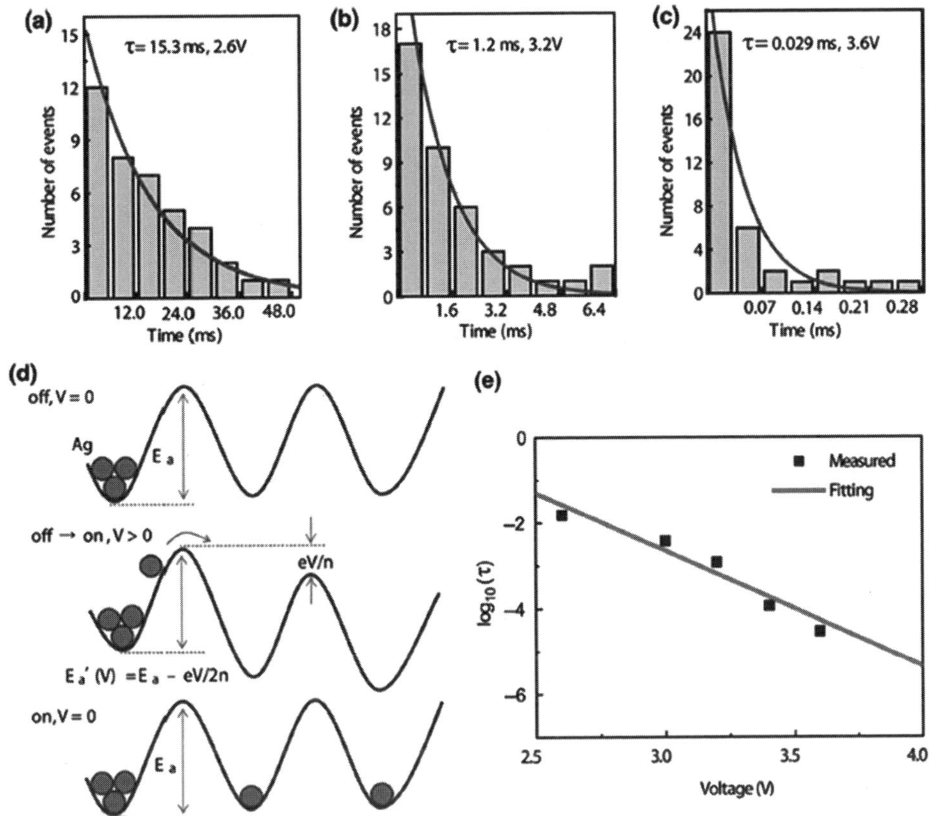

Figure 15. Bias-dependent switching characteristics in RRAM. (a–c) Histograms of the individual wait times before the first switching step at bias voltages of 2.6, 3.2, and 3.6 V for an *a*-Si-based RRAM. The solid lines are fitting results using Eq. (7), (d) schematic diagram of the ion hopping process, (e) relationship between the characteristic wait time τ versus voltage V that shows an exponential voltage dependence. Reprinted with permission from [97], S. H. Jo et al., *Nano Lett.* 9, 496 (2009). © 2009, American Chemical Society.

the threshold voltage also depends on the wait time. Waiting longer means the switching can be observed even at low voltages; however, applying a higher voltage will ensure an exponentially faster switching time (on average). These and future studies that can quantify the device characteristics, including temporal and special variations, will be highly necessary to guide future memory and logic operations based on resistive-switching devices.

4.1.1.2. Direct Characterizations of Metal Filaments.

Although electrical analyses have shown good agreement with the filament mechanism, direct evidence on the formation and evolution of metal filaments is still highly desirable to fundamentally elucidate the microscopic nature of the filaments and understand the switching kinetics. A lot of efforts have been devoted to reveal the nature of conducting filaments both in amorphous and crystalline materials, while conductive atomic force microscopy (CAFM) and TEM studies provided the most effective and convincing results to date.

CAFM has proven to be an effective method for investigation of local filament growth and dissolution processes without involving difficult sample preparation processes [176–178]. Figure 16(a) shows the local I–V and R–V characteristics measured by CAFM from a random position of a fresh Ag–Ge–Se film surface deposited on Ag [124], where the Pt/Ir probe serves as the inert electrode. From Figure 16(a) it is evident that the device is electrically formed by applying a voltage of ~1.1 V. After that, a conductive filament with a diameter of ~20 nm can be observed (Fig. 16(b)) [124]. The direct correlation between electrical switching and the emergence of local conductive path supports the above-mentioned localized metal filament mechanism. The small size of the filament also indicates that the Ag–Ge–Se based ECM cells might be scaled down to a ~20 nm range.

The microscopic nature of the filaments such as the composition and the chemical state, on the other hand, can only be obtained by studies such as a cross-sectional TEM by taking advantage of the powerful TEM attachments. However, direct TEM visualization of the conducting filament is a very challenging task because the filament is formed in a very localized region buried inside the dielectric layer. Up until now, direct TEM observations and characterizations of conducting filaments have been achieved in several materials, including Ta_2O_5 [113], ZnO:Mn [23], Ag_2S [179], TiO_2 [175], and ZrO_2 [180]. Figures 17(a and b) show the TEM images of Cu/Ta_2O_5/Pt devices in the OFF and ON states, respectively. A conducting filament is clearly visible in Figure 17(b). The electrodiagnostic (EDX) study in Figure 17(c) further demonstrates that the filamentary region is rich in Cu [113]. These results offer direct morphological and chemical evidence for the electrochemical metallization mechanism described above. Nevertheless, many

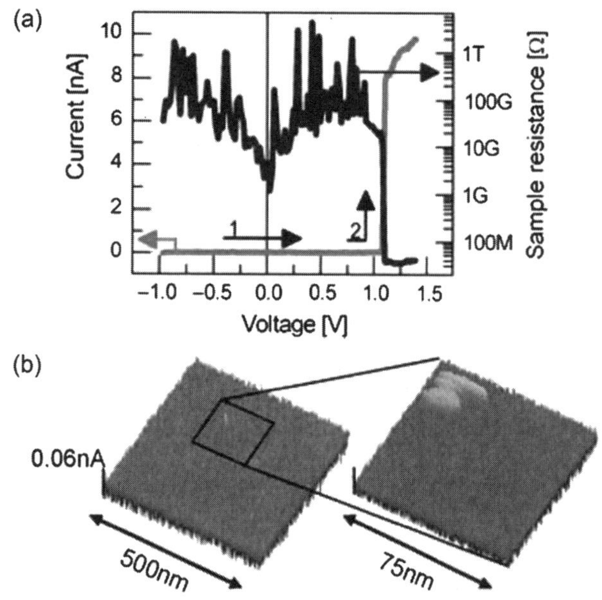

Figure 16. CAFM characterization of filament formation. (a) Local *I–V* and *R–V* curves measured from a random spot on the Ag–Ge–Se/Ag film surface by CAFM, (b) CAFM current image taken at 10 mV after the *I–V* measurement in (a). Reprinted with permission from [124], C. Schindler et al., *Phys. Stat. Sol. (RRL)* 2, 129 (2008). © 2008, Wiley-VCH Verlag GmbH and KGaA, Weinheim.

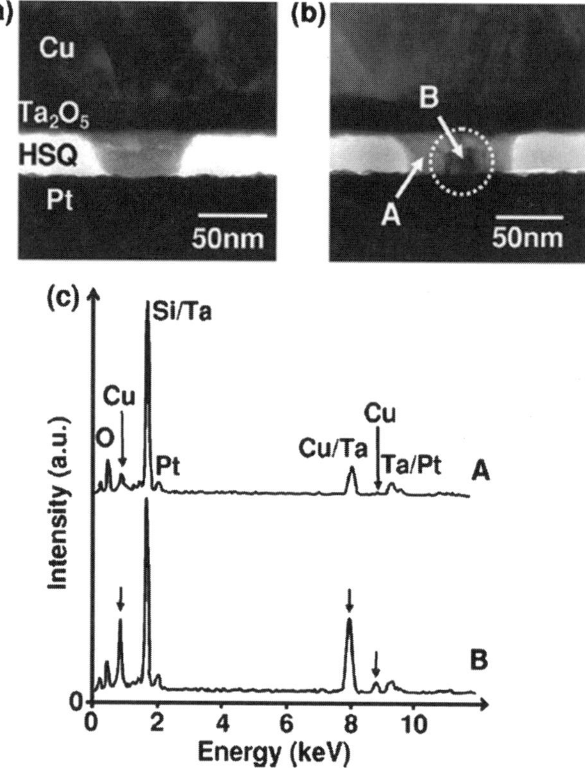

Figure 17. TEM images of a Cu/Ta_2O_5/Pt device; (a) in OFF state, (b) in ON state, (c) EDX spectrums taken from points A and B in (b). Reprinted with permission from [113], T. Sakamoto et al., *Appl. Phys. Lett.* 91, 092110 (2007). © 2007, American Institute of Physics.

questions remain unresolved especially regarding the switching kinetics, such as: Where does the filament growth start in the Set process? Where does the filament break during the Reset process? Is the dissolution of filament a local effect or through complete annihilation? Does the subsequent filament growth inherit previous nucleating sites? Understanding these issues will demand more detailed microscopic studies directly on the filaments. In particular, an *in situ* observation of the filamentary switching process under TEM will likely provide answers to many of the questions. As a payback, insight into the switching dynamics and kinetics will, in turn, guild the fabrication and optimization of resistive memory devices.

4.1.2. Drift of Oxygen Vacancies and Formation of Conducting Filaments

In many oxides, especially transition metal oxides (such as TiO_2), oxygen vacancies (V_O) are much more mobile than the metal cations [17], which result in another kind of resistive-switching mechanism based on the drift of oxygen vacancies. For example, in the case of TiO_2 based devices, it was found that the resistive switching is also a local effect, so the formation of conducting filaments could be assumed. Although different from the above-mentioned metal filament model, the conducting filament in TiO_2 is likely caused by the redistribution of V_O, which affects local conductivity and can, in turn, affect transport through the device (e.g., by affecting the transmission through the Pt/TiO_2 Schottky barriers in Ref. [152]). Specifically, in the study of Yang [152], the drift of oxygen vacancies toward the Pt/TiO_2 Schottky interface under the effect of electric field and the accumulation of V_O therein will create conducting channels that shunt the electronic barrier. In this case, the current of the device is determined by tunneling through a thin residual barrier that has not been penetrated by the filament, and the device is switched to the ON state. By applying the reverse electric field, the oxygen vacancies would drift away from the Schottky barrier, hence annihilating the conducting filaments. The electronic barrier is recovered, and the device is switched back to the OFF state [152]. In a separate study, the conducting filament in TiO_2 has been demonstrated to be formed by an oxygen-deficient Magnéli phase (Ti_4O_7) with the accumulation of oxygen vacancies, an effect that was directly confirmed by TEM studies [172, 181].

Similar mechanisms were found to drive the resistive switching in Pd/WO_3/W memristive devices [121]. In the scenario of V_O drift and filament formation at the Schottky interface, the overall conductance of the cell is considered to be composed of two parts in parallel: the tunneling path through the local conducting filaments and the path through the Schottky barrier in regions without filaments. Therefore, the overall current could be described as:

$$I = (1 - w)\alpha[1 - \exp(-\beta V)] + w\gamma \sin h(\delta V) \quad (8)$$

in which the first and second terms denote the contributions from the Schottky emission and the tunneling, respectively [121]. α, β, γ, and δ are all positive parameters determined by material properties, and the internal state variable w is a normalized area index reflecting the ratio of the contribution from the conducting filaments. Therefore, $w = 0$ indicates a fully Schottky-dominated conduction, while $w = 1$ implies a fully tunneling-dominated conduction. By considering both the drift and diffusion effects of V_O to calculate the growth rate of w, the simulated I–V curve satisfactorily captures the main features of resistive switching [121].

To clarify, the oxygen vacancies are simply re-distributed inside the oxide during the programming/erasing process, i.e., no net charge is created or lost during these processes. To create the oxygen vacancies that are needed in the resistive-switching process, a high-voltage or high-current electroforming process is usually necessary before reproducible resistive switching can be observed [152, 182]. The forming process is essentially an electroreduction of oxygen ions, which produces oxygen gas and leaves oxygen vacancies in the oxide films [172, 183]. On the other hand, he presence of the high-voltage forming process is not desirable for the integration of large-scale memory arrays. In addition, the eruption of oxygen gas can induce severe physical deformations on the devices. Recently, with the improved understanding of the electroforming and resistive-switching mechanism, the forming process have been successfully eliminated either by thinning down the oxide film to just keep the switching interface or by depositing an oxygen-deficient layer next to the switching layer in the fabrication process [183].

4.1.3. Filament Formation by Precipitation and Percolation of Secondary Phases

Beside the formation/dissolution of metal filaments that is normally suggested as the underlying mechanism in ECM cells, the conducting paths (filaments) in some chalcogenide films such as Ag–Ge–Se films were recently argued to be formed by a secondary phase, i.e., Ag_2Se [29] instead of redox of elemental metal ions. Figure 18 shows the microstructure evolution of the $Ag_{30}Ge_{17}Se_{53}$ films during the electrical treatment when a positive voltage of 1 V is applied to the Ag anode. One can see from the TEM image and the SAED pattern in Figure 18(a) that the as-deposited Ag–Ge–Se film has a typical amorphous structure. Over time, some crystalline precipitates begin to appear under positive bias, and then the precipitates tend to align themselves in a network as the number of precipitates increases. Finally, a network of precipitates is formed after electrical treatment for 480 min (Fig. 18(f)) whose SAED pattern could be indexed to orthorhombic Ag_2Se [29]. Therefore, it indicates that the conducting filaments in some Ag–Ge–Se-based devices may be, in fact, composed of Ag_2Se instead of elemental Ag as commonly believed. However, it should be noted that the programming conditions in Chen's study (Ref. [29], with a low programming field and very long programming time) are very different from those in previous studies (e.g., Ref. [28], with a high programming field and short programming time), and it is possible that different products—filaments based on the Ag_2Se phase or filaments based on elemental Ag—can be obtained. The other difference between the two possible explanations is that the metal filament is suggested to grow from the inert electrode to the active electrode in redox-based ECM cells [17, 23]; while, in the present percolation model, the Ag_2Se phase nucleates homogenously in the electrolyte matrix, showing no preferential growth direction.

The above-mentioned process involving microstructural evolution and phase separation has recently been qualitatively reproduced through a Monte Carlo simulation in Ag–Ge–Se electrolyte films [127]. Recently, a similar switching mechanism has also been revealed by an *in situ* TEM study in Ag_2S solid electrolyte in which the conducting filament was found to be composed of a more conductive secondary phase of Ag_2S (argentite) and Ag nanocrystals [179]. Therefore, the resistive-switching mechanism in Ag–Ge–Se and other chalcogenide electrolytes may be more complex than originally thought (based on redox and metal filament formation). More studies will be necessary to clarify these questions, especially ones aided by direct microscopic analyses.

4.2. Valence Change Mechanism at the Dielectric/Electrode Interface

It is well known that transition metal cations have complex valence states and nonstoichoimetries as well as multiphases are usually present in transition metal oxides. This gives rise to the possibility of another kind of resistive-switching mechanism controlled by the formation of a new phase at the dielectric/electrode interface. Since the new phase is formed by redox reactions and has a different valence state of cations than the original phase, the mechanism is sometimes called valence change mechanism (VCM). A typical amorphous material showing VCM controlled resistive switching is TaO_x. Wei et al. [76] proposed that the resistive switching in Pt/TaO_x/Pt cells was controlled by the following redox reaction:

$$Ta_2O_5 + 2e^- \longleftrightarrow 2TaO_2 + O^{2-} \quad (9)$$

Compared with the fully oxidized Ta_2O_5 phase, TaO_2 has a narrower band gap and a significantly higher conductivity. When contacted by metal electrodes, it offers a lower Schottky barrier and higher conductance. Thus the redox reaction described by Eq. (9) could lead to a resistance switching between the two semiconducting states (Fig. 19) The physical processes are as follows: According to Eq. (9), when the O^{2-} ions are repelled from the Pt/TaO_x interface, a portion of Ta_2O_5 would be reduced to TaO_2 at the interface region, which decreases the electrode/oxide Schottky barrier height and switches the device to ON state. However, by applying voltages with an opposite polarity, the O^{2-} ions are attracted to the Pt/TaO_x interface. The accumulation of O^{2-} ions will oxidize the TaO_2 back to Ta_2O_5. As a result, the barrier height is increased and the OFF state is recovered. A similar working mechanism was also suggested to explain resistive switching in Fe_3O_4 films, which could be described by the redox reactions between Fe_3O_4 and γ-Fe_2O_3 as follows [184]:

$$2Fe_3O_4 + O^{2-} \longleftrightarrow 3\gamma - Fe_2O_3 + 2e^- \quad (10)$$

Essentially, the VCM is also based on the formation of a new phase. In this aspect, it is similar to the mechanism of precipitation and percolation model discussed in

Figure 18. Microstructure evolution of the Ag–Ge–Se films during electrical treatment; (a) TEM image and corresponding SAED pattern of the as-deposited Ag–Ge–Se film, (b) TEM image of the film after electrical treatment for 3 min, showing that some crystalline precipitates begin to appear, (c–e) TEM images of the Ag–Ge–Se films after treatment of 60, 180, and 480 min. As the treatment time increases, the precipitates start to align into a network, (f) typical network formed after treatment of 480 min. Inset shows the corresponding SAED pattern. Reprinted with permission from [29], L. Chen et al., *Appl. Phys. Lett.* 94, 162112 (2009). © 2009, American Institute of Physics.

Section 4.1.3. Nevertheless, the active region of resistive switching differs in the two cases. In the precipitation and percolation model, the secondary phase nucleates randomly inside the dielectric layer, whereas in the VCM model the new phase is suggested to form only at the dielectric/electrode interface and hence is an interfacial effect. In addition, the precipitation and percolation of secondary phases would eventually lead to localized conducting paths and bridge the electrodes, while the formation of the new phases in the VCM model takes place homogeneously at the interface region. These differences in resistive switching are expected to affect the scaling limits of corresponding RRAM devices. For example, filament-based devices typically show better ON/OFF ratios that can be further improved with area scaling (since the ON state is determined by localized filaments and the leakage current in OFF state scales with cell area), while VCM devices normally have limited ON/OFF ratios that are also insensitive to area scaling (since both ON and OFF resistances scale with area).

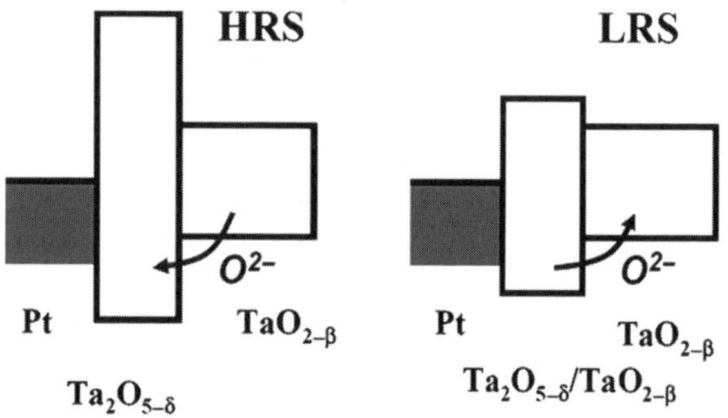

Figure 19. Schematic diagram of the resistive-switching mechanism in TaO_x that is induced by valence change. Reprinted with permission from [76], Z. Wei et al., " International Electron Devices Meeting," p. 293, 2008. © 2008, IEEE.

5. MULTILEVEL RESISTIVE SWITCHING IN AMORPHOUS MATERIALS

Besides continued scaling of the memory cells to smaller physical sizes, storing more than 1 bit of information in a single cell provides an alternative route to increase the density of data storage, which is one of the most important drivers of memory technologies. An attractive feature of resistive memories is that they usually possess a large ON/OFF ratio (> 10), which leaves space for possible intermediate resistance states between HRS and LRS, and provides a possibility for multivalue data storage. Up to now, a large number of amorphous materials have shown their potential of multilevel resistive switching such as Ag–Ge–Se [130], Ag–Ge–S [33, 134], *a*-Si [21, 97, 144], and TaO_x [157].

Multilevel data storage in chalcogenide-solid electrolytes is considered to be achieved by controlling the size of the conducting filaments. Figure 20 displays the multiple resistance states in Ag/Ag–Ge–S/W PMC devices in which the cell resistance R_C shows four different states: the OFF state ($R_C > 100$ kΩ) and three different ON states. The different resistance values of the ON states are obtained by programming operations with different compliance current of 5, 50, and 500 μA, respectively. All four resistance states are found to stably retain data for more than 10 hours at room temperature, demonstrating a 2-bit/cell

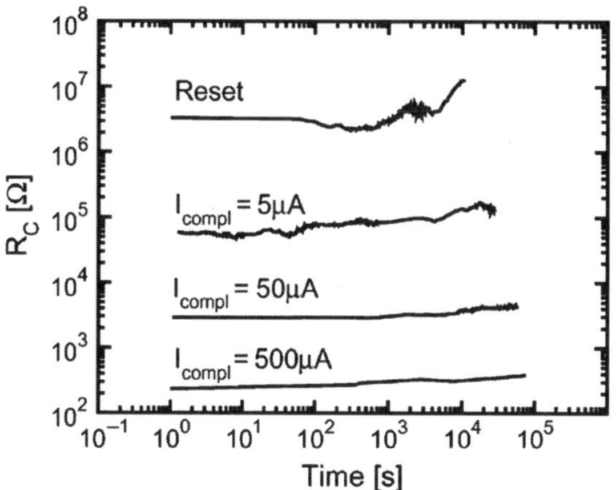

Figure 20. Multilevel storage capability of Ag–Ge–S ECM cells. Different cell resistance values were controlled by different current compliance during switching. Reprinted with permission from [33], U. Russo et al., *IEEE Trans. Electron Dev.* 56, 1040 (2009). © 2009, IEEE.

storage capability [33]. To help understand the switching process, Figure 21 shows the voltage drop on the memory cell in the resistive-switching process when a voltage pulse with amplitude of V_A and duration time of t_W is applied. The equivalent circuit of the experimental setup is shown in the inset, in which R_{load} represents the load resistor attached in series with the memory cell and R_S is the parasitic wire or contact resistance. The load resistor serves as a voltage divider for the cell and prevents excessive current flowing through the cell, essentially acting in a way equivalent to that of a CC [33]. It can be seen that most of the voltage drops on the cell when it is in the OFF state, i.e., $V_C \approx V_A$ in the beginning. As time increases, V_C suddenly decreases at $t = t_1$, indicating the connection of a conducting filament across the electrodes and hence, a large decrease of cell resistance R_C. After that, R_C decreases gradually between t_1 and t_W [33].

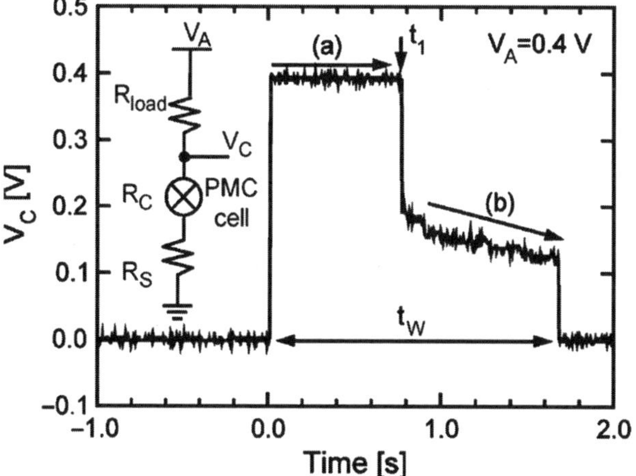

Figure 21. Cell voltage as a function of time during programming. Reprinted with permission from [33], U. Russo et al., *IEEE Trans. Electron Dev.* 56, 1040 (2009). © 2009, IEEE.

The evolution of R_C during programming suggests a two-step filament formation process: the initial formation of a narrow filament and its subsequent radial growth (or the subsequent formation of multiple filaments) [33]. The initial connection of the conducting filament corresponds to the drop of V_C at $t = t_1$. After that, the continued growth of the filament changes to a radial mode and the diameter of the filament is increased, manifesting as the gradual decrease of R_C between t_1 and t_W [33]. Since the filament growth is strongly dependent on the applied voltage (Section 4.1.1), the growth of the filament by controlling the CC (R_{load}), hence the cell resistance can be controlled and enable multilevel resistive-switching in ECM cells.

Similar effects have been observed in multilevel programming of *a*-Si-based RRAM devices [97]. In this study, multilevel programming is achieved by attaching a series resistor to the memory cell, so the voltage divider effect provides a feedback that reduces the voltage across the device after the filament is partially formed, and this significantly increases the wait time for the subsequent filament growth. As a result, the cell can be left in the intermediate ON states by adjusting the series resistor [97]. As displayed in Figure 22(a) eight different resistance values were obtained by applying identical programming pulses but with different series resistance, meaning that 3 bits of data can be stored in a single cell. Figure 22(b) further displays the

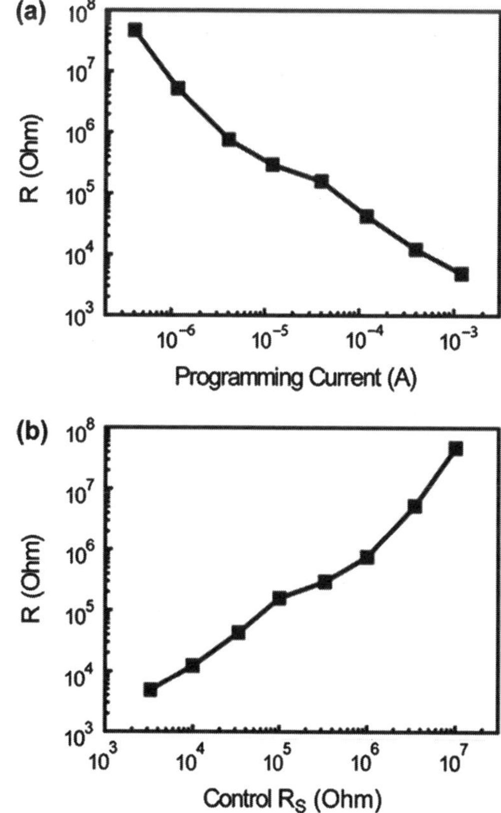

Figure 22. Multilevel resistive switching in *a*-Si-based RRAM. (a) The relationship between different ON resistance levels and the programming current, (b) correlation between the cell ON resistance and the series resistance. Reprinted with permission from [97], S. H. Jo et al., *Nano Lett.* 9, 496 (2009). © 2009, American Chemical Society.

direct correlation between the device resistance and the value of the series resistance, therefore highlighting the role of series resistance/CC in determining the final resistance of the device.

A different kind of multilevel resistive switching was reported in amorphous TaO_x thin films that are sandwiched between Cu and Pt electrodes. These devices have three stable resistance states:

(1) the HRS around 10^7–10^8 Ω,
(2) the LRS around 50 Ω, and
(3) another intermediate-resistance state (IRS) on the order of 10^4 Ω [157].

Multilevel resistive switching in the three states was attributed to a coupled mechanism [157]. Specifically, the switching between the HRS and the IRS seems to stem from the VCM between Ta_2O_5 and TaO_2 by redox reactions as interpreted in Section 4.2, while the LRS is induced by the further formation of Cu filaments inside the electrolyte. In view of the diversity of the various resistive-switching models, this type of device might serve as a model system for investigating the coupled effects between different switching mechanisms.

6. APPLICATIONS IN NONVOLATILE SRAM, ANALOG CIRCUITS, AND NEUROMORPHIC SYSTEMS

Beyond applications in high-density memory for mass data storage, resistive-switching devices have attracted interest in a broad range of applications such as nonvolatile SRAM [185, 186], reconfigurable logic, analog circuits, and neuromorphic systems.

A nonvolatile SRAM is expected to effectively reduce standby power consumption presently existing in conventional SRAM cells by storing the state information of SRAM in a pair of resistive-switching cells (Fig. 23), allowing the SRAM to be powered down during idling time to eliminate static power. When the SRAM cell needs to be accessed, the information can be obtained from the resistive-switching cells, therefore allowing nonvolatile operation. Proposed by Wang et al. in 2006 [185], this concept has been demonstrated in nonvolatile SRAM cells containing ZnCdS- [185] and Cu_xO-based [186] resistive-switching devices. Nonvolatile-SRAM based on a modified architecture employing metal-oxide-semiconductor field effect transistors and resistive-switching devices have also been recently demonstrated [187].

Resistive-switching cells can also be used as switchable interconnects in reconfigurable large-scale integration circuits such as field programmable gate arrays (FPGA) [77, 113, 188–191]. In such applications, the resistive devices are switched during the "programming" mode when voltages high enough are applied across them and remain unchanged during the "computing" mode when small signals are used for logic operations in the circuit. Compared with memory applications, higher programming/erasing threshold voltages are needed for devices in such applications in order to prevent unintentional switching during logic operations. For example, oxide solid electrolytes

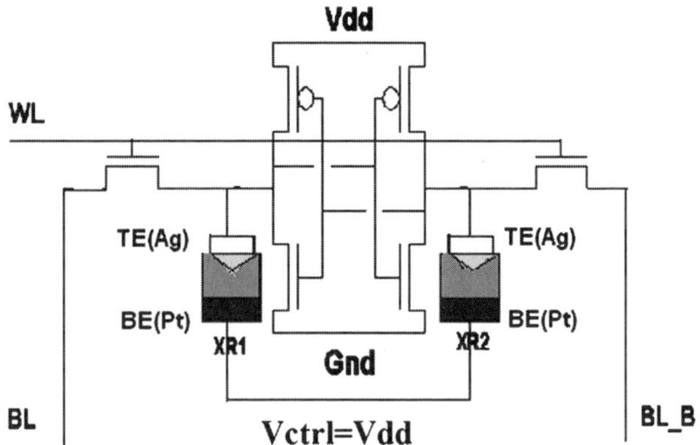

Figure 23. Nonvolatile SRAM cell structure. Reprinted with permission from [185], W. Wang et al., "International Electron Devices Meeting," p. 539 (2006). © 2006, IEEE.

with lower cation mobilities such as Ta_2O_5 were investigated for this purpose [77, 113]. Theoretical calculations on such FPGA circuits have predicted two orders of magnitude in improvements of the function density [189–191]. Recently, other circuit concepts, such as Boolean logic operations based on material implication, have also been demonstrated using resistive-switching devices [192].

Besides the classification of unipolar and bipolar switching discussed in Section 2, resistive switching can also be categorized into digital and analog type based on the width of the voltage window during which the device undergoes the ON–OFF transition. The digital-type devices with sharp switching (a narrow-switching window) normally possess promising attributes such as a large ON/OFF ratio, fast switching speed, high endurance, and long data retention, making them suitable for memory and reconfigurable logic applications. The analog-type devices with incremental resistive switching (a wide-switching window) could be used in analog circuits or hardware-based neuromorphic systems. Recently the analog devices have also been called memristors since their behaviors can be readily explained using Eqs. (1) and (2) (see Section 2). Similar to devices used in reconfigurable circuits, a two-mode operation is normally needed in circuits based on analog resistive-switching devices (memristors) with high non-linear characteristics. The cell states remain unchanged during the low-voltage logic operations (computing mode), while the cell states can be programmed during the high-voltage programming mode. Based on this concept, simulations of programmable analog circuits such as a threshold comparator, a gain amplifier, a switching threshold Schmitt trigger, and a frequency relaxation oscillator have been demonstrated using a memristor emulator [193].

In fact, an analog resistive-switching device (memristor) bears many resemblances with a synapse; they are both "two-terminal" resistive devices whose resistance can be incrementally modified by stimuli applied across them. Figures 24(a and b) show the concept of using a crossbar synapse network and CMOS-based neurons to emulate biologic systems in which every CMOS neuron in the pre-neuron layer is connected to every neuron in the post-neuron layer through a memristor synapse. In such an approach, a biologic system with high connectivity ($\sim 10^4$

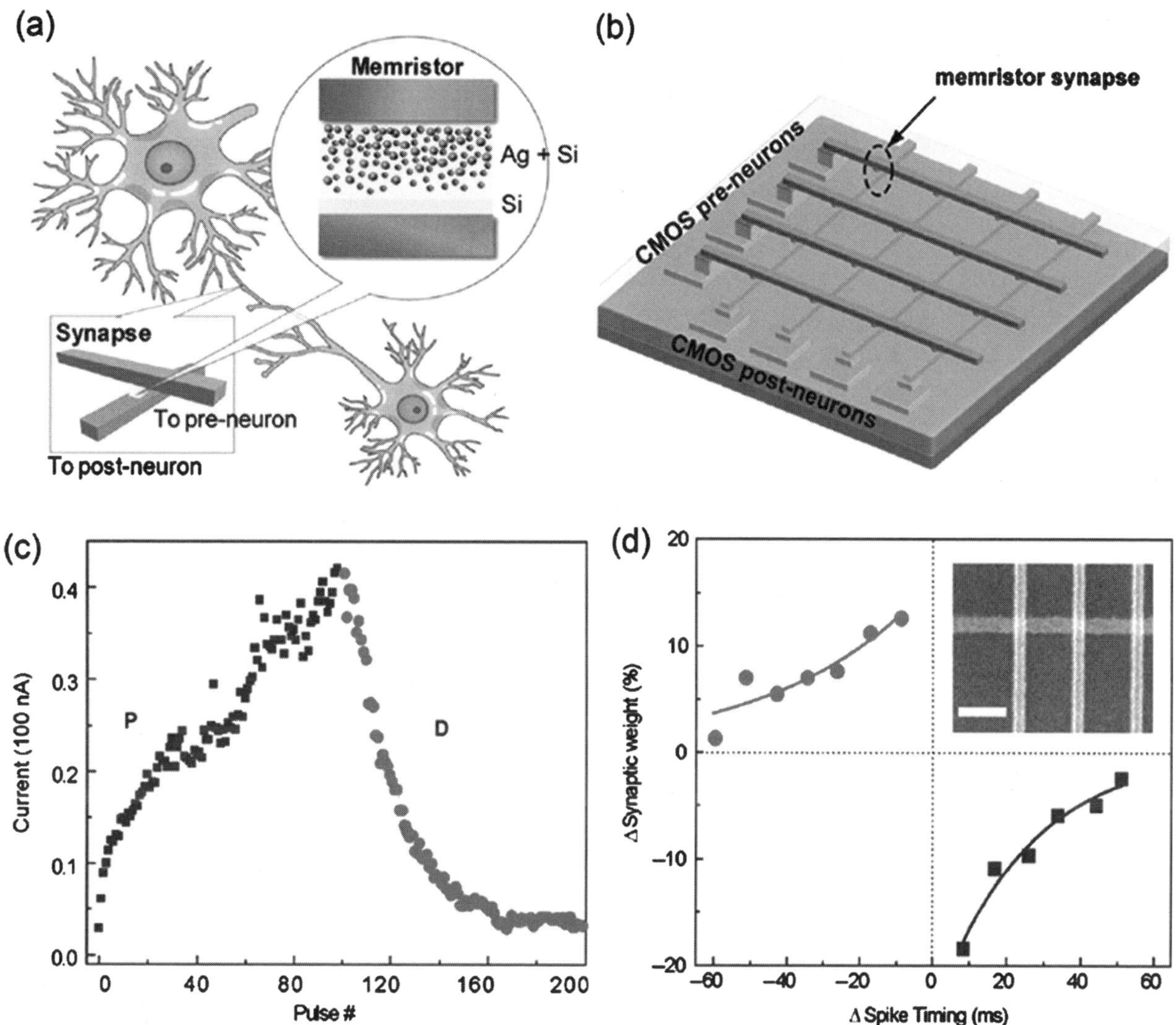

Figure 24. Neuromorphic systems employing c as synapse. (a) Schematic illustration of the concept. The inset shows the schematic of the memristor with co-sputtered Ag/Si active layer, (b) schematic of the hybrid system with CMOS neurons and memristor synapses in a crossbar structure, (c) incrementally modulated conductance of the memristor synapse by potentiating and depressing pulses, (d) change of the memristor synaptic weight as a function of the relative timing Δt of the CMOS neuron spikes, demonstrating STDP in the system. The inset shows a SEM image of a fabricated memristor crossbar array. Reprinted with permission from [143], S. H. Jo et al., *Nano Lett.* 10, 1297 (2010). © 2010, American Chemical Society.

synapses/neuron) and high density ($\sim 10^{10}$ synapses/cm^2) can be readily mapped into a hybrid memristor/CMOS circuit in a way that is impossible in CMOS-only circuits. In a recent demonstration of memristor-based neuromorphic circuits, the active layer of the memristor devices is composed of co-sputtered Ag/Si mixture with a semicontinuous Ag concentration gradient. The Ag redistribution, controlled by the applied voltage pulses, led to incremental conductance changes that are very similar to the behavior of biologic synapses [143]. Figure 24(c) shows the incremental adjustment of the conductance of the memristor synapse by a series of potentiating (3.2 V, 300 μs) and depressing (−2.8 V, 300 μs) pulses. Figure 24(d) further demonstrates that spike-timing-dependent-plasticity (STDP), an important synaptic modification rule for competitive Hebbian learning, can be achieved in the CMOS-neuron/memristor-synapse circuits [143]. In other studies, the formation of associative memory behavior has been simulated in a simple neural network using memristor emulators as electronic synapses [194]. These and further studies on memristor-based neuromorphic systems could one day serve as the building blocks for a new, different type of computer whose hardware resembles those of biologic systems and who can learn and adapt to carrying out challenging tasks in complex environments.

7. SCALING POTENTIAL, INTEGRATION, AND RELIABILITY

Compared with other candidates for high density memory, current research on RRAM devices has shown great scaling potential. For instance, a scalability down to sub-20 nm has been demonstrated in CBRAM arrays (Fig. 5) [20, 130], which already corresponds to a memory density as high as $> 10^{10}$ bit/cm^2. Essentially for all RRAM devices controlled by a filamentary mechanism, it is apparent that the scaling potential is ultimately determined by the minimum size of the conducting filaments. However, in practical devices the scaling limit should be at least two times of the minimum filament diameter in order to increase the cell stability and suppress crosstalk between cells [195]. Until now, microscopic studies have shown that the sizes of the filaments are on the nanoscale [23, 172, 175, 179], and conducting filaments with size as small as $\sim$10 nm were observed [172, 175]. Note that these numbers still may not represent the intrinsic limit of filaments due to measurement artifacts. Therefore, the scaling limit of RRAM devices is likely to be well below 20 nm and beyond that of present flash memory.

Among the candidate RRAM devices, filament-type devices such as ECM cells based on solid electrolytes might be the most maturely developed type at present. However, the cells need to further demonstrate their compatibility with conventional CMOS technologies. In particular, some of the ternary chalcogenide solid electrolytes such as Ag–Ge–Se have limited temperature tolerance for standard back-end-of-the-line CMOS integration. In this regard, oxide-based solid electrolytes such as SiO_2 or *a*-Si might be promising alternatives for the practical application of filament-type RRAM devices. For example, *a*-Si-based devices have shown high performance, high scalability, and excellent compatibility with the entrenched CMOS processes [21, 98]. Therefore, a relatively smooth integration of the *a*-Si based memory arrays with existing CMOS components could be expected. In addition, both digital- [21, 98] and analog-type [143] switching effects have been obtained in *a*-Si-based resistive-switching cells, making them promising not only in high-density memory arrays and logic switches but also in developing neuromorphic systems.

To achieve array-level integration, RRAM prototypes organized with one diode-one resistor ($1D$-$1R$) [26, 163] and $1T$-$1R$ [131, 134] structures have both been demonstrated. Compared with the $1T$-$1R$ matrix that employs active logic components at each cell, a passive crossbar matrix allows higher storage density, decoupling of the massive storage components from the (potentially much fewer) logic components to allow better scaling, and the ability to be stacked in a 3D fashion to allow even higher storage density. On the other hand, a pure passive crossbar array is vulnerable to undesirable sneak currents, thus a current steering/rectifying element with very high non-linear *I–V* characteristics such as a diode is needed in series with every memory cell. Both *p–n* diodes and Schottky diodes have been studied for this purpose. On the other hand, traditional silicon-based *p–n* diodes may not be the best candidate because of their high processing temperature, significant costs, and possible formation of silicide on a metal layer [166]. In a recent study, Lee et al. [196] prepared a low temperature NiO_x/TiO_x *p–n* diode with a high rectifying ratio of 10^5 at ± 3 V, a forward current density of $\sim 5 \times 10^3$ A cm^{-2}, and a turn-on voltage of 2 V. Although this oxide-based diode is fabricated at <300°C, its forward current density is still not high enough. Kang et al. [166] reported a room-temperature-grown amorphous $CuO_x/InZnO_x$ diode with a higher forward current density of 3.5×10^4 A cm^{-2} and a rectifying ratio of 10^6 at ± 2.45 V. Using this diode as the select element, NiO [26] and Al_2O_3 [163] resistive memories have been successfully integrated in the $1D$-$1R$ structure. In other studies, Schottky diodes such as Pt/TiO_2 have also been explored as the select element in $1D$-$1R$ memory arrays with an extremely high rectifying ratio of $\sim 10^9$ demonstrated at 1 V [197].

Nevertheless, it should be noted that the above-mentioned $1D$-$1R$ structure is only applicable to memory devices with unipolar switching characteristics that can only be switched ON or OFF by applying positive programming voltages so the serially-connected diode can remain forward-biased during programming/erasing. In order to solve the sneak path problem in bipolar switching systems, a complementary architecture by anti-serially connecting two resistive switches was proposed in which one of the switches is always kept in the OFF state to suppress unwanted leakage current [198]. On the other hand, the main disadvantage of this approach is its destructive read. However, the most elegant approach to address the sneak current problem for crossbar memory arrays based on bipolar resistive devices is probably finding devices with intrinsic nonlinear *I–V* characteristics so that current rectifying can be achieved without externally serially connected diodes. In this regard, the recent findings on intrinsic rectifying characteristics in *a*-Si-based RRAM devices are encouraging [21, 144], although investigations on the physical origin of this diode-like behavior and how effective it will be to suppress the sneak currents during high-speed programming pulses are still in progress.

The next level of integration beyond array demonstration is to build functional systems based on resistive-switching devices. Here, hybrid crossbar/CMOS architectures have emerged as the leading candidate since they combine the density advantages provided by the passive crossbar arrays with the reliability and flexibility of existing CMOS circuits [189, 190, 199]. A representative of the hybrid crossbar/CMOS approach is the so-called CMOS-molecule (CMOL) architecture that was first proposed by Likharev (Fig. 25) [189, 200]. In a CMOL circuit, two types of via-pins with different heights are used that connect the CMOS components to the top and bottom nanowire electrodes in the crossbar structure, respectively. The crossbar matrix on top of the CMOS circuit is rotated by an angle with respect to the CMOS layer so that each nanowire in the crossbar array could be accessed by exactly one CMOS cell, which allows the precise addressing of a particular crosspoint device in CMOL circuits (Fig. 25(b)) [189]. Due to the periodic nature of the crossbar arrays and CMOS cells, this concept does not require precise alignments [189, 190], and it allows a potentially very high density integration for memory [200], a reconfigurable circuit [189], and neuromorphic applications [201, 202].

Finally, the real commercial application potential for resistive-switching devices in the future will be determined not by the electrical performance in limited cells and time, but instead by the demonstration of large arrays with good cell-to-cell and long-term reliability [36, 203, 204]. Therefore, reliability issues in RRAM devices, such as the data retention, cell-to-cell uniformity, and cycle-to-cycle reproducibility, should be emphasized. Besides trying to improve cell performance through exhaustion of the parameter

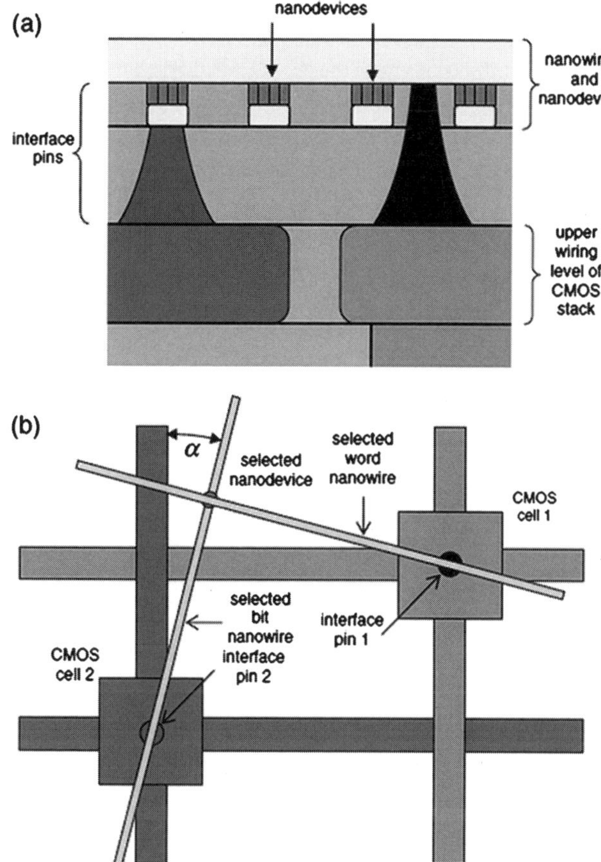

Figure 25. Schematic of the CMOL circuit with (a) side view, and (b) top view, highlighting the approach to address a specific crosspoint. Reprinted with permission from [189], D. B. Strukov and K. K. Likharev, *Nanotechnol.* 16, 888 (2005). © 2005, IOP Publishing Ltd.

space, it is also of crucial importance to understand how the devices function and fail and where the nonidealities come from in order to guide the device optimization and circuit applications.

8. SUMMARY AND OUTLOOK

We gave an overview of the resistive-switching phenomena in a range of amorphous materials including chalcogenide glasses, amorphous silicon and carbon, and amorphous oxides. The device level studies and small-scale demonstrations seem quite encouraging, with promising performance metrics such as switching speed of < 10 ns, high endurance of $> 10^{10}$, and long data retention. Different underlying mechanisms of resistive-switching effects have also been covered, including three types of filamentary models involving metal ions, oxygen vacancies, and secondary phases as the building blocks for local conducting filaments, respectively, as well as the VCM that focuses on changes at the dielectric/electrode interface. The rest of the discussions focused on multilevel resistive-switching effects in amorphous materials, the expanded applications of resistive devices, and reliability and integration issues that need to be addressed before the devices can be employed on a large scale.

Looking forward, we believe RRAM arrays based on amorphous films will have a bright future in memory applications with very high storage density, fast response, and low power consumption. Their employment in other applications such as reconfigurable circuits, analog circuits, or neuromorphic systems is also expected, mostly likely in the hybrid crossbar/CMOS form. In the meantime, certain issues such as reliability and sneak-path still remain to be addressed. Solving these problems may require a systematic attack involving system design, algorithm development, device engineering, material characterization, and optimization. The tasks are challenging, but the potential rewards will be significant and far-reaching for the semiconductor industry.

REFERENCES

1. G. I. Meijer, *Science* 319, 1625 (2008).
2. A. Chung, J. Deen, J. S. Lee, and M. Meyyappan, *Nanotechnol.* 21, 412001 (2010).
3. G. W. Burr, B. N. Kurdi, J. C. Scott, C. H. Lam, K. Gopalakrishnan, and R. S. Shenoy, *IBM J. Res. Dev.* 52, 449 (2008).
4. J. F. Scott and C. A. P. Dearaujo, *Science* 246, 1400 (1989).
5. B. H. Park, B. S. Kang, S. D. Bu, T. W. Noh, J. Lee, and W. Jo, *Nature* 401, 682 (1999).
6. P. Y. Chu, R. E. Jones, P. Zurcher, D. J. Taylor, B. Jiang, S. J. Gillespie, Y. T. Lii, M. Kottke, P. Fejes, and W. Chen, *J. Mater. Res.* 11, 1065 (1996).
7. D. Takashima and I. Kunishima, *IEEE J. Solid-St. Circ.* 33, 787 (1998).
8. K. Kim and S. Lee, *J. Appl. Phys.* 100, 051604 (2006).
9. J. C. S. Kools, *IEEE Trans. Magn.* 32, 3165 (1996).
10. S. S. P. Parkin, K. P. Roche, M. G. Samant, P. M. Rice, R. B. Beyers, R. E. Scheuerlein, E. J. O'Sullivan, S. L. Brown, J. Bucchigano, D. W. Abraham, Y. Lu, M. Rooks, P. L. Trouilloud, R. A. Wanner, and W. J. Gallagher, *J. Appl. Phys.* 85, 5828 (1999).
11. J. G. Zhu, Y. F. Zheng, and G. A. Prinz, *J. Appl. Phys.* 87, 6668 (2000).
12. S. Tehrani, J. M. Slaughter, M. Deherrera, B. N. Engel, N. D. Rizzo, J. Salter, M. Durlam, R. W. Dave, J. Janesky, B. Butcher, K. Smith, and G. Grynkewich, *Proc. IEEE* 91, 703 (2003).
13. S. M. Yoon, N. Y. Lee, S. O. Ryu, K. J. Choi, Y. S. Park, S. Y. Lee, B. G. Yu, M. J. Kang, S. Y. Choi, and M. Wuttig, *IEEE Electron Device Lett.* 27, 445 (2006).
14. D. J. Milliron, S. Raoux, R. Shelby, and J. Jordan-Sweet, *Nat. Mater.* 6, 352 (2007).
15. J. Hegedus and S. R. Elliott, *Nat. Mater.* 7, 399 (2008).
16. S. Raoux, G. W. Burr, M. J. Breitwisch, C. T. Rettner, Y. C. Chen, R. M. Shelby, M. Salinga, D. Krebs, S. H. Chen, H. L. Lung, and C. H. Lam, *IBM J. Res. Dev.* 52, 465 (2008).
17. R. Waser and M. Aono, *Nat. Mater.* 6, 833 (2007).
18. R. Waser, R. Dittmann, G. Staikov, and K. Szot, *Adv. Mater.* 21, 2632 (2009).
19. A. Sawa, *Mater. Today* 11, 28 (2008).
20. K. Aratani, K. Ohba, T. Mizuguchi, S. Yasuda, T. Shiimoto, T. Tsushima, T. Sone, K. Endo, A. Kouchiyama, S. Sasaki, A. Maesaka, N. Yamada, and H. Narisawa, "International Electron Devices Meeting," Washington, DC, 2007, p. 783.
21. S. H. Jo and W. Lu, *Nano Lett.* 8, 392 (2008).
22. C. Yoshida, K. Tsunoda, H. Noshiro, and Y. Sugiyama, *Appl. Phys. Lett.* 91, 223510 (2007).

23. Y. C. Yang, F. Pan, Q. Liu, M. Liu, and F. Zeng, *Nano Lett.* 9, 1636 (2009).
24. M. Fujimoto, H. Koyama, Y. Nishi, and T. Suzuki, *Appl. Phys. Lett.* 91, 223504 (2007).
25. S. L. Li, J. L. Gang, J. Li, H. F. Chu, and D. N. Zheng, *J. Phys. D: Appl. Phys.* 41, 185409 (2008).
26. M. J. Lee, S. I. Kim, C. B. Lee, H. X. Yin, S. E. Ahn, B. S. Kang, K. H. Kim, J. C. Park, C. J. Kim, I. Song, S. W. Kim, G. Stefanovich, J. H. Lee, S. J. Chung, Y. H. Kim, and Y. Park, *Adv. Funct. Mater.* 19, 1587 (2009).
27. T. W. Hickmott, *J. Appl. Phys.* 33, 2669 (1962).
28. M. N. Kozicki, M. Park, and M. Mitkova, *IEEE Trans. Nanotechnol.* 4, 331 (2005).
29. L. Chen, Z. G. Liu, Y. D. Xia, K. B. Yin, L. G. Gao, and J. Yin, *Appl. Phys. Lett.* 94, 162112 (2009).
30. C. Schindler, I. Valov, and R. Waser, *Phys. Chem. Chem. Phys.* 11, 5974 (2009).
31. M. N. Kozicki, M. Balakrishnan, C. Gopalan, C. Ratnakumar, and M. Mitkova, "Proceedings of Non-Volatile Memory Technology Symposium," p. 83, Dallas, TX, 2005.
32. M. Mitkova, M. N. Kozicki, H. C. Kim, and T. L. Alford, *Thin Solid Films* 449, 248 (2004).
33. U. Russo, D. Kamalanathan, D. Ielmini, A. L. Lacaita, and M. N. Kozicki, *IEEE Trans. Electron Dev.* 56, 1040 (2009).
34. S. J. Lee, S. G. Yoon, K. J. Choi, S. O. Ryq, S. M. Yoon, N. Y. Lee, and B. G. Yu, *J. Vac. Sci. Technol. B* 24, 2312 (2006).
35. C. J. Kim, S. G. Yoon, K. J. Choi, S. O. Ryu, S. M. Yoon, N. Y. Lee, and B. G. Yu, *J. Vac. Sci. Technol. B* 24, 721 (2006).
36. R. Soni, P. Meuffels, H. Kohlstedt, C. Kugeler, and R. Waser, *Appl. Phys. Lett.* 94, 123503 (2009).
37. R. Soni, P. Meuffels, A. Petraru, M. Weides, C. Kugeler, R. Waser, and H. Kohlstedt, *J. Appl. Phys.* 107, 024517 (2010).
38. Y. Hirose and H. Hirose, *J. Appl. Phys.* 47, 2767 (1976).
39. C. H. Liang, K. Terabe, T. Hasegawa, and M. Aono, *Nanotechnol.* 18, 485202 (2007).
40. Z. M. Liao, C. Hou, Q. Zhao, D. S. Wang, Y. D. Li, and D. P. Yu, *Small* 5, 2377 (2009).
41. B. Yang, H. X. Guo, K. B. Yin, Y. D. Xia, L. Chen, J. Yin, and Z. G. Liu, *J. Electroceram.* 22, 87 (2009).
42. J. R. Zhang and J. Yin, "Second IEEE International Nanoelectronics Conference," Vol. 1–3, pp. 1020, Mitaka, Japan, 2008.
43. T. Sakamoto, H. Sunamura, H. Kawaura, T. Hasegawa, T. Nakayama, and M. Aono, *Appl. Phys. Lett.* 82, 3032 (2003).
44. D. T. Schoen, C. Xie, and Y. Cui, *J. Am. Chem. Soc.* 129, 4116 (2007).
45. K. M. Kim, B. J. Choi, B. W. Koo, S. Choi, D. S. Jeong, and C. S. Hwang, *Electrochem. Solid-State Lett.* 9, G343 (2006).
46. C. Y. Lin, C. Y. Wu, C. Y. Wu, C. Hu, and T. Y. Tseng, *J. Electrochem. Soc.* 154, G189 (2007).
47. C. Schindler, S. C. P. Thermadam, R. Waser, and M. N. Kozicki, *IEEE Trans. Electron Dev.* 54, 2762 (2007).
48. C. Schindler, M. Weides, M. N. Kozicki, and R. Waser, *Appl. Phys. Lett.* 92, 122910 (2008).
49. B. J. Choi, D. S. Jeong, S. K. Kim, C. Rohde, S. Choi, J. H. Oh, H. J. Kim, C. S. Hwang, K. Szot, R. Waser, B. Reichenberg, and S. Tiedke, *J. Appl. Phys.* 98, 033715 (2005).
50. C. Rohde, B. J. Choi, D. S. Jeong, S. Choi, J. S. Zhao, and C. S. Hwang, *Appl. Phys. Lett.* 86, 262907 (2005).
51. K. M. Kim, B. J. Choi, Y. C. Shin, S. Choi, and C. S. Hwang, *Appl. Phys. Lett.* 91, 012907 (2007).
52. M. Fujimoto, H. Koyama, M. Konagai, Y. Hosoi, K. Ishihara, S. Ohnishi, and N. Awaya, *Appl. Phys. Lett.* 89, 223509 (2006).
53. S. Seo, M. J. Lee, D. H. Seo, E. J. Jeoung, D. S. Suh, Y. S. Joung, I. K. Yoo, I. R. Hwang, S. H. Kim, I. S. Byun, J. S. Kim, J. S. Choi, and B. H. Park, *Appl. Phys. Lett.* 85, 5655 (2004).
54. D. C. Kim, S. Seo, S. E. Ahn, D. S. Suh, M. J. Lee, B. H. Park, I. K. Yoo, I. G. Baek, H. J. Kim, E. K. Yim, J. E. Lee, S. O. Park, H. S. Kim, U. I. Chung, J. T. Moon, and B. I. Ryu, *Appl. Phys. Lett.* 88, 202102 (2006).
55. D. C. Kim, M. J. Lee, S. E. Ahn, S. Seo, J. C. Park, I. K. Yoo, I. G. Baek, H. J. Kim, E. K. Yim, J. E. Lee, S. O. Park, H. S. Kim, U. I. Chung, J. T. Moon, and B. I. Ryu, *Appl. Phys. Lett.* 88, 232106 (2006).
56. U. Russo, D. Ielmini, C. Cagli, and A. L. Lacaita, *IEEE Trans. Electron Dev.* 56, 186 (2009).
57. S. Spiga, A. Lamperti, C. Wiemer, M. Perego, E. Cianci, G. Tallarida, H. L. Lu, M. Alia, F. G. Volpe, and M. Fanciulli, *Microelectron. Eng.* 85, 2414 (2008).
58. Y. C. Yang, F. Pan, F. Zeng, and M. Liu, *J. Appl. Phys.* 106, 123705 (2009).
59. Y. C. Yang, F. Pan, and F. Zeng, *New J. Phys.* 12, 023008 (2010).
60. W. Y. Chang, Y. C. Lai, T. B. Wu, S. F. Wang, F. Chen, and M. J. Tsai, *Appl. Phys. Lett.* 92, 022110 (2008).
61. Q. Liu, S. B. Long, W. Wang, Q. Y. Zuo, S. Zhang, J. N. Chen, and M. Liu, *IEEE Electron Device Lett.* 30, 1335 (2009).
62. W. H. Guan, S. B. Long, Q. Liu, M. Liu, and W. Wang, *IEEE Electron Device Lett.* 29, 434 (2008).
63. C. Y. Lin, C. Y. Wu, T. Y. Tseng, and C. M. Hu, *J. Appl. Phys.* 102, 094101 (2007).
64. C. Y. Lin, C. Y. Wu, T. C. Lee, F. L. Yang, C. Hu, and T. Y. Tseng, *IEEE Electron Device Lett.* 28, 366 (2007).
65. H. Y. Lee, P. S. Chen, T. Y. Wu, Y. S. Chen, C. C. Wang, P. J. Tzeng, C. H. Lin, F. Chen, C. H. Lien, and M. J. Tsai, "International Electron Devices Meeting," San Francisco, CA, 2008, p. 297.
66. S. Lee, W. G. Kim, S. W. Rhee, and K. Yong, *J. Electrochem. Soc.* 155, H92 (2008).
67. M. Y. Chan, T. Zhang, V. Ho, and P. S. Lee, *Microelectron. Eng.* 85, 2420 (2008).
68. L. Tang, P. Zhou, Y. R. Chen, L. Y. Chen, H. B. Lv, T. A. Tang, and Y. Y. Lin, *J. Korean Phys. Soc.* 53, 2283 (2008).
69. P. Zhou, H. B. Lv, M. Yin, L. Tang, Y. L. Song, T. A. Tang, Y. Y. Lin, A. Bao, A. Wu, S. Cai, H. Wu, C. Liang, and M. H. Chi, *J. Vac. Sci. Technol. B* 26, 1030 (2008).
70. M. Yin, P. Zhou, H. B. Lv, T. A. Tang, B. A. Chen, Y. Y. Lin, A. Bao, and M. H. Cui, "Ninth International Conference on Solid-State and Integrated-Circuit Technology," Beijing, China, 2008, Vol. 1–4, p. 917.
71. D. Lee, D. J. Seong, I. Jo, F. Xiang, R. Dong, S. Oh, and H. Hwang, *Appl. Phys. Lett.* 90, 122104 (2007).
72. X. Sun, B. Sun, L. F. Liu, N. Xu, X. Y. Liu, R. Q. Han, J. F. Kang, G. C. Xiong, and T. P. Ma, *IEEE Electron Device Lett.* 30, 334 (2009).
73. L. F. Liu, X. Sun, B. Sun, J. F. Kang, Y. Wang, X. Y. Liu, R. Q. Han, and G. C. Xiong, "IEEE International Memory Workshop," Monterey, CA, 2009, p. 9.
74. S. Zhang, S. B. Long, W. H. Guan, Q. Liu, Q. Wang, and M. Liu, *J. Phys. D: Appl. Phys.* 42, 055112 (2009).
75. M. K. Yang, J. W. Park, T. K. Ko, and J. K. Lee, *Appl. Phys. Lett.* 95, 042105 (2009).
76. Z. Wei, Y. Kanzawa, K. Arita, Y. Katoh, K. Kawai, S. Muraoka, S. Mitani, S. Fujii, K. Katayama, M. Iijima, T. Mikawa, T. Ninomiya, R. Miyanaga, Y. Kawashima, K. Tsuji, A. Himeno, T. Okada, R. Azuma, K. Shimakawa, H. Sugaya, I. Takagi, R. Yasuhara, K. Horiba, H. Kumigashira, and M. Oshima, "International Electron Devices Meeting," San Francisco, CA, 2008, p. 293.
77. N. Banno, T. Sakamoto, N. Iguchi, H. Sunamura, K. Terabe, T. Hasegawa, and M. Aono, *IEEE Trans. Electron Dev.* 55, 3283 (2008).
78. W. C. Chien, Y. C. Chen, E. K. Lai, Y. D. Yao, P. Lin, S. F. Horng, J. Gong, T. H. Chou, H. M. Lin, M. N. Chang, Y. H. Shih,

K. Y. Hsieh, R. Liu, and C. Y. Lu, *IEEE Electron Device Lett*. 31, 126 (2010).

79. E. K. Lai, W. C. Chien, Y. C. Chen, T. J. Hong, Y. Y. Lin, K. P. Chang, Y. D. Yao, P. Lin, S. F. Horng, J. Gong, S. C. Tsai, C. H. Lee, S. H. Hsieh, C. F. Chen, Y. H. Shih, K. Y. Hsieh, R. Liu, and C. Y. Lu, *Jpn. J. Appl. Phys*. 49, 04DD17 (2010).
80. Y. T. Lu, S. B. Long, Q. Liu, Q. Wang, M. H. Zhang, H. B. Lv, L. B. Shao, Y. Wang, S. Zhang, Q. Y. Zuo, S. Liu, and M. Liu, *Phys. Stat. Sol. (RRL)* 4, 124 (2010).
81. I. H. Inoue, S. Yasuda, H. Akinaga, and H. Takagi, *Phys. Rev. B* 77, 035105 (2008).
82. Z. Q. Wang, X. H. Li, H. Y. Xu, W. Wang, H. Yu, X. T. Zhang, Y. X. Liu, and Y. C. Liu, *J. Phys. D: Appl. Phys*. 43, 385105 (2010).
83. H. Shima, F. Takano, H. Muramatsu, H. Akinaga, Y. Tamai, I. H. Inoue, and H. Takagi, *Appl. Phys. Lett*. 93, 113504 (2008).
84. X. Gao, Y. D. Xia, B. Xu, J. Z. Kong, H. X. Guo, K. Li, H. T. Li, H. N. Xu, K. Chen, J. A. Yin, and Z. G. Liu, *J. Appl. Phys*. 108, 74506 (2010).
85. N. G. Subramaniam, J. C. Lee, and T. W. Kang, *Appl. Phys. Lett*. 87, 212907 (2005).
86. C. Y. Liu, P. H. Wu, A. Wang, W. Y. Jang, J. C. Young, K. Y. Chiu, and T. Y. Tseng, *IEEE Electron Device Lett*. 26, 351 (2005).
87. C. C. Lin, B. C. Tu, C. H. Lin, and T. Y. Tseng, *IEEE Electron Device Lett*. 27, 725 (2006).
88. J. W. Park, *J. Appl. Phys*. 99, 124102 (2006).
89. K. Szot, W. Speier, G. Bihlmayer, and R. Waser, *Nat. Mater*. 5, 312 (2006).
90. M. Janousch, G. I. Meijer, U. Staub, B. Delley, S. F. Karg, and B. P. Andreasson, *Adv. Mater*. 19, 2232 (2007).
91. Y. Watanabe, J. G. Bednorz, A. Bietsch, C. Gerber, D. Widmer, A. Beck, and S. J. Wind, *Appl. Phys. Lett*. 78, 3738 (2001).
92. S. F. Alvarado, F. La Mattina, and J. G. Bednorz, *Appl. Phys. A—Mater. Sci. Process*. 89, 85 (2007).
93. K. Shibuya, R. Dittmann, S. B. Mi, and R. Waser, *Adv. Mater*. 22, 411 (2010).
94. S. Q. Liu, N. J. Wu, and A. Ignatiev, *Appl. Phys. Lett*. 76, 2749 (2000).
95. D. S. Shang, Q. Wang, L. D. Chen, R. Dong, X. M. Li, and W. Q. Zhang, *Phys. Rev. B* 73, 245427 (2006).
96. T. Zhang, H. J. Chen, M. M. Ni, Z. H. Su, and W. F. Zhang, *J. Appl. Phys*. 105, 083708 (2009).
97. S. H. Jo, K. H. Kim, and W. Lu, *Nano Lett*. 9, 496 (2009).
98. S. H. Jo, K. H. Kim, and W. Lu, *Nano Lett*. 9, 870 (2009).
99. M. Jafar and D. Haneman, *Phys. Rev. B* 49, 13611 (1994).
100. F. Kreupl, R. Bruchhaus, P. Majewski, J. B. Philipp, R. Symanczyk, T. Happ, C. Arndt, M. Vogt, R. Zimmermann, A. Buerke, A. P. Graham, and M. Kund, "International Electron Devices Meeting," San Francisco, CA, 2008, p. 521.
101. M. Pyun, H. Choi, J. B. Park, D. Lee, M. Hasan, R. Dong, S. J. Jung, J. Lee, D. J. Seong, J. Yoon, and H. Hwang, *Appl. Phys. Lett*. 93, 212907 (2008).
102. F. Zhuge, W. Dai, C. L. He, A. Y. Wang, Y. W. Liu, M. Li, Y. H. Wu, P. Cui, and R. W. Li, *Appl. Phys. Lett*. 96, 163505 (2010).
103. J. C. Scott and L. D. Bozano, *Adv. Mater*. 19, 1452 (2007).
104. Y. Yang, J. Ouyang, L. P. Ma, R. J. H. Tseng, and C. W. Chu, *Adv. Funct. Mater*. 16, 1001 (2006).
105. U. Russo, D. Ielmini, C. Cagli, A. L. Lacaita, S. Spiga, C. Wiemer, M. Perego, and M. Fanciulli, "International Electron Devices Meeting," Washington, DC, 2007, p. 775.
106. L. M. Chen, T. Y. Lin, C. C. Chang, S. C. Chang, and T. S. Chin, *Thin Solid Films* 518, 7352 (2010).
107. J. Song, A. I. Inamdar, B. Jang, K. Jeon, Y. Kim, K. Jung, H. Im, W. Jung, H. Kim, and J. P. Hong, *Appl. Phys. Express* 3, 091101 (2010).
108. S. Kim and Y. K. Choi, *Appl. Phys. Lett*. 92, 223508 (2008).
109. W. Zhu, T. P. Chen, Z. Liu, M. Yang, Y. Liu, and S. Fung, *J. Appl. Phys*. 106, 093706 (2009).
110. S. M. Yu, B. Gao, H. B. Dai, B. Sun, L. F. Liu, X. Y. Liu, R. Q. Han, J. F. Kang, and B. Yu, *Electrochem. Solid-State Lett*. 13, H36 (2010).
111. M. Hasan, R. Dong, H. J. Choi, D. S. Lee, D. J. Seong, M. B. Pyun, and H. Hwang, *Appl. Phys. Lett*. 92, 202102 (2008).
112. L. Chen, Y. Xu, Q. Q. Sun, H. Liu, J. J. Gu, S. J. Ding, and D. W. Zhang, *IEEE Electron Device Lett*. 31, 356 (2010).
113. T. Sakamoto, K. Lister, N. Banno, T. Hasegawa, K. Terabe, and M. Aono, *Appl. Phys. Lett*. 91, 092110 (2007).
114. D. S. Jeong, H. Schroeder, and R. Waser, *Electrochem. Solid-State Lett*. 10, G51 (2007).
115. L. Goux, J. G. Lisoni, M. Jurczak, D. J. Wouters, L. Courtade, and C. Muller, *J. Appl. Phys*. 107, 024512 (2010).
116. S. Lee, H. Kim, J. Park, and K. Yong, *J. Appl. Phys*. 108, 76101 (2010).
117. L. O. Chua, *IEEE Trans. Circuit Theory* 18, 507 (1971).
118. L. O. Chua and S. M. Kang, *Proc. IEEE* 64, 209 (1976).
119. D. B. Strukov, G. S. Snider, D. R. Stewart, and R. S. Williams, *Nature* 453, 80 (2008).
120. D. B. Strukov, J. L. Borghetti, and R. S. Williams, *Small* 5, 1058 (2009).
121. T. Chang, S. H. Jo, K. H. Kim, P. Sheridan, S. Gaba, and W. Lu, *Appl. Phys. A – Mater. Sci. Process*. 102, 857 (2011).
122. H. Y. Jeong, J. Y. Lee, and S. Y. Choi, *Appl. Phys. Lett*. 97, 042109 (2010).
123. J. Kawamura, N. Kuwata, and T. Tanji, *Comp. Sys*. 982, 135 (2008).
124. C. Schindler, K. Szot, S. Karthauser, and R. Waser, *Phys. Stat. Sol. (RRL)* 2, 129 (2008).
125. M. N. Kozicki, M. Mitkova, M. Park, M. Balakrishnan, and C. Gopalan, *Superlattices Microstruct*. 34, 459 (2003).
126. D. Brauhaus, C. Schindler, U. Bottger, and R. Waser, *Thin Solid Films* 516, 1223 (2008).
127. L. Chen, Q. C. Li, H. X. Guo, L. G. Gao, Y. D. Xia, J. Yin, and Z. G. Liu, *Appl. Phys. Lett*. 95, 242106 (2009).
128. L. Chen, H. X. Guo, Y. D. Xia, J. Yin, and Z. G. Liu, *Appl. Phys. A—Mater. Sci. Process*. 100, 309 (2010).
129. H. Choi, K. H. Nam, Y. W. Koo, and H. B. Chung, *J. Electroceram*. 23, 322 (2009).
130. M. Kund, G. Beitel, C. U. Pinnow, T. Rohr, J. Schumann, R. Symanczyk, K. D. Ufert, and G. Muller, "International Electron Devices Meeting," Washington, DC, 2005, p. 773.
131. S. Dietrich, M. Angerbauer, M. Ivanov, D. Gogl, H. Hoenigschmid, M. Kund, C. Liaw, M. Markert, R. Symanczyk, L. Altimime, S. Bournat, and G. Mueller, *IEEE J. Solid-St. Circ*. 42, 839 (2007).
132. S. J. Lee, S. G. Yoon, K. J. Choi, S. O. Ryu, S. M. Yoon, N. Y. Lee, and B. G. Yu, *Electrochem. Solid-State Lett*. 9, G364 (2006).
133. M. N. Kozicki, C. Gopalan, M. Balakrishnan, M. Park, and M. Mitkova, "Proceedings of Non-Volatile Memory Technology Symposium," Orlando, FL, 2004, p. 10.
134. P. Schrögmeier, M. Angerbauer, S. Dietrich, M. Ivanov, H. Hönigschmid, C. Liaw, M. Markert, R. Symanczyk, L. Altimime, S. Bournat, and G. Müller, "Proceeding of the IEEE Symposium on VLSI Circuits," Kyoto, Japan, 2007, p. 186.
135. M. Sakurai, F. Kakinuma, E. Matsubara, and K. Suzuki, *J. Non-Cryst. Solids* 312–314, 585 (2002).
136. S. K. Dey, *J. Vac. Sci. Technol*. 17, 445 (1980).
137. W. den Boer, *Appl. Phys. Lett*. 40, 812 (1982).
138. A. E. Owen, P. G. Lecomber, J. Hajto, M. J. Rose, and A. J. Snell, *Int. J. Electron*. 73, 897 (1992).
139. M. Jafar and D. Haneman, *Phys. Rev. B* 49, 4605 (1994).
140. A. Avila and R. Asomoza, *Solid-State Electron*. 44, 17 (2000).
141. J. Hu, H. M. Branz, R. S. Crandall, S. Ward, and Q. Wang, *Thin Solid Films* 430, 249 (2003).
142. H. K. Charles and C. Feldman, *J. Appl. Phys*. 46, 819 (1975).
143. S. H. Jo, T. Chang, I. Ebong, B. B. Bhadviya, P. Mazumder, and W. Lu, *Nano Lett*. 10, 1297 (2010).

144. K. H. Kim, S. H. Jo, S. Gaba, and W. Lu, *Appl. Phys. Lett.* 96, 053106 (2010).
145. X. M. Guan, Y. He, L. A. Zhao, J. Y. Zhang, Y. Wang, H. Qian, and Z. P. Yu, "International Electron Devices Meeting," Baltimore, MD, p. 845, 2009.
146. Y. Pauleau, F. Thiery, V. V. Uglov, A. K. Kuleshov, S. N. Dub, and M. P. Samtsov, *Rev. Adv. Mater. Sci.* 4, 139 (2003).
147. J. Imahori, T. Oku, and M. Murakami, *Thin Solid Films* 301, 142 (1997).
148. H. Choi, M. Pyun, T. W. Kim, M. Hasan, R. Dong, J. Lee, J. B. Park, J. Yoon, D. J. Seong, T. Lee, and H. Hwang, *IEEE Electron Device Lett.* 30, 302 (2009).
149. J. Y. Huang, S. Chen, Z. F. Ren, G. Chen, and M. S. Dresselhaus, *Nano Lett.* 6, 1699 (2006).
150. D. S. Jeong, H. Schroeder, and R. Waser, *Appl. Phys. Lett.* 89, 082909 (2006).
151. Y. B. Nian, J. Strozier, N. J. Wu, X. Chen, and A. Ignatiev, *Phys. Rev. Lett.* 98, 146403 (2007).
152. J. J. Yang, M. D. Pickett, X. M. Li, D. A. A. Ohlberg, D. R. Stewart, and R. S. Williams, *Nat. Nanotechnol.* 3, 429 (2008).
153. J. Yao, Z. Z. Sun, L. Zhong, D. Natelson, and J. M. Tour, *Nano Lett.* 10, 4105 (2010).
154. H. Y. Jeong, J. Y. Lee, M. K. Ryu, and S. Y. Choi, *Phys. Stat. Sol. (RRL)* 4, 28 (2010).
155. Y. Li, G. Y. Zhao, X. F. Zhou, L. N. Pan, and Y. Ren, *J. Sol–Gel Sci. Technol.* 56, 61 (2010).
156. C. Y. Lin, D. Y. Lee, S. Y. Wang, C. C. Lin, and T. Y. Tseng, *Surf. Coat. Technol.* 203, 628 (2008).
157. Y. C. Yang, C. Chen, F. Zeng, and F. Pan, *J. Appl. Phys.* 107, 093701 (2010).
158. M. N. Kozicki, C. Gopalan, M. Balakrishnan, and M. Mitkova, *IEEE Trans. Nanotechnol.* 5, 535 (2006).
159. J. Choi, J. Song, K. Jung, Y. Kim, H. Im, W. Jung, H. Kim, Y. H. Do, J. S. Kwak, and J. Hong, *Nanotechnol.* 20, 175704 (2009).
160. M. Fujimoto, H. Koyama, S. Kobayashi, Y. Tamai, N. Awaya, Y. Nishi, and T. Suzuki, *Appl. Phys. Lett.* 89, 243504 (2006).
161. K. Tsunoda, Y. Fukuzumi, J. R. Jameson, Z. Wang, P. B. Griffin, and Y. Nishi, *Appl. Phys. Lett.* 90, 113501 (2007).
162. Y. R. Chen, W. Tian, H. Li, X. B. Wang, and W. Z. Zhu, *IEEE Electron Device Lett.* 31, 866 (2010).
163. S. E. Ahn, B. S. Kang, K. H. Kim, M. J. Lee, C. B. Lee, G. Stefanovich, C. J. Kim, and Y. Park, *IEEE Electron Device Lett.* 30, 550 (2009).
164. C. Schindler, G. Staikov, and R. Waser, *Appl. Phys. Lett.* 94, 072109 (2009).
165. J. J. Yang, M. X. Zhang, J. P. Strachan, F. Miao, M. Pickett, R. D. Kelley, G. Medeiros-Ribeiro, and R. S. Williams, *Appl. Phys. Lett.* 97, 232102 (2010).
166. B. S. Kang, S. E. Ahn, M. J. Lee, G. Steftinovich, K. H. Kim, W. X. Xianyu, C. B. Lee, Y. Park, I. G. Baek, and B. H. Park, *Adv. Mater.* 20, 3066 (2008).
167. M. J. Rozenberg, I. H. Inoue, and M. J. Sanchez, *Phys. Rev. Lett.* 92, 178302 (2004).
168. A. Asamitsu, Y. Tomioka, H. Kuwahara, and Y. Tokura, *Nature* 388, 50 (1997).
169. G. I. Meijer, U. Staub, M. Janousch, S. L. Johnson, B. Delley, and T. Neisius, *Phys. Rev. B* 72, 155102 (2005).
170. R. Fors, S. I. Khartsev, and A. M. Grishin, *Phys. Rev. B* 71, 045305 (2005).
171. J. Y. Son and Y. H. Shin, *Appl. Phys. Lett.* 92, 222106 (2008).
172. D. H. Kwon, K. M. Kim, J. H. Jang, J. M. Jeon, M. H. Lee, G. H. Kim, X. S. Li, G. S. Park, B. Lee, S. Han, M. Kim, and C. S. Hwang, *Nat. Nanotechnol.* 5, 148 (2010).
173. J. W. Seo, S. J. Baik, S. J. Kang, Y. H. Hong, J. H. Yang, L. Fang, and K. S. Lim, *Appl. Phys. Lett.* 96, 053504 (2010).
174. K. Terabe, T. Hasegawa, T. Nakayama, and M. Aono, *Nature* 433, 47 (2005).
175. C. P. Hsiung, H. W. Liao, J. Y. Gan, T. B. Wu, J. C. Hwang, F. Chen, and M. J. Tsai, *ACS Nano* 4, 5414 (2010).
176. K. Szot, R. Dittmann, W. Speier, and R. Waser, *Phys. Stat. Sol. (RRL)* 1, R86 (2007).
177. S. C. Chae, J. S. Lee, S. Kim, S. B. Lee, S. H. Chang, C. Liu, B. Kahng, H. Shin, D. W. Kim, C. U. Jung, S. Seo, M. J. Lee, and T. W. Noh, *Adv. Mater.* 20, 1154 (2008).
178. R. Munstermann, J. J. Yang, J. P. Strachan, G. Medeiros-Ribeiro, R. Dittmann, and R. Waser, *Phys. Stat. Sol. (RRL)* 4, 16 (2010).
179. Z. Xu, Y. Bando, W. L. Wang, X. D. Bai, and D. Golberg, *ACS Nano* 4, 2515 (2010).
180. Q. Liu, S. Long, H. Lv, W. Wang, J. Niu, Z. Huo, J. Chen, and M. Liu, *ACS Nano* 4, 6162 (2010).
181. J. P. Strachan, M. D. Pickett, J. J. Yang, S. Aloni, A. L. D. Kilcoyne, G. Medeiros-Ribeiro, and R. S. Williams, *Adv. Mater.* 22, 3573 (2010).
182. Y. C. Yang, B. Fan, F. Zeng, and F. Pan, *J. Nanosci. Nanotechnol.* 10, 7370 (2010).
183. J. J. Yang, F. Miao, M. D. Pickett, D. A. A. Ohlberg, D. R. Stewart, C. N. Lau, and R. S. Williams, *Nanotechnol.* 21, 339803 (2010).
184. A. Odagawa, Y. Katoh, Y. Kanzawa, Z. Wei, T. Mikawa, S. Muraoka, and T. Takagi, *Appl. Phys. Lett.* 91, 133503 (2007).
185. W. Wang, A. Gibby, Z. Wang, T. W. Chen, S. Fujita, P. Griffin, Y. Nishi, and S. Wong, "International Electron Devices Meeting," San Francisco, CA, 2006, p. 539.
186. X. Y. Xue, G. Jin, J. Zhang, L. Xu, Y. Q. Ding, Y. F. Xie, C. H. Zhao, B. A. Chen, and Y. Y. Lin, "Ninth International Conference on Solid-State and Integrated-Circuit Technology," Beijing, China, Vol. 1–4, p. 869.
187. S. Yamamoto, Y. Shuto, and S. Sugahara, *Jpn. J. Appl. Phys.* 49, 040209 (2010).
188. S. Kaeriyama, T. Sakamoto, H. Sunamura, M. Mizuno, H. Kawaura, T. Hasegawa, K. Terabe, T. Nakayama, and M. Aono, *IEEE J. Solid-St. Circ.* 40, 168 (2005).
189. D. B. Strukov and K. K. Likharev, *Nanotechnol.* 16, 888 (2005).
190. K. K. Likharev, *J. Nanoelectron. Optoelectron.* 3, 203 (2008).
191. G. S. Snider and R. S. Williams, *Nanotechnol.* 18, 035204 (2007).
192. J. Borghetti, G. S. Snider, P. J. Kuekes, J. J. Yang, D. R. Stewart, and R. S. Williams, *Nature* 464, 873 (2010).
193. Y. V. Pershin and M. Di Ventra, *IEEE Trans. Circ. Syst. I, Reg. Papers* 57, 1857 (2010).
194. Y. V. Pershin and M. Di Ventra, *Neural Networks* 23, 881 (2010).
195. R. Waser, R. Dittmann, M. Salinga, and M. Wuttig, *Int. J. Mater. Res.* 101, 182 (2010).
196. M. J. Lee, S. Seo, D. C. Kim, S. E. Ahn, D. H. Seo, I. K. Yoo, I. G. Baek, D. S. Kim, I. S. Byun, S. H. Kim, I. R. Hwang, J. S. Kim, S. H. Jeon, and B. H. Park, *Adv. Mater.* 19, 73 (2007).
197. W. Y. Park, G. H. Kim, J. Y. Seok, K. M. Kim, S. J. Song, M. H. Lee, and C. S. Hwang, *Nanotechnol.* 21, 195201 (2010).
198. E. Linn, R. Rosezin, C. Kugeler, and R. Waser, *Nat. Mater.* 9, 403 (2010).
199. W. Lu and C. M. Lieber, *Nat. Mater.* 6, 841 (2007).
200. D. B. Strukov and K. K. Likharev, *Nanotechnol.* 16, 137 (2005).
201. Ö. Türel, J. H. Lee, X. Ma, and K. K. Likharev, *Int. J. Circuit Theory App.* 32, 277 (2004).
202. Ö. Türel, J. H. Lee, X. Ma, and K. K. Likharev, *Neurocomputing* 64, 271 (2005).
203. R. Oligschlaeger, R. Waser, R. Meyer, S. Karthauser, and R. Dittmann, *Appl. Phys. Lett.* 88, 042901 (2006).
204. A. Demolliens, C. Muller, D. Deleruyelle, S. Spiga, E. Cianci, M. Fanciulli, F. Nardi, C. Cagli, and D. Ielmini, "IEEE International Memory Workshop," Monterey, CA, 2009, p. 25.

CHAPTER 8

Overview of Metal-Oxide Resistive Memory

ChiaHua Ho, Fu-Liang Yang
National Nano Device Laboratories (NDL), Hsinchu City 300, Taiwan

CONTENTS

1. INTRODUCTION

Colossal magneto resistance (CMR) material has been studied for use in highly sensitive and nonvolatile memories or sensors [1]. Unlike purely metallic giant magnetoresistance structures that are composed of periods of alternated ferromagnetic/nonferromagnetic multilayers, such as Ruderman–Kittel–Kasuya–Yosida-based multilayers [2] or spin-valve structures [3], and purely direct tunneling based tunneling magnetoresistance systems composed of magnetic tunnel junctions [4], CMR functionality comes from a perovskite structured single film material with manganese-oxide, such as $La_xCa_{1-x}MnO_3$ [5] and $La_xSr_{1-x}MnO_3$ [6]. The resistance of CMR material can be sensitively switched by an external magnetic field (Fig. 1). Charge-ordering between Mn^{3+} and Mn^{4+} by an external magnetic field causes a double-exchange interaction that changes the film resistance. This can be well examined by the Jahn-Teller effect [7].

In earlier literature, Liu et al. [8] reported an unexpected room-temperature resistance switching effect by electric-pulse-induced reversible in another type of CMR material, $Pr_{0.7}Ca_{0.3}MnO_3$ thin film. $Pr_{1-x}Ca_xMnO_3$ with $x = 0.3\sim0.5$ is, however, a paramagnetically insulated phase of which the ferromagnetic Curie temperature is lower than room temperature. Instead of conventional CMR operation methodologies, the resistance of $Pr_{0.7}Ca_{0.3}MnO_3$ thin film can be switched with a ratio of higher than 1700% by an external electrical pulse with a pulse width of 100 ns at room temperature, without the application of a magnetic field. Furthermore, this resistance switching phenomena is reversible, nonvolatile, and reproducible (Fig. 2). A positive electrical pulse can switch the film resistance from the high resistance state (HRS) to the low resistance state (LRS), and a negative electrical pulse can return the state from LRS to HRS. This so-called bipolar resistance-switching mode will be described in Section 2.2. Due to the low ferromagnetic Curie temperature and lack of a magnetic field, the reported nonvolatility of $Pr_{0.7}Ca_{0.3}MnO_3$ thin film cannot be well examined by current magnetism theory. On the other hand, this kind of film stack was applied to a 1 transistor plus 1 resistor (1T-1R) test circuit and also achieved reproducible resistance-cycle result successfully [9] (Fig. 3) by a programming pulse of less than 5 V and a pulse width as narrow as 10 ns. Such nonvolatile memory is called resistance random access memory (RRAM or ReRAM).

Regarding the resistance-switching phenomena of initially insulated materials controlled by many kinds of electrical field stressing, including current-sweep (CS) control, voltage-sweep (VS) control, and the electrical pulse, resistance bi-stability was formerly referred to as current-control-negative-resistance (CCNR) phenomena in the early

ISBN: 1-58883-251-1

Nonvolatile Memories: Materials, Devices and Applications
Edited by Tseung-Yuen Tseng and Simon M. Sze
Volume 2: Pages: 185–224

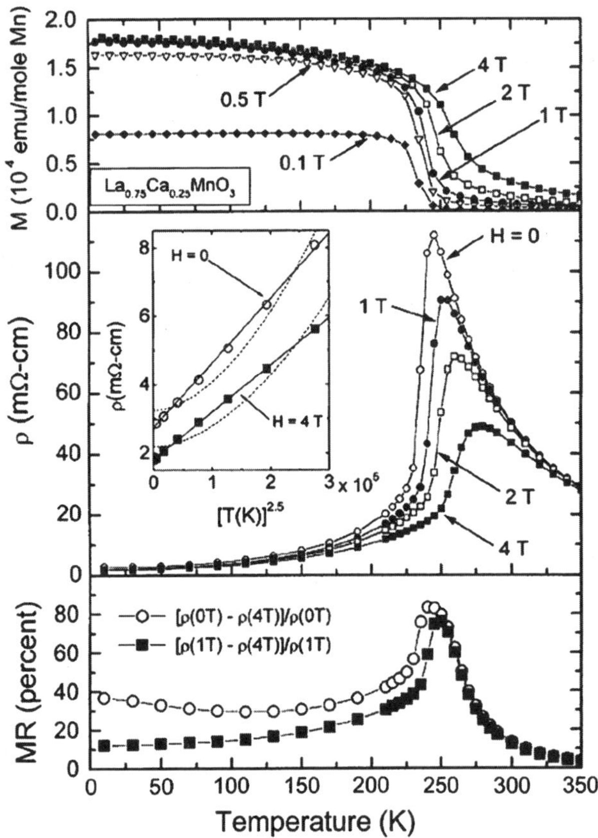

Figure 1. Top: magnetization versus temperature (M–T curve) of one CMR material, $La_{0.75}Ca_{0.25}MnO_3$, with various magnetic fields; middle, resistivity versus temperature with various fields; bottom, magnetoresistance (MR) versus temperature. Reprinted with permission from [1], A. P. Ramirez, *J. Phys. Condens. Matter* 9, 8171 (1997). © 1997, Institute of Physics.

literature on Nb–Nb_2O_5-metal structured diodes in 1965 (Fig. 4) [10, 11]. The influence of CS and VS controlling on resistance switching characteristics will be described in Section 2.1. In Figure 4, the diode structure is broken down

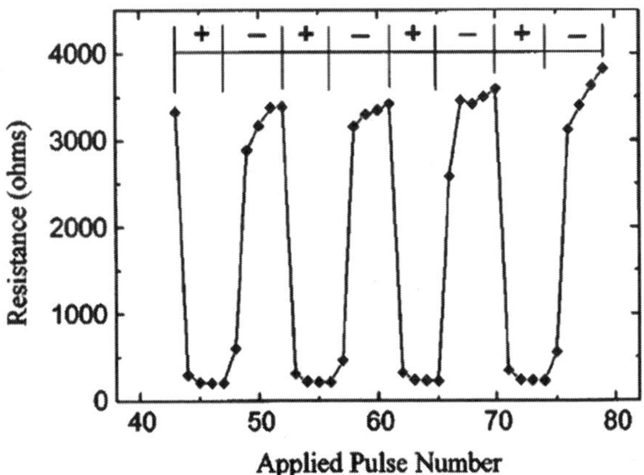

Figure 2. The pulse number dependent steady state resistance of a PrCaMnO/YBaCuO thin film sample. The + and – represent change in the applied pulse polarity. Reprinted with permission from [8], S. Q. Liu et al., *Appl. Phys. Lett.* 76, 2749 (2000). © 2000, American Institute of Physics.

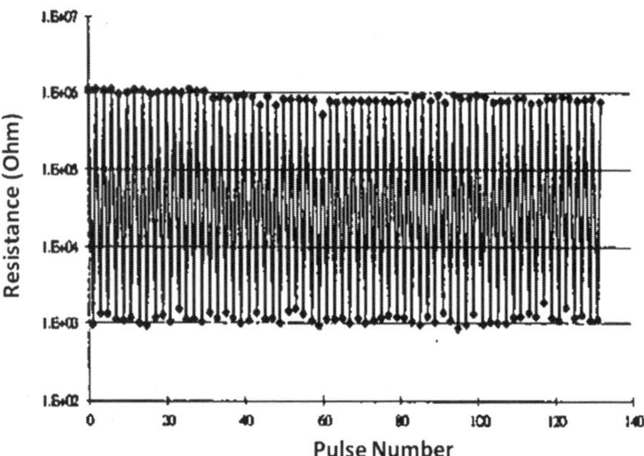

Figure 3. The cycle performance of PCMO CMR memory resistor by electrical pulse driving. Reprinted with permission from [9], W. W. Zhuangl et al., "IEEE International Electron Devices Meeting (IEDM) Technical Digest," p. 193, San Francisco, CA, 2002. © 2002, The Institute of Electrical and Electronics Engineers (IEEE).

in the beginning to obtain a high conductance state, i.e., the LRS revealed in curve "a". When the applied current or voltage alternates the polarity, curve "b", the resistance of this diode structure shows a sudden switching behavior to the low conductance state, i.e., the HRS at around −0.4 V. If a positive current or voltage is further applied to this diode structure, the HRS is switched again to a LRS, revealed by curve "c". Both resistances, HRS and LRS, are stable and nonvolatile. A similar CCNR effect was also found for the Nb–Nb_2O_5–Bi [10] and Nb–Nb_2O_5–Au [11] structured diode, implying that the niobium-oxide breakdown plays a dominant role in the CCNR effect.

Beside niobium-oxide, in 1970, a stoichiometric polycrystalline nickel-oxide (NiO) thin film was found to exhibit negative resistance, with resistance-switching behavior at room temperature and also without a magnetic field [12]. Because the antiferromagnetic Néel temperature of NiO is much lower than room temperature, as in $Pr_{0.7}Ca_{0.3}MnO_3$ thin film, this resistance alternation cannot be described by current magnetism theory. The initially low-conductive state of NiO film can be changed to a highly conductive state under a strong electrical field of 3×10^4 V/cm^2. The resistance ratio under alternation even reaches three orders of magnitude. In addition, the electrical resistivity of the LRS monotonically increases with temperature, indicating that the LRS behaves "metallically." The formation of metallic nickel filaments and rupturing are discussed in the prior figure.

Thus far, many metal oxides have been observed to have resistance-switching behaviors in response to electric stress. These are presented in the periodic table shown in Figure 5. Elements marked with bold-frame exhibit resistance bi-stability that can be controlled by electric stress. Some are controlled by bipolar operation (Fig. 4). Others are controlled by unipolar operation, in which both LRS and HRS states can be obtained by voltage stresses with the same electric polarity (see Section 2.3). Still others exhibit both bipolar and unipolar operations, the so-called nonpolar operation. Since most of the metallic elements with

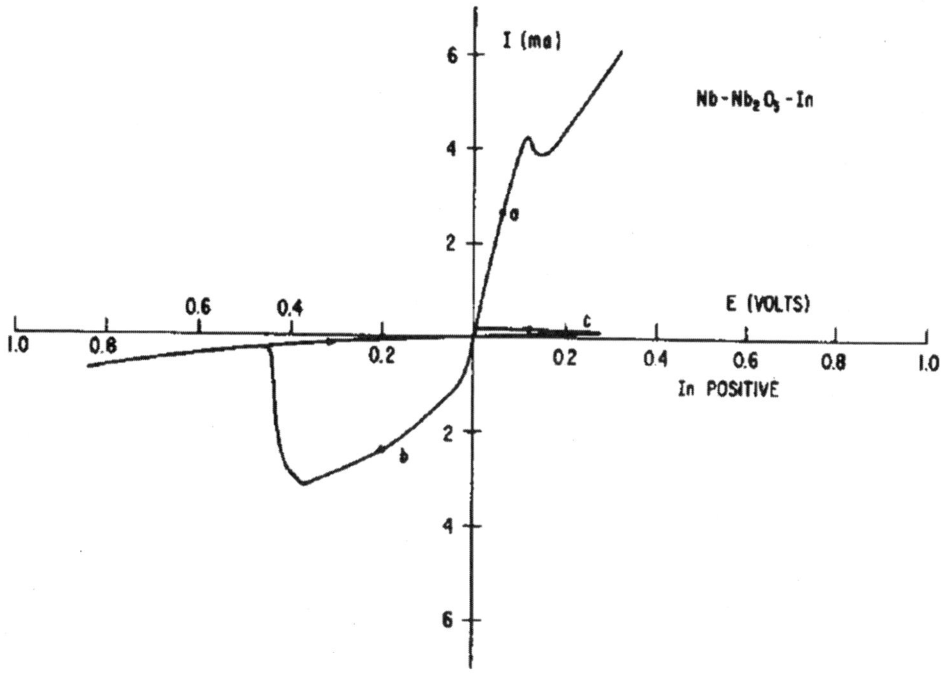

Figure 4. The CCNR induced resistance bi-stability of an Nb–Nb_2O_5–In diode. Oxide thickness is 1250 Å. Reprinted with permission from [10], W. R. Hiatt and T. W. Hickmott, *Appl. Phys. Lett.* 6, 106 (1965). © 1965, American Institute of Physics.

resistance-bistability switching (Fig. 5) are transition metals, resistance memories based on these transition metal oxides are called transition-metal-oxide RRAM (TMO-RRAM or TMO-ReRAM) or binary TMO-RRAM (BTMO-RRAM or BMO-RRAM). As shown in Figure 5, some elements of TMO-RRAM are fully compatible with complementary metal–oxide–semiconductor (CMOS), such as titanium (Ti), zirconium (Zr), hafnium (Hf), tantalum (Ta), tungsten (W), cobalt (Co), nickel (Ni), aluminum (Al), and copper (Cu). TMO-RRAM has recently been extensively studied due to its superior characteristics, namely simple structure, high density, fast operation speed, and low power. More details about TMO-RRAM are provided in Section 2.

The physical effects, such as the anode and cathode electrode, ion-doping, vertical and horizontal dimensions, on TMO-RRAM are described in detail in Sections 2.1–2.3. Accordingly, some conduction transport mechanisms and resistance-switching models of resistive memory have been proposed in recent years to thoroughly examine such a complex system.

Another branch of RRAM is based on the electrical voltage or current stress control of a programmable metallization formation and destruction in certain solid-state electrolytes. It has been variously called conductive-bridging RAM (CBRAM), ionic memory, programmable metallization cell, solid-state electrolyte memory, or nanobridge [13]. Metallic elements such as Cu, Ag, or Zn with a highly migrated mobility in certain solid-state electrolytes, e.g., metal sulfides [14, 15], metallic or semiconductor oxides [16–19], or Ge-based chalcogenides [20, 21], are extensively studied in CBRAM research. Figure 6 shows a typical direct-current (DC) voltage double sweeping effect on resistance of one CBRAM structure, W/GeSe/Ag, with a size of 850 nm [22]. The resistance can be suddenly dropped by around six orders of magnitude from the initial HRS at a critical voltage of 240 mV. This LRS remains in a stable state if the applied voltage is removed. Furthermore, this LRS can be switched back to the HRS by a voltage stress with the opposite polarity of around 100 mV. The switching behavior is similar to a bipolar operation, such as that of the Nb–Nb_2O_5–In diode in Figure 4. The formation and destruction of the programmable Ag-based conductive bridge in GeSe by applied voltage stress makes CBRAM one of the most promising nonvolatile new memory candidates.

2. RESISTANCE-SWITCHING MODES OF RESISTIVE MEMORY

2.1. Forming Process

The forming process is an initially dominant key factor in most RRAM systems, including TMO-RRAMs, perovskite insulating memories, polymer-based memories, and some of CBRAMs, although it is just a transient process during RRAM operation. A good and fine-tuned "forming process" can help to prevent the degradation of the cycle endurance in the active region from damage and also help the resistance ON/OFF ratio. Figure 7 [23] is a typical forming process current–voltage (I–V) curve (light-gray curve) of one TMO-RRAM device based on VS control, an HfO_2 active region with Ti electrode. The current compliance (CC) is set to 1 μA by the semiconductor parameter analyzer (SPA) to avoid an uncontrollable and irreversible low resistance state due to complicated conducting filaments (CF) formation in the active region. The concept of CF will be described later.

As compared with the low Reset voltage of around −2 V (the sharp reset curve, resistance transition from the LRS

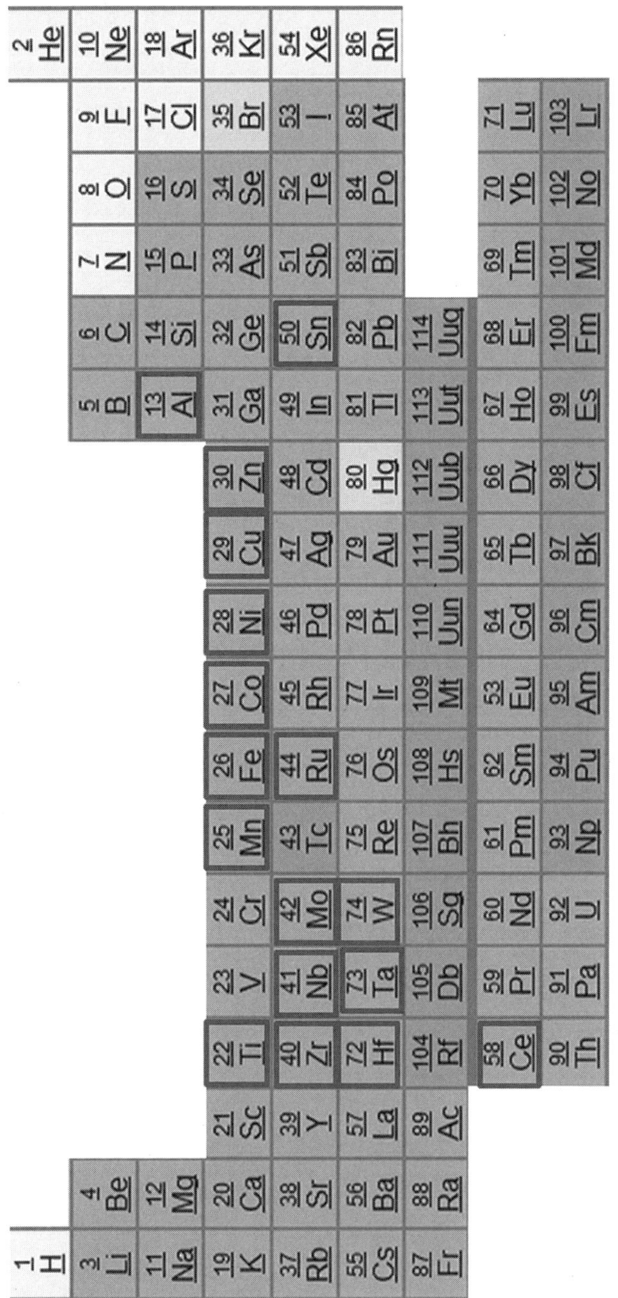

Figure 5. Elements (marked by bold-frame) for which metal oxides were found to exhibit resistance bi-stability controlled by bipolar and/or unipolar electric stress.

to HRS), the forming process, unfortunately, needs a relatively high voltage, reaching 12 V, to switch the resistance of the TMO-RRAM memory device from the initially HRS to the LRS. However, this highly applied voltage for the forming process (forming voltage) is a burden for circuit design and testing [24]. Meanwhile, a high-forming voltage means many accumulated charges will flow in the CFs when reaching a critical formation weak point, causing an abnormally high first Reset current [25]. To lower the forming voltage or eliminate it, i.e., forming free, is an important task in the RRAM field.

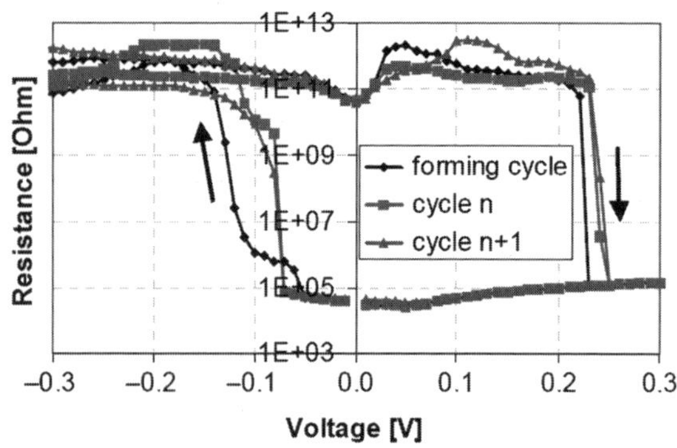

Figure 6. DC voltage sweeping effect on the resistance of the CBRAM structure, W/GeSe/Ag, of 850-nm size at room temperature. Reprinted with permission from [22], M. Kund et al., "IEEE International Electron Devices Meeting (IEDM) Technical Digest," p. 754, Washington DC, 2005. © 2005, The Institute of Electrical and Electronics Engineers (IEEE).

Physically, the forming process is a breakdown [26] or soft-breakdown process of the insulating material. The degree of breakdown level by CC (Fig. 7) can determine how low the LRS resistance of an RRAM device is. From recent literature, especially for the TMO-RRAM system, there are seven key intrinsic parameters that seriously affect the forming voltage amplitude and even the uniformity of performance of the forming voltage:

(1) the thickness of the active region of the RRAM device [24, 27–34];
(2) the dielectric constant of the active region of the RRAM device [33, 35];
(3) the cell size of the RRAM device [24, 27–31, 36–38];
(4) additional doping with a lower valence value [39–46];
(5) the material of the surrounding environment [36–38];

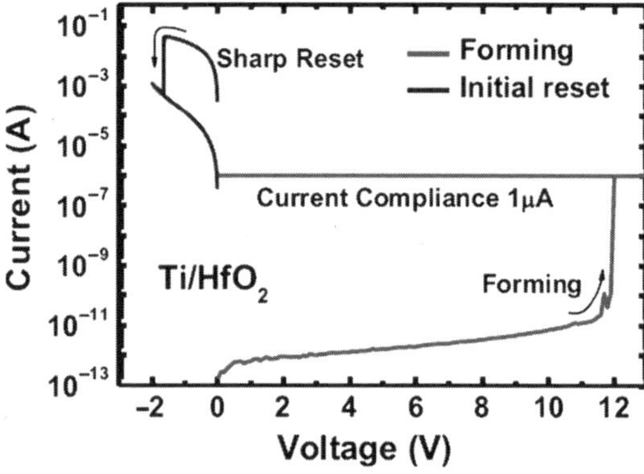

Figure 7. A typical forming process I–V curve of one TMO-RRAM device, an HfO_2 active region with a Ti electrode based on the voltage-sweep (V-S) operation. Large voltage and small compliance current are applied. The reset programming curve shows rather large initial reset current. Reprinted with permission from [23], B. Gao et al., "Proceedings of IEEE International Symposium on VLSI Technology Systems and Applications (VLSI-TSA)," p. 144, Hsinchu, Taiwan, 2010. © 2010, The Institute of Electrical and Electronics Engineers (IEEE).

(6) the material of the anode and cathode electrode [25, 31, 47]; and
(7) the density of oxygen vacancy in the active region (the stoichiometric effect) of the RRAM device [48–50].

On the other hand, for perovskite-insulating memory and polymer-based memory, which is a much more complex system (e.g., in composition and structure) than binary TMO-RRAM, the environmental processing can easily influence the forming voltage [51–54]. More information collected from experimentation and theory can help to organize a clear picture. For CBRAM [13, 55], because of cations provided by an oxidizable electrode, such as Ag or Cu, migrate through the electrolyte material by external electric field, the forming process in most CBRAM systems can be eliminated. For example, a metal-insulator-metal (MIM)-structured CBRAM system, Au/ZrO_2/Ag [55], was found to be operating forming-free because of the highly diffusive coefficient of Ag cations in the ZrO_2 electrolyte.

Except in the above internal intrinsic parameters, some external methodologies can also successfully reduce damage to the device caused in the forming process by unexpected current peaks. One example is using a CS-controlled forming process, rather than VS control [23, 26, 56–58]; another example is a degraded gate-voltage, V_G, of a 1T-1R structure during the forming process [59]. Here, we would like to probe the details of seven intrinsic parameters and two external methodologies for decreasing damage to an RRAM system during the forming process.

2.1.1. Internal Physical Parameters of Forming Voltage

2.1.1.1. Effect of the Active Region Thickness on Forming Voltage. Figure 8 shows a typical diagram of the thickness dependent-forming voltage of one TMO-RRAM system: an MIM-structured TiN/Ti/HfO_x/TiN device. As depicted, forming voltage decreases monotonically from 6 V to 2 V as the thickness of the active region decreases from 20 nm to 5 nm. According to Ref. [29], a forming-free operation can be successfully achieved by continuously thinning down the active region (HfO_x) thickness to below 3 nm.

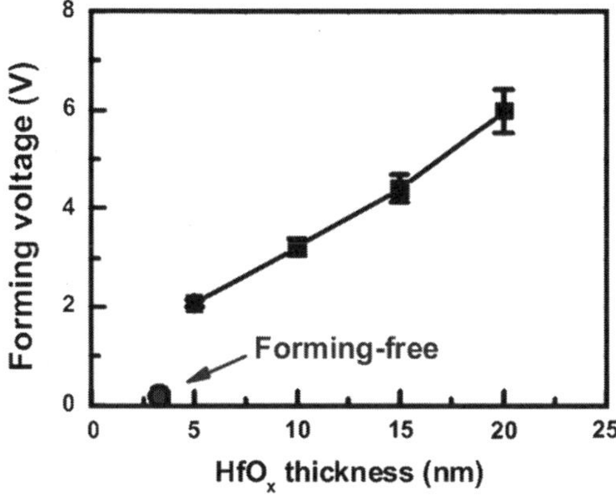

Figure 8. Example of an active region (HfO_x) thickness effect on forming the voltage of one binary TMO-RRAM: a TiN/Ti/HfO_x/TiN device. The forming voltage shows a monotonic decrease with active region thickness. A very thin active region can achieve free-forming operation. Reprinted with permission from [29], C. H. Lien et al., "Proceedings of the 10th IEEE International Conference on Solid-State and Integrated Circuit Technology (ICSICT)," p. 1084, Shanghai, China, 2010. © 2010, The Institute of Electrical and Electronics Engineers (IEEE).

Similar characteristics were also found in several TMO-RRAM systems, such as the hybrid bilayer atomic-layer-deposited HfO_x and sputtering deposited ZrO_x [31], an MIM-structured Pt/NiO/Pt [32], a radio-frequency reactive sputtered MIM-structured TiO_2 system [33], and a hetero-structured AlO_x/TiO_x bilayer system [34]. The dependence of the thickness of the active region on the forming voltage statistically lies between a linearly proportional and exponentially proportional relationship, and it depends on the initial transport mechanism before the forming process. For example, a preforming stated metal-insulator-semiconductor structure with an *e*-beam evaporated NiO thick film on a heavily *n*-doped Si-substrate has Pool-Frankel (PF) emission behavior [58], so the forming voltage, i.e., the breakdown voltage, follows the thickness dependent PF transport. On the other hand, the exponentially proportional dependence of the forming voltage on the active region thickness occurs in the hetero-structured AlO_x/TiO_x bilayers because the electron transportation in AlO_x follows Fowler-Nordheim tunneling in the high electric field region [34].

2.1.1.2. Dielectric Constant Effect of the Active Region on Forming Voltage. Figure 9 shows that the soft-breakdown electric field, i.e., it is proportional to the forming voltage for a constant active region thickness, is dependent on the dielectric constant (ε) of the TMO active region. Accordingly, lower forming voltage can be obtained in a TMO-RRAM system with a higher dielectric constant. In Figure 9, all data points approach the universal line, which describes the strong correlation of the forming voltage

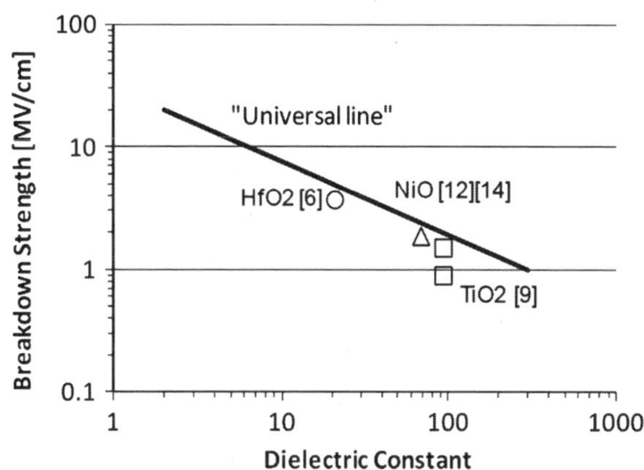

Figure 9. Example of an active region dielectric constant effect on the forming voltage of a binary TMO-RRAM. Reprinted with permission from [33], K. Hosotani et al., "Proceedings of the IEEE International Integrated Reliability Workshop (IRW) Final Report," p. 11, South Lake Tahoe, CA, 2009. © 2009, The Institute of Electrical and Electronics Engineers (IEEE).

with the dielectric constant and has the following relationship [33]:

$$V_{\text{Forming}} \propto \sqrt{1/\varepsilon} \tag{1}$$

2.1.1.3. Effect of Device Cell Size on the Forming Voltage. Figure 10 shows the effect of device cell size on the forming voltage of MIM-stacked TiN/HfO_x/ZrO_x/Pt with recessed via profile [31]. The thickness of HfO_x is 4 nm. Inconsistent forming voltage in Figures 8 and 10 might be due to (1) a different dielectric constant (discussed in Subsection 2.1.1.2 of Section 2.1.1), and (2) a stoichiometric effect (discussed in Subsection 2.1.1.7 of Section 2.1.1). A monotonically increased forming voltage with a decreasing cell size of the TMO device is obviously found. For device scaling down to 50 nm, the forming voltage is further increased to around 2.8 V. Similar characteristics were also found in amorphous hafnium-silicate thin-film [27], a MIM-structured TiN/Ti/HfO_x/TiN with recessed and pillar profiles [30, 36, 37], and self-aligned electrical-field-enhanced W/WO_x/TiN MIM stacks [38]. The device cell size depends on the forming voltage, thus it can be examined by an empirical model as [12]:

$$\beta \ln\left(\frac{V_{\text{BD}}}{V_0}\right) = -\ln\left(\frac{A}{A_0}\right) \tag{2}$$

where β is the Weibull parameter, V_{BD} is the breakdown voltage, indicating the forming voltage, A is the device cell size; V_0 is a reference breakdown voltage; and A_0 is a reference for the device cell size. The reduction of defects (e.g., kinds of oxygen vacancy and ions) and shrinking the device cell size is believed to be the reason for Figure 10 and Eq. (2).

Unfortunately, from Eq. (2), the forming voltage ($\sim V_{\text{BD}}$) trend is logarithmically proportional to the device area (A), which is opposite to the device scaling-down law. Advanced knobs for scaling the forming voltage of RRAM devices should be further investigated.

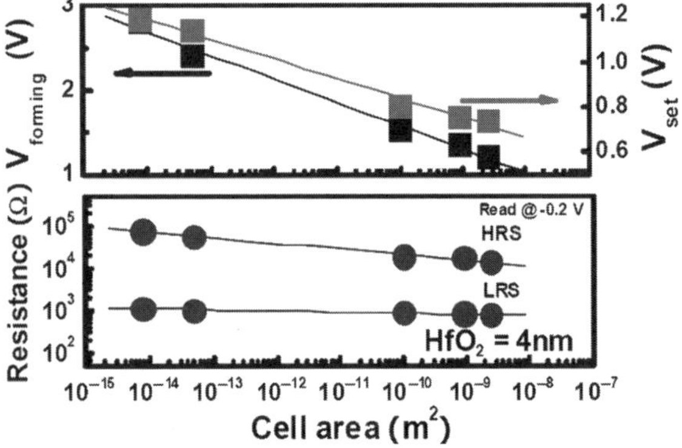

Figure 10. The forming voltage with respect to device cell size from a large dimension to 50-nm wide. Reprinted with permission from [31], J. Lee et al., "IEEE International Electron Devices Meeting (IEDM) Technical Digest," p. 452, San Francisco, CA, 2010. © 2010, The Institute of Electrical and Electronics Engineers (IEEE).

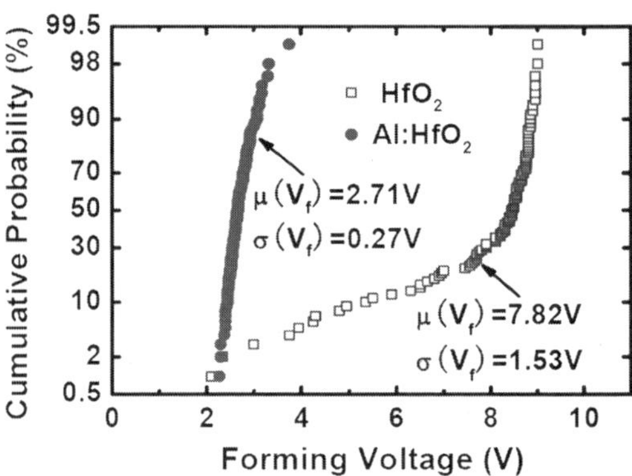

Figure 11. Cumulative probability of the forming voltage difference between two active regions, pure HfO_x and Al doped HfO_x. Both the forming voltage level and the uniformity can be improved by additional Al doping. Reprinted with permission from [43], B. Gao et al., "IEEE Symposium on VLSI Technology Digest of Technical Papers," p. 30, Kyoto, Japan, 2009. © 2009, The Institute of Electrical and Electronics Engineers (IEEE).

2.1.1.4. Additional Doping for the Forming Voltage. The effect of ionic doping into the active region of a TMO-RRAM device has been widely studied because it can help us understand the transition mechanism between the initially insulated states to the LRS. Figure 11 shows the cumulative probability of the forming voltage difference between two kinds of active materials, pure HfO_x and Al doped HfO_x [43]. Obviously, Al doping in the HfO_x TMO matrix can successfully improve not only the forming voltage amplitude but also the forming voltage uniformity. To date, a series of experiments and theories have been published according to this similar concept on topics such as Al-doped NiO [39], Ti-doped NiO [44], Al-doped TiO_x [40], Ti-doped ZrO_2 [41], Al-doped ZrO_2 [46], Al/La/Ga-doped HfO_2 and ZrO_2-[43], and Ti/La/Al-doped HfO_2, and ZrO_2 [45]. Based on these experimental and theoretical results, the effect of metallic ion doping in the TMO matrix on the forming voltage can be summarized in Table 1. Here, "O" means that the effect of metallic ion doping is positive for scaling the forming voltage or lowering the formation energy; Δ means the metallic ion doping effect is not clear. In order to clarify the doping effect in more detail, a monoclinic ZrO_2 supercell of 96 atoms is built for calculation (Fig. 12) [46]. The formation energy $E_f(X^Q)$ of neutral and charged oxygen vacancy, V_O, is a function of the electron chemical potential and can be described as:

$$E_f(X^Q) = E_{\text{total}}(V_o^Q) - E_{\text{total}}(\text{bulk}) + Q(\varepsilon_f + \varepsilon_v + \Delta V) + \mu_o \tag{3}$$

where $E_{\text{total}}(V_o^Q)$ is the total energy of the supercel, with V_O containing charge Q in the nearest neighbor of dopant; $E_{\text{total}}(\text{bulk})$ is the total energy of the supercell without V_O (that is a vacancy-free system); ε_f is the energy of the Fermi level with respect to the edge of the valence-band (VB); ε_v, ΔV is the shift of ε_v caused by the introduced charge of V_O defect in the supercell; μ_o is the chemical potential of the oxygen-atom, which is one-half of the oxygen-molecular potential energy at ground state. Here, we first consider anion migration [13], instead of cation migration, since the thermal diffusivity of metallically ionic dopants in Table 1

Table 1. Effect of adding metallically ionic dopant into binary transition-metal–oxide on forming voltage or formation energy. O means the effect is positive; Δ means the effect is not clear.

	Dopant				
	Al	Ti	La	Au	Ga
TMO					
HfO_2	O [43]	D [43]	O [43]	–	–
ZrO_2	O [43]	D [43]	O [43]	–	O [43]
ZrO_2	–	O [41]	–	O [41]	–
NiO	O [39]	–	–	–	–
TiO_2	–	O [42]	–	O [42]	–
ZrO_2	O [46]	D [46]	O [46]	–	–
HfO_2	O [45]	D [45]	O [45]	–	–
ZrO_2	O [45]	D [45]	O [45]	–	–

is not as high as those TMO materials. Hence, under an electrical voltage stress, O^{2-} migration in a TMO matrix is reasonable and is widely accepted to play the crucial role of resistance switching [46]. From stochastic modeling [60], it is also reasonable that O^{2-} migrates to interstitial sites and further forms oxygen vacancies. A weak point in TMO film, probably at the grain boundary [50] of the poly-crystalline binary metal–oxide film or at a site with highly distributed nonstoichiometric metallic oxide (discussed in Subsection 2.1.1.7 of Section 2.1.1) would form a "channel" composed of a series of oxygen vacancies. The electron transport between oxygen vacancies and between oxygen vacancy and cathode or anode is assumed to be an electron-hopping mechanism [60–64] based on the stochastic model, unified model, and ion-transport-recombination model. Once a conductive path is successfully formed with much lower resistance than the initially high resistance stated TMO material by a forming process, this conductive path is called a CF.

Let's return to Eq. (3) and Figure 12. For a trivalent dopant, such as Al^{3+} or La^{3+}, by replacing the tetravalent Zr^{4+}, it becomes a negatively charged "acceptor," while the oxygen vacancy at the nearest neighboring interstitial site is a positively charged "donor." The electrical dipole formation between the acceptor and donor causes Coulomb interaction energy shift (a negative energy) and further results in a shift of the edge of the valence band, ΔV. In turn, the formation energy $E_f(X^Q)$ will be decreased by adding a metallically trivalent ionic dopant into the monoclinic ZrO_2 matrix with tetravalent Zr^{4+}. Lowering the formation energy implies that there is a positive effect on the forming voltage. In addition, since the HfO_2 matrix has a very similar physical structure and tetravalent phase, trivalent Al^{3+} and La^{3+} would also cause a positive effect on the forming voltage. On the other hand, according to this model, there is no such benefit for Ti doping in HfO_2 and ZrO_2 due to the absence of the shift of the VB edge from the Coulomb dipole interaction.

In Table 1, Ti doping into the TiO_2 matrix [42] also shows a positive effect on the forming voltage. This result is inconsistent with formation energy model that predicts an insensitive effect of Ti doping. However, Ti is known to have an excellent ability of oxygen gettering; more and more oxygen vacancies are further generated if the Ti metallically ionic dopants are embedded into the matrix. On the other hand,

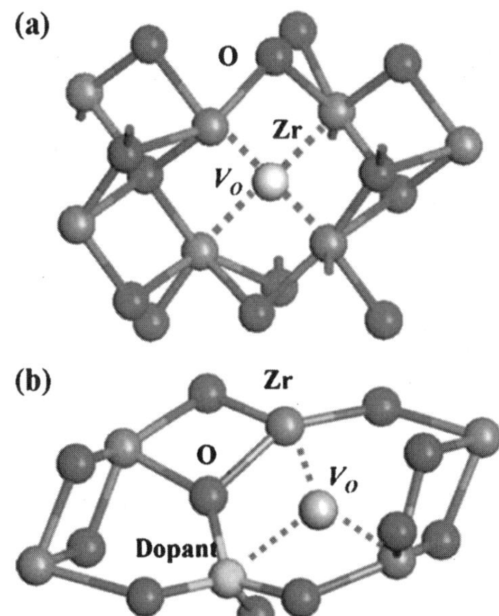

Figure 12. (a) Schematic diagram of an introduced supercell containing V_O in ZrO_2 without a metallic ion dopant, (b) a supercell containing V_O in ZrO_2 matrix with a metallic ion dopant. Here, the supercell is a monoclinic ZrO_2 structure. With trivalent doping, such as Al^{3+} or La^{3+}, replacing the tetravalent Zr^{4+} becomes a negatively charged acceptor, while V_O is a positively charged donor. The electrical dipole in turn is formed between the acceptor and donor. This causes to the energy shift due to the Coulomb interaction. Reprinted with permission from [46], H. Zhang et al., *Appl. Phys. Lett.* 96, 123502 (2010). © 2010, American Institute of Physics.

the further decreased formation energy after releasing helps the scaling down of the forming voltage. The explanations by the formation energy model discussed above can be well fitted to Gibb's free energy ΔG [36, 37].

Another explanation of the forming voltage improvement can start from the density of state of the HfO_2 (left side of Fig. 13) and Al-doped HfO_2 (right side of Fig. 13) with neutrally charged oxygen vacancies [45]. A deep level trap state is formed in HfO_2 with a neutrally charged oxygen vacancies. *Metallically trivalent* Al^{3+} *ion dopant in* HfO_2 *can shift this deep trap level upward.* A shallower trap center indicates that the reliability of Al-doped HfO_2 is different from that of pure HfO_2.

Figure 14 shows the effect of the ion radius and dopant doping in the ZrO_2 matrix on formation energy. Obviously, the forming process is insensitive to the ion radius. Trivalent Al^{3+} or La^{3+} replacing tetravalent Zr^{4+} plays the dominant role in lowering the formation energy.

2.1.1.5. Material in the Surrounding Environment on the Forming Voltage. Figure 15 shows an example knob for forming voltage improvement with a scaled MIM-structured device memory cell. Pillar-type structured TMO-RRAM with stacked HfO_2/Ti/TiN is prepared on the TiN bottom electrode [36, 37]. The encapsulating layer of SiO_2 and Si_3N_4 are studied for the interlayer dielectric. The conventional MIM stack in Figure 15 shows the forming voltage increasing with device cell size scaling (discussed in Subsection 2.1.1.3 of Section 2.1.1) and could be organized by

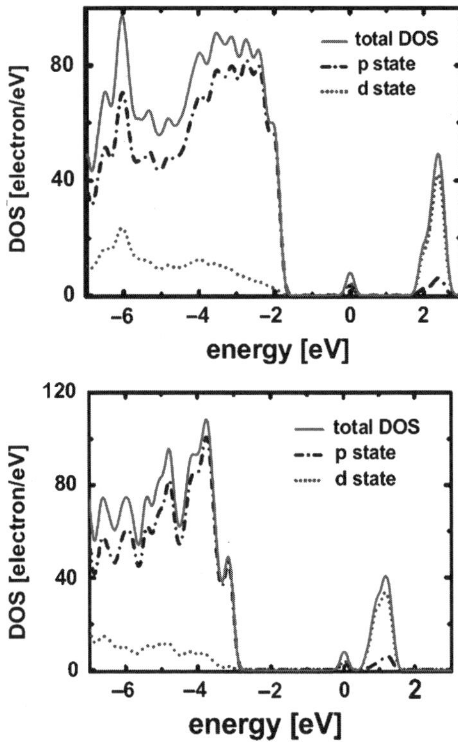

Figure 13. Left, the simulated density of state of HfO_2 with oxygen vacancy, V_O. The Fermi-level is at 0 eV; right, the simulated density of state of Al:HfO_2 with oxygen vacancy, V_O, at the nearest neighbor site to the dopant. The shifted upward deep level leads to the shallow deep level. Reprinted with permission from [45], H. Zhang et al., "Proceedings of the IEEE International Conference on Simulation of Semiconductor Processes and Devices (SISPAD'09)," p. 155, San Diego, CA, 2009. © 2009, The Institute of Electrical and Electronics Engineers (IEEE).

Eq. (2). However, a pillar-type structured TMO-RRAM with SiO_2 encapsulating unexpectedly worsens the forming voltage. For cell size < 50 nm, the increased forming voltage is higher than the extrapolated value of the predicted line with around 1 V. Because of the oxygen gettering ability of Ti, an enhanced oxygen concentration at the corner of

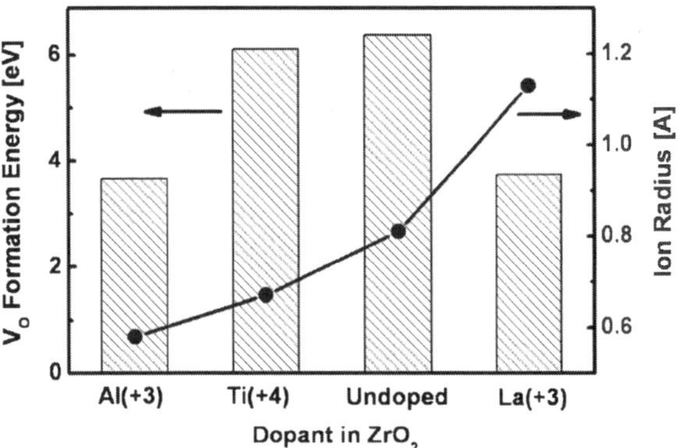

Figure 14. Effect of the ion radius and dopant in ZrO_2 on the formation energy. The ion radius is insensitive to the forming voltage. Reprinted with permission from [46], H. Zhang et al., *Appl. Phys. Lett.* 96, 123502 (2010). © 2010, American Institute of Physics.

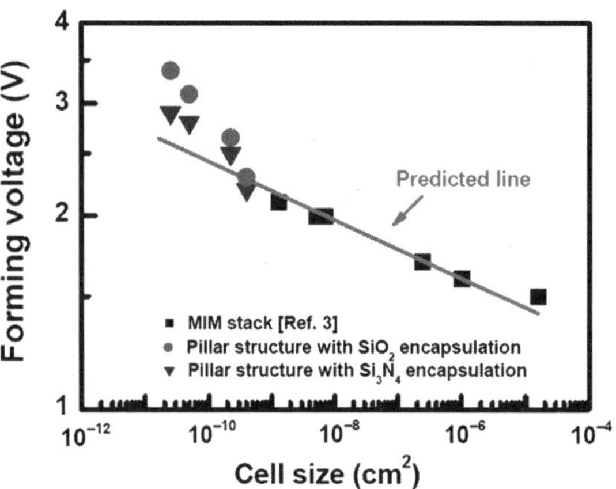

Figure 15. Encapsulation material effect on the forming voltage of the device. SiN as the encapsulation of a pillar-type TMO-RRAM device cell slightly improves the forming voltage. Reprinted with permission from [36], P.-Y. Gu et al., "Proceedings of IEEE International Symposium on VLSI Technology Systems and Applications (VLSI-TSA)," p. 146, Hsinchu, Taiwan, 2010. © 2010, The Institute of Electrical and Electronics Engineers (IEEE).

the pillar structure from the SiO_2 environment was found to seriously affect the reliability of such a TMO-RRAM device. With scaling of the device, the effect of the corner would play a more important role in RRAM performance. This can result in different behaviors between the pillar-structured device and the conventional MIM-stacked device. To improve the corner-enhanced oxygen concentration, an encapsulating layer of Si_3N_4 was used to replace the SiO_2. In Figure 15, a forming voltage improvement of around 600 mV for a device cell size of 50 nm is clearly observed, indicating the degraded corner oxygen effect by encapsulating.

The second example of the surrounding effect on forming voltage can be realized by Figure 16, which shows

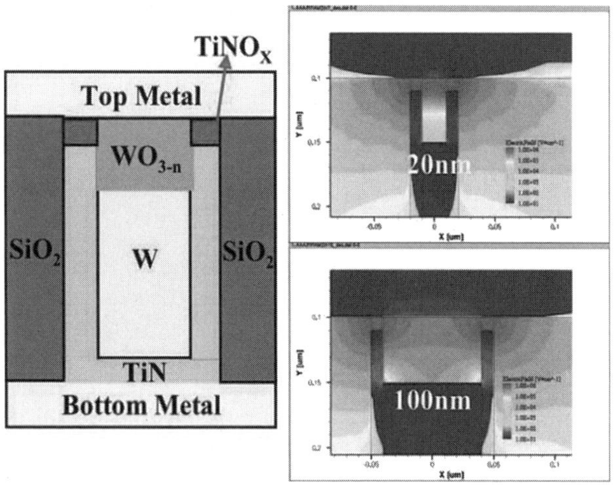

Figure 16. Schematic view of electric field-enhanced structure and field distribution for WO_x devices with various cell sizes. A 10-nm thick TiN barrier is oxidized as an insulating $TiNO_x$ layer. Reprinted with permission from [38], W. C. Chien et al., "IEEE International Electron Devices Meeting (IEDM) Technical Digest," p. 440, San Francisco, CA, 2010. © 2010, The Institute of Electrical and Electronics Engineers (IEEE).

a self-aligned and fully CMOS compatible tungsten-oxide (WO_x) based binary TMO-RRAM system [38, 65–70]. By oxidizing the TiN barrier to become an insulated $TiNO_x$ layer (10 nm thick), the WO_x is forced to protrude above the remaining TiN, thus achieving a higher electric field when a voltage is applied. Unlike the previous encapsulating result, the structure with the enhancing electric field exactly follows the semiconductor-scaling rule, i.e., the formation energy is degraded with cell size.

2.1.1.6. Material of the Anode and Cathode Electrode on the Forming Voltage. Similar to the doping-dependent forming voltage behavior (discussed in Subsection 2.1.1.4 of Section 2.1.1), the electrode effect on the TMO-RRAM is also an important issue not only because of the formation energy but also the nonvolatility performance [62, 71], such as cycle endurance, data retention, and the ON/OFF ratio.

In Figure 10, the effect of electrode material on the forming voltage is also illustrated for a HfO_2-based TMO-RRAM with a fixed TiN bottom electrode [31]. Changing the top electrode from platinum (Pt) to Pt/Ti and Pt/Zr shows different results: zirconium plays a dominant role in reducing the forming voltage, while the effect of titanium is minor. On the other hand, similar experiments were done by replacing the TiN top electrode with a composite TiN/Ti for HfO_2-, ZrO_2-, and TiO_2-based, MIM-stacked TMO-RRAMs, retaining the bottom electrode of TiN [25]. The performance of the reducing forming voltages are positive for "all" TMO matrices, even for the HfO_2-based TMO matrix.

For the bottom electrode dependency, replacing a Pt bottom electrode of Ta_2O_5/TiO_2 hybrid TMO-RRAM by ruthenium (Ru) and a composite Ru/Ti shows un-preference results with keeping the top electrode as ruthenium [47]. A pure Ru bottom electrode can increase the forming voltage by < 1 V. And both Pt and Ru bottom electrodes can provide stable forming voltage of Ta_2O_5/TiO_2 hybrid TMO-RRAM with a fluctuation range of < 0.5 V. If stacked Ru/Ti is used for the bottom electrode, a huge voltage fluctuation of forming process, with a range of about 6 V, complicates the analysis. All of the above results are presented in Table 2.

Pt is a noble metal, indicating that the reaction of the oxygen ions with Pt can be minimized during the forming process. This means that the TMO-RRAM characteristics with the Pt electrode can be used as a reference comparison:

(1) Pt → Ru: The increased forming voltage of around < 1 V by replacing Pt ($\phi = 5.65$ eV) with Ru ($\phi = 4.71$ eV) might result from the work-function difference;
(2) Pt → Zr: The improved forming voltage of around 1.6 V by replacing Pt with Zr ($\phi = 4.05$ eV) is due to the reoxidation of Zr at interface. The formation of ZrO_x at interface and thinning of HfO_2 indicates the rearrangement of the density of oxygen vacancies. This effect will be described in Subsection 2.1.1.7 of Section 2.1.1. Meanwhile, the dielectric constant changing (described in Subsection 2.1.1.2 of Section 2.1.1) and the HfO_x thinning effect (described in Subsection 2.1.1.1 of Section 2.1.1) of the forming voltage might contribute to the reduced forming voltage; and
(3) Pt →Ti or Ru/Ti: As previously discussed, Ti is ($\phi = 4.33$ eV) has a strong oxygen gettering ability.

This means that the unpredictable results of an electrode replacement with Ti depend on the interfacial oxygen dynamics between Ti and the TMO matrix. For the TiO_2-based TMO matrix, top electrode replacement from TiN to TiN/Ti reveals a positive effect on the forming voltage due to the high density of oxygen vacancies [25]. In contrast, the initial trap density at the interface might easily result in a huge fluctuation of the forming voltage [47]. The improved forming voltage and highly fluctuating forming voltage are tradeoffs in TiO_2-based TMO-RRAM.

The complexity of the electrode effect of TMO-RRAM depends on the oxygen ion diffusivity, local electric field [56, 57], and interfacial barrier of both the electrode material and memory layer. The movement or migration of oxygen ions can be well understood by two items, the diffusion and the drift [71]. The former is a function of temperature and is independent of electric polarity. The latter depends directly on the local electric field. The time-dependent evolution of oxygen concentration can be accordingly written as [62]:

$$\frac{\partial C_i}{\partial t} = B_i\left[Z_i e\frac{\partial \phi}{\partial x}\frac{\partial C_i}{\partial x} + k_B T\frac{\partial^2 C_i}{\partial x^2}\right] \tag{4}$$

where C_i is concentration of oxygen ions, B_i is diffusion coefficient, $\partial\phi/\partial x$ means the local electric field with electric potential of ϕ, T is temperature, and $Z_i e$ is electric quantity of oxygen ions. The first item on the right side of Eq. (4) represents the drift of oxygen ions by electric field driving, while the second item relates to temperature dependent oxygen ion diffusion. The boundary conditions of Eq. (4) are determined by the interfacial dynamics between electrode and TMO matrix: (1) If there is no barrier for the oxygen ion diffusion between the interfaces, the boundary condition of Eq. (4) is:

$$\begin{aligned} &C(x, t=0) = N\delta(x) \\ &\frac{\partial}{\partial x}C(x=l, t) = 0 \\ &\frac{\partial}{\partial x}C(x=0, t) = 0 \end{aligned} \tag{5}$$

Here, l is the active region thickness of the TMO layer, and N is the total amount of oxygen ions at interface. In the beginning, $t = 0$, all oxygen ions are at the interface and follow a delta function. Since there is no barrier, there is no oxygen ion accumulation at the top and bottom interfaces at any time; however, (2) if there is a barrier for the oxygen ion migration at the interface between the electrode and TMO matrix layer, the boundary condition of Eq. (4) needs to be modified as:

$$\begin{aligned} &C(x>0, t=0) = 0 \\ &\frac{\partial}{\partial x}C(x=l, t) = 0 \\ &\frac{\partial}{\partial x}C(x=0, t) = C_0 \end{aligned} \tag{6}$$

Here, C_0 is the fixed oxygen ion concentration at the interface and at any time that the amount is lower than total amount of oxygen ions, N. Similar to Eq. (5), in the beginning, $t = 0$, there is no oxygen ion concentration in the bulk

Table 2. Effect of top and bottom electrodes on the forming voltages of TMO based RRAM system. Here, replacing the electrode with titanium shows unpredictable results, indicating a complex system. O means the effect on forming voltage is positive; Δ means the effect is not clear; *X* means the effect on forming voltage is negative; Unstable means a huge fluctuation was found.

	Top electrode			Bottom electrode	
	TiN to TiN/Ti	Pt to Pt/Ti	Pt to Pt/Zr	Pt to Ru	Pt to Ru/Ti
TMO					
TiO_2	O [25]	–	–	–	–
ZrO_2	O [25]	–	–	–	–
HfO_2	O [25]	Δ [31]	O [31]	–	–
Ta_2O_5/TiO_2	–	–	–	*X* [47]	Unstable [47]

of the TMO matrix. At any time, only the interface, $x = 0$, retains a constant oxygen ion concentration, C_0, which is a function of electric voltage due to the drift effect.

From Eqs. (4)~(6), one can simulate the effect of the top and bottom electrodes according to the characteristics of the electrode material. For example, the boundary condition of Eq. (5) can be used to explain the Pt electrode since there is almost no interaction with oxygen ions. The boundary condition of Eq. (6) can be implemented on the Ti electrode due to the strong oxygen gettering ability. The characteristics of a TMO matrix with a TiN electrode can be realized from both Eqs. (5) and (6). Except for the consideration of the oxygen ion migration barrier, the influence of various electrodes on the local electric field would also affect the results of Eq. (4).

2.1.1.7. Effect of Density of Oxygen Vacancy on the Forming Voltage. From the discussion in Subsection 2.1.1.4 of Section 2.1.1, oxygen vacancy dynamics (relating to oxygen ion migration) plays the key role in CF formation or the formation energy. Any perturbation on the density of the oxygen vacancy at the interface or in bulk would result in a quite different conclusion. The change of oxygen ion concentration at the interface could be achieved by the alternation of the electrode with various oxygen ion activities (described in Subsection 2.1.1.6 of Section 2.1.1). On the other hand, the change in bulk could be done by additionally suitable doping in the TMO matrix (described in subsection 2.1.1.4 of Section 2.1.1). Methodologies of both the electrode alternation and additional doping are extrinsic. In this Subsection, the forming voltage improvement by an intrinsic behavior (stoichiometric control) inside the bulk of the TMO matrix is discussed.

Figure 17 depicts the forming process improvement by stoichiometric controlling of plasma-oxidized copper-oxide [49]. The left side of the figure is an auger electron spectroscopy (AES) depth profile before and after thermal annealing at 300°C. The surface layer shows a transition from CuO to Cu_2O, while the inner layer between the surface and bottom electrode is nonstoichiometric CuO_x that is more conductive causing from the graded oxygen vacancy than the surface CuO before thermal annealing. Thus, this needs a high-forming voltage across CuO for CF formation (Fig. 17). With enough formation energy, a CF composed of a series of oxygen vacancies produces a LRS in this memory device. If the preforming sample is annealed in a N_2 or Ar environment (oxygen deficient ambient), the high-forming voltage is successfully eliminated, as shown by the gray curve on the right side of Figure 17. Furthermore, to clarify the inner-graded CuO_x characteristics, the surface CuO layer was removed carefully by focus-ion-beam time mode etching control [48]. A graded CuO_x-based TMO-RRAM with free forming process was also obtained.

Similar TMO-RRAM systems without forming processes were also achieved in graded tungsten-oxide (WO_x) [65, 66] and in nonstoichiometric tungsten-oxide (Fig. 18) [67]. The resistance of nano-scaled graded or nonstoichiometric WO_x is much lower than the surface WO_3 layer since the enhanced density of oxygen vacancies.

2.1.2. External Methodologies of Forming Voltage

2.1.2.1. CS Control. VS control is often operated on dielectric breakdown or soft breakdown reliability topics, such as time-dependent-dielectric-breakdown. The previous discussion in Section 2.1.1 about the intrinsic parameters of forming voltage is also summarized from VS control with a defined CC of SPA. However, in Section 2.2, the life time (τ) of recombination between an oxygen ion (O^{2-}) and oxygen-vacancy (V_O) or precipitation between a metal and oxygen ion might be on the order of less than 10 ns [71]. CC controlling by SPA (order of sub-μs) is much slower than the lift time, indicating that the complex CF formation in the TMO matrix might be prepared during this compliance time by the following models:

(1) One CF with various radii [50];

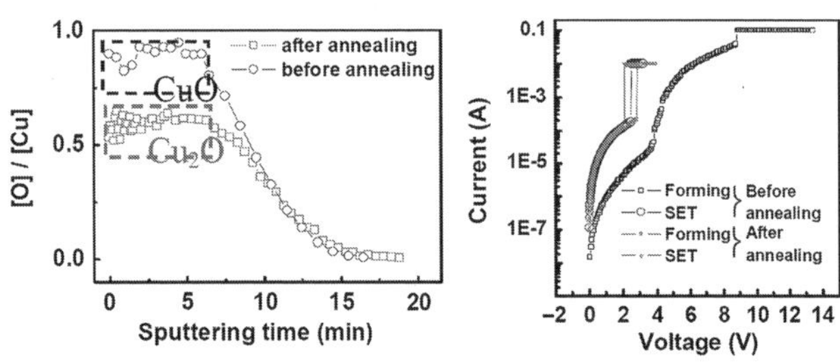

Figure 17. Left, Auger (AES) depth profiles of an oxidized sample pre- and post-annealing. The Cu_2O surface is formed from CuO; right, *I–V* curves pre- and post-annealing. The forming behavior is obviously improved by optimized annealing process. Reprinted with permission from [49], H. B. Lv et al., "Proceedings of the Joint 2008 Non-Volatile Semiconductor Memory Workshop and 2008 International Conference on Memory Technology and Design (NVSMW/ICMTD)," p. 52, Monterey, CA, 2008. © 2008, The Institute of Electrical and Electronics Engineers (IEEE).

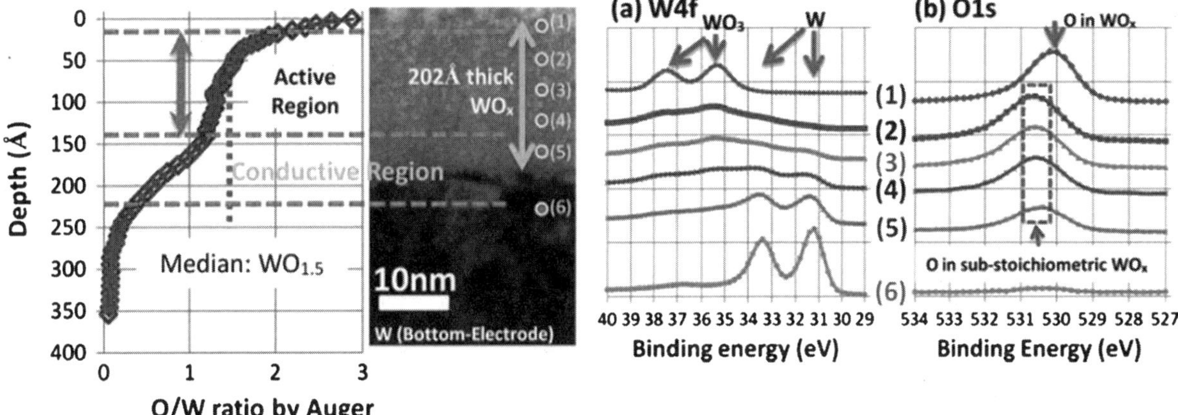

Figure 18. Left, AES depth profile of O/W ratio for RTO oxidized WO_x film; right, (a) W^{4f} and (b) O^{1s} by XPS. Depths (1), (2)... represent the location in the left-hand TEM figure. Reprinted with permission from [67], C. H. Ho et al., "IEEE International Electron Devices Meeting (IEDM) Technical Digest," p. 436, San Francisco, CA, 2010. © 2010, The Institute of Electrical and Electronics Engineers (IEEE).

(2) several CFs connected in parallel [25, 26, 32, 38];
(3) complex CF with multiple branches [30, 31, 39, 72]; and
(4) denser CF with very short distances between hopping sites.

All of above four cases would generate lower resistance than that of the LRS such that the first Reset current is abnormally higher than the others [56]. Some prior arts have mentioned that a stable cycle operation can be finally obtained after the first few Reset-Set operation cycles. Therefore, a stable CF configuration after the forming process is important.

As an alternative to VS control, CS control [23, 26, 56–58] was proposed to boost the RRAM performance (Fig. 19). The left side of Figure 19 is a typical I–V characteristic of a MIM-stacked TiN (top electrode)/HfO_2 (10 nm)/Pt (bottom electrode) TMO-RRAM memory device for forming and Reset/Set processes under VS control. Compared with the gradual resistance transition by CS control, abrupt forming and Set processes are observed by VS control. It is noted that the forming voltage of both the VS and CS control methods are similar, all around 7 V, but the current levels of both methods are different. The CC level of the VS control is set at around 4 μA, while the current of CS control is measured at around 2 μA. This implies that the "actual" formation energy is not as high as that of the VS control. After the CF formation, the excess energy will be released to strengthen the CF so that the current of the first Reset process (I_{Reset}) is much higher than the others. This is the reason for the first abnormally high Reset current. The gradual-resistance switching might come from the complicated rupture of the CF. In contrast, since moderated formation energy is injected by the CS control, the rupture of only one CF is obviously found during the Reset process.

2.1.2.2. Degraded Gate-Voltage for the Forming Process. A real TMO-RRAM device with a 1T-1R structure is shown in the left side of Figure 20 [59]. All Forming, Reset, Set, and Read processes need to turn on the transistor channel by applying suitable gate voltage simultaneously. With the same potential difference between the drain and source sides (V_{DS}), the drain current (I_D) monotonically increases with increasing gate voltage (V_G) before the saturation region. To minimize the current through the TMO matrix, a degraded gate voltage (< 1 V) is proposed to minimize the cross-section area of the CF, A_{CF}, which was

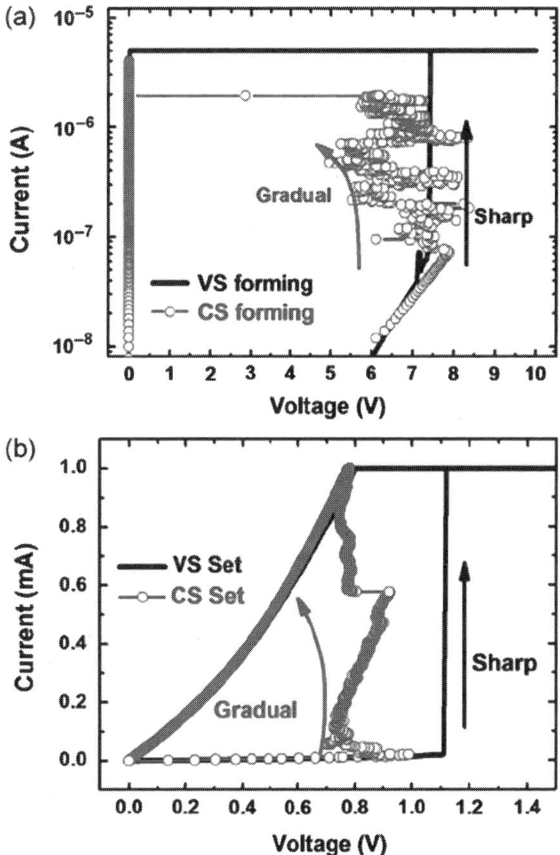

Figure 19. Left, typical I–V curves of device for forming process under voltage-sweep (VS) and current-sweep (CS) controls. Right side: Typical I–V curves of device for Set process under VS and CS controls. Gradual Set transition by CS control is observed. Reprinted with permission from [57], B. Chen et al., *IEEE Electron. Device Lett.* 32, 282 (2011). © 2011, The Institute of Electrical and Electronics Engineers (IEEE).

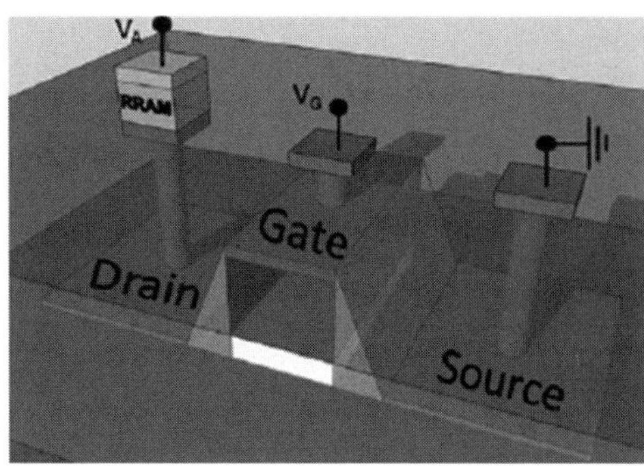

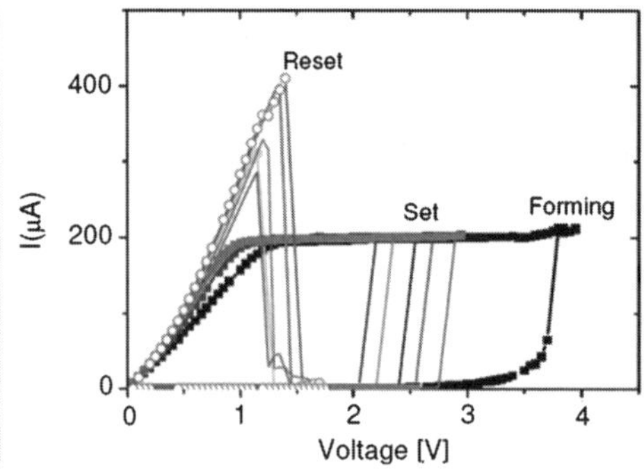

Figure 20. Left, schematic diagram of the 1T-1R structure; right, Forming/Reset/Set characteristics. Low gate-voltage, V_G, is used during the Forming and Set processes for a minimum drain current, I_D, and area of CF, A_{CF}. Reprinted with permission from [59], F. Nardi et al., *J. Solid-State Electron.* 58, 42 (2011). © 2011, Elsevier.

discussed previously. The black curve on the right side of Figure 20 shows the successful forming process with well-controlled V_G and V_{DS}.

2.2. Bipolar Resistance Switching

The currently developed but still emerging nonvolatile memories based on resistance alternation by external injection power into a device include spin-torque-transferring magnetic RAM (STT-MRAM), phase-change RAM (PCRAM), and the presented RRAM. The resistance of magnetic tunnel junctions of the STT-MRAM can be switched between the HRS and LRS by an injection of current with alternated electric polarity. This is called bipolar resistance switching. On the other hand, the resistance of the chalcogenide material of PCRAM, such as GeSbTe, can be successfully switched by injection current with modulated pulse width and amplitude, while keeping the same electric polarity. This is called unipolar resistance switching. In RRAM, the situation is more complicated than those of STT-MRAM and PCRAM. Some systems have bipolar resistance switching; some have unipolar resistance switching; and some have both bipolar and unipolar resistance switching. In this section, we focus on the bipolar resistance switching of TMO-RRAM. The unipolar resistance switching of RRAM is discussed in Section 2.3.

Figure 21 shows a typical I–V curve of bipolar resistance switching mode of an MIM-structured TMO-RRAM memory device with a TMO of NiO film after the forming process. After forming, this TMO-RRAM device is in the "ON state," in which the resistance is lower. When a negative voltage sweep is applied, this TMO-RRAM device transfers its state from the initial "ON state" (LRS) to the "OFF state" (HRS), with higher resistance at a critical transition voltage point of around −0.8 V. This clockwise curve is called the "Reset" process. When a positive voltage sweep is further applied to this TMO-RRAM device, the resistance state is alternated from the "OFF state" to the "ON state" again at a critical transition voltage point of around 0.8 V. This counterclockwise curve is called the "Set" process. Both the HRS and LRS are stable even without the application of external voltage, indicating the nonvolatility of this TMO-RRAM memory device.

2.2.1. TMO-RRAM Materials with Bipolar Resistance Switching

Figure 22 describes the elements that were shown to exhibit resistance switching with the binary (transition) metal–oxide based bipolar resistance-switching mode (marked with gray) and the binary (transition) metal–oxide-based unipolar resistance-switching mode (marked with light-gray and discussed in Section 2.3). Examples of the former and the latter are hafnium-oxide (HfO_2) and tungsten-oxide (WO_x), respectively. The element marked with dark-gray was used for the proposed electrode application in resistance memory. La, Cr, Ga, and Al were used to study the ionic doping effect on resistance memory, especially TMO-RRAM.

In Figure 22, we can summarize binary metal–oxide-based bipolar resistance-switching operations that occur for the TMO matrix, such as TiO_x [74, 75], FeO_x [76], CoO_x [77], NiO_x [78], CuO_x [79, 80], ZnO_x [81], ZrO_x [82], NbO_x [83], HfO_x [36, 84], TaO_x [85], and WO_x [38, 65, 67], and $4f$-group metal oxides, such as CeO_x [86] and GdO_x [87], as well as the p-group metal oxides, such as AlO_x [34] and graphene-oxide [88]. To simplify the naming, all of these materials are referred to as TMO-RRAM in this chapter. On the other hand, some TMO-RRAM materials even have unipolar resistance-switching behavior, such as TiO_x [89],

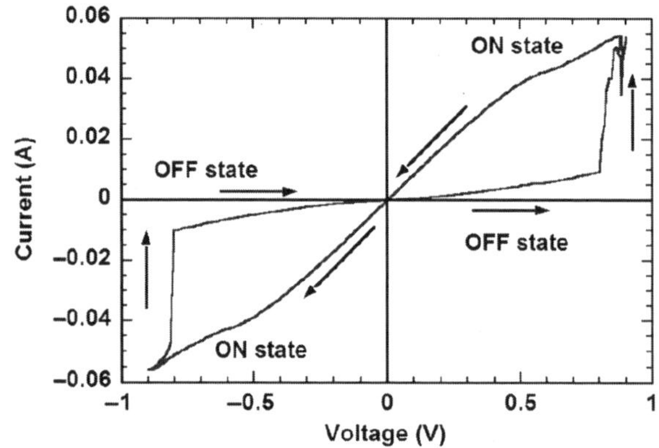

Figure 21. A typical DC hysteretic I–V characteristic for a MIM-structured bipolar resistive-switching RRAM. Reprinted with permission from [73], O. Ginez et al., Proceedings of the 14th IEEE European Test Symposium (ETS'09)," p. 61, Sevilla, Spain, 2009. © 2009, The Institute of Electrical and Electronics Engineers (IEEE).

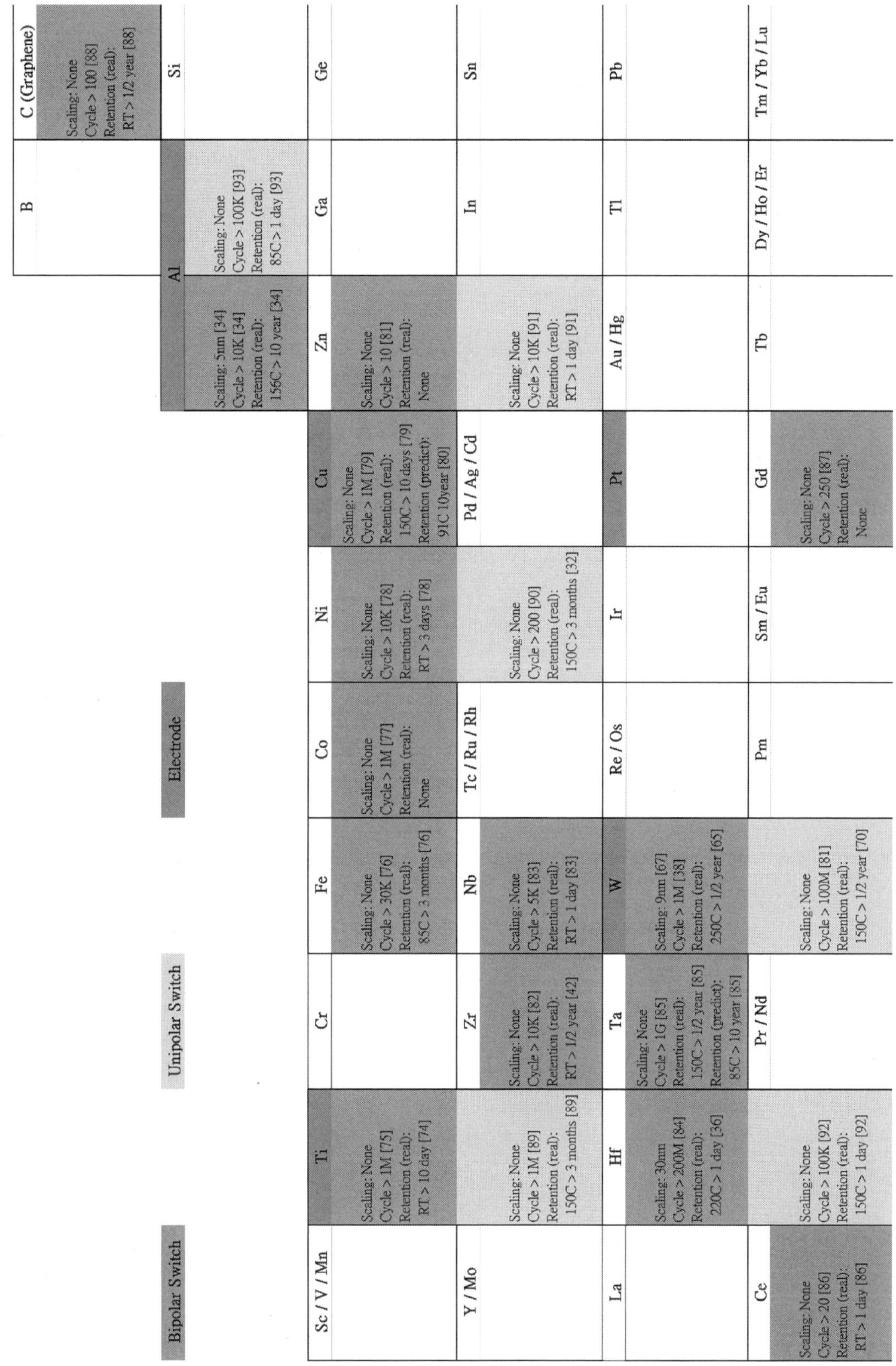

Bipolar Switch		Unipolar Switch		Electrode				B	C (Graphene)
									Scaling: None Cycle > 100 [88] Retention (real): RT > 1/2 year [88]
							Al		Si
							Scaling: 5nm [34] Cycle > 10K [34] Retention (real): 156C > 10 year [34]	Scaling: None Cycle > 100K [93] Retention (real): 85C > 1 day [93]	
Sc / V / Mn	Ti	Cr	Fe	Co	Ni	Cu	Zn	Ga	Ge
	Scaling: None Cycle > 1M [75] Retention (real): RT > 10 day [74]		Scaling: None Cycle > 30K [76] Retention (real): 85C > 3 months [76]	Scaling: None Cycle > 1M [77] Retention (real): None	Scaling: None Cycle > 10K [78] Retention (real): RT > 3 days [78]	Scaling: None Cycle > 1M [79] Retention (real): 150C > 10 days [79] Retention (predict): 91C 10year [80]	Scaling: None Cycle > 10 [81] Retention (real): None		
Y / Mo		Zr	Nb	Tc / Ru / Rh		Pd / Ag / Cd		In	Sn
	Scaling: None Cycle > 1M [89] Retention (real): 150C > 3 months [89]	Scaling: None Cycle > 10K [82] Retention (real): RT > 1/2 year [42]	Scaling: None Cycle > 5K [83] Retention (real): RT > 1 day [83]		Scaling: None Cycle > 200 [90] Retention (real): 150C > 3 months [32]		Scaling: None Cycle > 10K [91] Retention (real): RT > 1 day [91]		
La	Hf	Ta	W	Re / Os	Ir	Pt	Au / Hg	Tl	Pb
	Scaling: 30nm Cycle > 200M [84] Retention (real): 220C > 1 day [36]	Scaling: None Cycle > 1G [85] Retention (real): 150C > 1/2 year [85] Retention (predict): 85C > 10 year [85]	Scaling: 9nm [67] Cycle > 1M [38] Retention (real): 250C > 1/2 year [65]						
Ce		Pr / Nd		Pm	Sm / Eu	Gd	Tb	Dy / Ho / Er	Tm / Yb / Lu
Scaling: None Cycle > 20 [86] Retention (real): RT > 1 day [86]	Scaling: None Cycle > 100K [92] Retention (real): 150C > 1 day [92]		Scaling: None Cycle > 100M [81] Retention (real): 150C > 1/2 year [70]			Scaling: None Cycle > 250 [87] Retention (real): None			

Figure 22. The elements that were shown to exhibit resistance switching with the binary (transition) metal–oxide-based bipolar resistance switching mode (marked with gray) and the binary (transition) metal–oxide-based unipolar resistance switching mode (marked with light gray).

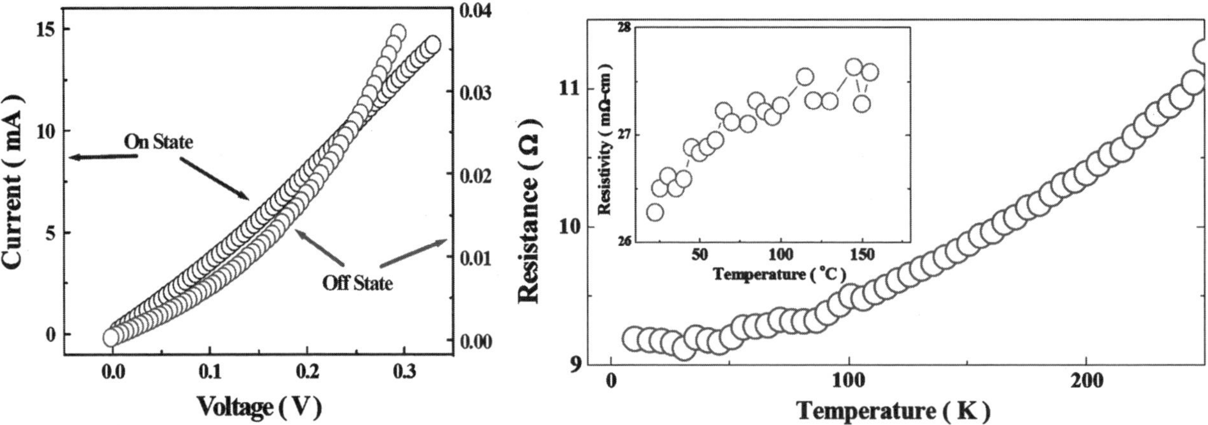

Figure 23. LRS of TMO-RRAM with an Ohmic transportation such that the current is proportional to voltage. Reprinted with permission from [65], C. H. Ho et al., "IEEE Symposium on VLSI Technology Digest of Technical Papers," p. 228, Kyota, Japan, 2007. © 2007, The Institute of Electrical and Electronics Engineers (IEEE).

NiO_x [32, 90], ZnO_x [91], HfO_x [92], WO_x [69, 70], and AlO_x [93]. It should be realized that the organization in Figure 22 is not complete yet, since additional analyses and experiments are ongoing and not published yet.

2.2.2. Reset Process

The Reset process is the first programming step in TMO-RRAM after the Forming process, if needed. The Reset process of the bipolar resistance-switching mode here is defined as the state transition of the memory device from the LRS to HRS by applying voltage or current stress or pulse with electrical polarity opposite to the Forming process. Because the initial state before the Reset process has lower resistance, the required maximum current during the Reset process, naming the Reset current, I_{Reset}, is an important factor in memory design. This is similar to PCRAM development; the reduction ability of I_{Reset} of a designed new structure determines the device scalability.

In Figure 19 (CS control), the amplitude of the first Reset current is seriously affected by controlling the Forming process. The higher Reset current for the Forming current overshooting induced by VS control indicates that the Reset process is very sensitive to the dynamics of CF formation, i.e., it is sensitive to the history of the LRS.

Additional literature has discussed the various LRS electron transportations of TMO-RRAM: the metallic transportation (Ohmic transport) [50, 65, 78, 79, 87, 94], the electron hopping transportation [34, 60–64, 67, 71, 95, 96], the Schottky emission [75, 85, 97–99], and the space-charge limited-current (SCLC) [24, 28, 94, 100–104], etc. The relationships of the temperature and voltage dependent current (density) are generally used to analyze the electron transport mechanism, as described below:

$$\text{Ohmic: } I \propto V \cdot \exp\left(-E_{\text{ae}}/kT\right) \tag{7}$$

$$\text{Schottky emission: } J = A * T^2 \cdot \exp\left[-\frac{q}{kT}\left(\phi_B - \sqrt{\frac{qE}{4\pi\varepsilon_i}}\right)\right] \tag{8}$$

$$\text{SCLC: } J = 8\varepsilon_i \mu V^2/9d^3 \tag{9}$$

Electron hopping (e.g., variable-range electron hopping):

$$\begin{aligned} J_{(V\sim 0)} &\propto \tfrac{qRE}{kT}\exp\left[-BT^{-1/4}\right] \\ J_{(V\gg 0)} &\propto \exp\left[\tfrac{qRE}{kT} - BT^{-1/4}\right] \end{aligned} \tag{10}$$

where E_{ae} in Eq. (7) is the activation energy of electrons, k is the Boltzman constant; A in Eq. (8) is an effective Richardson constant; ϕ_B in Eq. (8) is the barrier sheight, E is the electric field; d in Eq. (9) is the insulator thickness in which $V = E^*d$; ε_i in Eqs. (8) and (9) is dynamic insulator permittivity; R in Eq. (10) is the electron hopping distance; B in Eq. (10) is a hopping correlation parameter that is a function of density of state near Fermi level, $N_e(E_F)$, and the electron wave-function delay parameter, α.

An example of Ohmic transportation in the LRS can be seen in Figure 23. The TMO-RRAM material is a highly graded WO_x by an optimized down-stream plasma oxidation condition [65]. As discussed in Eq. (7) of Section 2.1.1, a forming process is not required in this kind of TMO material. The left side of Figure 23 shows a typical linear I–V curve, indicating the Ohmic transportation. The right side of Figure 23 displays a metallic-like temperature-dependent resistance.

An example of Schottky emission transportation in the LRS can be pointed out in Figure 24. MIM-structured $IrO_x/Ta_2O_5/W$ shows that both the HRS and LRS follow the Schottky emission transportation with barrier heights of 1.05 eV and 0.94 eV, respectively [97]. On the other hand, Figure 25 depicts the SCLC dominated I–V characteristic of α-TiO_x-based MIM structure with an Al electrode [101]. The result shows a transition from initially Ohmic transportation to the SCLC after 200 mV of applied voltage.

Regarding the I–V characteristics in Figures 23 to 25, another explanation can be achieved by the electron-hopping transportation in Eq. (10). For an applied voltage very close to zero, Eq. (10) can be rewritten as $\ln(I) \propto \text{constant} + \ln(V)$, indicating the slope of 1 in the low-voltage region of Figure 25. However, if the applied

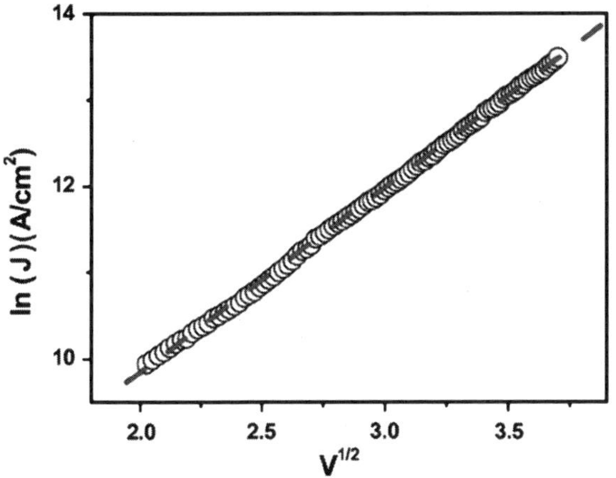

Figure 24. LRS I–V behavior of NiO-based TMO system, implying transportation by Schottky emission. Reprinted with permission from [99], M.-D. Lee et al., *IEEE Trans. Magn.* 43, 939 (2007). © 2007, The Institute of Electrical and Electronics Engineers (IEEE).

voltage is high enough but lower than the resistance switching, Eq. (10) becomes $\ln(I) \propto$ constant $+ (qR/kTd)V$; i.e., $\ln(I) \propto (qR/kTd)e^{\ln V}$. The current follows a voltage-dependent exponential growth trend with the coefficient relating to the hopping distance, insulator film thickness, and temperature. Note that the higher voltage region in Figure 25supports $\log V \sim 0$; Eq. (10) can be approximated as $\ln I \propto$ constant $+ (qR/kTd)\ln V$. The slope change in Figure 25 with an increase in the applied voltage from 1 to 2 can be furthermore realized by electron-hopping transportation. The hopping distance from the previous literature is summarized in Figure 26. All of the LRS hopping distances of TiO_x-, HfO_x-, and GeO_x/HfON-based TMO-RRAM are evaluated in the simplified Eq. (10), $\ln(I) \propto$ constant $+ (qR/kTd)\ln V$. The LRS hopping distance of 2.5 Å~10 Å for various TMO matrices indicates that the highly CF path was formed by a previous Forming process or Set process. Note that the HRS hopping distance of WO_x, ~15 Å, was obtained by fitting the measured I–V and I–T curves. The evidence of electron-hopping transportation can also be achieved by Mott's formula for alternate current

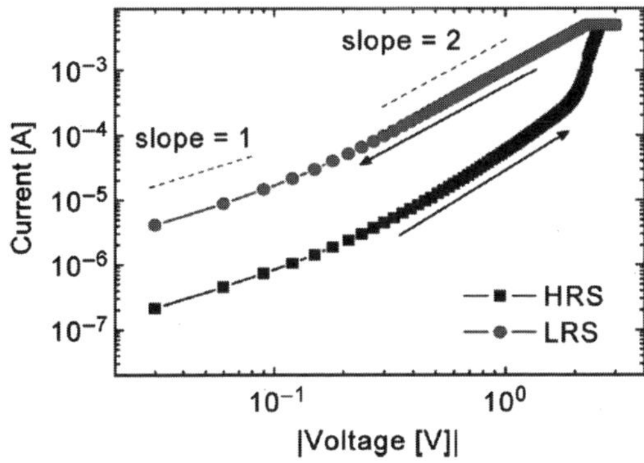

Figure 25. LRS I–V behavior of α-TiO_x-based TMO with an Al electrode, implying space-charge-limited-current (SCLC) transportation. Reprinted with permission from [101], J.-K. Lee et al., *IEEE Electron. Device. Lett.* 31, 603 (2010). © 2010, The Institute of Electrical and Electronics Engineers (IEEE).

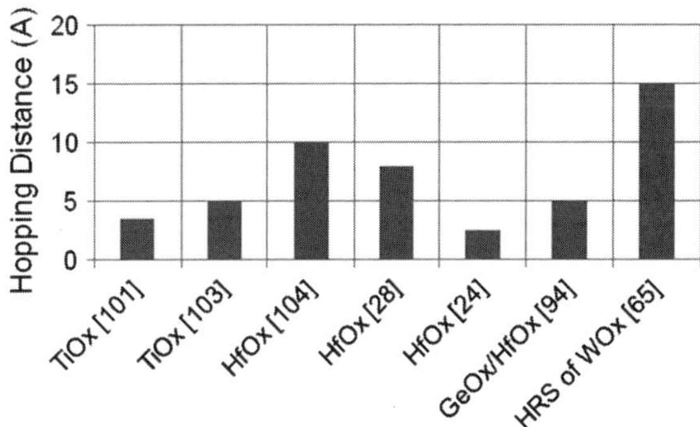

Figure 26. Evaluated distance of electron hopping from the literature for TiO_x-, HfO_x- and GeO_x/HfON-based RRAM. Compared with that of HRS of WO_x RRAM, the lower hopping distance of LRS indicates the highly CF path.

(AC) conductance [61]:

$$\sigma(\omega) = \frac{\pi^4}{96} * \left(\frac{e^2}{\alpha^5}\right) * [N(EF)]^2 kT\omega * \left[\ln\left(\frac{v_p h}{\omega}\right)\right]^4 \quad (11)$$

The electron-hopping transportation mechanism between oxygen vacancies, the cathode ←→ oxygen vacancy, and the anode ←→ oxygen vacancy have been proposed recently by the stochastic model [60, 63, 64, 96], unified model [61], and ion-transport-recombination model [62]. Figure 27 shows the assumption of the CF of the LRS by the stochastic model [64]. During the Forming process or Set process, oxygen ions are moved to the nearest interstitial position (if this position is empty) with the probability of Γ_n'; furthermore, the oxygen vacancies are formed. Hence, the CF is generated by localized oxygen vacancies or domains of oxygen vacancies [60]. Thus, the LRS can be interpreted as an electron transport along a CF in an oxygen vacancy-rich region or along the grain boundary region with oxygen vacancies precipitation by a high-oxygen vacancies concentration, which are presented in Hafnia on the order of 10^{18}~10^{19}/cm^2 [50, 106]. On the other hand, because $a+1$ charged state of oxygen vacancy, $V_O + 1$, is not stable [106]; formed oxygen vacancies have two stable charged states: $2 + (V_O + 2)$ and neutral $(V_O + 0)$. The former has the highest migration barrier, ~5.9 eV; the barrier height of the latter is only 3.8 eV. The Fermi energy (E_F) is raised above the valence-band maximum (VBM) and near the mid-gap from the insulating state of Fermi energy (E_F) near the VBM. This implies that all the dynamics of the Reset process can be achieved by neutral oxygen vacancy.

Figure 28 is an example of partial and total density-of-state with and without oxygen vacancies [105]. The band-gap of 2.99 eV from the simulation of Figure 28 is close to the experimental result of 3.0 eV. Due to the oxygen vacancy creation, a defect state is observed within the energy gap. A similar result was also simulated according to the NiO-based TMO-RRAM with six oxygen vacancies in the ⟨110⟩ direction for LRS. The density-of-state of LRS near Fermi energy (E_F) comes from four metallic Ni atoms having 10 valence electrons [106], causing the almost metallic transportation through metallic Ni atoms.

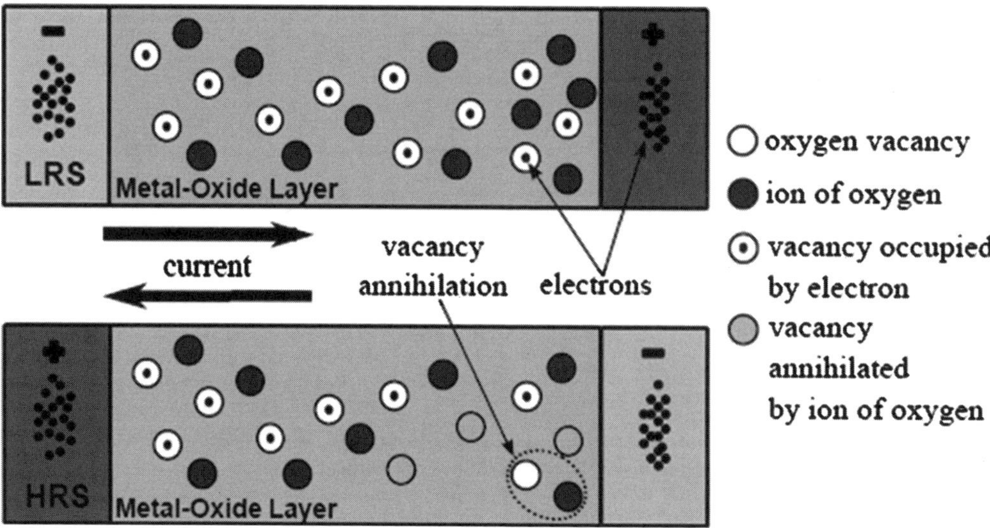

Figure 27. The assumption of the CF of LRS by stochastic model. Transportation by electron hopping between oxygen vacancies, and cathode ←→ oxygen vacancy, and anode ←→ oxygen vacancy. Reprinted with permission from [64], A. Makarov et al., "Proceedings of the European Solid-State Device Research Conference (ESSDERC)," p. 396, Seville, Spain, 2010. © 2010, The Institute of Electrical and Electronics Engineers (IEEE).

According to the electron-hopping transportation between oxygen vacancies, cathode ←→ oxygen vacancies, and anode ←→ oxygen vacancies, the Monte Carlo simulation is started from the electron hopping rate as [60, 63, 64, 96]:

$$\Gamma_{nm} = A_e * \frac{dE}{1 - \exp(-dE/T)} * \exp(-R_{nm}/a) \tag{12}$$

where A_e is a coefficient, $dE = E_n - E_m$ is the electron energy difference positioned between site n and m, R_{nm} is the hopping distance, and a is the localization radius. The generated hopping transportation current can be calculated as:

$$I = q_e * \frac{\sum dx}{\sum[\sum_m \Gamma_m]^{-1}} \tag{13}$$

Here, q_e is the electron charge and dx is hopping distance. For simplification, the oxygen vacancies are assumed to be either empty ($V_o + 0$) or occupied by one electron ($V_o + 1$), and all oxygen vacancies have the same energy level without applied voltage and temperature. The temperature-insensitive simulation result of occupation probability was obtained according to Eqs. (12) and (13); unfortunately, the

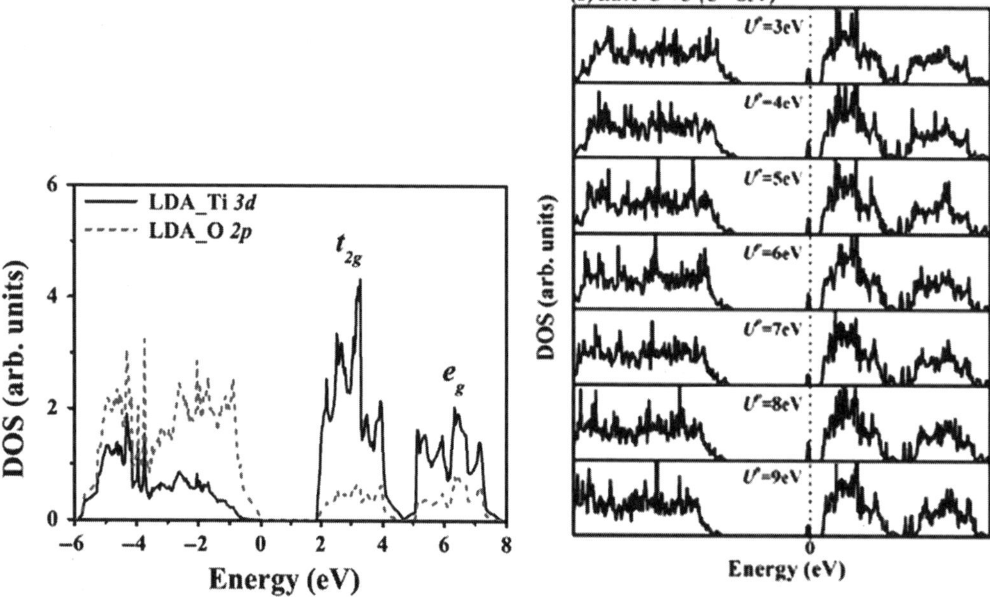

Figure 28. Left, the partial density of states of Ti 3d and O 2p orbitals in the rutile TiO_2 unit cell calculated by LDA + U^{d+p}; right, the total density of states of the rutile TiO_2 supercell with one oxygen vacancy obtained by LDA + U^{d+p} ($U^d = 8$ eV and various U^p). Fermi level is set to zero. Reprinted with permission from [105], S.-G. Park et al., *Phys. Rev. B* 82, 115109 (2010). © 2010, American Physical Society.

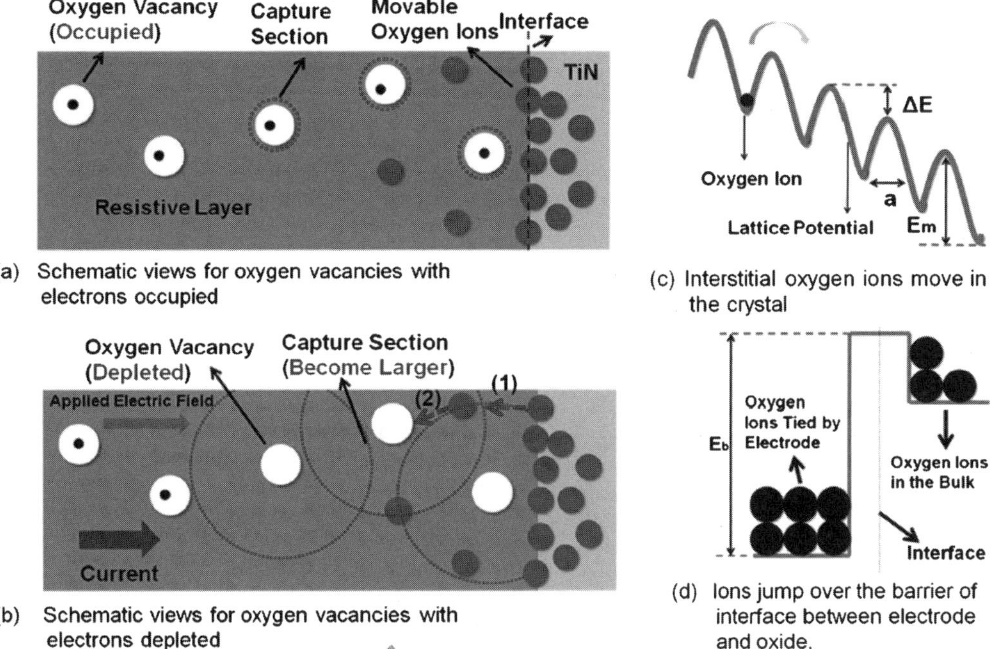

Figure 29. Schematic modeling diagrams of depleted-recombination. (a and b), increased capture section of oxygen ions by electron-depletion; (c and d), ion-transport behaviors of oxygen ions in the oxide bulk and at the interface. Reprinted with permission from [62], B. Gao et al., "IEEE International Electron Devices Meeting (IEDM) Technical Digest," p. 563, San Francisco, CA, 2008. © 2008, The Institute of Electrical and Electronics Engineers (IEEE).

movement rate of oxygen ions moving to the nearest interstitial position was needed to be further considered.

Regarding the Reset process, the movement of oxygen ions plays the most important role in rupturing of the conductive filament. As described in Eqs. (4) to (6), the movement of oxygen ions can be determined by both the diffusion migration and the drift migration [62, 71]. The diffusion migration, which is a temperature-sensitive dependent, is independent on the voltage polarity. A faster Reset process, and thus shorter Reset time, will occur at a higher operation temperature. The drift migration, which is sensitive to electrical voltage, is also dependent on the electric polarity. A higher Reset voltage can successfully operate TMO-RRAM with a shorter Reset time.

Figure 29 presents a schematic view of the ion-transport-recombination model. In Figure 29(a), as in the previous discussion, oxygen vacancies are occupied by electrons and electrically neutral. If the applied voltage is much lower than the Reset voltage, the capture section (dashed circle on oxygen vacancy) of the electron-occupied oxygen vacancy to the nearest interstitially positioned oxygen ions is very small due to the electron-shielding effect. The probability of ion-transport-recombination can be thus neglected. In Figure 29(b), when the applied voltage reaches the Reset voltage, the electric neutral oxygen vacancy close to the cathode with initial occupied electrons is depleted, and the capture sections have a significant increase in oxygen ions. The probability of the recombination between the oxygen vacancies and oxygen ions increases with the applied voltage until the Reset voltage. On the other hand, the recombination also depends on the oxygen ion concentration near the oxygen vacancies. Both the diffusion and drift migrations of oxygen ions can determine the oxygen ion concentration, indicating that the recombination is related to oxygen movement.

Figure 29(c) describes the movement of oxygen ions through the barrier. Similar to the electron hopping between oxygen vacancies, the movement rate of oxygen ions can be described as:

$$\Gamma_n' = A_i * \frac{\Delta E}{1 - \exp(-\Delta E/T)} \tag{14}$$

where A_i is a distance dependent coefficient, and ΔE represents the formation energy or annihilation energy of oxygen vacancies when oxygen ions move to the interstitial site or back to oxygen vacancies, respectively. Figure 29(d) describes another factor that affects the oxygen ion concentration in bulk. The barrier means the reaction ability of the anode or cathode with oxygen ions. For example, a Pt electrode has a very low barrier so that the boundary condition of Eq. (5) is suitable for resolving the partial differential equation of Eq. (4). The boundary condition of Eq. (6) for a high barrier can be used for an electrode of made of TiN. Since the oxygen ion concentration near the oxygen vacancies is affected by the barrier of the electrode material, the impact factors of the Reset process can be organized as four items:

(1) diffusive migration of oxygen ions;
(2) drifted migration of oxygen ions;
(3) recombination between oxygen ions and oxygen vacancies; and
(4) the interface barrier height between the cathode and bulk.

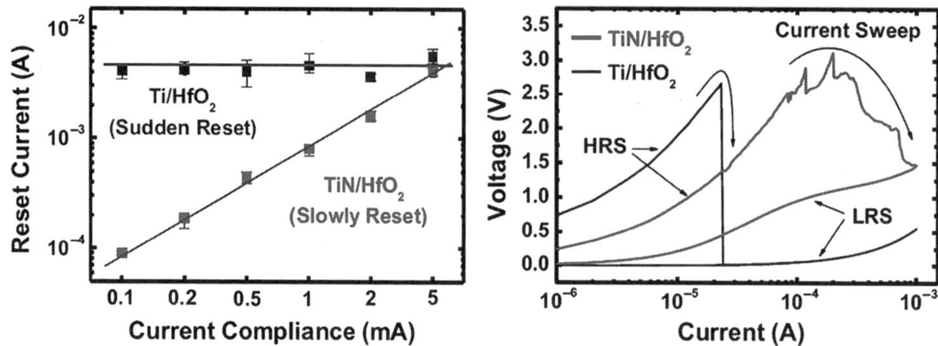

Figure 30. Left, CC of the Set process dependence of the Reset current. The Reset current of devices with a TiN electrode monotonically depends on the CC, but devices with a Ti electrode are independent; right, typical current-sweep *I–V* curves of Ti/HfO_2 and TiN/HfO_2 in the Set process. Reprinted with permission from [23], B. Gao et al., "Proceedings of IEEE International Symposium on VLSI Technology Systems and Applications (VLSI-TSA)," p. 144, Hsinchu, Taiwan, 2010. © 2010, The Institute of Electrical and Electronics Engineers (IEEE).

In the following discussion, some experimental results of the Reset process from the recent literature are organized and analyzed.

2.2.2.1. CC Effect on the Reset Process. The left side of Figure 30 presents the Set CC effect on the Reset current [23]. Here, the Set processes were done by CS control instead of the VS control. Two distinguishable phenomena are clearly observed for HfO_2 TMO-RRAM devices with TiN and Ti electrodes. The reset current of devices with TiN electrodes depends on the CC amplitude of the Set process both monotonically and linearly, but devices with Ti electrodes are independent with the Set process. The right side of Figure 30 shows the typical *I–V* characteristics of Ti/HfO_2 and TiN/HfO_2 in a CS-controlled Set process. A sharp resistance transition of Ti/HfO_2 is obtained at the critical current amplitude. On the other hand, the transition is gradual in TiN/HfO_2-based TMO-RRAM. The difference in the CF formation of a TMO-RRAM device between the Ti and TiN electrodes might play an important role. Due to the gradual resistance switching of the device with a TiN electrode from the HRS to LRS, multiple CFs induced by the Set process are believed to be the root cause of the CC linearly dependent Reset current. In contrast, a single CF formation can explain the sudden Reset and Set processes of devices with Ti electrodes.

Because the Ti and TiN electrodes have different oxygen gettering abilities, the barrier height at the interface between the bulk and electrode is different (see Fig. 29(d)). The evaluated time and location-dependent oxygen ion concentrations in bulk contribute to the differences in recombination between the oxygen vacancies and oxygen ions. Meanwhile, the oxygen concentration also depends on the grain boundary condition [50, 106]; a different grain boundary performance might also contribute to the different Reset process of Figure 30.

2.2.2.2. Temperature Effect on the Reset Process. From the various resistance switching models, the temperature dependence plays a key factor in not only the oxygen ion diffusion but also the recombination between the oxygen ions and oxygen vacancies. The left side of Figure 31 shows a temperature-dependent Reset process of TMO-RRAM with HfO_2 matrix. A monotonic Reset voltage decrease with an increasing temperature indicates the thermally assistant oxygen ions diffusion and recombination dynamics during Reset process [107, 109, 110]. The time revolution of the oxygen ion concentration can be understood by Eq. (4). The degraded drift movement of oxygen ions migration caused by the applying voltage can be achieved by increasing the temperature, i.e., increasing the oxygen ion diffusion movement. On the other hand, since the drift movement of oxygen ions migration depends on voltage polarity, the temperature dependent Reset and Set processes should be asymmetric. The left side of Figure 30 provides evidence that the Set process is more temperature insensitive than the Reset process. For recombination between oxygen ions and oxygen vacancies, since the capture section depends on the ability to depleted electrons by applying voltage (Figs. 29(a and b)), an enhanced electron depletion by thermal assistance can decrease the Reset voltage.

However, the right side of Figure 31 presents a temperature effect unlike that of the figure on the left. A temperature-insensitive behavior is found on TMO-RRAM devices with the TaO_x matrix and TiN electrode [108]. The reason has not been discussed in detail in the previous literature. Based on the unified and ion-transport-recombination models, one can give a possible root cause as indicated below.

Because both the Reset and Set voltages are smaller than those of most TMO-RRAM systems, the oxygen vacancies formation of the CFs can be understood as oxygen ion movement to the nearest interstitial position. Thus, the requirement of the capture section for the recombination becomes smaller. Also, because of an interfacial layer, TiON, formation, the oxygen ion barrier at the interface between the bulk and the electrode no longer plays the role of the Reset process. During the Reset process, i.e., the rupture of the CF, the diffusion of oxygen ions becomes a weak impact factor. The only impact factor is the oxygen ion drift movement, which depends on the voltage and the voltage polarity and it is independent of temperature.

2.2.2.3. Device Cell Size Effect on the Reset Process. The majority of the experimental results from the prior literature describe the Reset process as almost insensitive

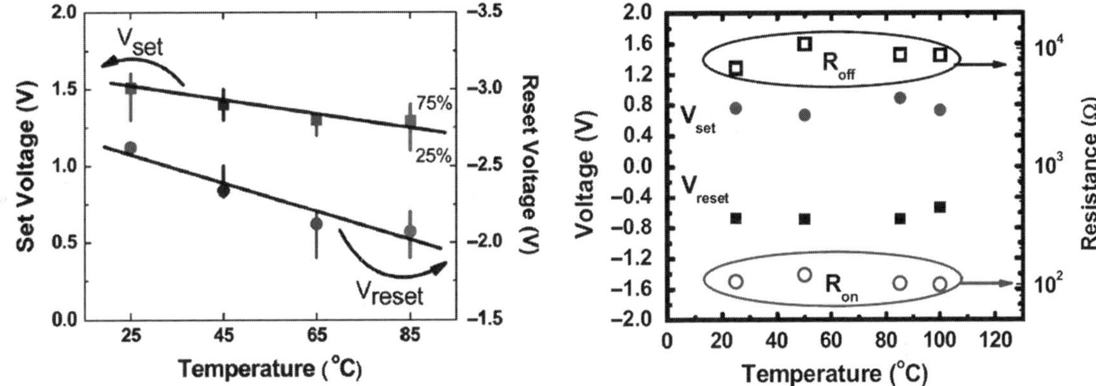

Figure 31. Left, temperature-dependent Reset process of the TMO with HfO_2 matrix. A monotonic Reset voltage decrease with increasing temperature indicates the thermally assistant diffusion and recombination processes during the Reset; right, opposite to the left side, an RRAM device with a TaO_x matrix and TiN electrode reveals the temperature insensitive Reset process. Reprinted with permission from [107], Z. Fang et al., "Proceedings of 2010 IEEE International Reliability Physics Symposium (IRPS)," p. 964, Anaheim, CA, 2010. © 2010, The Institute of Electrical and Electronics Engineers (IEEE); and from [108], L. Zhang et al., "Proceedings of the 10th IEEE International Conference on Solid-State and Integrated Circuit Technology (ICSICT)," p. 1160, Shanghai, China, 2010. © 2010, The Institute of Electrical and Electronics Engineers (IEEE).

to device cell size [24, 28, 103]. Figure 32 shows the cell-size dependent Reset voltage and Reset current of HfO_2-based TMO-RRAM memory devices [24]. The upper figure in Figure 32 reveals that the Reset voltage is insensitive to device cell size, while the lower figure depicts a very slow Reset current degradation with the device cell size. Due to the rupture of the CF during the Reset process, the Reset power (including the voltage and current) depends only on the properties of the CF, e.g., the number of CFs, the effective radius of the CF, and the dynamics between the electrode and TMO matrix, instead of device cell size.

Recently, several promising results of TMO-RRAM devices with device cell sizes of less than 10 nm have attracted investigation. Currently, performances of the devices have shown a totally different trend than those larger than 30 nm. Both figures in Figure 33 show that the programming current has a dramatic drop beyond the critical dimension of 10 nm [34, 67]. The left side of Figure 33 is based on a dash-bottom electrode with the smallest dimension of 5 nm. The device is an AlO_x-based TMO-RRAM with an area of 5 nm by 65 nm and with a conductive electrode of TiO_x. The right side of Figure 33 has a small recessed via structure with a critical dimension of 9 nm. The device is WO_x-based TMO-RRAM with top electrode of TiON. Except for the programming current, the success of Figure 33 indicates the TMO-RRAM has potential to scale-down till nano-meter size, implying the replacement of current mainstream non-volatile memory devices in the future. Attractively developed TMO-RRAM for nano-meter scaled device still needs more persuasive evidence in order to illustrate a resistance switching mechanism, since device cell size is comparable to that of conductive filament.

2.2.2.4. Electrode Effect on the Reset Process.

In Subsection 2.1.1.6 of Section 2.1.1, we discussed the electrode effect on the Forming process, including the cathode and anode. The different boundary conditions for TMO-RRAM with and without a barrier are described in Eqs. (5) and (6), respectively. The electrode effect on both Reset and Set processes is, however, more complicated because the TMO-RRAM can sometimes change its resistance-switching mode from bipolar to unipolar resistance switching under the electrode alternation [71]. The Reset process of the unipolar resistance switching is totally different from that of the bipolar version. The former needs a voltage stress with the same electric polarity as the Forming and Set processes and Joule

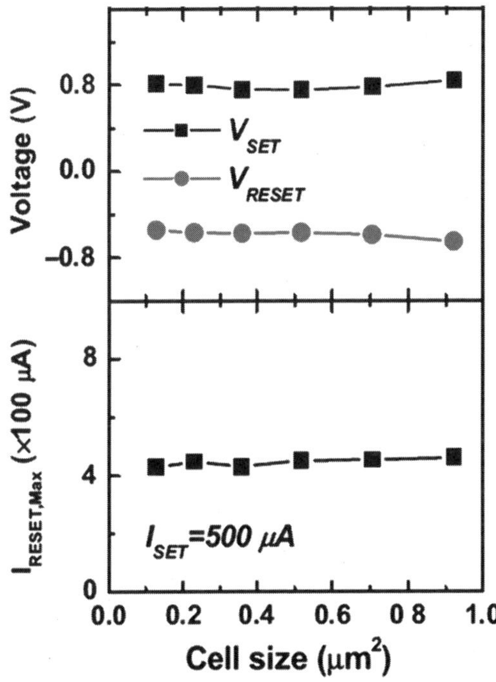

Figure 32. Device cell size dependence of various resistance switching parameters in TMO-based RRAM. The upper figure shows that the Reset voltage is insensitive to the device cell size. The lower figure shows a very slow Reset current degradation with the device cell size. Reprinted with permission from [24], Y.-S. Chen et al., "Proceedings of IEEE International Symposium on VLSI Technology Systems and Applications (VLSI-TSA)," p. 37, Hsinchu, Taiwan, 2009. © 2009, The Institute of Electrical and Electronics Engineers (IEEE).

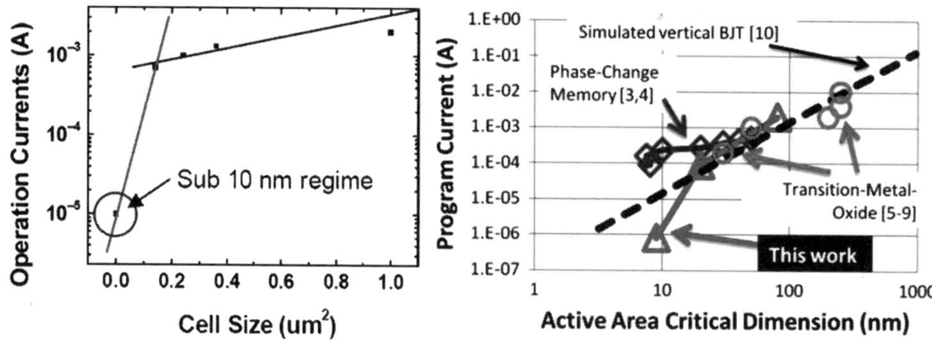

Figure 33. Left, an abrupt programming currents transition appears at around the sub-10-nm region; right, programming current versus RRAM device size. Reprinted with permission from [34], M. J. Kim et al., "IEEE International Electron Devices Meeting (IEDM) Technical Digest," p. 444, San Francisco, CA, 2010. © 2010, The Institute of Electrical and Electronics Engineers (IEEE); and from [67], C. H. Ho et al., "IEEE International Electron Devices Meeting (IEDM) Technical Digest," p. 436, San Francisco, CA, 2010. © 2010, The Institute of Electrical and Electronics Engineers (IEEE).

heating assistance to rupture the CF. The latter needs a voltage stress with opposite electric polarity to the Forming and Set processes and recombination between oxygen ions and vacancies. Electron transportation between oxygen vacancy and electrode might play an important role in the resistance switching. In general, TMO-RRAM with a noble metal electrode is observed as a unipolar mode, such as Pt/ZrO_2/Pt, Pt/HfO_2/Pt and Pt/ZnO/Pt. TMO-RRAM with oxidizable metal is frequently found to be a bipolar mode, such as Ti/ZrO_2/Pt, TiN/HfO_2/Pt, and TiN/ZnO/Pt. Detail of the unipolar resistance switching is described in Section 2.3. From Eq. (11), the hopping rates between electrode (0 or $N+1$ state) and oxygen vacancy (state "m") can be described as:

$$\Gamma_m^{iC} = \alpha * \Gamma_{0m}, \quad \Gamma_m^{oC} = \alpha * \Gamma_{m0} \tag{15}$$

$$\Gamma_m^{iA} = \beta * \Gamma_{(N+1)m}, \quad \Gamma_m^{oA} = \beta * \Gamma_{m(n+1)} \tag{16}$$

where α and β are coefficients of the boundary conditions on the cathode and anode, respectively. A and C mean anode and cathode. i and o represent the electron hopping on the site and out of the site. The stochastic model predicts that both α and β values can decide resistance switching between bipolar and unipolar modes [60]. If α and β are larger than 1, the low occupation region is formed near the anode and has unipolar resistance switching. If α and β are lower than 1, the low occupation region is close to the cathode and has bipolar resistance switching. Figure 34 shows the variations of resistance switching parameters in Ti/ZrO_2/Pt, Pt/ZrO_2/Pt, and Al/ZrO_2/Pt memory devices. V_{off} and V_{on} mean the voltage of Reset and Set processes, respectively. Different resistance switching modes are observed between the Ti and Pt top electrodes. The former is the bipolar resistance-switching mode; the latter is the unipolar mode.

The oxygen ion barrier at the interface of the bulk and electrode was discussed in Subsection 2.1.1.6 of Section 2.1.1. Ti as the electrode of TMO-RRAM has a higher barrier than the Pt electrode so that many oxygen ions can accumulate at the interface. This not only can help the stability of the Reset-Set cycle endurance but also the prevention of multiple CFs in bulk. Hence, a stable Reset current can be successfully achieved by replacing the top electrode of TiN with TiN/Ti for TiO_x, ZrO_x, and HfO_x-based TMO-RRAM [25].

2.2.2.5. Reset Voltage-Dependent HRS. Because of the electron-hopping transportation and the rupture of the CF by a recombination of oxygen ions and oxygen vacancies during the Reset process, the resistance of the HRS is expected to be a function of the Reset voltage. When introducing enough applied Reset voltage (not only DC VS control but also the electric pulse) for the state transition from the LRS to HRS, both the increased drift movement of the oxygen ion and the increased capture section of oxygen vacancy for recombination result in the disappearance of some oxygen vacancies in the CF. The increased hopping distance in turn exponentially enhances the resistance. Figure 35 reveals the increasing of the HRS resistance by applying the Reset voltage with DC VS and electric pulse [57, 111]. Furthermore, an extreme case can be predicted: all oxygen vacancies in

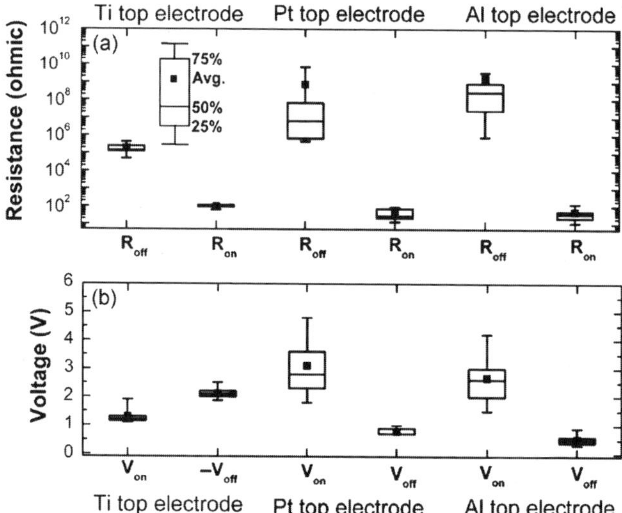

Figure 34. Resistance-switching parameters of Ti/ZrO_2/Pt, Pt/ZrO_2/Pt, and Al/ZrO_2/Pt devices. Reprinted with permission from [82], C.-Y. Lin et al., *IEEE Electron. Device. Lett.* 28, 366 (2007). © 2007, The Institute of Electrical and Electronics Engineers (IEEE).

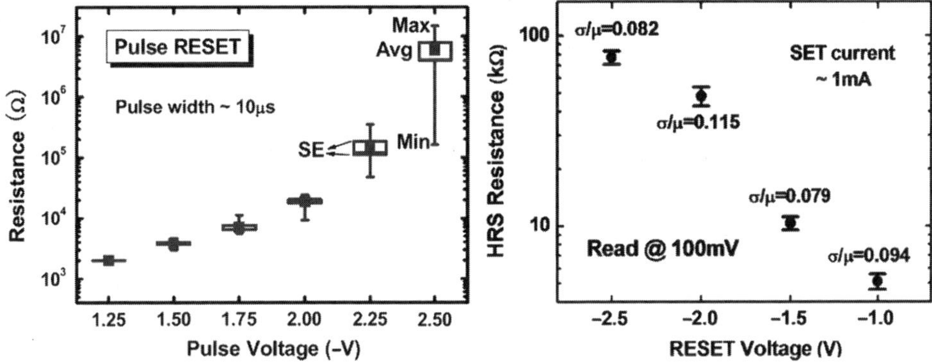

Figure 35. Left, pulse voltage-dependent resistance of a TMO-RRAM device during the Reset process; right, effect of the Reset voltage on HRS resistance under DC voltage-sweep control with current-sweep control for the Set process. Reprinted with permission from [111], B. Gao et al., "Proceedings of the 10th IEEE International Conference on Solid-State and Integrated Circuit Technology (ICSICT)," p. 1145, Shanghai, China, (2010). © 2010, The Institute of Electrical and Electronics Engineers (IEEE); and from [57], B. Chen et al., *IEEE Electron. Device. Lett.* 32, 282 (2011). © 2011, The Institute of Electrical and Electronics Engineers (IEEE).

the bulk are disappeared by a very strong Reset voltage. This state would be irreversible, resulting in a return to the initial state before the Forming process.

2.2.2.6. Reset Voltage Dependent on the Reset Time.

Figure 36 depicts the relationship between the Reset voltage and Reset time of ZnO-based TMO-RRAM with various top electrodes and thicknesses [62]. The Reset process includes the oxygen ion movement by diffusion and drift as well as the recombination between oxygen ion and oxygen vacancy. The former needs a movement time, τ_m; the latter needs a recombination time, τ_r. Total Reset time is the sum of τ_m and τ_r:$\tau_{\text{Reset}} = \tau_m + \tau_r$. As discussed in Section 2.2.2, recombination is a function of the oxygen ion concentration near electron-low-occupied oxygen vacancy. On the other hand, since the oxygen concentration near the low occupation oxygen vacancy depends on the oxygen movement, τ_m is also a function of τ_m. In the left side of Figure 36, two different slopes of Reset time versus Reset voltage indicate different dominant reactions. In the low voltage region, the Reset time, τ_{Reset}, strongly depends on the applied Reset voltage before turning point. The recombination time, τ_r, becomes a dominant factor of resistance switching because τ_r is much larger than τ_m. This is making sense because electron depletion of oxygen vacancy strongly depends on the applied voltage. A higher voltage of the Reset process would enhance the recombination probability between the oxygen ion and depleted oxygen vacancy. On the other hand, if the applied voltage is high enough, such that $\tau_r \approx \tau_m$, the total Reset time includes both τ_r and τ_m. A weaker Reset voltage dependence of Reset time than τ_r dominated is found after the turning point.

The right side of Figure 36 presents the low-field characteristics of TMO-RRAM with various cathode materials and various TMO-RRAM thicknesses. The slope and τ_{Reset} are found to be insensitive to TMO-RRAM thicknesses, indicating the recombination process occurs near the interface. Furthermore, a very low oxygen ion barrier at the interface between the bulk and Pt cathode electrode can greatly enhance the recombination probability such that the Reset time is much lower than TMO-RRAM with oxidizable cathode, such as TiN, under the same applied voltage.

2.2.3. Set Process

Like the Forming process discussed in Section 2.1, the Set process is operated to change the resistance state of

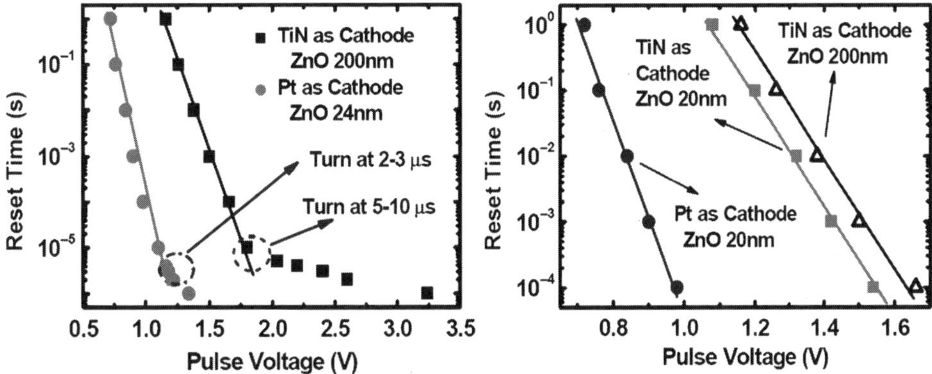

Figure 36. Left, effect of the pulse voltage on the measured Reset time for a ZnO RRAM device; right, pulse voltage-dependent Reset time of ZnO RRAM with various thicknesses and electrodes. Reprinted with permission from [62], B. Gao et al., "IEEE International Electron Devices Meeting (IEDM) Technical Digest," p. 563, San Francisco, CA, 2008. © 2008, The Institute of Electrical and Electronics Engineers (IEEE).

TMO-RRAM from the HRS to LRS. Instead of the initially ultra-high resistance of the TMO-RRAM memory device, here the HRS is obtained by rupturing the CF during the Reset process. The reversible Set process can regenerate the CF again and further provide the LRS of the TMO-RRAM memory device. Similar to the Reset process, the Set process depends on the device characteristics or resistance of the preprogramming (pre-Set) process, too. Effectively obtaining a CF is important in TMO-RRAM device design. On the other hand, the strength of formed CF in TMO-RRAM can determine how strong the CF is at room or higher temperature. Some researchers have mentioned that improving the Set process and data retention issues is a tradeoff. In order clarify the formation dynamics of CFs in detail, in this subsection, we will describe following five topics:

(1) transport-mechanism of the HRS;
(2) data retention;
(3) the HRS stability;
(4) modeling; and
(5) some experimental results.

Due to the nonlinear I–V characteristics of the HRS, many prior articles have discussed its transportation mechanism, including the Schottky emission of Eq. (8) [85, 94, 97–100], the SCLS of Eq. (9) [24, 28, 74, 87, 101–104, 112, 113], the electron-hopping conduction Eq. (10) [60–65, 67, 79, 95, 96], the PF emission [112], and tunneling [34, 50, 107, 110]. Examples of electron hopping can be understood through Figure 37, which describes the temperature and voltage effects on the HRS read-current or resistance of TMO-RRAM memory device. The TMO material here is a highly graded WO_x produced by an optimized plasma oxidation condition [65]. The characteristics of its LRS are presented in Figure 23 with a typical linear I–V curve and monotonically increased resistance with temperature, indicating the Ohmic transportation. In Figure 37, the variable range hopping (VRH; dash-dot curve and white-dashed line in the inset) with both

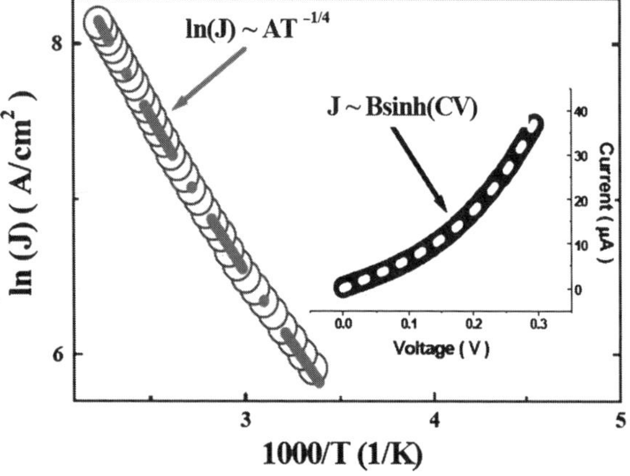

Figure 37. HRS read-current as functions of temperature and voltage. Variable Range Hopping (VRH, dash-dot curve and white-dashed line in inset) is proposed to explain the transport. Reprinted with permission from [65], C. H. Ho et al., "IEEE Symposium on VLSI Technology Digest of Technical Papers," p. 228, Kyota, Japan, 2007. © 2007, The Institute of Electrical and Electronics Engineers (IEEE).

$\ln(J) \propto T^{-1/4}$ and $J \propto \sin h(V)$ can explain the transportation mechanism. According to the fitting results, the hopping distance of ~15 Å is observed, implying that many of the oxygen vacancies in the bulk between hopping sites or between the electrode and hopping sites are recombined with migrated oxygen ions during the Reset process. Figure 38 shows the simulated scheme of the formation and rupture of the CF during the Reset and Set processes [96]. In Figure 38(d), the density of oxygen vacancies with and without electron occupation degrades greatly under the Reset process compared with the LRS after the Set process. This indicates the HRS of the TMO-RRAM memory device due to the large hopping distances between oxygen vacancies and between the electrode and oxygen vacancies.

By moderating the impact parameters of hopping conduction, such as the hopping distance (R), decay constant of the electron wave-function (α), and the density-of-state near the Fermi level ($N(E_F)$), many TMO-RRAM systems can be examined. Instead of the interface charge trapping by the Schottky emission model or bulk trapping by the SCLC model and the PF emission model, the transition of

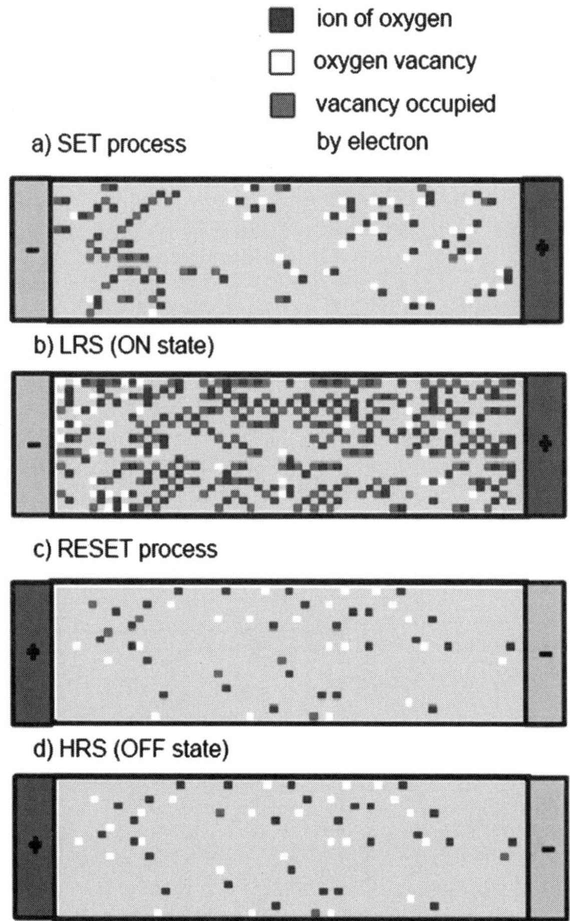

Figure 38. Simulated modeling of a bipolar-mode TMO memory cell: (a) Set process, (b) CF in LRS, (c) Reset process, and (d) CF in HRS. Reprinted with permission from [96], A. Makarov et al., "Proceedings of the 14th IEEE International Workshop on Computational Electronics (IWCE)," p. 35, Pisa, Italy, 2010. © 2010, The Institute of Electrical and Electronics Engineers (IEEE).

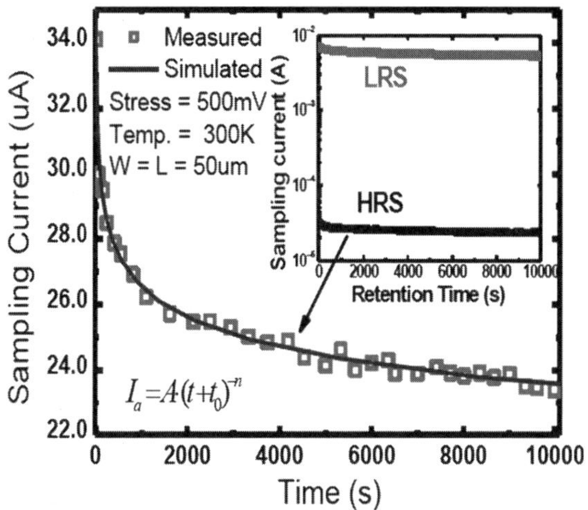

Figure 39. Relaxation behavior of a ZnO-based TMO device with a TiN top electrode. Reprinted with permission from [61], N. Xu et al., "IEEE Symposium on VLSI Technology Digest of Technical Papers," p. 100, Honolulu, HI, 2008. © 2008, The Institute of Electrical and Electronics Engineers (IEEE).

the electron-hopping transportation between the high and low density oxygen vacancies is used to simplify the discussion below and explain the transition between the LRS and HRS by the Set and Reset processes, respectively. Figure 39 provides evidence of resistance switching controlled by the formation and rupture of the CF in a ZnO-based TMO-RRAM memory device with a TiN top electrode [61]. The stress voltage of 500 mV is lower than the transition voltage (Set voltage). Both the relaxation curves of the HRS and LRS as functions of stress time can be well fitted by the Pillai model, the black curve in Figure 39, and described as:

$$I_a = A * (t + t_0)^{-n} \tag{17}$$

These equations relate to the polarization effect caused by oxygen ion migration in the dielectric.

Due to the formation and recombination dynamics of the oxygen vacancy for the Set and Reset processes, respectively, electron emission and capture in the trapping center, such as oxygen vacancies without occupation, should be considered [47, 75, 101]. Also, the normalized noise power spectral density based on normalized $1/f$ noise of a planar diode resistor can be described as:

$$S_i/I^2 = S_v/V^2 = \frac{\alpha qL}{5\varepsilon AV} * \left(\frac{1}{f}\right)^{\gamma} \tag{18}$$

where γ is a fitting parameter, f is the measuring frequency, ε is the dielectric constant of TMO-RRAM material, A is the cross-sectional area, q is the elementary electron charge, and α is the Hooge's parameter, which can determine the noise level in different devices or materials. Measurements of the normalized noise power spectral density on various TMO-RRAM memory devices showed $\gamma \sim 1$, indicating that the bipolar resistance switching TMO-RRAM still obeys the classical $1/f$ noise theory in both the HRS and LRS [47, 101]. According to the right side of Figure 40 and Eq. (18), Hooge's parameters of ~14000 and ~1500 are obtained for the HRS and LRS, respectively (Table 3).

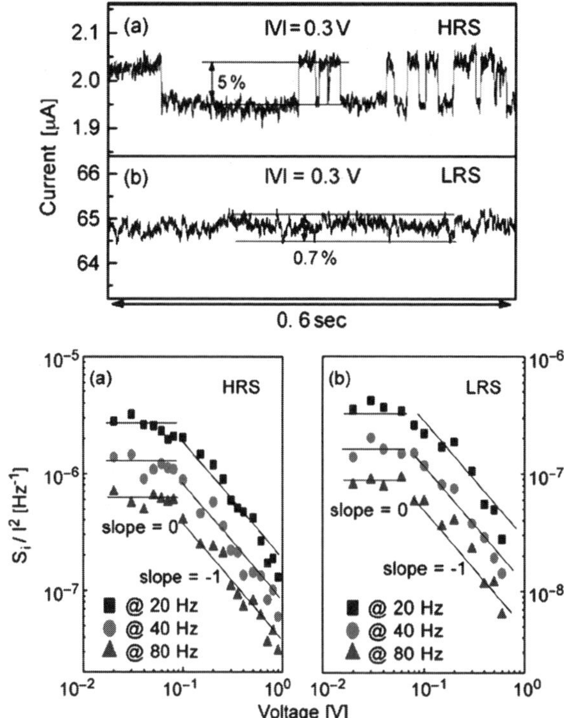

Figure 40. Left, read current fluctuations of both (a) HRS and (b) LRS. RTN is obviously found in HRS; right, voltage dependent S_i/I^2 at various frequencies for (a) HRS and (b) LRS. Reprinted with permission from [101], J.-K. Lee et al., *IEEE Electron. Device Lett.* 31, 603 (2010). © 2010, The Institute of Electrical and Electronics Engineers (IEEE).

Note that the noise level of the HRS of a TiO_x-based TMO-RRAM device is much higher than those of general metal oxides. The observed material with the highest noise level is CMR material, which is discussed in Section 1 [101]. One order of magnitude higher of Hooge's parameter for the HRS than for LRS can also be found by a random telegraph noise (RTN) measurement (Fig. 40). The magnitude of the noise current fluctuation is ~5% in the HRS, but it is ~0.7% in the LRS. The memory device showing the RTN in the HRS is the same as the one that shows the largest S_i/I^2. A similar result was also found in an MIM-structured Ta_2O_5/TiO_2 TMO-RRAM device with a Ru bottom electrode [47]. The capture and emission of the electrons with the oxygen vacancy near the CF result in the fluctuation of the measured current in the LRS. In the HRS of the TMO-RRAM memory device, the measured current fluctuation results from the oxygen vacancy near the CF and in the tunneling barrier.

Table 3. Hooge's parameter of various materials. The noise level of HRS of TiO_x-based TMO device is much higher than general metal–oxides. The highest noise level is in the CMR material discussed in introduction.

	Ordinary metal	Fe_3O_4	LRS of TiO_x	CrO_2	HRS of TiO_x	CMR
Hooge's parameter (α)	< 0, 01	~80	1,500	~2,000	14,000	> 100, 000

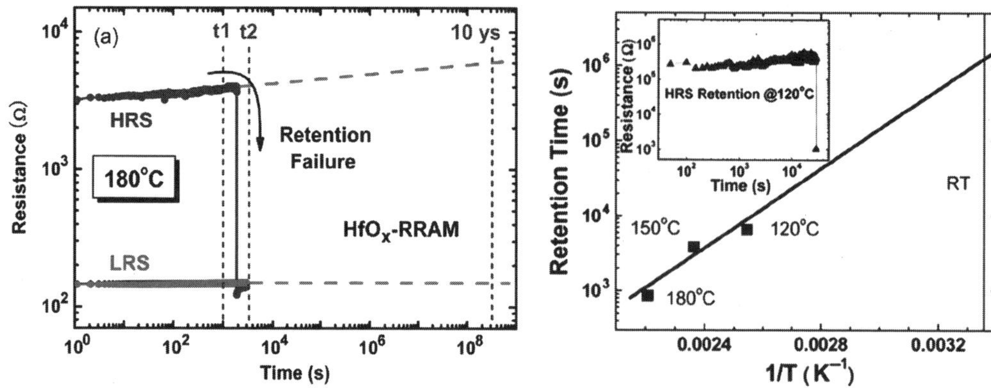

Figure 41. Left, 180°C data retention of a TMO-RRAM device and projected lifetime by traditional retention evaluation method; right, temperature-dependent HRS retention time. The retention time is defined at the point where the resistance state suddenly changes; see the inset. Reprinted with permission from [114], B. Gao et al., *IEEE Electron. Device. Lett.* 32, 276 (2011). © 2011, The Institute of Electrical and Electronics Engineers (IEEE); and from [110], Z. Fang et al., *IEEE Electron. Device. Lett.* 31, 476 (2010). © 2010, The Institute of Electrical and Electronics Engineers (IEEE).

The HRS of TMO-RRAM suffers issues of not only the high read-current fluctuation within a very short time-scale, including the RTN and low frequency noise, but also data retention failure over a very long time scale. Figure 41 displays the typical HRS and LRS data retention behaviors of a Ga-doped HfO_2-based TMO-RRAM memory device at 180°C and the projected lifetime by the traditional retention evaluation method, shown in the purple dash-lines [114]. More than 10 years of data retention ability at 180°C can be easily predicted. However, the reality is that the HRS of a TMO device drops its resistance value from an initially high resistance to a lower one suddenly at around 2000 sec. This sudden-dropped failure of the resistance state is complete different from that of conventional nonvolatile memories, such as floating-gate flash memory. Thus, the retention projection methodology is the most important work in the nonvolatility study of RRAM. Since the resistance switching of TMO-based devices comes from the formation and rupture of the CF (see Section 2.1.1), thermally activated process-induced oxygen vacancy generation in the ruptured CF is assumed to be the HRS failure model. This assumption is reasonable due to the temperature-dependent oxygen ion diffusive movement and thermally assisted oxygen vacancy formation in the ruptured CF. Accordingly, the formation energy of the oxygen vacancy, $E_f(X^Q)$ discussed in Eq. (3) of Section 2.1.1, is a key factor of the TMO-RRAM failure mode. Based on crystal defect and probability theories, the targeted retention time (t_E) and the time revolution failure probability of the HRS failure ($F(t;\ V, T)$) can be written as [114]:

$$F(t; V, T) \approx F(t) * \exp(QLV/2dkT)$$
$$t_E \approx \alpha^{-1} * \exp[E_f(x^Q) - (QLV/2d)/kT]; \quad \alpha = \frac{n}{t_0} \quad (19)$$

where Q is the electric charge quantity of oxygen vacancy described in Eq. (3); L is the lattice constant; d is the effective length of the ruptured CF; α is a constant and equal to n/t_0; n is the total amount of possible sites for oxygen vacancy; t_0 is the vibration period for lattice oxygen atoms; V is applied voltage stress; and T is the environment temperature. Equation (19) implies that the Arrhenius plot with various temperatures can successfully predict the data retention ability of the HRS of a TMO-RRAM memory device (Fig. 41) with the HRS retention time as a function of temperature. The inset shows the HRS data retention at 120°C, and the retention time is defined as the point where resistance suddenly drops. Similarly, the left side of Figure 42 reveals the retention time as a function of temperature for different formation energy keeping the parameters of Q, L, and d. Once the formation energy of the oxygen vacancy is measured, the retention time can be easily estimated. The expected retention time is better than 10 years if the formation energy of the oxygen vacancy is larger than 1.3 eV. The right side of Figure 42 displays the calculated formation energy of oxygen vacancy for various TMO matrixes of HfO_2, ZrO_2, and TiO_2 with various dopants of Ti, Al, La, and Ga [43]. Decreasing the oxygen vacancy formation energy causes data retention issues, although it can improve the Forming process and uniformity as well (see Section 2.1.1). Poor data retention of Ga-doped HfO_2-based TMO-RRAM memory device shown in the left side of Figure 41 comes from the degraded formation energy of oxygen vacancy by trivalent dopant in tetravalent host material, so the oxygen vacancies are generated in the rupture region of the CF. In turn, the resistance suddenly drops to the LRS once the oxygen vacancies are generated.

Although the LRS of TMO-RRAM behaves around one order of magnitude lower than Hooge's parameter noise level (α) from Eq. (18) within a very short time scale, its data retention ability under a very long time scale is still an issue. The left side of Figure 43 shows the time-to-failure of the LRS at 110°C, 125°C, and 135°C for an MIM-stacked TiN/Cu_xO/Cu TMO-RRAM memory device cell. Similar to the HRS failure mode, the LRS of a TMO-RRAM memory device also presents a temperature-dependent resistance sudden transition. The retention time degradation at a higher temperature indicates the thermally assisted rupture of the CF. In addition, since the LRS also follows the Arrhenius plot (see Fig. 43) with the activation energy of 1.8 eV, the activation energy here

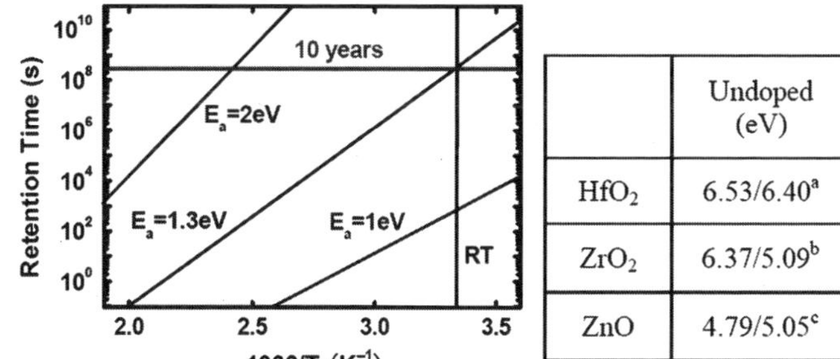

	Undoped (eV)	Ti (eV)	Al (eV)	La (eV)	Ga (eV)
HfO_2	6.53/6.40[a]	6.48	4.09	3.42	–
ZrO_2	6.37/5.09[b]	6.11	3.66	3.74	3.77
ZnO	4.79/5.05[c]	–	–	–	–

Figure 42. Left, temperature dependent retention time for various formation energies; right, calculated energy of the oxygen vacancy for various TMO matrixes with various dopants. Decreasing of the formation energy improves the forming process and uniformity as well, but this results in data retention issues. Reprinted with permission from [115], B. Gao et al., "Proceedings of the European Solid-State Device Research Conference (ESSDERC)," p. 392, Seville, Spain, 2010. © 2010, The Institute of Electrical and Electronics Engineers (IEEE); and from [43], B. Gao et al., "IEEE Symposium on VLSI Technology Digest of Technical Papers," p. 30, Kyoto, Japan, 2009. © 2009, The Institute of Electrical and Electronics Engineers (IEEE).

relates to the recombination process between the oxygen ion and oxygen vacancy, which is similar to what is seen in the Reset process. As described in Section 2.2.2, the increased environmental temperature can reduce the Reset voltage due to the enhanced oxygen ion diffusion movement and enhanced electron depletion by thermal assistance. Thus, the temperature dependent LRS failure mode can be realized.

From the discussion of HRS data retention, the failure mode of the HRS results from the thermally assisted generation of the oxygen vacancy in the ruptured CF. In Eqs. (15) and (16), if α and β are greater than 1, the low occupation region is formed near the anode and behaves like unipolar resistance switching. On the contrary, the low occupation region is close to the cathode and presents bipolar resistance switching. The dynamics of the CF near the cathode play key roles in the Set and Reset processes. The formation of the CF might generate oxygen vacancy during the oxygen ion movement to the nearest interstitial position [60, 63, 64, 96] or accumulate at the interface between the cathode and insulator [62]. Another resistance-switching mechanism by redox reaction was proposed by Bersuker

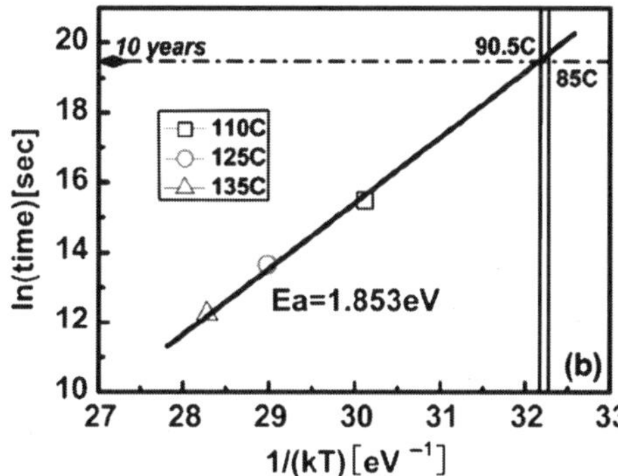

Figure 43. Arrhenius plot and extrapolation for LRS data retention time. Reprinted with permission from [134], H. Wan, et al., "Proceedings of the 10th IEEE International Conference on Solid-State and Integrated Circuit Technology (ICSICT)," p. 1100, Shanghai, China, 2010. © 2010, The Institute of Electrical and Electronics Engineers (IEEE).

et al. [50]. The trap-assisted-tunneling and metallically Ohmic conduction are believed to be the transportation of TMO-RRAM in the HRS and LRS, respectively. The simulation indicates that the CF of the HRS is separated from the cathode by a tunneling barrier of about 9 Å of HfO_2 dielectric. This is consistent with our previous result (shown in Fig. 26), implying that the hopping distance between oxygen vacancies or between the cathode and oxygen vacancy is around 15 Å for the HRS of a WO_x-based TMO-RRAM device [65]. Once the Set process is performed on a HRS of a TMO-RRAM memory device, the grain boundary current reaches a critical value that causes a sufficient Joule heating temperature for the oxygen dissociation under a provided bias condition and formation of a metal-rich CF. Figure 44 reveals the details of the formation and rupture of a CF with a conical shape. The simulated ultra-high temperature profile within the separation, d, supports this redox reaction.

Regarding the redox-reaction mechanism, a few studies have begun to explain the resistance alternation under the Set and Reset processes. Examples of the redox reaction for WO_x- and TaO_x-based TMO-RRAM memory devices can be realized as [85, 116]:

$$WO_{3-n} + nO^{2-} \longleftrightarrow 2ne^- + WO_3 \tag{20}$$

$$2TaO_2 + O^{2-} \longleftrightarrow 2e^- + Ta_2O_5 \tag{21}$$

The right sides of the equations represent the HRS after the Reset process, while the left sides of the equations represent the LRS after the Forming and Set processes. Both Eqs. (20) and (21) can be applied in Figure 44. Since heat is confined in the separation region of the CF, most of the redox reaction occurs near the cathode.

Beside the discussed elementary resistance-switching mechanisms, circuit-like modeling based on the two-variable resistors model [102, 113] and compact model [117] are also frequently used to simplify the transition. The two-variable resistor model can be understood by reviewing Figure 45 [113]. The example structure is based on a conventional two-point measurement of TiO_x thin film, i.e., the top-left figure of Figure 45. The top-right figure of Figure 45 represents the equivalent of an MIM-stacked TMO-RRAM memory device with a LRS filled-trap region and a HRS unfilled-trap region in the TiO_x matrix.

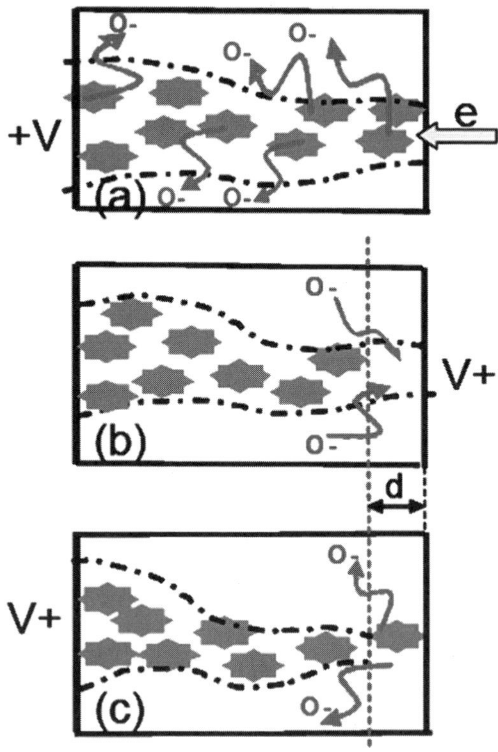

Figure 44. Schematic diagrams of the (a) forming, (b) Reset, and (c) Set processes. The region filled with stars represents the CF. Reprinted with permission from [50], G. Bersuker et al., "IEEE International Electron Devices Meeting (IEDM) Technical Digest," p. 456, San Francisco, CA, 2010. © 2010, The Institute of Electrical and Electronics Engineers (IEEE).

There are four assumptions of the two-variable resistor model [102, 113]:

(1) oxygen vacancy in the oxygen-deficient layer act as a trap for electrons, and they are uniformly distributed in the insulating layer;

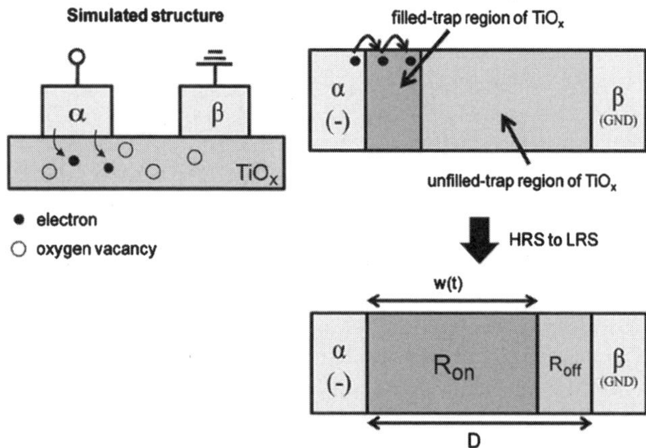

Figure 45. Schematic views of modeled resistance switching in an MIM-structured TMO device, Al (top electrode)/TiO_x/Al (top electrode), considering the variation of the LRS filled-trap region of TiO_x by injected carriers. Reprinted with permission from [113], S. Kim and Y.-K. Choi, *IEEE Trans. Electron. Device.* 56, 3049 (2009). © 2009, The Institute of Electrical and Electronics Engineers (IEEE).

(2) the insulating layer is divided into two parts, a good conducting part of thickness, $\omega(t)$, and a less conductive part of thickness, $D - \omega$;
(3) the filled-trap region of the insulating layer shows good conductivity, i.e., R_{LRS}; and
(4) the unfilled-trap region of the insulating layer shows poor conductivity, i.e., R_{HRS}.

Accordingly, one can describe the total resistance of Figure 45 as:

$$R_{\text{Total}} = R_{\text{LRS}} * \frac{\omega(t)}{D} + R_{\text{HRS}} * \left(1 - \frac{\omega(t)}{D}\right) \tag{22}$$

The bipolar resistance switching can be obtained under a designed time-revolution applied voltage and $\omega(t)/D$.

Figure 46 illustrates another circuit-like modeling, i.e., the compact model. There are three different resistances to be mentioned in Figure 46(a):

(1) the resistance of the CF, R_f;
(2) the resistance of the resistive-switching layer outside the CF, R_H; and
(3) the resistance of the anode and cathode, R_L.

The effective circuit of Figure 46(a) can be presented as Figures 46(b and c) is the flow chart of the compact model based on Set and Reset process controlled by CS and VS, respectively. Modeling can start from the following equation:

$$\text{Reset process: } R_f = R_0 m^{(1/b_v)};\quad m = m_0 + \int_{t_1}^{t_2} V(t)^{a_v}\, dt \tag{23}$$

$$\text{Set process: } 1/R_f = \sigma_0 \omega^{(1/b_i)};\ \omega = \omega_0 + \int_{t_1}^{t_2} I(t)^{a_i}\, dt \tag{24}$$

where ω_0 and m_0 are original states for the Set and Reset processes, respectively, and $1/b$ is the saturation coefficient. The bipolar resistance switching based on Eqs. (23) and (24) can be achieved by optimizing the parameters and coefficients, such as a_i, a_v, b_i, b_v, R_0, and σ_0.

In the following discussion, some experimental results of the Reset process from the recent literature are organized and analyzed.

2.2.3.1. Temperature Effect on the Reset Process. The left side figure of Figure 31 in Section 2.2.2 reveals a temperature-dependent Set process of HfO_2-based TMO-RRAM. A monotonic Set voltage that is decreasing with an increasing environment temperature indicates the thermally assistant oxygen ion diffusion and recombination processes during Set process. From the previous discussions of the HRS failure mode, the oxygen vacancy generation in the ruptured CF by the thermally activated process is the root cause of the temperature dependence of the Set process.

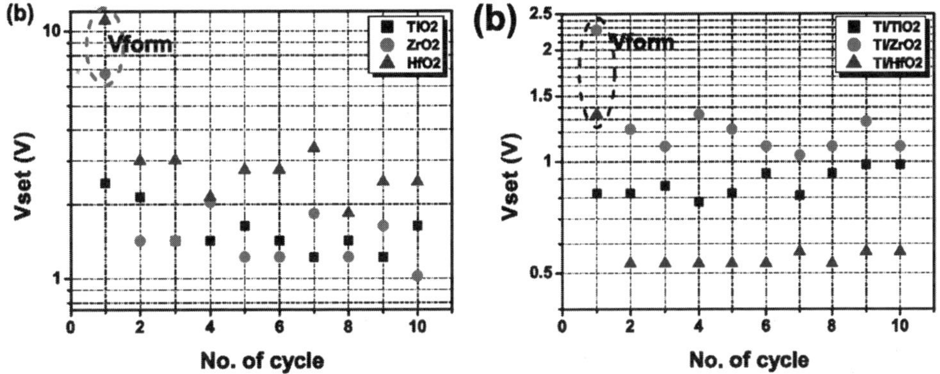

Figure 47. Left, the Set voltage distribution of a TMO device with TiN top and bottom electrodes under cycling; right, the Set voltage distribution of a TMO device with a TiN/Ti top electrode and a TiN bottom electrode under cycling. Reprinted with permission from [25], W. G. Kim et al., "Proceedings of the European Solid-State Device Research Conference (ESSDERC)," p. 400, Seville, Spain, 2010. © 2010, The Institute of Electrical and Electronics Engineers (IEEE).

2.2.3.2. Device Cell Size Effect on the Set Process. Figure 32 in Section 2.2.2 shows the Set voltage independent of the device cell size [24]. Due to the formation of the CF during the Set process, Set power (including voltage and current) therefore depends only on the characteristics of the CF, such as the number of CFs, the effective radius of the CFt, and the dynamics between the electrode and TMO-RRAM, instead of the size of the device cell.

2.2.3.3. Electrode Effect on the Set Process. Figure 47 depicts the effect of the top electrode replacing TiN to TiN/Ti on the Reset process of HfO_2-, ZrO_2-, and TiO_2-based TMO-RRAM memory devices [25]. Since the Ti insertion between the TiN and TMO matrix can act as an oxygen ion reservoir due to the high barrier to oxygen ions at the interface (see Section 2.2.2), a more stable Reset/Set cycle endurance can be predicted by the ion-transport-recombination resistance-switching mechanism than with TiN electrode. On the other hand, besides the stabilization, the Ti electrode also greatly improves the Set voltage from the TiN electrode. The reason is similar to that described in the Subsection 2.1.1.6 of Section 2.1.1.

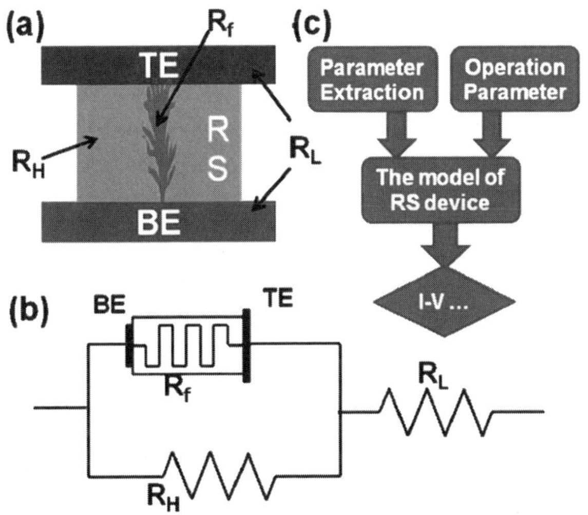

Figure 46. (a) Schematic view of MIM-structured TMO-RRAM; the CF with resistance R_f is in the resistive switching layer, (b) the equivalent circuit, and (c) the flowchart of the model. Reprinted with permission from [117], B. Chen et al., "Proceedings of the 10th IEEE International Conference on Solid-State and Integrated Circuit Technology (ICSICT)," p. 1829, Shanhai, China, 2010. © 2010, The Institute of Electrical and Electronics Engineers (IEEE).

2.2.3.4. Set Current Dependent LRS. Because of the electron-hopping transport mechanism and the formation of the CF by oxygen vacancy generation with oxygen ion movement during the Set process, the resistance of the LRS is expected to be a function of the Set current. The decreased hopping distance in turn exponentially enhances the conductance. Figure 48 presents the decrease of the LRS resistance by an applied Set current with a DC CS and electric pulse [57, 111]. The excellent tuning ability of the LRS resistance by the Set current is demonstrated.

2.3. Unipolar Resistance Switching

Similar to PCRAM, unipolar resistive memory has more advances in the scalability of nonvolatile memory than bipolar resistive memory due to the bit-share of a three-dimensional (3D) stackable one diode + one resistor structure and a cross-pointed cell design. This can be achieved with the same voltage polarity for all of the Forming, Reset, and Set processes. In contrast to unipolar resistance switching, since bipolar resistive memory needs a Reset process with an opposite voltage polarity to perform the resistance alternation, only a transistor-like selector can drive the bipolar resistive memory, including the metal–oxide–semiconductor field effect transistor, bipolar junction transistor, and so on. The feature size based on bipolar resistive memory of around 5~6 F^2 is larger than the unipolar one of around 4~5 F^2. Meanwhile, due to the poly-crystalline P/N diode, 3D stackable unipolar resistive memory becomes possible if some issues of unipolar resistive memory are resolved, including a very ultra-high Reset current, a high Forming voltage, programming instability, and data retention. Although some of these examples also occur in bipolar resistive memory, they are clearly minimized by a physical picture. In this section, we will review potential ways to resolve the bottlenecks of unipolar resistive memory.

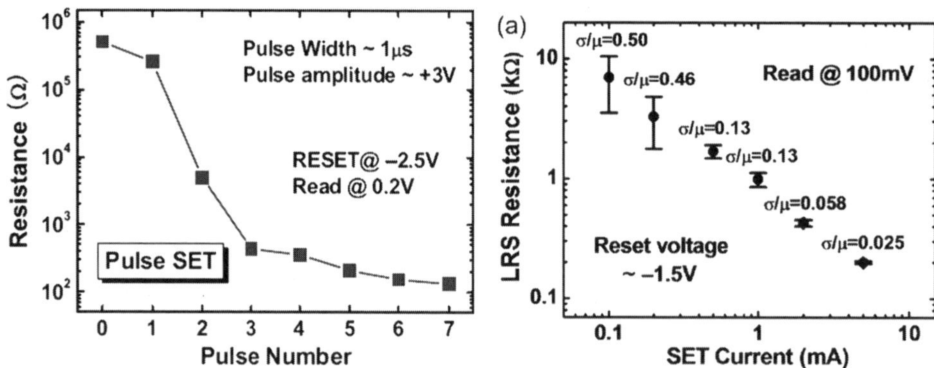

Figure 48. Left, number of Set pulse dependence of resistance on the Set process; right, measured LRS resistance as a function of the Set current under the DC current-sweep controlling. Reprinted with permission from [111], B. Gao et al., "Proceedings of the 10th IEEE International Conference on Solid-State and Integrated Circuit Technology (ICSICT)," p. 1145, Shanghai, China, 2010. © 2010, The Institute of Electrical and Electronics Engineers (IEEE); and from [57], B. Chen et al., *IEEE Electron. Device. Lett.* 32, 282 (2011). © 2011, The Institute of Electrical and Electronics Engineers (IEEE).

Figure 49 shows a typical unipolar resistance switching (left side) of a NiO-based MIM-stacked TMO-RRAM memory device and its cross-sectional image (right side). The Forming process (curve 1 → 2) is achieved by a positive electrical voltage stress of around 3.6 V. After forming, this RRAM device is in the "ON state," in which the resistance is lower (LRS). Note that the Forming process is performed by CS control, rather than VS control, due to the fine control of the CF (see Section 2.1.2). When a VS with the same electrical polarity as the Forming process is applied to the device, this TMO-RRAM memory device transfers its state from an initial LRS to a HRS at a critical transition voltage point of around 650 mV, or it may stay at a critical transition current level of around 10 mA. This clockwise curve is called a "Reset" process. When a CS with the same electrical polarity as the Forming and Reset processes is further applied to this device, the resistance state is changed from a HRS to a LRS again at a critical transition voltage point of around 2.4 V. This counterclockwise curve is called a "Set" process. Both the HRS and LRS are stable, even without the application of external voltage, thus indicating the nonvolatility of this RRAM device.

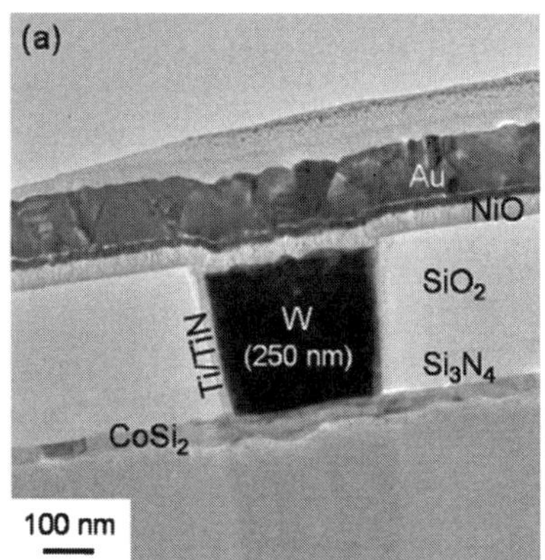

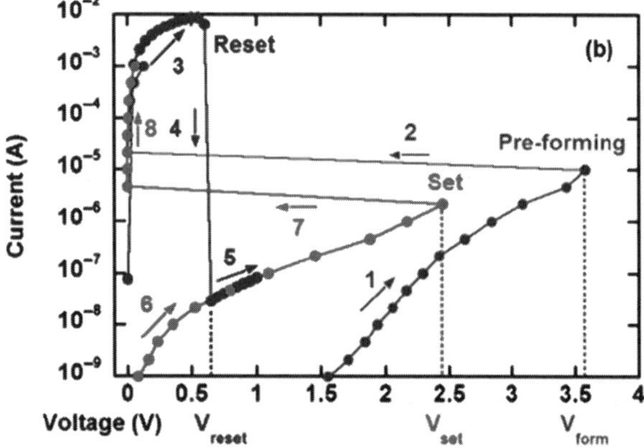

Figure 49. (a) Cross-sectional image of an MIM-structured NiO based unipolar memory cell, and (b) typical unipolar resistance switching I–V behaviors. Reprinted with permission from [90], A. Demolliens et al., "Proceedings of the IEEE International Memory Workshop (IMW)," p. 25, Seoul, South Korea, 2009. © 2009, The Institute of Electrical and Electronics Engineers (IEEE).

Since unipolar resistance-switched TMO-RRAM attracts much more attention due to its wide applications, we will focus on the material and possible programming and resistance switching mechanisms of this kind of memory device in this section.

2.3.1. TMO-RRAM Materials with Unipolar Resistance Switching

In Section 2.2, we mentioned the materials that exhibit resistance switching by electrical voltage, current, or pulse stress; those are also summarized in Figure 21. Unipolar resistance-switched TMO-RRAM includes TiO_x [89], NiO_x [32, 90], ZnO_x [91], HfO_x [92], WO_x [69, 70], and AlO_x [93]. On the other hand bipolar resistance switching characteristics are also found in those TMO materials (see Section 2.2.2). An electrode candidate plays an important role in the resistance-switching type because it can determine the location of a low-occupied oxygen vacancy region in the CF by the difference of the hopping probability between oxygen vacancies, oxygen vacancy, and the electrode. Thus, we believe there may be more systems not yet discovered involve unipolar resistance switching besides the organized elements in Figure 21.

From Section 1, we have illustrated the development of unipolar resistance switching in the perovskite material

$Pr_{0.7}Ca_{0.3}MnO_3$. Currently, in addition to the TMO-RRAM, some perovskite-based RRAM systems, some CBRAM-based systems and some polymer-based systems also present unipolar resistance switching. On the other hand, most of the materials or structures in the above four systems exhibit both unipolar and bipolar resistance-switching modes, such as a WO_x-based TMO device [67, 69, 70], Cu:ZrO_2-based CBRAM [118, 119], and V:$SrZrO_3$-based perovskite devices [120, 121]. A clearer physical understanding of resistance switching, especially unipolar, can help us to confidently clarify these complicated behaviors.

2.3.2. Reset Process and Reliability

The Reset process is the first programming step in RRAM after the Forming process, if needed. The Reset process of the unipolar resistance-switching mode is defined here as the state transition of a memory device from the LRS to HRS by the application of voltage or current stress or electrical pulse with the same electrical polarity as seen in the Forming process; this is unlike bipolar resistance switching. However, just as seen in bipolar resistance switching, the required high Reset current, which is sensitive to CF formation dynamics in the insulating host during the Reset process, plays a key role in nonvolatile memory applications.

2.3.2.1. LRS Dependent Reset Process. Figure 50 shows the drain current (I_D) dependent resistance of the LRS and the Reset current for a NiO-based TMO-RRAM device with an additional transistor selector and other systems, such as CuO_x-, Ti doped NiO-, and HfO_2-based TMO-RRAM devices [59]. Even though various systems are organized in Figure 50, a clear trend can be observed, i.e., that the Reset current decreases monotonically with the increasing resistance value of the LRS. By describing Figure 50 in more detail, one can find that the Reset current is exactly inversely proportional to the resistance of the LRS.

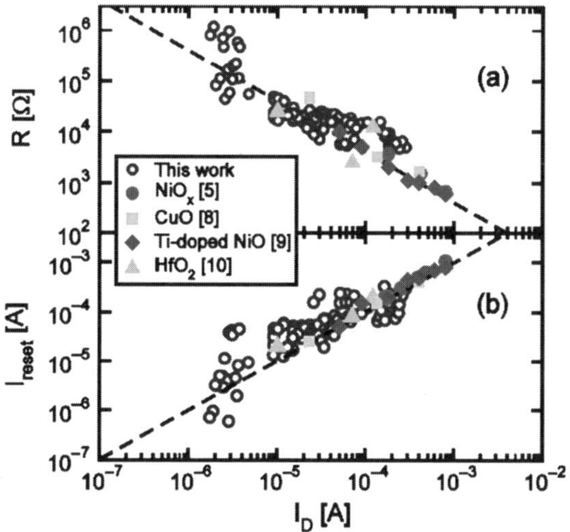

Figure 50. (a) Resistance of LRS, and (b) the Reset current as a function of drain current. The resistance of LRS decreases and the Reset current increases with increased drain current, as result of increasing the effective area of the CF (A_{CF}). Reprinted with permission from [59], F. Nardi et al., *J. Solid-State Electron* 58, 42 (2011). © 2011, Elsevier.

The relationship between the Reset current and the resistance of the LRS can be written as:

$$I_{\text{Reset}} = \alpha * (\Delta T_{\text{crit}})^{1/2} * (R * R_{\text{th}})^{-1/2} \tag{25}$$

where α is the fitting parameter, ΔT_{crit} is the critical temperature increase for the CF oxidation, or diffusion, or other, and R and R_{th} are the effective electrical resistance and thermal resistance of the CF, respectively. Accordingly, in turn, the optimization of the low Reset current can be achieved to be less than 10 μA (Fig. 51). Various resistances of the LRS under various Set processes indicate the control of the CF. Here, we introduce an effectively CF diameter, ϕ, to represent the resistance of the LRS by assuming a cylindrical CF (Fig. 52). There are four states to be distinguished:

(1) full or over Set state;
(2) the intermediate state with a smaller metallically CF;
(3) the intermediate state with a separated CF; and
(4) the full or over Reset state.

Whether the CF is contributed from metal atoms [39, 59], oxygen vacancies [33, 39, 44, 123], defects [58], or another contributor, a CF with a large diameter can provide a lower resistance. Thus, this implies that the comparison of the effective diameter of a CF of the various states in Figure 51 should be thus: 9.5 μA curve > 4.5 μA curve > 3.5 μA curve > 2 μA curve. On the other hand, since the CF with a smaller effective diameter has a higher resistance, the Reset voltage must also be higher [58]. In addition to the Reset current and voltage dependence of the resistance value of the LRS of TMO-RRAM, the Reset power can be easily predicted to be inversely proportional to the resistance value of the LRS. Sakotsubo et al. [124] demonstrated a complete Reset power dependency with various resistances of a LRS by various plasma oxidation treatments on a TiO_x-based TMO-RRAM device. A slight difference in slope of the Reset power versus the conductance of a LRS between heavily oxidized TiO_x and lightly oxidized TiO_x indicates that the above assumptions about the CF need modification.

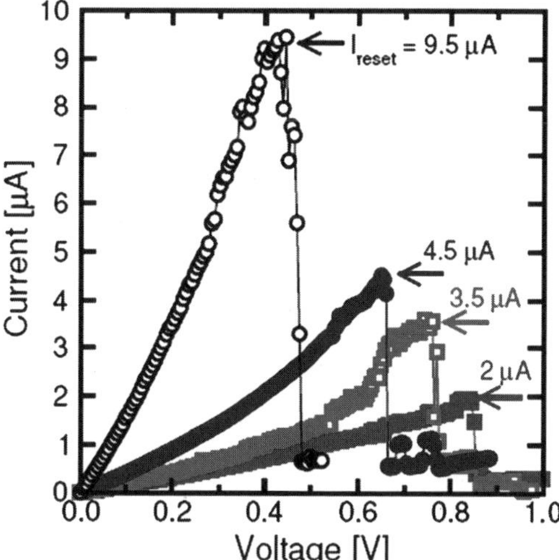

Figure 51. Measured *I–V* curves for LRS with variable resistance. Reprinted with permission from [59], F. Nardi et al., *J. Solid-State Electron.* 58, 42 (2011). © 2011, Elsevier.

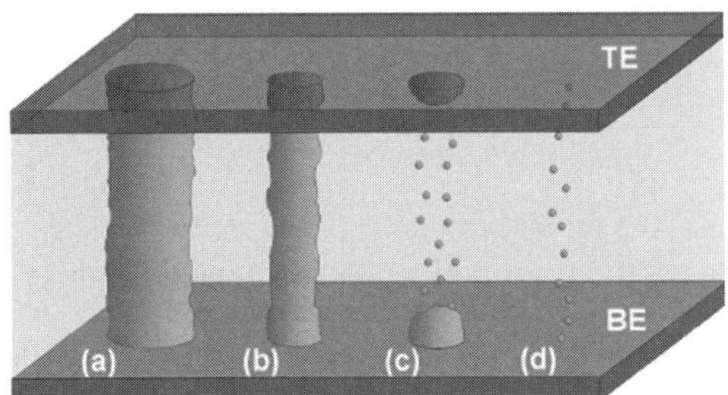

Figure 52. Schematic view for a TMO-RRAM cell with multiple statuses: (a) full or over the Set state, (b) intermediate state with a smaller metal-like CF, (c) intermediate state with a separated CF, and (d) full or over the Reset state. Reprinted with permission from [122], D. Ielmini et al., "Proceedings of the IEEE International Reliability Physics Symposium (IRPS)," p. 620, Anaheim, CA, 2010. © 2010, The Institute of Electrical and Electronics Engineers (IEEE).

The first item that needs to be modified is the temperature dependence of the CF [125]. In bipolar resistance switching, several transportation mechanisms of the LRS were illustrated, including the metallically Ohmic transport, Schottky emission, SCLC, and electron hopping. Similar discussions have been proposed to explain the transportation of the LRS in unipolar resistance switching, with the noted exception of the Schottky emission. Most of the literature has stated that metallic Ohmic conduction dominates the resistance of LRS [58, 92, 124, 125]. However, although linear I–V curves are found in the low voltage region, all resistances with various states have nonlinear characteristics in the high-voltage region before the beginning of the Reset process (Fig. 51). If the cylindrical CF assumption is maintained, introducing the temperature modification in resistance is proposed to fit the retention model [125]. If the resistance of the LRS is lower than 0.5 kΩ, the following equation describes the metallic behavior for temperature-dependent resistance:

$$R = R_0 * (1 + \alpha * \Delta T) \quad (26)$$

where R_0 is the resistance at a reference temperature, such as room temperature; T_0, ΔT is the temperature difference between T and T_0; and α is a temperature coefficient. If the resistance of a LRS is higher than 0.5 kΩ, according to the Arrhenius law, the LRS resistance can be written as:

$$R = \rho_0 \frac{t_{\mathrm{TMO}}}{A} * \exp\left(\frac{E_a}{kT}\right) \quad (27)$$

where A is the area of effectively CF, t_{TMO} is the thickness of the TMO film, E_a is the activation energy for conduction, and ρ_0 is the Arrhenius pre-exponential resistivity factor. This resistance equation of the LRS is semiconductor-like (e.g., resistance decreases with increasing temperature) and follows the Arrhenius plot. Both Eqs. (26) and (27) present the temperature-dependent resistances of the CFs occurring for metallic (Fig. 53) and semiconductive transportations (Fig. 51), respectively.

The second item that needs to be modified is the shape of the CF. Joule heating-induced CF reduction/reoxidation [39, 59], defect diffusion [33], or anodization by oxygen ion diffusion [44] have been proposed to examine the Reset process in unipolar resistance switching. Both the electric current flow and thermal heat flow in a CF with various shapes determine the hot-spot formation in a CF. Accordingly, we introduce the Poisson equation and Fourier heat-flow equation as:

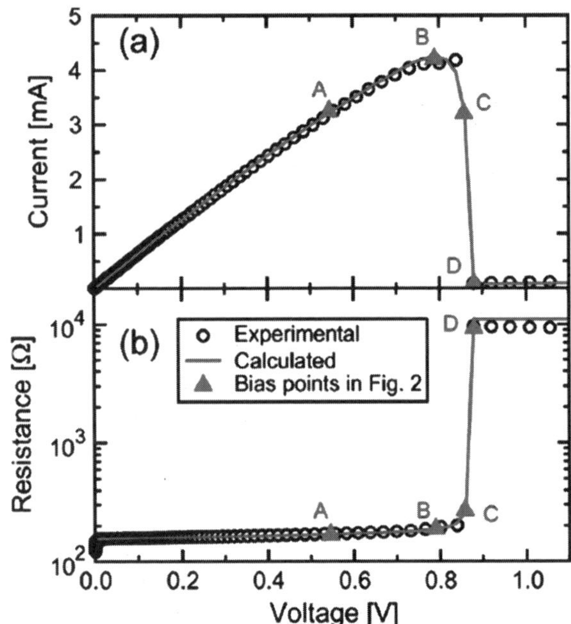

Figure 53. Experimental and simulated (a) I–V and (b) R–V behaviors. Resistance slightly increases with the voltage, i.e., increasing the temperature in the CF. A metallic CF is thus believed to be the transportation of LRS. Reprinted with permission from [126], U. Russo et al., *IEEE Trans. Electron. Device.* 56, 193 (2009). © 2009, The Institute of Electrical and Electronics Engineers (IEEE).

$$\begin{aligned} \nabla \cdot \left(\tfrac{1}{\rho}\nabla V\right) &= 0 \\ -\nabla \cdot (\kappa \nabla T) &= \rho J^2 \end{aligned} \quad (28)$$

with a Dirichlet boundary condition of $V = V_a$ at the top electrode and $V = 0$ at the bottom electrode, and the boundary condition of $T = T_0$ at both electrodes. Based on the Ohmic law, $J = \nabla V/\rho$. Here, ρ is electrical resistivity, and ρ of the CF, ρ_{CF}, is much lower than that of the insulating TMO film, ρ_{bulk}; κ is thermal conductivity, which includes κ of CF, κ_{CF}, and of TMO film, κ_{bulk}. Because of the low ρ_{CF} of the CF, the thermal conductivity of the CF can be described as the sum of the phonon effect and the electrical effect:

$$\kappa_{\mathrm{CF}} = \kappa_{\mathrm{CF,ph}} + \kappa_{\mathrm{CF,el}} \quad (29)$$

Based on the Wiedeman-Franz law, $\kappa_{\mathrm{CF,el}}$ is inversely proportional to ρ_{CF}. Figure 54 shows the schematic and simulated temperature profile of a CF with the usual cylindrical shape and with a cone shape. In the left side of Figure 54, after the Reset current injection, the middle of the CF increases its temperature so that CF reduction/re-oxidation occurs. The rupturing of the CF provides the high resistance of a HRS. On the other hand, due to the cone-shaped CF, the hot spot appears close to the position with a smaller CF diameter (Fig. 54). The formation and rupturing of the

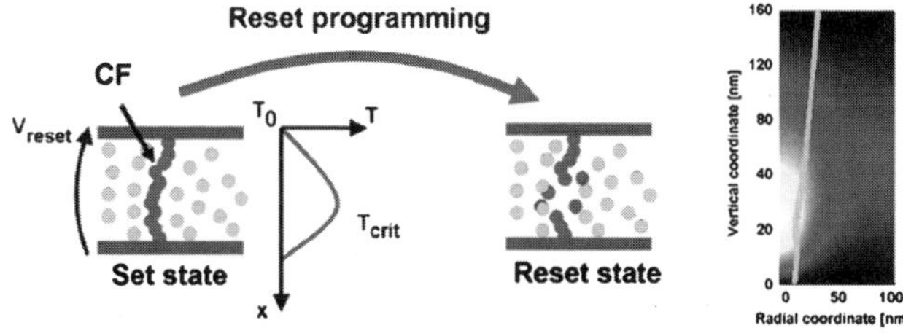

Figure 54. Left, Reset process schematic dynamics; right, simulated temperature in TMO-RRAM structure with a cone-shaped CF. Reprinted with permission from [126], U. Russo et al., *IEEE Trans. Electron. Device.* 56, 193 (2009). © 2009, The Institute of Electrical and Electronics Engineers (IEEE).

CF occurs near the anode side, which is believed to be the reaction region of the unipolar resistance-switching mode. Figure 55 reveals other possibilities for the shape geometry of the formed CF in the insulating TMO matrix. The left side of Figure 55 has formation/rupturing behaviors similar to those of the CF in the left side of Figure 54. Due to the Joule heat dissipation, the left side of Figure 55 needs more Reset current than that of Figure 54. The middle figure of Figure 55 has a CF with branches in insulating TMO material; irregular resistance switching occurs during the Set process [72], so the initial Reset/Set cycles show resistance instability.

In summary, the several impact factors of the effect of the LRS resistance on the Reset process can be organized as:

(1) temperature-dependent resistance of the CF;
(2) the shape of the CF;
(3) the thermal and electrical conductivities of the CF and insulating TMO material; and
(4) the defect diffusivity in the insulating TMO film.

All four factors are coupled with each other. Thus, in reality, the Reset process is a greatly complex dynamic process. Once Reset power is injected into a given CF of a TMO system that has been defined by a previous Set process, the increased temperature in the CF causes a change in resistance, thus causing a simultaneous change in the electrical and thermal conductivities. The former is achieved by temperature-dependent resistivity; the latter depends on the former and additional phonon interaction. When the injected Reset power gradually increases, some defects start to diffuse according to the Joule heating around the CF. The shape of the CF is further changed such that the alternations of the electrical and thermal conductivities of the CF occur again. The resistance of the CF is believed to increase with a decreasing diameter. Feedback to the Joule heating will speed up the diffusion of defects such that the CF is further broken within a limited time. The example of the calculated maximum temperature is shown in Figure 56, in which the complexity is simplified by fixing the geometry of the CF. The critical temperature, T_{crit}, means the CF starts to break, i.e., the Reset process begins. The voltage value corresponding to the critical temperature is the Reset voltage. T_0 means room temperature. It is noted that the maximum temperature during the Reset process occurs within the voltage range of resistance rising, instead of the beginning or ending of a transition (Fig. 57). Four marked states in Figures 57(A–D), represent the LRS, Early-On, Early-Off, and HRS, respectively. The marked states A and D are stable states, even with the external programming power off. However, states B and C are transient states in which the self-accelerated thermal dissolution is under processing [126]. The peak temperature occurs at state C, although the peak current occurs at state B. Since the dissolution effect causes the shrinkage of the CF, the effective diameter of the CF at state B degrades very fast. Meanwhile, the greatly enhanced resistance of the CF contributes more heat accumulation and accelerates the dissolution process until state C, in which the current suddenly drops due to the broken CF. This performs the Reset process.

2.3.2.2. Reset-Set Instability. Similar to bipolar resistance switching, the Reset current reduction of unipolar resistance switching can be achieved by the CC of the Set process. The left side of Figure 58 presents the Reset current of 1T plus one transistor plus one TMO resistor (1T + 1TMO) and 1TMO resistor circuits as functions of the CC of the Set process. A drastic Reset current reduction is found for the 1T + 1TMO circuit [44]. Similar results are also found in the right side of Figure 58 [130]: The mean Reset current values of thirty "Reset" cycles of MIM-structured Pt/NiO/Pt alone (open squares), 1T in 1TMO (open circles), and 1T in 1TMO without pad (closed circles). Instead of a 1T + 1TMO structure with both bipolar and unipolar resistance switching modes and the single TMO-resistor circuit with bipolar resistance switching mode (Fig. 30) [23], the single TMO-resistor circuit with unipolar-type is quite insensitive to the CC of the Set process. In Figure 58, the difference between the 1T + 1TMO and single TMO-resistor circuits indicates that the compliance by the SPA limits the Reset current reduction performance, which is described in Section 2.2. The lifetime of recombination between the oxygen ion and oxygen vacancy or the precipitation between the metal and oxygen ion might be less than 10 ns [71]. CC control by the SPA (on the order of sub micron-seconds) is much slower than the lift time, indicating that the complicated formation of CF(s) in the TMO matrix might be prepared during this compliance time. And, hence, the generated lower resistance of the LRS results in the high Reset current.

Due to the formation and rupturing of the CF in the TMO-insulating film, both the Set and Reset processes depend on the threshold switching under a transition time. For constant pulse Reset and Set voltage conditions, the times to alternate the state from the LRS to HRS and from the HRS to LRS are the Reset time, τ_{Reset}, and the Set time, τ_{Set}, respectively. For the Reset process, we assume that the CF, structured the same as the left side of Figure 54, decreases its diameter within the process time by a thermally activated diffusion of defects, described as:

$$\frac{d\phi}{dt} = -V_{G0} * \exp\left(\frac{E_a}{KT}\right) \tag{30}$$

where ϕ is diameter of the CF, E_a is the activation energy, and ν_{G0} is a pre-exponential constant. The Reset time, τ_{Reset}, means the required time for scaling the diameter of the CF

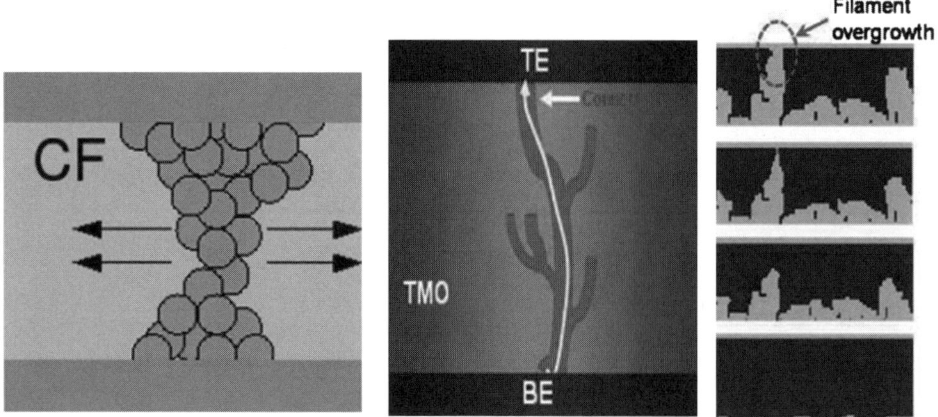

Figure 55. Left, a symmetrically CF shape with the region with the smallest diameter at the center; middle, CF with branches in insulating TMO material; right, asymmetric CF simulated by the kinetic Monte Carlo (KMC) method. Reprinted with permission from [127], C. Cagli et al., "IEEE International Electron Devices Meeting (IEDM) Technical Digest," p. 301, San Francisco, CA, 2008. © 2008, The Institute of Electrical and Electronics Engineers (IEEE); and from [72], K.-C. Ryoo et al., "Proceedings of the IEEE Silicon Nanoelectronics Workshop (SNW)," p. 63, Honolulu, HI, 2010. © 2010, The Institute of Electrical and Electronics Engineers (IEEE); Reprinted with permission from [128], F. Pen and V. Subramanian, "Proceedings of the IEEE International Conference on Simulation of Semiconductor Processes and Devices (SISPAD'10)," p. 19, Bologna, Italy, 2010. © 2010, The Institute of Electrical and Electronics Engineers (IEEE).

from an initial value of ϕ_0 to 0, indicating that the Reset time can be described as:

$$\tau_{\text{Reset}} = \frac{\phi_0}{2v_{G0}} * \exp\left(\frac{E_a}{KT}\right) \tag{31}$$

On the other hand, since the diffusion of defects in the CF depends on an enhanced temperature by the external Reset voltage on cell, the temperature and its increasing rate can be written as:

$$\begin{aligned} T &= T_0 + V_{\text{cell}}^2 * \frac{R_{\text{th}}}{R} \\ \beta_T &= 2\beta V_{\text{Cell}} * \frac{R_{\text{th}}}{R} \end{aligned} \tag{32}$$

where V_{Cell} is voltage drop across the TMO film, $\beta_T = dV/dt$ is the increasing rate of CF temperature, $\beta = dV_{\text{Cell}}/dt$ is the voltage ramp speed, R and R_{th} are electrical and thermal resistances of teh CF, and T_0 is room temperature. According to Eqs. (30) to (32), one can conclude the relationship between V_{Cell} and $\beta = dV_{\text{Cell}}/dt$ as well as τ_{Reset}. On the other hand, for the Set process, a similar relationship can be derived as:

$$\begin{aligned} V_{\text{Set}} &= V_0 * \ln\left(\frac{\beta\tau_0}{V_0}\right) \\ \tau_{\text{Set}} &= \tau_0 * \exp\left(\frac{-V_{\text{Cell}}}{V_0}\right) \end{aligned} \tag{33}$$

Both the Set and Reset voltages monotonically increase with increasing the voltage ramp speed, $\beta = dV_{\text{Cell}}/dt$ for a wide range from 10^{-4} V/s to 10^7 V/s (raise voltage to 1 V within 100 ns). Meanwhile, both the Set and Reset time monotonically and exponentially decrease with the cell voltage. For an MIM-structured Pt/NiO/Pt TMO-RRAM system, less than

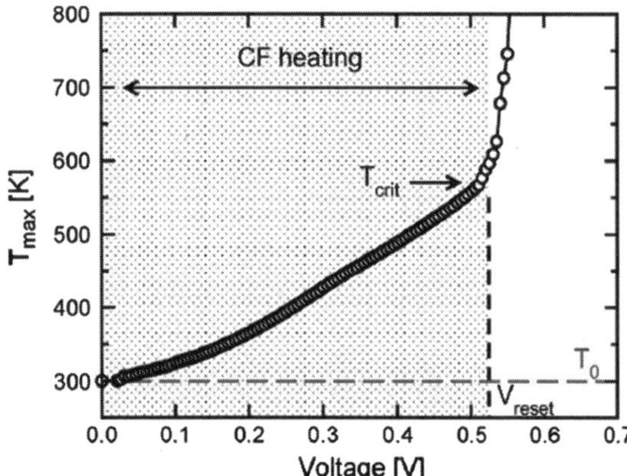

Figure 56. Voltage-dependent maximum temperature in the CF. Reprinted with permission from [129], U. Russo et al., *IEEE Trans. Electron. Device.* 56, 186 (2009). © 2009, The Institute of Electrical and Electronics Engineers (IEEE).

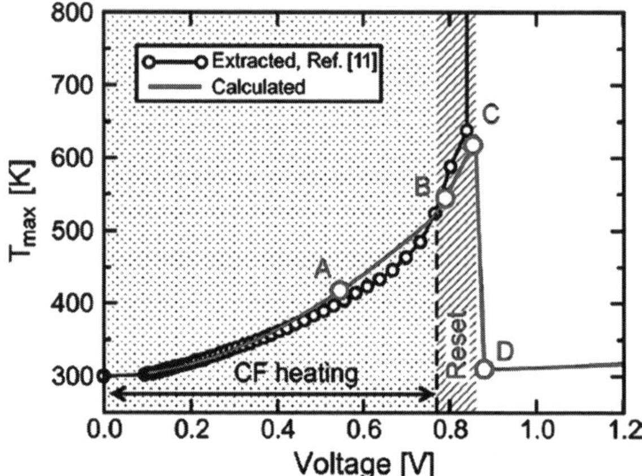

Figure 57. Simulated and experimental voltage-dependent CF temperature. Reprinted with permission from [126], U. Russo et al., *IEEE Trans. Electron. Device.* 56, 193 (2009). © 2009, The Institute of Electrical and Electronics Engineers (IEEE).

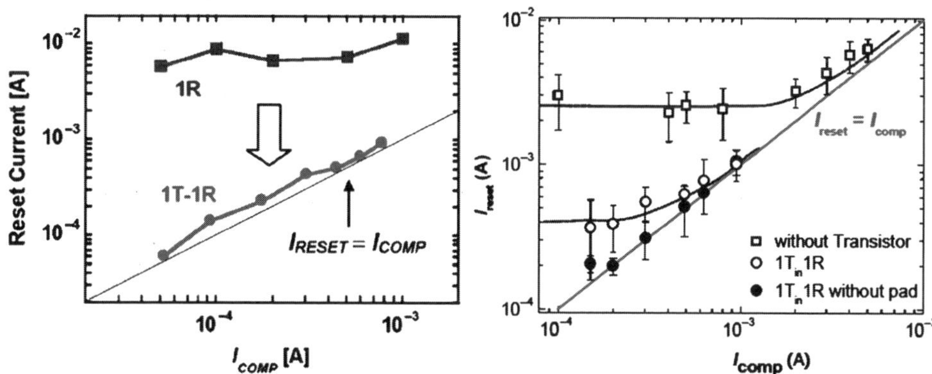

Figure 58. Left, the Reset current of 1T + 1TMO and 1TMO circuits as functions of the CC of the Set process. The drastic Reset current reduction is found for 1T + 1TMO circuit; right, Reset current values of a MIM structured Pt/NiO/Pt alone (open squares), 1T in 1TMO (open circles), and *1T* in 1TMO without a pad (closed circles). Reprinted with permission from [44], K. Tsunoda et al., "IEEE International Electron Devices Meeting (IEDM) Technical Digest," p. 767, Washington, DC, 2007. © 2007, The Institute of Electrical and Electronics Engineers (IEEE); and from [130], K. Kinoshita et al., "Proceedings of the 22nd IEEE Non-Volatile Semiconductor Memory Workshop (NVSMW)," p. 66, Monterey, CA, 2007. © 2007, The Institute of Electrical and Electronics Engineers (IEEE).

a 20 ns set time and a 60 ns Reset time can be achieved by a Set voltage of 2.5 V and a Reset voltage of 4 V, respectively [127]. Even a shorter Reset time of 5 ns with an applied voltage of 1.8 V can be achieved by a NiO-based TMO-RRAM device with an additional doping effect [44]. The threshold characteristics for both the Set and Reset processes can examine the Reset current insensitive to the CC during the Set process for the one TMO-resistor circuit in Figure 58. Current overshooting by the SPA with the time that is several orders of magnitude higher than the Set and Reset times complicates the analysis. On the other hand, the switching instability during the Set and Reset processes can also be realized: (1) the secondary Reset switching during the Set process [127], and (2) the secondary Set switching during the Reset process [32].

Figure 59 shows resistance-switching examples of successful (a) → (c) → (e) and unsuccessful (b) → (d) → (f), Set processes on a Pt/NiO/Pt MIM-structured TMO-RRAM device. For a successful 100 ns Set process, a cell with an initially high resistance has a high voltage drop of around 2 V, and then drops its voltage due to the state transition from the HRS to LRS at 60 ns (Fig. 59(a)). At the same time, the high current peak reaches around 10 mA at the transition time because of the capacitance effect:

$$I_{\text{Cell}} = \frac{V_A - V_{\text{Cell}}}{R_L} - C * \frac{dV_{\text{Cell}}}{dt} \tag{34}$$

The current peak in Figure 59(c) might result from a capacitance of 15 pF. Since the CF is formed at that time, a high current peak also produces a high local temperature (Fig. 59(e)). The stable transition from the HRS to LRS is done after these current and temperature peaks. On the other hand, Figure 59(b) displays an unsuccessful Set process. Similar to Figure 59(a), the state transition occurs at around 60 ns. However, because of the capacitance, the same as 15 pF, and a very high dV_{Cell}/dt, the current peak is much higher than in Figure 59(c). So, the produced local temperature is high enough. This further generates the reduction/reoxidation or defect diffusion or anodization by oxygen ion diffusion in the CF, which can again become the Reset process. Hence, the state changes and recovers to a HRS again after the transition time of 60 ns. This is the secondary Reset switching during the Set process.

In contrast to the secondary Reset switching during the Set process, the similar case is the secondary Set switching during the Reset process. Figure 60 reveals the resistance of the HRS as a function of the Reset voltage for a conventional MIM-structured NiO-based TMO-RRAM device [44]. Before the Reset voltage of 1.4 V, the resistance monotonically increases with Reset voltage and reaches the threshold switching at 1.4 V. The higher Reset voltage, however, enables the resistance of the HRS to suddenly drop more than three orders of magnitude. Once a Reset voltage is applied to the TMO-RRAM device, the rupturing

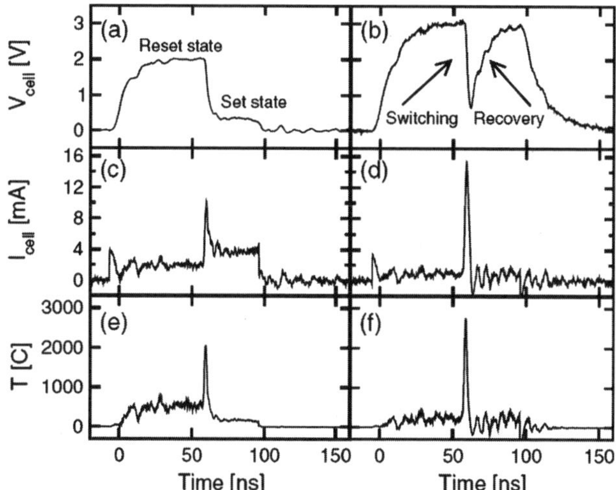

Figure 59. Voltage drop on TMO cell (a, b) during set pulses, corresponding current (c, d), and temperature (e, f). Threshold-switched LRS can evolve into a persistent Set state (a, c, e) or disappear by HRS recovery (b, d, f). Reprinted with permission from [127], C. Cagli et al., "IEEE International Electron Devices Meeting (IEDM) Technical Digest," p. 301, San Francisco, CA, 2008. © 2008, The Institute of Electrical and Electronics Engineers (IEEE).

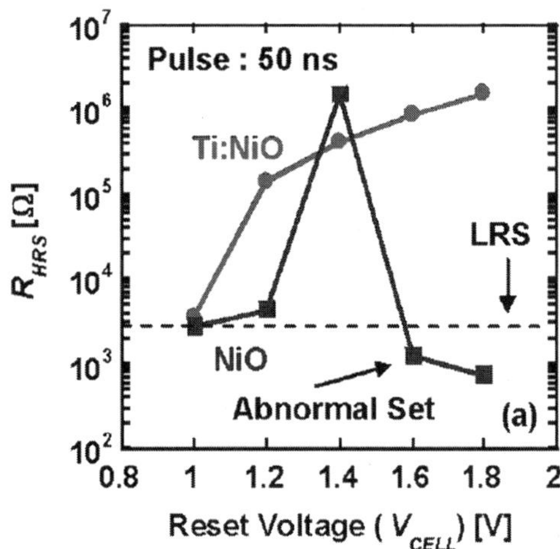

Figure 60. Effect of pulsed Reset voltage on resistance of HRS. The secondary Set at a voltage of 1.6 V shows an abnormal Set phenomena during the Reset process in conventional MIM-structured NiO devices (black). Improved abnormal phenomena are achieved by an advanced Ti-doped, NiO-based TMO device. Reprinted with permission from [44], K. Tsunoda et al., "IEEE International Electron Devices Meeting (IEDM) Technical Digest," p. 767, Washington, DC, 2007. © 2007, The Institute of Electrical and Electronics Engineers (IEEE).

of the CF increases the device resistance, meaning that the post-Reset voltage drop on the TMO-RRAM device also increases. If this post-Reset voltage drop exceeds the threshold-switching voltage of the Set process, the device will change the resistance state again from a HRS to LRS. This is the secondary Set switching during the Reset process. This phenomenon can be improved by advanced circuit design [32] and by altering the TMO material (see the black curve of Fig. 60).

Both the secondary Set resistance switching during the Reset process and the secondary Reset resistance switching during the Set process are undesirable for proper unipolar RRAM operation and are called Reset-Set instability [131, 132] due to the similar amplitude and time of the voltage pulse required for Set and Reset. Based on the stochastic model described in Section 2.2, we assume the probability for the cell to be in Set or in Reset as P_{Set} and P_{Reset}, and a Poisson statistic time variation of P_{Set} can be written as:

$$\frac{dP_{\text{Set}}}{dt} = -\frac{P_{\text{Set}}}{\tau_{\text{Reset}}} + \frac{P_{\text{Reset}}}{\tau_{\text{Set}}} \tag{35}$$

where the first and second terms of the right side of Eq. (35) describe the decreasing of the Reset rate and increasing of the Set rate, respectively. Due to the continuity relation, $P_{\text{Set}} + P_{\text{Reset}} = 1$, one can get:

$$\begin{aligned} P_{\text{Set}} &= \frac{\tau_0}{\tau_{\text{Set}}} * \left(1 + \frac{\tau_{\text{Set}}}{\tau_{\text{Reset}}} * \exp(-t/\tau_0)\right) \\ P_{\text{Reset}} &= \frac{\tau_0}{\tau_{\text{Reset}}} * (1 - \exp(-t/\tau_0)) \end{aligned} \tag{36}$$

where $\tau_0 \equiv \tau_{\text{Set}} * \tau_{\text{Reset}}/(\tau_{\text{Set}} + \tau_{\text{Reset}})$. The steady-state values from Eq. (36) can be obtained as $P_{\text{Set}} = \tau_{\text{Reset}}/ (\tau_{\text{Set}} + \tau_{\text{Reset}})$ and $P_{\text{Reset}} = \tau_{\text{Set}}/(\tau_{\text{Set}} + \tau_{\text{Reset}})$. To get a complete Reset process and avoid Reset-Set instability, we need $P_{\text{Reset}} \cong 1$ at the end of Reset programming, indicating $\tau_{\text{Set}} \gg \tau_{\text{Reset}}$. On the other hand, if $P_{\text{Set}} \cong 1$ is at the end of Set programming, we need $\tau_{\text{Set}} \ll \tau_{\text{Reset}}$. The voltage dependent τ_{Set} and τ_{Reset} can be obtained by Eqs. (30) to (33); one can determine a suitable operation condition to degrade the Reset-Set instability effect based on individual TMO device characteristics.

2.3.2.3. *Engineering of the Anode Interface and Electrode.* The formation and rupturing of the CF in TMO

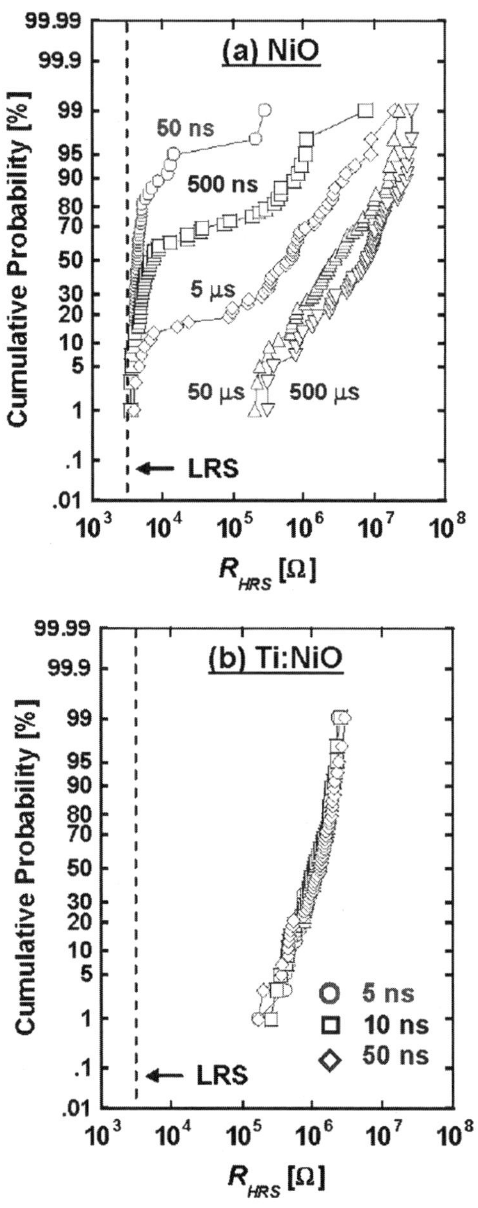

Figure 61. Reset programming pulse width dependent accumulation plot of HRS resistance of a MIM-structured TMO with (a) NiO, and (b) Ti:NiO. An ultra-high speed Reset time of 5 ns is achieved in Ti:NiO. Voltage of the TMO cell is 1.0 V for NiO-based and 1.8 V for Ti:NiO-based TMO-RRAM. Gate-voltage is 1.8 V. For the Set process, a cell voltage of 2.8 V with a time of 10 ns and gate-voltage of 0.8 V are used. Reprinted with permission from [44], K. Tsunoda et al., "IEEE International Electron Devices Meeting (IEDM) Technical Digest," p. 767, Washington, DC, 2007. © 2007, The Institute of Electrical and Electronics Engineers (IEEE).

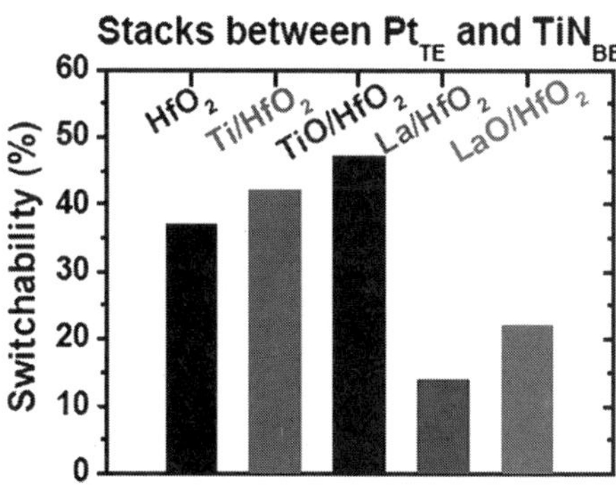

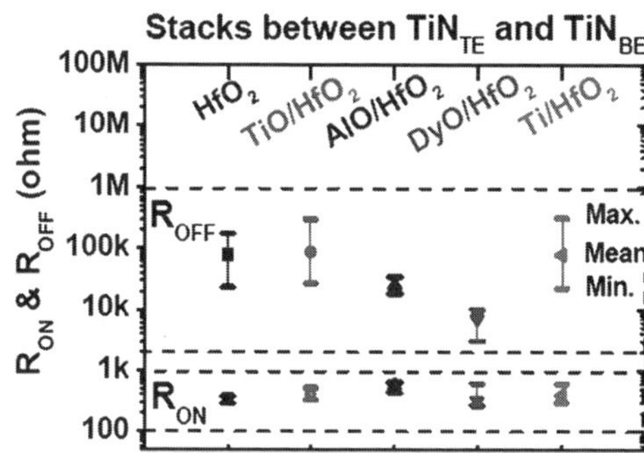

Figure 62. Left, switchability of HfO_2-based TMO-RRAM with a Pt top electrode and TiN bottom electrode; right resistance of LRS and HRS distribution for the HfO_2-based TMO-RRAM with various capping layers. Reprinted with permission from [133], X. P. Wang et al., "Proceedings of the IEEE International Symposium on VLSI Technology Systems and Applications (VLSI-TSA)," p. 140, Hsinchu, Taiwan, 2010. © 2010, The Institute of Electrical and Electronics Engineers (IEEE).

insulating film have been widely accepted for the realization of reversibly bipolar and unipolar resistance-threshold switching between the HRS and LRS. The CF might be composed of oxygen vacancies generated by the Forming process (see Section 2.2). From the previous discussion, some knobs are used for improving the switchability, power reduction, or the switching uniformity. Those include

(1) the low formation energy of the oxygen vacancies by addition doping;
(2) electrode candidates for the oxygen ion reservoirs;
(3) environment to improve the sidewall effect; and
(4) nonstoichiometric TMO film effects.

Here, we discuss the effects of additional doping in NiO film and various electrodes of HfO_2 film on the unipolar resistance switching of TMO-RRAMs.

From the ion-transport-recombination model and stochastic model discussed in Section 2.2, because of the low barrier height at the interface between bulk and electrode, such as Pt, TMO-RRAM with a noble metal-based electrode has a high possibility to exhibit unipolar resistance switching. The reaction region is close to the anode in the CF. TMO-RRAM with a MIM-structured Pt/NiO/Pt [44] thus presents the unipolar resistance switching with a wide distributed resistance of the HRS (Fig. 61). For a very fast Reset pulse time of < 500 ns, the resistance of the HRS shows the soft-error due to the indistinguishable bistability. From the right side of Figure 61, the distribution of the HRS reveals great improvement. This might be due to the slight disordering of the Ni–O bonds that enhance the population and diffusion of the oxide ions during the Reset process. A stable and fast Reset speed in turn can be achieved. Another Al-insertion doping effect into the NiO-based TMO matrix on the reduction of the Reset and Set currents of unipolar resistance switching has been proposed [39] due to the increase in the oxygen vacancies at the cell interface. The noble metal of Ir is used for the electrode. The oxidizable metallic dopant in a TMO-RRAM structure with a noble metal electrode is found to enhance the dynamics of the oxygen vacancy movement during the programming.

The electrode effect on resistance switching is related to the Gibb's free energy (see Section 2.2). Figure 62 shows the switchability and the ratio of HRS to LRS by various cap layers and electrodes of HfO_2-based TMO-RRAM. Due to the much higher Gibb's free energy for oxidization of La (−1706 KJ/mol) and Dy (−1771 KJ/mol) than Hf (−1088 KJ/mol) and Ti (−889 KJ/mol), the cap layer of La and LaO_x as well as the DyO_x on HfO_2-based TMO film exhibits poor resistance switchability and a poor ratio of the HRS to LRS (Fig. 61) [133]. The Gibb's free energy of Al (−1582 KJ/mol) for oxidization has a value between Hf and La, so the ratio of the HRS to LRS has a median performance.

2.3.2.4. Data Retention. Both the temperature dependent HRS (Fig. 42) and the LRS (Fig. 43) retention time of the bipolar resistance switching, described in Section 2.2, obey the Arrhenius law, shown in Eq. (19). The retention time is inversely exponentially proportional to the environment temperature due to the thermally activated ion-transport-recombination effect between an oxygen ion and oxygen vacancy. In unipolar resistance switching, because the Joule heating induces the defect diffusion outward from the conductive filament, the resistance of the LRS is also expected to be temperature dependent.

Ielmini and colleagues proposed a retention model with variables of temperature and the diameter of a CF, described as [122]:

$$\tau_R = \tau_{R0} * \left(\frac{\phi}{\phi_0}\right)^2 * \exp\left(\frac{E_{AR}}{kT}\right) \tag{37}$$

where E_{AR} is the activation energy of the Arrhenius law. The structure of the left side of Figure 55 and the cylindrical coordinate diffusion equation are used with the conductive concentration degradation by a factor of 10 or 100 by diffusion process. The retention time is proportional to ϕ^2, indicating that the LRS with lower resistance has the better retention performance. Meanwhile, the increased diameter of the conductive filament, i.e., the decreased resistance of LRS, implies that the required Reset power is increased. The effect of diameter of conductive filament on the critical Reset temperature, T_{Reset}, can be described as:

$$T_{Reset} = \frac{E_{AR}}{k * \log[(\tau_{Reset}/\tau_{R0}) * (\phi/\phi_0)^2]} \tag{38}$$

Figure 63 shows the experimental and calculated data retention time τ_R, the required Reset voltage V_{Reset}, and the

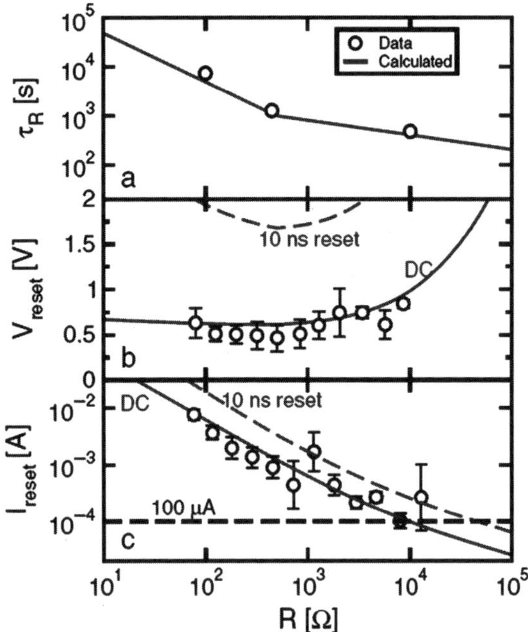

Figure 63. Effect of LRS resistance on (a) data retention time, (b) required Reset voltage V_{Reset}, and (c) the required Reset current I_{Reset}. Sample is a MIM-structured NiO-based TMO film deposited on a W-plug with a Pt top electrode. Reprinted with permission from [122], D. Ielmini et al., "Proceedings of the 2010 IEEE International Reliability Physics Symposium (IRPS)," p. 620, Anaheim, CA, 2010. © 2010, The Institute of Electrical and Electronics Engineers (IEEE).

required Reset current I_{Reset}, as functions of resistance of LRS of a MIM-structured NiO-based TMO film deposited on a W-plug and with a Pt top electrode. Both DC and pulsed (10 ns) Reset conditions are shown. In Figure 63(c), it corresponds to the effect of the LRS resistance on the Reset current, as described previously. The lower the resistance of the LRS of TMO film, the higher the Reset current must be due to the increased diameter of the CF. Because of the absence of the higher LRS resistance, the experimental data reveals consistent results with the calculated model (Fig. 63(b)). According to Eq. (37) and Figure 63(c), due to the enhanced CF diameter, the data retention time depicts a monotonic increase with decreasing LRS resistance. The tradeoff between data retention time and the Reset current is obvious in Figure 63. The simulation results based on Eq. (37) with the diffusion-activated degradation of the conductive concentration in the CF by a factor of 10 or 100 are shown in Figure 64(a) [125] and are consistent with previous discussions. According to experimental results in a 250°C environment, a much lower LRS resistance of $< 100\ \Omega$ is predicted to exhibit reliable data retention of higher than 10 years at 85°C (Fig. 64(b)).

3. SUMMARY

In traditional semiconductor devices, defect issues always confuse engineers and researchers because those defects affect device reliability and leakage current, regardless of how small the advanced device can be. Those undesirable defects include anions and cations in the interlayer dielectric. This implies that defects have a much better scalability than traditional semiconductor devices.

When the development of a nonvolatile memory device reached nanometer-scaled dimensions, because of the limited storage elements, most nonvolatile memory concepts suffered degraded performance and further instability in the target environment. A limited number of electrons trapped in the floating-gate of advanced flash memory with a node of less than 20 nm results in data retention issues, especially at higher temperature. The superparamagnetism issue of magnetic memory causes a tradeoff between scalability and temperature-induced instability. The difficulty of scaling down the programming current of phase change memory beyond 30 nm also limits development. So far, the defect-dominated memory presents a great possibility to achieve future memory with nanometer or subnanometer dimensions.

Anion-based defects in BTMOs play an important role in the formation and rupturing of CFs, which are probably composed of oxygen vacancies with controllable hopping

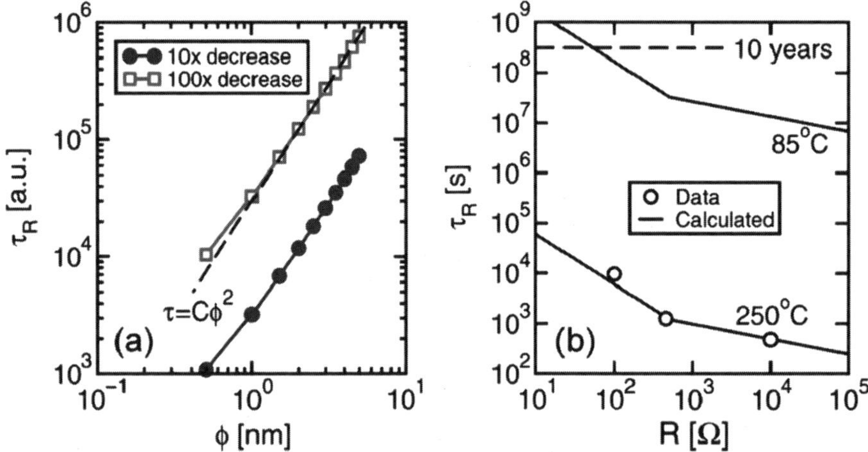

Figure 64. (a) Simulated retention time as a function of the CF, and (b) the experimental and simulated retention time as a function of the LRS resistance. Reprinted with permission from [125], D. Ielmini et al., *IEEE Electron. Device. Lett.* 31, 353 (2010). © 2010, The Institute of Electrical and Electronics Engineers (IEEE).

distances. Each filament might have dimensions of a few nanometers or less. The scalability limitation of the BTMOs is currently under study. Thus, good control of the defect movements is an interesting topic and makes BTMO-RRAM a rich field of research opportunities. The proposed ion-transport-recombination modeling between oxygen ions and oxygen vacancies and electrochemical/thermal reaction modeling are widely accepted as the resistance-switching mechanism. On the other hand, various resistance-switching operations by bipolar and unipolar modes enrich the applications of BTMO-RRAM.

Unfortunately, due to defect domination, the BTMO-RRAM may have limited nonvolatility performance, such as reliability, retention, and endurance, and industrial level uniformity. Thus, optimization by electrode engineering, metal–oxide film engineering, integrated structure engineering, and testing engineering are ongoing to enhance the binary transition metal oxide RRAM non-volatility performance and uniformity.

Finally, the BTMO-RRAM with fully CMOS compatible materials may present the opportunity for highly scalable production with low-cost, median reliability, a niche market, or embedded applications.

REFERENCES

1. A. P. Ramirez, *J. Phys. Condens. Matter* 9, 8171 (1997).
2. C. H. Ho, C. K. Lo, Y. D. Yao, S. F. Lee, I. Klik, M.-T. Lin, Y. Liou, D. Y. Chiang, and D. R. Chang, "Material Research Society Series Symposium Proceedings," Vol. 517, p. 73, San Francisco, CA, 1998.
3. C. K. Lo, C. H. Ho, I. Klik, Y. D. Yao, S. F. Lee, H. H. Huang, Y. C. Chen, C. Y. Wu, D. Y. Chiang, C. A. Chang, M.-T. Lin, and D. R. Chang, "Material Research Society Series Symposium Proceedings," Vol. 517, p. 67, San Francisco, CA, 1998.
4. C. H. Ho, M.-T. Lin, Y. D. Yao, S. F. Lee, C. C. Liao, F. R. Chen, and J. J. Kai, *J. Appl. Phys.* 90, 6222 (2001).
5. X. W. Li, Y. Lu, G. Q. Gong, G. Xiao, A. Gupta, P. Lecoeur, J. Z. Sun, Y. Y. Wang, and V. P. Dravid, *J. Appl. Phys.* 81, 5509 (1997).
6. S. Y. Tang, W. L. Kuang, C. H. Ho, W. S. Tse, M.-T. Lin, S. F. Lee, Y. Liou, and Y. D. Yao, *J. Magn. Magn. Mater.* 226–230, 703 (2000).
7. B. J. Campbell, R. Osborn, D. N. Argyriou, L. Vasiliu-Doloc, J. F. Mitchell, S. K. Sinha, U. Ruett, C. D. Ling, Z. Islam, and J. W. Lynn, *Phys. Rev. B.* 65, 014427 (2001).
8. S. Q. Liu, N. J. Wu, and A. Ignatiev, *Appl. Phys. Lett.* 76, 2749 (2000).
9. W. W. Zhuangl, W. Pan, B. D. Ulrich, J. J. Lee, L. Stecker, A. Burmaster, D. R. Evans, S. T. Hsul, M. Tajiri, A. Shimaoka, K. Inoue, T. Naka, N. Awaya, K. Sakiyama, Y. Wang, S. Q. Liu, N. J. Wu, and A. Ignatiev, "IEEE International Electron Devices Meeting (IEDM) Technical Digest," p. 193, San Francisco, CA, 2002.
10. W. R. Hiatt and T. W. Hickmott, *Appl. Phys. Lett.* 6, 106 (1965).
11. K. L. Chopra, *J. Appl. Phys* 36, 184 (1965).
12. J. C. Bruyere and B. K. Chakraverty, *Appl. Phys. Lett.* 16, 40 (1970).
13. A. Chen, "Proceedings of the 9th IEEE Annual Non-Volatile Memory Technology Symposium (NVMTS)," pp. 1–5, Pacific Grove, CA, 2008.
14. K. Terabe, T. Hasegawa, T. Nakayama, and M. Aono, *Nature* 433, 47 (2005).
15. S. Kaeriyama, T. Sakamoto, H. Sunamura, M. Mizuno, H. Kawaura, T. Hasegawa, K. Terabe, T. Nakayama, and M. Aono, *IEEE J. Solid-State Circuit* 40, 168 (2005).
16. T. Sakamoto, N. Banno, N. Iguchi, H. Kawaura, H. Sunamura, S. Fujieda, K. Terabe, T. Hasegawa, and M. Aono, "IEEE Symposium on VLSI Technology Digest of Technical Papers," p. 38, Kyota, Japan, 2007.
17. M. N. Kozicki, C. Gopalan, M. Balakrishnan, M. Park, and M. Mitkova, "Proceedings of the 5th IEEE Non-Volatile Memory Technology Symposium (NVMTS)," p. 10, Orlando, CA, 2004.
18. C. Schindler, S. C. P. Thermadam, R. Waser, and M. N. Kozicki, *IEEE Trans. Electron Device* 54, 2762 (2007).
19. K. Tsunoda, Y. Fukuzumi, J. R. Jameson, Z. Wang, P. B. Griffin, and Y. Nishi, *Appl. Phys. Lett* 90, 113501 (2007).
20. S. Dietrich, M. Angerbauer, M. Ivanov, D. Gogl, H. Hoenigschmid, M. Kund, C. Liaw, M. Markert, R. Symanczyk, L. Altimime, S. Bournat, and G. Mueller, *IEEE J. Solid-State Circuit* 42, 839 (2007).
21. M. N. Kozicki, M. Balakrishnan, C. Gopalan, C. Ratnakumar, and M. Mitkova, "Proceedings of the 6th IEEE Non-Volatile Memory Technology Symposium (NVMTS)," p. 83, Dallas, TX, 2005.
22. M. Kund, G. Beitel, C.-U. Pinnow, T. Röhr, J. Schumann, R. Symanczyk, K.-D. Ufert, and G. Müller, "IEEE International Electron Devices Meeting (IEDM) Technical Digest," p. 754, Washington, DC, 2005.
23. B. Gao, W. Y. Chang, B. Sun, H. W. Zhang, L. F. Liu, X. Y. Liu, R. Q. Han, T. B. Wu, and J. F. Kang, "Proceedings of the IEEE International Symposium on VLSI Technology Systems and Applications (VLSI-TSA)," p. 144, Hsinchu, Taiwan, 2010.
24. Y.-S. Chen, T.-Y. Wu, P.-J. Tzeng, P.-S. Chen, H.-Y. Lee, C.-H. Lin, F. Chen, and M.-J. Tsai, "Proceedings of the IEEE International Symposium on VLSI Technology Systems and Applications (VLSI-TSA)," p. 37, Hsinchu, Taiwan, 2009.
25. W. G. Kim, M. G. Sung, S. J. Kim, J. Y. Kim, J. W. Moon, S. J. Yoon, J. N. Kim, B. G. Gyun, T. W. Kim, C. H. Kim, J. Y. Byun, W. Kim, T. O. Youn, J. H. Yoo, J. W. Oh, H. J. Kim, M. S. Joo, J. S. Roh, and S. K. Park, "Proceedings of the European Solid-State Device Research Conference (ESSDERC)," p. 400, Seville, Spain, 2010.
26. R. Degraeve, Ph. Roussel, L. Goux, D. Wouters, J. Kittl, L. Altimime, M. Jurczak, and G. Groeseneken, "IEEE International Electron Devices Meeting (IEDM) Technical Digest," p. 632, San Francisco, CA, 2010.
27. M. N. Saleh, D. K. Venkatachalam, K. Belay, T. Kim, and R. G. Elliman, "Proceedings of the 2010 Conference on Optoelectronic and Microelectronic Materials and Devices (COMMAD)," p. 185, Canberra, Australia, 2010.
28. H. Y. Lee, P. S. Chen, T. Y. Wu, Y. S. Chen, C. C. Wang, P. J. Tzeng, C. H. Lin, F. Chen, C. H. Lien, and M.-J. Tsai, "IEEE International Electron Devices Meeting (IEDM) Technical Digest," p. 297, San Francisco, CA, 2008.
29. C. H. Lien, Y. S. Chen, H. Y. Lee, P. S. Chen, F. T. Chen, and M.-J. Tsai, "Proceedings of the10th IEEE International Conference on Solid-State and Integrated Circuit Technology (ICSICT)," p. 1084, Shanghai, China, 2010.
30. Y. S. Chen, H. Y. Leel, P. S. Chen, P. Y. Gu, C. W. Chen, W. P. Lin, W. H. Liu, Y. Y. Hsu, S. S. Sheu, P. C. Chiang, W. S. Chen, F. T. Chen, C. H. Lien, and M.-J. Tsai, "IEEE International Electron Devices Meeting (IEDM) Technical Digest," p. 105, Washington, DC, 2009.
31. J. Lee, J. Shin, D. Lee, W. Lee, S. Jung, M. Jo, J. Park, K. P. Biju, S. Kim, S. Park, and H. Hwang, "IEEE International Electron Devices Meeting (IEDM) Technical Digest," p. 452, San Francisco, CA, 2010.
32. Y. Sato, K. Tsunoda, K. Kinoshita, H. Noshiro, M. Aoki, and Y. Sugiyama, *IEEE Trans. Electron. Device.* 55, 1185 (2008).
33. K. Hosotani, S.-G. Park, and Y. Nishi, "Proceedings of the IEEE International Integrated Reliability Workshop (IRW) Final Report," p. 11, South Lake Tahoe, CA, 2009.
34. M. J. Kim, I. G. Baek, Y. H. Ha, S. J. Baik, J. H. Kim, D. J. Seong, S. J. Kim, Y. H. Kwon, C. R. Lim, H. K. Park, D. Gilmer, P. Kirsch, R. Jammy, Y. G. Shin, S. Choi, and C. Chung, "IEEE International Electron Devices Meeting (IEDM) Technical Digest," p. 444, San Francisco, CA, 2010.

35. M. Terai, S. Kotsuji, H. Hada, N. Iguchi, T. Ichihashi, and S. Fujieda, "Proceedings of the 47th IEEE Annual International Reliability Physics Symposium (RPS)," p. 134, Montreal, Canada, 2009.
36. P.-Y. Gu, Y.-S. Chen, H.-Y. Lee, P.-S. Chen, W.-H. Liu, W.-S. Chen, Y.-Y. Hsu, F. Chen, and M.-J. Tsai, "Proceedings of the IEEE International Symposium on VLSI Technology Systems and Applications (VLSI-TSA)," p. 146, Hsinchu, Taiwan, 2010.
37. Y.-S. Chen, H.-Y. Lee, P.-S. Chen, P.-Y. Gu, W.-H. Liu, W.-S. Chen, Y.-Y. Hsu, C.-H. Tsai, F. Chen, M.-J. Tsai, and C. Lien, *IEEE Electron Device Lett.* 32, 390 (2011).
38. W. C. Chien, Y. R. Chen, Y. C. Chen, A. T. H. Chuang, F. M. Lee, Y. Y. Lin, E. K. Lai, Y. H. Shih, K. Y. Hsieh, and C.-Y. Lu, "IEEE International Electron Devices Meeting (IEDM) Technical Digest," p. 440, San Francisco, CA, 2010.
39. K.-C. Ryoo, J.-H. Oh, S.-H. Jung, and B.-G. Park, "Proceedings of the IEEE Nanotechnology Materials and Devices Conference (NMDC)," p. 356, Monterey, CA, 2010.
40. J.-H. Oh, K.-C. Ryoo, S. Jung, K. S. Oh, H. Shin, and B.-G. Park, "Proceedings of the IEEE Silicon Nanoelectronics Workshop (SNW)," pp. 1–2, Honolulu, HI, 2010.
41. Q. Liu, M. Liu, S. Long, W. Wang, M. Zhang, Q. Wang, and J. Chen, "Proceedings of the European Solid-State Device Research Conference (ESSDERC)," p. 221, Athens, Greece, 2009.
42. Q. Liu, S. Long, W. Wang, Q. Zuo, S. Zhang, J. Chen, and M. Liu, *IEEE Electron. Device. Lett.* 30, 1335 (2009).
43. B. Gao, H. W. Zhang, S. Yu, B. Sun, L. F. Liu, X. Y. Liu, Y. Wang, R. Q. Han, J. F. Kang, B. Yu, and Y. Y. Wang, "IEEE Symposium on VLSI Technology Digest of Technical Papers," p. 30, Kyoto, Japan, 2009.
44. K. Tsunoda, K. Kinoshita, H. Noshiro, Y. Yamazaki, T. Jizuka, Y. Ito, A. Takahashi, A. Okano, Y. Sato, T. Fukano, M. Aoki, and Y. Sugiyama, "IEEE International Electron Devices Meeting (IEDM) Technical Digest," p. 767, Washington, DC, 2007.
45. H. Zhang, B. Gao, S. Yu, L. Lai, L. Zeng, B. Sun, L. Liu, X. Liu, J. Lu, R. Han, and J. Kang, "Proceedings of the IEEE International Conference on Simulation of Semiconductor Processes and Devices (SISPAD'09)," p. 155, San Diego, CA, 2009.
46. H. Zhang, B. Gao, B. Sun, G. Chen, L. Zeng, L. Liu, X. Liu, J. Lu, R. Han, J. Kang, and B. Yu, *Appl. Phys. Lett.* 96, 123502 (2010).
47. M. Terai, Y. Sakotsubo, Y. Saito, S. Kotsuji, and H. Hada, "IEEE International Electron Devices Meeting (IEDM) Technical Digest," p. 775, Washington, DC, 2009.
48. H. B. Lv, M. Yin, P. Zhou, T. A. Tang, B. A. Chen, Y. Y. Lin, A. Bao, and M. H. Chi, "Proceedings of the 9th IEEE International Conference on Solid-State and Integrated Circuit Technology (ICSICT)," p. 52, Shanghai, China, 2008.
49. H. B. Lv, M. Yin, P. Zhou, T. A. Tang, B. A. Chen, Y. Y. Lin, A. Bao, and M. H. Chi, "Proceedings of the Joint 2008 Non-Volatile Semiconductor Memory Workshop and 2008 International Conference on Memory Technology and Design (NVSMW/ICMTD)," p. 52, Monterey, CA, 2008.
50. G. Bersuker, D. C. Gilmer, D. Veksler, J. Yum, H. Park, S. Lian, L. Vandelli, A. Padovani, L. Larcherl, K. McKenna, A. Shluger, V. Iglesias, M. Porti, M. Nafría, W. Taylor, P. D. Kirsch, and R. Jammy, "IEEE International Electron Devices Meeting (IEDM) Technical Digest," p. 456, San Francisco, CA, 2010.
51. M. P. Tendulkar, J. R. Jameson, P. B. Griffin, J. P. McVittie, and Y. Nishi, "Proceedings of the 10th IEEE Annual Non-Volatile Memory Technology Symposium (NVMTS)," p. 48, Portland, OR, 2009.
52. M.-H. Lin, M.-C. Wu, Y.-H. Huang, C.-H. Lin, and T.-Y. Tseng, *IEEE Trans. Electron. Device.* 58, 1182 (2011).
53. S. B. Lee, A. Kim, J. S. Lee, S. H. Chang, H. K. Yoo, T. W. Noh, B. Kahng, M.-J. Lee, C. J. Kim, and B. S. Kang, *Appl. Phys. Lett.* 97, 093505 (2010).
54. M.-H. Lin, M.-C. Wu, C.-H. Lin, and T.-Y. Tseng, *IEEE Trans. Electron. Device.* 57, 1801 (2011).
55. Y. Li, S. Long, M. Zhang, Q. Liu, L. Shao, S. Zhang, Y. Wang, Q. Zuo, S. Liu, and M. Liu, *IEEE Electron. Device. Lett.* 31, 117 (2010).
56. B. Chen, B. Gao, S. W. Sheng, L. F. Liu, X. Y. Liu, Y. S. Chen, Y. Wang, J. F. Kang, and B. Yu, "Proceedings of the IEEE Silicon Nanoelectronics Workshop (SNW)," pp. 1–2, Honolulu, HI, 2010.
57. B. Chen, B. Gao, S. W. Sheng, L. F. Liu, X. Y. Liu, Y. S. Chen, Y. Wang, R. Q. Han, B. Yu, and J. F. Kang, *IEEE Electron. Device. Lett.* 32, 282 (2011).
58. U. Russo, D. Jelmini, C. Cagli, A. L. Lacaita, S. Spigat, C. Wiemert, M. Peregot, and M. Fanciullit, "IEEE International Electron Devices Meeting (IEDM) Technical Digest," p. 775, Washington, DC, 2007.
59. F. Nardi, D. Ielmini, C. Cagli, S. Spiga, M. Fanciulli, L. Goux, and D. J. Wouters, *J. Solid-State Electron.* 58, 42 (2011).
60. A. Makarov, V. Sverdlov, and S. Selberherr, "Proceedings of the IEEE International Conference on Simulation of Semiconductor Processes and Devices (SISPAD'10)," p. 237, Bologna, Italy, 2010.
61. N. Xu, B. Gao, L. F. Liu, B. Sun, X. Y. Liu, R. Q. Han, J. F. Kang, and B. Yu, "IEEE Symposium on VLSI Technology Digest of Technical Papers," p. 100, Honolulu, HI, 2008.
62. B. Gao, S. Yu, N. Xu, L. F. Liu, B. Sun, X. Y. Liu, R. Q. Han, J. F. Kang, B. Yu, and Y. Y. Wang, "IEEE International Electron Devices Meeting (IEDM) Technical Digest," p. 563, San Francisco, CA, 2008.
63. A. Makarov, V. Sverdlov, and S. Selberherr, "Proceedings of the 17th IEEE International Symposium on the Physical and Failure Analysis of Integrated Circuits (IPFA)," pp. 1–4, Singapore, 2010.
64. A. Makarov, V. Sverdlov, and S. Selberherr, "Proceedings of the European Solid-State Device Research Conference (ESSDERC)," p. 396, Seville, Spain, 2010.
65. C. H. Ho, E. K. Lai, M. D. Lee, C. L. Pan, Y. D. Yao, K. Y. Hsieh, R. Liu, and C.-Y. Lu, "IEEE Symposium on VLSI Technology Digest of Technical Papers," Kyota, Japan, 2007, p. 228.
66. C. H. Ho, M.-D. Lee, C.-L. Pan, E.-K. Lai, Y.-D. Yao, K.-Y. Hsieh, R. Liu, and C.-Y. Lu, "Proceedings of the IEEE International Symposium on VLSI Technology Systems and Applications (VLSI-TSA)," p. 98, Hsinchu, Taiwan, 2007.
67. C. H. Ho, C.-L. Hsu, C.-C. Chen, J.-T. Liu, C.-S. Wu, C.-C. Huang, C. Hu, and F.-L. Yang, "IEEE International Electron Devices Meeting (IEDM) Technical Digest," p. 436, San Francisco, CA, 2010.
68. W. C. Chien, Y. C. Chen, K. P. Chang, E. K. Lai, Y. D. Yao, P. Lin, J. Gong, S. C. Tsai, S. H. Hsieh, C. F. Chen, K. Y. Hsieh, R. Liu, and C.-Y. Lu, "Proceedings of the IEEE International Memory Workshop (IMW)," p. 15, Seoul, South Korea, 2009.
69. W. C. Chien, Y. C. Chen, E. K. Lai, Y. D. Yao, P. Lin, S. F. Horng, J. Gong, T. H. Chou, H. M. Lin, M. N. Chang, Y. H. Shih, K. Y. Hsieh, R. Liu, and C.-Y. Lu, *IEEE Electron. Device. Lett.* 31, 126 (2010).
70. W.-C. Chien, E.-K. Lai, K.-P. Chang, C.-H. Yeh, M.-H. Hsueh, Y.-D. Yao, T. Luoh, S.-H. Hsieh, T. H. Yang, K. C. Chen, Y.-C. Chen, K.-Y. Hsieh, R. Liu, and C.-Y. Lu, "Proceedings of IEEE International Symposium on VLSI Technology Systems and Applications (VLSI-TSA)," p. 144, Hsinchu, Taiwan, 2008.
71. S. Yu and H.-S. P. Wong, *IEEE Electron. Device. Lett.* 31, 1455 (2010).
72. K.-C. Ryoo, J.-H. Oh, H. Jeong, and B.-G. Park, "Proceedings of the IEEE Silicon Nanoelectronics Workshop (SNW)," p. 63, Honolulu, HI, 2010.
73. O. Ginez, J.-M. Portal, and C. Muller, "Proceedings of the 14th IEEE European Test Symposium (ETS'09)," p. 61, Sevilla, Spain, 2009.
74. S. Jung, T.-W. Kim, H. Choi, J. Kong, J.-B. Park, M. Jo, S. Kim, W. Lee, J. Lee, T. Lee, K. Lee, and H. Hwang,

"International Semiconductor Device Research Symposium (ISDRS'09)," pp. 1–2, College Park, MD, 2009.

75. Y. H. Tseng, W. C. Shen, C.-E. Huang, C. J. Lin, and Y.-C. King, "IEEE International Electron Devices Meeting (IEDM) Technical Digest," p. 636, San Francisco, CA, 2010.
76. S. Muraoka, K. Osano, Y. Kanzawa, S. Mitani, S. Fujii, K. Katayama, Y. Katoh, Z. Wei, T. Mikawa, K. Arita, Y. Kawashima, R. Azuma, K. Kawai, K. Shimakawa, A. Odagawa, and T. Takagi, "IEEE International Electron Devices Meeting (IEDM) Technical Digest," p. 779, Washington, DC, 2007.
77. S. Kawabata, M. Nakura, S. Yamazaki, T. Shibuya, Y. Inoue, J. Onishi, Y. Tabuchi, Y. Tamai, Y. Yaoi, K. Ishihara, Y. Ohta, H. Shima, H. Akinaga, Natsuki Fukuda, H. Kurihara, Y. Yoshida, Y. Kokaze, Y. Nishioka, K. Suu, K. Nakayama, A. Kitagawa, S. Ohnishi, and N. Awaya, "Proceedings of the IEEE International Memory Workshop (IMW)," pp. 1–2, Seoul, South Korea, 2010.
78. M.-J. Lee, C. B. Lee, S. Kim, H. Yin, J. Park, S. E. Ahn, B. S. Kang, K. H. Kim, G. Stefanovich, I. Song, S. W. Kim, J. H. Lee, S. J. Chung, Y. H. Kim, C. S. Lee, J. B. Park, I. G. Baek, C. J. Kim, and Y. Park, "IEEE International Electron Devices Meeting (IEDM) Technical Digest," p. 85, San Francisco, CA, 2008.
79. M. Wang, W. J. Luo, Y. L. Wang, L. M. Yang, W. Zhu, P. Zhou, J. H. Yang, X. G. Gong, and Y. Y. Lin, "IEEE Symposium on VLSI Technology Digest of Technical Papers," p. 89, Honolulu, HI, 2010.
80. P. Zhou, H. J. Wan, Y. L. Song, M. Yin, H. B. Lv, Y. Y. Lin, S. Song, R. Huang, J. G. Wu, and M. H. Chi, "Proceedings of the IEEE International Memory Workshop (IMW)," pp. 1–2, Seoul, South Korea, 2009.
81. K. Kinoshita, T. Okutani, H. Tanaka, T. Hinoki, H. Agura, K. Yazawa, K. Ohmi, and S. Kishida, "Proceedings of the IEEE International Memory Workshop (IMW)," pp. 1–2, Seoul, South Korea, 2010.
82. C.-Y. Lin, C.-Y. Wu, C.-Y. Wu, T.-C. Lee, F.-L. Yang, C. Hu, and T.-Y. Tseng, *IEEE Electron. Device Lett.* 28, 366 (2007).
83. L. Chen, Y. Xu, Q.-Q. Sun, H. Liu, J.-J. Gu, S.-J. Ding, and D. W. Zhang, *IEEE Electron. Device. Lett.* 31, 356 (2010).
84. S.-S. Sheu, P.-C. Chiang, W.-P. Lin, H.-Y. Lee, P.-S. Chen, Y.-S. Chen, T.-Y. Wu, F. T. Chen, K.-L. Su, M.-J. Kao, K.-H. Cheng, and M.-J. Tsai, "IEEE Symposium on VLSI Technology Digest of Technical Papers," p. 82, Kyota, Japan, 2009,.
85. Z. Wei, Y. Kanzawa, K. Arita, Y. Katoh, K. Kawai, S. Muraoka, S. Mitani, S. Fujii, K. Katayama, M. Iijima, T. Mikawa, T. Ninomiya, R. Miyanaga, Y. Kawashima, K. Tsuji, A. Himeno, T. Okada, R. Azuma, K. Shimakawa, H. Sugaya, and T. Takagi, R. Yasuhara, K. Horiba, H. Kumigashira, and M. Oshima, "IEEE International Electron Devices Meeting (IEDM) Technical Digest," p. 293, San Francisco, CA, 2008.
86. L. F. Liu, X. Sun, B. Sun, J. F. Kang, Y. Wang, X. Y. Liu, R. Q. Han, and G. C. Xiong, "Proceedings of the IEEE International Memory Workshop (IMW)," pp. 1–2, Seoul, South Korea, 2009.
87. K.-C. Liu, W.-H. Tzeng, K.-M. Chang, Y.-C. Chan, C.-C. Kuo, and C.-W. Cheng, "Proceedings of the 3rd IEEE International Nanoelectronics Conference (INEC)," p. 898, Hong Kong, China, 2010.
88. S. K. Hong, J. E. Kim, S. O. Kim, S.-Y. Choi, and B. J. Cho, *IEEE Electron. Device. Lett.* 31, 1005 (2010).
89. Y. H. Tseng, C.-E. Huang, C.-H. Kuo, Y.-D. Chih, Y.-C. King, and C. J. Lin, *IEEE Trans. Electron. Device.* 58, 53 (2011).
90. A. Demolliens, C. Muller, D. Deleruyelle, S. Spiga, E. Cianci, M. Fanciulli, F. Nardi, C. Cagli, and D. Ielmini, "Proceedings of the IEEE International Memory Workshop (IMW)," p. 25, Seoul, South Korea, 2009.
91. S. Kim, H. Moon, D. Gupta, S. Yoo, and Y.-K. Choi, *IEEE Trans. Electron. Device.* 56, 696 (2009).
92. X. A. Tran, H. Y. Yu, Y. C. Yeo, L.Wu, W. J. Liu, Z. R. Wang, Z. Fang, K. L. Pey, X. W. Sun, A. Y. Du, B. Y. Nguyen, and M. F. Li, *IEEE Electron. Device. Lett.* 32, 396 (2011).
93. S. Kim, S.-J. Choi, and Y.-K. Choi, *IEEE Trans. Electron. Device.* 56, 2670 (2009).
94. C. H. Cheng, A. T. Chin, and F. S. Yeh, *IEEE Electron. Device. Lett.* 32, 366 (2011).
95. C. H. Cheng, C. Y. Tsai, A. Chin, and F. S. Yeh, "IEEE International Electron Devices Meeting (IEDM) Technical Digest," p. 448, San Francisco, CA, 2010.
96. A. Makarov, V. Sverdlov, and S. Selberherr, "Proceedings of the 14th IEEE International Workshop on Computational Electronics (IWCE)," p. 35, Pisa, Italy, 2010.
97. C. I. Lin, A. Prakash, and S. Maikap, "International Semiconductor Device Research Symposium (ISDRS'09)," pp. 1–2, College Park, MD, 2009,.
98. C.-H. Hsu and S.-Y. Lin, "Proceedings of the 3rd IEEE International Nanoelectronics Conference (INEC)," p. 1236, Hong Kong, China, 2010.
99. M.-D. Lee, C.-H. Ho, C.-K. Lo, T.-Y. Peng, and Y.-D. Yao, *IEEE Trans. Magn.* 43, 939 (2007).
100. C. H. Cheng, K. Y. Chou, A. Chin, and F. S. Yeh, "IEEE International Electron Devices Meeting (IEDM) Technical Digest," p. 512, San Francisco, CA, 2010.
101. J.-K. Lee, H. Y. Jeong, I.-T. Cho, J. Y. Lee, S.-Y. Choi, H.-I. Kwon, and J.-H. Lee, *IEEE Electron. Device. Lett.* 31, 603 (2010).
102. L. Wang, Z. Jia, and T. Ren, "IEEE International Conference of Electron Devices and Solid-State Circuits (EDSSC)," pp. 1–3, Hong Kong, China, 2010.
103. L.-E. Yu, S. Kim, M.-K. Ryu, S.-Y. Choi, and Y.-K. Choi, *IEEE Electron Device Lett.* 29, 331 (2008).
104. H. Y. Lee, P.-S. Chen, T.-Y. Wu, Y. S. Chen, F. Chen, C.-C. Wang, P.-J. Tzeng, C. H. Lin, M.-J. Tsai, and C. Lien, *IEEE Electron. Device Lett.* 30, 703 (2009).
105. S.-G. Park, B. Magyari-Köpe, and Y. Nishi, *Phys. Rev. B* 82, 115109 (2010).
106. H. D. Lee and Y. Nishi, "Proceedings of the 2010 IEEE GLOBECOM Workshops (GC Wkshps)," Miami, Florida, p. 1886, 2010.
107. Z. Fang, H. Y. Yu, W. J. Liu, K. L. Pey, X. Li, L. Wu, Z. R. Wang, P. G. Q. Lo, B. Gao, and J. F. Kang, "Proceedings of the 2010 IEEE International Reliability Physics Symposium (IRPS)," p. 964, Anaheim, CA, 2010.
108. L. Zhang, R. Huang, D. Gao, Y. Pan, S. Qin, Z. Yu, C. Shi, and Y. Wang, "Proceedings of the 10th IEEE International Conference on Solid-State and Integrated Circuit Technology (ICSICT)," p. 1160, Shanghai, China, 2010.
109. Z. Fang, H. Y. Yu, X. Li, K.-L. Pey, and W. Liu, "Proceedings of the 2009 12th IEEE International Symposium on Integrated Circuits (ISIC'09)," p. 144, Singapore, 2009.
110. Z. Fang, H. Y. Yu, W. J. Liu, Z. R. Wang, X. A. Tran, B. Gao, and J. F. Kang, *IEEE Electron. Device. Lett.* 31, 476 (2010).
111. B. Gao, B. Chen, Y. Chen, L. Liu, X. Liu, R. Han, and J. Kang, "Proceedings of the 10th IEEE International Conference on Solid-State and Integrated Circuit Technology (ICSICT)," p. 1145, Shanghai, China, 2010.
112. A. Chen, S. Haddad, and Y.-C. Wu, *IEEE Electron. Device Lett.* 29, 38 (2008).
113. S. Kim and Y.-K. Choi, *IEEE Trans. Electron. Device.* 56, 3049 (2009).
114. B. Gao, H. Zhang, B. Chen, L. Liu, X. Liu, R. Han, J. Kang, Z. Fang, H. Yu, B. Yu, and D.-L. Kwong, *IEEE Electron. Device. Lett.* 32, 276 (2011).
115. B. Gao, J. F. Kang, H. W. Zhang, B. Sun, B. Chen, L. F. Liu, X. Y. Liu, R. Q. Han, Y. Y. Wang, B. Yu, Z. Fang, H. Y. Yu, and D.-L. Kwong, "Proceedings of the European Solid-State Device Research Conference (ESSDERC)," p. 392, Seville, Spain, 2010.
116. Y.-C. Chen, W.-C. Chien, Y.-Y. Lin, F.-M. Lee, K.-Y. Hsieh, and C.-Y. Lu, "Proceedings of the 10th IEEE International Conference on Solid-State and Integrated Circuit Technology (ICSICT)," p. 1065, Shanghai, China, 2010.

117. B. Chen, Q. Y. Jun, B. Gao, F. F. Zhang, K. L. Wei, Y. S. Chen, L. F. Liu, X. Y. Liu, J. F. Kang, and R. Q. Han, "Proceedings of the 10th IEEE International Conference on Solid-State and Integrated Circuit Technology (ICSICT)," p. 1829, Shanghai, China, 2010.
118. Q. Liu, S. Long, W. Wang, S. Tanachutiwat, Y. Li, Q. Wang, M. Zhang, Z. Huo, J. Chen, and M. Liu, *IEEE Electron. Device. Lett.* 31, 1299 (2010).
119. W. Guan, S. Long, Q. Liu, M. Liu, and W. Wang, *IEEE Electron. Device Lett.* 29, 434 (2008).
120. C.-C. Lin, B.-C. Tu, C.-C. Lin, C.-H. Lin, and T.-Y. Tseng, *IEEE Electron. Device Lett.* 27, 725 (2006).
121. C.-C. Lin, C.-Y. Lin, M.-H. Lin, C.-H. Lin, and T.-Y. Tseng, *IEEE Trans. Electron. Device* 54, 3146 (2007).
122. D. Ielmini, F. Nardi, C. Cagli, and A. L. Lacaita, "Proceedings of the IEEE International Reliability Physics Symposium (IRPS)," p. 620, Anaheim, CA 2010.
123. S. Deshpande and V. V. Nair, "Proceedings of the International Conference on Advances in Computing, Control, and Telecommunication Technologies (ACT'09)," p. 471, Trivandrum, Kerala, India, 2009.
124. Y. Sakotsubo, M. Terai, S. Kotsuji, Y. Saito, M. Tada, Y. Yabe, and H. Hada, "IEEE Symposium on VLSI Technology Digest of Technical Papers," p. 87, Honolulu, HI, 2010.
125. D. Ielmini, F. Nardi, C. Cagli, and A. L. Lacaita, *IEEE Electron. Device. Lett.* 31, 353 (2010).
126. U. Russo, D. Ielmini, C. Cagli, and A. L. Lacaita, *IEEE Trans. Electron. Device.* 56, 193 (2009).
127. C. Cagli, D. Ielmini, F. Nardi, and A. L. Lacaita, "IEEE International Electron Devices Meeting (IEDM) Technical Digest," p. 301, San Francisco, CA, 2008.
128. F. Pan and V. Subramanian, "Proceedings of the IEEE International Conference on Simulation of Semiconductor Processes and Devices (SISPAD'10)," p. 19, Bologna, Italy, 2010.
129. U. Russo, D. Ielmini, C. Cagli, and A. L. Lacaita, *IEEE Trans. Electron. Device.* 56, 186 (2009).
130. K. Kinoshita, K. Tsunoda, Y. Sato, H. Noshiro, Y. Yamazaki, T. Fukano, S. Yagaki, M. Aoki, and Y. Sugiyama, "Proceedings of the 22nd IEEE Nnon-Volatile Semiconductor Memory Workshop (NVSMW)," p. 66, Monterey, CA, 2007.
131. D.-K. Kim, D.-S. Suh, and J. Park, *IEEE Electron. Device. Lett.* 31, 600 (2010).
132. D. Ielmini, *IEEE Electron. Device. Lett.* 31, 552 (2010).
133. X. P. Wang, Y. Y. Chen, L. Pantisano, L. Goux, M. Jurczak, G. Groeseneken, and D. J. Wouters, "Proceedings of the IEEE International Symposium on VLSI Technology Systems and Applications (VLSI-TSA)," p. 140, Hsinchu, Taiwan, 2010.
134. H. Wan, X. Tian, Y. Song, W. Luo, M. Wang, Y. Wang, P. Zhou, and Y. Lin, "Proceedings of the 10th IEEE International Conference on Solid-State and Integrated Circuit Technology (ICSICT)," p. 1100, Shanghai, China, 2010.

CHAPTER 9

Resistive-Switching Memory Devices Based on Metal Oxides: Modeling of Unipolar Switching, Reliability, and Scaling

Carlo Cagli, Daniele Ielmini
Dipartimento di Elettronica e Informazione and IU.NET, Politecnico di Milano, Piazza L. da Vinci 32, 20133 Milano (MI), Italy

CONTENTS

1. INTRODUCTION

As the scaling of standard CMOS memory, as flash and DRAM, becomes increasingly difficult, the interest to explore novel storage concept for non-volatile memories is constantly growing [1, 2]. Given the high technological level reached by standard Flash memory, the task of finding an alternative device with comparable performance, density and scalability is extremely challenging. The requirements for a future non-volatile random access memory are in fact very difficult to fulfill in terms of cost, power consumption and bit density. Moreover any non-volatile memory device should exhibit a high reliability in terms of retention and endurance, and at the same time display fast read and write access times.

ISBN: 1-58883-251-1

Nonvolatile Memories: Materials, Devices and Applications
Edited by Tseung-Yuen Tseng and Simon M. Sze
Volume 2: Pages: 225–248

Among non-volatile memory devices, which are considered for a possible flash replacement in future generations, the resistive switching memory (RRAM) is one of the most promising for simplicity of the storage concept and prospected scalability [3–6]. In a RRAM, the resistance R of an insulating layer, most typically a metal-oxide film, is electrically changed between a high-resistance state and a low-resistance state. The transition from high to low R is called set process, while the reverse transition is called reset process. The high and low resistance states are also referred to as reset and set states in the literature. The most popular RRAM concepts are based on electrically induced nanoionic transport and redox reactions within metal–insulator–metal (MIM) structures [5, 7]. These capacitor-like devices are very promising from the scaling viewpoint, since they are well suited to fit in crossbar integrated architecture. In a crossbar array, every memory element is sandwiched between a word-line and a perpendicular bit-line, thus allowing for a minimum area and maximum density of the device [8, 9]. The single device area is in fact given by $4F^2$, where F is the minimum feature size characterizing a given technology generation [10].

RRAM devices include a wide range of different materials and switching modes, all sharing the same basic concept of fast, voltage-driven transitions between the set and reset states. In literature a plethora of materials with different stacks and composition can be found [11], although the physical switching mechanisms can vary prominently and so far very little has been understood about the actual switching mechanisms. In this frame, a useful taxonomy has been provided by Waser and Aono [5], providing a classification of three different basic switching mechanisms and devices, namely

(i) thermo-chemical memory,
(ii) valence-change memory and
(iii) electrochemical memory.

The three different switching modes can be generally observed in metal oxides, and sometimes a metal oxide MIM can display more than one switching mode [11]. According to the classification in [7], a necessarily coarse overview of the different RRAM devices and switching modes is given in Figure 1 and described in the following.

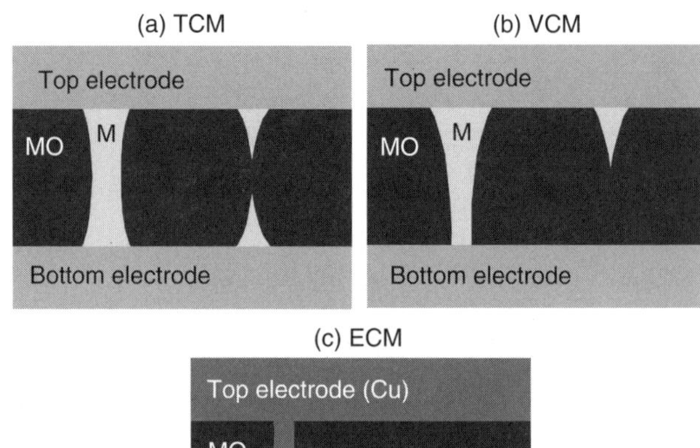

Figure 1. Schematic representation of the three main RRAM categories as proposed by Waser in Ref. [7], namely (a) thermochemical memory (TCM), (b) valence change memory (VCM and (c) electrochemical memory (ECM).

1.1. Thermochemical Memory

A thermochemical memory (TCM) is a RRAM device where the resistance switching is due to thermally-induced chemical reactions, typically reduction and oxidation (Fig. 1(a)) [7, 12]. These reactions are typically localized at one spot in the metal oxide layer, which will be referred to as the conductive filament (CF) [13–15]. The CF is initially obtained through a forming operation, which causes a local reduction of the metal oxide and results in the formation of a metallic-rich CF with low resistance. Next, the CF can be oxidized by application of a voltage and the consequent release of a Joule heat accelerating diffusion and chemical reaction [16, 17]. The composition in the oxidized CF is closer to the metal oxide, thus displays a higher resistance. The two resistance states can be used as the two logic states of the memory. The localized nature of unipolar switching can be supported by the fact that the set-state resistance is generally independent from the device area, since R is controlled by the CF area and conductivity [16, 18]. This has significant implications in terms of reduction of the switching current and scaling of the cell size in a real array [16]. The most important signature of this switching mode is its *unipolar* character, where both set and reset processes are achieved by the application of a pulse with the same (e.g., positive) polarity. This allows a straightforward implementation of a crossbar array architecture through TCM devices, with a relatively simple periphery circuitry and unipolar rectifying diodes as select elements [10, 19, 20].

1.2. Valence-Change Memory (VCM)

The second class of resistance switching devices, schematically shown in Figure 1(b), is similar to TCMs, in that it is observed in metal oxides and displays transition between a high and a low resistance states. However, differently from TCM, the switching requires a change of bias polarity between the set and the reset operations, and is thus referred to as *bipolar* switching. Bipolar switching in VCMs can be explained by a physical mechanism similar to TCMs, however involving a significant thermally- and voltage-assisted ion migration [5]. After the forming operation, the CF is dissolved by migration of ions toward the electrodes, namely positive ions (e.g., metallic ions or oxygen vacancies) drift toward the cathode and negative ions (oxygen ions) drift toward the anode. In the set process, instead, the CF is recovered by migration of the ions back to the previous position. This allows a low-resistance connection between the electrodes by a continuous metal-rich (or oxygen-vacancy rich) CF. The vertical migration of ions, instead of the mostly-radial diffusion of conductive species in the TCM, thus forms the basis for the bipolar switching process in VCMs.

Several transition metal oxides have been shown to display bipolar VCM switching. Examples are ZrO_x [21, 22], $SrTiO_x$ [23, 24], Nb_2O_5 [25, 26], TiO_x [11, 13, 27–31] and HfO_x [31–36], with no specific requirements regarding the electrodes and doping. Electroforming is generally required to initiate the resistance switching, but the reset and set parameters generally vary depending on the materials and the cell structures.

Similar to TCM devices, VCM devices generally display filamentary switching, in that ion migration is localized at a specific CF defined by the initial forming operation. An important exception to this general rule is the uniform switching observed in VCM devices based on complex oxides such as PrCaMnO (PCMO) and other perovskytes [37–39]. These devices show an area-dependent switching, in that both the set-state and reset-state resistances are inversely proportional to the device area, contrary to TCM. Ion migration in these materials is probably uniform, leading to an increase of the oxygen concentration to the anode side and a resulting oxidation. Formation of bubbles at the anode side has been shown as an evidence for a uniform, field-induced oxygen migration [40]. The partial oxidation of the electrode results in the formation of an interface layer with a high potential barrier for electrons, thus causing the increase of resistance in the uniform-switching VCM [41]. Uniform-switching VCM are attracting a growing interest since the reset current can be reduced linearly with the device area, in contrast to filamentary switching RRAM where the reset current in area independent. However, the deposition and control of complex ternary/quaternary oxides is generally not straightforward and the reliability issues and mechanisms are still not clear, thus these devices appear to be not yet sufficiently mature as compared to filamentary TCMs and VCMs.

1.3. Electro-Chemical Memory (ECM)

Bipolar switching is also displayed by the electrochemical memory (ECM), also known as programmable metallization cell (PMC) or conductive-bridge RAM (CBRAM) [42, 43]. In an ECM, schematically shown in Figure 1(c), one of the electrode is made of an active metal such as Ag or Cu, characterized by easy oxidation and diffusion within solid-state electrolytes such as amorphous sulphides/selenides [42], metal oxides [5, 44], silicon dioxide [45], amorphous silicon [46] and organic insulators [47]. The field-driven migration and electrodeposition of cations result in the local formation of metallic CFs responsible for the low resistance state. Active cations are electrodeposited at the anode, usually an inert metal such as Pt, Au or W. The solid electrolytes are generally doped with the active ions from the beginning, to facilitate the initial formation of the filament. The typical technique for cation doping is photo-dissolution within the chalcogenide matrix to obtain a ternary compound [48]. Due to the very high mobility of Ag or Cu in the solid electrolyte, ECM devices can achieve very low-current/low-power switching, although a tradeoff between data retention and reset current has been highlighted [49].

The set process in an ECM is achieved in three main steps [7]. First, due to the application of a positive voltage to the active electrode, the electric field causes the active metal M to ionize on the electrode surface by electron release. Then, positive ions (e.g., M^+, assuming a singly charged ion) migrates toward the inert cathode. Finally, ions are reduced at the cathode by $M^+ + e \rightarrow M$, thus resulting in the growth of a metallic dendrite. This leads to the formation of the thin conductive filament that eventually causes the resistance change to low values. Being field-activated, the process tends to grow filaments along the field direction. The very first evidence of field-induced CF formation was given in the 1976 by Hirose and Hirose in lateral cells based on Ag-photodoped As_2S_3 [50]. The high resistance is finally restored by a reset process with the application of a negative bias to the inert electrode, resulting in ions M^+ being released from the CF and migrating back to the active electrode, thus resulting in the disconnection of the CF. The resistance switching in ECMs is bipolar, since positive and negative voltages are needed to form/dissolve the CF by ion migration in two opposite directions. A current compliance is generally used during set to control the size of the CF, hence the value of the set-state resistance [45, 51]. Generally, low values of the set and reset operating voltages are shown, thus evidencing the low-voltage potential advantage of EMC as compared to Flash technology.

From the previous description, it is clear that RRAM includes several different switching modes (unipolar, bipolar, filamentary, uniform switching) and physical mechanisms (Joule heating, thermally activated diffusion, ion migration, chemical reduction and oxidation). As a result, a comprehensive review of all RRAM devices would be very difficult. In the following, the focus will be the physical understanding and modeling of TCMs, or unipolar RRAM based on metal oxides. After a description of the cell structure, physical models for the set/reset transitions, for CF conduction mechanisms and for physical phenomena potentially affecting reliability will be described. The consequences of these physical models on device scaling will be pointed out.

2. CELL STRUCTURE AND ELECTRICAL CHARACTERIZATION

The first report about resistive switching on disordered materials (in particular on NiO) is dated 1964 [52], but only recently this technology has attracted a serious interest both in academy and industry, thanks to the rapid improvements of deposition techniques, material science and device-modeling capabilities. Among all metal-oxide candidates for active material in RRAM technology, NiO is considered a promising material due to its *unipolar* switching behavior. However, a wide range of other metal oxides has been the object of RRAM studies, for instance TiO_2, HfO_2, and many others (see as example Refs. [5] or [11] for a list of materials). The device has a very simple capacitor structure, consisting of two metallic electrodes sandwiching the active material.

The working principle of RRAM relies on the reversible transition of the oxide between two different resistance values. This occurs by alternating formation and rupture of one or more CFs, which shunts the relatively large resistance of the oxide layer in the low resistive state. The filamentary nanoscale nature of the switching mechanism has been established by C-AFM experiments and by electrical measurements [53]. Figure 2 shows an experiment performed by Son et al. where a drop of Hg was used as top electrode on a NiO thin film [15]. After resistance switching in this experimental device, the Hg drop was removed and C-AFM was used to test the conductivity of the underling oxide in a set or reset state. As can be seen, several filamentary paths were observed as responsible of the low and high resistivity in the set and reset state respectively. Further evidence for the filamentary switching in NiO is provided by the lack of an area-dependence of the resistance and the reset current in the low-resistance state. This is shown in Figure 3, were the reset current is reported as a function of contact area for different NiO-based devices, namely Ti-doped NiO [54] and undoped NiO [55–57]. A part from one case [54], the reset current remains constant irrespective of the device area, due to the filamentary nature of the low resistance state. The area dependent I_{reset} in [54] might be due to a set state featuring many independent CFs, as shown in Figure 2. The fact that the multifilament state is obtained for Ti-doped NiO suggests that the number of CFs may strongly depend on the doping and composition of the active metal oxide.

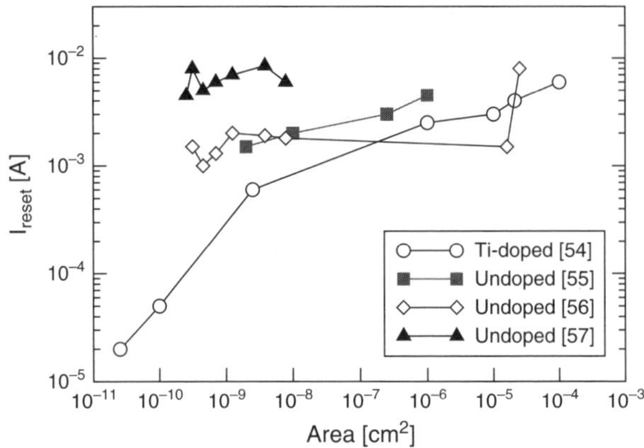

Figure 3. Reset current as a function of contact area for different NiO-based devices. Except for one case [54], the reset current remains constant while cell diameter scales down. This supports the filamentary nature of the resistive switching in this kind of device. Reprinted with permission from [17], D. Ielmini et al., *Phase Transition* 84, 570 (2011), © 2011, Taylor and Francis.

Figure 4 shows typical programming *I–V* curves for a NiO-based RRAM device. The sample initially displays a large resistance of several GΩ, with a characteristics Pool-Frenkel conduction characteristic with an activation energy of about 0.4 eV [58]. The pristine state (black trace) shows a sudden current increase at a relatively high voltage (around 4.2 V) marking the transition to the low resistance set state. This is referred to as the forming operation, namely the dielectric breakdown operation where the CF is first initiated through the insulating layer. Note that the current is limited by a compliance system to 500 mA in the figure, to prevent the irreversible breakdown of the cell. The following applied voltage sweep causes the transition from the set to the reset state at a voltage V_{reset}, typically below 1 V. After reset, the cell shows a high resistance, although typically lower than the pristine value before the forming process. The cell can recover its low resistance state by the set operation, where the applied voltage sweep results in a new sudden transition to low resistance at a voltage V_{set}, larger than V_{reset} and smaller than the forming voltage. A current compliance is used to prevent irreversible damage as in the forming process. Figure 5 schematically summarized the forming, set and reset process.

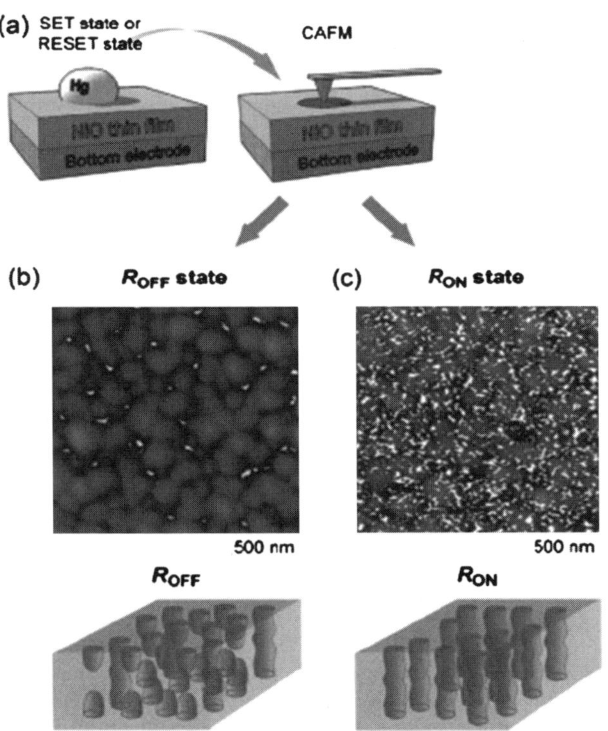

Figure 2. (a) A drop of Hg is used as top electrode. Once the cell is programmed, removing the Hg allows analyzing the NiO film via C-AFM. (b and c) show respectively the distribution of the conductivity for OFF and ON states. Reprinted with permission from [15], J. Y. Son and Y.-H. Shin, *Appl. Phys. Lett.* 92, 222106 (2008). © 2008, American Institute of Physics.

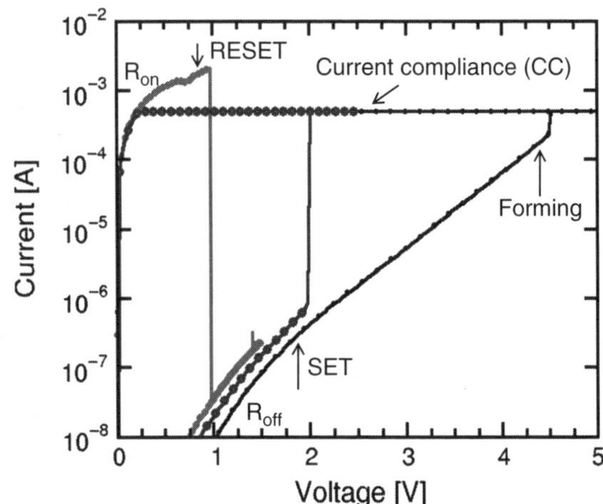

Figure 4. Example of unipolar forming, set and reset curves on NiO-based cell obtained with DC measurements. Reprinted with permission from [17], D. Ielmini et al., *Phase Transition* 84, 570 (2011). © 2011, Taylor and Francis.

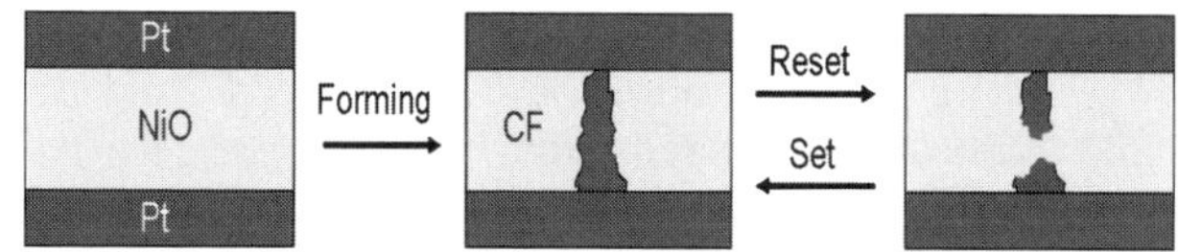

Figure 5. Schematic picture of RRAM working principle. Forming process generates a CF that shunts the two electrodes. Once the CF is formed, reset and set operations make the cell resistance to change, dissolving and rebuilding the filament respectively.

Our analysis allows for a preliminary understanding of the set and reset states: the set state in fact consists of a continuous metallic CF with low resistance, while the reset state is the result of the total or partial oxidation of the CF [16]. Also, the forming/set/reset operations in Figure 4 allows to point out the critical role of the current compliance in avoiding a possible irreversible breakdown at the CF location. Most importantly, the current compliance I_C was shown to define the set resistance, which has been shown to obey an inverse relationship $R = V_0/I_C$, where V_0 is close to 0.4 V [59]. This relationship can be useful for two main purposes: First, it may allow the cell to work with a multilevel approach, storing more bits in a single cell, with each bit represented by a certain resistance value. On the other hand, the limitation of the set-state R allows to reduce the reset current needed to dissolve the CF in the reset operation [60, 61]. This allows a strong reduction of the power consumption for device operation, which is among the main issues of RRAM technology [58].

3. SET MODEL

The set transition can be viewed as a soft breakdown phenomenon that causes the formation of the CF. This process is critical since it determines most of the characteristics of the switching behavior of the cell. In fact, the set operation determines the resistance of the set state, which in turn controls the reset current as described in Section 4. Given its importance, a good understanding and modeling of this process is necessary to develop and improve RRAM devices and arrays. To this purpose, the kinetics of the set transition is critical.

Figure 6 shows typical results for pulsed set experiments on NiO-based RRAM devices [62]. The set pulse was applied to RRAM cell in the reset state with a load resistance R_L connected in series as shown in Figure 6(a). This experimental setup allows to monitor V_{cell} while a voltage pulse with amplitude V_A is applied to node A. From V_{cell}, one can estimate the cell resistance during time according to:

$$R = R_L V/(V_A - V) \tag{1}$$

thus allowing for a study of the kinetic of the set transition. Figures 6(b and c) show V_{cell} during the application of voltage pulses with 100 ns width on the same RRAM cell. The load resistance was $R_L = 1\ \mathrm{k\Omega}$. In both cases, V_{cell} displays a sudden drop indicating the decrease of R to a low value according to Eq. (1). In case (b) the cell switches permanently to the low-R state, consistently with results in Figure 4 for the set operation under DC conditions. On the other hand, the low-R state in (c) is unstable, and the high-R reset state is soon re-established by a recovery process. DC measurement of the resistance after the pulse of Figure 6(c) confirmed that no stable set state was obtained. The recovery process in Figure 6(c) could be interpreted as a fast reset process, occurring right after the set transition due to the relatively high voltage across the cell. However, the recovery time in Figure 6(b) is at least 2 orders of magnitude shorter than the typical reset time at the V_{cell} in the set state. On the other hand, the fast V_{cell} drop and recovery in Figure 6(b) are consistent with *threshold switching*, that is a reversible electronic transition from high to low resistance generally observed in chalcogenides glasses and other amorphous semiconductors [63, 64]. At the onset of threshold switching, an electronic filament with a very high current density is formed, therefore causing a sudden decrease of resistance. Note that the switching is due to an electronic mechanism with no structural modification in the NiO layer, at least initially. After the buildup of the electronic filament, the high local temperature due to Joule heating accelerates the set process, e.g., due to local chemical reduction by oxygen radial diffusion from the electronic filament location. This results in the formation of a CF, consisting of locally segregated metallic Ni or NiO_x suboxide ($x < 1$), shunting the two electrodes with a low resistance path. The fast drop of the cell voltage, due to the presence of the load resistance or of the current compliance in the experimental setup, results in a fast temperature decrease, thus inhibiting further growth of the CF or thermally induced degradation.

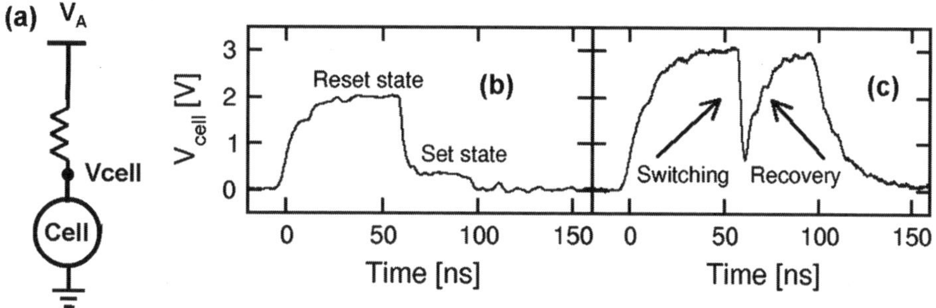

Figure 6. (b) Voltage-time trace of a set transition marked by the voltage drop. This is due to the resistance partition of the cell and a load "bit-line" resistance (a). (c) After a sudden drop of voltage, the signal rapidly recovers. This has been recognized as a signature of threshold switching. Reprinted with permission from [62], C. Cagli et al., "IEEE IEDM," p. 1, San Francisco, CA, 2008. © 2008, IEEE EDS.

According to this picture, the set transition is thus viewed as a two-step process, as sketched in Figure 7. First, threshold switching locally enhances conductivity, hence Joule heating. Then CF growth can take place thanks to thermally activated chemical reactions and diffusion/migration [65]. This can account for the establishment of a stable set state in Figure 6(b), while the switching/recovery effects in Figure 6(c) can be explained as an unsuccessful formation of the CF after the threshold switching. Due to the conductivity increase, the cell voltage decreases soon after threshold switching, thus falling below the holding voltage necessary to sustain the ON-state of the electronic filament. This causes the electronic filament to vanish, thus leaving the cell in a high resistance state again [65].

The finding of threshold switching as a key initiating step in the set process has important consequences from the viewpoint of modeling. In particular, the set parameters, such as set voltage V_{set} and the delay time for the initiation of the set process τ_{set}, are controlled by the threshold switching mechanism. Therefore, to correctly predict the set parameters, a good understanding of threshold switching is strictly necessary. Threshold switching followed by set is generally assumed to take place at a "weak" spot, possibly at the position of the previous CF which has been partially dissolved by the reset process. This is in fact the location of maximum current density prior to switching in the reset state. Also, the electric field is believed to be locally higher, due to a possible local thinning of the metal oxide or to a non-uniform distribution of the electric field. In support of threshold switching as the initiating step in the set transition, note that threshold switching is routinely observed in transition metal oxides, such as NiO [66, 67]. The tendency of NiO to threshold switching (Fig. 6(c)) as opposed to memory switching (Fig. 6(b)) has been attributed to oxygen concentration in NiO [66] and thickness of the electrodes, possibly affecting the thermal behaviour of the stack [67].

To calculate the set voltage V_{set} under a given voltage sweep rate or the delay time for set τ_{set} under a given applied voltage, a threshold-switching model is needed. Lavizzari et al. developed a model for switching delay in chalcogenide-based phase change memory (PCM) devices [68] that can be used to evaluate the probability for threshold switching to apply. According to this model the threshold switching is activated by intrinsic fluctuation of the current during the application of a voltage to the device. The current fluctuations with a $1/f$ power spectrum are generally well known to occur in disordered materials with Poole-Frenkel transport mechanism [69, 70]. As the current approaches the threshold current I_T, the probability for a fluctuation to exceed I_T the increases rapidly, and eventually causes the switching to take place. According to this picture, V_{set} is expected to increase for increasing sweep rate, since the time available for fluctuation to attempt the transition decreases, thus can only be successful at a higher voltage. On the other hand, τ_{set} decreases for increasing cell voltage, since the threshold point for the switching is approached. Both experimental evidences were observed in NiO RRAM, in agreement with this picture [62].

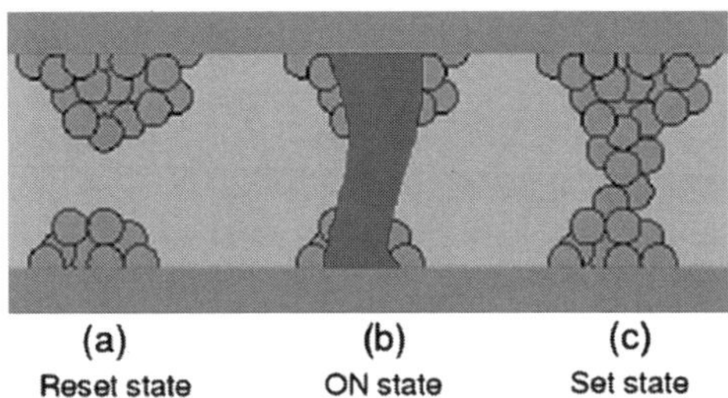

Figure 7. Schematic representation of set transition as a two-stage process. In the first step (b) threshold switching activates conduction in an electronic filament. Successively (c) the increase of temperature yields to the formation of a structural CF. Reprinted with permission from [71], C. Cagli et al., *IEEE Trans. Electron Devices* 56, 1712 (2009). © 2009, IEEE EDS.

3.1. Time Dependence of V_{set}

To address the time dependence of the set parameters, we consider the simple case of a triangular pulse of applied voltage V_A, where the voltage increases linearly with time according to $V_A = \beta t$, where $\beta = dV/dt$ is the sweep rate. To this purpose, we can use an empirical model for the probability dP_{set}/dt for threshold switching given by [71]:

$$dP_{set}/dt = \exp(V_{cell}/V_0)/t_0 \quad (2)$$

where V_0 and t_0 are constants. Equation (2) describes an exponential increase of threshold switching probability for increasing voltage, which is in agreement with the observed voltage dependence of the delay time for switching in chalcogenide materials [72]. Figure 8 shows the probability dP_{set}/dt calculated from Eq. (2) as a function of time during a voltage sweep. To calculate the set voltage, the voltage sweep can be first approximated as a staircase of rectangular pulses, each with a constant voltage V_k for a pulse time Δt_k. To compute the probability that switching takes place in a given time Δt_i, we need to evaluate the conditional probability that switching occurs in Δt_i, provided that it has not occurred in a previous time Δt_k $(k < i)$. Calling ΔP_i the conditional probability for switching in Δt_i and $\Delta P_i'$ the probability that switching has not occurred in any previous Δt_k, we get:

$$\begin{aligned}\Delta P_i &= \Delta t_i \frac{dP_{set}(V_i)}{dt} \Delta P_i' \\ &= \Delta t_i \frac{dP_{set}(V_i)}{dt} \prod_{k=1}^{i-1} \left(1 - \Delta t_k \frac{dP_{set}(V_k)}{dt}\right)\end{aligned} \quad (3)$$

where V_k and V_i are the voltage values at time steps Δt_k and Δt_i, respectively, with $(k < i)$.

Figure 8(b) shows the calculated ΔP_i as a function of V_{cell}, for β increasing from 1 to 10^3 Vs^{-1}. The probability ΔP_i was calculated for a constant voltage step $\Delta t_i = \Delta V/\beta$ during each sweep, corresponding to the time needed to cover a voltage step $\Delta V = 1$ mV. Note in Figure 8(b) that ΔP_i is maximum at a characteristics voltage which increases with β: These maxima identify the average set voltage, and correspond to the voltage values at which the probability $\Delta P_i'$

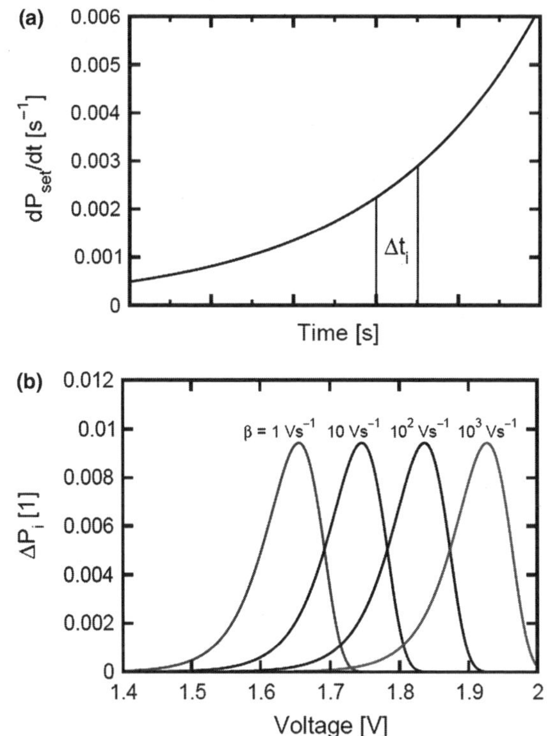

Figure 8. Calculated probability for switching dP/dt according to Eq. (2) (a) and calculated switching probability during a voltage sweep ΔP_i normalized to a temporal step $\Delta t = 1$ mV/β (b). Reprinted with permission from [71], C. Cagli et al., *IEEE Trans. Electron Devices* 56, 1712 (2009). © 2009, IEEE EDS.

that switching has not occurred until Δt_i equals e^{-1}. More in details:

$$\Delta P'_i = \exp\left(\sum_{k=1}^{i-1} \log\left(1 - \frac{\Delta t_k}{\tau_0} e^{V_k/V_0}\right)\right) \approx \exp\left(-\sum_{k=1}^{i-1} \frac{\Delta t_k}{\tau_0} e^{V_k/V_0}\right) = e^{-1}$$

Passing from the staircase sweep to a more realistic, continuous voltage sweep, one obtains:

$$\int_0^{\tau_{set}} \frac{\exp(V_{cell}/V_0)}{\tau_0} dt \approx V_0 \frac{\exp(V_{set}/V_0)}{\beta\tau_0} = 1 \qquad (4)$$

where τ_{set} is the time for set during the voltage sweep computed according to $V_{cell} = \beta t$, and $V_{set} = \beta\tau_{set}$. The set voltage can thus be evaluated as:

$$V_{set} = V_0 \log\left(\frac{\beta t_0}{V_0}\right) \qquad (5)$$

which gives the β dependence of V_{set} for triangular voltage pulses. As previously pointed out, V_{set} increases for increasing β. This can be understood noting that, for increasing β, the time scale of the set experiment decreases: less time is available for the cell to switch, thus a larger voltage must be reached to ensure a sufficient set probability. Figure 9 shows measured V_{set} as a function of β and calculations according to Eq. (5). Data were obtained from DC (quasi static) and AC (pulsed) experiments, for $\beta < 10$ Vs^{-1} and $\beta \geq 10$ Vs^{-1}, respectively, covering over 10 decades of sweep rate [71]. The inset shows a typical waveform of V_{cell}, measured during the application of a triangular voltage pulse with $\beta = 10^6$ Vs^{-1} on the cell setup in Figure 6(a). The sudden drop of the voltage indicates the set transition and allows for the detection of the set voltage V_{set} for any sweep rate β.

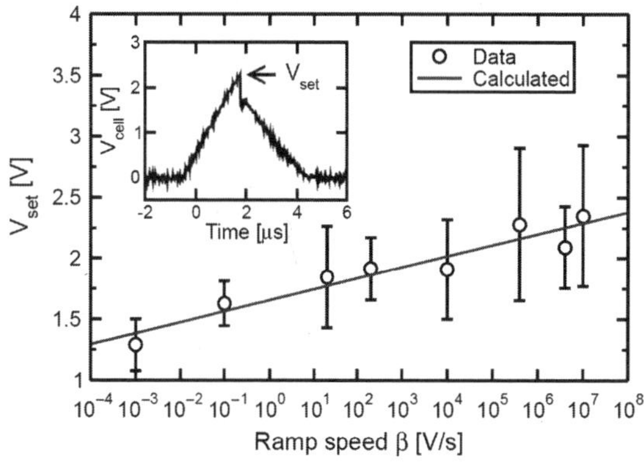

Figure 9. Measured and calculated V_{set} as a function of β. Data and calculations indicate a logarithmic increase of V_{set} over 10 decades of β. The inset shows the typical V_{cell} waveform during a triangular pulse: the sudden drop of V_{cell} indicates a reduction of resistance, which is the set transition. Reprinted with permission from [71], C. Cagli et al., *IEEE Trans. Electron Devices* 56, 1712 (2009). © 2009, IEEE EDS.

Using the same empirical model for threshold switching in Eq. (2), one can also evaluate the case of a rectangular pulse with constant cell voltage V_{cell} and variable pulsewidth. This is relevant for practical purposes, since constant voltage pulses are generally used in RRAM device to maximize the programming speed. The model in Eq. (2) allows us to calculate the set delay time τ_{set} for the onset of threshold switching (hence of set) under a constant voltage V_{cell}. Simple algebra leads to:

$$\tau_{set} = t_0 \exp(-V_{cell}/V_0) \qquad (6)$$

showing that τ_{set} follows an exponential dependence on V_{cell}. Figure 10 shows measured and calculated τ_{set} as a function of V_{cell}. Calculations based on Eq. (6) can reproduce the data within the large statistical spread, using the same empirical parameters V_0 and t_0 of Figure 9. Note that the measured τ_{set} in the figure was limited by the RC rise time of the pulse of about 15 ns. Therefore, much shorter intrinsic set times may be possible in NiO RRAM devices.

3.2. Resistance Dependence of V_{set}

The key role of threshold switching in initiating the set transition in RRAM allows to evaluate the set voltage as a function of the memory resistance. Predicting V_{set} for a memory state allows to estimate the statistical fluctuations of the switching voltage in large arrays. The variability of V_{set} is, in fact, one key point in limiting the feasibility of high-density crossbar arrays [10]. Methods to reduce V_{set} variability would thus strongly improve the array size and design margins.

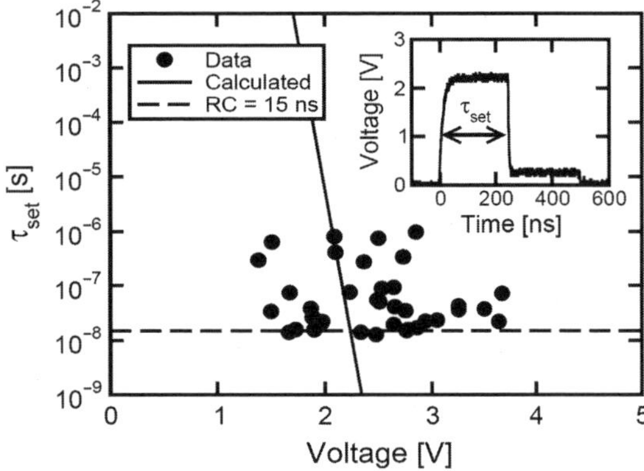

Figure 10. Measured and calculated τ_{set} as a function of V_{cell}. Calculations performed by Eq. (6) only approximately reproduce data. However experimental points are effected of a large statistical spread. The inset shows the measured V_{cell} during a voltage pulse. The dashed line indicates the highest experimental resolution due to parasitic capacitances, which limited the least recordable time to RC = 15 ns. Reprinted with permission from [71], C. Cagli et al., *IEEE Trans. Electron Devices* 56, 1712 (2009). © 2009, IEEE EDS.

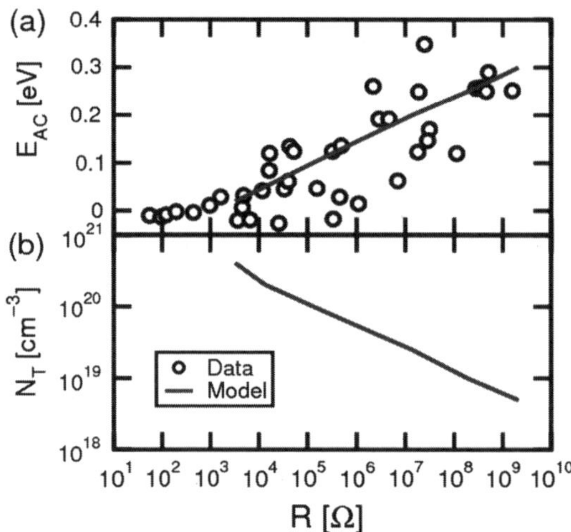

Figure 11. (a) Correlation between measured and calculated resistance R and activation energy E_{AC} for conduction in the reset state [10]. (b) N_T modulation used in Eq. (7) to obtain simulation in (a). Reprinted with permission from [10], D. Ielmini et al., *Nanotechnology* 22 (2011). © 2011, IOPScience.

Several physical models for threshold switching have been proposed to date, and the discussion about the physical switching mechanisms has no conclusive answer yet. Physical models include impact ionization [73, 74], polaron instability [75], field-induced nucleation [76], and structural/carrier heating [77, 78]. The heating models probably feature the necessary generality to account for threshold switching in a large variety of material, from amorphous chalcogenides [64, 73] to metal oxides [66, 67]. Therefore, to evaluate V_{set} as a function of RRAM resistance, we used a threshold-switching model for carrier heating during Poole-Frenkel (PF) conduction [64].

PF conduction can be assumed at the broken CF region, consisting of a degraded metal oxide with high concentration of defects associated with grain boundaries, oxygen vacancies and wrong bonds (e.g., Ni–Ni bonds). To correctly describe the broken CF region, we used a model for PF conduction, where resistance is given by [10, 79]:

$$R = \frac{kT\tau_0 t_{\text{NiO}}}{q^2 A_{\text{CF}} N_T \Delta z^2} e^{(E_{\text{AC}}/kT)} \tag{7}$$

where t_0 is the attempt-to-escape characteristic time for the carrier from the localized state, t_{NiO} if the thickness of the NiO layer, corresponding to the nanofilament length, N_T is the density of dopants, A_{CF} is the nanofilament area and Δz is the distance between positively charged defects, where electrons are trapped in their PF transport [79]. Figure 11(a) shows the correlation between measured and calculated resistance R and activation energy E_{AC} for conduction in the reset state [10]. Calculations were obtained from Eq. (7), where N_T was changed according to Figure 11(b): the decrease of N_T for increasing R describes the gradual reset from a highly defective region, corresponding to the CF, to an almost stoichiometric NiO (full reset state). With these assumptions, Eq. (7) can provide a close prediction of the dependence between activation energy and resistance in NiO broken CFs.

The evaluation of microscopic parameters N_T and E_{AC} in Figure 11 allows to physically model the threshold switching phenomenon using the PF carrier-heating model in Ref. [64]. According to this model, carriers moves along a trap chain (represented by a filament with a relatively high R with low N_T) and increase their kinetic energy due to the application of a high electric field based on the following equation:

$$\frac{d(E_F - E_{F0})}{dz} = qF - \frac{qn_T}{J}\frac{E_F - E_{F0}}{\tau_{\text{rel}}} \tag{8}$$

where E_F and E_{F0} are the quasi Fermi and the equilibrium Fermi levels, respectively, τ_{rel} is the characteristic time for carrier energy relaxation, J is the current density and n_T is the concentration of trapped carriers [64]. In Eq. (8), the energy gain is given by the balance between a field-driven energy gain (qF) and an energy relaxation effects, similar to the case of hot-electron effects [80] in the conduction band. Since the electron-hopping rate exponentially increases with the difference between the quasi Fermi level (representative of the electron population probability being 1/2) and the band edge, even small increases in E_F results in a large conductivity increases. For instance, the condition $E_F = E_{F0} + kT$ results in a conductivity enhancement by a factor "e" with respect to the equilibrium case. This provides a simplified criterion for the onset of threshold switching, which corresponds to a power density P_T''' given by [64]:

$$P_T''' = \frac{N_T(kT)^2}{\tau_{\text{rel}}(E_C' - E_{\text{F0}})} \tag{9}$$

where E_C' is the minimum conduction band energy. From Eq. (9), the critical electrical power can be obtained simply as $P_{\text{set}} = P_T'''W$, where W is the threshold switching volume, computed as the volume of the switching filament, evaluated from the CF area times the NiO thickness.

Figure 12 shows the measured and calculated V_{set} (a), I_{set} (b) and $P_{set} = V_{set}I_{set}$ (c), as a function of R. Data were obtained from NiO RRAM devices under DC conditions, where the set transition was operated at constant current. The dependence of P_{set} on resistance can be explained by Eq. (9): as R decreases, the activation energy for conduction E_{AC} decreases (Fig. 11(a)) and N_T increases (Fig. 11(b)), thus the concentration of trapped carriers that must be excited for the onset of threshold switching increases, resulting in an increase of P_{set}. The behaviors of V_{set} and I_{set} are a consequence of the P_{set} dependence on R. In fact, assuming a linear increase of I with V and noting that P_{set} approximately decreases as $R^{-0.5}$ from Figure 12(c), we can write:

$$V_{set}I_{set} = RI_{set}^2 = P_{set} \propto R^{-0.5}$$

which results in the approximated power-law dependences $I_{set} \propto R^{-0.75}$ and $V_{set} = IR \propto R^{0.25}$. These power laws qualitatively account for the shallow increase of V_{set} with R and for the strong decrease of I_{set} for increasing R in Figures 12(a and b). The calculated results in the figures were obtained using a numerical model for PF conduction and threshold switching, thus accounts for the non-linear I–V curves. These results support the picture for threshold-switching-initiated set, thus allowing for a prediction of set parameters V_{set}, I_{set}, P_{set} and set kinetics for unipolar RRAMs depending on the high-R state microscopic parameters, such as resistance defect density and activation energy.

A closer look at data in Figure 12 reveals that V_{set} increases almost linearly with R, while I_{set} remains constant, for relatively low values of R. This may be understood considering low-R states as CF affected by a gap of thickness Δ along the filament as a result of a partial reset operation. In this case, the switching applies across a thinner NiO layer, with a smaller V_{set}. Calculations of threshold switching for interrupted CFs accounts for the linear increase of V_{set} with R and for the constant I_{set} [81]. On the other hand, V_{set} and I_{set} increase rapidly as R approaches the pristine state around 10^9 Ω. This is because the background leakage current across the whole MIM capacitor provides a maximum R value which cannot be exceeded experimentally. As a result, all data for variable broken CFs appear at the pristine R, thus appearing as a steep increase of V_{set} and I_{set} [10].

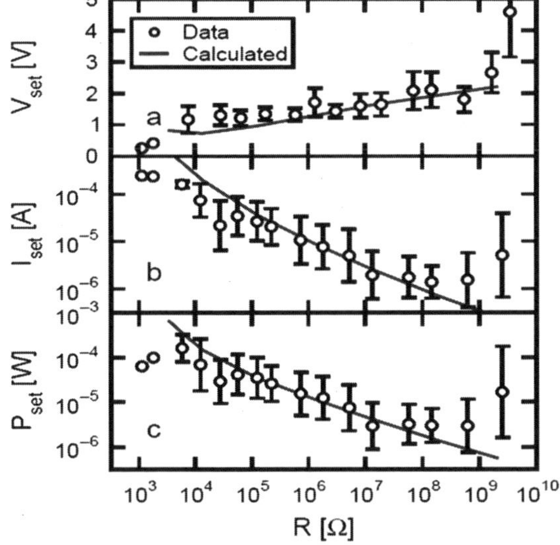

Figure 12. Measured and calculated V_{set} (a), I_{set} (b) and $P_{set} = V_{set}I_{set}$ (c) as a function of initial resistance R_0. Reprinted with permission from [10], D. Ielmini et al., *Nanotechnology* 22 (2011). © 2011, IOPScience.

4. RESET MODEL

In the reset process, the CF is dissolved by thermal and chemical phenomena, thus resulting in a transition to a high resistance. There is a wide consensus on the dominant role of Joule heating in the reset transition, at least for unipolar RRAM device. The reset transition, schematically shown in Figure 13, can be described as a radial diffusion of conductive species (e.g., Ni atoms, oxygen vacancies) and/or an oxidation of the excess Ni within the CF [16]. The thermally activated solid-state processes of diffusion and oxidation eventually result in a breakdown of the CF and in a corresponding sudden increase of resistance. Several experiments have provided clues about it: for instance, it was shown that an increase of the ambient temperature results in a corresponding decrease of the reset power in NiO, due to the lower heating needed to reach the critical oxidation point [58, 82]. Also, an Arrhenius temperature-activation law was obtained by a Kissinger analysis of reset voltage for variable sweep rate [83, 71]. Finally, it has been experimentally demonstrated that reset can be operated by a high-temperature annealing of the sample [84, 85].

A simple model to describe the dissolution of the CF is based on a thermally activated rate of reduction of the CF diameter ϕ, as a result of diffusion/oxidation effects. This can be expressed by a (negative) growth velocity v_G with Arrhenius temperature dependence, namely:

$$v_G = -1/2\ d\phi/dt = v_{G0}\exp(-E_A/kT) \qquad (10)$$

where E_A is the activation energy and v_{G0} is a pre-exponential factor of the dissolution process. Note that this kind of approach is not sensitive to the specific microscopic processes responsible for the CF dissolution: in fact, diffusion of metallic species or oxygen vacancies or chemical oxidation could in principle be treated by the same basic model, provided that the Arrhenius-like character of the processes is assumed.

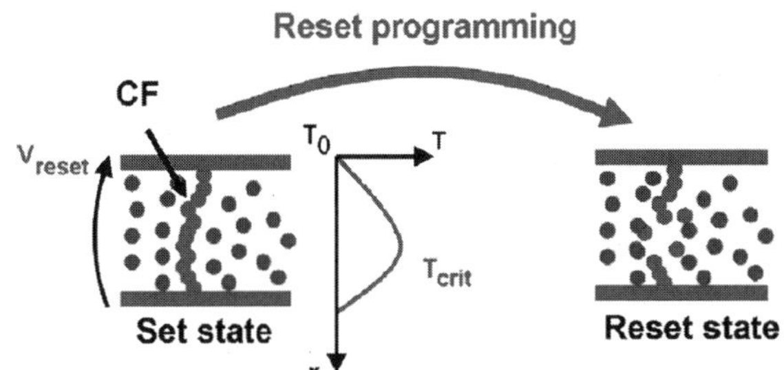

Figure 13. Schematic representation of reset process. The temperature profile along the CF is nearly parabolic due to the stack symmetry. Reprinted with permission from [83], U. Russo et al., *IEEE Trans. Electron Devices* 56, 186 (2009). © 2009, IEEE EDS.

The modeling of the reset process is an essential part of the RRAM physical description, since reset largely contributes to the power consumption and the consequent scalability of the RRAM device concept. In fact, the reset transition is the most demanding in terms of the current that needs to be provided for Joule heating and CF dissolution. The reset current also dictates the area of the select device that must accompany the cell within a practical memory array. Thus, limiting the power dissipation and the cell area requires a reduction of the reset current, which in turn could be possible only by an accurate understanding of the physical mechanisms for reset.

4.1. Time Dependence of V_{reset}

To understand the kinetic of the reset transition, we might follow the same approach of the set transition in Section 4.1, thus first considering the case of a triangular pulse with a voltage sweep rate $\beta = dV/dt$ [71]. As the cell voltage V_{cell} across the CF increases, the maximum temperature increases according to the equation:

$$T = T_0 + V^2 R_{th}/R \tag{11}$$

where T_0 is the room temperature and R_{th} is the effective thermal resistance of the CF. The thermal resistance includes two contributions: one is heat conduction along the CF, toward the top and bottom electrodes serving as heat sinks. This is the most important contribution when the CF cross-section is relatively large compared to the CF length. On the other hand, if the CF is relatively thin, a second contribution becomes predominant, which is the heat dissipation through the surrounding insulating oxide. A compact modeling of the two contributions will be given in Section 4.2.

To estimate the reset point along a voltage sweep, one should be able to estimate the temperature increase within the CF and compute the CF reduction according to Eq. (10). Assuming that reset process actually takes place in a relatively short time, when the voltage is close to the critical value V_{reset}, Eq. (11) can be approximated by a linear expansion around the critical value T_{reset}, thus leading to:

$$T \approx T_0 + \beta_T (t - t_{extr}) \tag{12}$$

where t_{extr} is an appropriate time constant and β_T is the rate for temperature increase around T_{reset}. The temperature increase rate can be obtained by differentiating Eq. (11), which gives:

$$\beta_T = dT/dt = 2\beta V_{reset} R_{th}/R \tag{13}$$

Considering that reset is completed when the CF diameter ϕ vanishes, and integrating Eq. (10) as a function of time allows to compute the time needed to achieve a full reset, hence T_{reset} and V_{reset}. In particular, it has been shown that integration of Eq. (10) leads, after some approximation, to the Kissinger law [71]:

$$\beta_T / T_{reset}^2 = (2v_{G0}/kE_A) \exp[-(E_A/kT_{reset})] \tag{14}$$

Figure 14 shows experimental data of β_T/T_{reset}^2 as a function of $1/kT_{reset}$. Data below 1500°C follow an approximately straight line, where the slope indicates an estimated activation energy E_A of 1.4 eV. At higher temperatures, data deviate from the Kissinger law, which may be explained noting that the local CF temperature is approaching the melting point of the materials used in the stack, namely Ni, NiO and the electrode material Pt. In fact, the melting point for Ni, NiO and Pt are 1728 K, 2041 K and 1998 K, respectively [71]. It is thus reasonable to assume different kinetics depending on different temperature ranges. In particular, a lower $E_A = 0.35$ eV can be used to describe the smaller temperature dependence at high T.

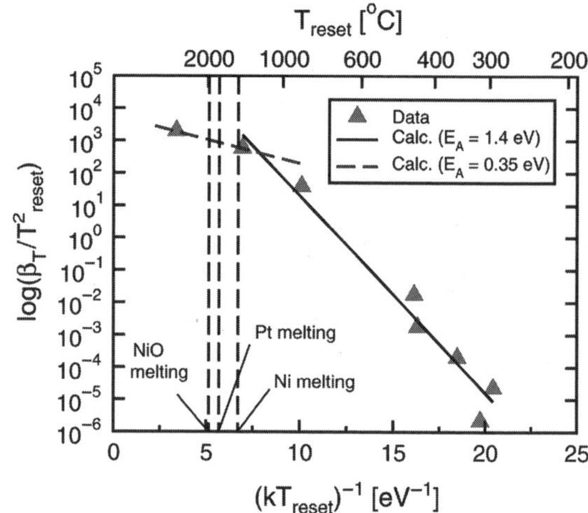

Figure 14. Experimental data of β_T/T_{reset}^2 as a function of $1/kT_{reset}$. Below 1500°C a linear fit leads to activation energy E_A of 1.4 eV. At higher temperatures, closer to the melting point of the materials integrated, a lower activation energy was extracted. Reprinted with permission from [71], C. Cagli et al., *IEEE Trans. Electron Devices* 56, 1712 (2009). © 2009, IEEE EDS.

From Eq. (14) and using Eq. (11) for V_{reset} as a function of T_{reset} and Eq. (13) for β_T as a function of β, one can evaluate the V_{reset} as a function of β. Data and calculations are shown in Figure 15. Both the low-β and high-β activation energies extracted from the Kissinger plot are used to account for data. The inset also shows a typical voltage

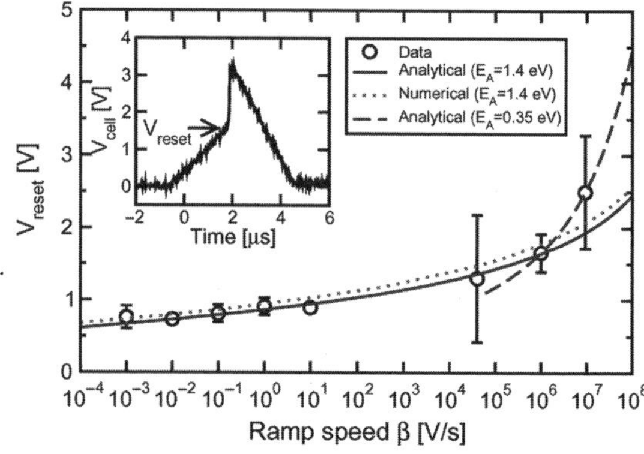

Figure 15. Reset voltage V_{reset} (b) as a function of the voltage sweep rate $\beta = dV/dt$. Data are obtained with triangular pulses. The insets show typical V–t traces. The reset transition is also marked. Reprinted with permission from [71], C. Cagli et al., *IEEE Trans. Electron Devices* 56, 1712 (2009). © 2009, IEEE EDS.

waveform obtained during the application of a triangular pulse on a RRAM cell in the set state. The reset transition is marked by a sudden increase of V_{cell}, due to the voltage partition between the cell and the load resistance in series with the cell. Note that using the value of E_A obtained in the low-β regime may lead to a large underestimation of the V_{reset} at high speed, which is of the highest interest from the application viewpoint. Also note that a large statistical spread affects data, in particular for $\beta > 10^4$ Vs^{-1}, which can be attributed to the variability in CF geometry, stoichiometry and, consequently, on microscopic parameters such as as the activation energy and v_{G0} [71].

As a second case, most relevant from the application point of view, we consider the reset kinetics under a rectangular pulse as depicted in the inset of Figure 16. Here, the cell is subjected to a constant V_{cell}, thus the differential Eq. (10) can be straightforwardly solved leading to:

$$\tau_{reset} = \phi_0^2/v_{G0} \exp(-E_A/kT_{reset}) \tag{15}$$

where τ_{reset} is the delay time to the onset of the reset transition, namely the time it takes to dissolve the CF given a certain T_{reset}. To link the temperature to the applied voltage, Eq. (11) can again be used, leading to the V_{reset}–τ_{reset} plot shown in Figure 16. The figure shows calculations for both low-β and high-β activation energies, demonstrating that an accurate estimation of E_A is indeed critical for a correct prediction of reset parameters, such as V_{reset} and τ_{reset}.

More accurate numerical simulations solving Eq. (11) in a 3D geometry are required to calculate the time evolution of the reset process. Assuming a cylindrical shape of the CF in the set state (line in Fig. 17(a–d)), one can numerically calculate the temperature profile of the filament and the time evolution of the CF cross section [58]. Figure 17 shows the temperature map for increasing applied voltage, namely (a) 0.53, (b) 0.78, (c) 0.85, and (d) 0.87 V. Note that the temperature profile is almost parabolic, as shown in the right panel of Figure 17, thus the reset process is mainly accelerated at the middle of the CF. Here, the cross section is

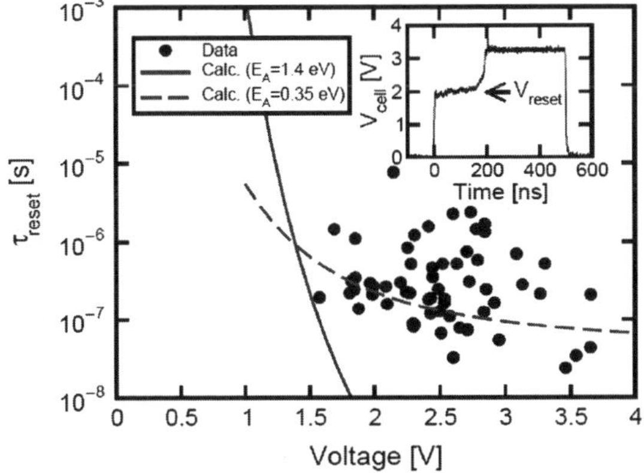

Figure 16. Measured and calculated time to reset (τ_{reset}) as a function of V_{cell}. The figure shows calculation performed with two different activation energy, to reproduce both high-β and low-β regimes. Inset shows a typical reset obtained with rectangular pulses. Reprinted with permission from [71], C. Cagli et al., *IEEE Trans. Electron Devices* 56, 1712 (2009). © 2009, IEEE EDS.

abruptly reduced thus leaving a high-resistivity open gap in the conductive path. As soon as the gap starts forming by CF dissolution, the current density locally increases, thus enhancing Joule heating and the rate of CF dissolution. As a result, the reset process is self-accelerated until CF completely opens. This simulation results allow for a microscopic interpretation of the abrupt reset transition which is typically observed in Pt/NiO/Pt devices, thus further supporting the critical role of Joule-heating and diffusion/oxidation effects in the reset process. Note that the position of the reset-induced gap along the CF might depend on the actual CF geometry [86]. For instance, reset transition was shown to take place near the electrodes in the case of a conical CF, due to the asymmetric thermal and electrical resistances of the CF [86].

4.2. Resistance Dependence of Reset Parameters

One of the main scaling issues of RRAM is the generally excessive reset current. To reduce the reset current, a control of the resistance of the filament has been shown to be essential [58, 60, 61, 83]. From this standpoint, understanding the relationship between the set-state resistance and the reset voltage and current in the cell is a key requirement for identifying the best selector, architecture and programming scheme for a RRAM array.

To control the resistance of a RRAM device, two schemes have been demonstrated. On the one hand, the resistance can be controlled by a limitation of the current flowing during the set operation. This can be achieved by (1) a current compliance system, or (2) a load resistance or transistor in series with the cell. However, the current limitation may be affected by overshoot effects, possibly due to (1) the finite time response of the compliance adjustment, usually in the 10–100 ms timescale, and/or (2) the unavoidable presence of a parasitic capacitance in parallel to the RRAM device. In the latter case, as the RRAM switches to a low resistance as a result of threshold switching/set transition, the capacitance may discharge through the cell, thus causing a parasitic current lasting for a relatively long time given by RC, approximately given by the product of the minimum between the load and the cell resistances and the parasitic capacitance. The RC time is typically of the order of 1 kΩ × 10 pF = 10 ns, while the maximum current in the capacitance discharge is approximately given by the set voltage divided by the final set resistance, thus it may easily reach the few mA range [65]. Clearly, current overshoots impede the proper control of the resistance, thus they should be avoided by limiting the parasitic capacitance as much as possible, e.g., by load resistance or select transistors integrated on the same chip of the RRAM cell [60, 61]. This has been shown to allow for a set resistance in the order of 100 kΩ and for reset current below 10 mA [61].

The second approach to control the RRAM resistance is to exploit the gradual reset transition, which is sometimes observed in NiO cells. To highlight this behavior, Figure 18 shows I–V characteristics of NiO RRAM [16], measured during reset sweeps where the final reset voltage was increased gradually from 0.3 V to higher values. After

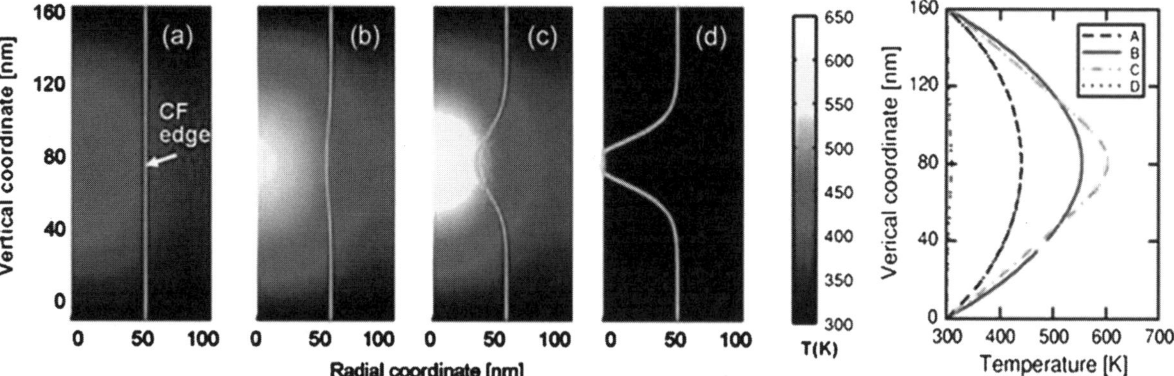

Figure 17. Electro-thermal simulations of reset process. Pictures from (a to d) show progressive CF radius reduction due to the temperature-activated dissolution process. Gray map indicates temperature within the cell. On the right end side temperature profile along the CF axis is reported for (a to d) simulation steps. Reprinted with permission from [86], U. Russo et al., *IEEE Trans. Electron Devices* 56, 193 (2009). © 2009, IEEE EDS.

each sweep, the resistance increased by approximately 20%, thus allowing for a precise tuning of the resistance.

Figure 19 shows the measured V_{reset} (a) and I_{reset} (b) as a function of initial resistance in the set state. The initial state was obtained either by partial set with a limited current within a 1T1R structure (filled square) or by a partial reset (open circles) with a limited reset voltage. At first glance, in both cases the reset voltage remains roughly constant, ranging between 0.5 and 1 V. As a consequence, I_{reset} decreases as $1/R$ while R spans between 100 Ω and 10^4 Ω. However, a closer view reveals that the reset voltage displays a shallow U shape. For increasing R in fact, V_{reset} first decreases up to a minimum, around 300 Ω, then increases again. The increase of V_{reset} at high R may be described by size-dependent Joule heating and heat dissipation effects [10]. A key role is played by the effective thermal resistance of the CF, which contains two contributions, one due to the heat dissipation along the CF axis through the electrodes and the second due to the thermal dissipation through the lateral CF surface and the surrounding NiO [83]. To evaluate the first contribution, R'_{th}, the following equation can be adopted:

$$R'_{th} = 1/8(k_{th}) * t_{NiO}/A_{CF} \quad (16)$$

where k_{th} is the CF thermal conductivity, t_{NiO} is the cell thickness, which is assumed to be equal to the CF length, and A_{CF} is the CF cross section. The corrective factor of 1/8 is due to the parabolic temperature profile of the CF, caused by the presence of the electrodes acting as thermal reservoirs.

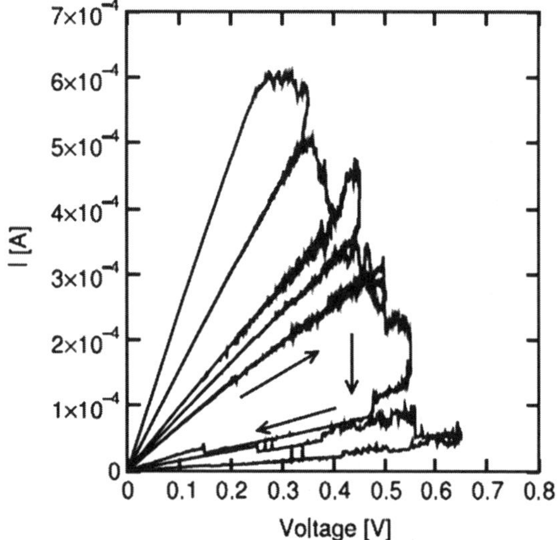

Figure 18. Progressive reset process obtained increasing the maximum value of the voltage sweep. The first reset starts to increase cell resistance at about 0.3 V. Further voltage increases (0.4 V, 0.45 V, 0.5 V, 0.55 V and 0.65 V) cause the resistance to become higher, approaching the reset state. Reprinted with permission from [10], D. Ielmini et al., *Nanotechnology* 22, 254022 (2011). © 2011.

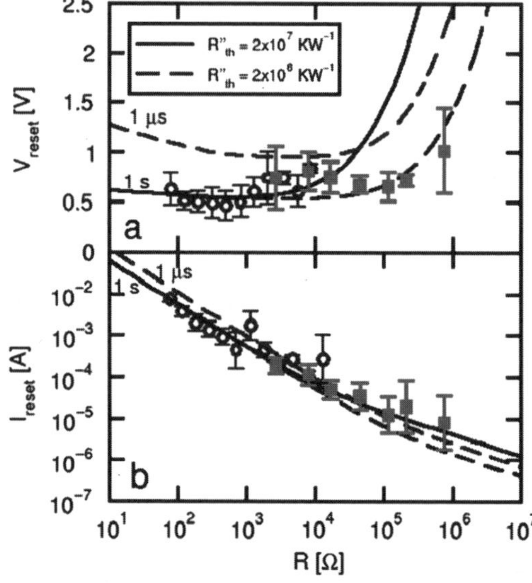

Figure 19. Data and calculations of V_{reset} and I_{reset} as a function on initial resistance. Open points represent reset process, showing a shallow U-shaped behaviour. Close squares show reset operations on cells programmed with a mosfet selector as current limiter. Calculations are reported for DC measurement (1 s time-frame) and "fast" programming (1 μs time-frame). Reprinted with permission from [10], D. Ielmini et al., *Nanotechnology* 22 (2011). © 2011, IOPScience.

Evaluating the second contribution to thermal resistance requires 3D numerical simulations to take into account Joule heating and heat dissipation, which are strongly affected by geometry [10]. To calculate the pure parallel contribution to R_{th}, i.e., R'_{th}, Poisson and Fourier equations were solved for a cylindrical filament under an applied voltage of 0.2 V, surrounded by perfectly insulating NiO. The effective thermal resistance was then calculated from the equation $R_{th} = R(T - T_0)/V^2$, which can be derived by Eq. (11). R here is the known electrical resistance of the CF and T the maximum temperature reached in the filament. The NiO thermal conductivity was then changed between 0 and 4 Wm^{-1} K^{-1} to assess the impact of lateral heat conduction on R_{th}. Figure 20 shows summarized simulation results for R_{th} as a function of A_{CF} at different NiO thermal conductivities. The curve for $k_{th} = 0$, corresponding to perfectly insulating NiO, gives the value of R'_{th}, since the surrounding oxide does not contribute to heat dissipation. For different values of k_{th}, the total effective thermal resistance can be approximately viewed as the parallel of two separated contributions R'_{th} and R''_{th}. For large filaments, thus for low CF resistance, the overall thermal resistance is not significantly affected by the lateral heat loss, that on the contrary becomes more and more dominant for thinner filaments. This reflects the fact that for large CFs the surface/volume ratio is relatively small, thus the heat is mainly dissipated through the electrodes and only a small fraction, compared to the overall amount, dissipates in the NiO. Figure 21 shows results obtained by the same simulations, at constant $k_{th} = 2$ Wm^{-1} K^{-1}, for different CF diameter, namely 20 nm, 8 nm and 2.5 nm. Results indicate that at a given voltage, the temperature decreases as A_{CF}. This can be explained by the fact that, in the R/R_{th} ratio, R_{th} decreases faster than R for decreasing A_{CF}. As a consequence, the temperature in Eq. (11) will be smaller at constant applied voltage for decreasing CF size, or, conversely, a higher voltage will be required to achieve the critical temperature for CF dissipation. This in turn explains the slight increase of reset voltage at higher resistances, as shown in Figure 19.

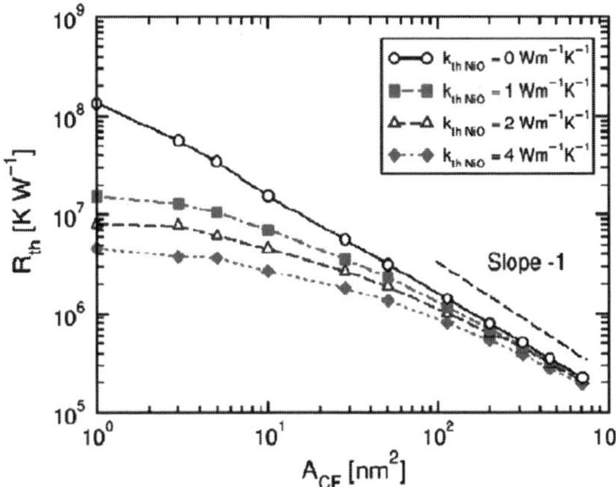

Figure 20. Calculated R_{th} for different values of NiO thermal conductivity. For larger filaments the heat dissipation through the surrounding oxide becomes significant and thermal resistance saturates. Reprinted with permission from [10], D. Ielmini et al., *Nanotechnology* 22 (2011). © 2011, IOPScience.

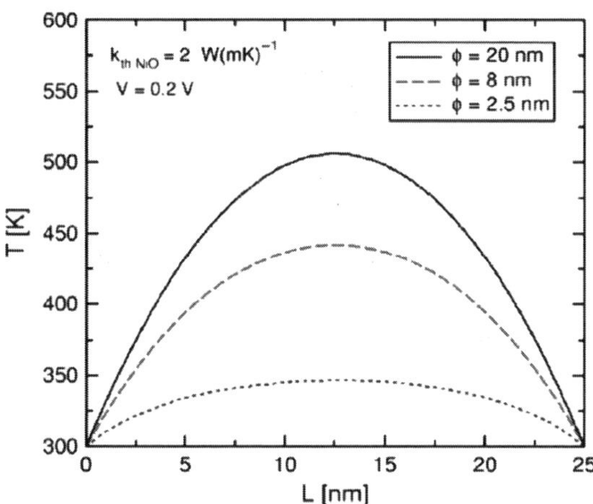

Figure 21. Calculated temperature profiles along the CF axis as a function of CF radius. For thinner filaments heat dissipation through the surrounding oxide causes the temperature to decrease. Moreover the profiles lose their parabolic shape to become more flat, as the effect of the electrodes as thermal sinks diminishes. Reprinted with permission from [10], D. Ielmini et al., *Nanotechnology* 22 (2011). © 2011, IOPScience.

However, the same argument cannot explain the increase of V_{reset} at very low resistance, below 0.5 kΩ, corresponding to a relatively large filament with rather constant R_{th}/R ratio. The increase of V_{reset} for decreasing R may be explained by the increasing size of the CF, which thus requires a longer time/temperature for reset [85, 10]. Assuming that the filament disruption is due to oxidation or diffusion of, e.g., Ni atoms [87], the diffusion equation in radial coordinates can be used to describe the diffusion-reaction process for CF reset, namely:

$$\frac{\partial n}{\partial t} = D\frac{1}{r}\frac{\partial}{\partial r}\left(r\frac{\partial n}{\partial r}\right) \tag{17}$$

where n is the concentration of conductive species (or dopants), D is the diffusion coefficient and r is the radial coordinate. Eq. (17) can be analytically solved assuming that the initial state has a Gaussian dopant concentration, leading to [10]:

$$n(r, t_0) = N(z, t_0)/4\pi D t_0 \exp(-r^2/4Dt_0) \tag{18}$$

where N is the integral of n on an horizontal plane, perpendicular to the CF axis, namely $\int 2\pi r n(r, t)dr$. The standard deviation of the Gaussian-shaped distribution in Eq. (18) increases with time according to $\sigma = (2Dt)^{-1/2}$, while the peak concentration, reached on the CF axis, will decrease according to $n(0, t) = N(2\pi\sigma^2)^{-1/2}$. Defining a reset time $t_{1/2}$ as the time for which the peak concentration is reduced by a factor 2, and assuming an initial standard deviation σ_0, the condition for reset reads:

$$n(0, t_{1/2})/n(0, t_0) = \sigma_0^2/(2Dt_{1/2}) = 1/2 \tag{19}$$

We can thus calculate the time to obtain a reset as:

$$t_{reset} = t_{1/2} - t_0 = \sigma_0^2/2D \div A_{CF} \div R^{-1} \tag{20}$$

Equation (20) shows that the time to reset is proportional to the initial CF area, thus it is inversely proportional to the initial resistance. Equivalently, given a certain time frame or pulse-width in which reset must be accomplished, the temperature for reset must be increasingly higher for larger CFs, thus voltage must increase. This in turn explains the increase of reset voltage at decreasing resistance in a large-CF regime. Another relevant consequence of the size-dependent reset is the resistance dependence of the retention, where CFs with relatively large size (small resistance) have relatively long retention time. This will be discussed in Section 6.

Finally note that the increase of V_{reset} at small resistances may also be affected by series resistance effects [88]. Considering the schematic of Figure 22, the 'apparent' reset voltage V_{reset} is related to the 'true' reset voltage V'_{reset} across the cell by:

$$V_{reset} = V'_{reset}(1 + R_S/R) \tag{21}$$

where R_S is the series resistance. According to Eq. (21), V_{reset} may largely increase when R becomes very small with respect to R_S. This may account for the steep increase of V_{reset} observed in unipolar devices at relatively small R [89, 90].

4.3. Scaling of the Reset Current

Due to the filamentary nature of resistive switching in most unipolar RRAM devices, the scaling of the device contact area does not necessarily result in a reduction of the reset current or voltage (see Fig. 3). This can negatively impact the scalability of memory arrays, since the reset current dictates the area of the select element in the array. A lack of area scaling of the reset current would thus impede a proper downscaling of the device area in the array. The reduction of the reset current can however be pursued by limiting the current during the set operation, thus resulting in a control of the set state resistance which is inversely proportional to the reset current (Fig. 19). To limit the current during set, three different approaches can be used, as summarized in Figure 23 [60]. The first approach uses the current limitation by a parameter analyzer which however suffers from the relatively slow adjustment of voltage to limit the current level through the device. The second approach uses a load resistance connected to the cell, while configuration 3 consists in a 1T-1R structure with the select transistor (1T) and the RRAM cell (1R) integrated within the same ship. Figure 24 summarizes data for the reset current as a function of the compliance current using the different limitation approaches. As the compliance current decreases, the set-state R increases, thus the reset current decreases due to the approximately constant reset voltage in Figure 19(a). This is experimentally confirmed in Figure 24, showing that I_{reset} increases linearly with I_{compl} for all different approach in Figure 23. However, the reset current saturates to a relatively large value for configuration 1: this is because the relatively small compliance current is exceeded during the adjustment transient of the parameter analyzer, resulting in a current overshoot and in a correspondingly high I_{reset}. A similar result is obtained with configuration 2, due this time to the current overshoot resulting from the capacitance

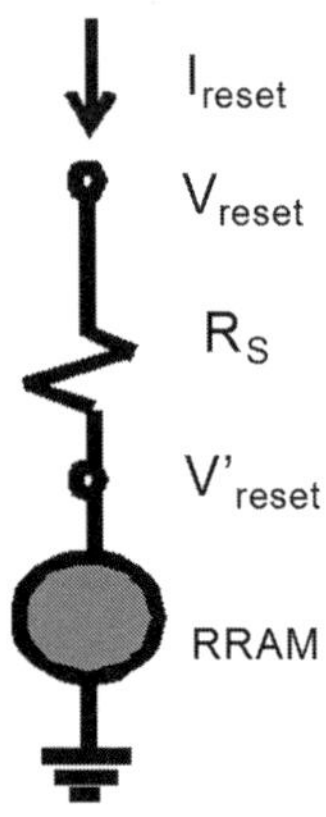

Figure 22. Schematic representation of the RRAM device with a series parasitic resistance R_S. The drop of potential across R_S must be taken into account to correctly evaluate voltages across the cell.

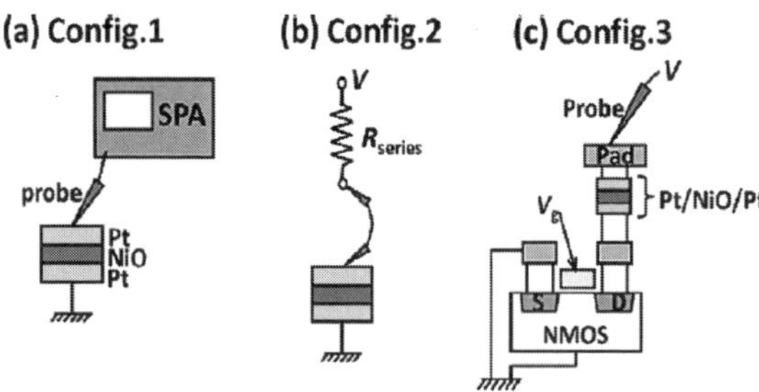

Figure 23. Different possible setup configurations were compared to better control the set resistance, limiting the current supplied during set. Config. 1 only uses the semiconductor parameter analyzer to limit the current (current compliance). Config. 2 uses a load resistance, while in 3 an integrated mosfet is exploited. An external mosfet is implemented in config. 4, while config. 5 is the same as 3 with a monitor pad (configs. 4 and 5 not shown). The different performances of these configurations are shown in Figure 24. Reprinted with permission from [60], K. Kinoshita et al., *Appl. Phys. Lett.* 93, 033506 (2008). © 2008, American Institute of Physics.

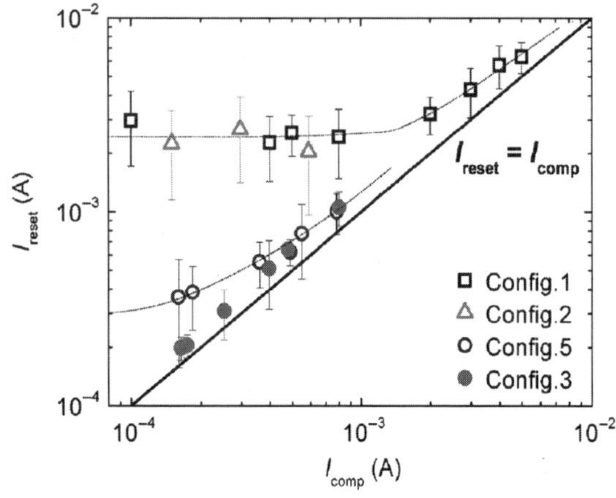

Figure 24. The effectiveness of the current limiting during set is reported for the configurations shown in Figure 23. Reprinted with permission from [60], K. Kinoshita et al., *Appl. Phys. Lett.* 93, 033506 (2008). © 2008, American Institute of Physics.

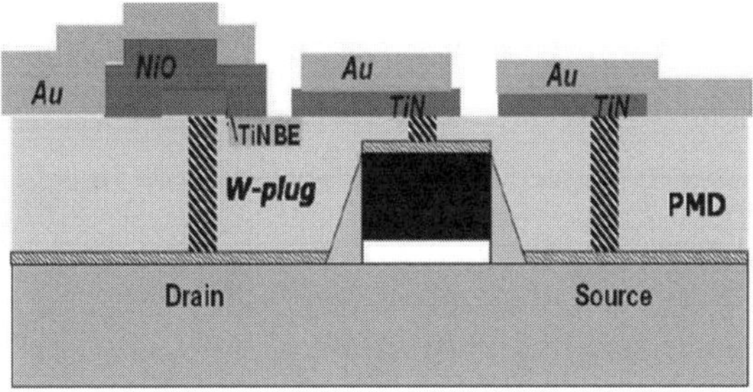

Figure 25. Schematic representation of the stack used in 1T1R device in Ref. [57]. Here a mosfet is exploited as current limiter. Reprinted with permission from [57], F. Nardi et al., "IEEE IMW," p. 66, Seoul, Korea, 2010. © 2010.

discharge through the cell. Configuration 3, with a full 1T1R structure, provides instead the best current control, with no sign of saturation at small I_{reset}.

The use of 1T1R structures for proper control of CF size and I_{reset} is reported by many authors and for many different metal oxides materials [82, 60, 91]. Figure 25 shows a typical 1T1R architecture with a NiO-based RRAM [57]. The n-MOSFET selector was made with a standard 130 nm process. The channel length was 1 μm, the width 10 μm and the gate oxide thickness was 1.6 nm. The MOSFET drain was connected on a 90-nm W plug, connected to the TiN bottom electrode in the RRAM device. The active NiO layer was 35 nm thick and was capped with Au as top electrode.

Figure 26 shows typical programming curves for forming, set and reset for device in [57]. During forming and set, a low gate voltage is used so that the MOSFET works in saturated regime, thus limiting the available current through the cell. The integrated structure ensures the absence of any significant parasitic capacitance, thus avoiding current overshoot effects. On the other hand, the gate is biased at high voltage during reset, to provide the reset current required for CF dissolution. The value of the gate voltage during set controls the current compliance, hence the set state resistance. The resistance control can allow reset current reduction and multilevel operation of the cell, which may be useful for high-density application.

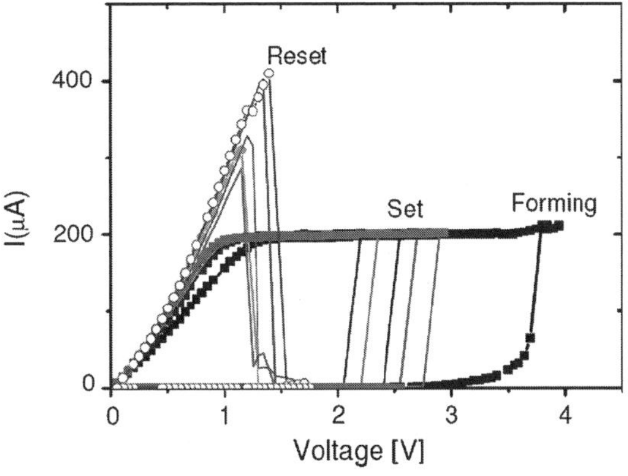

Figure 26. I–V curve of set and reset transition in 1T1R structure. During forming and set the mosfet provide the current compliance (around 200 μA in the figure), while during reset no current limitation is imposed. Reprinted with permission from [57], F. Nardi et al., "IEEE IMW," p. 66, Seoul, Korea, 2010. © 2010.

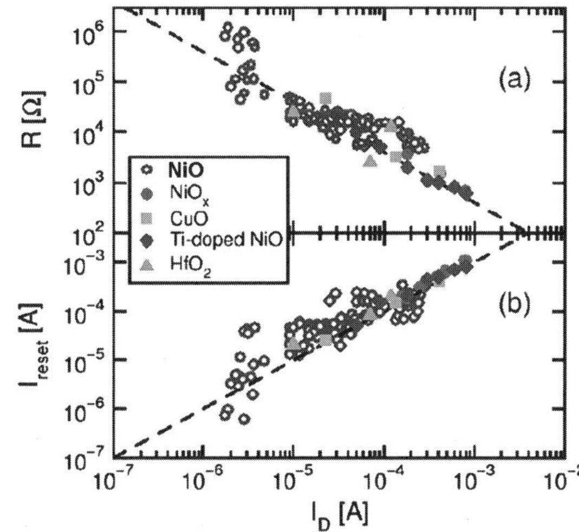

Figure 27. R_{set} and I_{reset} as a function of drain current (I_D) provided by transistor selector during set operation. At lower I_D correspond higher set resistances and thus lower reset current. The same trend is shown on different devices implementing different material (NiO [61], NiO_x [82], CuO [60], Ti-doped NiO [91] and HfO_2 [20].), demonstrating universal behaviour of these curves. Reprinted with permission from [61], F. Nardi et al., *Solid-State Electronics* 58, 42 (2011). © 2011, Elsevier.

Figure 27(a) shows measured R as a function of the drain current I_D during set, while Figure 27(b) shows measured reset current are shown as a function of I_D. Reducing I_D results in an increase of R and a corresponding decrease of I_{reset} [61]. Different metal oxides are compared in the same plot, namely NiO_x [60], CuO_x [82], Ti-doped NiO [91] and HfO_2 [20]: however, the set and reset characteristics display a universal behavior, irrespective of the active material used for switching [59]. The reset current can be reduced down to below 10 mA in Figure 27(b), thanks to the good control of the compliance current in the 1T-1R structure. The I–V curves with the reset transitions are shown in Figure 28. The reset current can be as small as 2 mA under DC conditions.

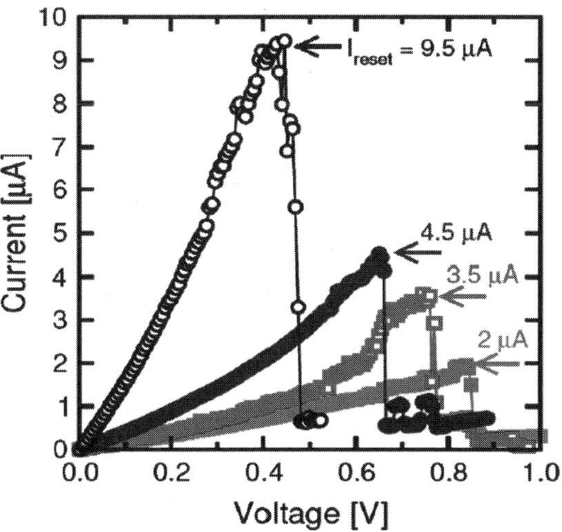

Figure 28. Least current demanding reset achieved with 1T1R structures. Reprinted with permission from [61], F. Nardi et al., *Solid-State Electronics* 58, 42 (2011). © 2011, Elsevier.

5. CF CONDUCTION MODEL

Although the CF is usually considered a metallic phase for simplicity, a more detailed conduction model can be developed based on experimental evidences [10]. Figure 29 shows the Arrhenius plot of RRAM resistance after set or partial reset. The plot indicates different conduction mechanisms depending on the resistance level. For very low resistive states, around 100 Ω in figure, a clear metallic behavior is observed, where resistance linearly increases with temperature. This dependence is reproduced by the equation:

$$R = R_{0m}(1 + a(T - T_0)) \qquad (22)$$

where R_{0m} is the metallic resistance observed at the reference temperature T_0, and a is the temperature coefficient that links R and T [83]. For higher R, the R–T dependence indicates a semiconductor behavior, where the resistance increases for decreasing T. Data show a straight line on the $R - 1/kT$ plot, thus R can be expressed by the Arrhenius law:

$$R = R_{0s} \exp(E_{AC}/kT) \qquad (23)$$

where R_{0s} represent the resistance at infinite temperature and E_{AC} is the activation energy for conduction. The activation energy describes the relative position of the Fermi level with respect to the relevant conduction band edge, within a simple Poole-Frenkel (PF) conduction model [79]. The same equation may apply to either electron (n-type semiconductor) or hole (p-type semiconductor) transport. The increase of activation energy for conduction at increasing R can be described as a shift of the Fermi level with respect to the relevant conduction band edge, as depicted on the right panel of Figure 29. This highlights that the major contribution to the increase of resistance is not simply due to a different CF geometry, but most importantly to a different position of the Fermi level with respect to the semiconductor bands, resulting in different values for the activation energy.

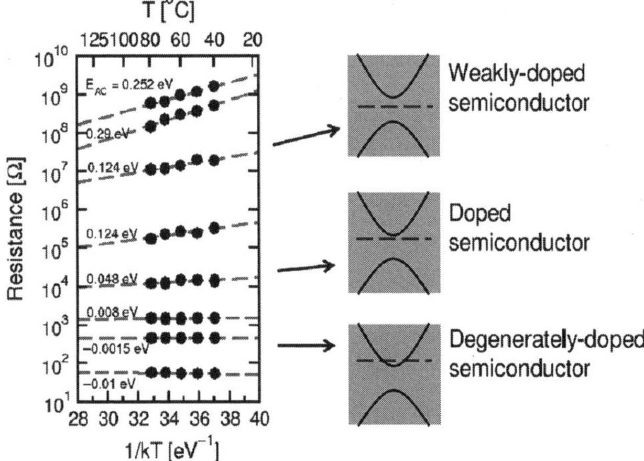

Figure 29. Resistance as a function of $1/kT$ for different resistance states. Low resistance states show metallic behavior, with a slight increase of resistance at increasing temperature. This is attributed to a very high free carrier density. At higher resistances the conduction mechanism becomes more semiconductor-like, as the resistance decreases at increasing temperature. Reprinted with permission from [10], D. Ielmini et al., *Nanotechnology* 22 (2011). © 2011, IOPScience.

The microscopic mechanism responsible for the Fermi level shift is still a matter of debate. Several explanations have been proposed. In 2010 Lee, in Phys. Rev. B 81, 193202, demonstrated with "*ab initio*" simulations that oxygen-deficient NiO can explain conductivity changes in the CF, suggesting that different O concentration could be responsible for the formation of a conductive path. Similarly, metallic doping, which introduces wrong-bond defects in the metal oxide structure, could also contribute to the CF conductivity. A reasonable picture, thus, could be a locally different Ni–O balance as a possible responsible of the Fermi level shift. Oxygen excess causes the material to gain p-type conductivity, while O deficiency (or Ni excess) may lead to n-type character. Therefore the different temperature dependences of R in Figure 29 may be regarded as the result of a Fermi level shift due to different NiO stoichiometries. This leads to a decrease of E_{AC} from a deep level in the band gap to more shallow levels for increasing defect/doping concentration. Above a concentration threshold, the Fermi level may be above the conduction band edge, thus leading to the observed metallic behavior. The carrier concentration in this case is not exponentially influenced by the temperature, thus an ohmic I–V behavior with metallic temperature dependence is observed. Note that a similar transition from metallic to semiconductor-like behavior is generally observed in the drain current of bulk [92, 93] and SOI MOS transistor [94] for increasing gate voltage. In these cases the explanation is similarly based on the Fermi level shift, due to a different gate bias.

While the metallic CF states display an ohmic behavior, semiconductor states are not ohmic, since a simple drift-diffusion model of conduction is not adequate. Figure 30 shows measured I–V curves for different resistance states, namely a full set state and partial reset states with increasing resistance of 44 kΩ, 100 kΩ, 1 MΩ and 27 MΩ. The preforming state is also reported for reference. The I–V curves show an increasing non-linear behavior, which is compatible with PF conduction. To confirm the PF behavior, Figure 31 reports the same data as in Figure 30 as a function

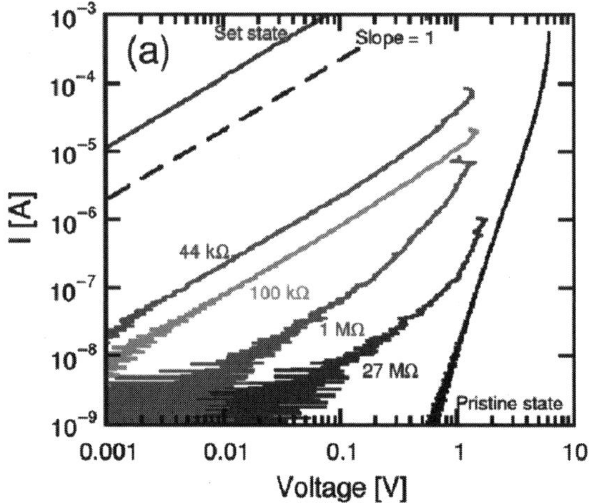

Figure 30. Log–log IV plot of different resistance states. As can be shown at higher resistances the IV curve becomes more and more over-linear. Reprinted with permission from [10], D. Ielmini et al., *Nanotechnology* 22 (2011). © 2011, IOPScience.

of the square root of the voltage $V^{1/2}$. Data for $R = 1$ and 27 MΩ are consistent with the typical exponential law for PF transport, namely $I = I_0 \exp(\beta V^{1/2})$, where I_0 and β are constants. While I_0 impacts on the current magnitude in Figure 31, parameter β dictates the slope of the I–V characteristic, and is given by $\beta = q^{3/2}/(\pi\varepsilon t_{NiO}k^2T^2)^{1/2}$, where ε is the dielectric constant. The different slopes for the curves at $R = 1$ and 27 MΩ may indicate different values of ε. This can be due to different CF characteristics, such as defect concentration or impurities [10].

The transition from metallic to semiconductive CF conduction is schematically represented in Figure 32, showing CF corresponding to increasing resistance values. Starting from a continuous, metallic CF with a relatively large diameter (a), an increasing resistance can be first obtained by a decrease in the CF dimension (b), then by a decrease in the concentration of defects such as excess Ni atoms and O vacancies. Figure 32(c and d) shows two percolation paths, corresponding to intermediate states with relatively large R, such as the states with $R = 1$ and 27 MΩ in Figure 31, where an increasing resistance reflects a decreasing concentration of conductive defects. Correspondingly, the Fermi level shifts to increasingly deep energies as a result of the improved order within the metal-oxide structure and chemical composition.

From Figure 32, it is clear that both the CF resistance is the results of two key parameters, namely (i) the CF size and (ii) the CF resistivity, associated to the position of the Fermi level, namely [85]:

$$R = \rho_0 t_{NiO}/A \exp(E_{AC}/kT) \tag{24}$$

where ρ_0 is the infinite-temperature resistivity of the CF, t_{NiO} is the NiO thickness which is assumed equal to the CF length and $A = \pi(\phi/2)^2$ is the CF cross section. From the equation, the main part of the resistance change is due to the change of E_{AC}, which exponentially impacts R, rather than from the CF size A. Figure 33(a) shows the measured values of activation energies (same as the data in Fig. 11), extracted

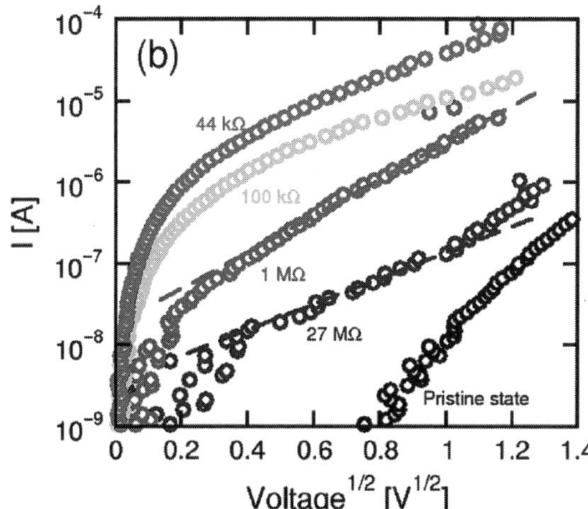

Figure 31. Same data as Figure 30 in a log–log I–$V^{1/2}$ plot. Data aligned on straight lines in the graph indicates good agreement with a Poole-Frenkel conduction mechanism. Reprinted with permission from [10], D. Ielmini et al., *Nanotechnology* 22 (2011). © 2011, IOPScience.

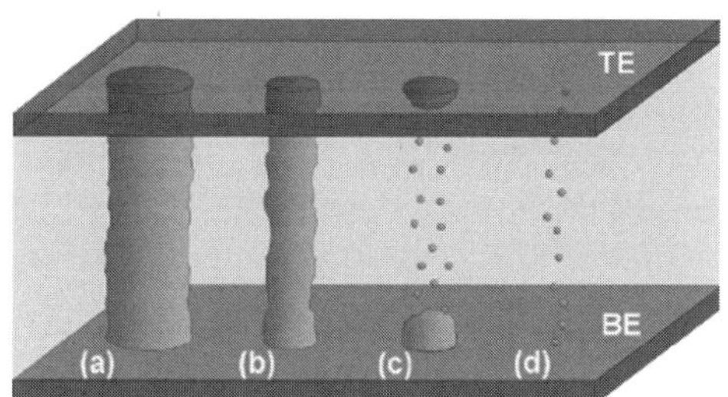

Figure 32. Schematic picture representing a progressive reset operation. From (a to d) CF dissolves, eventually leaving only traces that form a percolation path between the electrodes. Reprinted with permission from [84], D. Ielmini et al., "International Reliability Physics Symposium," pp. 620–626, 2010. © 2010, IEEE EDS.

from the slope in the Arrhenius plot as in Figure 29, as a function of R measured at room temperature (about 25°C). From R and E_{AC}, it is possible to estimate the effective CF area A, using $\rho_0 = 100\ \mu\Omega$ cm [83]. The latter can be viewed as a typical electrical resistivity for metallic nanowires of relatively small size, which is markedly higher than the bulk value due to surface carrier scattering effects [95–97]. The estimated CF diameter is shown in Figure 33(b): despite a change of resistance within range of almost 10 decades, the estimated diameter only changes by a factor 20, as a result of the change in activation energy. It should be noted that the estimated ϕ should be viewed as an effective CF size, assuming a cylindrical shape of the CF. A conic shape [98] or non-uniform percolation conduction [99] may significantly affect the estimated effective diameter.

6. RELIABILITY AND SCALING

For non-volatile memory applications, a key requirement is memory cell reliability, in terms of switching variability, data retention, cycling endurance and data stability against

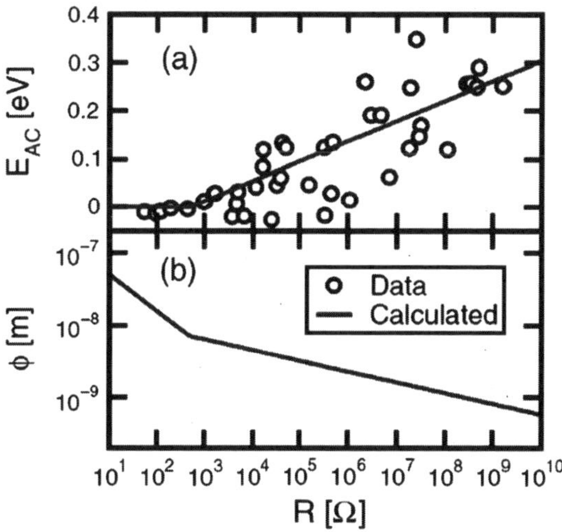

Figure 33. (a) Activation energy for conduction as a function of resistance. (b) CF diameter ϕ estimation as a function of resistance, obtained inverting Eq. (24). Reprinted with permission from [84], D. Ielmini et al., "International Reliability Physics Symposium," pp. 620–626, 2010 © 2010, IEEE EDS.

time and temperature variations. For RRAM, reliability is intimately connected to other memory requirements, such as the need to reduce the reset current or to improve the resistance window. For instance, it has been reported that RRAM devices in a set state with relatively large resistance, thus consisting of a relatively small CF, are affected by a short retention time [85]. At the same time, a high resistance in the set state is usually desired to reduce the reset current, thus posing an important issue for RRAM scaling at maintained reliability. On the other hand, the multilevel capability of RRAM is among the key objectives to allow for high-density memory arrays. Storage of two bits within the same physical cell can in fact allow for doubling the array capacity while maintaining the same technology node. From this viewpoint, the stability of data in the set and intermediate states is very important to allow for fast readout and high reliability of the multilevel memory. Finally, the variability of switching parameters, such as the set or reset voltage, affects the scaling potential of RRAM, since high-density crossbar arrays are only possible for relatively tight distribution of switching voltages. Therefore, algorithms to control the RRAM resistance, hence the switching parameters, in the set/reset states are essential for crossbar array functionality and scaling.

6.1. Data Retention

To highlight the link between reliability and initial resistance state, Figure 34 shows the correlation plot of the resistance values measured before (R_{pre}) and after annealing (R_{post}) at $T = 280°C$. The initial resistance covered a range between about 70 and 600 Ω. The straight line in the figure indicates $R_{pre} = R_{post}$. From the comparison between R_{pre} and R_{post}, it is clear that resistance states below 200 Ω are less likely to be erased by the thermal annealing, while higher resistances show a larger tendency to data loss. This can be explained by size-dependent diffusion of dopants from the CF during accelerated annealing, similar to the previous discussion of the reset phenomenon in Section 4. A similar resistance-dependent retention time was reported for bipolar CuO-based RRAMs [82] and Cu-doped MoO_x/GdO_x capacitors [100].

To quantitatively assess the temperature-dependence of the retention time and the impact of resistance, experiments were performed at fixed temperature on cells programmed at a given initial resistance. The resistance was measured at room temperature after each annealing step, for a sample set of 50 samples. Figure 35 shows the cumulative distribution of measured R for increasing annealing time at 300°C, for an initial resistance between 0.2 and 1 kΩ. For increasing annealing times, the resistance distribution shifts to higher R and develop a statistical tail, indicating that more cells are failing. Note the relatively sharp transition from low to high resistance within each distribution, suggesting a sudden increase of cell resistance at retention failure. The resistance increase can be attributed to thermally activated CF dissolution through diffusion and oxidation. Note that all experiments were performed in air, thus diffusion of oxygen from the atmosphere could play a role in the observed oxidation.

Figure 36 shows the time evolution of resistance extracted from Figure 35 at fixed percentiles $f = 25$, 50, 75 and 90%. Data in the figure confirm the abrupt transition from set to reset state for percentile higher than 25%. A retention time τ_R can be defined as the time for a resistance increase by a factor 10. Similar experiments and analysis can be repeated for variable annealing temperatures, allowing to extract the failure time as a function of temperature. Figure 37(a) shows the measured τ_R as a function of $1/kT$, where T is the annealing temperature. Data are reported for different percentiles f: note the relatively large spread of τ_R for different percentiles, which might be due to the random nature of diffusion/oxidation in presence of non-uniform

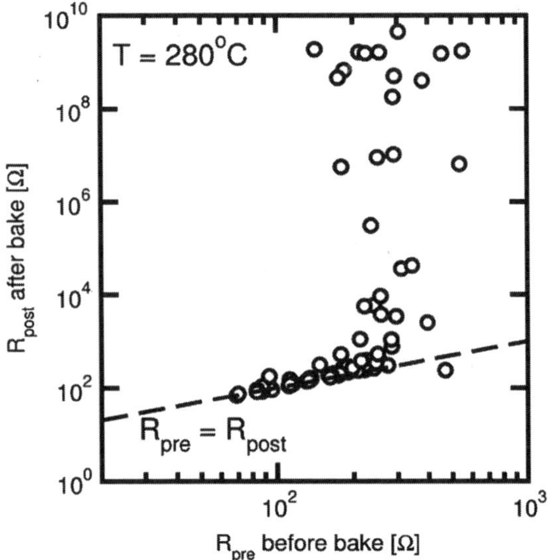

Figure 34. Correlation plot between resistance before (R_{pre}) and after (R_{post}) annealing at $T = 280°C$. As can be seen cell programmed at higher initial resistance are more affected by the thermal budget. Reprinted with permission from [84], D. Ielmini et al., "International Reliability Physics Symposium," pp. 620–626, 2010. © 2010, IEEE EDS.

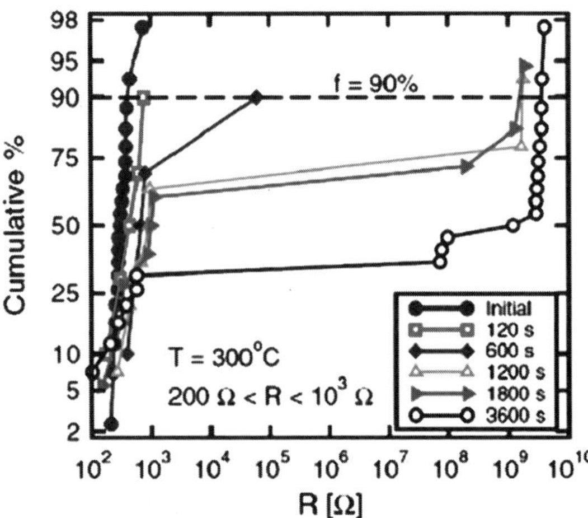

Figure 35. Resistance distributions of cells after annealing at $T = 300°C$ for increasing time. Initial resistances were selected between 200 and 10^3 Ω. Reprinted with permission from [84], D. Ielmini et al., "International Reliability Physics Symposium," pp. 620–626, 2010. © 2010, IEEE EDS.

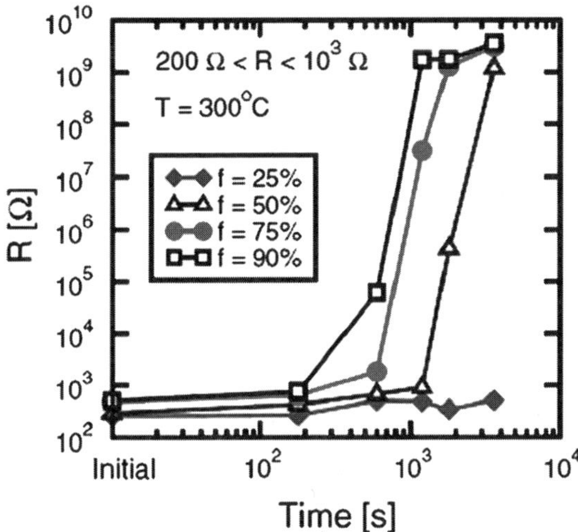

Figure 36. Time evolution of resistance during baking at $T = 300°C$ for different percentiles referred to distributions of Figure 35. Reprinted with permission from [84], D. Ielmini et al., "International Reliability Physics Symposium," pp. 620–626, 2010. © 2010, IEEE EDS.

CFs. All data satisfactorily obey the Arrhenius law, with an activation energy of $E_A = 1.21$ eV at $f = 50\%$. This value is in good agreement with previous estimation of the activation energy for the reset mechanism, based on the Kissinger analysis of V_{reset} as a function of β (see Fig. 14) [71]. Figure 37(b) reports a similar Arrhenius plot of τ_R for different initial resistance, namely $R < 200\ \Omega$, R between 200 and 1 kΩ and $R > 1$ kΩ, at $f = 90\%$. Data in the figure confirm that the failure time decreases for increasing initial resistance, in agreement with data in Figure 34.

Based on the size dependent retention time in Eq. (20), the retention time can be estimated according to [85]:

$$\tau_R = \tau_{r0}\left(\frac{\phi}{\phi_0}\right)^2 \exp\left(\frac{E_{\text{AR}}}{kT}\right) \tag{25}$$

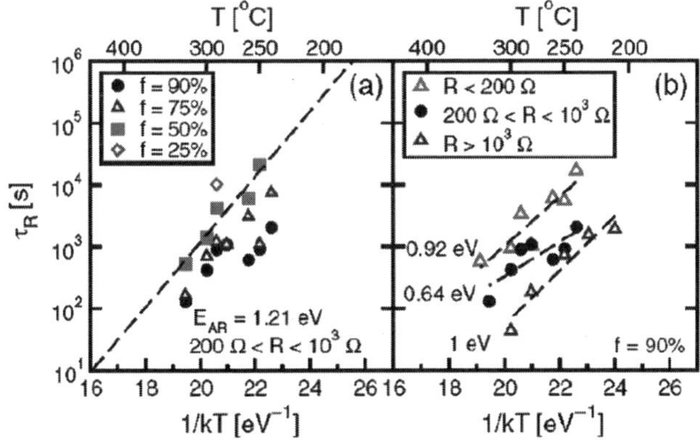

Figure 37. (a) Arrhenius plot showing failure time, τ_R, as a function of $1/kT$ for different percentiles. Activation energy for retention $E_{\text{AR}} = 1.21$ eV was extracted. (b) Same results obtained on cells prepared in different resistance states, namely $R < 200\ \Omega$, $200 < R < 10^3\ \Omega$ and $R > 10^3\ \Omega$. Reprinted with permission from [84], D. Ielmini et al., "International Reliability Physics Symposium," pp. 620–626, 2010. © 2010, IEEE EDS.

where τ_{r0} and ϕ_0 are constants and E_{AR} is the activation energy for retention. Figure 38(a) shows the calculated retention time according to numerical solutions of Eq. (25) [85], showing that τ_R increases with the ϕ^2 irrespective of the retention criterion used (i.e., a resistance increase of a factor 10 or 100 in the figure). Figure 38(b) shows experimental values of τ_R as a function of R at an annealing temperature $T = 250°C$. The figure also shows calculated results according to Eq. (25) were ϕ was evaluated according to Figure 33 and an activation energy of $E_{\text{AR}} = 1.2$ eV was assumed, in agreement with results in Figure 37(a). As R increases due to the CF size decrease, the retention time decreases, thus leading to a size-dependent retention effect [85]. This indicates that the CF diameter should be maximized for best data retention, which however conflicts with the need for a reduction of the reset current, as discussed in Section 4.3. As a result, an improvement of the data retention generally

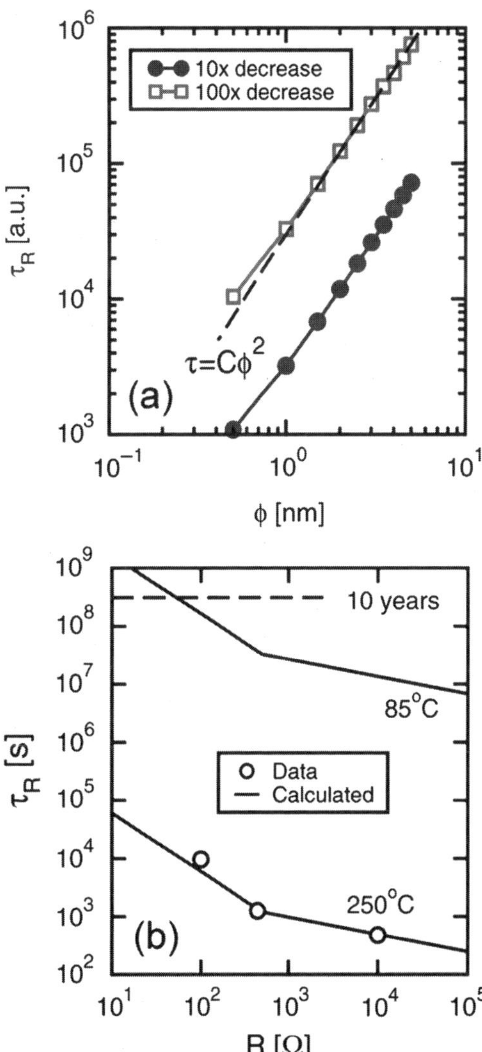

Figure 38. (a) Calculated retention time according to numerical solutions of Eq. (25). τ_R increases with the ϕ^2 irrespective of the retention criterion used. (b) Experimental values of τ_R as a function of R at an annealing temperature $T = 250°C$. Reprinted with permission from [84], D. Ielmini et al., "International Reliability Physics Symposium," pp. 620–626, 2010. © 2010, IEEE EDS.

can be obtained at the expense of a higher power consumption during reset.

6.2. Random-Telegraph-Signal Noise (RTN)

Another relevant issue, which particularly affects multi-level cell reliability and small CFs for extreme reduction of the reset current, is the random-telegraph noise [101]. Figure 39 shows typical RTN measurements for NiO-based devices at intermediate resistance states [101]. For these cells, the full-set state has a resistance around 100 Ω, while the full-reset state has a resistance higher than 100 MΩ. Therefore, several intermediate states could be established in the cell, which could serve as states within a multi-level memory with e.g., 4 or 8 resistance levels, corresponding to 2 and 3 bits in the same physical cell, respectively. The resistance in the figure was evaluated as $R = V/I$, where the current I was measured while the voltage was swept during the measurement along the low-field region between 0 and 0.4 V. The figure shows data for several intermediate states at resistances between about 3 kΩ and 3 MΩ. All measured resistances clearly indicate the presence of a RTN, namely a bistable fluctuations between two discrete levels of resistance [102–104]. The two resistance levels R' and $R > R'$ are separated by a resistance difference $\Delta R = R' - R$. From data in the figure, the relative amplitude of RTN, namely $\Delta R/R = (R - R')/R'$, significantly depends on the value of R [101–104]. In fact, $\Delta R/R$ ranges between 2×10^{-3} for metallic CFs with low resistance to about 0.5 for semiconductor-like conduction. In agreement with previous interpretations of RTN in MOSFETs and Flash memories [105], RTN in RRAM was explained by a fluctuating-charge effect as schematically shown in Figures 40(a and b). According to this model, the resistance fluctuation is described by a change in the effective cross section of the CF, from the geometrical value $A = \pi\phi^2/4$ to a smaller value, where an area ΔA is depleted by carriers due to the repulsive interaction with a negative trapped

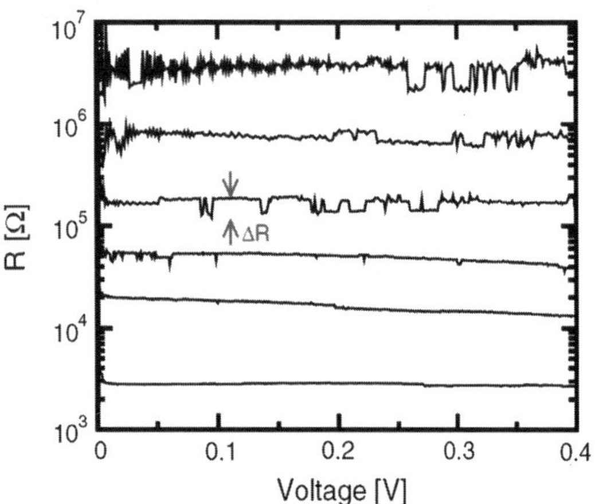

Figure 39. Resistance as a function of voltage applied in a low field range. Different resistance states are shown. As can be seen higher resistances display stronger RTN signal, while low-R states are not effected by the telegraphic noise. Reprinted with permission from [101], D. Ielmini et al., *Appl. Phys. Lett.* 96, 053503 (2010). © 2010, American Institute of Physics.

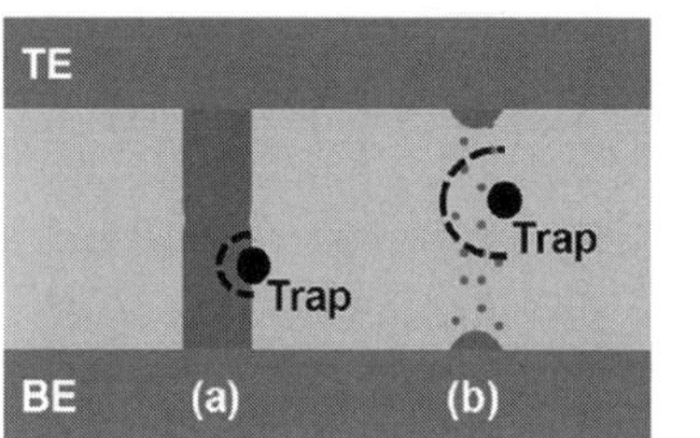

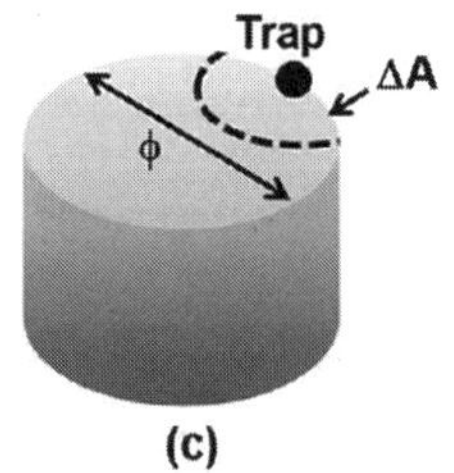

Figure 40. Schematic representation of a single trap, located on the CF border, affecting conduction in the filament. In case of low-R state this effect is efficiently shielded by the free carriers. On high-R states on the contrary the radius of influence of the trap is longer. (c) Shows a closer view of the CF, where it is reported the area of influence of the trap. Reprinted with permission from [101], D. Ielmini et al., *Appl. Phys. Lett.* 96, 053503 (2010). © 2010, American Institute of Physics.

charge. The CF is modelled as a cylindrical nanowire with length equal to the NiO layer thickness, and the fluctuating charge is assumed to be located on the CF surface. The fluctuating charge could be a trap, responsible of a carrier emission/capture, or an oxygen ion or vacancy that may switch between two energetically-comparable configurations with neutral/negative charge. First note that the different resistance may correspond to (i) a different CF size or (ii) a different activation energy for conduction, resulting in a different concentration of free carriers in the CF, or both. For a large, metallic CF with a large concentration of carriers, the fluctuating defect charge may be effectively screened by the high-density carriers within the CF, thus a very short interaction range and a very small depleted area are expected in this case. This should therefore lead to a low RTN relative amplitude $\Delta R/R$ for low resistance states. On the other hand, high R states with semiconductor-like transport display a larger interaction radius as a result of weak screening by the low density of free carriers. This results in a large depleted area and a correspondingly larger $\Delta R/R$.

To estimate the depleted area in the CF, we estimate the screening interaction range according to the Debye length λ_D, given by:

$$\lambda_D = \sqrt{\frac{\varepsilon kT}{q^2 n}} \tag{26}$$

where ε is the dielectric constant, q the electron charge and n is the free carrier density. To evaluate the free carrier density, we use the Boltzmann statistic to calculate the amount of carriers thermally promoted to the relevant conduction band edge, namely [106]:

$$n = n_0 \exp(E_{\mathrm{AC}}/kT) \tag{27}$$

where n_0 is the effective density of states and E_{AC} the activation energy for conduction. To evaluate the depleted region of the CF, a sphere with λ_D radius was intersected with the CF. To approximate the intersection surface, the half circle with area $\Delta A = \pi\lambda_D^2/2$ was used. This is an acceptable approximation as long as $\lambda_D \ll \phi$. On the other hand, the resistance change can be evaluated referring to a segment of CF length equal to d_{CF}, where the presence of the charged defect disturbs the conduction. The low resistance level R' (which corresponds to neutral charge trapped) is thus computed as $\rho d_{CF}/A$, while the high level R is evaluated as the parallel between two different contributions. The first contribution refers to the *screened* resistance R_s through the undepleted area $A - \Delta A$. This contribution is not altered by the presence of the charged defect, because of effective screening by the free carriers. The second contribution is the *unscreened* resistance R_u, due to the depleted region ΔA. The two contributions can be evaluated as follows:

$$R_s = \rho d_{CF}/(A - \Delta A) \quad (28)$$

$$R_u = \rho a d_{CF}/\Delta A \quad (29)$$

In Eq. (29), a is a factor describing the increase of resistivity due to electrostatic repulsion of free carriers in the depleted area ($a > 1$). The equations above only apply for partial-screening condition, which means $\Delta A < A$. When this condition is not satisfied, i.e., $\Delta A > A$, R is uniquely given by R_u in Eq. (29) replacing ΔA with A. Finally to evaluate the relative resistance change $\Delta R/R$, the following equation applies:

$$\Delta R/R = (R - R')/R = \Delta A/A(1 - 1/a) \quad (30)$$

For no screening (or total depletion, namely $\Delta A > A$), the latter yields to the particular case $\Delta R/R = 1/a$. The dependence of the relative resistance ratio as a function of the current resistance, can then be understood from Eq. (30) in terms of the increased ΔA and decreased A. To evaluate the CF cross section area A the model in Section 5 was used. Figure 41 shows the measured and calculated $\Delta R/R$ as a function of R, for NiO devices [101] and other metallic nanobridges in the literature, namely Cu [102, 103] and Ag nanofilament [104]. Note the universal behavior of $\Delta R/R$ as a function of R, from which a dependence $\Delta R \propto R^2$ can be derived [59]. This can be understood noting that $\Delta A \propto \lambda_D^2 \propto n^{-1}$, while, for a given R, the CF area is given by $A \propto n^{-1}R^{-1}$. As a result, we obtain:

$$\Delta R/R \propto \Delta A/A \propto R \quad (31)$$

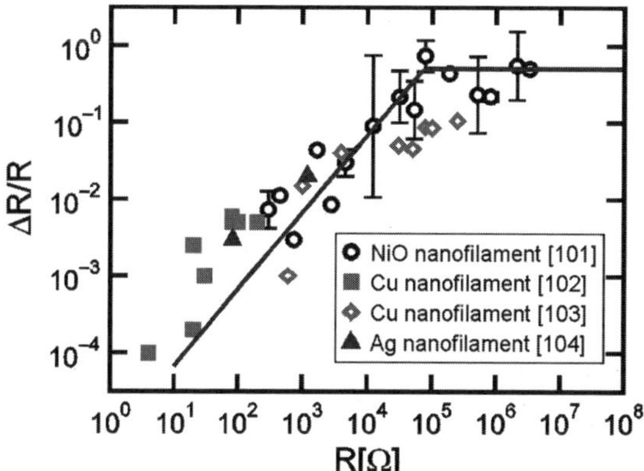

Figure 41. Measured and calculated DR/R as a function of R, for NiO devices [101] and other devices reported in the literature [102–104]. A universal behavior of $\Delta R/R$ as a function of R can be clearly noted. Reprinted with permission from [101], D. Ielmini et al., *Appl. Phys. Lett.* 96, 053503 (2010). © 2010, American Institute of Physics.

in agreement with results in Figure 41. This behavior is obeyed in both the metallic and the semiconductor-like regimes, since Eq. (31) is independent of E_{AC}. Calculation results were obtained for the same filament size estimated in Figure 33, a factor a equal to 2, a density of states of $n_0 = 10^{20}$ cm^{-3} and a relative dielectric constant of 12, in agreement with [107].

From the figure, a clear change of regime is found at $R = 10^5$ Ω. This corresponds to the change in the screening regime, from conduction partially affected by the charged trap to conduction completely effected (no screening, or complete depletion with $\Delta A = A$), for which $\Delta R/R = (1 - 1/a) = 0.5$, in good agreement with data. Note that the analytical RTN model presented here is slightly simplified, in that the mechanism of interaction between the charged trap and the CF could be, more realistically, described by a redistribution of current, in particular in the semiconductor regime. The presence of the charged trap could be the reason of a change in the percolation path that addresses the current and hence the resistivity. This may also include the case in which a fluctuating defect (e.g., oxygen ion or vacancy) affects the percolation path of the hopping conduction, similar to previous explanations of post-breakdown gate current noise in silicon dioxide [108]. Moreover the abrupt distinction between screened and unscreened regimes is unrealistic. A much more gradual shift from the first situation to the second would be preferable. For all these reasons we should consider a as the parameter that takes into account all these oversimplifications and provides corrections to the neglected effects of current redistribution and modulations.

6.3. Scaling Perspectives

To guarantee the necessary reliability of many cells within a large array, the control of CF formation and disruption are key issues. This is particularly true in high-density applications, where cross-point architectures provide the highest scaling potential. Statistical set and reset voltage spread must be as small as possible, to reliably program and erase cells within the array. To highlight the need for a narrow distribution of set voltages V_{set}, consider the $V/2$ programming algorithm shown in Figure 42 [109]. To set a memory element (light gray in Fig. 42(a)), a certain programming voltage V_{prog} higher than the required set voltage V_{set} must be applied at the bit-line (BL). To address the cell, the corresponding world-line (WL) is grounded so that the cell under programming is biased correctly at V_{prog}. Since all other BLs and WLs are left at $V_{prog}/2$, the cells on unselected BL and/or WL will have zero voltage across them, while unselected cells sharing the same BL or WL of the selected cell will experience an applied voltage equal to $V_{prog}/2$. Figure 42(b) shows the bias conditions of the cells, to comply with the $V_{prog}/2$ method. The window of acceptable V_{set} is between $V_{prog}/2$ and V_{prog}, in that V_{reset} must be lower than $V_{prog}/2$ to avoid unwanted erase. This means that the two voltage distributions must be relatively narrow and well separated. At the same time, the reset current must be as low as possible to comply with the limited forward current of selectors in a cross-bar arrays. For instance, semiconductor diodes may

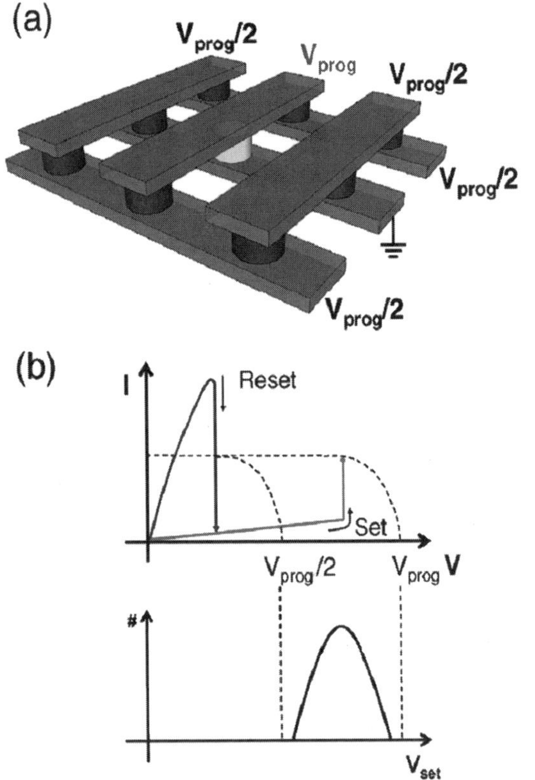

Figure 42. (a) Example of cross-bar array, showing the $V_{prog}/2$ programming schema. (b) Set voltage distribution compatible with the programming approach. Reprinted with permission from [10], D. Ielmini et al., *Nanotechnology* 22 (2011). © 2011, IOPScience.

be used for unipolar RRAM devices, allowing for a minimum area consumption with respect to select transistors as in the 1T1R structure.

To highlight the relationship between reset current reduction and device area scaling, Figure 43 shows the calculated

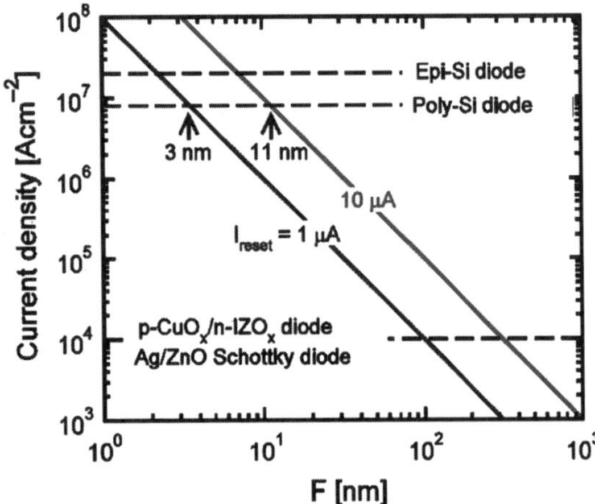

Figure 43. Current density expected for 10 μA and 1 μA reset currents at different technological nodes F. Current density supplied by different diodes (Epi-Si diode [110], Poly-Si [111], p-CuO_x/n-IZO_x [112], Schottky diode [113]) are reported for reference. Reprinted with permission from [61], F. Nardi et al., *Solid-State Electronics* 58, 42 (2011). © 2011, Elsevier.

forward current density $j = I_{reset}/F^2$ as a function of the technological node F. The figure shows calculations for $I_{reset} = 1$ and 10 μA, assumed as examples. As a reference, current densities for reported diodes are shown, including epitaxial Si [110], poly-Si [111], Ag–ZnO oxide-based diodes [112] and Schottky diodes [113]. The latter is particularly interesting in view of 3D stackable memory arrays, where multiple memory layers are vertically stacked. To this purpose, the availability of low-temperature oxide-based diodes for select purposes is essential. However, oxide-based diodes display a relatively small current density of about 10^4 A cm^{-2} that would correspond to device size of about 100 nm for a reset current of 1 μA. This clearly highlights the need for a major breakthrough in the development of select devices and materials for high density crossbar arrays.

7. CONCLUSIONS

The chapter has summarized the main aspects of electrical characterization and physical modelling for unipolar resistance switching memory (RRAM) devices based on NiO. Device experimental behaviour has been extensively discussed evidencing the main critical issues linked to the technology for both set and reset transitions. Moreover detailed physical based models have been described, capable to reproduce experiment data and provide precious predictions. These represent an important insight in a still debated field. Many gaps remain to be filled in both technology and comprehension domains. From one side RRAM is still immature to undergo production due to key issues as current scaling, performance reproducibility and scaling potential assessment. From the other side the physical mechanisms of the resistive switching are still unclear and extensive studies are required to fill numerous gaps. Different interpretations have been proposed in literature regarding different aspects of device behavior but still we lack a conclusive comprehension. Clear understanding of the working principle of RRAM device would eventually widen engineering possibility to improve materials and operation schemas. Finally, new architectures for high density applications such as cross-bar or 3D stacks must be developed. Possible implementations in logic circuits and reprogrammable arrays must be also discussed to fully pinpoint and exploit RRAM potentials.

REFERENCES

1. J. G. Beck, Bednorz, C. Gerber, C. Rossel, and D. Widmer, *Appl. Phys. Lett.* 77, 139 (2000).
2. E. Green, J. W. Choi, A. Boukai, Y. Bunimovich, E. Johnston-Halperin, E. DeIonno, Y. Luo, B. A. Sheriff, K. Xu, Y. S. Shin, H.-R. Tseng, J. F. Stoddart, and J. R. Heath, *Nature London* 445, 414 (2007).
3. G. Atwood, *IEEE Trans. Device Mater. Relat.* 4, 5 (2004).
4. J. J. Yang, M. D. Pickett, X. Li, D. A. Ohlberg, D. R. Stewart, and R. S. Williams, *Nat. Nanotechnol.* 3, 429 (2008).
5. R. Waser and M. Aono, *Nat. Mat.* 6, 833 (2007).
6. G. Baek, M. S. Lee, S. Seo, M. J. Lee, D. H. Seo, D.-S. Suh, J. C. Park, S. O. Park, H. S. Kim, I. K. Yoo, U.-In Chung, and J. T. Moon, *Tech. Dig. Int. Electron Devices Meet.* 1, 587 (2004).
7. R. Waser, R. Dittmann, G. Staikov, and K. Szot, *Adv. Mat.* 21, 2632 (2009).

8. G. F. Cerofolini, M. Ferri, E. Romano, F. Suriano, G. P. Veronese, S. Solmi, and D. Ducci *Semiconduct. Sci. Tech.* 26, 045005 (2011).
9. C. Kugeler, R. Rosezin, E. Linn, R. Bruchhaus, and R. Waser, *Appl. Phys. A-Mat. Sci. Process.* 102, 791 (2011).
10. D. Ielmini, F. Nardi, and C. Cagli, *Nanotechnology* 22, 254022 (2011).
11. H. Akinaga and H. Shima, *Proceed. IEEE* 98, 2237 (2010).
12. L. J. Zhang, R. Huang, M. H. Zhu, S. Q. Qin, Y. B. Kuang, D. J. Gao, C. Y. Shi, and Y. Y. Wang, *IEEE Electron Device Lett.* 31, 966 (2010).
13. S. G. Park, B. Magyari-Kope, and Y. Nishi, *IEEE Electron Devic. Lett.* 32, 197 (2011).
14. J. Y. Ye, Y. Q. Li, J. Gao, H. Y. Peng, S. X. Wu, and T. Wu, *Appl. Phys. Lett.* 97, 132108 (2010).
15. J. Y. Son and Y.-H. Shin, *Appl. Phys. Lett.* 92, 222106 (2008).
16. D. Ielmini, S. Spiga, F. Nardi, C. Cagli, A. Lamperti, E. Cianci, and M. Fanciulli, *J. Appl. Phys.* 109, 034506 (2011).
17. D. Ielmini, R. Bruchhaus, and R. Waser, *Phase Transition* 84, 570 (2011).
18. J. Park, M. Jo, E. M. Bourim, J. Yoon, D.-J. Seong, J. Lee, W. Lee, and H. Hwang, *IEEE Electron Device. Lett.* 31, 5 (2010).
19. I. G. Baek, D. C. Kim, M. J. Lee, H.-J. Kim, E. K. Yim, M. S. Lee, J. E. Lee, S. E. Ahn, S. Seo, J. H. Lee, J. C. Park, Y. K. Cha, S. O. Park, H. S. Kim, I. K. Yoo, U.-In Chung, J. T. Moon, and B. I. Ryu, "IEDM Tech. Dig.," pp. 750–753, 2005.
20. M.-J. Lee, Y. Park, B.-S. Kang, S.-E. Ahn, C. Lee, K. Kim, W. Xianyu, G. Stefanovich, J.-H. Lee, S.-J. Chung, Y.-H. Kim, C.-S. Lee, J.-B. Park, and I.-K. Yoo, *IEDM Technol. Dig.* 771 (2007).
21. B. Sun, Y. X. Liu, L. F. Liu, N. Xu, Y. Wang, X. Y. Liu, R. Q. Han, and J. F. Kang, *J. Appl. Phys.* 105, 6 (2009).
22. Q. Liu, S. Long, W. Wang, Q. Zuo, S. Zhang, J. Chen, and M. Liu, *Electron Devic. Lett. IEEE* 30, 12 (2009).
23. X. B. Yan, Y. D. Xia, H. N. Xu, X. Gao, H. T. Li, R. Li, J. Yin, and Z. G. Liu, *Appl. Phys. Lett.* 97, 11 (2010).
24. S. B. Lee A. Kim, J. S. Lee S. H. Chang, H. K. Yoo, T. W. Noh, B. Kahng, M.-J. Lee, C. J. Kim, and B. S. Kang, *Appl. Phys. Lett.* 97, 9 (2010).
25. H. Sim, D. Choi, D. Lee, S. Seo, M.-J. Lee, I.-K. Yoo, and H. Hwang, *Electron Devic. Lett. IEEE* 26, 5 (2005).
26. X. T. Zhang, Q. X. Yu, Y. P. Yao, and X. G. Li, *Appl. Phys. Lett.* 97, 22 (2010).
27. W. G. Kim and S. W. Rhee, *Microelectronic Engineering* 87, 98 (2010).
28. L.-E. Yu, S. Kim, M.-K. Ryu, S.-Y. Choi, and Y.-K. Choi, *IEEE Electron Devic. Lett.* 29, 331 (2008).
29. H. Y. Jeong, S. K. Kim, J. Y. Lee, and S.-Y. Choi, *Appl. Phys. A: Materials Science and Processing* 102, 967 (2011).
30. K. P. Biju, L. X. Jun, E.-M. Bourim, I. Kim, S. Jung, M. Siddik, J. Lee, and H. Hwang, *Jour. Phys. D: Appl. Phys.* 43, 495104 (2010).
31. A. Fantini, J. F. Nodin, C. Guedj, A. Persico, J. Buckley, S. Tirano, P. Lorenzi, R. Vignon, H. Feldis, S. Minoret, H. Grampeix, A. Roule, S. Favier, E. Martinez, P. Calka, N. Rochat, G. Auvert, J. P. Barnes, P. Gonon, C. Vallee, L. Perniola, and B. De Salvo, *Solid-State Electronics* 58, 62 (2011).
32. X. A. Tran, H. Y. Yu, Y. C. Yeo, L. Wu, W. J. Liu, Z. R. Wang, Z. Fang, K. L. Pey, X. W. Sun, A. Y. Du, B. Y. Nguyen, and M. F. Li, *IEEE Electron Devic. Lett.* 32, 396 (2011).
33. H. Zhang, L. Liu, B. Gao, Y. Qiu, X. Liu, J. Lu, R. Han, J. Kang, and B. Yu, *Appl. Phys. Lett.* 98, 042105 (2011).
34. Y.-S. Chen, H.-Y. Lee, P.-S. Chen, T.-Y. Wu, C.-C. Wang, P.-J. Tzeng, F. Chen, M.-J. Tsai, and C. Lien, *IEEE Electron Devic. Lett.* 31, 1473 (2010).
35. C. H. Lien, Y. S. Chen, H. Y. Lee, P. S. Chen, F. T. Chen, and M.-J. Tsai, "10th IEEE International Conference on Solid-State and Integrated Circuit Technology," p. 4, 2010.
36. H. Y. Lee, Y. S. Chen, P. S. Chen, T. Y. Wu, F. Chen, C. C. Wang, P. J. Tzeng, M.-J. Tsai, and C. Lien, *IEEE Electron Devic. Lett.* 31, 44 (2010).
37. S.-L. Li, D. S. Shang, J. Li, J. L. Gang, and D. N. Zheng, *J. Appl. Phys.* 105, 033710 (2009).
38. M. Hasan, R. Dong, H. J. Choi, D. S. Lee, D.-J. Seong, M. B. Pyun, Hwang, and Hyunsang, *Appl. Phys. Lett.* 92, 202102 (2008).
39. D.-J. Seong, *IEEE Electron Device Lett.* 30, 919 (2009).
40. Sanchez, R. Myer, and W. Kinney, "Unity Semiconductor Corporation." Sunnyvale, CA, 2009.
41. D.-J. Seong, J. Park, N. Lee, M. Hasan1, S. Jung, H. Choi1, J. Lee, M. Jo, W. Lee, S. Park, S. Kim, Y. H. Jang, Y. Lee, M. Sung, D. Kil, Y. Hwang, S. Chung, S. Hong, J. Roh, and H. Hwang, "UT-Dallas MSE Colloquium," p. 805, 2009.
42. M. N. Kozicki, M. Park, and M. Mitkova, *IEEE Trans. Nanotechnol.* 4, 331 (2005).
43. M. Kund, G. Beitel, C.-U. Pinnow, T. Rohr, J. Schumann, R. Symanczyk, K.-D. Ufert, and G. Müller, "IEDM Technol Dig.," p. 751, San Francisco, 2005.
44. M. N. Kozicki, C. Gopalan, M. Balakrishnan, and M. Mitkova, *Nanotechnology, IEEE Transactions* 5, 535 (2006).
45. M. Weides, M. N. Kozicki, and R. Waser, *Appl. Phys. Lett.* 92, 122910 (2008).
46. Y. Dong, G. Yu, M. C. McAlpine, W. Lu, and C. M. Lieber, *Nano Lett.* 8, 386 (2008).
47. J. Billen, S. Steudel, R. Müller, J. Genoe, and P. Heremans, *Appl. Phys. Lett.* 91, 263507 (2007).
48. M. Mitkova and M. N. Kozicki, *J. Non-Cryst. Solids* 299, 2 (2002).
49. D. Kamalanathan, U. Russo, D. Ielmini, and M. N. Kozicki, *IEEE Electron Device Lett.* 30, 553 (2009).
50. Y. Hirose and H. Hirose, *J. Appl. Phys.* 47, 2767 (1976).
51. U. Russo, D. Kamalanathan, D. Ielmini, A. L. Lacaita, and M. N. Kozicki, *Transactions on Electron Devices* 56, 5 (2009).
52. J. F. Gibbons, *Solid-State Electr.* 7, 785 (1964).
53. R. Yasuhara, K. Fujiwara, K. Horiba, H. Kumigashira, M. Kotsugi, M. Oshima, and H. Takagi, *Appl. Phys. Lett.* 95, 012110 (2009).
54. S.-E. Ahn, M.-J. Lee, Y. Park, B. S. Kang, C. B. Lee, and K. H. Kim, *Adv. Mater.* 20, 924 (2008).
55. I. G. Baek, M. S. Lee, S. Seo, M. J. Lee, D. H. Seo, D.-S. Suh, J. C. Park, S. O. Park, H. S. Kim, I. K. Yoo, U.-I. Chung, and I. T. Moon, "IEDM Technol Dig.," pp. 587–590, 2004.
56. D. Ielmini, C. Cagli, F. Nardi, and A. L. Lacaita, "International Symposium on Integrated Ferroelectrics," Hong Kong, 2010.
57. F. Nardi, D. Ielmini, C. Cagli, S. Spiga, M. Fanciulli, L. Goux, and D. J. Wouters, "IEEE IMW," p. 66, Seoul, Korea, 2010,
58. U. Russo, D., C., A. L., S.C., M. Perego, and M. Fanciulli "IEEE International Electron Devices Meeting," Vols. 1 and 2, pp. 775–8, 2007.
59. D. Ielmini, F. Nardi, and C. Cagli, "IEEE Semiconductor Interface Specialist Conference (SISC)," San Diego, CA, 2010.
60. K. Kinoshita, K. Tsunoda, Y. Sato, H. Noshiro, S. Yagaki, M. Aoki, and Y. Sugiyama, *Appl. Phys. Lett.* 93, 033506 (2008).
61. F. Nardi, D. Ielmini, C. Cagli, S. Spiga, M. Fanciulli, L. Goux, and D. J. Wouters, *Solid-State Electronics* 58, 42 (2011).
62. C. Cagli, F. Nardi, and D. Ielmini, "IEEE IEDM," p. 1, San Francisco, CA, 2008.
63. D. Ielmini, D. Mantegazza, A. L. Lacaita, A. Pirovano, and F. Pellizzer, *Solid-State Electronics* 49, 1826 (2005).
64. D. Ielmini, *Phys. Rev. B* 78, 035308 (2008).
65. D. Ielmini, C. Cagli, and F. Nardi, *Appl. Phys. Lett.* 94, 063511 (2009).
66. S. Seo, M. J. Lee, D. H. Seo, E. J. Jeoung, D.-S. Suh, Y. S. Joung, I. K. Yoo, I. R. Hwang, S. H. Kim, I. S. Byun, J.-S. Kim, J. S. Choi, and B. H. Park, *Appl. Phys. Lett.* 85, 5655 (2004).

67. S. H. Chang, S. C. Chae, S. B. Lee, C. Liu, T. W. Noh, J. S. Lee, B. Kahng, J. H. Jang, M. Y. Kim, D.-W. Kim, and C. U. Jung, *Appl. Phys. Lett.* 92, 183507 (2008).
68. S. Lavizzari, D. Sharma, and D. Ielmini, *IEEE Trans. Electron Devices* 57, 1047 (2010).
69. P. Fantini, G. B. Beneventi, A. Calderoni, L. Larcher, P. Pavan, and F. Pellizzer, "IEDM Tech. Dig.," pp. 219–22, 2008.
70. D. Fugazza, D. Ielmini, S. Lavizzari, and A. L. Lacaita, "IEEE IRPS," p. 743, 2010.
71. C. Cagli, F. Nardi, and D. Ielmini, *IEEE Trans. Electron Devices* 56, 1712 (2009).
72. S. Lavizzari, D. Ielmini, and A. L. Lacaita, *IEEE Transactions on Electron Devices* 57, 8 (2010).
73. A. Pirovano, A. L. Lacaita, A. Benvenuti, F. Pellizzer, and R. Bez, *IEEE Trans. Electron Devices* 51, 452 (2004).
74. D. Adler, M. S. Shur, M. Silver, and S. R. Ovshinsky, *J. Appl. Phys.* 51, 3289 (1980).
75. D. Emin, *Phys. Rev. B* 74, 035206 (2006).
76. V. G. Karpov, Y. A. Kryukov, S. D. Savransky, and I. V. Karpov, *Appl. Phys. Lett.* 90, 123504 (2007).
77. A. C. Warren, *IEEE Trans. Electron Devices* 20, 123 (1973).
78. A. Bogoslovskij and K. D. Tentsin, *J. Non-Cryst. Sol.* 357, 992 (2011).
79. D. Ielmini and Y. Zhang, *J. Appl. Phys.* 102, 054517 (2007).
80. Wolfe, M. Charles, Holonyak, Nick, Stillman, and E. Gregory, "Physical Properties of Semiconductors." Prentice Hall, Englewood Cliffs, NJ, 1989.
81. D. Ielmini, F. Nardi, A. Vigani, E. Cianci, and S. Spiga, "IEEE Semiconductor Interface Specialist Conference (SISC)," Arlington, VA, 2009.
82. T.-N. Fang, S. Kaza, S. Haddad, A. Chen, Y.-C. Wu, Z. Lan, S. Avanzino, D. Liao, C. Gopalan, S. Choi, S. Mahdavi, M. Buynoski, Y. Lin, C. Marrian, C. Bill, M. VanBuskirk, and M. Taguchi, "IEDM Tech. Dig.," pp. 789–92, 2006.
83. U. Russo, D. Ielmini, C. Cagli, and A. L. Lacaita, *IEEE Trans. Electron Devices* 56, 186 (2009).
84. D. Ielmini, F. Nardi, C. Cagli, and A. L. Lacaita, "International Reliability Physics Symposium," Anaheim, CA, pp. 620–626, 2010.
85. D. Ielmini, *IEEE Electron Devic. Lett.* 31, 552 (2010).
86. U. Russo, D. Ielmini, C. Cagli, and A. L. Lacaita, *IEEE Trans. Electron Devices* 56, 193 (2009).
87. S. A. Makhlouf, *Thin Solid Films* 516, 3112 (2008).
88. D. Ielmini, "219th ECS Symposium," Montreal, Canada, 2011.
89. K. M. Kim and C. S. Hwang, *Appl. Phys. Lett.* 94, 122109 (2009).
90. Y.-M. Kim and J.-S. Lee, *J. Appl. Phys.* 104, 114115 (2008).
91. K. Tsunoda, K. Kinoshita, H. Noshiro, Y. Yamazaki, T. Iizuka, Y. Ito, A. Takahashi, A. Okano, Y. Sato, T. Fukano, M. Aoki, and Y. Sugiyama, "IEDM Tech. Dig.," p. 767, 2007.
92. P. F. Heiman and H. S. Miller, *IEEE Trans. Electron Devices* 12, 142 (1965).
93. K. Kanda, K. Nose, H. Kawaguchi, and Sakurai, *IEEE J. Solid-State Circuits* 36, 1559 (2001).
94. G. Groeseneken, J.-P. Colinge, H. E. Maes, J. C. Alderman, and S. Holt, *IEEE Electron Device Lett.* 11, 329 (1990).
95. T. Ohgai, L. Gravier, X. Hoffer, M. Lindeberg, K. Hjort, R. Spohr, and J.-P. Ansermet, *J. Phys. D, Appl. Phys.* 36, 3109 (2003).
96. N. D. Davydov, J. Haruyama, D. Routkevitch, B. W. Statt, D. Ellis, M. Moskovits, and J. M. Xu, *Phys. Rev. B, Condens. Matter* 57, 13550 (1998).
97. M. N. Ou, T. J. Yang, S. R. Harutyunyan, Y. Y. Chen, C. D. Chen, and S. J. Lai, *Appl. Phys. Lett.* 92, 063101 (2008).
98. K. M. Kim and C. S. Hwang, *Appl. Phys. Lett.* 94, 122109 (2009).
99. S. C. Chae, J. S. Lee, S. Kim, S. B. Lee, S. H. Chang, C. Liu, B. Kahng, H. Shin, D.-W. Kim, C. U. Jung, S. Seo, M.-J. Lee, and T. W. Noh, *Adv. Mater.* 20, 1154 (2008).
100. J. Park, M. Jo, E. M. Bourim, J. Yoon, D.-J. Seong, J. Lee, W. Lee, and H. Hwang, *IEEE Electron Device Lett.* 31, 485 (2010).
101. D. Ielmini, F. Nardi, and C. Cagli, *Appl. Phys. Lett.* 96, 053503 (2010).
102. K. S. Ralls and R. A. Buhrman, *Phys. Rev. B* 44, 5801 (1991).
103. R. Soni, P. Meuffels, A. Petraru, M. Weides, C. Kügeler, R. Waser, and H. Kohlstedt, *J. Appl. Phys.* 107, 024517 (2010).
104. P. A. M. Holweg, J. Caro, A. H. Verbruggen, and S. Radelaar, *Phys. Rev. B* 45, 9311 (1992).
105. A. S. Spinelli, C. M. Compagnoni, R. Gusmeroli, M. Ghidotti, and A. Visconti, *Jpn. J. Appl. Phys.* 47, 2598 (2008).
106. D. Ielmini and Y. Zhang, *Appl. Phys. Lett.* 90, 192102 (2007).
107. K. V. Rao and A. Smakula, *J. Appl. Phys.* 36, 2031 (1965).
108. T. P. Chen, M. S. Tse, X. Zeng, and S. Fung, *Semicond. Sci. Technol.* 16, 793 (2001).
109. K. E. Van Landingham, *IEEE Trans. Electron Devices* 20, 178 (1973).
110. J. H. Oh, J. H. Park, Y. S. Lim, H. S. Lim, Y. T. Oh, J. S. Kim, J. M. Shin, J. H. Park, Y. J. Song, K. C. Ryoo, D. W. Lim, S. S. Park, J. I. Kim, J. H. Kim, J. Yu, F. Yeung, C. W. Jeong, J. H. Kong, D. H. Kang, G. H. Koh, G. T. Jeong, H. S. Jeong, and K. Kim, "International Electron Devices Meeting," San Francisco, CA, Vols. 1 and 2, pp. 515–518, 2006.
111. Y. Sasago, M. Kinoshita, T. Morikawa, K. Kurotsuchi, S. Hanzawa, T. Mine, A. Shima, Y. Fujisaki, H. Kume, H. Moriya, N. Takaura, and K. Torii, "Symposium On VLSI Technology," New Dehli, pp. 24–25, 2009.
112. H. Y. Lee, P. S. Chen, T. Y. Wu, Y. S. Chen, C. C. Wang, P. J. Tzeng, C. H. Lin, F. Chen, C. H. Lien, and M. J. Tsai, "IEEE International Electron Devices Meeting," San Francisco, CA, pp. 297–300, 2008.
113. G. Tallarida, N. Huby, B. Kutrzeba-Kotowska, S. Spiga, M. Arcari, G. Csaba, P. Lugli, A. Redaelli, and R. Bez, "IEEE International Memory Workshop," Monteray, CA, pp. 6–8, 2009.

CHAPTER 10

Organic and Polymer Nonvolatile Memories: Materials, Devices, and Working Mechanisms

Wei Lek Kwan[1], Yang Yang[2]

[1]*School of Electrical and Electronic Engineering, Singapore Polytechnic, Singapore 139651*
[2]*Department of Materials Science and Engineering, University of California, Los Angeles, CA 90095, USA*

CONTENTS

1. INTRODUCTION

Organic and polymer nonvolatile memories are two terminal devices with tunable resistance [1–5] and can be considered as variants of resistive-based memory. The resistance across the device can be controlled simply by applying different voltage pulses across the terminals. Since the first reports of electrical switching in polymer and organic films in the 1970s [6–9], a wide range of organic materials have been found to show resistive switching behavior. Most of these early devices used an insulating polymer film as the active layer and were very similar to inorganic metal-insulator-metal (MIM) memory devices [10–13].

ISBN: 1-58883-251-1

Nonvolatile Memories: Materials, Devices and Applications
Edited by Tseung-Yuen Tseng and Simon M. Sze
Volume 2: Pages: 249–264

Renewed interests in organic memory is spurred by an increase in research activities in organic-based devices such as organic thin film transistors (OTFT) [14], light emitting diodes (OLED/PLED) [15, 16], and photovoltaic [17], and an urgent need to replace the ubiquitous flash memory [5]. In the 1990s, researchers, while working on PLED, discovered resistive switching behavior in their diodes, which they classified as anomalous electrical characteristics [18–20]. When the devices were tested in vacuum, very large current flowed through the device even at low voltages. When a much larger voltage was applied to it, the current dropped back to the normally low levels. This phenomenon was highly repeatable; therefore, these devices could be used as a nonvolatile memory [18]. It was later found that reliable resistive switching can also be achieved by introducing metallic or semiconducting nanoparticles into the organic layer [21–27], although the exact reason is still under debate. Many other novel materials systems and device structures have since been developed and explored for their applications in organic memory. These devices will be further elaborated in the following sections.

The term 'organic memory' is usually used to denote devices that apply small organic molecules as the active material, but it is also used to describe polymer memory. Polymer memory, on the other hand, specifically uses long chain polymer molecules with hundreds or thousands of repeating monomer units as the active layer. In this chapter, however, for conciseness, the terms 'organic' and 'polymer' are used interchangeably, unless the context requires the differentiation of these two. In International Technology Roadmap for Semiconductors reports (Ref. [5]), the name 'macromolecular memory' is used.

The main advantages of organic materials are their low cost and ease of processing. Besides thermal evaporation, small organic molecules and polymer can be dissolved in a solvent and processed using a wide range of solution-based techniques such as spin coating, spray-coating [28], inkjet printing [29] and other low cost, high-throughput printing methods [30]. These low temperature processes enable the use of flexible plastic substrates, which is especially critical in low-cost applications where roll-to-roll fabrication is often used. These deposition methods are also intrinsically compatible with current integrated circuit processes and can be used in the integration of organic memory with complementary metal oxide semiconductor (CMOS) technology [27, 31, 32].

Besides the ease of processing, electronic and physical properties of organic materials can also be easily fine tuned by changing the chemical structure of the molecule. For example, the molecular packing of an organic molecule can be adjusted to change the crystallinity of the organic thin film. This will, in turn, affect the mobility of the charge carriers and the resistance of the device. Polymer films can also be cross-linked after deposition to improve robustness, thus enabling photolithography and multilayer coatings of the polymer films [27, 28, 33].

Figure 1 shows three representative device structures of the organic memory. The simplest structure (Fig. 1(a)) consists of two electrodes and a thin layer of organic film. Although earlier devices used insulating polymers like polystyrene as the active medium, more recent devices make use of semiconducting conjugated organic molecules. Ma of the University of California–Los Angeles demonstrated that reliable switching of an organic memory could be achieved with a layer of aluminum nanoparticles sandwiched between two layers of organic films (Fig. 1(b)) [21]. Similar resistive switching can also be achieved by replacing the three layers of organic/metallic nanoparticles/organic with a single layer of polymer with embedded nanoparticles (Fig. 1(c)) [22, 24].

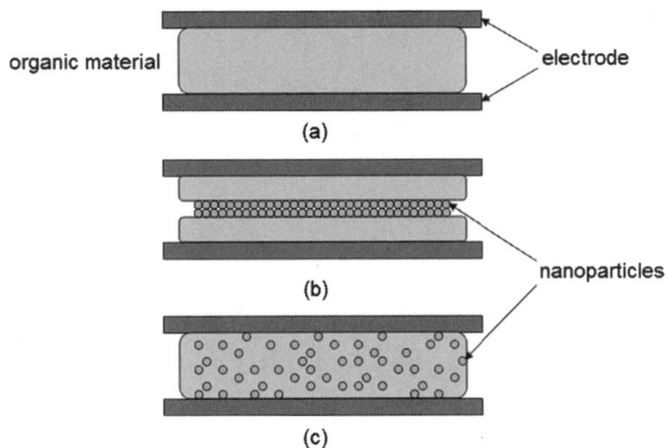

Figure 1. Typical device structures of organic memory. (a) Single layer of organic material sandwiched between two electrodes, (b) three-layer structure consisting of organic/nanoparticles/organic between the electrodes, and (c) single layer organic layer with nanoparticles dispersed in it.

Despite intense research efforts over the past few decades, there is still significant disagreement among researchers over the origins of the switching mechanism. A wide range of materials and device structures has been reported to show resistance switching with similar characteristics. To complicate matters, electrical characterizations carried out by various groups are often different and difficult to compare, and the results are often contradictory [1–4].

This chapter aims to summarize the materials, devices, and current understanding of the working mechanisms of organic memory devices. Section 2 describes the electrical characteristics of organic memory, while Section 3 outlines the properties of the organic materials (both small molecules and polymer), their conduction mechanism, and the organic-metal interface. Section 4 summarizes the results of significant and representative devices utilizing small organic molecules and polymer and also important integration issues in organic memories. The discussion in Section 3 helps facilitate the discussion of the working mechanisms in Section 5.

2. ELECTRICAL CHARACTERISTICS OF ORGANIC MEMORY DEVICES

The resistance across an organic memory device can be changed by applying voltage pulses to it. Both bipolar and unipolar operations in nonvolatile organic memory devices have been reported. In bipolar operation, voltages of different polarities are used to switch the device between the resistive states. Conversely, in unipolar operation, only voltages of the same polarity are used in switching.

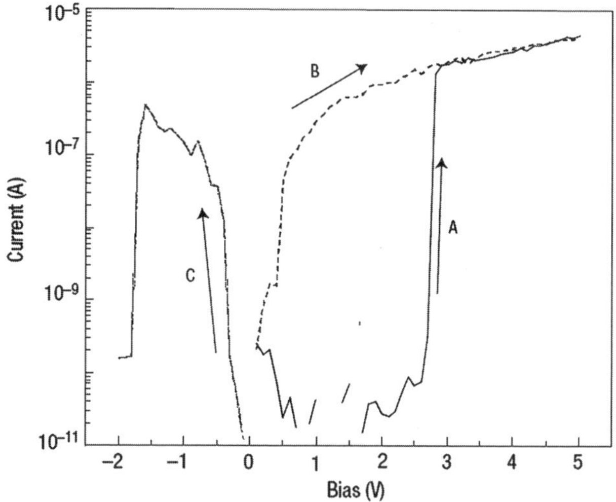

Figure 2. I–V curve of a polymer memory device. The lines A, B, and C represent the response of the device when scanned in that order. Reprinted by permission from [22], J. Ouyang et al., *Nat. Mat.* 3, 918 (2004). © 2004, Nature Publishing Group.

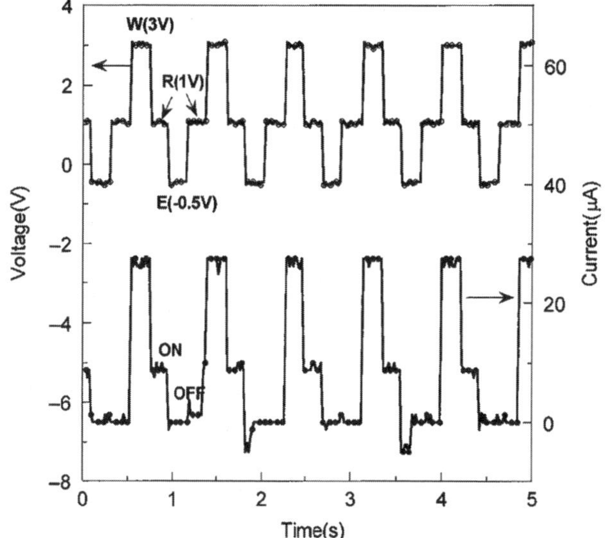

Figure 3. Current response of an organic memory device during write-read-erase-read cycles. The write voltage was set at 3 V, the erase voltage at −0.5 V, and the device was read at 1 V. Reprinted with permission from [21], L. P. Ma et al., *Appl. Phys. Lett.* 80, 2997 (2002). © 2002, American Institute of Physics.

Figure 2 shows an example of a device operating in the bipolar mode. When the voltage bias is swept in the positive direction, the resistance of the device decreases abruptly (as shown by the sudden increase in current) after the threshold voltage (V_{th}) is reached. The device retains its low resistance state indefinitely until the voltage is swept in the negative direction. The resistance states can also be changed by applying positive and negative voltage pulses to the device. It has been reported that the pulse duration can be as short as 20 ns [21] and is often limited by the resistive-capacitive delay of the test circuit. An electrical readout can be easily achieved by applying a small voltage ($\ll V_{th}$) and then measure the current through a current sensing circuit. Organic memory generally exhibits very high readout stability. Very little change to the resistance was measured even after more than 1 million read pulses had been applied [34]. The low-resistance state can be defined as the 'on' state or logic 1 and the high resistance state can be defined as the 'off' state or logic 0. Figure 3 shows the switching characteristics of an organic memory device with the current readout at 1 V. Although there is no proper investigation on the stability of the resistive states, it is found to be generally stable and in one case, the states remained the same for up to 1 year when stored at room temperature [39].

Figure 4 shows the current–voltage (I–V) characteristics of a typical unipolar device. Similar to the bipolar device, the resistance of the device switches after the threshold voltage is reached. However, as the voltage is swept beyond the threshold voltage, the current of the device reaches a maximum at V_{max} and begins to decrease (negative differential resistance [NDR]) until it reaches a minimum at V_{min}. The current starts to increase again after the minimum point. Voltage pulses with magnitude between V_{th} and V_{max} can be used to switch the device to the 'on' state and voltages at V_{min} and beyond can be used to switch the device back to the 'off' state [23]. Intermediate resistive states can also be attained by switching the device from the 'on' state with voltages between V_{max} and V_{min} [23, 36].

Unipolar operation has considerable advantage over bipolar operation because the device can be connected in series with a diode and configured as a crosspoint array [37, 38]. The series diode is used to reduce crosstalk between neighboring cells in a cross-point array (Fig. 5). In a crosspoint array, each memory cell only occupies an area of $4F^2$, where F is the half-pitch distance. If the crosspoint array is stacked into multiple layers [27, 31, 35, 39], each cell size can be further reduced to $4F^2/n$, where n is the number of layers of stacked memory. Therefore, organic memory in a crosspoint array has significant advantages over current flash memory technology in terms of higher memory density and scalability. The demonstrated device performance of organic memory is summarized in Table 1.

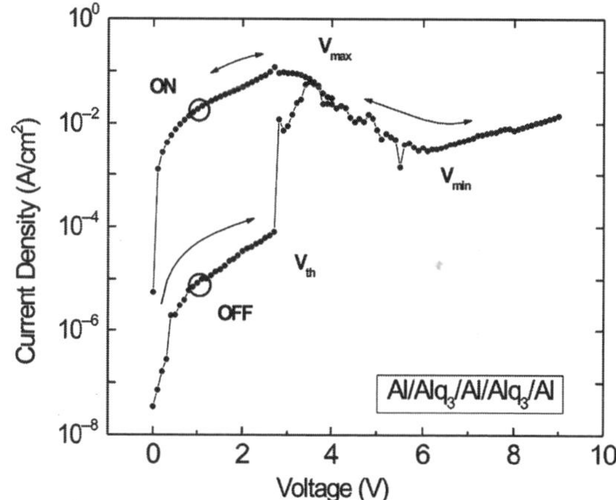

Figure 4. I–V curve of an organic memory device showing unipolar characteristics. Reprinted with permission from [23], L. D. Bozano et al., *Appl. Phys. Lett.* 84, 607 (2004). © 2004, American Institute of Physics.

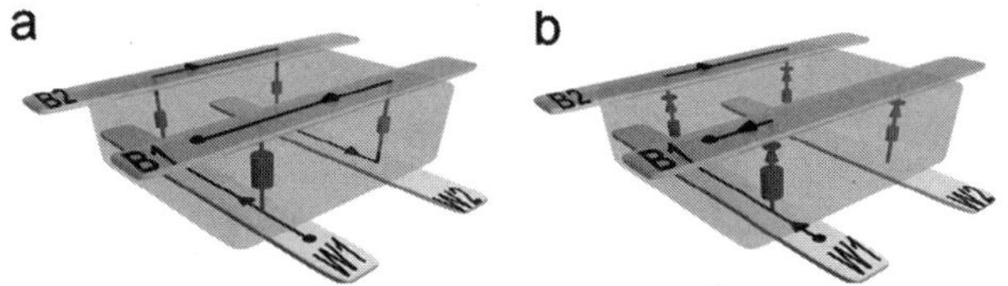

Figure 5. Schematic diagram of a 4-bit memory array. The darker gray element (W1B1) is at high-resistance state, while the lighter elements are at the low-resistance state. Without the rectifying diodes, (a) error readout is possible as there are alternative low-resistance pathways through the lighter gray elements. However, with a diode attached in series with the memory element, only one current pathway is possible, eliminating the cross-talk between other elements not addressed. Reprinted with permission from [129], K. Asadi et al., *Appl. Phys. Lett.* 97, 193308 (2010). © 2010, American Institute of Physics.

Table 1. Demonstrated performance of organic memory devices.

Cell elements	1T-1R or 1D-1R
Device area	200 × 200 nm [124]
Read time	10 ns [21]
Write/erase time	10 ns [21]
Retention time	> 1 year [35]
Write cycles	> 1,000,000 [21]
	> 4000 [31]
	> 30,000 [110]
Write voltage	~ ± 2 V [21]
	4–9 V [31]
Read voltage	1 V [21, 31]

It has been reported that a 'forming' process is required in certain devices to ensure repeatable and reliable switching [35, 40–42] (Fig. 6). The forming process consists of applying a high voltage (typically 10 V or higher) or multiple voltage sweeps to the device. Verbakel et al. suggested that this is due to the soft breakdown of the aluminium oxide formed between the aluminium electrode and the polymer layer. Due to the high electric field generated at nonuniform edges of the electrode during the forming process, metal atoms from the electrode can also migrate into the polymer film during the 'forming' process [43–45]. This is similar to some inorganic MIM memory devices where a high voltage is used to force nanoparticles into the polymer film [13].

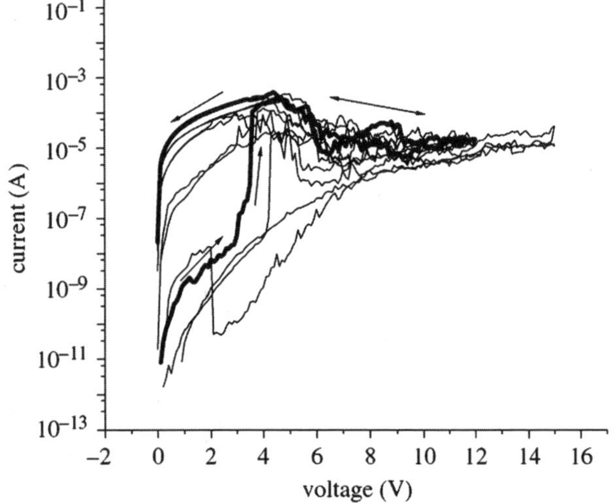

Figure 6. *I–V* sweep showing the forming process. The *I–V* curve becomes stable (bold line) after multiple voltage sweeps to 16 V. Reprinted with permission from [35], W. L. Kwan et al., *Philos. Trans. R. Soc. A* 367, 4159 (2009). © 2009, The Royal Society.

Besides bipolar and unipolar switchable devices, write-once-read-many organic memory devices have also been demonstrated [46–50]. In these memory devices, the active layer is permanently changed after applying a voltage pulse to the device. Since the resistance state is very stable after the switch, the device can be easily read out by applying a small voltage. However, the resistance change is not reversible and therefore, it has limited applications.

3. MATERIALS

3.1. Organic Materials

In many organic memory devices, the organic materials used are often the similar to the materials used in OLED, OTFT, and solar cell devices [51–53]. Organic materials are a class of carbon-based chemical compounds. Elements like oxygen, nitrogen, and sulfur are also commonly found in organic compounds. The size of each molecule may range from a few atoms to tens of thousand of atoms (polymer). In organic electronic devices, molecules with a π conjugated system are commonly used. These π conjugated molecules consist of alternating single and multiple bonds between carbon atoms. Benzene is an example of such a molecule. The carbon atoms in the benzene ring form σ bonds through sp^2 hybridized orbitals. The remaining *p*-orbitals weakly overlap allowing the electrons in the *p*-orbitals (π electrons) to delocalized over a few atoms.

In a ground-state molecule, electrons occupy molecular orbitals with lower energies. The highest orbital that is occupied is called, not surprisingly, the highest occupied molecular orbital (HOMO) and the lowest orbital that is unoccupied is called lowest unoccupied molecular orbital (LUMO). This is analogous to the valence and conduction bands of the inorganic semiconductors. However, unlike the inorganic semiconductor, organic molecules interact only weakly between molecules by van der Waals forces with little overlap of wave functions between the molecules. As a result, band transport of charge carriers is seldom observed, especially, in amorphous organic solids at room temperature. The weak interaction between the molecules is also the reason why organic materials have low melting points and can be easily processed at room temperature.

Usually in organic devices, semiconducting molecules with energy gaps (difference between LUMO and HOMO levels) between 1.5 to 3.5 eV are used [51]. As a result, undoped organic materials at room temperature usually have very few free charge carriers and thus, can sometimes be considered 'insulators.' Therefore, it is not uncommon in the literature to classify organic memory as a special class of MIM memory. In fact, some of the organic memories have very similar characteristics as inorganic MIM memory devices [10–13], and the working mechanisms developed on inorganic MIM devices have also been used to explain organic memory [12, 13].

The electrical and physical properties of organic materials are governed by their chemical structures. The degree of crystallinity of an organic thin film is dependent on the planarity of the molecules and also the π–π interactions between the molecules. Due to the weak interactions between molecules, impurities, chemical defects, and long molecular chains for polymer, the level of crystallinity is typically much lower when compared with inorganic materials. Even for a highly crystalline organic film, there are still significant regions that are amorphous. For organic memory, amorphous films are usually desired because this will reduce the nonuniformity of the device when it is scaled down to nanometer size. In general, the charge mobility of an amorphous film is much lower than that of a crystalline film. This is usually advantageous in an organic memory device because it will also reduce the 'off' state current and thus increase the on–off ratio of the device.

3.2. Conduction Processes in Organic Memory Devices

In organic materials, when an additional electron is added or removed from a molecule, the molecular structure and polarization field will distort significantly to accommodate the change in charge density. This lowers the total energy of the system and leads to a structurally relaxed state called polaron. In the literature, for simplicity, these electron and hole polarons are generally referred to as electrons and holes respectively.

Charge transport in organic materials involves the transfer of charges between nearby molecules over an energy barrier. The hopping process is often used to describe this transfer of charges between molecules. Since the energy state of a molecule is affected by its chemical structure, e.g., variations in the local environment, defects, impurities, conformations, it is difficult to describe a general microscopic process for all organic materials [54]. One method, described by Bässler, is to use Gaussian distribution to model the energy distribution and simulate the interactions using Monte Carlo simulations [55]. This results in the following temperature dependence of the charge mobility:

$$\mu = \mu_0 \exp(-T_0/T)^2 \tag{1}$$

where T is the temperature and T_0 denotes the energetic disorder. A prefactor μ_0 can be obtained by extrapolating T to infinity. This expression deviates from the Arrhenius law, but, in general, both Bässler's and Arrhenius's expressions are able to fit experimental results quite well within the experimental limits.

In the disordered materials often used in organic memory devices, the charge mobility also often display a Poole–Frenkel type of behavior [54], although the basis of this relation is unclear:

$$\mu(F) = \mu_0 \exp(\gamma\sqrt{F}) \tag{2}$$

where F is the electric field in the device and γ is a temperature dependent variable. There are several techniques that are used to characterize charge transport in organic materials e.g., time-of-flight (TOF) [56, 57], field effect transistor (FET) [58], and I–V measurements. However, when studying charge transport mechanism in organic memory, TOF and FET methods are usually not used. In a TOF measurement, the thickness of the organic film is required to be at least a few μm thick. But, at this thickness, the probability of switching in organic memory is very low [42]. The same problem lies in a FET configuration. As a result, many mechanism studies on organic memory rely solely on the I–V characteristics of the device, which do not yield conclusive results. More information on the transport characteristics can be obtained by measuring the I–V curves at different temperatures, usually in a vacuum probe station. However, the range of accessible temperature is limited by the large difference in thermal expansion coefficient of the organic material and the electrode [59]. This is further complicated by the instability of the device at higher voltage bias close to the threshold voltage. Nevertheless, the temperature dependence of the I–V characteristics will give some indication on the transport mechanism.

If the space-charge limited current (SCLC) is attainable in the device, it can be used to measure the mobility of the organic material. In an SCLC measurement, the electrode is chosen in such a way that only one type of charge (electron or hole) is injected into the organic film and one of the contacts is ohmic with respect to the charge that it is injecting. As the injected charges are not shielded adequately in the organic material, the charges prevent additional charges from injecting at the electrostatic potential, resulting in the following I–V characteristics [60]:

$$J = \frac{9}{8}\varepsilon_0\varepsilon_r\mu\frac{V^2}{L^3} \tag{3}$$

where J is the current density, L is the device thickness, V is the voltage bias, and $\varepsilon_0\varepsilon_r$ is the dielectric constant. True SCLC is not easily observed in an organic memory device because the metal-organic contact is often nonohmic, and the voltage range applicable to the memory device is limited by the switching voltage of the memory device.

Impurities or defects present in the organic material can drastically affect charge transport properties. This is especially the case when the impurities have energy levels that fall between the HOMO and LUMO of the host material. Thus, the impurity acts as a trap for the charge carriers. If the difference between the trap level and charge transporting levels are of the order of kT, then the trap is considered a shallow trap since thermal energy is sufficient to detrap the charges. If the trap level is much deeper than kT, then it is considered as a deep trap and will have a larger influence on the transport properties of the organic material.

If the current of the organic memory device is not bulk limited but instead is injection limited, the I–V characteristics and its temperature dependence will reflect the charge injection mechanism of the device. Thermionic emission, Fowler–Nordheim tunnelling, and carrier hopping from metal into disordered states of organic materials [61–64] have been used to describe the charge injection mechanism in organic devices. For Thermionic emission and Fowler–Nordheim tunnelling [61, 64], the current dependence on voltage and temperature are as

Thermionic emission:

$$J \propto T^2 \exp(+\sqrt{qV/4\pi\varepsilon_i}/T - q\phi_B/kT) \quad (4)$$

and

$$\text{Fowler–Nordheim: } J \propto V^2 \exp(-k/V) \quad (5)$$

where T is the temperature, V is the voltage bias, q is the elementary charge, ε_i is the material dynamic permittivity, ϕ_B is the barrier height, and k is the Boltzmann constant. The voltage and temperature dependence of the current can give an indication of the dominant conduction mechanism of the organic memory device. An important note here is that these $I–V$ characteristics and temperature dependence are based on the assumption that the current is uniformly distributed. The $I–V$ and temperature relationships become more complicated when parallel pathways with different transport mechanisms in the device exist.

3.3. Electrode and Organic: Metal Interface

When a metal and an organic surface come together, an interface similar to the Schottky barrier is formed [65, 66]. An injection barrier for electrons and holes is formed between the metal and organic interface due to the difference between the Fermi level of the metal and the LUMO (or conduction level) or HOMO (valence level) levels of the organic materials. The interface becomes more complex with the formation of the interfacial dipole layer, which can result from charge transfer across the interface, chemical reactions between the metal and organic layer, and the alignment of polar molecules. When the contact is formed by the deposit of metal on organic materials by evaporation, hot metal atoms may penetrate the soft organic layer, thus forming a diffused junction and making a quantitative analysis even more difficult. However, unlike other organic electronic devices, where the electrodes are chosen or modified to reduce the injection barrier into the organic layer, the role of the electrode or interface is not clear in organic memory.

Aluminum, indium tin oxide, copper, silver, and gold are among the most commonly used electrode materials in organic memory devices. In particular, aluminum is the most important because of its low cost and compatibility with CMOS processes. A thin layer of native oxide, which is an insulator, readily forms on the surface of aluminum during device fabrication. The thickness and density of the aluminium oxide can be increased by the ultraviolet (UV) ozone or oxygen plasma treatment of the aluminium surface. The aluminum oxide is said to play an important role in the switching properties of the device [41, 67, 68]. This will be discussed in more detail in Section 5.

The adhesion between the electrode and polymer may play an important role in the stability and cycle endurance of the memory device. The interface can be improved by depositing a thin layer of self-assembled monolayer that covalently bonds with the aluminum oxide on the surface [69, 70]. Phosphonic acids are known to absorb on aluminium oxide surface through an acid-base reaction. After treatment of the aluminum oxide surface with 4-nitrophenyl dichloride phosphate, the switching reproducibility of the organic device was improved [27]. This was attributed to the improvement of adhesion and charge injection properties of the interface.

4. ORGANIC MEMORY DEVICES

4.1. Organic-Nanoparticles Memory

Ma of the University of California–Los Angeles introduced the first organic-nanoparticle memory device in 2002 (Fig. 1(a)) [21]. The middle layer of the aluminum nanoparticles is formed by depositing a very thin layer of aluminum at low deposition rate (< 0.5 A/s) [71] using thermal evaporation. At such a low deposition rate, aluminum oxide readily forms on the surface of the aluminum nanoparticles due to residual oxygen and moisture in the vacuum chamber. Since the report of this device, many other groups, including IBM, have fabricated similar organic memory devices with various nanoparticles like magnesium, silver, chromium, and gold [23, 24, 72, 73].

Despite the similarities between the University of California–Los Angeles and IBM devices, the electrical characteristics are very different. The University of California–Los Angeles device showed bipolar switching characteristics (Fig. 2), while the IBM device displayed NDR and unipolar switching characteristics (Fig. 3). Wang et al. solved the apparent inconsistency in these results by demonstrating that both bipolar and unipolar characteristics can be attained from the same device depending on the measurement environment [72, 73]. For their device, when measured under ambient conditions, the electrical characteristics were similar to that of the device from the University of California–Los Angeles. However, when the device was measured in vacuum, NDR appeared and the device was able to switch in the unipolar mode. This result shows that oxygen or moisture from the air affects how the device switches from the low-resistance state to the high-resistance state.

Subsequently, it was discovered that similar switching behavior can also be achieved by blending metallic nanoparticles in solution-processable polymer films. Interestingly, a wide range of organic-nanoparticles blends showed switching characteristics: gold nanoparticles embedded in insulating polystyrene (PS) with [22] and without a donor molecule [73]; gold nanoparticles embedded in a semiconducting polymer [24, 33, 75, 76]; gold nanoparticles with polyaniline embedded in poly(vinyl alcohol [PVA]) [77]; platinum nanoparticles with tobacco mosaic virus embedded in PVA [78], and more. The metallic particles are stabilized by ligands that may play an important role in the switching characteristics [79].

Many devices with nonmetallic nanoparticles blended in organic materials that displayed switching capabilities were also reported: (6,6)-phenyl-C61 butyric acid methyl ester (PCBM) with tetrathiafulvalene as a donor in PS [26]; PCBM or C_{60} in insulating polymer [27, 39, 68, 80, 81]; semiconducting quantum dots in a polymer [25, 82, 84]; copper phtalocyanine in aluminum tris(8-hydroxyquinolate) (Alq_3) [24], and more.

In these devices, the nanoparticles are mostly assumed to play the role of charge storages, thus explaining the need for an insulating organic matrix or ligands surrounding the nanoparticles. However, in at least one report [74], it was explained that the nanoparticles facilitated the formation of metallic filaments in the device. This will be discussed again in Section 5.

4.2. Homogenous Single Layer Organic Memory (MIM Structure)

A wide range of materials has been used in the MIM structured organic memory. Perhaps the most confusing aspects of organic memory comes from the large variety of organic small molecules and polymers that display resistance switching and the numerous mechanisms proposed by various groups explaining the phenomena.

The materials reported in MIM devices range from 'true' insulators like PS and poly(methyl methacrylate) [5–8] to semiconducting small molecules like Rose Bengal, Alq_3, pentacene [40, 85–95], and semiconducting polymers like polyfluorene and poly(2-methoxy-5(2′-ethyl)hexoxy-phenylenevinylene) [18–20, 31, 34, 36, 46, 67, 96–101]. The typical thickness of the organic film is less than 100 nm. A comprehensive list of polymers that exhibit memory behavior can be found in Ref. [3].

A forming process is usually required before these devices will display switching characteristics. As mentioned earlier, metallic particles may be driven into the polymer film during the forming process. If this is true, these devices are similar to the organic-nanoparticle devices.

The other common feature among these devices is the use of aluminum as the electrode. In some cases, the aluminum oxide, which is formed between the electrode and the polymer layer, is critical for switching to occur [67].

4.3. CuTCNQ Memory

In 1979, Potember introduced a metal-organic charge transfer complex, copper tetracyanoquinodimethane (CuTCNQ) as the switching medium [102]. The CuTCNQ layer is formed by reaction of a thin layer of copper with TCNQ in solution or vapour phase. A typical *I–V* curve of a CuTCNQ memory is shown in Figure 7 [103]. Since the device operates in the bipolar mode, Potember postulated that electric-field-induced charge transfer or redox reaction was the cause of the resistive switch. However, recent experiments showed that a thin layer of oxide is required to form between the CuTCNQ and the electrode to observe the switching effect [103–107]. It was found that the oxide layer acted as a switching layer for the electrochemical formation and dissolution of copper filaments. Besides aluminum oxide, hafnium oxide, zirconium oxide, and silicon dioxide can also be used as a matrix for the growth of the filament [107]. Thus, CuTCNQ memory can also be classified as a type of programmable metallization cells or nano-ionics-based resistive memory [108].

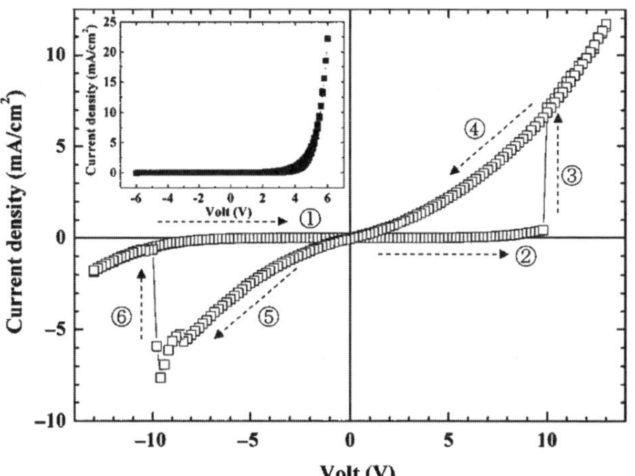

Figure 7. A typical *I–V* curve of a CuTCNQ memory showing bipolar characteristics. Reprinted with permission from [103], T. Oyamada et al., *Appl. Phys. Lett.* 83, 1252 (2003). © 2003, American Institute of Physics.

4.4. Copper Ion Memory

The device structure of a copper ion memory consists of an organic layer sandwiched between two copper electrodes [109–111]. The switching mechanism of copper ion memory is very similar to that of the CuTCNQ memory. Copper ions are ionized and drifted into the organic layer to form filaments under a very high electric field [111]. It was found that metallic filaments can be formed in polymers that form a strong complex with the metal ion. The reproducibility of the device depends heavily on the type of polymer used. Samsung demonstrated that reliable switching could be achieved in a copper ion memory device by carefully selecting the polymer used in the metallization layer [110]. Their device was shown to be able to switch more than 30,000 times without any failure (Fig. 8).

In copper ion memory, the switching delay time is dependent on the polymer thickness [112]. When the device is fabricated in a noncleanroom environment, dust particles on the device can cause local nonuniformity in the device thickness. Since the dust particles are of various sizes, the delay time also varies over a large distribution. Joo et al. discovered that the spread in delay time over switching cycles could be reduced by depositing PS nanospheres of a uniform 300-nm diameter before the deposition of the bottom electrode (figure). Since the PS nanospheres are larger than most dust particles, the effect of the dust particles on the device is minimized. As expected, the variance in the delay time is reduced for the PS nanosphere devices. This is an important result because it points out the effect of nonuniformity of the device thickness.

4.5. Organic Mobile Ion Memory

Ions in the organic layer can change the electrical behavior of organic devices in two ways: (1) by increasing the conductivity of the organic material by doping [113], and (2) by changing the injection barrier of charges by ion accumulation and electrochemical doping of the electrode [114–116]. Both of these methods have been utilized in organic mobile ion memory devices [117–121]. In such devices, a layer rich in the mobile ions is deposited next to the organic layer and electric field is used to drive the ions into the organic layer (figure (a, b)). The main difference between this type of memory and the previously discussed CuTCNQ and copper ion memory is that the ions itself do not form a conductive filament. Instead, the organic layer remains as the main medium for charge conduction.

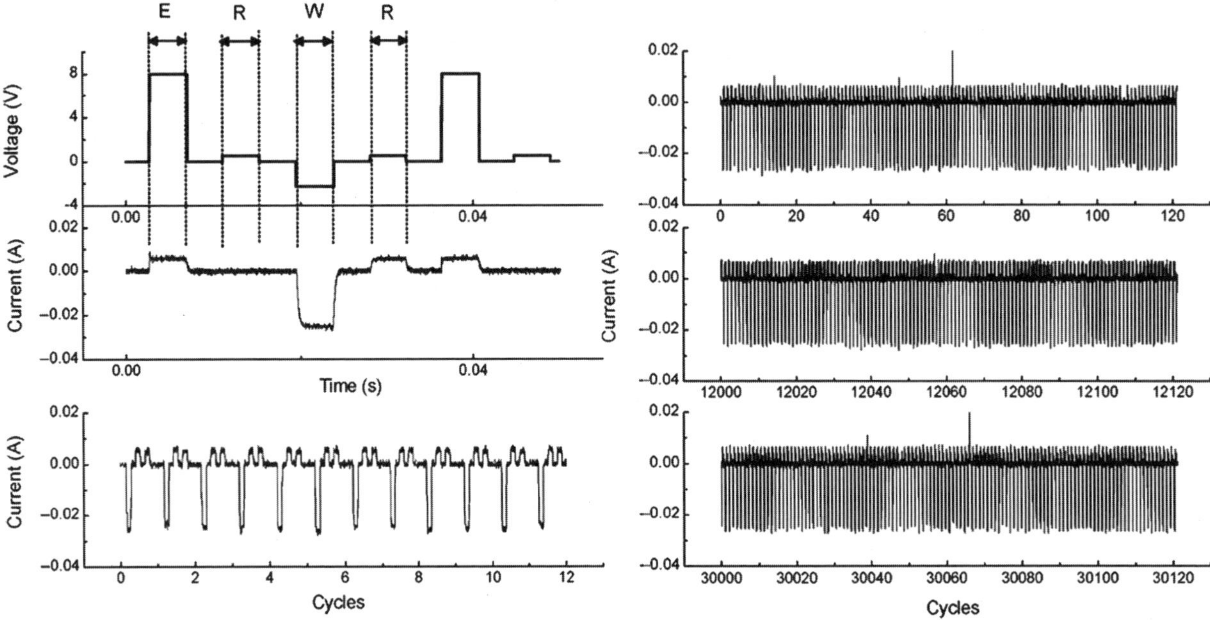

Figure 8. Write-read-erase-read cycles of copper ion memory showing 30,000 cycles without error. Reprinted with permission from [110], W.-J. Joo et al., *J. Phys. Chem. B* 110, 23812 (2006). © 2006, American Chemical Society.

4.6. Polymer Ferroelectric-Based Memory Diode

Polymer ferroelectric capacitor and transistor-based memory devices are based on their inorganic counterparts. The ferroelectric property of an organic material is derived from the dipole moment of its polar molecule. In a ferroelectric polymer like polyvinylidene fluoride or poly(vinylidene fluoridetrifluoroethylene), the dipole moment of the polymer originates from the highly electronegative fluorine atoms. When an electric field is applied to the ferroelectric polymer, the polymer molecule will roll over to align its dipole moment in the direction of the applied field.

Despite a clear understanding in the working mechanisms, these devices are not desirable for practical applications due to the destructive readout of the capacitor-based device and the complexity in structure of the transistor-type device. More information about these devices can be found in Refs. [3, 122].

A breakthrough in ferroelectric polymer-based memory device came from the Blom's group [123, 129]. They proposed a diode-type device with a phase-separated blend of semiconducting and ferroelectric polymer as the active layer. This device is a two-terminal device with a nondestructive current readout similar to other organic memories. In this device, when a sufficiently high voltage is applied to the electrode, the electric field changes the direction of the polarization of the polymer (Fig. 9). To read the polarization state of the device, a smaller voltage is applied to it. The polarization of the ferroelectric polymer in the blend will either increase or decrease the injection barrier of charges depending on the direction. However, the scalability of this device is limited by the phase separation of the polymer blend. Nevertheless, this device offers an interesting solution for low-cost memory applications.

4.7. Integration of Organic and Polymer Memory Devices

For organic memory to be successful, two important issues need to be addressed: (1) compatibility with conventional patterning and CMOS processing, and (2) integration with other circuit elements, e.g., the transistor and diode, to achieve random access.

In most laboratory demonstrations of organic memory, the device area is usually defined by the overlapping area

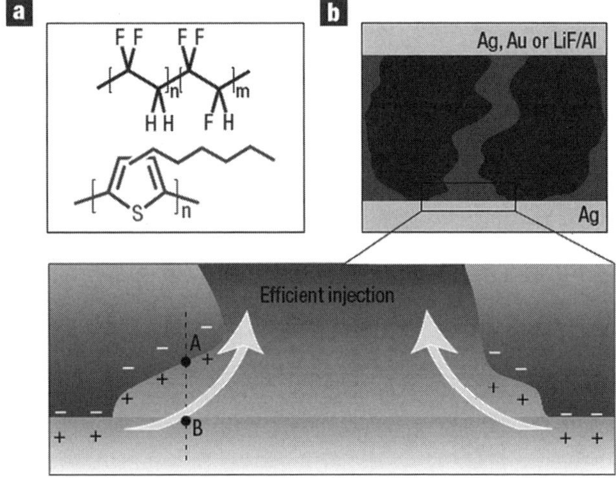

Figure 9. (a) The chemical structure of the ferroelectric polymer P(VDF–TrFE) and semiconducting polymer P3HT used in the polymer blend, and (b) the dark gray area represent P(VDF–TrFE) and the light gray area represents P3HT. The polarization in P(VDF–TrFE) modified the injection barrier for holes into P3HT. Reprinted by permission from [123], K. Asadi et al., *Nat. Mater.* 7, 547 (2008). © 2008, Nature Publishing Group.

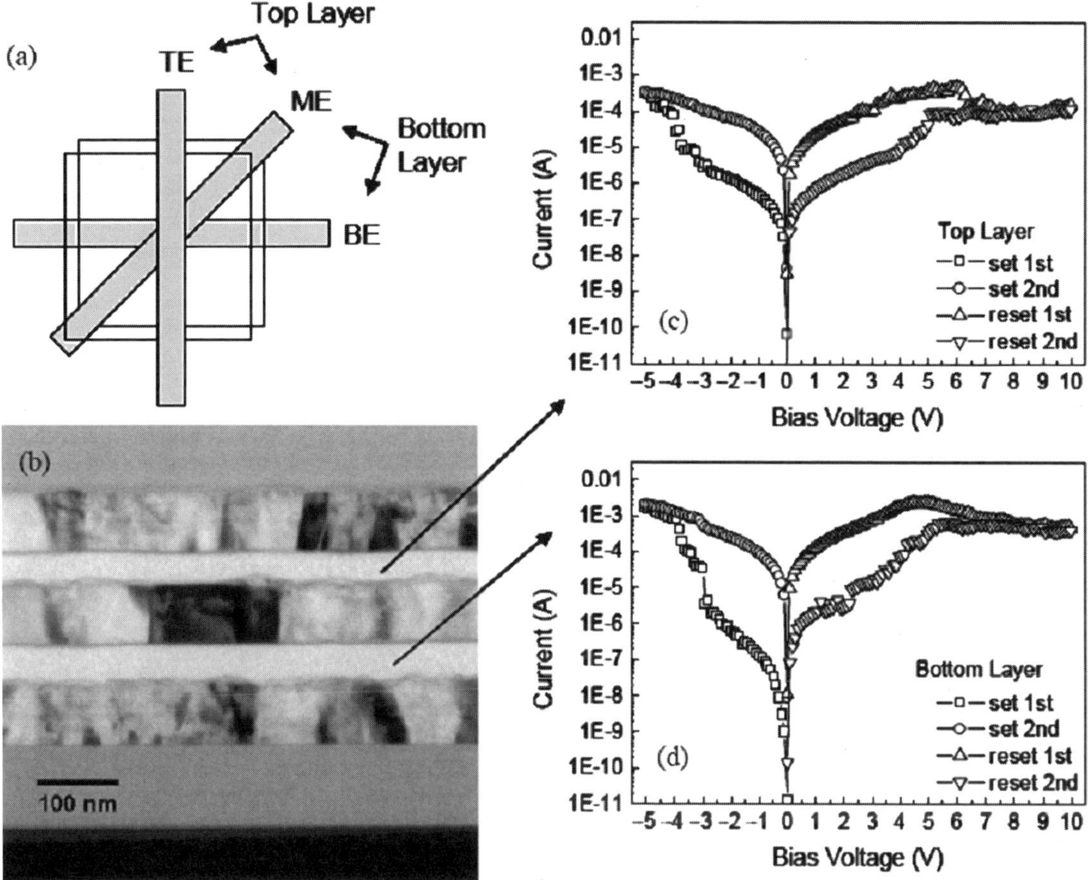

Figure 10. (a) Schematic diagram of a two-layer polymer memory device, (b) cross-sectional TEM image of the two-layer memory device, (c) I–V curve of the top layer device, and (d) I–V curve of the bottom layer device. Reprinted with permission from [27], B.-O. Cho et al., "International Electronic Devices Meeting," p. 1, San Francisco, CA, 2006. © 2006, IEEE.

of the top and bottom electrodes. For process simplicity, the top electrode is usually patterned using a shadow mask during the deposition process, and the narrowest width of the electrode is limited to a few hundred micrometers due to this shadow effect. However, for practical applications of organic memory, the device area of each memory cell has to be less than 1 μm^2 [1]. Devices as small as 200 × 200 nm have been reported in via-hole structures, demonstrating the scalability of the organic memory device [124]. To achieve such dimensions in a useful device structure, the electrode has to be patterned using lithographic methods instead of shadow masking. However, most of the organic materials and polymer used in memory devices are soluble in common organic solvents; therefore, they are incompatible with conventional photolithography.

Lee and colleagues circumvented this problem by using a direct metal transfer method to fabricate an 8 × 8 crossbar memory array with device area of 2 × 2 μm [125]. The top electrode was first patterned on a glass stamp and then transferred on to the active polymer layer by applying pressure and heat to the substrate. Using this technique, the underlying polymer is not exposed to solvents usually used in the patterning process. Although this method is promising because it removes the restrictions on the organic materials, conventional lithography remains the preferred method in large-scale production of the memory device.

In 2006, Samsung reported a two-layer memory device that used a thermally cured polyamide-based polymer blended with PCBM as the active layer [27]. After the polymer layer is cured at 300°C, it became insoluble in its original solvent. Thus, an additional layer can be spin-coated on top of it to form a second layer of the device (Fig. 10). The cured polymer layer is thermally robust to withstand multiple thermal cycles. Up to three layers of memory arrays have been demonstrated using this polyamide-based system [39].

Alternatively, semiconducting polymers can be cross-linked to achieve similar robustness against solvent and heat. A thermally cured semiconducting polymer like polyfluorene can be synthesized by attaching 4-phenylethenyl groups to the both ends of the polymer chain [33, 126, 127]. After spin-coating the polymer solution, the polymer film is cross-linked by heating the substrate to 150°C on a hotplate. Multilayer device architectures of organic memory have been demonstrated using these polymers [24].

Besides thermal curing, photocurable polymers were also used to fabricate memory devices. UV curable polymers are achieved by including an oxetane group to the main chain of the polymer [31, 43, 128]. A photo acid, selected based on its absorption spectra and solubility, is then added to the polymer blend. The cross-linking process of the oxetane group is triggered by the creation of photo acid when the polymer film is exposed to the UV light. Once the polymer chains

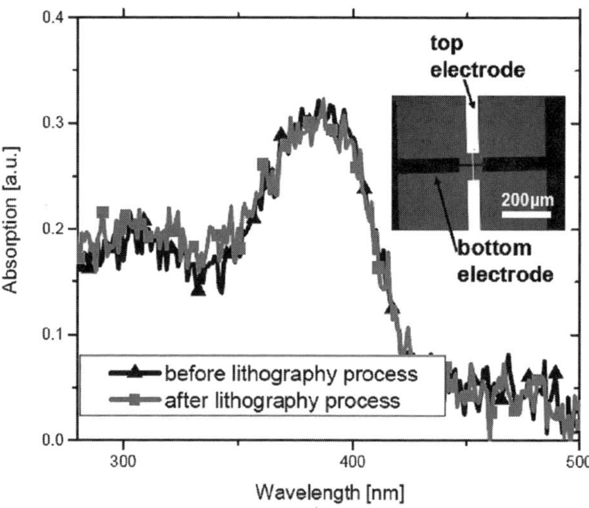

Figure 11. UV-Vis absorption spectra of the photo cross-linked polymer before and after the photolithography process. The two spectra did not change much, indicating that the cross-linked polymer is robust enough to withstand the lithography process. Inset: optical microscope image of a 4 × 4 μm polymer memory device. Reprinted with permission from [31], W. L. Kwan et al., "International Electronic Devices Meeting Technology Digest," p. 237, Washington DC, 2007. © 2007, IEEE.

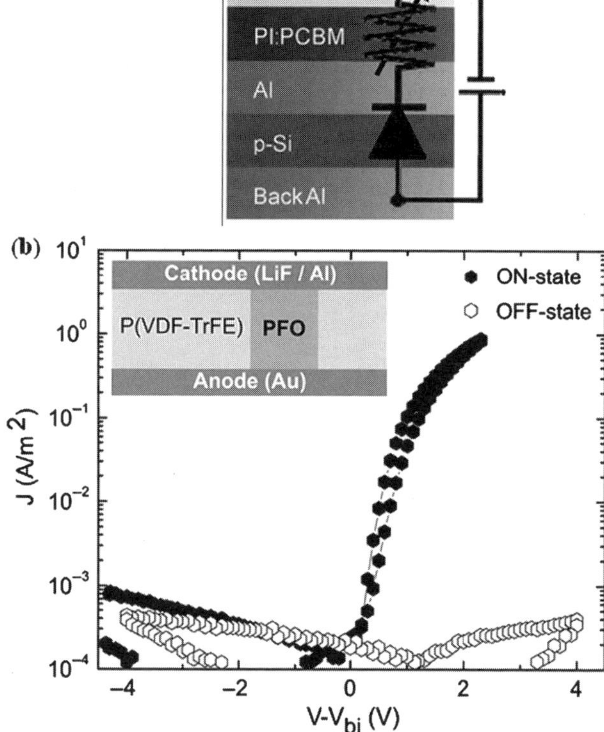

Figure 12. (a) Schematic diagram of a polymer memory with a silicon-based diode. Reprinted with permission from [38], B. Cho et al., *Adv. Mater.* 22, 1228 (2010). © 2010, Wiley-VCH Verlag GmbH & Co. KGaA. (b) *I–V* curve of a polymer ferroelectric-based memory diode. The diode is formed by using electrodes of different work function. Inset: schematic diagram of the device structure. Reprinted with permission from [129], K. Asadi et al., *Appl. Phys. Lett.* 97, 193308 (2010). © 2010, American Institute of Physics.

are cross-linked, the polymer film become robust enough to withstand photolithography and multiple coatings of the polymer. A 4 × 4 μm memory device and a two-layer cross-point memory array were fabricated using this UV-cured polymer (Fig. 11). One additional advantage of a UV curable polymer is that it enables the direct patterning of the polymer layer through a photomask, thus reducing the number of patterning steps in the process.

There are two main methods to achieve random addressability in memory devices: a one transistor-one resistor (1T-1R) with the transistor acting as the bit selector, and a one diode-one resistor (1D-1R) in a crosspoint array. The fabrication processes of the transistor and diode elements have to be compatible with organic memory processes. Kim et al. reported the integration of organic memory with a silicon field effect transistor [32]. In their process, the transistor was first fabricated on to a silicon substrate followed by the integration of the organic memory. This demonstrated the compatibility of the organic memory fabrication process with CMOS technology. Alternatively, memory elements can also be addressed individually by integrating a diode with the memory device in a crosspoint configuration (Figs. 12(a and b)) [38, 129, 130].

5. WORKING MECHANISM OF ORGANIC MEMORY

The working mechanism of the organic memory has been under much debate for a very long period of time. With the exception of copper ion, mobile ion, CuTCNQ, and polymer ferroelectric memories discussed in Section 4, of which the working mechanisms are relatively clearer with strong experimental evidences, the switching mechanism of the remaining resistive-based organic memories remains ambiguous. Despite the wide range of device architectures and materials used in these organic memories, the electrical characteristics remain remarkably similar. Therefore, it is not unreasonable to speculate that there exists an underlying mechanism that can explain the phenomena observed in an organic memory. In this section, a few of the major proposed mechanisms are discussed.

5.1. Electric-Field-Induced Charge Transfer

When a voltage pulse of a few volts in magnitude is applied to an organic film of about 100 nm, an electric field close to 1 MV/cm can be generated. It is believed that this electric field could induce a charge transfer between donors and acceptors within the organic film. An electron donor is usually a moiety, an organic molecule or a polymer with relatively higher LUMO level than the acceptor molecule. An acceptor can be a metallic or semiconductor nanoparticle, or an organic molecule. Examples of donors and acceptors can be found in figure (D–A). To prevent the backflow of charges after the charge transfer process, the donors and acceptors are separated by an insulating material.

The electric field induced charge transfer mechanism is used to explain the bipolar nature of some devices. Since a charge transfer complex is formed after the charge transfer process, it is postulated that the reverse process can be achieved by changing the polarity of the electric field. In Ma's three layer device, he explained that the change in resistance of his device is due to the induced charges in the organic film caused by the charged nanoparticles after the charge transfer process between the organic layers and the metallic nanoparticles [71]. In Ouyang's polymer devices with embedded gold nanoparticles and 8-hydroxyquinoline (8HQ), he suggested that the LUMO and HOMO levels become partially filled after the charge transfer process, resulting in an increase in the carrier concentration [22, 48, 79].

Capacitance measurements were done on the device to prove that there were trapped charges in the device after the charge transfer process. Figure 13 shows the result of one such experiment [71]. At the 'on' state, the device capacitance is an order of magnitude higher than the 'off' state. This shows that the extra charges trapped in the metal particles contributed to the increase in capacitance. Recent results from electrostatic force microscopy study also proved that gold nanoparticles in a polymer matrix could be used to store charges, while the insulating polymer acts as the insulator to prevent charge loss [131].

Ling et al. provided an alternative view on the electric-field-induced effect. He explained that a charge transfer complex, which can be either conductive [99] or insulating [34], can be formed after a threshold voltage is reached. The threshold voltage is determined by the charge injection barrier of the electron and the hole from the electrode. Once the threshold voltage is reached, electrons will start filling up the LUMO of the acceptor moiety and holes will fill up the HOMO of the donor moiety, forming a dipole between the positively charged donor and a negatively charged acceptor. Because the charge transfer state is not very stable, the process can be easily reversed by applying an opposite bias to the device.

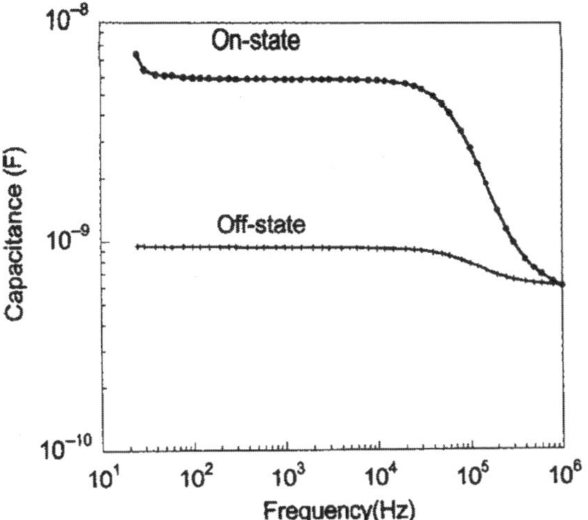

Figure 13. Capacitance versus frequency of an organic memory device at the 'on' and 'off' states. Reprinted with permission from [71], L. Ma et al., *Appl. Phys. Lett.* 82, 1419 (2003). © 2003, American Institute of Physics.

5.2. Charge Trap

As mentioned in Section 3.2, impurities can act as charge traps in organic material. Traps can also be intentionally introduced into the organic thin film by adding metallic or semiconducting nanoparticles to the host material [82–84, 132]. An electron trap is considered to be deep when the Fermi level lies above its energy level. At thermal equilibrium, the traps are filled based on Fermi-Dirac statistics. According to the space charge model introduced by Lampert and Mark [60], at the low-charge injection level, the device operates under the Ohm law because the injected charges are less than the thermal charge concentration in the material. As the voltage bias increases, more charges are injected into the device, thereby raising the quasi-Fermi level in the device and filling more deep level traps. The voltage at which all the deep level traps are filled is the trap-filled-limit voltage, denoted by V_{TFL}. After V_{TFL}, the current increases rapidly and reaches the same level as the trap-free SCLC [60]. Lin et al. used this model to describe the resistance-switching phenomena. In their device, they introduced gold nanoparticles to act as traps in PS.

Bozano et al. however, used the Simmons and Verderder model to explain the switching phenomena in organic-nanoparticles memories [13, 23]. According to the model, when the traps are empty, the device is at the low-resistance state. This is because the impurity band in the insulator is available for electrical conduction. When the voltage bias is increased beyond a maximum point, injected electrons cannot reach the impurity band due to the lowered band energies. As a result, the current that can flow through the device decreases even when the voltage increases (NDR). During this process, some of the charges are trapped near the top of the impurity band. These charges continue to remain there even after the voltage bias is removed from the device. The trapped charges create an internal electric field that lowers the impurity band of the insulator, thus reducing the probability of charge injection. These trapped charges can be removed by applying a large enough voltage to switch the device back to the low-resistance state.

5.3. Metal Oxide Switching

Cölle et al. first observed that the yield of organic memory devices is increased when a thin layer of aluminum oxide is inserted between the aluminum electrode and organic layer [67]. Since most organic memory devices used aluminum as electrode, Cölle et al. proposed that the resistive switching in organic memory devices could actually be due to the switching in the *oxide* layer, not the *organic* layer. It was suggested that the organic layer merely acts as a current limiting series resistor to the switching element. Resistive switching in metal oxide is a well-known effect [133], so it seems plausible that the aluminum oxide is the cause of the switching.

By using an infrared microscope, Cölle et al. noticed that most of the current flowed through a few hot spots in the device during the low-resistance state. As a result,

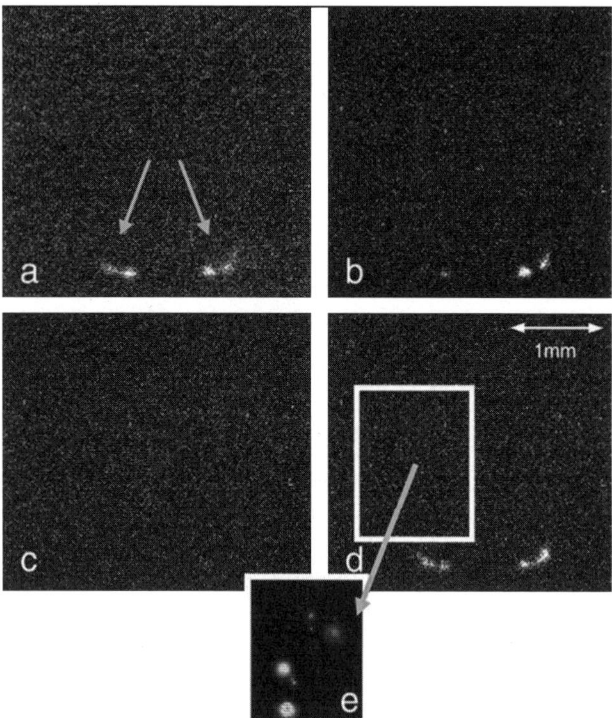

Figure 14. A series of infrared microscope images when the device is read at 1 V. The brighter spots indicate higher temperature that means higher current density. The device was switch from the 'on' state (a) to the intermediate state, (b) to the 'off' state, and (c) the 'on' state (d) again. The bright spots reappeared at the same positions as (a). This implies that filaments are actually not destroyed but reactivated, (e) enlarged image of (d) readapt 3 V. The bright spots indicate that the filaments are not just localized in a few spots but distributed around the device. Reprinted with permission from [67], M. Cölle et al., *Org. Electron.* 7, 305 (2006). © 2006, Elsevier.

the current density flowing through these hotspots is probably much higher than the limit organic materials can transport. They also observed that these hotspots kept reappearing at the same spots after multiple cycles of switching (Fig. 14). All these point to the fact that highly conductive filaments are formed in the organic film and the aluminum oxide acts as a switch to turn on or off the device.

Verbakel et al. extended this idea by fabricating a memory device consisting of solution-processable metal oxide nanoparticles sandwiched between a polymer layer and the electrode [134]. The switching behavior is similar to that of a polymer-based device, but no forming process was required.

One group, however, observed that oxide might not be the only cause of NDR in organic devices [135]. When studying electron-only devices for measuring electron mobility, they noticed that NDR does not occur if the bottom electrode is very smooth, even if a thin layer of oxide is present. They concluded that the surface inhomogeneities or surface roughness of the bottom electrode is the main reason why NDR is observed in organic devices [135].

5.4. Filament Formation

Filamentary switching in organic memory has been observed in various devices using a conductive atomic force microscope [136, 137], infrared microscope [40, 67], and scanning electron microscope (SEM) [6, 35]. Figure 15 shows the SEM image of the top electrode of an organic memory device after multiple cycles of switching [35]. The damages on the electrode show that the current density at those localized area is very high during the switching of the device. Formation and destruction of carbon [8], metallic [42, 43, 74, 92, 138–140], and other filamentary pathways [141–145] have been suggested to explain the filamentary nature of the device. However, due to the difficulty of directly observing the filaments, the precise nature and formation mechanism of the filaments are still not clear.

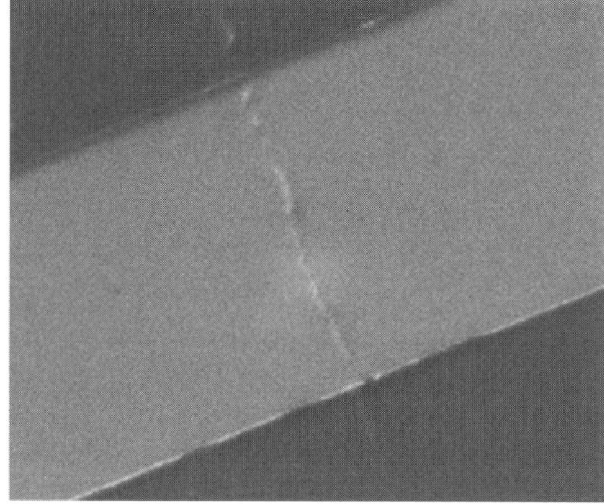

Figure 15. SEM image of the damage found on the top electrode of a polymer memory device. Reprinted with permission from [35], W. L. Kwan et al., *Philos. Trans. R. Soc. A* 367, 4159 (2009). © 2009, The Royal Society.

Electron microscopy has been widely used to study filament formation in inorganic memory. Filaments have been observed in both planar [146–148] and vertical device [149–150] structures in inorganic devices. It is only recently that the formation of the filament in organic memory has been directly observed using high-resolution transmission microscopy [43, 151]. Cross-sections of the polymer memory device were carefully prepared using a focused ion beam (Fig. 16). It was found that localized nonuniformity in the electrode is the cause of the filament formation [42, 43]. Figure 17 shows that gold atoms from the metal electrode were injected into organic film due to the enhanced electric field at the sharp edge of the electrode during the forming process. When the device was switched to the low-resistance state, a metallic bridge was formed between the top and bottom electrodes at these localized points (Fig. 16). The filament can be destroyed by Joule heating from the high current density when a high voltage is applied to the device. Transient current characteristics of the device (Fig. 18) show that the formation and rupture of the filaments is a dynamic process. During the period when the write and erase pulses were applied to the device, the current momentarily decreased and increased, possibly indicating the dynamic formation and annihilation of filaments. These processes could explain the relative instability shown by many devices in the NDR region of the device [42].

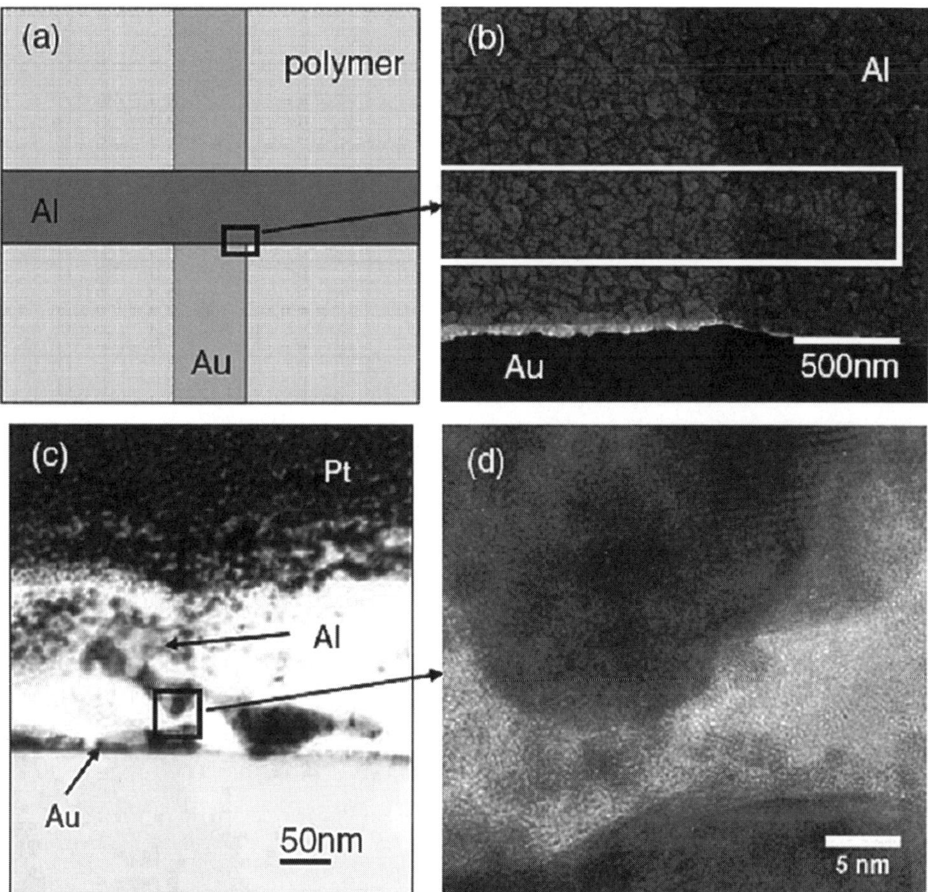

Figure 16. (a) Schematic diagram of the top view of a polymer memory device, (b) high magnification SEM image of the device showing slight damage to the to electrode, (c) cross-sectional TEM image of the area in (b), and (d) high-resolution TEM image of the box in (c), showing that a metallic bridge is formed between the top and bottom electrode. Reprinted with permission from [43], W. L. Kwan et al., *J. Appl. Phys.* 105, 124516 (2009). © 2009, American Institute of Physics.

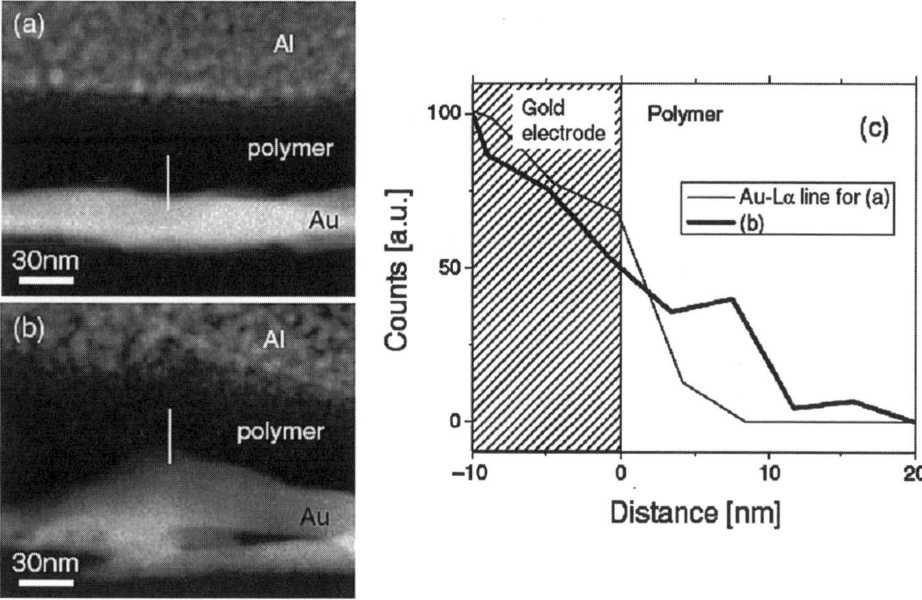

Figure 17. Cross-sectional STEM images of a polymer memory device. (a) The bottom electrode is flat, (b) the bottom electrode is protruding, and (c) TEM-EDS line scan data of the device at (a and b). This shows that when the electrode is irregular, more gold atms penetrated into the polymer after the forming process. Reprinted with permission from [43], W. L. Kwan et al., *J. Appl. Phys.* 105, 124516 (2009). © 2009, American Institute of Physics.

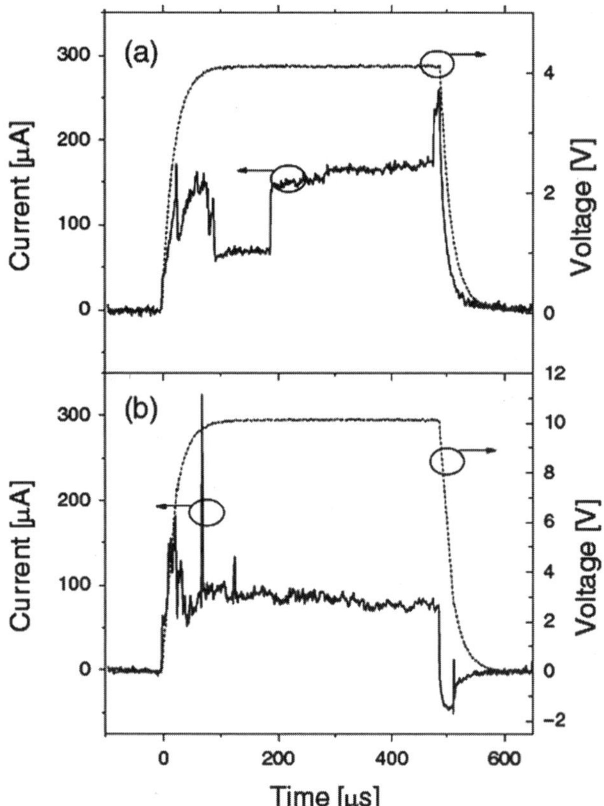

Figure 18. Transient current characteristics of the device during the write (a) process and erase (b) process. Current spikes during the write and erase pulse show that resistive switching of the device is a dynamic process. Reprinted with permission from [43], W. L. Kwan et al., *J. Appl. Phys.* 105, 124516 (2009). © 2009, American Institute of Physics.

6. SUMMARY AND OUTLOOK

In this chapter, the current status and understanding of organic memory has been summarized. Although no conclusion can be drawn on the switching mechanisms of organic memory, the latest experimental results show that we are much closer in achieving a unifying understanding.

Currently, organic memory is limited by its low cycling endurance and reproducibility. However, these obstacles can be overcome by a better understanding of the device mechanism through continual research and collaboration between physicists, chemists, material scientists, and engineers. Even though the device structure of an organic memory is very simple, many factors are known to affect the yield and electrical properties of the device, including the nanoscale morphology of polymer [145, 154], charge and ionic mobility [117–121], metal affinity of polymer [110], metal-organic interface [41, 67], nanostructure of electrodes [43, 135], and the testing environment [72, 73]. It is only recently that these factors have become better understood.

Although it has been shown that nano-size scaling is achievable and organic memory processes are compatible with CMOS processes, the best chance for the commercialization of organic memory lies in the area of disposable and flexible low-cost memory [152, 153]. For low cost application in radio frequency identity tags and disposable storage, the main concern is the cost, so compromise in performance can be tolerated. It is also expected that these devices are driven by low-power electronics; therefore, the power consumption of the organic memory device during switching needs to be closely examined in future research.

REFERENCES

1. L. D. Bozano and J. C. Scott, *Adv. Mater.* 19, 1452 (2007).
2. Y. Yang, J. Ouyang, L. Ma, R. J.-H. Tseng, and C.-W. Chu, *Adv. Funct. Mater.* 16, 1001 (2006).
3. Q.-D. Ling, D.-J. Liaw, C. Zhu, D. S.-H. Chan, E.-T. Kang, and K.-G. Neoh, *Prog. Polym. Sci.* 33, 917 (2008).
4. D. Prime and S. Paul, *Philos. Trans. R. Soc. A* 367, 4141 (2009).
5. "International Technology Roadmap for Semiconductors." 2009, http://www.itrs.net/.
6. H. Carchano, R. Lacoste, and Y. Segui, *Appl. Phys. Lett.* 19, 414 (1971).
7. H. K. Henisch and W. R. Smith, *Appl. Phys. Lett.* 24, 589 (1974).
8. L. F. Pender and R. J. Fleming, *J. Appl. Phys.* 46, 3426 (1975).
9. Y. Segui, B. Ai, and H. Carchano, *J. Appl. Phys.* 47, 140 (1976).
10. E. L. Cook, *J. Appl. Phys.* 41, 551 (1970).
11. M. Shatzkes, M. Av-Ron, and R. M. Anderson, *J. Appl. Phys.* 45, 2065 (1974).
12. G. Dearnaleya, D. V. Morgana, and A. M. Stonehama, *J. Non-Cryst. Solids* 4, 593 (1970).
13. J. G. Simmons and R. R. Verderber, *Proc. R. Soc. London Ser. A* 301, 77 (1967).
14. C. D. Dimitrakopoulos and P. R. L. Malenfant, *Adv. Mater.* 14, 99 (2002).
15. J. H. Burroughes, D. D. C. Bradley, A. R. Brown, R. N. Marks, K. Mackay, R. H. Friend, P. L. Burns, and A. B. Holmes, *Nature* 347, 539 (1990).
16. C. W. Tang and S. A. VanSlyke, *Appl. Phys. Lett.* 51, 913 (1987).
17. C. W. Tang, *Appl. Phys. Lett.* 48, 183 (1986).
18. V. Cimrová and D. Neher, *Synth. Met.* 76, 125 (1996).
19. J. Manta, W. Bijnens, R. Kiebooms, J. D'Haen, M. D'Olieslaeger, T.-D. Wu, W. D. Ceuninck, L. D. Schepper, D. Vanderzande, J. Gelan, and L. Stals, *Opt. Mater.* 9, 134 (1998).
20. S. Berleb, W. Batting, and M. Schwoere, *Synth. Met.* 102, 1034 (1999).
21. L. P. Ma, J. Liu, and Y. Yang, *Appl. Phys. Lett.* 80, 2997 (2002).
22. J. Ouyang, C.-W. Chu, C. R. Szmanda, L. Ma, and Y. Yang, *Nat. Mater.* 3, 918 (2004).
23. L. D. Bozano, B. W. Kean, V. R. Deline, J. R. Salem, and J. C. Scott, *Appl. Phys. Lett.* 84, 607 (2004).
24. L. Bozano, B. Kean, M. Beinhoff, K. Carter, P. Rice, and J. Scott, *Adv. Funct. Mater.* 15, 1933 (2005).
25. F. Verbakel, S. C. J. Meskers, and R. A. J. Janssen, *Appl. Phys. Lett.* 89, 102103 (2006).
26. C.-W. Chu, J. Ouyang, J.-H. Tseng, and Y. Yang, *Adv. Mater.* 17, 1440 (2005).
27. B.-O. Cho, T. Yasue, H. Yoon, M.-S. Lee, I.-S. Yeo, U-I. Chung, J.-T. Moon, and B.-I. Ryu, "International Electronic Devices Meeting," p. 1, San Francisco, CA, 2006.
28. L.-M. Chen, Z. Hong, W. L. Kwan, C.-H. Lu, Y.-F. Lai, B. Lei, C.-P. Liu, and Y. Yang, *ACS Nano* 4, 4744 (2010).
29. J. Bharathan and Y. Yang, *Appl. Phys. Lett.* 72, 2660 (1998).
30. F. C. Krebs, M. Jrgensen, K. Norrman, O. Hagemann, J. Alstrup, T. D. Nielsen, J. Fyenbo, K. Larsen, and J. Kristensen, *Sol. Energy Mater. Sol. Cells* 93, 422 (2009).
31. W. L. Kwan, R. J. Tseng, W. Wu, Q. Pei, and Y. Yang, "International Electronic Devices Meeting," p. 237, Washington DC, 2007.
32. T.-W. Kim, H. Choi, S.-H. Oh, G. Wang, D.-Y. Kim, H. Hwang, and T. Lee, *Adv. Mater.* 21, 2497 (2009).
33. M. Beinhoff, L. D. Bozano, J. C. Scott, and K. R. Carter, *Macromolecules* 38, 4147 (2005).

34. Q. Ling, Y. Song, S. J. Ding, C. Zhu, D. S. H. Chan, D.-L. Kwong, E.-T. Kang, and K.-G. Neoh, *Adv. Mater.* 17, 455 (2005).
35. W. L. Kwan, R. J. Tseng, W. Wu, Q. Pei, and Y. Yang, *Philos. Trans. R. Soc. A* 367, 4159 (2009).
36. M. Lauters, B. McCarthy, D. Sarid, and G. E. Jabbour, *Appl. Phys. Lett.* 89, 013507 (2006).
37. F. L. E. Jakobsson, X. Crispin, and M. Berggren, *Appl. Phys. Lett.* 87, 063503 (2005).
38. B. Cho, T.-W. Kim, S. Song, Y. Ji, M. Jo, H. Hwang, G.-Y. Jung, and T. Lee, *Adv. Mater.* 22, 1228 (2010).
39. S. Song, B. Cho, T.-W. Kim, Y. Ji, M. Jo, G. Wang, M. Choe, Y. H. Kahng, H. Hwang, and T. Lee, *Adv. Mater.* 22, 5048 (2010).
40. F. L. E. Jakobsson, X. Crispin, M. Cölle, M. Büchel, D. M. de Leeuw, and M. Berggren, *Org. Electron.* 8, 559 (2007).
41. F. Verbakel, S. C. J. Meskers, R. A. J. Janssen, H. L. Gomes, M. Cölle, M. Büchel, and M. D. de Leeuw, *Appl. Phys. Lett.* 91, 192103 (2007).
42. B. Lei, W. L. Kwan, Y. Shao, and Y. Yang, *Org. Electron.* 10, 1048 (2009).
43. W. L. Kwan, B. Lei, Y. Shao, S. V. Prikhodko, N. Bodzin, and Y. Yang, *J. Appl. Phys.* 105, 124516 (2009).
44. X. Zhou, J. He, L. S. Liao, M. Lu, X. M. Ding, X. Y. Hou, X. M. Zhang, X. Q. He, and S. T. Lee, *Adv. Mater.* 12, 265 (2000).
45. J. He, X. Zhou, J. R. Cao, K. L. Wang, L. S. Liao, Z. B. Deng, X. M. Ding, X. Y. Hou, and S. T. Lee, *Thin Solid Films* 363, 240 (2000).
46. S. Möller, C. Perlov, W. Jackson, C. Taussig, and S. R. Forrest, *Nature* 426, 166 (2003).
47. E. Y. H. Teo, Q. D. Ling, Y. Song, Y. P. Tan, W. Wang, E. T. Kang, D. S. H. Chan, and C. Zhu, *Org. Electron.* 7, 173 (2006).
48. J. Ouyang, C.-W. Chu, D. Sieves, and Y. Yang, *Appl. Phys. Lett.* 86, 123507 (2005).
49. S. Möller, S. R. Forrest, C. Perlov, W. Jackson, and C. Taussig, *J. Appl. Phys.* 94, 7811 (2003).
50. M. A. Mamo, W. S. Machado, W. A. L. van Otterlo, N. J. Coville, and I. A. Hümmelgen, *Org. Electron.* 11, 1858 (2010).
51. F. So, "Organic Electronics: Materials, Processing, Devices and Applications," CRC Press, Florida, USA, 2009.
52. R. Farchioni and G. Grosso, "Organic Electronic Materials: Conjugated Polymers and Low Molecular Weight Organic Solids." Spinger-Verlag, Berlin, Heidelberg, 2001.
53. M. Pope and C. E. Swenberg, "Electronic Processes in Organic Crystals and Polymers." 2nd Edition, Oxford University Press, New York, 1999.
54. V. Coropceanu, J. Cornil, D. A. da Silva Filho, Y. Olivier, R. Silbey, and J.-L. Brédas, *Chem. Rev.* 107, 926 (2007).
55. H. Bassler, *Phys. Status Solid B* 175, 15 (1993).
56. R. G. Kepler, *Phys. Rev.* 119, 1226 (1960).
57. O. H. Leblanc, *J. Chem. Phys.* 33, 626 (1960).
58. G. Horowitz, *Adv. Mater.* 10, 365 (1998).
59. W. L. Kwan, Stackable Polymer Memory Device and Its Working Mechanism, Ph.D. Dissertation, UCLA, 2009.
60. M. A. Lampert and P. Mark, "Current Injection in Solids." Academic Press, New York, 1970.
61. S. M. Sze, 'Physics of Semiconductor Devices." 2nd Edition, Wiley-Interscience, USA, 1981.
62. V. I. Arkhipov, U. Wolf, and H. Bassler, *Phys. Rev. B* 59, 7514 (1999).
63. V. I. Arkhipov, E. V. Emelianova, Y. H. Tak, and H. Bassler, *J. Appl. Phys.* 84, 848 (1998).
64. I. D. Parker, *J. Appl. Phys.* 75, 1656 (1994).
65. H. Ishii, K. Sugiyama, E. Ito, and K. Seki, *Adv. Mater.* 11, 605 (1999).
66. S. Braun, W. R. Salaneck, and M. Fahlman, *Adv. Mater.* 21, 1450 (2009).
67. M. Cölle, M. Büchel, and D. M. de Leeuw, *Org. Electron.* 7, 305 (2006).
68. B. Cho, S. Song, Y. Ji, and T. Lee, *Appl. Phys. Lett.* 97, 063305 (2010).
69. I. Maege, E. Jaehne, A. Henke, H.-J. P. Adler, C. Bram, C. Jung, and M. Stratmann, *Prog. Org. Coat.* 34, 1 (1997).
70. Y. Vaynzof, T. J. Dennes, J. Schwartz, and A. Kahn, *Appl. Phys. Lett.* 93, 103305 (2008).
71. L. Ma, S. Pyo, J. Ouyang, Q. Xu, and Y. Yang, *Appl. Phys. Lett.* 82, 1419 (2003).
72. H. P. Wang, S. Pigeon, R. Izquierdo, and R. Martel, *Appl. Phys. Lett.* 89, 183502 (2006).
73. H. P. Wang, S. Pigeon, R. Izquierdo, and R. Martel, *Mater. Res. Soc. Symp. Proc.* 997, 9 (2007).
74. T. Tsukamoto, S. Liu, and Z. Bao, *Jpn. J. Appl. Phys.* 46, 3622 (2007).
75. A. Prakash, J. Ouyang, J. L. Lin, and Y. Yang, *J. Appl. Phys.* 100, 054309 (2006).
76. P. Y. Lai and J. S. Chen, *Appl. Phys. Lett.* 93, 153305 (2008).
77. R. J. Tseng, J. Huang, J. Ouyang, R. B. Kaner, and Y. Yang, *Nano Lett.* 5, 1077 (2005).
78. R. J. Tseng, C. L. Tsai, L. P. Ma, J. Y. Ouyang, C. S. Ozkan, and Y. Yang, *Nat. Nanotechnol.* 1, 72 (2006).
79. J. Ouyang, C.-W. Chu, R. J. Tseng, A. Prakash, and Y. Yang, *Proc. IEEE* 93, 1287 (2005).
80. J. K. Baral, H. S. Majumdar, A. Laiho, H. Jiang, E. I. Kauppinen, R. H. A. Ras, J. Ruokolainen, O. Ikkala, and R. Österbacka, *Nanotechnology* 19, 035203 (2008).
81. S. Paul, A. Kanwal, and M. Chhowalla, *Nanotechnology* 17, 145 (2006).
82. F. Li, D.-I. Son, H.-M. Cha, S.-M. Seo, B.-J. Kim, H.-J. Kim, J. H. Jung, and T. W. Kim, *Appl. Phys. Lett.* 90, 222109 (2007).
83. F. Li, D.-I. Son, B. J. Kim, and T. W. Kim, *Appl. Phys. Lett.* 93, 021913 (2008).
84. F. Li, D.-I Son, S.-M. Seo, H.-M. Cha, H.-J. Kim, B. J. Kim, J. H. Jung, and T. W. Kim, *Appl. Phys. Lett.* 91, 122111 (2007).
85. D. G. Ma, M. Aguiar, J. A. Freire, and I. A. Hummelgen, *Adv. Mater.* 12, 1063 (2000).
86. A. Bandyopadhyay and A. J. Pal, *Chem. Phys. Lett.* 371, 86 (2003).
87. A. Bandhopadhyay and A. J. Pal, *J. Phys. Chem. B* 107, 2531 (2003).
88. A. Bandyopadhyay and A. J. Pal, *Appl. Phys. Lett.* 82, 1215 (2003).
89. A. Bandyopadhyay and A. J. Pal, *Appl. Phys. Lett.* 84, 999 (2004).
90. A. Szymanski, D. C. Larson, and M. M. Labes, *Appl. Phys. Lett.* 14, 88 (1969).
91. A. R. Elsharkawi and K. C. Kao, *J. Phys. Chem. Solids* 38, 95 (1977).
92. D. Tondelier, K. Lmimouni, D. Vuillaume, C. Fery, and G. Haas, *Appl. Phys. Lett.* 85, 5763 (2004).
93. A. K. Mahapatro, R. Agrawal, and S. Ghosh, *J. Appl. Phys.* 96, 3583 (2004).
94. W. Tang, H. Shi, G. Xu, B. S. Ong, Z. D. Popovic, J. Deng, J. Zhao, and G. Rao, *Adv. Mater.* 17, 2307 (2005).
95. M. Terai, K. Fujita, and T. Tsutsui, *Jpn. J. Appl. Phys. Part1* 45, 3754 (2006).
96. H. S. Majumdar, A. Bandyopadhyay, A. Bolognesi, and A. J. Pal, *J. Appl. Phys.* 91, 2433 (2002).
97. Q. D. Ling, Y. Song, S. L. Lim, E. Y. H. Teo, Y. P. Tan, C. X. Zhu, D. S. H. Chan, D. L. Kwong, E. T. Kang, and K. G. Neoh, *Angew. Chem. Int. Ed.* 45, 2947 (2006).
98. Y. Song, Q. D. Ling, C. Zhu, E. T. Kang, D. S. H. Chan, Y. H. Wang, and D.-L. Kwong, *IEEE Electron Device Lett.* 27, 154 (2006).
99. Q.-D. Ling, S.-L. Lim, Y. Song, C.-X. Zhu, D. S.-H. Chan, E.-T. Kang, and K.-G. Neoh, *Langmuir* 23, 312 (2007).
100. Q. D. Ling, F. C. Chang, Y. Song, C. X. Zhu, D. J. Liaw, D. S. H. Chan, E. T. Kang, and K. G. Neoh, *J. Am. Chem. Soc.* 128, 8732 (2006).

101. L. Li, Q. D. Ling, S. L. Lim, Y. P. Tan, C. Zhu, D. S. H. Chan, E. T. Kang, and K. G. Neoh, *Org. Electron.* 8, 401 (2007).
102. R. S. Potember, T. O. Poehler, and D. O. Cowan, *Appl. Phys. Lett.* 34, 405 (1979).
103. T. Oyamada, H. Tanaka, K. Matsushige, H. Sasabe, and C. Adachi, *Appl. Phys. Lett.* 83, 1252 (2003).
104. T. Kever, U. Böttger, C. Schindler, and R. Waser, *Appl. Phys. Lett.* 91, 083506 (2007).
105. J. Billen, S. Steudel, R. Müller, J. Genoe, and P. Heremans, *Appl. Phys. Lett.* 91, 263507 (2007).
106. A. Hefczyc, L. Beckmann, E. Becker, H. H. Johannes, and W. Kowalsky, *Phys. Status Solid A* 205, 647 (2008).
107. R. Müller, C. Krebs, L. Goux, D. J. Wouters, J. Genoe, P. Heremans, S. Spiga, and M. Fanciulli, *IEEE Electron Device Lett.* 30, 620 (2009).
108. R. Waser and M. Aono, *Nat. Mater.* 6, 833 (2007).
109. L. Ma, Q. Xu, and Y. Yang, *Appl. Phys. Lett.* 84, 4908 (2004).
110. W.-J. Joo, T.-L. Choi, J. Lee, S. K. Lee, M.-S. Jung, N. Kim, and J. M. Kim, *J. Phys. Chem. B* 110, 23812 (2006).
111. W.-J. Joo, T.-L. Choi, K.-H. Lee, and Y. Chung, *J. Phys. Chem. B* 111, 7756 (2007).
112. W.-J. Joo, T.-L. Choi, and K.-H. Lee, *Thin Solid Films* 516, 3133 (2008).
113. A. G. MacDiarmid, *Rev. Mod. Phys.* 73, 701 (2001).
114. L. Edman, M. A. Summers, S. K. Buratto, and A. J. Heeger, *Phys. Rev. B* 70, 115212 (2004).
115. Q. Pei, G. Yu, C. Zhang, Y. Yang, and A. J. Heeger, 269, 1086 (1995).
116. J. C. deMello, N. Tessler, S. C. Graham, and R. H. Friend, *Phys. Rev. B* 57, 12951 (1998).
117. Q. Lai, Z. Zhu, Y. Chen, S. Patil, and F. Wudl, *Appl. Phys. Lett.* 88, 133515 (2006).
118. J. H. Zhao, D. J. Thomson, R. G. Pillai, and M. S. Freund, *Appl. Phys. Lett.* 94, 092113 (2009).
119. Q. Lai, L. Zhang, Z. Li, W. F. Stickle, R. S. Williams, and Y. Chen, *Appl. Phys. Lett.* 95, 213503 (2009).
120. J. Smits, S. J. Meskers, R. Janssen, A. Marsman, and D. de Leeuw, *Adv. Mater.* 17, 1169 (2005).
121. J. H. Krieger, S. V. Trubin, S. B. Vaschenko, and N. F. Yudanov, *Synth. Met.* 122, 199 (2001).
122. R. C. G. Naber, K. Asadi, P. W. M. Blom, D. M. de Leeuw, and B. de Boer, *Adv. Mater.* 22, 933 (2010).
123. K. Asadi, D. M. de Leeuw, B. de Boer, and P. W. M. Blom, *Nat. Mater.* 7, 547 (2008).
124. T.-W. Kim, H. Choi, S.-H. Oh, M. Jo, G. Wang, B. Cho, D.-Y. Kim, H. Hwang, and T. Lee, *Nanotechnology* 20, 025201 (2009).
125. T.-W. Kim, K. Lee, S.-H. Oh, G. Wang, D.-Y. Kim, G.-Y. Jung, and T. Lee, *Nanotechnology* 19, 405201 (2008).
126. G. Klärner, J.-I. Lee, V. Y. Lee, E. Chan, J.-P. Chen, A. Nelson, D. Markiewicz, R. Siemens, J. C. Scott, and R. D. Miller, *Chem. Mater.* 11, 1800 (1999).
127. J. P. Chen, G. Klaerner, J. I. Lee, D. Markiewicz, V. Y. Lee, R. D. Miller, and J. C. Scott, *Synth. Met.* 107, 129 (2000).
128. C. D. Müller, A. Falcou, N. Reckefuss, M. Rojahn, V. Wiederhirn, P. Rudati, H. Frohne, O. Nuyken, H. Becker, and K. Meerholz, *Nature* 421, 829 (2003).
129. K. Asadi, M. Li, N. Stingelin, P. W. M. Blom, and D. M. de Leeuw, *Appl. Phys. Lett.* 97, 193308 (2010).
130. E. Y. H. Teo, C. Zhang, S. L. Lim, E.-T. Kang, D. S. H. Chan, and C. Zhu, *IEEE Electron Device Lett.* 30, 487 (2009).
131. D. Prime and S. Paul, *Appl. Phys. Lett.* 96, 043120 (2010).
132. H.-T. Lin, Z. Pei, and Y.-J. Chan, *IEEE Electron Device Lett.* 28, 569 (2007).
133. A. Sawa, *Mater. Today* 11, 28 (2008).
134. F. Verbakel, S. C. J. Meskers, D. M. de Leeuw, and R. A. J. Janssen, *J. Phys. Chem. C* 112, 5254 (2008).
135. R. Steyrleuthner, S. Bange, and D. Neher, *J. Appl. Phys.* 105, 064509 (2009).
136. S. Baek, D. Lee, J. Kim, S.-H. Hong, O. Kim, and M. Ree, *Adv. Funct. Mater.* 17, 2637 (2007).
137. T.-W. Kim, S.-H. Oh, H. Choi, G. Wang, H. Hwang, D.-Y. Kim, and T. Lee, *Appl. Phys. Lett.* 92, 253308 (2008).
138. J. Tyczkowski, *Thin Solid Films* 199, 335 (1991).
139. C.-M. Huang, Y.-S. Liu, C.-C. Chen, K.-H. Wei, and J.-T. Sheu, *Appl. Phys. Lett.* 93, 203303 (2008).
140. C.-L. Liu, J.-C. Hsu, W.-C. Chen, K. Sugiyama, and A. Hirao, *ACS Appl. Mater. Interface* 1, 1974 (2009).
141. M. L. Wang, J. Zhou, X. D. Gao, B. F. Ding, Z. Shi, X. Y. Sun, X. M. Ding, and X. Y. Hou, *Appl. Phys. Lett.* 91, 143511 (2007).
142. S. G. Hahm, S. Choi, S.-H. Hong, T. J. Lee, S. Park, D. M. Kim, J. C. Kim, W. Kwon, K. Kim, M.-J. Kim, O. Kim, and M. Ree, *J. Mater. Chem.* 19, 2207 (2009).
143. T. J. Lee, C.-W. Chang, S. G. Hahm, K. Kim, S. Park, D. M. Kim, J. Kim, W.-S. Kwon, G.-S. Liou, and M. Ree, *Nanotechnology* 20, 135204 (2009).
144. T. J. Lee, S. Park, S. G. Hahm, D. M. Kim, K. Kim, J. Kim, W. Kwon, Y. Kim, T. Chang, and M. Ree, *J. Phys. Chem. C* 113, 3855 (2009).
145. M. Vilkman, K. Solehmainen, A. Laiho, H. G. O. Sandberg, and O. Ikkala, *Org. Electron.* 10, 1478 (2009).
146. H. Pagnia and N. Sotnik, *Phys. Status Solid A* 108, 11 (1988).
147. Y. Hirose and H. Hirose, *J. Appl. Phys.* 47, 2767 (1976).
148. Y. Naitoh, M. Horikawa, H. Abe, and T. Shimizu, *Nanotechnology* 17, 5669 (2006).
149. M. Saji and K. C. Kao, *J. Non-Cryst. Solids* 22, 223 (1976).
150. G. S. Park, X.-S. Li, D.-C. Kim, R.-J. Jung, M.-J. Lee, and S. Seo, *Appl. Phys. Lett.* 91, 222103 (2007).
151. W. L. Kwan, B. Lei, Y. Shao, and Y. Yang, *Curr. Appl. Phys.* 10, e50 (2010).
152. A. Laiho, H. S. Majumdar, J. K. Baral, F. Jansson, R. Osterbacka, and O. Ikkala, *Appl. Phys. Lett.* 93, 203309 (2008).

CHAPTER 11

Material, Device, and Circuit of Organic Nonvolatile Memory

Zingway Pei[1], Heng-Tien Lin[2]

[1]*Graduate Institute of Optoelectronic Engineering, Department of Electrical Engineering, National Chung Hsing University, 250 Ku-Kang Rd., Taichung, 40227, Taiwan, R.O.C.*
[2]*Circuit and System Design Technology Department, Flexible Electronics Technology Division, Electronics and Optoelectronics Research Laboratories, Industrial Technology Research Institute (ITRI), 195, Sec. 4, Chung Hsing Rd., Chutung, Hsinchu, 31040, Taiwan, R.O.C.*

CONTENTS

ISBN: 1-58883-251-1

Nonvolatile Memories: Materials, Devices and Applications
Edited by Tseung-Yuen Tseng and Simon M. Sze
Volume 2: Pages: 265–287

1. INTRODUCTION OF ORGANIC NONVOLATILE BISTABLE MEMORY (ONBM)

1.1. Motivation

In recent years, there has been a growing interest in flexible electronics for their potential advantages of user friendly, lightweight, low cost, and safety on plastic substrate. The progress of the organic light-emitting diodes (OLEDs) for high-performance display in the past few years [1, 2] have proven organic materials as promising candidates in the manufacturing of flexible optoelectronics. Besides OLEDs, the devices fabricated from organic materials also include photovoltaic cells [3], sensors [4], and thin film transistors [5]. However, to extend the application of organic materials to varieties of flexible electronics, such as radio-frequency identification (RFID)-tags, electronic papers, and electronic signs, a memory is a necessary device to store information.

There is an enormous effort to develop new memory devices. In general, three features are requested for the new memory. They include the high operation speed, nonvolatility, and low cost. Many methods have been reported for achieving memory that fulfills the above-mentioned requirement. They include phase-change memory [6, 7, 20, 21], mechanical switches [8, 9], quantized atomic switches [10], quantum dots [11, 12], and nanocrystal memory [13], ferroelectric random access memory (RAM) [16, 17], magnetic random access memory [18, 19]. For the flexible electronics, they strongly demand low cost and simple process. An organic nonvolatile memory with simple processes and a high performance on plastic substrate is an adequate candidate for flexible electronics [14, 15].

1.2. Overview

The organic memory devices are basically categorized by two types of structure: two terminal bistable [50–55] and three terminal transistor-like memory devices [16, 17]. The two terminal bistable memory devices offer the advantages of a low-operation voltage and a simple process over three terminal transistor-like devices. Therefore, much attention is paid to bistable organic memory devices. The two-terminal organic nonvolatile bistable memory (ONBM) is a resistance-based memory. The memory states are determined by the resistance. Devices incorporating switchable resistive materials are generically classified as resistive random access memory (RRAM). The RRAM element switching between high and low resistances is achieved by means of an appropriate electrical pulse, and the read-out process consists of applying a lower voltage to probe the state of the resistance. A number of organic device structures have been reported to show resistive switching. By the organic material system, they could be classified as a simple polymer [22–24], small molecules [25–29], mobile ion [30–39], donor–acceptor complex [40–48] and nano-particles [49–61] as shown in Figure 1. The structure, material, and switching properties have been reviewed in details in a previous work [62]. The general behavior of organic bistable memory is described as follows: Upon applied voltage, which exceeds a certain value, the conductivity changes abruptly from a low-conductivity state to a high-conductivity state with a difference of several orders of magnitude. This high-conductivity state will be memorized until a negative (or larger positive) bias is applied to erase it. Although many groups have explored the ONBM, which exhibits an interesting performance, they are far from practical applications in memories, especially the endurance and retention time. Besides, the carrier transport path is rarely investigated, especially the rapid increase on the current from a low-conductivity state to a high-conductivity state of the conductive mechanism.

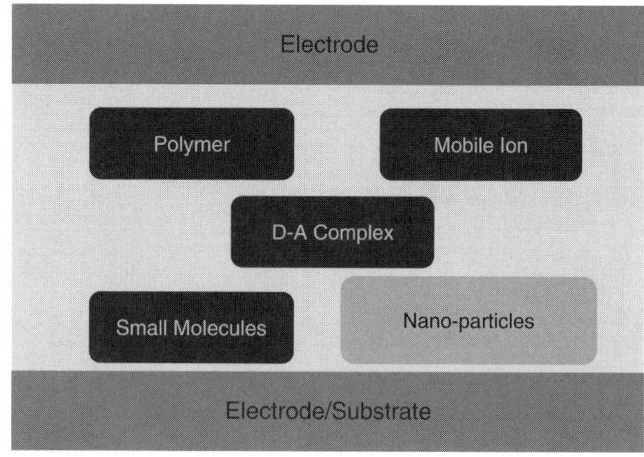

Figure 1. The building blocks of the organic material systems used in a two-terminal nonvolatile bistable memory.

1.3. Organization

In this review, we will focus on the transport mechanism, stability, and circuit of nano-particles based organic nonvolatile bistable memory; for a specific reason, the progress of this type of memory is moved ahead over other type of organic memories.

In Section 2, the gold nanoparticles (Au–NPs) were embedded in polymer to fabricate the memory in Al/PS + Au–NPs/Al structure to study the transport mechanism. Through the comparison to pure postscript device, the memory is correlated to the presence of the Au–NPs. A trap-filled space-charge-limited current (SCLC) model is proposed to explain the transport mechanism in this memory device. The experimental results fit the theoretical prediction quite well. The retention time for this device is more than 400 minutes. The light-induced conductivity change further supports the SCLC model.

In Section 3, the polymer chain is used to stabilize gold nanoparticles and blend in the host polymer as the memory active layer to get a stable ONBM. Therefore, the Al/polymer + Au − Polymer/Al memory device is demonstrated. The transmission electron microscopy (TEM) image shows the polymer stabilized Au–NPs are well dispersed in the polymer matrix. The electrical bi-stability of the device can be precisely controlled by applying a positive voltage pulse or a negative voltage pulse, respectively. Two orders of magnitude current difference between the on and off state can be easily achieved under air environment. This memory can be switched on and off more than 2000 times without appreciable performance degradation. In addition, the memory state can be retained for over 3 days in air environment.

In Section 4, a 16-byte addressable ONBM array on the plastic substrate has been demonstrated. The memory cell can be switched on and off for more than 1,000 times and the longest retention time without functional failure can be estimated to be nearly 1 year in the air. In the analysis of the mechanical flexibility, the electrical properties of this ONBM are fairly stable during the application of compressive stress down to 5 mm in bending radius. After connecting the ONBM array to the current-sensing circuit, the ONBM array can be correctly addressed and operated while maintaining low-power consumption.

In Section 5, an ultraviolet (UV) light erasable stacked diode-switch ONBM (DS-ONBM) using polymer stabilized Au–NPs on the plastic substrate in the ambient air was demonstrated. The absorption spectrum of the gold nanoparticles shows UV absorption. Therefore, UV light was used to erase data in the DS-ONBM. The function of UV-erasing and the diode-switch could greatly simplify the required peripheral circuits. This DS-ONBM was demonstrated to be able to read, write, and retain the data and was reusable by UV light illumination. Hence, the UV-erasable DS-ONBM was fully applicable for key applications in printed electronics.

2. TRANSPORT MECHANISM OF GOLD NANOPARTICLE-BASED ONBM

The memory devices utilize nanomaterials exhibit distinguished bistable memory characteristics. The most popular material system was reported by Ounyang and colleagues [54] who utilized gold nanoparticles and 8-hydroxyqulinone in acceptor–donor pairs embedded in the polystyrene (PS) matrix to form a diode-type device. Upon applied voltage, which exceeds a certain value, the conductivity changes abruptly from a low-conductivity state to a high-conductivity state with a difference of several orders of magnitude. This high-conductivity state will be memorized until a negative bias is applied to erase it. Despite the superior performance, the mechanisms for the bistable memory are not understood at that time. The proposed mechanisms suggest that current transport through available energy levels is accomplished either by internal charge transfer between the donor–acceptor pairs or by the hopping process due to the charged or non-charged metallic nanomaterials based on the Simmons and Verderber (SV) model [63]. Although these models can give a reasonable explanation on the bistable states of the nanomaterial-based memory, the carrier transport path is not clear, especially the rapid increase on the current from a low-conductivity state to a high-conductivity state and the unusual switching to a low-conductivity state based on the presence of light. Since those models are based on charge transfer through the nanomaterials, devices with only one nanomaterial are better explored to clarify the charge transport mechanism for a memory effect in an organic memory [64]. The device with a pure

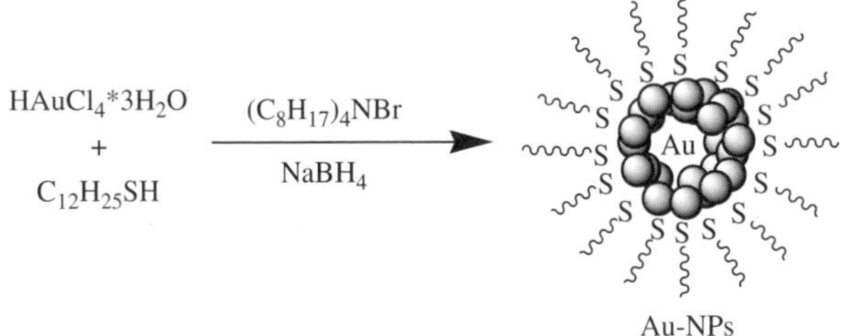

Figure 2. The schematic diagram of the Brust-Schiffrin method for the preparation of AuNPs.

host dielectric material (polystyrene) was also fabricated to clarify the possible memory effect of the host material.

2.1. Device Fabrication Process

An organic bistable nonvolatile memory was fabricated by dissolved Au nanoparticles in the PS matrix. The experimental preparation and purification procedure of gold nanoparticles was by the Brust-Schiffrin method (Fig. 2). It is a two-phase synthesis and stabilization of metal nanoparticles [65]. An accurate determination of particle size distributions is crucial for developing nanoscale electronic devices with advanced functionality because the electronic structure of gold nanoparticles is size dependent [66–70]. A conventional method for determining the size of nanoparticles is through TEM [71]. Au–NPs were prepared with a size distribution of 2–5 nm.

The memory devices were prepared through the following processes. At first, glass substrates were cleaned by detergent solution, de-ionized water, acetone, and isopropanol (IPA) using ultrasonic cleaner for 20 minutes, sequentially; and then, they were dried in a vacuum oven for 30 minutes at 105°C. Prior to the bottom electrode deposition, the glass substrates were treated in a UV-ozone environment for 30 minutes. After this process, a 75-nm thick aluminum (Al) bottom electrode was deposited by a thermal evaporator at a base pressure of 2×10^{-6} Torr using a shadow metal mask attached to it. The UV-ozone treatment was repeated again to activate the Al surface. The PS organic film with 1-dodecanethiol protected Au–NPs was spin-coated sequentially. The solution containing Au–NPs and PS was prepared with 0.4% and 1.2% by weight in 1,2-dichlorobenzene, respectively, under a nitrogen environment. The thickness of organic film was about 30 nm and was determined by the TEM. An Al layer was then deposited in a thermal evaporator using a second shadow mask as the top electrode. The area for the memory cell was 0.2×0.2 mm^2. The process flow of Al/PS + Au–NPs/Al organic memory is schematically shown in Figure 3, while the cross-sectional TEM images of Al/PS + Au NPs/Al devices are shown in Figure 4.

2.2. Electrical Characteristics of the Device

The current–voltage (*I–V*) characteristics of the memory devices were measured by an HP 4156A semiconductor analyzer in air (Fig. 5). A low-conductivity state, approximately 10^{-9} A, was recorded from 0 to 1.5 volt for the first voltage scan, which was corresponding to "0" state of a bistable

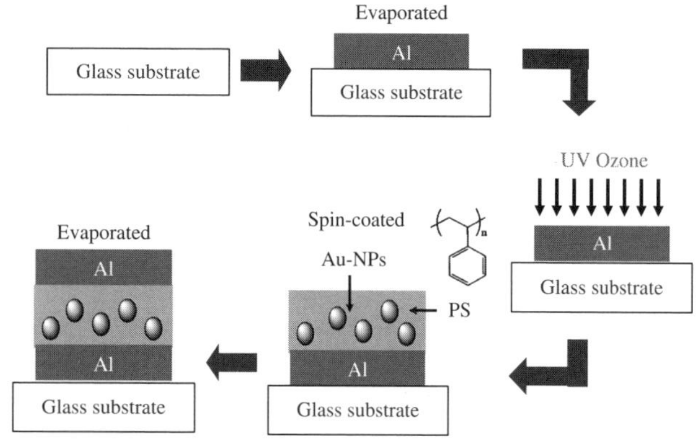

Figure 3. The process steps for fabricating the Al/PS + Au nanoparticles/Al organic bistable memory.

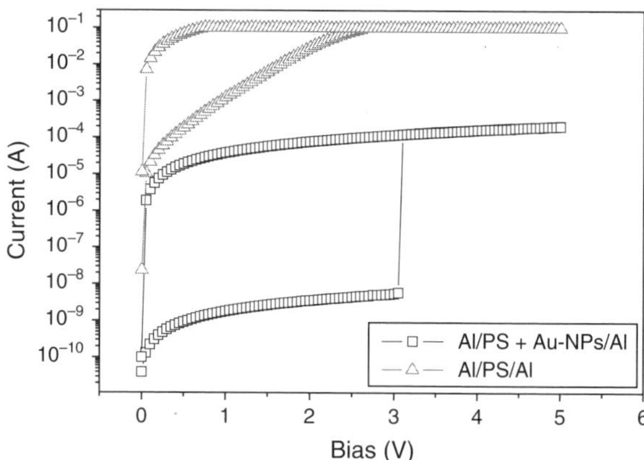

Figure 5. The *I–V* curves of the Al/PS + AuNPs/Al memory and the PS memory. Reprinted with permission from [64], H. T. Lin et al., *IEEE Electron Device Lett.* 28, 569 (2007). © 2007, IEEE.

memory. The device kept in the low-conductivity state until the applied voltage approaching to 3 V; then, a remarkable abrupt current transition from 10^{-9} to 10^{-4} A was observed. After this transition, the current through the memory device remained at an order of 10^{-4} A even at a low voltage, which manifested a nonvolatile characteristic. This situation indicated a high-conductivity state, which was corresponding to "1" state of a memory. The operation window for this memory was therefore four to five orders of magnitude. The high-conductivity states could be sustained for more than 400 minutes in a dark ambient environment. However, once this device was exposed to optical illumination, it switched back to a low-conductivity state immediately (Fig. 6). For comparison, the memory device using a pure PS without adding Au–NPs was also fabricated. Although the *I–V* behavior showed a memory effect, the abrupt current transition was not observed and the memory window was quite small when compared with the Al/PS + Au–NPs/Al memory. This implied that the abrupt current transition was strongly correlated to the presence of Au–NPs.

2.3. Carrier Transport Mechanism

Several mechanisms were commonly proposed to explain the abrupt current transition in a dielectric film. They were the intermediated-state enhanced tunneling transport [72], the traps-filled process affected by SCLC transport [73], the formation of the filament path [74], and the SV model as mentioned above. For the intermediate state tunneling process, an abrupt current transition is expected; but, the current will not remain in a high-conductivity state after the next voltage sweep. The formation of the conductive filament path was also not the mechanism for our memory since the permanent memory effect was not observed; the high conductance disappears immediately after light illumination. The SV model had an *N*-shaped *I–V* characteristic, and the pristine device was in a low-conductivity state. These phenomena were different from the characteristics, which we observed. The remaining possible mechanism was the trap-filled SCLC current model.

To examine this possibility, the *I–V* characteristics of the memory depicted in a log *I*–log *V* chart shown in Figure 7. Four major regions for the *I–V* relationship can be easily distinguished. At low voltages, from 0 to around 0.5 V, the current increased linearly with the increase of the bias voltage (region I). Then, the current showed the voltage-square dependence for the bias voltage between ~0.5 and

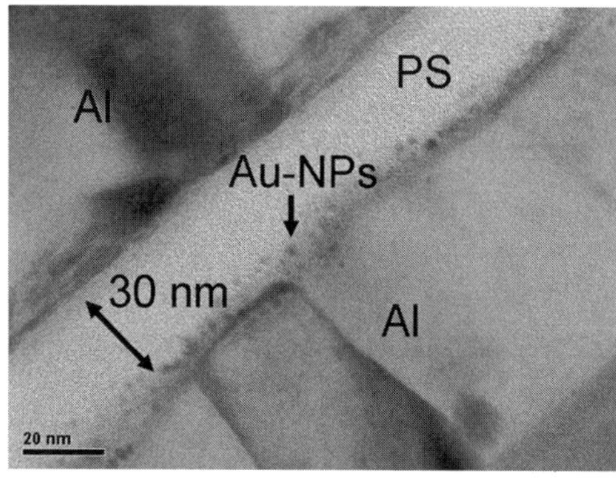

Figure 4. The cross section TEM image of the organic bistable memory. The AuNPs aggregate together.

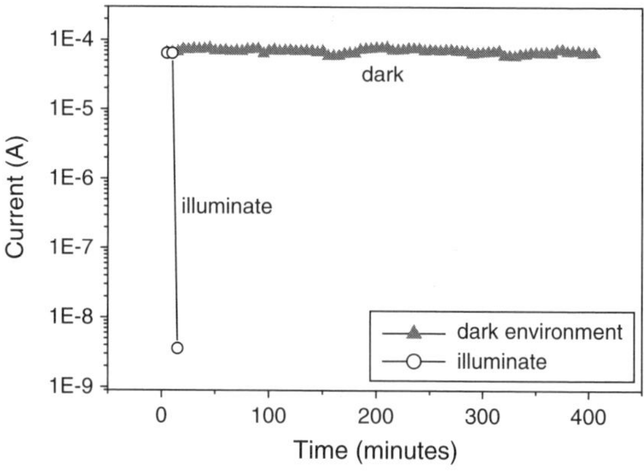

Figure 6. The retention test of the Al/PS + AuNPs/Al memory in a high-conductivity state could be sustained for more than 400 minutes in a dark ambient environment. This device was exposed to optical illumination; it switched back to a low-conductivity state immediately.

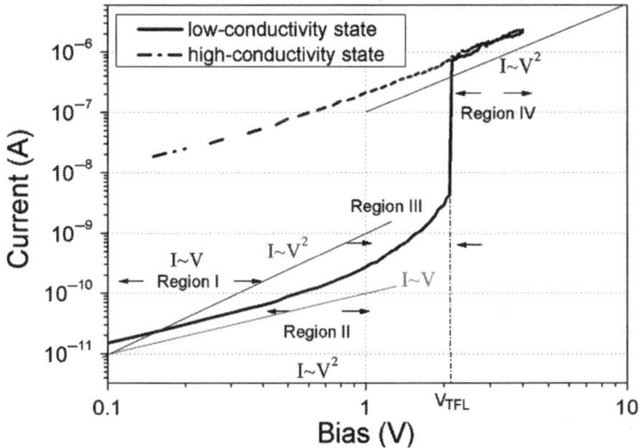

Figure 7. The log I–log V curves of Al/PS + Au–NPs/Al bistable memory. Reprinted with permission from [64], H. T. Lin et al., *IEEE Electron Device Lett.* 28, 569 (2007). © 2007 IEEE.

1.5 V (region II). With a continuous increase of bias voltage, the current increased exponentially until it reached an abrupt current transition voltage, which was marked as "VTFL" (region III). After VTFL, the current showed the voltage-square dependence again (region IV).

The I–V characteristic for the trap-filled SCLC transport was proposed by Lampert and Mark [73]. In addition to the writing process, the current at a high-conductivity state also showed a voltage-square dependence. A theoretical model of the shallow trap-affected current through a dielectric layer sandwiched by two electrodes in which the Fermi level of the dielectric lies below the shallow trap level had been derived [73] by the following two equations for "with traps" and "traps filled," respectively:

$$J = \frac{9n\varepsilon\mu}{8n_t}(V^2/L^3), \quad \text{(with traps)} \tag{1}$$

and

$$J = \frac{9\varepsilon\mu}{8n_t}(V^2/L^3), \quad \text{(traps filled)} \tag{2}$$

where J was the transport current, n was the free carrier concentration and was proportional $\exp(qV/KT)$, n_t was the concentration of trapped charge, ε was the dielectric constant of the dielectric layer, μ was free carrier mobility, V was the applied voltage, and L was the dielectric layer thickness. The depictions of this mechanism were schematically shown in Figures 2–9(a to d). At low voltages (Fig. 8(a)), the current was due to the thermally generated free carriers, which showed a linear voltage dependence. At a higher applied electric field (Fig. 8(b)), the carriers injected into the dielectric were from a thermionic process across the barrier. As a consequence, n was much lower than n_t. The I–V follows (1), which showed a V^2 dependence. With further applied voltage (Fig. 8(c)), in addition to thermionic emission, Fowler–Nordeim tunneling may occur where the injected carriers, n, increased rapidly and the traps were nearly filled. The current thus had an exponential relationship to voltage instead of V^2 dependence. At the last stage with the highest applied voltage (Fig. 8(d)), the traps were completely filled; the I–V characteristics follow the trap-filled model. As described in (2), which the

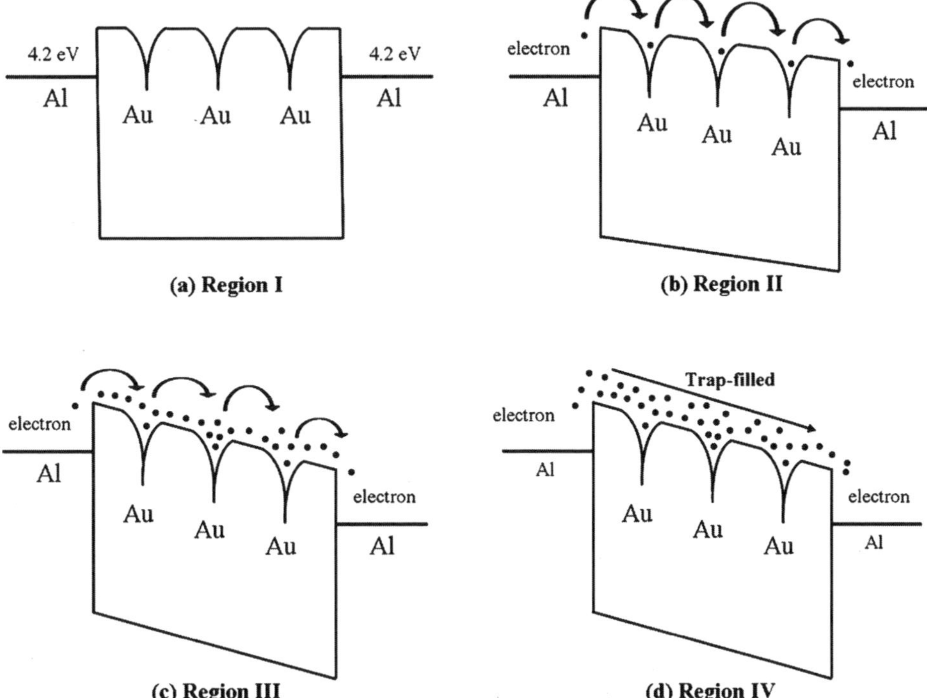

Figure 8. Schematic band diagrams for the transport mechanism of trapped-filled SCLC. (a) Region I: thermally generated carrier conduction, (b) region II: with traps, (c) region III: nearly filled, and (d) region IV: traps filled. Reprinted with permission from [64], H. T. Lin et al., *IEEE Electron Device Lett.* 28, 569 (2007). © 2007, IEEE.

current once back to have a V^2 dependence but with a constant 9/8 instead of n/n_t dependence in (1). Since the ratio of n/n_t was rather small in region II, and the trap-filled current was much higher than the current with traps, the *I–V* characteristics exhibited an abrupt enhancement.

In the Al/PS + Au–NPs/Al memory device, Au–NPs exhibited a work function around 5.1 eV, which was lower than the lowest occupied molecular orbit of PS. Therefore, Au–NPs can be treated as a trap in the PS. As a consequence, the current in our memory at regions I, II, III, and IV of Figure 7 can be explained by the trap-filled SCLC model, which fit the experimental results rather well.

To summarize, the Al/PS + Au–NPs/Al memory devices were demonstrated in this section. The *I–V* characteristics showed that the device switches from an initial low-conductivity state to a high-conductivity state upon application of external electric field at room temperatures. The current transition exhibited in a very narrow voltage range, causing an abrupt increase of the current. The conduction mechanism in nanoparticles contained polymer memory was experimentally and theoretically investigated. Through the comparison to a pure PS device, the memory was correlated due to the presence of the Au–NPs. A trap-filled SCLC model was proposed to explain the transport mechanism in this memory device. The experimental results fitted the theoretical prediction rather well. The retention time for this device was more than 400 minutes. The light-induced conductivity change further supported the SCLC model.

3. POLYMER STABILIZED GOLD NANOPARTICLE FOR ONBM

During the operation of the bistable memory [51, 55], the device is electrical-biased to generate a distinctive amount of current, which determines the memory states of the device. Although many works have been reported on bistable memory devices, there are hardly any works that discuss the reproducibility, retention, and endurance of the device performance especially in an air environment, which is crucial for a memory device in a real application. For the generally used material system, e.g., the Au–NPs embedded in polystyrene that we used to discuss the transport mechanism in the previous section, the *I–V* characteristics of device were generally unstable. The *I–V* behavior became unpredictable after several write-erase cycles (Fig. 9). The reason was clearly understood by the cross-sectional TEM image in Figure 4: the Au–NPs aggregated in the host polymer. We proposed polymer stabilized Au–NPs in the host polymer to ensure a stable device. Figure 10 shows the schematic diagram. Polymer with a higher T_g (temperature of glass transition) has been used to replace PS to obtain better thermal stability. By this concept, an ONBM device features a long retention time and a high endurance under air environment [75, 76].

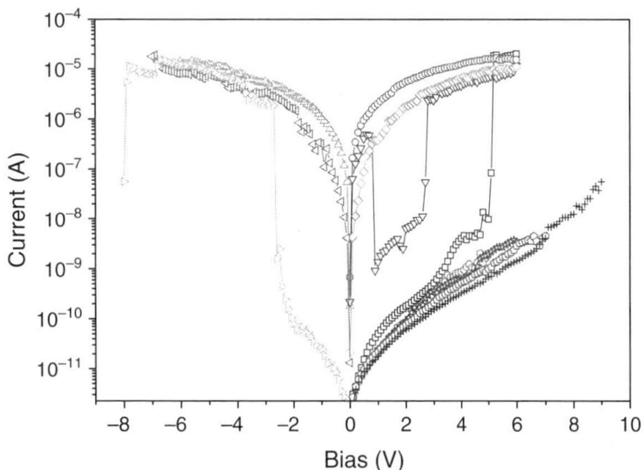

Figure 9. The *I–V* curves of a typical Al/Au-NPs + PS/Al memory device.

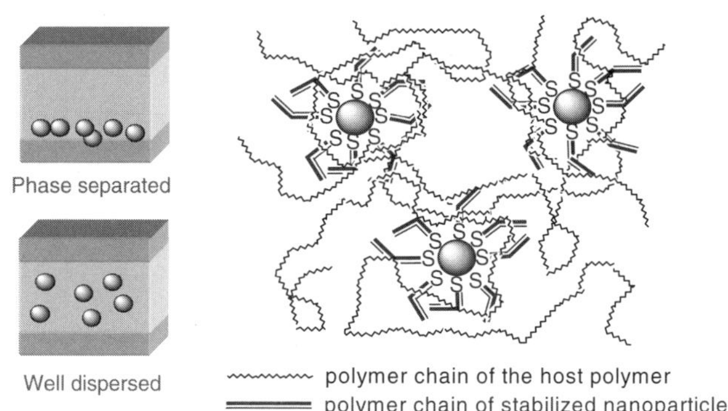

Figure 10. The concept of polymer stabilized AuNPs.

3.1. Preparation

3.1.1. Material Analysis

The polymer used in this experiment was [4-Cyano-2,4,4-trimethyl-2-methylsulfanylthiocarbonylsulfanyl-poly(butyric acid 1-adamantan-1-yl-1-methyl-ethyl ester)], also called PCm (Fig. 11). The polymer chains were attached to a sulfur atom at each end that stabilized the Au clusters by an S-Au bond to form the Au–PCm. The polymer stabilized Au–NPs were postulated to be immobile in the same host polymer material and to have highly stable memory properties during electrical operation.

The thermal stability of pure Au–PCm powder was investigated by thermal gravimetric analysis (TGA), which was

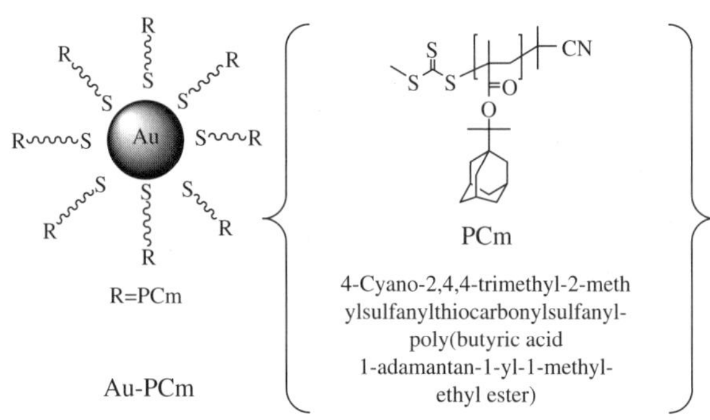

Figure 11. The chemical structure of polymer stabilized AuNPs. Reprinted with permission from [75], H. T. Lin et al., *IEEE Electron Device Lett.* 28, 951 (2007). © 2007, IEEE.

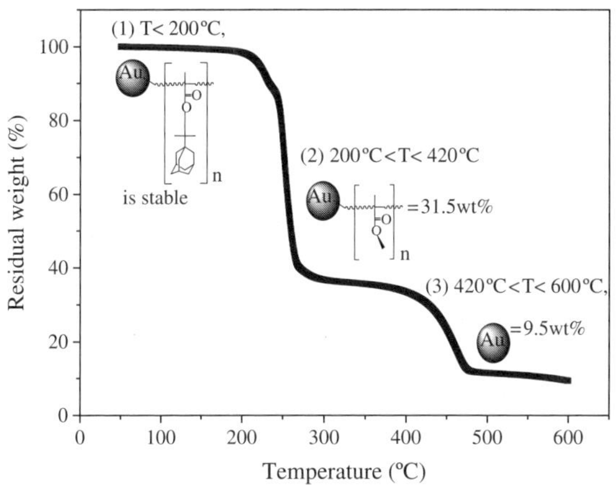

Figure 12. The thermal gravimetric analysis plot of pure Au–PCm powder. Reprinted with permission from [76], J.-R. Chen et al., *Nanotechnology* 20, 255706 (2009). © 2009, IOP Publishing.

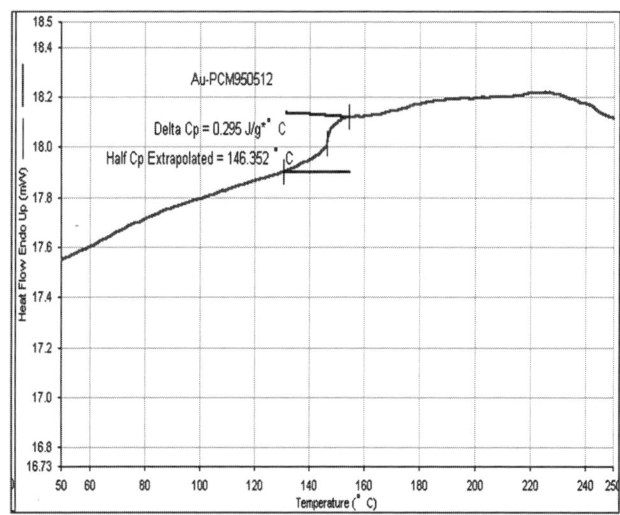

Figure 13. The differential scanning calorimeter plot of Au–PCm.

used to characterize the thermal stability and the metal content of a metal-nanoparticle system. The TGA for Au–PCm is shown in Figure 12. There were three distinct temperature zones in the TGA plot:

(1) $T < 200°C$, the Au–PCm was thermally stable for no weight loss, suggesting that the result was at a thermal equilibrium state;
(2) $200°C < T < 420°C$, the C–O bond in ester groups breaking at $T = 205\sim250°C$ caused the organic 1-adamantan-1-yl-1-methyl-ethyl fragments evaporation, leaving Au–NPs with 4-Cyano-2,4,4-trimethyl-2-methylsulfanylthocarbonylsulfanyl-polybutyric acid chains in 31.5% by weight; and
(3) $T > 420°C$, Au–S bonds break and all the organics were volatile, leading to only Au clusters left 9.5% by weight as $T > 600°C$. Therefore, the Au clusters content of the Au–PCm was about 9.5% by weight.

The temperature of the T_g of the polymer, PCm, was also measured by a differential scanning calorimeter (DSC). The DSC of PCm is shown in Figure 13. Obviously, an abrupt increasing trace in heat flow indicated that the phase change occurred for PCm at about 146°C.

3.1.2. Organic Memory with a Different Formula

The process for fabricating memory devices is the same as in the previous section. The solution containing the Au–PCm and PCm host polymer was prepared with 0.1% and 2.4% by weight in 1,2-dichlorobenzene, respectively, under a nitrogen environment. The thickness of the organic film was about 50 nm, which was determined by the TEM. The area for the memory cell was 2×2 mm^2. The concentration and molecular weight (MW) of the polymer selection is a key to achieve reproducible and stable properties of ONBM. Table 1 lists how the formulation was chosen and the generated modulate. For step 1, the MW of PCm chosen for Au–PCm and the host polymer was 2399. The solution containing Au–PCm and PCm was prepared with 0.05 or 0.1% and 1.2% by weight dissolved in 1,2-dichlorobenzene, respectively. The solution was fabricated as an active layer to the ONBM devices. However, the yield of the devices was only about 5% and the devices are not erasable. The thickness of the film is too thin that a large conduction current through the memory devices that the device was not erased might be possible reason.

Consequently, the concentration of the Au–PCm and PCm were increased in step 2. The solution containing the Au–PCm and PCm host polymer was prepared with 0.4, 0.8, 2.4, 3.6, and 2.0, 1.6, 0, and 0 percent by weight in dichlorobenzene, respectively, to fabricate the ONBM devices. The yield of devices improved, but the devices were still not erasable. The *I–V* characteristics of devices for 0.4% Au–PCm and 2.0% PCm are shown in Figure 14(a). Although a better bistable effect was observed, the device was still not erasable by a high-negative voltage sweep around −6 V. The memory device for 0.8% Au–PCm and 1.6% PCm achieved similar *I–V* characteristics. The memory devices containing 2.4% of the Au–PCm higher conduction current causes instability (Fig. 14(b)). As the concentration of Au–PCm increased to 3.6%, the thickness of the memory layer increase that decrease the on-current to less than 1 mA (Fig. 14(c)). However, the on-state current is still too high to erase. Consequently, the thickness of the film was not sufficient; a larger MW for polymer was selected.

For step 3, the MW of the PCm in the nanoparticle and host layer was 112,226 g/mol. The solution containing the Au–PCm and PCm host polymer was prepared with 0.4, 0.8, 2.4, and 3.6 and 0.8, 0.4, 0, and 0 percent by weight dissolved in dichlorobenzene, respectively, to fabricate ONBM devices. A better film quality was achieved by using a higher MW in Au–PCm and PCm. The memory device was erasable and a yield of 60% was obtained. Since the concentration of Au–PCm is the same as in step 2, the thickness of the memory layer plays an important role. The *I–V* characteristics of the device for 0.4% Au–PCm and 0.8% PCm is shown in Figure 15. The devices exhibit a bistable effect and are erasable by a high-negative voltage sweep. The on-state current level was around $10^{-3}\sim10^{-4}$ A. Although the devices could be rewritten, the deviation of the turn-on voltage was too large. This might be due to the fact that the Au content

Table 1. The formulas on molecular weight used for AuNp PCms and for host polymer in the organic nonvolatile bistable memory.

	NPs material (Au–PCm)		Host material (PCm)		
Recipes	Concentration of Au–PCm (Wt% = g/100 mL)	Molecular weight of PCm (g)	Concentration of PCm (Wt% = g/100 mL)	Molecular weight of PCm (g)	Yield (%)
[1]	0.1/0.05	2399	1.2	2399	~5
[2]	0.4/0.8/2.4/3.6	2399	2.0/1.6/0/0	2399	~50
[3]	0.4/0.8/2.4/3.6	112,226	0.8/0.4/0/0	112,226	~60
[4]	0.05/0.1/0.2	2399	2.35/1.1/1.2	112,226	~90

is not high enough because of the large MW of the connected polymer. Consequently, a small MW of polymer bond to the Au–NPs could decrease the Au–PCm that increased the Au solid content. However, the on-state current has to maintain a suitable range, from 10^{-3} to 10^{-4} A, to achieve the ability to be an erasable memory device, so the concentration of Au–PCm has to be decreased. For step 4, a smaller MW (2399 g/mol) of polymer was used to bond the Au–NPs. The host polymer PCm, has a larger MW (112,226 g/mol). The solution containing the Au–PCm and PCm host polymer was prepared with 0.05 or 0.1 and 2.35 or 1.2% by weight dissolved in dichlorobenzene, respectively, to fabricate ONBM devices. The memory device with 0.05% Au–PCm and 2.35% PCm has a yield as high as 90%. The *I–V* characteristic of the device is shown in Figure 16. The device exhibited a low off-state current of about 10^{-8} A at 1 V. An electrical transition took place at 2.3 V with an abrupt current increase from 10^{-8} A to 10^{-4} A. The high-conductivity state could be returned to the low-conductivity state by applying a high-negative bias pulse. After the device had returned to the low-conductivity state, it could be switched back to the high-conductivity state. The electrical bi-stability of the device could be precisely controlled by applying a suitable voltage sweep numerous times without any significant degradation.

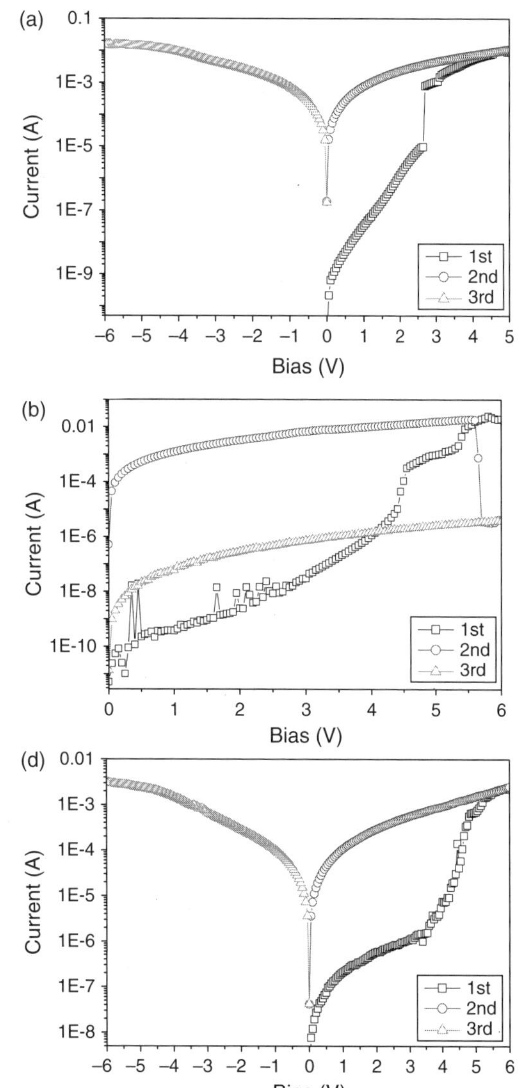

Figure 14. (a) The *I–V* characteristics of device for 0.4% Au–PCm and 2.0% PCm. The MWs of Au–PCm and PCm were 2399, (b) the *I–V* characteristics of device for 2.4% Au–PCm. The MW of Au–PCm was 2399, and (c) the *I–V* characteristics of device for 3.6% Au–PCm. The MW of Au–PCm was 2399.

3.1.3. Organic Memory with Different Polymers

The concept that the polymer stabilizes Au nanoparticles is not a limit to PCm. Other polymers are also adopted to demonstrate the generalization. The poly(methyl methacrylate) (PMMA) and PS were used to stabilize the Au–NPs and used as the host polymer. The chemical structures of PS and PMMA are shown in Figure 17(a). The memory fabrication process was the same as Al/PCm + Au–PCm/Al structure. For the PS polymer, the solution containing the Au-PS and PS host polymer was prepared with 0.1% and

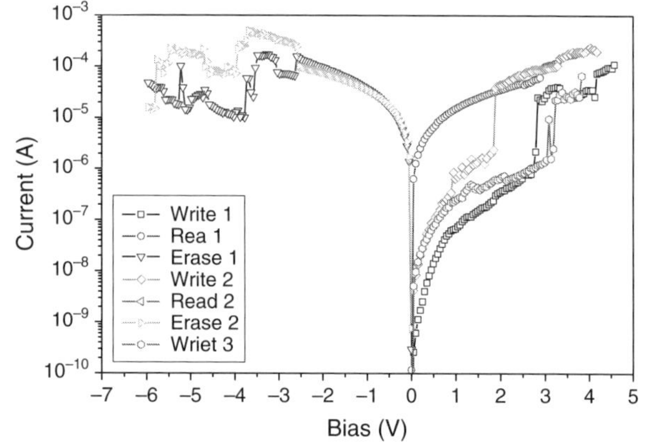

Figure 15. The *I–V* characteristics of device for 0.4% Au–PCm and 0.8% PCm. The MWs of Au–PCm and PCm were 112226.

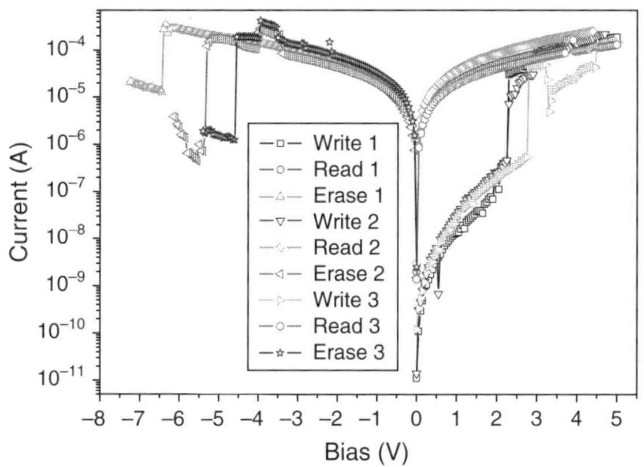

Figure 16. The *I–V* characteristics of device for 0.05% Au–PCm and 2.35% PCm. The MWs of Au–PCm and PCm were 2399 and 112226, respectively.

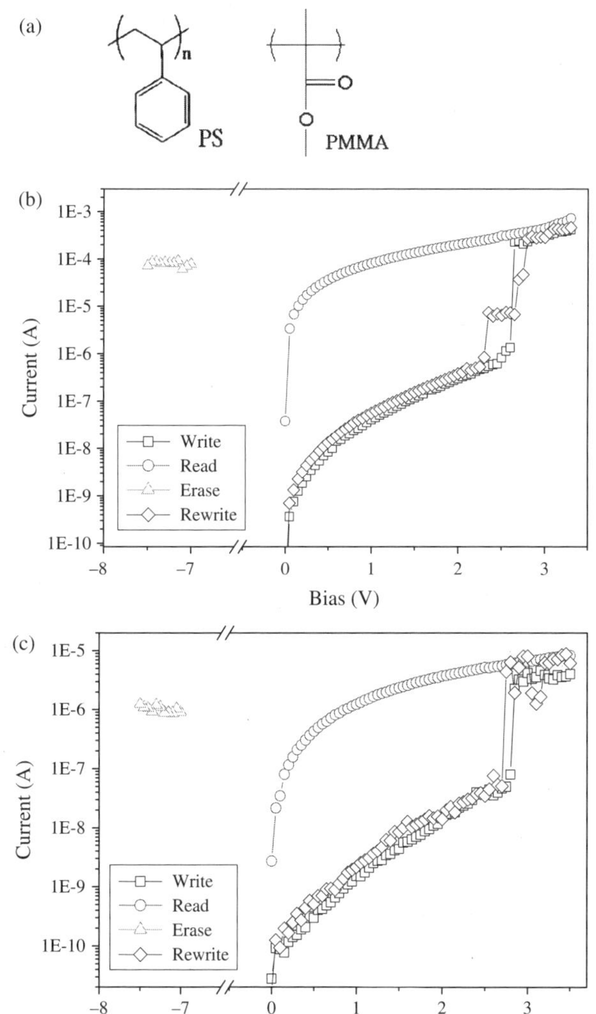

Figure 17. (a) The chemical structures of PS and PMMA, (b) the *I–V* characteristics of the Al/PS + Au-PS/Al sandwiched memory device, and (c) The *I–V* characteristics of the Al/PMMA + Au-PMMA/Al sandwiched memory device.

1.2% by weight dissolved in dichlorobenzene, respectively, under nitrogen environment. The *I–V* characteristics of the Al/PS + Au-PS/Al sandwiched memory device are shown in Figure 17(b). The device exhibited a low current of about 10^{-8} A at 1 V. An electrical transition took place at 2.6 V with an abrupt current increase from 10^{-8} A to 10^{-4} A. The high-conductivity state could be returned to the low-conductivity state by applying a high-negative bias pulse. After the device had returned to the low-conductivity state, it could be switched back to the high-conductivity state.

For the PMMA polymer, the solution containing the Au–PMMA and PMMA host polymer was prepared with 0.1% and 2.4% by weight dissolved in dichlorobenzene, respectively, under nitrogen environment. Similar behaviors were observed for the Al/PMMA + Au–PMMA/Al memory device (Fig. 17(c)). The current on/off ratio for this ONBM was four orders of magnitude. The electrical bistability of the device could be precisely controlled by applying a suitable voltage numerous times without any significant degradation. The concept of polymer-stabilized Au nanoparticles was demonstrated to be useful for organic nonvolatile bistable memory.

3.2. Electrical Characteristics of the ONBM

3.2.1. The I–V Characteristics

The *I–V* characteristics of the typical Al/PCm + Au–PCm/Al sandwiched memory device are shown in Figure 18. Two distinct conducting states were clearly observed. A low-conductivity state with a current of approximately 10^{-8} A is recorded from 0 to 1.5 V for the first voltage sweep, which corresponded to the "0" state of a bistable memory. When the applied voltage was approaching 2.3 V, a remarkable abrupt current increase from 10^{-8} to 10^{-4} A was observed. After this high voltage was removed, the current still remained around 10^{-4} A by a small (~1 V) detection voltage, which manifested a nonvolatile characteristic. This situation indicated a high-conductivity state, which corresponded to the "1" state of a memory. In addition, a high-conductivity state can be returned to a low-conductivity state by applying a negative voltage sweep from 0 to –6 V or by a high negative voltage pulse. After that,

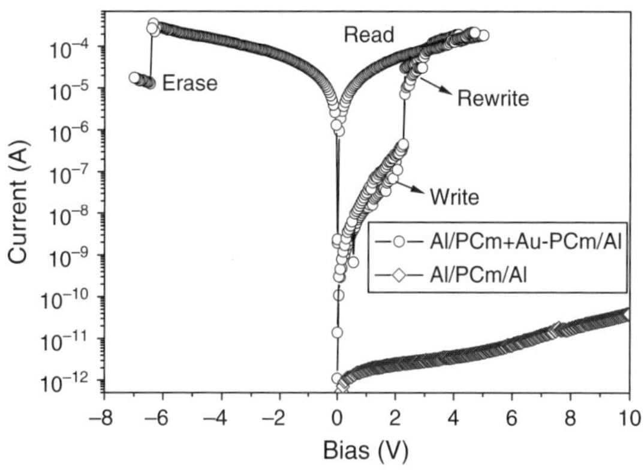

Figure 18. The typical *I–V* characteristics of the Al/PCm + Au–PCm/Al organic memory device. Reprinted with permission from [75], H. T. Lin et al., *IEEE Electron Device Lett.* 28, 951 (2007). © 2007, IEEE.

the device was restored to a low-conductivity state, and it was able to repeat the turn-on behavior as the first positive voltage sweep with very similar *I–V* characteristics. Therefore, this device was a rewritable nonvolatile memory device. For comparison, the memory device using a pure PCm without Au–NPs was also demonstrated in Figure 18. Even after the applied voltage increased to 10 volts, the *I–V* behavior still showed a low-conductivity state. This implied that the memory effect was strongly correlated to the presence of Au–NPs.

3.2.2. Localized Transport of ONBM

After demonstrating that the memory is an appropriate nonvolatile memory, the transport investigation by a scanning laser beam-induced thermal energy transfer method was applied. This method is usually called the optical beam-induced resistance change (OBIRCH) method [77]. Figure 19 illustrates the basic setup. The memory is preset to either the "1" or "0" state, which was biased by a constant voltage (1 V for example) for the ORBICH measurement. At the same time, an infrared (IR) laser with a wavelength of 1.3 μm scans the top surface of ONBM. The absorption of the IR energy will heat the ONBM locally, causing a local resistance change. The current change (ΔI) caused by the resistance change is expressed as [77]:

$$\Delta I = -\frac{\Delta R}{V} \cdot I^2 \tag{3}$$

where ΔR is the resistance change due to the localized thermal energy, and I is the current passing the ONBM at a constant applied voltage V. The ΔI is therefore the induced current change. Since the equation indicating the ΔI corresponds to the square of the current (I) at constant voltage (V), the mapping of the ΔI reflects the transport phenomena of the ONBM. This implies that, if the mapping of ΔI for the ONBM shows a localized property, the transport path in an ONBM is localized.

Figure 20 illustrates the ORBICH results on an ONBM. A nearly 3-V voltage was applied to write the ONBM. At this voltage, a relatively high current (1.05 mA) was recorded, which corresponds to the logic "1" state. Several specific points that have a large negative ΔI were found (Fig. 20(a)). This demonstration current transport in an ONBM is localized. After the writing process, a read voltage at 1 V was applied to detect the transport current. The transport current is 0.126 mA and is similar to the current in Figures 3–25 at 1 V for a high-conductivity state. This indicates that the ONBM still remains at a logic "1" state. Some points having a large ΔI after ΔR laser scanning, shown in Figure 20(b), were observed, which almost coincide to the ΔI mapping in the writing process. This implies that once the localized current transport path is established in the writing process, the transport current as a read process will follow the same paths.

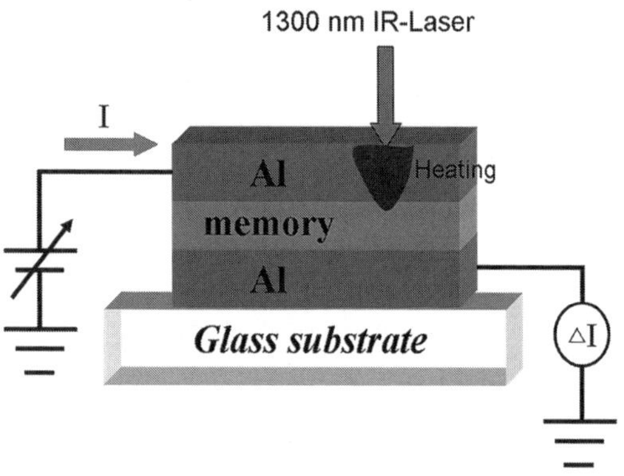

Figure 19. Schematic setup of an OBIRCH method.

The remaining question is how thermal energy alters the transport current through Au–NPs in an ONBM device. The transport mechanism is suggested and proved in the previous section, which corresponds to the trap-filled SCLC. The transport path will be established if the potential well formed by both the Au–NPs and surrounding polymer is filled with carriers. Therefore, the current in the ONBM is correlated to the probability (f) of electrons trapped in Au–NPs to the total amounts of electrons, which can be expressed as [78],

$$f = \frac{1}{1 + (N_c/N_d) \cdot \exp(-(\text{LUMO} - E_d)/kT)} \tag{4}$$

where LUMO is the lowest unoccupied molecular orbit of the host polymer, N_c is the effective density of states at LUMO, N_d is the density of the Au–NPs, the E_d is the energy states of the Au–NPs, k is the Boltzman constant, and T is the temperature. By this equation, as the T increased, the f decreased. The Au–NPs are less filled at high temperature, resulting in a lower transport current. As a consequence, the ΔI is negative.

To further investigate the stability of the localized transport path, a voltage of −7 V was applied to erase the ONBM. After erasing, a 1-V read voltage was applied to read the ONBM, and there is a negligible current in the ONBM (Fig. 21). Almost no thermally induced ΔI is found. However, after a voltage of 3 V was applied to write the ONBM, a transport current of 1.34 mA was recorded, indicating that the ONBM has been written to the logic "1" state. The localized transport paths were found again (Fig. 20(c)). However, these transport paths are not the same as compared with the previous transport paths shown in Figure 20(a). After writing the ONBM, a read voltage at 1 V was applied and the localized paths were found again, which almost coincide with the previous one shown in Figure 20(d). The transport mechanism of an Au-NP is similar to what was discussed previously, i.e., the carriers remained in the Au-NP potential well dominate the formation of the transport path. After the erasing process, the filled Au-NP potential wells were evacuated by a negative voltage and the transport current was negligible (Fig. 21). The originally built-up conducting paths were totally eliminated, and the ONBM returned to the prewriting state. After re-applying a 3-V writing voltage, the Au-NPs were randomly filled depending on the carrier status of each potential well. As a consequence, the transport paths are not necessary the same for each writing process. These transport paths will remain, and the ONBM is sustained in an "1" state until the following erase process.

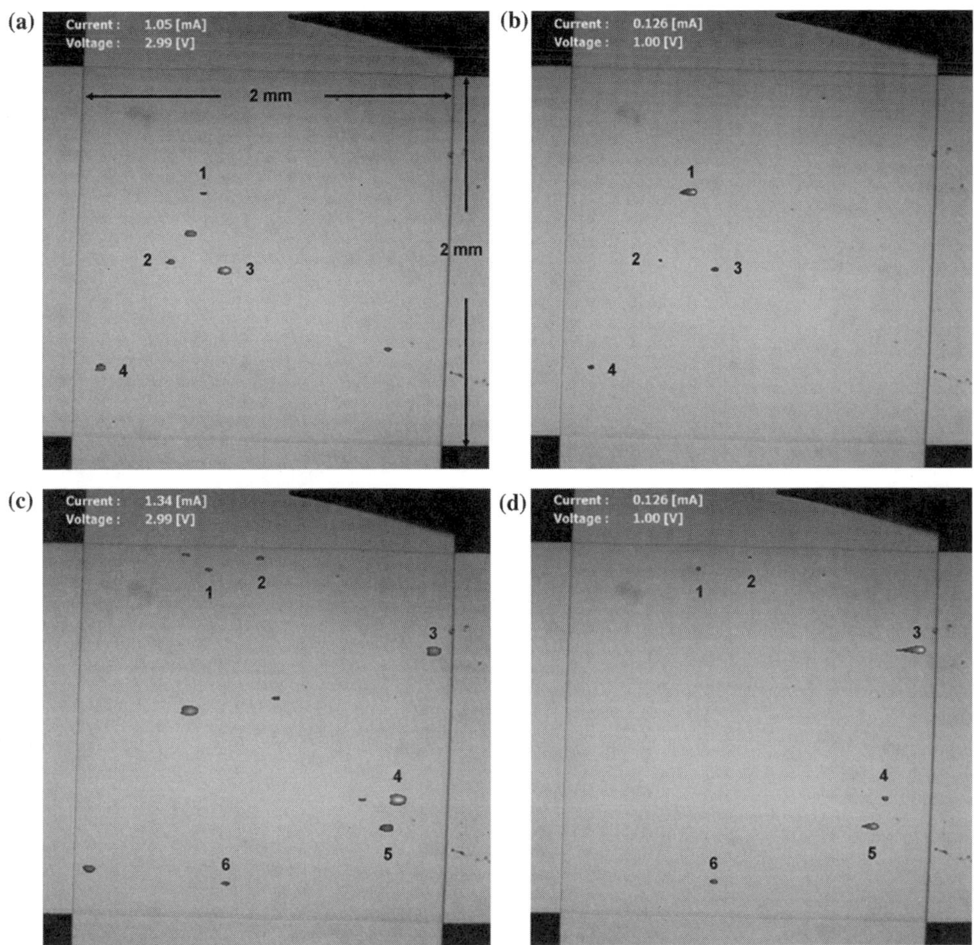

Figure 20. (a) The OBIRCH image of ONBM is at write-state for 3 V and several specific points of ONBM, (b) the OBIRCH image of ONBM at the read state for 1 V after the writing process. The localized current transport path established in the writing process; the transport current at read process will follow the same path, (c) the OBIRCH image of ONBM is at the rewrite state for 3 V, and (d) the OBIRCH image of ONBM is at the read state for 1 V, and the localized paths are found again.

Figure 21. After erasing, a 1-V read voltage was applied to read the ONBM; there is negligible current transport in the OBIRCH image of ONBM.

3.3. Reliability of the ONBM

3.3.1. Reproducibility

To further demonstrate the advantage of polymer-stabilized Au nanoparticle as a polymer material, the reproducibilities were investigated [79]. For comparison, two memory structures were used. The first one was the Al/PCm + Au–PCm/Al structure, and the second one was a Al/PCm + Au–NPs/Al device. Sixty samples were made to compare their *I–V* characteristics. The yields of the Al/PCm + Au–NPs/Al and Al/PCm + Au–PCm/Al were 40% and 82%, respectively (Fig. 22). For the Al/PCm + Au–NPs/Al devices, the turn-on voltage was widely distributed from 2.1 to 3.6 V. The average turn-on voltage was about 2.7 V with a 0.4-V standard deviation.

For the Al/PCm + Au–PCm/Al, a well-reproducible electrical bistability could be achieved with a high workable yield of about 82%. The turn-on voltage was converged on 1.8~2.5 V. The average of the turn-on voltage was about 2.1 V and it had a smaller standard deviation at 0.16 V. The turn-on voltages of the polymer-stabilized Au–NPs were lower and concentrated compared with the blending system. Therefore, the Au–NPs would be more likely to move under

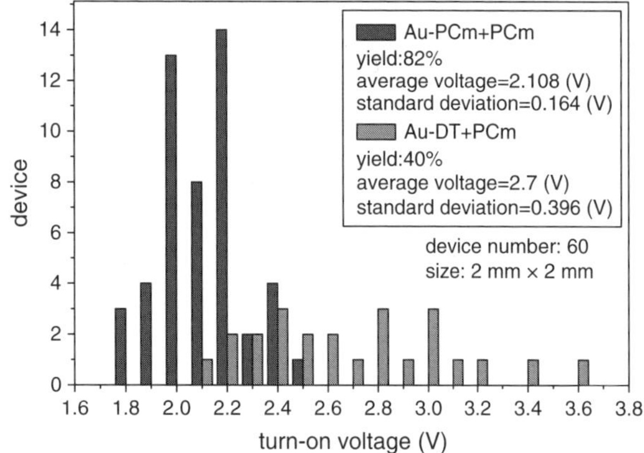

Figure 22. The reproducibility of the Al/PCm + Au-NPs/Al and Al/PCm + Au–PCm/Al was 40% and 82%, respectively. Reprinted with permission from [76], J.-R. Chen et al., *Nanotechnology* 20, 255706 (2009). © 2009, IOP Publishing.

a thermal process or electrical stress because they were randomly blended in the host polymer. That would make the memory unstable under ambient conditions, implying that the reproducibility of ONBM devices was strongly correlated with polymer stabilized Au–NPs.

To further demonstrate this, the cross-sectional TEM images of Al/PCm + Au–PCm/Al and Al/PCm + Au–NPs/Al devices are shown in Figures 23(a and b), respectively. The TEM images showed that the polymer stabilized Au–NPs were well dispersed in the polymer matrix. Due to the uniform distribution of the Au–NPs, a well reproducible of electrical bi-stability can be achieved. In contrast, the Au–NPs without stabilization showed undesirable Au–NPs aggregation in the host polymer after operation. The concept of stabilizing Au–NPs using the polymer chain offered some unique functions for ONBM devices.

3.3.2. Endurance and Retention

Since the device was a rewritable ONBM device, a "write-read-erase-read" sequence test was conducted in air. According to the *I–V* characteristics in Figure 18, the write, the read and erase voltages were selected as 3, 1, and −7 V respectively. The endurance result was shown in Figure 24. A 3-V voltage pulse drove the device to a high-conductivity "1" state with a current level between 10^{-3} and 10^{-4} A. With regard to the read pulse, 1-V read voltage yielded around a 3×10^{-5} A current level. After the write and read positive pulse, a −7 V voltage pulse erased the memory device to a low-conductivity "0" state. This "0" state again was detected by a 1-V pulse; the current was around 10^{-7} A. The current levels shown in Figure 24 were different from Figure 18, which was due to the difference in pulse mode and the direct current mode operation. Therefore, the on/off current ratio was about two orders of magnitude during the pulse operation. The electrical bi-stability of the device could be precisely controlled by applying a suitable voltage pulse numerous times without any significant degradation. A shorter pulse below 0.1 second was conducted to confirm the memory consistency. In addition to the rewriting capability, the cycling endurance over 2000 times on/off switching was demonstrated in Figure 25. This endurance was not

(a)

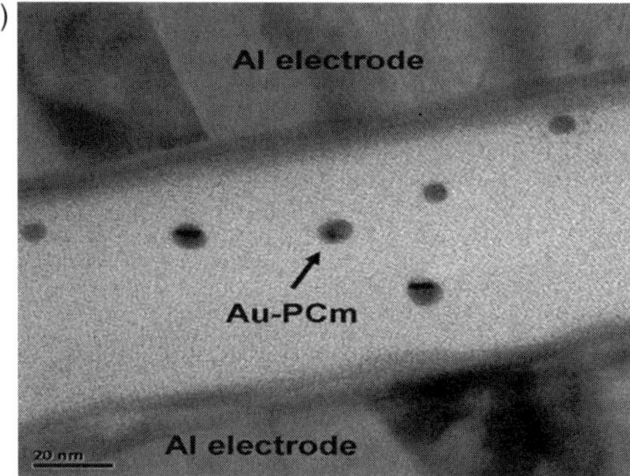

(b)

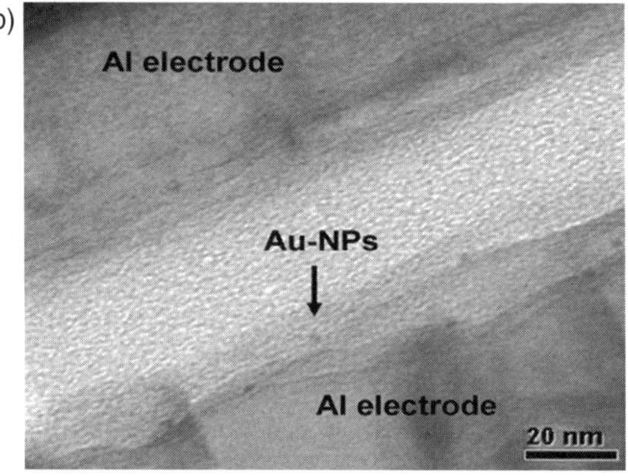

Figure 23. (a) The Au–PCm stabilized by the polymer chains was well dispersed in the PCm, and (b) the random blended of the Au–NPs were aggregated in the host polymer. Reprinted with permission from [76], J.-R. Chen et al., *Nanotechnology* 20, 255706 (2009). © 2009, IOP Publishing.

limited by 2000 times since no appreciable degradation was recorded.

Besides the endurance, the retention time was an important parameter for a memory device. The retention ability

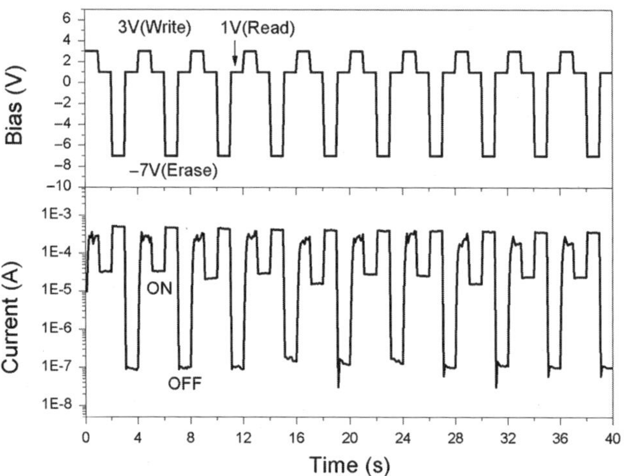

Figure 24. The write-read-erase-read sequence operation of the AuPCm memory device. The sequence of voltage pulse is 3 V/1 V/−7 V/1 V. Reprinted with permission from [75], H. T. Lin et al., *IEEE Electron Device Lett.* 28, 951 (2007). © 2007, IEEE.

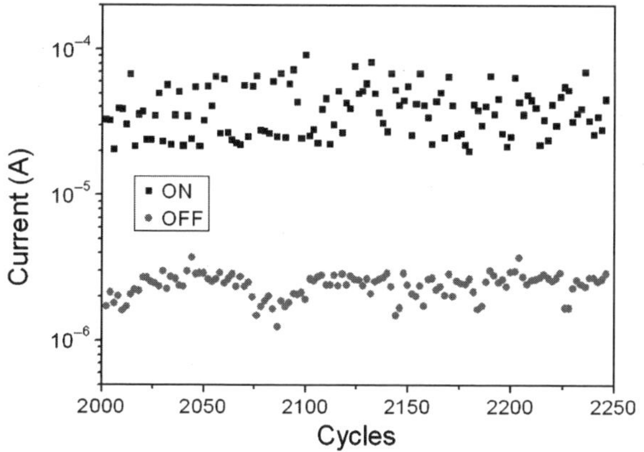

Figure 25. The current level of on and off states at a 1-V read voltage for more than 2000 cycles.

was tested (Fig. 26); at first, a positive voltage pulse of 3 V was applied to the memory device to achieve a high-conductivity state. Then, a 1-V voltage pulse was given to the device to read the memory state. After this read voltage, the bias was removed and the device was stored in ambient air for 3 days. After 3 days, a 1-V voltage was applied to read the state of this memory. It was found that the device still sustained in the "1" state with only a slight degradation after more than 3 days in an air environment. The device exhibited a good retention characteristic after a time period of 3 days in air. The rewritable, bi-stable, and nonvolatile organic memory either required a donor–acceptor pair [41] or it operated a relative high voltage or was not stable. The stabilization of nanoparticles by the polymer chain offers a unique function for organic memory devices. This polymer bonded to Au clusters could clasp the host polymer material physically to tightly bind the Au NPs and the host polymer material together.

To summarize, we demonstrated a stable organic bi-stable nonvolatile memory by using polymer chain stabilized Au–NPs in a host polymer as the memory active layer. The reproducibility of the Al/PCm + Au–NPs/Al and Al/PCm + Au–PCm/Al was 40% and 82%, respectively. The TEM images show that the polymer-stabilized Au–NPs are well dispersed in the polymer matrix. This memory can be switched on and off more than 2000 times without appreciable performance degradation. In addition, the memory state can be retained for more than 3 days in an air environment. Therefore, this device is a potential candidate for the next-generation of nonvolatile memory to be applied in an all-printed RFID, smart card, or system-integrated display.

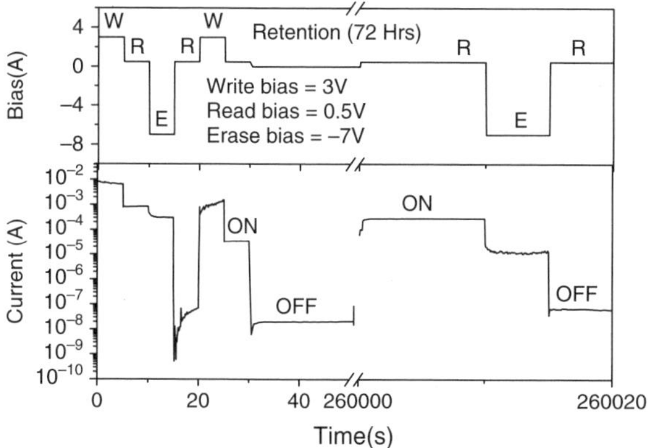

Figure 26. The retention time test for the Al/PCm + Au–PCm/Al memory. Over 3 days retention time was observed in air. Reprinted with permission from [79], H. T. Lin et al., "IEEE International Electron Device Meeting, Technical Digest," pp. 233–236, 2007. © 2007, IEEE.

4. 16-BYTE ONBM ARRAY ON PLASTIC

4.1. Fabrication

The 16-byte ONBM array [79] was prepared by the procedures shown in Figure 27 and described in detail as the following: A polycarbonate (PC) plastic sheet was used as the substrate and cleaned by detergent solution, de-ionized water, acetone, and isopropanol (IPA) using an ultrasonic cleaner for 20 minutes, sequentially; then, it was dried in a vacuum oven for 30 minutes at 105°C. The poly-4-vinyl phenol (PVP) solution was spun onto the PC substrate as the smooth layer. The polymer solution was prepared containing 80 mg/ml PVP and 40 mg/ml (melamine-co-formaldehyde) methylated (PMF) dissolved in the propylene glycol monomethyl ether acetate in which the PMF was used as the cross-linking agent. This solution was then spun onto the PC substrate at 3000 rpm for 60 seconds. The PVP was baked on a hotplate at 90°C for 20 minutes and then illuminated by UV light (254 nm) for 20 minutes.

A 75-nm-thick aluminum (Al) bottom electrode was deposited using a thermal evaporator with a shadow metal mask at a base pressure of 2×10^{-6} torr. The bottom electrode mask is shown in Figure 28(a). The UV ozone was treated to activate the Al surface. The memory active layer consisted of host polymer material and polymer stabilized Au–NPs. The memory solution containing 0.1% Au–PCm and 2.0% PCm host polymer was dissolved in 1,2-dichlorobenzene. This solution was then spin-coated on the bottom Al electrodes. Then, toluene was used to wipe out the memory layer in the connected area. Another Al layer was then deposited on the top as the top electrode. The top electrode mask is shown in Figure 28(b). The top and bottom electrodes had line widths of 1 mm and were aligned

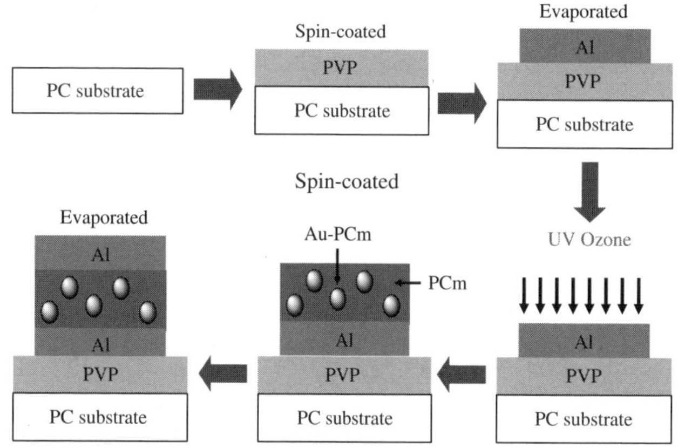

Figure 27. The schematic process flows for fabricating Al/PCm + Au-NPs/Al ONBM.

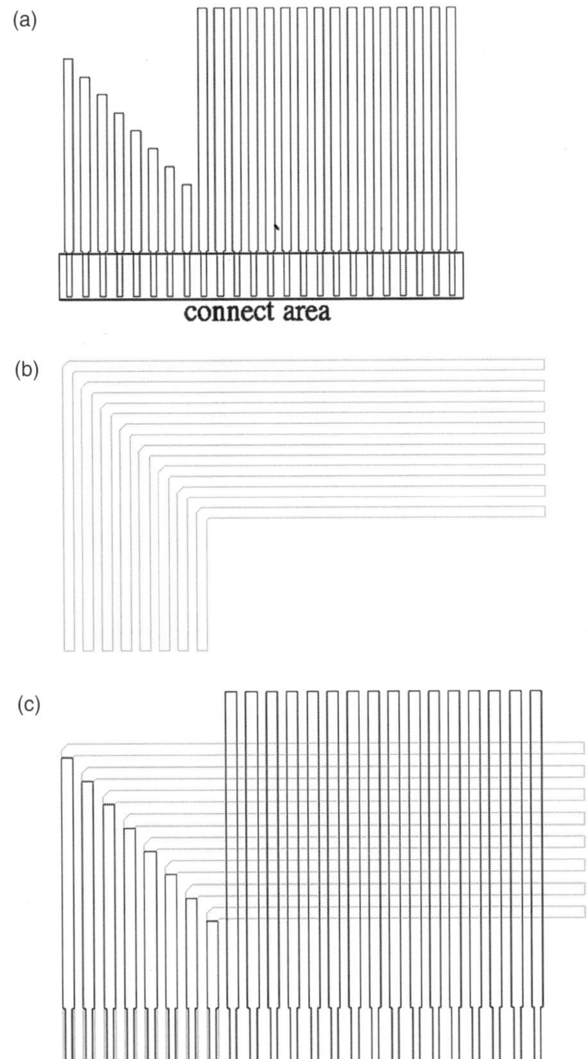

Figure 28. (a) The bottom electrode mask of a 16-byte ONBM array, (b) the top electrode mask of a 16-byte ONBM array, and (c) the top and bottom electrodes had line widths of 1 mm and were aligned perpendicular to each other on the 16-byte ONBM array.

perpendicular to each other (Fig. 28(c)). The device area for the memory cell was 1 mm^2. The Au-PCms were distributed well without aggregation phenomenon. The thickness of the 16-byte ONBM array was about 50 nm.

4.2. Design of the External Driving Circuit

The 16-byte ONBM array was designed in the cross-bar structure with eight rows and 16 column outputs and pasted up the converter board (Figs. 29(a and b)). To access a specific memory cell, the column [n] and row [m], as shown in Figure 30, the mth bit row [m] of the ONBM array was connected to the current-sensing circuit and was supplied with the voltage −7, 0, and floating, depending on the sensing situation. The word line, column [n], was supplied to the voltage 3, 0.5, and floating when we accessed the nth byte as the write, read, and idle states. The relationship between the state and supply voltage is summarized in Table 2.

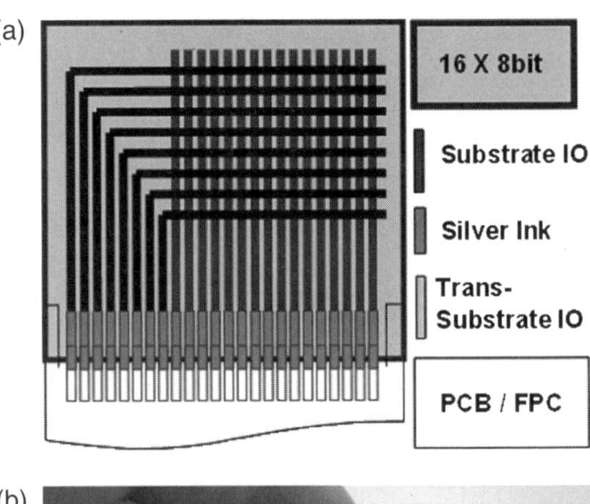

Figure 29. (a) The schematic diagram of a 16-byte ONBM, and (b) the photograph of a 16-byte ONBM array on the plastic substrate. Reprinted with permission from [79], H. T. Lin et al., "IEEE International Electron Device Meeting, Tech. Dig.," pp. 233–236, 2007. © 2007, IEEE.

Because the current comes from a memory cell flowing through the bit line, the current sensing circuit in Figure 31 will determine the output state, either a logic "1" or logic "0", by comparing the Row_ref[m] with-(IRH-IRL)*R/2; the mean value of IRH was 0.05 mA and mean value of IRL was 5 μA. Since we chose R as 100 K-ohm, Vref_R was then

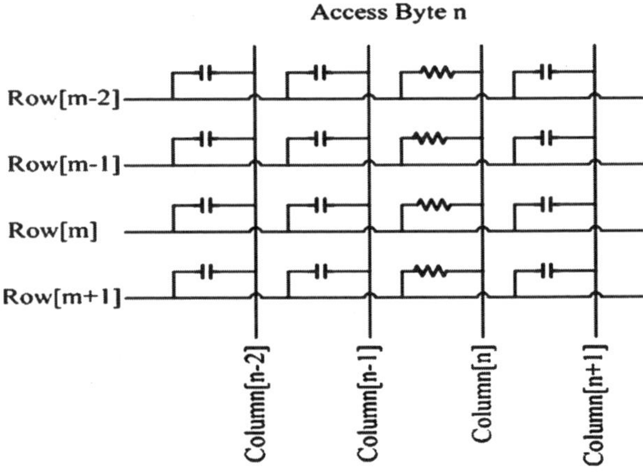

Figure 30. The crossbar ONBM array. To access a specific memory cell, the column [n] and row [m] were selected. Reprinted with permission from [79], H. T. Lin et al., "IEEE International Electron Device Meeting, Technical Digest," pp. 233–236, 2007. © 2007, IEEE.

Table 2. The voltages used to address and drive an ONBM array in the "write" "read" and "idle" conditions.

	Write 0 (V)	Write 1 (V)	Read (V)	Idle
Column [*n*] (Byte *n*)	3	3	0.5	Floating
Row [*m*] (Bit *m*)	−4	0	0	Floating

2.25 V. The IRH was the output current of ONBM at the "on" state and IRL was the output current of ONBM at the "off" state.

The evaluation system consisted of a PC, control circuit, and software (Fig. 32(a)). The output of the ONBM control software is shown in Figure 32(b). The input data is shown on the right of the figure, while the output data is shown on the left. By reading the output, we know that the ONBM array was correctly addressed, read, and written.

4.3. Reliability

4.3.1. Flexibility

For the practical use of organic memory and its flexible integrated circuits, it is very important to understand the strain effect [80]. Consequently, the electrical properties of ONBM under bending for several curvature radiuses were investigated. The bending apparatus was a precision stage for a probe station (Fig. 33). The *I–V* characteristics were measured by applying compressive strains of the various bending curvature radius for 25 mm, 15 mm, and 5 mm. The *I–V* characteristics of the original, 25 mm, 15 mm, and 5 mm are shown in Figure 34. For the original memory device, two distinct conducting states were observed. A low conduction current around 10^{-8} A could be observed from 0 to 1 volts for the first voltage sweep, which corresponded to the "0" state of the bistable memory. When the applied voltage approached 2.2 V, a remarkably abrupt current increment from 10^{-8} to 10^{-4} A was observed. Without further operation, the conduction current remained at around 10^{-4} A by using a small (~0.5 V) detection voltage. This manifested nonvolatile memory characteristics. This relatively high current indicated a high-conductivity state, which corresponded to the "1" state of the memory. This high-conductivity state could then return to the low-conductivity state by applying either a negative voltage sweep from 0 to −7 V or a high-negative voltage pulse. After the device returned to a low-conductivity state, it could be once again turned on, and it exhibited similar *I–V* characteristics to those in

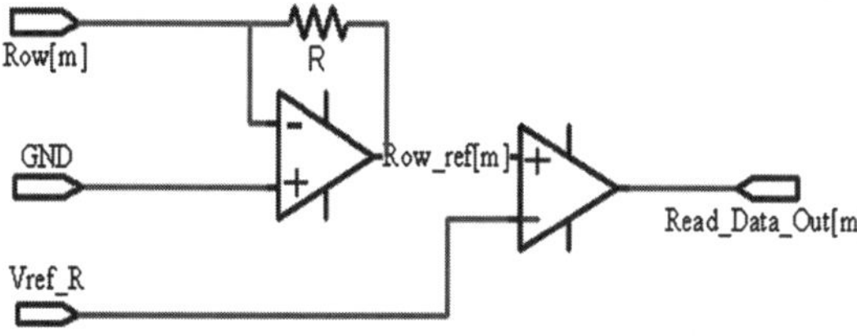

Figure 31. The current-sensing circuit to determine the logic "1" or logic "0" of the ONBM. Reprinted with permission from [79], H. T. Lin et al., "IEEE International Electron Device Meeting, Technical Digest," pp. 233–236, 2007. © 2007, IEEE.

(a)

(b)

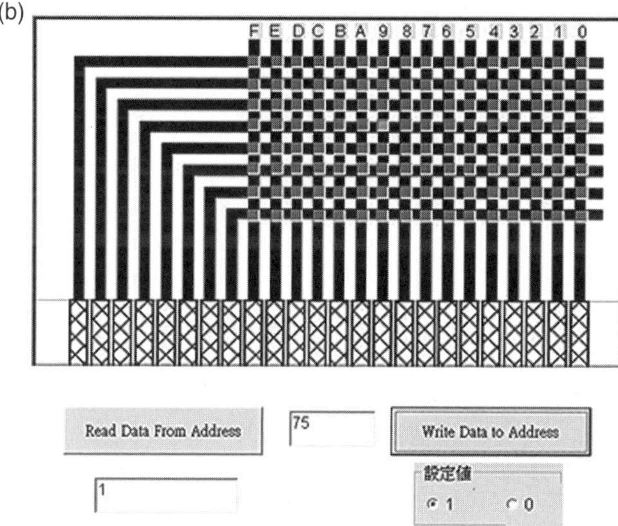

Figure 32. (a) The evaluation system consisted of a PC, control circuit, and software, and (b) the output of ONBM control software. The input data are shown on the right, and the output data are shown on the left. From this graph we could see the consistent results. Reprinted with permission from [79], H. T. Lin et al., "IEEE Intternational Electron Device Meeting, Technical Digest" pp. 233–236, 2007. © 2007, IEEE.

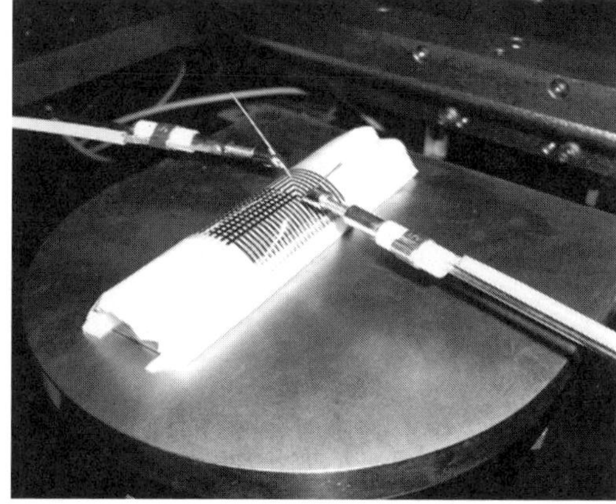

Figure 33. The bending test apparatus with a precision stage in a probe station.

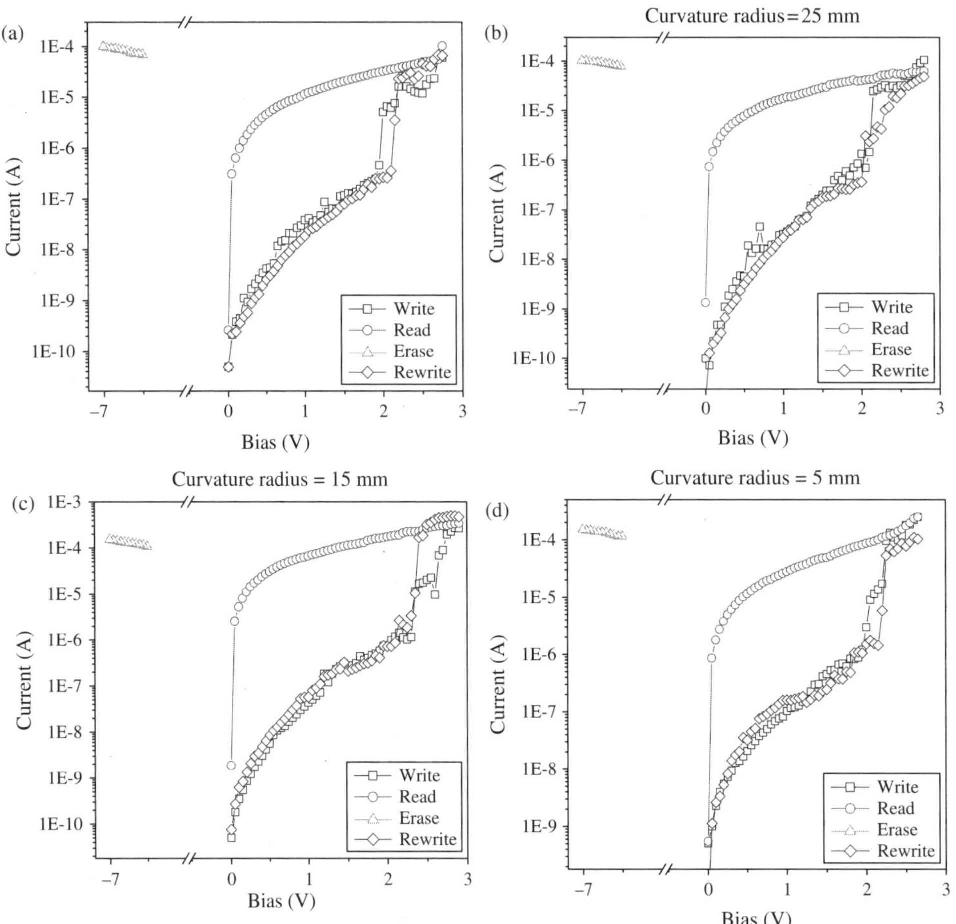

Figure 34. (a) The *I–V* characteristics of the Al/PCm + Au–PCm/Al memory device before bending test, (b) the *I–V* characteristics measured in the bending radius of 25 mm, (c) the *I–V* characteristics measured in the bending radius of 15 mm, and (d) the *I–V* characteristics measured in the bending radius of 5 mm.

the first voltage sweep. Therefore, this device was demonstrated as a rewritable nonvolatile memory device. For the "bended" memory, the on/off ratio and turn-on voltage had not changed for the various bending curvature radii.

4.3.2. Endurance and Retention

Since the device is a rewritable nonvolatile memory, a "write-read-erase-read" sequence test was carried out in the air (Fig. 35). The voltage of write, read, and erase was performed at 3, 0.5, and −7 V, respectively. A 3-V voltage pulse drove the device to a high-conductivity "1" state, with a current level between 10^{-3} and 10^{-4} A. As for the reading function, a 0.5-V read voltage yielded around 5×10^{-5} A current level. After the write and read positive pulse, a −7 V voltage pulse was applied to erase the memory device to a low-conductivity "0" state. This "0" state again was also detected using a 0.5-V detect pulse, yielding a current level around 10^{-7} A. The electrical bi-stability of the device can be precisely controlled by applying a suitable voltage pulse for numerous times, thereby not observing any significant degradation. In addition to the rewriting capability, cycling endurance for more than 1000 times of ON/OFF switching for ONBM on a plastic substrate was demonstrated in

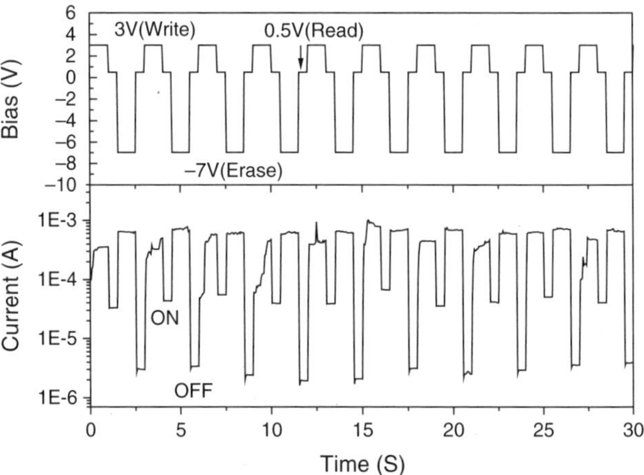

Figure 35. The write-read-erase-read sequence operation of the Au–PCm memory device on a plastic substrate. The sequence of voltage pulse was 3 V/0.5 V/−7 V/0.5 V. Reprinted with permission from [79], H. T. Lin et al., "IEEE International Electron Device Meeting, Technical Digest," pp. 233–236, 2007. © 2007, IEEE.

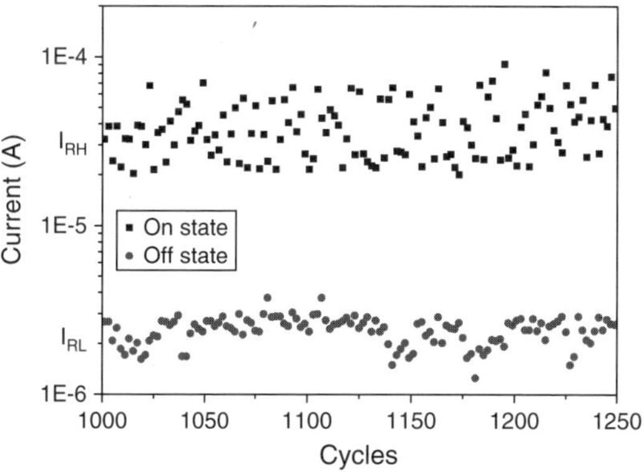

Figure 36. The current level of "on" and "off" states for an ONBM on plastic substrate at 0.5-V read voltage for more than 1000 cycles. Reprinted with permission from [79], H. T. Lin et al., "IEEE International Electron Device Meeting, Technical Digest," pp. 233–236, 2007. © 2007, IEEE.

Figure 36. Since no appreciable degradation was recorded, the endurance was not limited to 1000 times.

On the other hand, since the retention capability is an important parameter for the nonvolatile memory, the retention time was tested for more than 10 days in the ambient air (Fig. 37). A 3-V voltage pulse was applied to the memory device for 2 seconds to achieve the high-conductance state. A 0.5-V voltage pulse was then followed to drive the memory to the read state. After these operations, the bias was then removed and the memory device was stored in the ambient air for 10 days. After 10 days, a 0.5-V voltage pulse was again applied to read the data retained in the memory. The device can still keep in the high-conductance state with only slight degradation after 10 days. The *I–V* characteristics of the memory were shown at different read times in Figure 38. The ΔV was defined between the "0" and turn-on voltage. To estimate the ultimate retention time, the memory was turned to a high-conductance state and was detected at different time intervals. The current of the memory was decreased as time passed, and the ΔV was also decreased. By plotting the ΔV as a function of time, the longest retention time without a functional failure can be

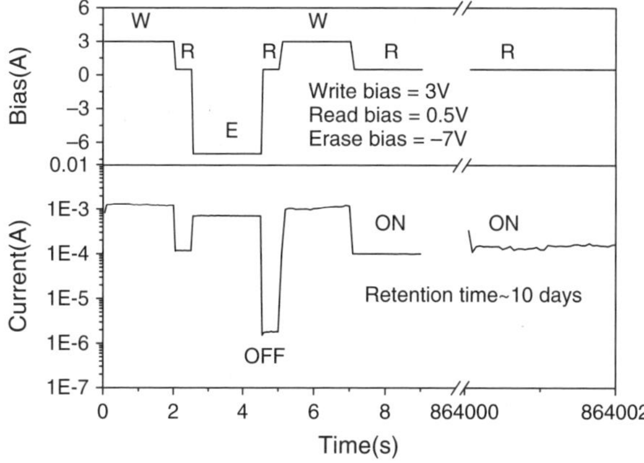

Figure 37. More than 10 days of retention time of the memory is observed in the air. Reprinted with permission from [81], H. T. Lin et al., *IEEE Electron Device Lett.* 30, 18 (2009). © 2009, IEEE.

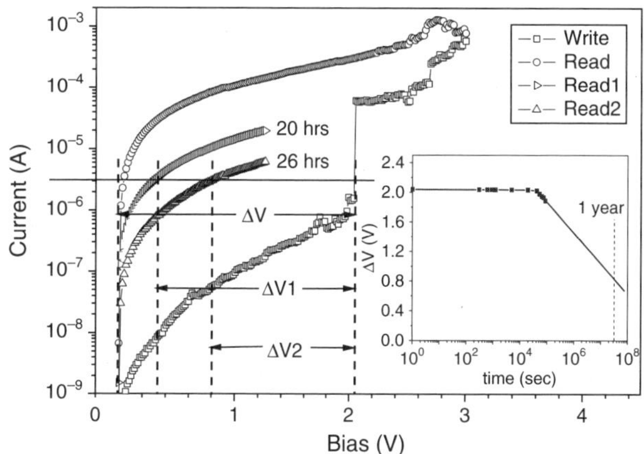

Figure 38. The longest retention time without functional failure can be estimated to be nearly 1 year. Reprinted with permission from [81], H. T. Lin et al., *IEEE Electron Device Lett.* 30, 18 (2009). © 2009, IEEE.

estimated through a linear exploration method and was estimated to nearly 1 year (Fig. 38, inset).

5. DIODE-SWITCH ONBM ON PLASTIC

An actively addressed organic memory device is essential for flexible electronic systems to eliminate the requirements of external circuits [81]. A DS-ONBM cell is one of the most promising candidates in flexible electronics [82–86]. In this section, a robust and stacked DS-ONBM on the plastic substrate operated in the ambient air was demonstrated. Compared with the last section in which the switch-diode is not included, the demonstrated diode switch can provide an active memory array on the plastic substrate. In general, to erase the data retained in the organic bistable memory, a high voltage at the reverse polarity is required [54, 55]. This indicates that both positive and negative voltages are required to realize an organic memory circuit and they result in a complicated external circuit architecture. This difficulty could be solved by UV light. From the transport mechanism [82, 83], the carriers stored in the metal nanoparticles are essential to ensure large current transport through a metal nanoparticle organic bistable memory. Removing this carrier could restrict current transport and provide erase function in the organic memory. Therefore, the photo response of an organic memory is studied and UV light is utilized to erase the data in the DS-ONBM. In this schematic structure, the erase circuit and "negative" voltage in the direct current/direct current converter for a passively addressed ONBM could be eliminated to make the peripheral circuit even simpler (Fig. 39).

5.1. Design of the Diode-Switch ONBM

The fabrication of the diode-switch ONBM could be separated into three major parts, including structure design, surface roughness, and process solvent selection. Since several kinds of organic material, including semiconductor, poly(3,4-ethylenedioxythiophene)/poly(styrenesulfonate) (PEDOT:PSS), and memory have been dissolved in different solvent as toluene, de-ionized water, and

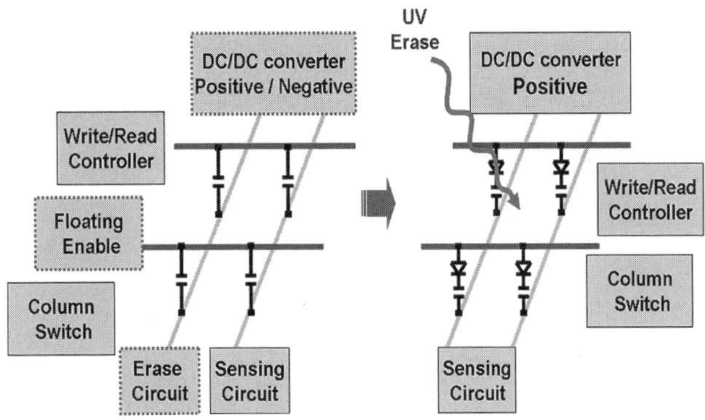

Figure 39. The erase circuit and "negative" voltage in the direct current/direct current converter in the passive ONBM array could be eliminated to make a peripheral circuit even simpler by a DS-ONBM. The schematic structure of a UV erasable DS-ONBM array is shown on the right.

dichlorobenzene, respectively, this might cause a different interaction between interfaces. There are two different kinds of design for device structure, including Al/memory/Al/semiconductor/PEDOT:PSS/Au and Au/PEDOT:PSS/semiconductor/Al/memory/Al (Fig. 40).

For the Au/PEDOT:PSS/semiconductor/Al/memory/Al device, the PEDOT:PSS layer was spin-coated on the bottom Au electrodes uniformly (Fig. 41(a)). Sequentially, the organic semiconductor layer was spin-coated on

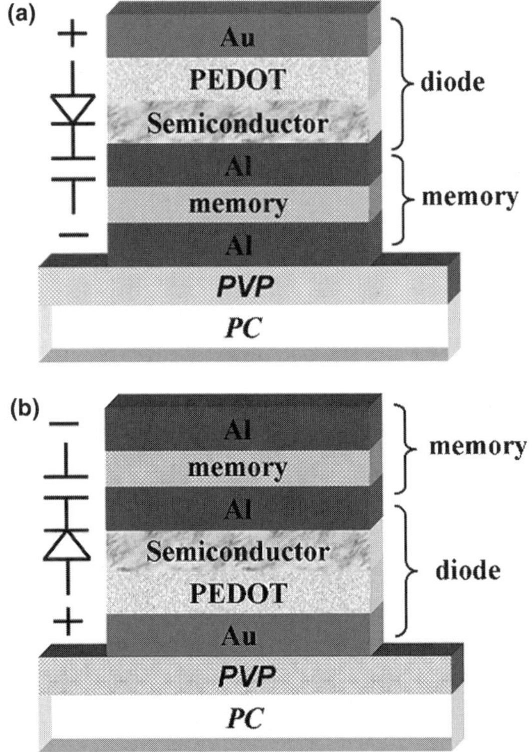

Figure 40. (a) The schematic structure of the Al/memory/Al/semiconductor/PEDOT/Au device, and (b) the schematic structure of the Au/PEDOT/semiconductor/Al/memory/Al device. Reprinted with permission from [81], H. T. Lin et al., *IEEE Electron Device Lett.* 30, 18 (2009). © 2009, IEEE.

Figure 41. (a) The PEDOT:PSS layer distributed uniformly on the bottom Au electrodes, (b) the photograph for a spin-coated organic semiconductor layer on the PEDOT:PSS film. The surface of organic semiconductor film was rugged, and (c) the memory solution eroded the dried organic semiconductor layer instantaneously due to the strong dichlorobenzene solvent.

the PEDOT:PSS film; the surface roughness of organic semiconductor film was rugged (Fig. 41(b)). Afterward, the medium Al electrode was deposited on the organic semiconductor film. Then, the memory layer was spin-coated on the medium of the Al electrodes. Finally, an Al layer as the top electrode was deposited on the memory layer. The device was completed, but the memory solution eroded the dried organic semiconductor layer instantaneously due to the strong solvent of dichlorobenzene (Fig. 41(c)). The *I–V* characteristics of the

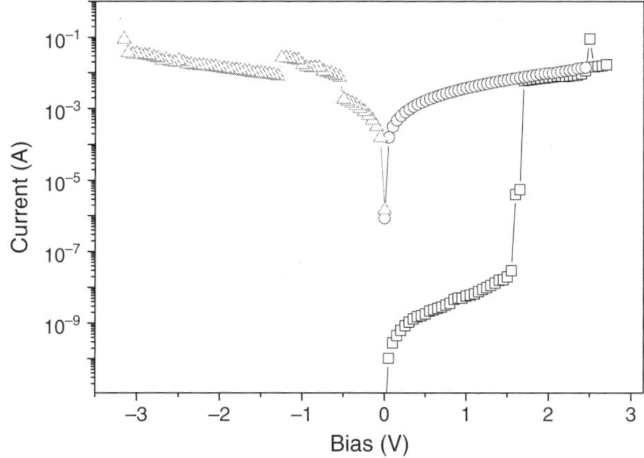

Figure 42. The *I–V* characteristics of the Au/PEDOT/semiconductor/Al/memory/Al device only had memory phenomenon without diode property.

Au/PEDOT:PSS/semiconductor/Al/memory/Al device only had memory phenomenon without diode property (Fig. 42).

For the Al/memory/Al/semiconductor/PEDOT:PSS/Au device, the memory layer was spin-coated on the bottom of the Al electrodes. Sequentially, the medium Al electrode was deposited on the memory film. Then, the organic semiconductor layer was spin-coated on the medium of the Al electrodes. Finally, the PEDOT layer was spin-coated on the organic semiconductor layer and the top of Au electrode was deposited. The optical image of the finished device

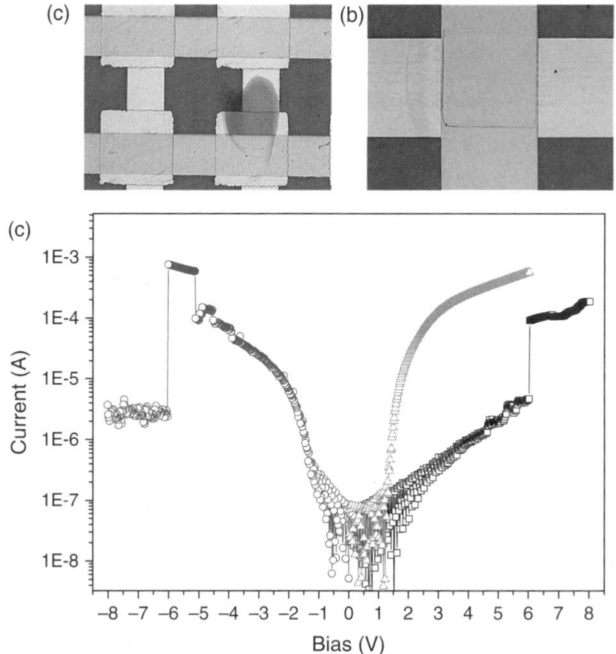

Figure 43. (a) The PEDOT:PSS aggregated on the hydrophobic semiconductor layer, and (b) employed a PEDOT:PSS to IPA ratio of 1:0.4 modify the hydrophilic surface of PEDOT:PSS. The aggregation of PEDOT:PSS layer disappears, and (c) the *I–V* characteristics of the Al/memory/Al/semiconductor/PEDOT/Au device were unstable without modifying the PEDOT:PSS.

is shown in Figure 43(a). The PEDOT:PSS aggregated on the surface of the hydrophobic semiconductor layer due to its hydrophilic property, cause device instability. The *I–V* characteristic of the device is shown in Figure 43(c). Therefore, a PEDOT:PSS to IPA ratio of 1:0.4 was used to modify the surface of the PEDOT:PSS, and the aggregation of PEDOT:PSS layer improved (Fig. 43(b)).

5.2. Fabrication of the Diode-Switch ONBM

By the 5-1, the structure depicted in Figure 40(b) is feasible for diode switch memory. The DS-ONBM cell was prepared using the following procedures: First, a PC plastic sheet was used as the substrate and cleaned by detergent solution, deionized water, acetone, and IPA using an ultrasonic cleaner for 5 minutes, sequentially; then, it was dried in a vacuum oven for 20 minutes at 100°C. Then, the PVP solution was spun onto the PC substrate. After that, the PVP was baked on a hotplate at 90°C for 20 minutes and then illuminated the UV light for 20 minutes. The cross-linked PVP was completed on the PC substrate as the smoothing layer.

A 75-nm-thick Al bottom electrode was deposited using a thermal evaporator with a shadow metal mask at a base pressure of 2×10^{-6} torr. The Al surface was activated by the UV-ozone treatment. Afterward, the memory solution was spin-coated. The solution for the memory layer, which contained Au–PCm and PCm host polymer, was prepared with 0.05% and 1.6% by weight in 1,2-dichlorobenzene, respectively, in nitrogen. The thickness of the dried organic film, which was determined by TEM, was about 37 nm. Another Al layer as the middle electrode was deposited in a thermal evaporator with second shadow mask. A 250 nm-thick organic semiconductor layer, poly(3-hexthiophene), was then spin-coated on top of the Al layer. This layer was baked at 110°C for 20 minutes. After this step, the PEDOT:PSS was also spin-coated and baked at 110°C for 20 minutes. Finally, an Au layer as the top electrode was then deposited in a thermal evaporator with a third shadow mask. The cross-section TEM image of the DS-ONBM is shown in Figure 44. The device has an area of 1×1 mm^2. The photograph of the DS-ONBM array on the plastic substrate is shown in Figure 45.

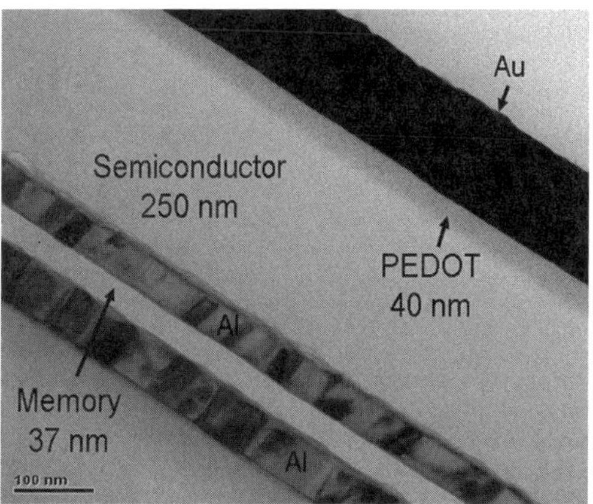

Figure 44. The cross-section TEM image of the DS-ONBM. Reprinted with permission from [81], H. T. Lin et al., *IEEE Electron Device Lett.* 30, 18 (2009). © 2009, IEEE.

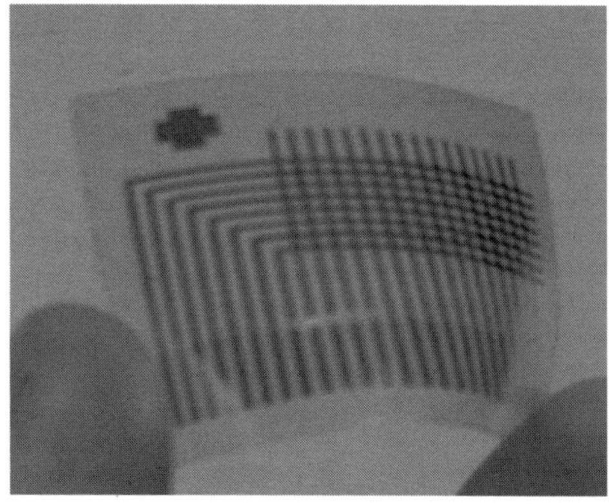

Figure 45. The photograph of DS-ONBM array on a plastic substrate.

5.3. Electrical Characteristics

The *I–V* characteristics of these devices (Fig. 46(a)) were measured by an HP 4156C semiconductor analyzer in air. A small amount of current could be observed from 0 to 3 V for the first voltage sweep, which corresponds to the "off" state of the DS-ONBM. When the applied voltage approaches 4.4 V, an abrupt current increment can be observed. A larger amount of current from 0 to 1.5 V for the second voltage sweep demonstrates the diode-switch characteristics. This amount of current remained high and can be measured using a small (~3 V) detection voltage. This manifests the nonvolatile memory characteristics. This high conductance current also indicates the "ON" state of the DS-ONBM. The *I–V* characteristics of the polymer diode had five orders of magnitude (Fig. 46(b)). The *I–V* characteristics of both organic diode and memory indicate the DS-ONBM is fully functional.

The absorbance of PCm and Au–PCm NPs was measured by a LAMBDA 950 UV/VIS/NIR Spectrophotometer (Fig. 47(a)). The absorption of Au–PCm had a peak at 310 nm, which was not observed for the PCm polymer film, thus indicating that this absorption was correlated to the Au–NPs. Consider the Au–NPs dissolved in PCm: this energy (~4 eV) might correspond to the carriers in the Au–NPs that escaped to the lowest unoccupied molecular orbit (LUMO) of the PCm on light illumination. Surface plasma absorption of Au-NP was excluded since the plasma absorption was at around 500 nm. Therefore, a UV light with a 254-nm wavelength was used to erase the DS-ONBM. This phenomenon could be explained by suggesting that, upon UV illumination, the carriers escaped from the Au–PCm nanoparticles, which restricted the current transport and

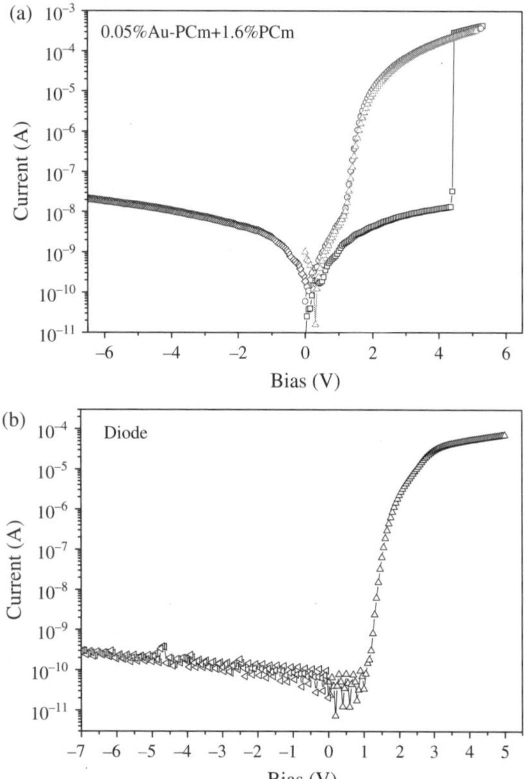

Figure 46. (a) The *I–V* characteristics of the DS-ONBM, and (b) the *I–V* characteristics of the polymer diode. Reprinted with permission from [81], H. T. Lin et al., *IEEE Electron Device Lett.* 30, 18 (2009). © 2009, IEEE.

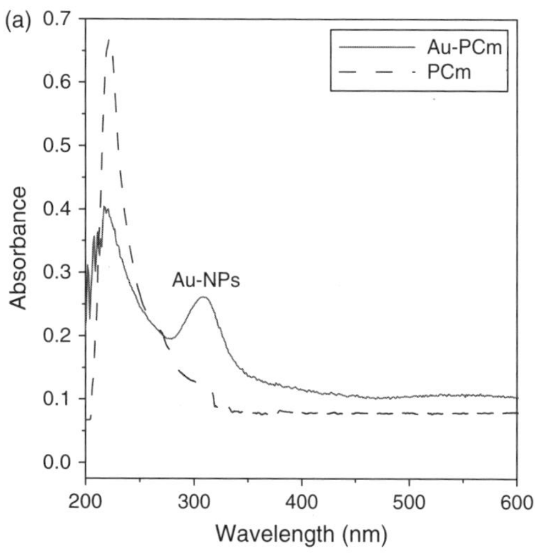

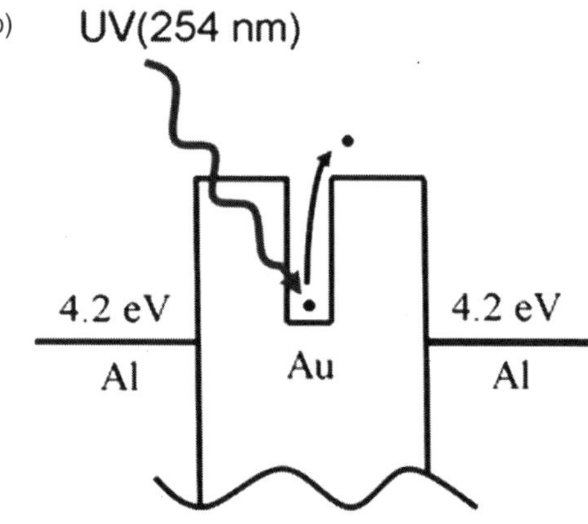

Figure 47. (a) The absorption spectra for pristine PCm and Au–PCm. A very clear Au-NP related absorption at around 310 nm was found, and (b) the schematic band diagram and UV erasing process. Reprinted with permission from [81], H. T. Lin et al., *IEEE Electron Device Lett.* 30, 18 (2009). © 2009, IEEE.

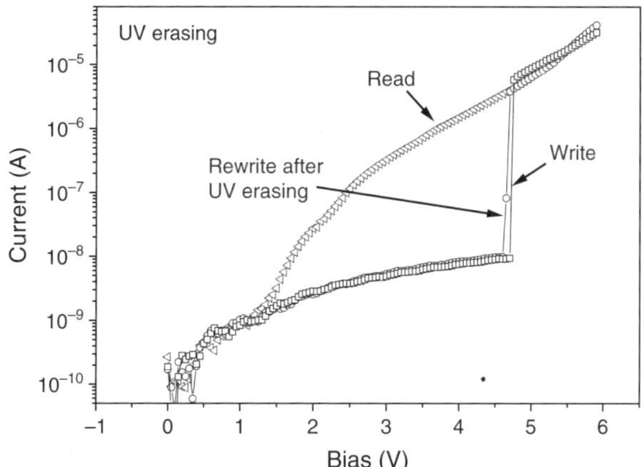

Figure 48. The *I–V* characteristics of the DS-ONBM by UV erasing. After the DS-ONBM was exposed to UV light for 30 seconds, the on state returned to the off state and completed the easing function. Reprinted with permission from [81], H. T. Lin et al., *IEEE Electron Device Lett.* 30, 18 (2009). © 2009, IEEE.

erased the retained data in the DS-ONBM. The schematic band diagram and UV erase process are shown in Figure 47(b).

Figure 48 shows the *I–V* characteristics of the UV erasing process. After the DS-ONBM was exposed to UV light for 30 seconds, the high-conductance current returned to the low-conductance current and completed the easing function. Once the device was erased and returned to low-conductance state, it could be written again and exhibit similar *I–V* characteristics (just as in the first voltage sweep). The bi-stability of the DS-ONBM could be controlled by applying a suitable voltage level. The nonvolatile memory function could last for a number of operations without observing significant degradation.

6. CONCLUSION

In this chapter, the introduction of ONBM has been briefly described. In the Section 2, the Au–NPs embedded in host polymer were utilized to fabricate the Al/PS + Au–NPs/Al memory device. The *I–V* characteristics show that the device switches from an initial low-conductivity state to a high-conductivity state after the application of an external electric field at room temperatures. The current transition exhibits in a very narrow voltage range causes an abrupt increase of the current. The conduction mechanism in nanoparticles contained in polymer memory was experimentally and theoretically investigated. By comparing with a pure PS device, the memory is correlated due to the presence of the Au–NPs. A trap-filled SCLC model is proposed to explain the transport mechanism in this memory device. The experimental results fit the theoretical prediction rather well. The retention time for this device is more than 400 minutes. The light-induced conductivity change further supports the SCLC model.

In the Section 3, in order to obtain a stable ONBM, the Au-PCms in a host polymer were used as the memory active layer. The Al/PCm + Au–PCm/Al memory device was demonstrated. The reproducibility of the Al/PCm + Au–NPs/Al and Al/PCm + Au–PCm/Al was 40% and 82%, respectively. The TEM images show that the polymer stabilized Au–NPs were well dispersed in the polymer matrix. We further demonstrated our concept that polymer stabilized Au–NPs are feasible, thus enabling Au–NPs to be well dispersed in the host polymer to fabricate the stable devices. The electrical bi-stability of the device can be precisely controlled by applying a positive voltage pulse or a negative voltage pulse, respectively. Two orders of magnitude current between the on and off state can be easily achieved in an air environment. This memory can be switched on and off more than 2000 times without appreciable performance degradation. In addition, the memory state can be retained for more than 3 days in an air environment. Therefore, this device is a potential candidate for the next-generation of nonvolatile memories to be applied in RFID, smart card, or system-integrated display.

In the Section 4, *a*-16-byte addressable ONBM array on the plastic substrate was demonstrated. The memory cell can be switched on and off more than 1000 times, and the longest retention time without functional failure can be estimated to be nearly 1 year in the air. In the analysis of the mechanical flexibility, the electrical properties of the ONBM were fairly stable during the application of compressive stress down to 5 mm in bending radius. After connecting the ONBM array to the current-sensing circuit, the ONBM array can be correctly addressed and operated while maintaining low-power consumption.

In Section 5, an UV erasable DS-ONBM that used a AU-PCms on the plastic substrate in the ambient air was demonstrated. The absorption spectrum of the AuNPs showed UV absorption. Therefore, UV light was used to erase the data in the DS-ONBM. The function of UV-erasing and the diode-switch could greatly simplify the required peripheral circuits. This DS-ONBM was demonstrated to be able to read, write, and retain the data, and it was also reusable by UV light illumination. Hence, the UV-erasable DS-ONBM is fully applicable for key applications in printed electronics.

REFERENCES

1. C. D. Müller, A. Falcou, N. Reckefuss, M. Rojahn, V. Wiederhirn, P. Rudati, H. Frohne, O. Nuyken, H. Becker, and K. Meerholz, *Nature* 421, 829 (2003).
2. S. C. Lo, T. D. Anthopoulos, E. B. Namdas, P. L. Burn, and I. D. W. Samuel, *Adv. Mat.* 17, 1945 (2005).
3. G. Dennler and N. S. Sariciftci, *Proceeding of the IEEE* 93, 1429 (2005).
4. G. Darlinski, U. Bottger, and R. Waser, *J. Appl. Phys.* 97, 093708 (2005).
5. M. Mizukami, N. Hirohata, T. Iseki, K. Ohtawara, T. Tada, S. Yagyu, T. Abe, T. Suzuki, Y. Fujisaki, Y. Inoue, S. Tokito, and T. Kurita, *IEEE Electron Device Let.* 27, 249 (2006).
6. K. Nakayama, K. Kojima, Y. Imai, T. Kasai, S. Fukushima, A. Kitagawa, M. Kumeda, Y. Kakimoto, and M. Suzuki, *Jap. J. Appl. Phys. Part* 1 42, 404 (2003).
7. H. J. Hovel and J. J. Urgell, *J. Appl. Phys.* 42, 5076 (1971).
8. T. Rueckes, K. Kim, E. Joselevich, G. Y. Tseng, C. L. Cheung, and C. M. Lieber, *Science* 289, 94 (2000).
9. R. L. Badzey, G. Zolfagharkhani, A. Gaidarzhy, and P. Mohanty, *Appl. Phys. Lett.* 86, 23106 (2005).
10. K. Terabe, T. Hasegawa, T. Nakayama, and M. Aono, *Nature* 433, 47 (2005).

11. N. Kouklin, S. Bandyopadhyay, S. Tereshin, A. Varfolomeev, and D. Zaretsky, *Appl. Phys. Lett.* 76, 460 (2000).
12. R. Ohab, N. Sugiyama, K. Uchida, J. Koga, and A. Toriumi, *IEEE Trans. Electron Device* 49, 1392 (2002).
13. M. L. Ostraat, J. W. De Blauwe, M. L. Green, L. D. Bell, M. L. Brongerma, J. R. Casperson, C. Flagan, and H. A. Atwater, *Appl. Phys. Lett.* 79, 433 (2001).
14. J. C. Scott, *Science* 304, 62 (2004).
15. R. H. Friend, R. W. Gymer, A. B. Holmes, J. H. Burroughes, R. N. Marks, C. Taliani, D. D. C. Bradley, D. A. Dos Santos, J. L. Brédas, M. Lögdlund, and W. R. Salaneck, *Nature* 397, 121 (1999).
16. T. P. Juan, C. Y Chang, and J. Y Lee, *IEEE Electron Device Lett.* 27, 217 (2006).
17. R. Schroeder, L. A. Majewski, M. Voigt, and M. Grell *IEEE Electron Device Lett.* 26, 69 (2005).
18. S. Fukami, H. Honjo, T. Suzuki, and N. Ishiwata, *IEEE Trans. Magnetic.* 43, 3512 (2007).
19. S. C. Li, J. M. Lee, M. F. Shu, J. P. Su, and T. H. Wu, *IEEE Trans. Magnetic.* 41, 899 (2005).
20. S. Kim and H. S. P. Wong, *IEEE Electron Device Lett.* 28, 697 (2007).
21. H. Y. Cheng, C. A. Jong, C. M. Lee, and T. S. Chin, *IEEE Trans. Magnetic.* 41, 1031 (2005).
22. L. V. Gregor, *Thin Solid Films* 2, 235 (1968).
23. H. Carchano, R. Lacoste, and Y. Segui, *Appl. Phys. Lett.* 19, 414 (1971).
24. L. F. Pender and R. J. Fleming, *J. Appl. Phys.* 46, 3426 (1975).
25. A. Szymanski, D. C. Larson, and M. M. Labes, *Appl. Phys. Lett.* 14, 88 (1969).
26. D. Tondelier, K. Lmimouni, and D. Vuillaume, *Appl. Phys. Lett.*, 85, 5763 (2004).
27. A. K. Mahapatro, R. Agrawal, and S. Ghosh, *J. Appl. Phys.* 96, 3583 (2004).
28. C. H. Tu, Y. S. Lai, and D. L. Kwong, *IEEE Electron Device Lett.* 27, 354 (2006).
29. M. Terai, K. Fujita, and T. Tsutsui, *Jap. J. Appl. Phys.* 45, 3754 (2006).
30. H. K. Henisch and W. R. Smith, *Appl. Phys. Lett.* 24, 589 (1974).
31. Y. Segui, B. Ai, and H. Carchano, *J. Appl. Phys.* 47, 140 (1976).
32. Y. S. Lai, C.-H. Tu, D.-L. Kwong, and J. S. Chen, *Appl. Phys. Lett.* 87, 122101 (2005).
33. H. S. Majumdar, A. Bandyopadhyay, A. Bolognesi, and A. J. Pal, *J. Appl. Phys.* 91, 2433 (2002).
34. L. D. Bozano, B. W. Kean, M. Beinhoff, K. R. Carter, P. M. Rice, and J. C. Scott, *Adv. Function. Mat.* 15, 1933 (2005).
35. M. Lauters, B. McCarthy, D. Sarid, and G. E. Jabbour, *Appl. Phys. Lett.* 89, 013507 (2006).
36. R. S. Potember, T. O. Poehler, and D. O. Cowan, *Appl. Phys. Lett.* 34, 405 (1979).
37. E. I. Kamitsos, C. H. Tzinis, and W. M. Risen, *Solid State Commun.* 42, 561 (1982).
38. K. Xiao, I. N. Ivanov, A. A. Puretzky, Z. Liu, and D. B. Geohegan, *Adv. Mat.* 18, 2184 (2006).
39. L. P. Ma, Q. F. Xu, and Y. Yang, *Appl. Phys. Lett.* 84, 4908 (2004).
40. H. J. Gao, K. Sohlberg, Z. Q. Xue, H. Y. Chen, S. M. Hou, L. P. Ma, X. W. Fang, S. J. Pang, and S. J. Pennycook, *Phys. Rev. Lett.* 84, 1780 (2000).
41. C. W. Chu, J. Ouyang, J. H. Tseng, and Y. Yang, *Adv. Mat.* 17, 1440 (2005).
42. Z. C. Liu, F. L. Xue, Y. Su, and K. Varahramyan, *IEEE Electron Device Lett.* 27, 151 (2006).
43. L. P. Ma, W. J. Yang, Z. Q. Xue, and S. J. Pang, *Appl. Phys. Lett.* 73, 850 (1998).
44. Q. Ling, Y. Song, S. J. Ding, C. Zhu, D. S. H. Chan, D.-L. Kwong, E.-T. Kang, and K.-G. Neoh, *Adv. Mat.* 17, 455 (2005).
45. Y. Song, Q. D. Ling, C. Zhu, E. T. Kang, D. S. H. Chan, Y. H. Wang, and D. L. Kwong, *IEEE Electron Device Lett.* 27, 154 (2006).
46. Y. Iwasa, T. Koda, S. Koshihara, Y. Tokura, N. Iwasawa, and G. Saito, *Phys. Rev. B* 39, 10441 (1989).
47. C. K. Chiang, C. R. Fincher, Y. W. Park, A. J. Heeger, H. Shirakawa, E. J. Louis, S. C. Gau, and A. G. McDiarmid, *Phys. Rev. Let.* 39, 1098 (1978).
48. Q. X. Lai, Z. H. Zhu, Y. Chen, S. Patil, and F. Wudl, *Appl. Phys. Lett.* 88, 133515 (2006).
49. L. P. Ma, J. Liu, S. M. Pyo, and Y. Yang, *Appl. Phys. Lett.* 80, 362 (2002).
50. L. P. Ma, J. Liu, and Y. Yang, *Appl. Phys. Lett.* 80, 2997 (2002).
51. L. D. Bozano, B. W. Kean, V. R. Deline, J. R. Salem, and J. C. Scott, *Appl. Phys. Lett.* 84, 607 (2004).
52. L. P. Ma, S. M. Pyo, J. Y. Ouyang, Q. F. Yu, and Y. Yang, *Appl. Phys. Lett.* 82, 1419 (2003).
53. J. Ouyang, C.-W. Chu, D. Sieves, and Y. Yang, *Appl. Phys. Lett.* 86, 123507 (2005).
54. J. Ouyang, C. W. Chu, C. R. Szmanda, L. Ma, and Y. Yang, *Nat. Mat.* 3, 918 (2004).
55. J. Ouyang, C. W. Chu, R. J. H. Tseng, A. Prakash, and Y. Yang, *Proceedings of the IEEE* 93, 1287 (2005).
56. A. Prakash, J. Ouyang, J. L. Lin, and Y. Yang, *J. Appl. Phys.* 100, 054309 (2006).
57. B. Prahdan, S. K. Batabyal, and A. J. Pal, *J. Phys. Chem. B* 110, 8274 (2006).
58. S. H. Kang, T. Crisp, I. Kymissis, and V. Bulovic, *Appl. Phys. Lett.* 85, 4666 (2004).
59. A. Kiesow, J. E. Morris, C. Radehaus, and A. Heilmann, *J. Appl. Phys.* 94, 6988 (2003).
60. R. J. Tseng, J. Ouyang, C. W. Chu, J. Huang, and Y. Yang, *Appl. Phys. Lett.* 88, 123506 (2006).
61. D. Y. Tu, C. S. Wang, Z. Y. Ji, W. P. Hu, and M. Liu, *IEEE Electron Device Solid-State Circuit* 19–21, 575 (2005).
62. J. C. Scott and L. D. Bozano, *Adv. Mater.* 19, 1452 (2007).
63. J. G. Simmons and R. R. Verderber, *Proc. Roy. Soc. Ser. A* 301, 77 (1967).
64. H. T. Lin, Z. Pei, and Y. J. Chan, *IEEE Electron Device Lett.* 28, 569 (2007).
65. O. Nagao, G. Harada, T. Sugawara, A. Sasaki, and Y. Ito, *Jap. J. Appl. Phys.* 43, 7742 (2004).
66. T. S. Ahmadi, Z. L. Wang, T. C. Green, A. Henglein, and M. A. El-Sayed, *Science* 272, 1924 (1996).
67. S. A. Harfenist, Z. L. Wang, M. M. Alvarez, I. Vezmar, and R. L. Whetten, *J. Phys. Chem.* 100, 13904 (1996).
68. C. R. Kagan, C. B. Murray, M. Nirmal, and M. G. Bawendu, *Phys. Rev. Lett.* 76, 1517 (1996).
69. S. A. Harfenist, Z. L. Wang, R. L. Whetten, I. Vezmar, and M. M. Alvarez, *Adv. Mat.* 9, 817 (1997).
70. S. Murthy, T. P. Bigioni, Z. L. Wang, J. T. Khoury, and R. L. Whetten, *Mat. Lett.* 30, 321 (1997).
71. P. D. Nellist and S. J. Pennycook, *Phys. Rev. Lett.* 81, 4156 (1998).
72. Z. Pei, A. Y. K. Su, and H. L. Hwang, *Appl. Phys. Lett.* 86, 063503 (2005).
73. M. A. Lampert and P. Mark, Current Injection in Solids, pp. 14–25, Academic Press, New York, 1970.
74. K. Efimenko, V. Rybka, V. Svorcik, and V. Hnatowicz, *App. Phys. A: Mat. Science Process.* 67, 503 (1998).
75. H. T. Lin, Z. Pei, J. R. Chen, G. W. Hwang, J. F. Fan, and Y. J. Chan, *IEEE Electron Device Lett.* 28, 951 (2007).
76. J.-R. Chen, H.-T. Lin, G.-W. Hwang, Y.-J. Chan, and P.-W. Li, *Nanotechnology* 20, 255706 (2009).
77. K. Nikawa, C. Matsumoto, and S. Inoue, *Jap. J. Appl. Phys.* 34, 2260 (1995).

78. D. A. Neamen, "Semiconductor Physics and Devices," Chap. 4, 3rd Edition, McGraw–Hill, New York, 2003.
79. H. T. Lin, Z. Pei, J. R. Chen, C. P. Kung, Y. C. Lin, C. M. Tseng, and Y. J. Chan, "IEEE Int. Electron Device Meeting Tech. Dig.," pp. 233–236, 2007.
80. T. Sekitani, S. Iba, Y. Kato, and T. Someya, *Jap. J. Appl. Phys.* 44, 2841 (2005).
81. H.-T. Lin, Z. Pei, J.-R. Chen, and Y.-J. Chan, *IEEE Electron Device Lett.* 30, 18 (2009).
82. D. T. Simon, M. S. Griffo, R. A. Dipietro, S. A. Swanson, and S. A. Carter, *Appl. Phys. Lett.* 89, 133510 (2006).
83. H. P. Wang, S. Pigeon, R. Izquierdo, and R. Martel, *Appl. Phys. Lett.* 89, 183502 (2006).
84. G. Gu, M. G. Kane, and S. C. Mau, *J. Appl. Phys.* 101, 014504 (2007).
85. J. Chen and D. Ma, *J. Appl. Phys.* 100, 034512 (2006).
86. T. Kondo, S. M. Lee, M. Malicki, B. Domercq, S. R. Marder, and B. Kippelen, *Adv. Function. Mat.* 18, 1112 (2008).

CHAPTER 12

Organic/Polymeric Films with Resistive-Switching Behavior and Their Application as Nonvolatile Memory Devices

Jianyong Ouyang

Department of Materials Science and Engineering, National University of Singapore, Singapore 117574

CONTENTS

1. INTRODUCTION

The demand for high-speed and high-density memory devices has been stronger and stronger with the rapid development of information technology. Flexible electronic devices are regarded as the next-generation devices, and high mechanical flexibility is also required for the future memory devices. Two-terminal organic or polymer devices with resistive switches have gained strong attention due to their unique advantages. They have strong application as memory devices, and they can be called organic/polymeric memristors. This article reviews the materials, fabrication, memory application, and resistive-switching mechanism of organic and polymeric memristors. The organic memristors are classified into hybrid organic memristors and pure organic memristors in terms of the active materials. Hybrid materials of inorganic nanoparticles (NPs) and organic molecules or polymers are the active materials of the former, while the latter uses only organic molecules and/or polymers for the active materials. Several mechanisms have been proposed for the resistive switches observed in organic/polymeric memristors. The major mechanisms for the resistive switches include the electric-field-induced charge transfer between two components or two units in one

ISBN: 1-58883-251-1

Nonvolatile Memories: Materials, Devices and Applications
Edited by Tseung-Yuen Tseng and Simon M. Sze
Volume 2: Pages: 289–307

molecule, the charge trapping on inorganic NPs or conjugated organic molecules, and electric-field-induced polarization. The organic/polymeric memristors can potentially solve technical problems in the present leading memory devices. Moreover, the organic/polymeric memristors can be flexible, and bending of the devices does not remarkably affect the electrical behavior. Electronic papers were also proposed by combining organic memristors with light-emitting diodes.

Organic electronics has been gaining strong attention. This area is fundamentally different from the electronics of metals and inorganic semiconductors due to the weak intermolecular interactions for organic molecules and polymers [1]. The development of organic electronics can be traced back to 1950s with the concept of organic semiconductors. Generally, conjugated organic molecules and polymers can be regarded as organic semiconductors, because they can have interesting optical and electrical properties. The organic semiconductors usually have low conductivity in the neutral state, and the conductivity can significantly increase after oxidation or reduction. Charge-transfer complexes of tetracyanoquinodimethane (TCNQ) can have a conductivity as high as 10^2 S cm^{-1}, in which TCNQ acts as an electron acceptor [2, 3]. Later, metallic conductivity was discovered on charge-transfer organic complexes, such as tetrathiafulvalene (TTF)-TCNQ [4, 5], and conducting polymers [6]. Even superconductivity was observed on organic solids, such as charge-transfer complexes of bis(ethylenedithio) TTF [7] and fullerene [8, 9]. In principle, organic or polymeric materials can function like metals or inorganic semiconductors in many electronic devices. Organic electronic devices, including light-emitting diodes, field-effect transistors, and solar cells, are regarded as the next-generation electronic devices. They have advantages of low fabrication cost and high mechanical flexibility in comparison with the inorganic semiconductor devices.

In the family of organic electronic devices, memory devices using organic molecules or polymers as the active material are relatively new members [10–14]. But, they have been arising strong interest because they are indispensable units for future electronics, particularly in the field of information technology. The memory application of the organic and polymer devices is the basis of resistive switches, i.e., the devices can be electrically switched between two or multiple states with significantly different resistances. The devices with resistive switches can have applications for memory, and they are also called memresitors [15]. The organic/polymeric memristors usually have a structure of an active layer sandwiched between two electrodes. They can have a short response time and an extremely high density. They can potentially solve all technical difficulties met in the three leading memory devices: dynamic random access memories (DRAMs), hard-disk drives (HDDs) and flash memories. DRAMs are volatile and need to refresh frequently, although they have very high switching speeds and a large number of write-erase cycles. HDDs can achieve a very high data density and have many write-erase cycles. But, they respond slowly to the magnetic field. Flash memories have the advantage of nonvolatility, and they are capable of storing information for a long period. However, they have a low write-erase speed and a limited number of rewrite cycles.

Moreover, organic and polymeric materials enable the organic memristors to be highly flexible, so that they are highly compatible with other flexible electronic devices that are regarded as the next-generation electronic devices. This can bring new applications for the memory devices, such as in biologic technologies and electronic books.

This article reviews the fabrication, electrical characterization, resistive-switching mechanism, and memory application of organic memristors. The organic memristors are classified into two categories in terms of the active materials: (1) hybrid organic memresitors, whose active materials are hybrid materials of inorganic NPs and organic/polymeric materials, and (2) pure organic memresitors, whose active materials are only organic molecules or polymers. Flexible organic memristors and the application of memristors in electronic papers are also included.

2. HYBRID ORGANIC MEMRISTORS

2.1. Materials, Device Architectures, and Fabrication Techniques

Most of the current research on organic memristors is focused on devices with hybrid materials consisting of inorganic NPs and organic or polymer materials as the active materials. Figure 1 presents the chemical structure of some organic molecules and polymers used in the hybrid organic memristors. Both thermal deposition and solution processing can be used to fabricate the active layer. The hybrid organic memristors can be classified into three types of devices in terms of the structure of the hybrid materials: triple layers, a polymer layer blended with NPs, and nanocomposites.

2.1.1. Devices with a Triple-Layer Structure

The first type of the hybrid organic memristors has architecture with a triple-layer structure sandwiched between two electrodes (Fig. 2(a)). The top and bottom layers of the triple-layer structure are made of organic semiconductors, while the middle metal layer is comprised of metal NP with an organic or oxide shell (Fig. 2(b)). Ma et al. [16] reported the first triple-layer memristor, and their device used Al NPs by thermal deposition as the middle layer, 2-amino-4,5-imidazoledicarbonitrile (AIDCN) as the two organic layers, and Al as the top and bottom electrodes. That device is presented with Al/AIDCN/Al NPs/AIDCN/Al in this review. Besides AIDCN and Al, aluminum tris(8-hydroxyquinoline) (Alq_3) [17, 18], *N*,*N*′-diphenyl-*N*,*N*′-bis(3-methyl-phenyl)-1,1′biphenyl-4,4′diamine (TPD) [19], and fullerene (C_{60}) [20] were also used for the top and bottom layers, and Cu, Ag, Au, and Ni were exploited for the middle layer [17, 21, 22]. Li et al. also used core/shell CdSe/ZnS NPs for the middle layer [20].

All of the three layers are usually fabricated by thermal deposition. The top and bottom organic layers have a thickness of 20–50 nm, and the middle metal layer has a thickness of around 10 nm. The electrical behavior of the hybrid memristors is strongly dependent on the thickness and the morphology of the three layers, particularly on the middle metal layer. The middle metal layer consists of metal NPs coated

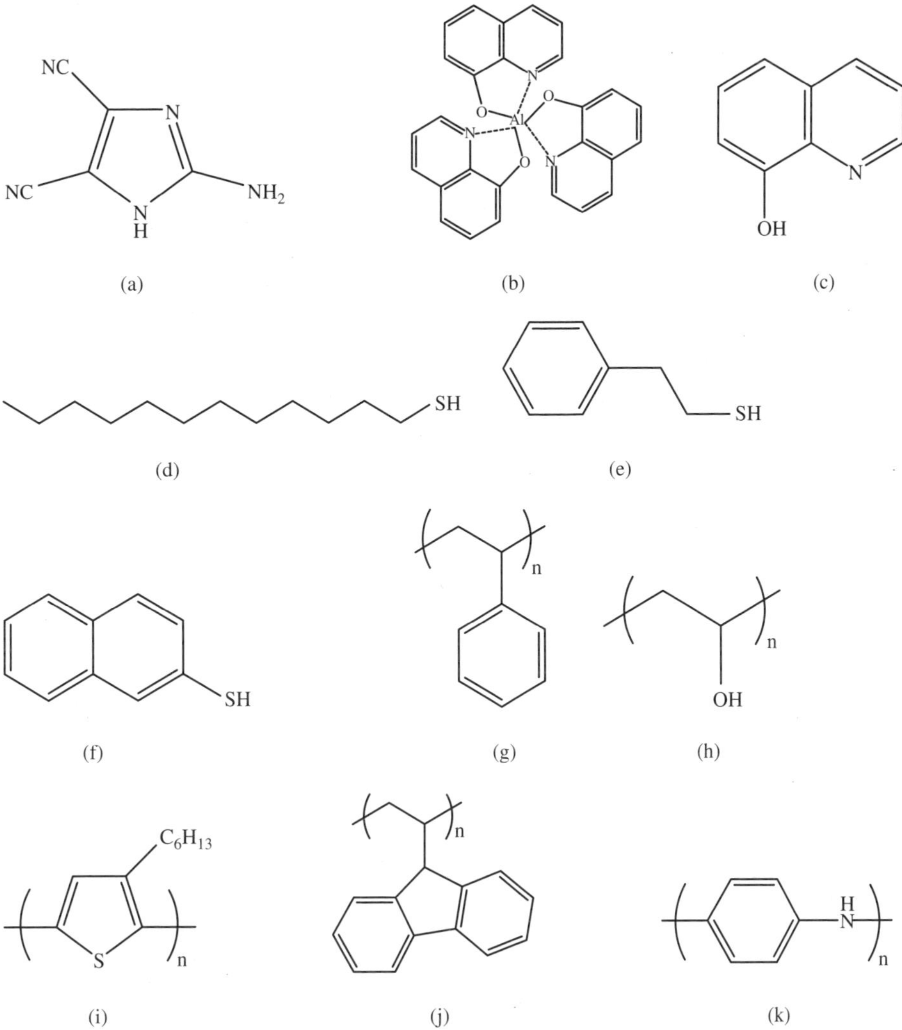

Figure 1. Chemical structure of (a) AIDCN, (b) aluminum tris(8-hydroxyquinoline) (Alq_3), (c) 8HQ, (d) 1-dodecanethiol, (e) 2-benzeneethanethiol (BET), (f) 2NT, (g) PS, (h) polyvinyl alcohol, (i) P3HT, (j) PVK, and (k) PANi.

with metal oxide, which resulted from the oxidation of the metal by the trace amount of oxygen in the chamber during the thermal evaporation [17, 21]. Reddy et al. observed such core–shell structures and the thickness of the oxide shell is nearly same (around 1.5–2.0 nm) for all sizes of NPs with transmission electron microscopy (TEM; Fig. 3) [18]. Thus, the morphology of the middle metal layer is quite sensitive to the experimental conditions during the thermal evaporation, such as the evaporation rate, vacuum level, temperature in chamber, and contamination of the chamber. The middle metal layer should be fabricated through a slow deposition process to achieve an assembly of NPs stabilized by metal oxide. The metal oxide stabilizes the metal NPs and constructs an energy barrier for the metal core. The shell can also be made of organic molecules, which are present in the evaporator chamber as contaminant.

2.1.2. Devices with a Polymer Layer Blended with Nanoparticles

The triple-layer structure can be replaced with a single polymer layer embedded with NPs (Fig. 4). Ouyang et al. were the first to report such devices in 2005 [23]. In that report, there were three components, gold NPs capped with 1-dodecanethiol (Au-DT NPs), conjugated 8-hydroxyquinoline (8HQ) and polystyrene (PS), in the active layer of the devices. The Au-DT NPs had an average diameter of 2.8 nm (Fig. 5). The device is represented by glass/Al/Au-DT NPs + 8HQ + PS/Al, when Al is used as the top and bottom electrode. The gold NPs can be prepared by chemical synthesis and are soluble in solvents. Thus, the active layer is usually fabricated by solution processing, such as spin coating.

The size and the shell of the gold NPs can be well controlled by the solution method. This solves the difficulty in preparing metal NPs by the thermal deposition. Besides gold NPs capped with thiols, gold NPs capped with dendrons [24] and silver NPs [25, 26] were also used. Semiconductor NPs, such as ZnO, CdS, CdSe, ZnS, Cu_2O, and core/shell CdSe/ZnS, were reported to replace the metal NPs in the active layer as well [27–33]. Kim et al. also reported memristors using magnetite NPs [34]. Besides the solution coating, other processing techniques, such as layer-by-layer

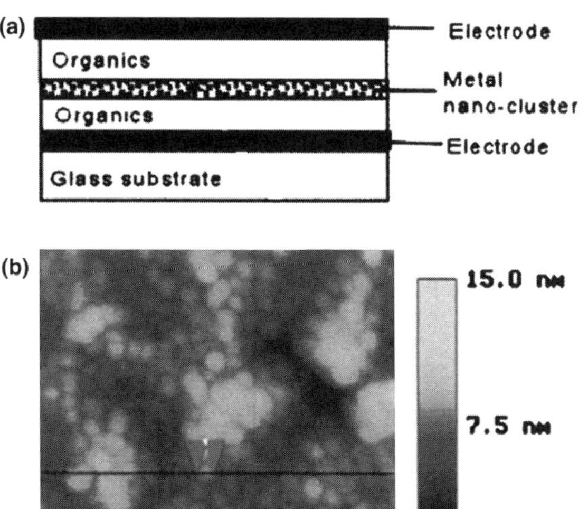

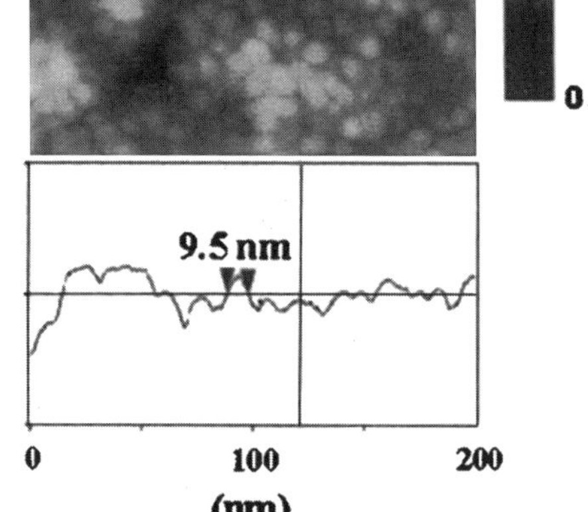

Figure 2. (a) Schematic architecture of a triple-layer device and (b) AFM image of the middle metal layer. Reprinted with permission from [21], L. Ma et al., *Appl. Phys. Lett.* 82, 1419 (2003). © 2003, American Institute of Physics.

electrostatic assembly of the NP and polymer layers, were also reported to fabricate the active layer [30].

Resistive switches were observed on a single polymer layer without an organic semiconductor for some devices, while the presence of the organic semiconductors can improve the stability of the devices in the low-resistance state. The inert polymer acts as the matrix, which does not contribute to the resistive switches. Hence, resistive switches were recently observed on assemblies of CdSe NPs and core/shell CdS/PbS NPs without organic semiconductors and a polymer matrix [35–37].

2.1.3. Devices with Nanocomposites

A variation of the NP and organic semiconductor mixtures is nanocomposites, in which metal NPs are directly attached to a conjugated polymer. The nanocomposites provide a unique way to control the positions and interactions of NPs and the polymers in the active layer, because the interaction between them is crucial for the resistive switches.

Tseng et al. reported the memristors using nanocomposites of polyaniline (PANi) nanofibers decorated with Au NPs [38]. The nanocomposite, whose TEM image is shown in Figure 6, was prepared by growing Au NPs on the PANi nanofibers through the reduction of chloroauric acid ($HAuCl_4$) in an aqueous solution containing the nanofibers [39, 40]. Polyvinyl alcohol was used as the matrix of the nanocomposites, and the active layer is prepared by spin coating. Later, nanocomposites of metal NPs and the tobacco mosaic virus were also used as the active material of memristors [41]. Nanocomposites of ZnO NPs and carbon nanotubes were reported as the active materials in the single-layer devices as well [57].

2.2. Electrical Behavior and Resistive Switches

2.2.1. Bipolar Resistive Switches

These hybrid organic devices exhibit resistive switches when an electrical voltage is applied. The electrical behavior is quite sensitive to the experimental conditions and materials. Generally, three types of resistive switches, i.e., bipolar and unipolar resistive switches and a single resistive switch, were observed [42, 43]. Figure 7 shows the typical current–voltage (I–V) curves of bipolar resistive switches observed on a device glass/Al/Au-DT NPs + 8HQ + PS/Al [23]. Initially, the device was in a high-resistance state. The current was approximately 10^{-11} A at 1 V. The current exhibited an abrupt transition at about 2.7 V to a low resistance state, which increased from 10^{-11} to 10^{-7} A in the first voltage scan (curve a). The high- and low-resistance states are defined as "OFF" and "ON" states, respectively. The device exhibited good stability in the ON state as indicated in the subsequent voltage scan (curve b). The ON state was able to return to the OFF state by applying a negative bias (curve c), where the current suddenly dropped to 10^{-10} A at −1.8 V.

The conduction mechanisms are different in the two states. The conduction mechanisms for the device glass/Al/Au-DT NP + 8HQ + PS/Al were revealed by the temperature dependence of currents and analysis of the current–voltage curves. The conduction mechanism in the OFF state may be due to small amounts of impurity or hot electron injection. The currents in the ON state do not vary significantly with the temperature (Fig. 8). The activation energy is only 1–1.7 meV for an applied voltage of 1–4 V. Thus, the electrical current in the ON state may be due to some temperature independent charge tunneling processes, such as direct tunneling (i.e., tunneling through a square barrier) and Fowler–Nordheim tunneling (i.e., tunneling through a triangular barrier) [44]. The I–V curve of the device in the ON state is nonlinear but cannot be fitted well by Fowler–Nordheim tunneling alone (Fig. 9), but it can be well modeled by a combination of direct tunneling and Fowler–Nordheim tunneling,

$$I = C_1 V e^{-(2d\sqrt{2m^*\Phi})/\hbar} + C_2 V^2 e^{-(4d\Phi^{3/2}\sqrt{2m^*})/(3q\hbar V)}$$

The first term on the right-hand side of the equation is the current contributed by direct tunneling, and the second term is the current by Fowler–Nordheim tunneling. Φ is the energy barrier height. At low voltage, $V < \Phi$, direct tunneling is the dominant conduction mechanism, and at high voltage, $V > \Phi$, Fowler–Nordheim tunneling becomes the dominant conduction mechanism.

The switch from the OFF to ON state could occur at either polarity, i.e., regardless whether the bottom electrode was positively or negatively biased at the first scan. But, the reverse switch from ON to OFF took place only

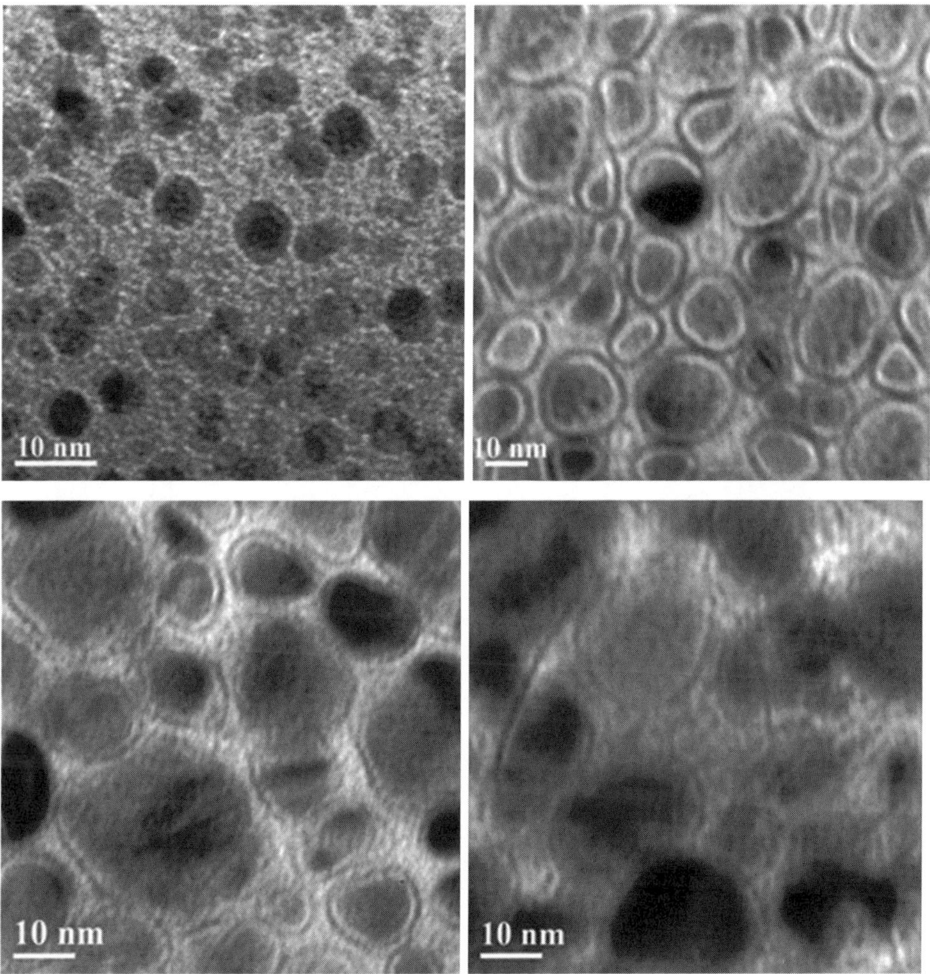

Figure 3. TEM images of the middle aluminum layers of various thicknesses: (a) 5 nm, (b) 10 nm, (c) 15 nm, and (d) 20 nm. Reprinted with permission from [18], V. S. Reddy et al., *Appl. Phys. Lett.* 94, 173304 (2009). © 2009, American Institute of Physics.

at the opposite polarity of the first scan. Thus, the electrical switches are bipolar resistive switches. Bipolar resistive switches were observed on many devices, including single-layer and triple-layer devices [11, 12]. Figure 10 presents the bipolar resistive switches reported by Ma et al. on Al/AIDCN/Al NPs/AIDCN/Al [21].

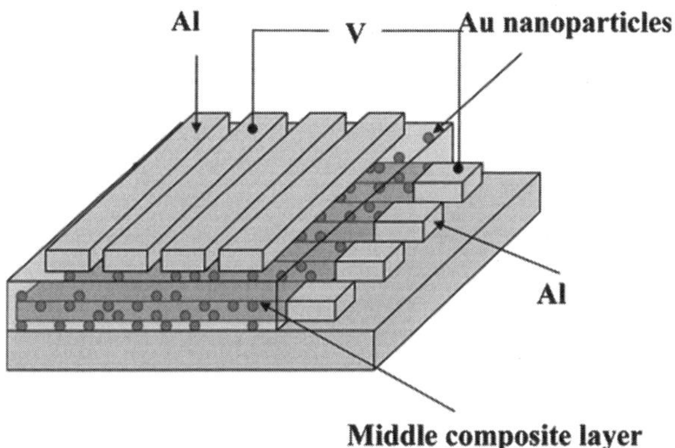

Figure 4. Schematic architecture of a single-layer device. The gray dots represent the metal NPs. Reprinted with permission from [11], Y. Yang et al., *Adv. Funct. Mater.* 16, 1001 (2006). © 2006, Wiley-VCH Verlag GmbH & Co. KGaA.

2.2.2. Unipolar Resistive Switches

The resistive switches are quite sensitive to the fabrication conditions and materials. Bozano et al. observed unipolar resistive switches on their triple-layer memristors with Alq_3 replacing AIDCN as the organic semiconductor (Fig. 11) [17]. The threshold voltage V_{th} from OFF to ON was about 2.8 V. The device was stable in the ON state if the scanning voltage kept below V_{max}, which was the voltage corresponding to the maximum current. The device was switched to the OFF state when the voltage was increased to V_{min}, which was the voltage corresponding to the minimum current. The device could be switched between the ON and OFF states by applying voltages at the same polarity. The decrease in the current at the voltage over V_{max} is called the negative differential resistance (NDR).

Unipolar resistive switches were also observed on the single-layer nanocomposite memristors. Figure 12 presents the I–V curves of the devices with PANi nanofiber/Au NP composites [38]. The transition voltage from OFF to ON is 3 V. NDR appears when the voltage is above 3 V.

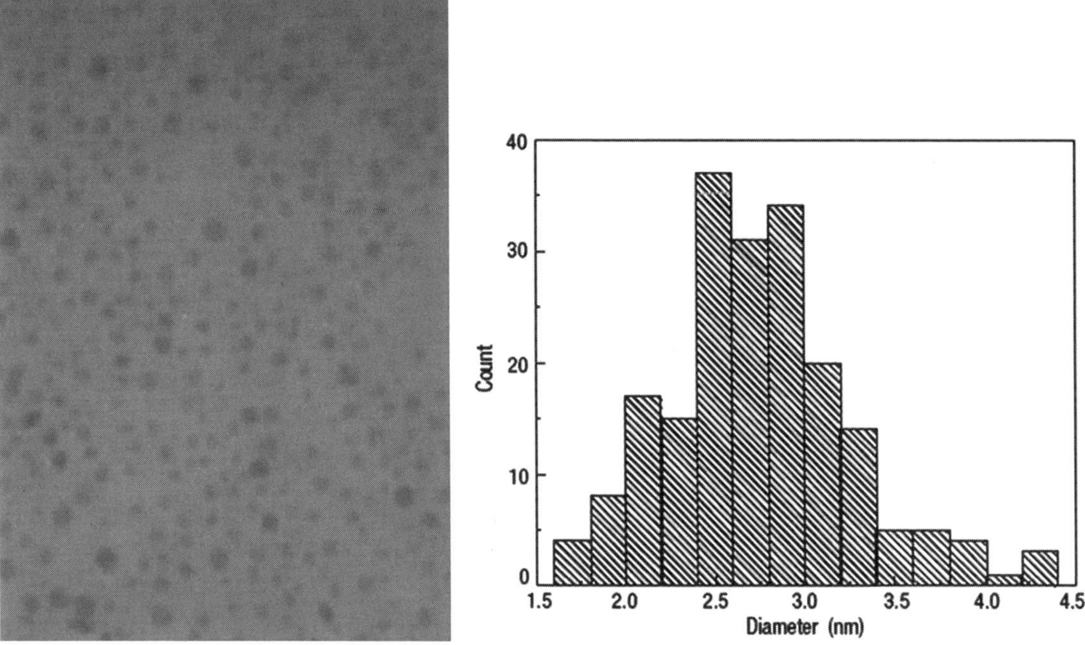

Figure 5. TEM image and size histogram of Au-D NPs. Reprinted with permission from [23], J. Ouyang et al., *Nat. Mater.* 3, 918 (2004). © 2004, Nature Publishing Group.

2.2.3. Single Resistive Switch

Besides the reversal resistive switches, some devices exhibit a single resistive switch, i.e., only one switch from OFF to ON, since the as-prepared devices are in the OFF state. The devices cannot be switched back to the OFF state by applying a voltage in the same or opposite polarity. One example is the devices with a PS layer blended with Au NPs capped with conjugated 2-naphthalenethiol (2NT) sandwiched between two Al electrodes. The *I–V* curves are shown in Figure 13 [45]. A single resistive switch was also observed on devices with ZnO NPs [27].

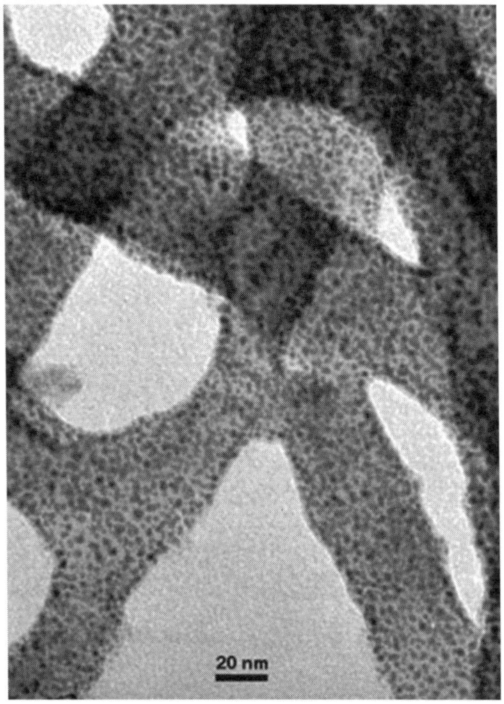

Figure 6. TEM image of a polyaniline nanofiber/gold NP composite. The black dots are 1 nm-size gold NPs within 30 nm-diameter polyaniline nanofibers. Reprinted with permission from [38], R. Tseng et al., *Nano Lett.* 5, 1077 (2005). © 2005, American Chemical Society.

2.3. Memory Application for Resistive-Switching Devices

The devices with resistive switches can have important applications as memory devices. Those devices with a single resistive switch can be used as write-once-read-many times

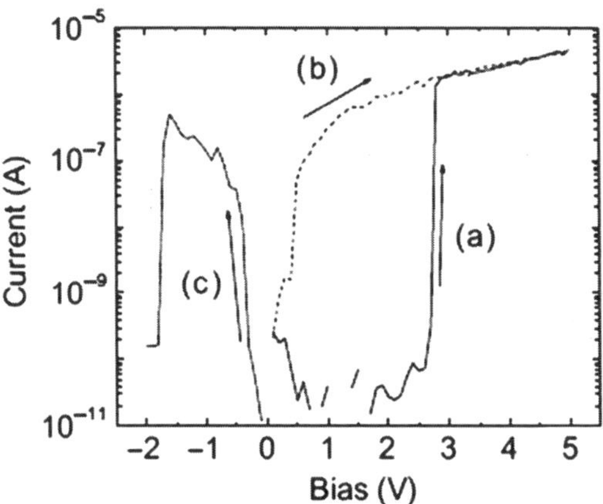

Figure 7. *I–V* curves of an Al/Au-DT NPs + 8HQ + PS/Al device tested in vacuum: (a) first-, (b) second-, and (c) third-bias scans. The arrows indicate the voltage-scanning directions. Reprinted with permission from [23], J. Ouyang et al., *Nat. Mater.* 3, 918 (2004). © 2004, Nature Publishing Group.

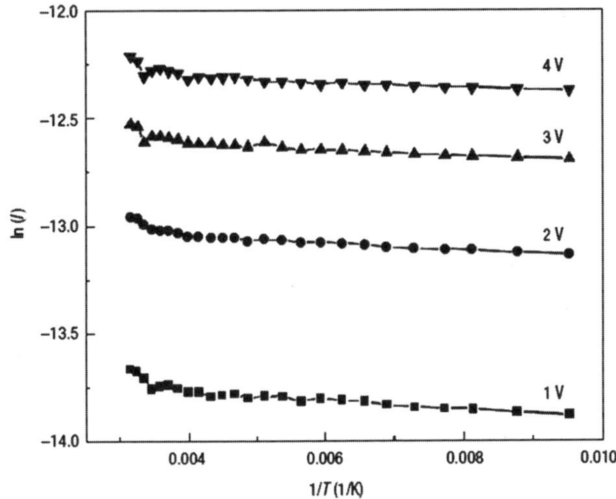

Figure 8. Arrhenius plot of the temperature dependence of currents at 1, 2, 3, and 4 V for Al/Au-DT NPs + 8HQ + PS/Al in the ON state. Reprinted with permission from [23], J. Ouyang et al., *Nat. Mater.* 3, 918 (2004). © 2004, Nature Publishing Group.

memory devices, while the others with repeatable reversal resistive switches can be used as nonvolatile memory devices.

Many hybrid organic memristors can be switched between the two resistance states numerous times, and the resistive switches can be achieved by applying short voltage pulses. A device glass/Al/Au-DT NPs + 8HQ + PS/Al is used as an example here. The transition time from OFF to ON is less than 25 ns [23]. The ON and OFF states can be defined as "1" and "0", respectively, e.g., in digital memories. The processes to turn the device from "0" to "1" or from "1" to "0" can then be defined as "write" and "erase," respectively. The two resistive states can be detected by applying a small voltage. Figure 14 shows the write-read-erase cycles of a device

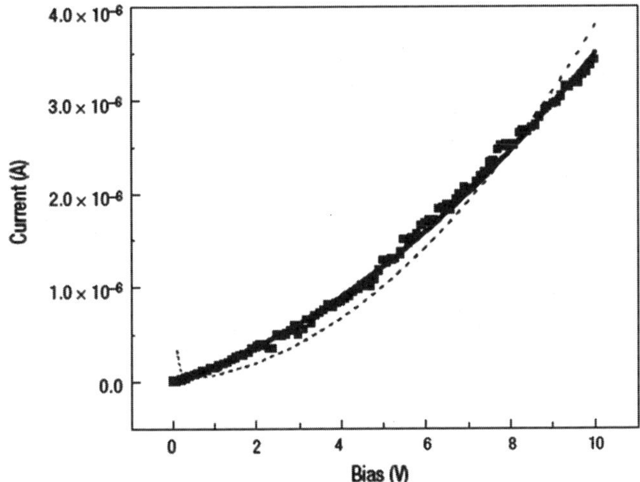

Figure 9. *I–V* curve of a device Al/Au-DT NPs + 8HQ + PS/Al in the ON state. The scattered points are the experimental results; the solid line is the data fit by combining direct tunneling and Fowler–Nordheim tunneling; and the broken line is the data fit by Fowler–Nordheim tunneling. Reprinted with permission from [23], J. Ouyang et al., *Nat. Mater.* 3, 918 (2004). © 2004, Nature Publishing Group.

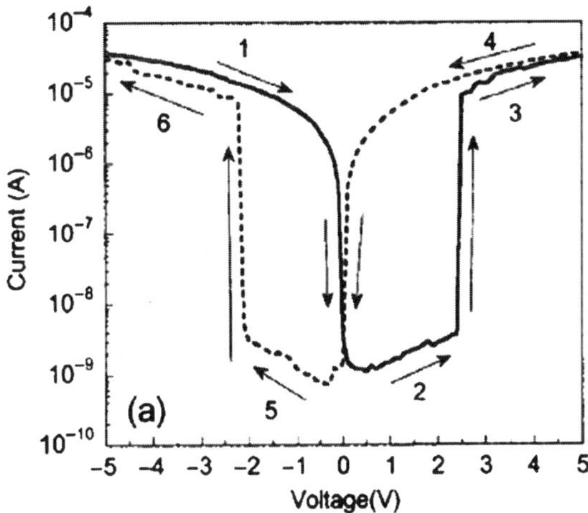

Figure 10. *I–V* curves of a device Al/AIDCN/Al/AIDCN/Al. Reprinted with permission from [21], L. Ma et al., *Appl. Phys. Lett.* 82, 1419 (2003). © 2003, American Institute of Physics.

Al/Au-DT NPs + 8HQ + PS/Al. The "write" and "erase" were performed by applying a pulse of 5 V and −2.1 V, respectively, and the "read" was carried out by applying a pulse of 1 V. The "read" current after "write" was higher than that after "erase" by two to three orders in magnitude. The cycles demonstrate that the device can be used as a nonvolatile memory device.

Another important parameter for a nonvolatile memory application is the stabilities of the devices in the two resistive states. Both the triple-layer and single-layer devices are initially in the OFF state and quite stable in the OFF state. They can also have good stability in the ON state. Figure 15 presents the current at 1 V for the device Al/Au-DT NPs + 8HQ + PS/Al in the ON state. Although the current decreases with time, it is still higher than that in the "OFF" state by one to two orders in magnitude after 4000 minutes [45].

These hybrid organic memristors can have an extremely high density when they have extremely small electrodes.

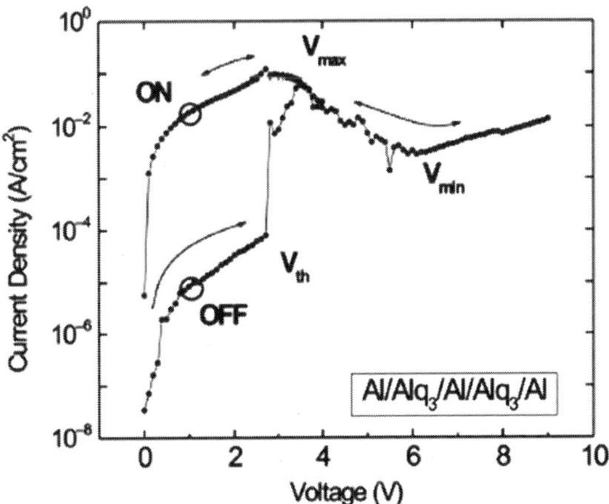

Figure 11. *I–V* curves of an Al (50 nm)/Alq_3 (50 nm)/Al (5 nm)/Alq_3 (50 nm) device. Reprinted with permission from [17], L. D. Bozano et al., *Appl. Phys. Lett.* 84, 607 (2004). © 2004, American Institute of Physics.

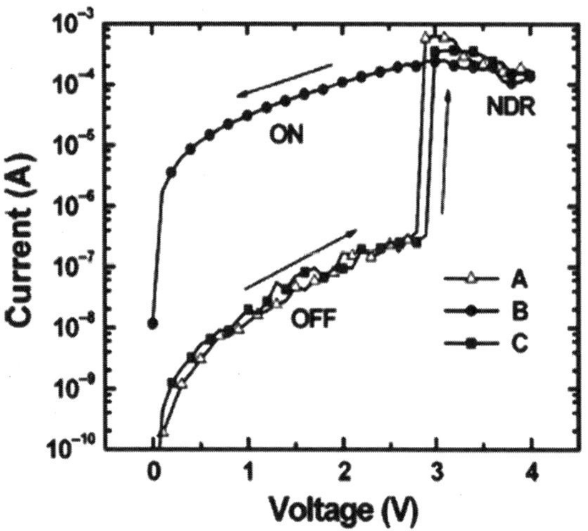

Figure 12. I–V curves of a polyaniline nanofiber/gold NP device. The voltage is scanned from (a) 0 to +4 V, (b) +4 to 0 V, and (c) 0 to +4 V. Reprinted with permission from [38], R. Tseng et al., *Nano Lett.* 5, 1077 (2005). © 2005, American Chemical Society.

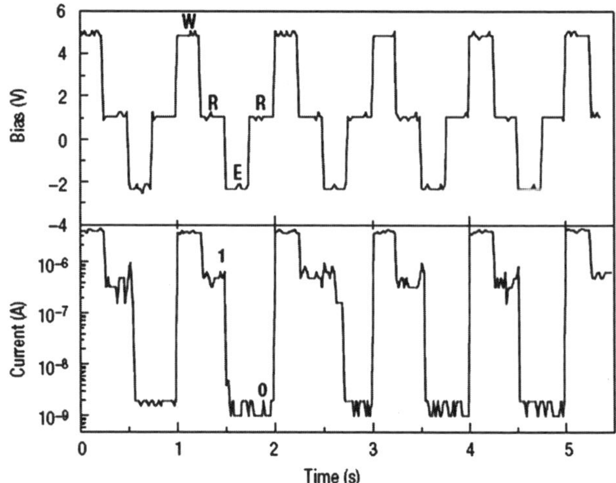

Figure 14. Write-read-erase cycles of a device Al/Au-DT NPs + 8HQ + PS/Al. The top and bottom curves are the applied voltage and the corresponding current, respectively. W, R and E in the top figure mean write, read and erase, respectively. The labels '1' and '0' in the bottom figure indicate the device in the ON and OFF states, respectively. Reprinted with permission from [23], J. Ouyang et al., *Nat. Mater.* 3, 918 (2004). © 2004, Nature Publishing Group.

Operation of these devices with an AFM tip as the top electrode was first demonstrated by Ouyang et al. (Fig. 16(a)) [23]. The device was fabricated by spin-coating a solution of Au-DT NPs, 8HQ, and PS on a conductive Si substrate. The conductive Si substrate was used as the bottom electrode, while an AFM tip was positioned on the polymer film and acted as the top electrode. Figure 16(b) shows a surface potential AFM picture of the Au-DT NPs + 8HQ + PS film. At first, an area of 20 μm × 10 μm of the film was scanned vertically in contact mode by applying a bias of 10 V through a 50-nm-size AFM tip coated with Au. Then, another area of 20 μm × 5 μm was scanned horizontally by applying a bias of −10 V through the tip. Finally, the scanning surface potential image was acquired with the tapping model by applying a bias of 4 V on the film through the AFM tip coated with Au. The two pretreated areas exhibited significantly different surface potentials. Hence, the "write," "erase," and "read" can be performed with an AFM tip. Extremely high-density memory cells may be achieved this way.

Tseng et al. also demonstrated the resistive switches of nanocomposites with a conductive AFM tip as the top electrode (Fig. 17). The AFM tip was directly in contact with the PANi nanofiber/Au NPs nanocomposites [38]. An external electric voltage was applied between the AFM tip and the bottom Al electrode. A resistive switch was observed when the voltage was scanned from 0 to −5 V.

2.4. Effect of Nanoparticles on Resistive Switches

The electrical behavior of these hybrid organic memristors is sensitive to the NPs. Ma et al. observed that the devices did not exhibit any electrical switch when the thickness of

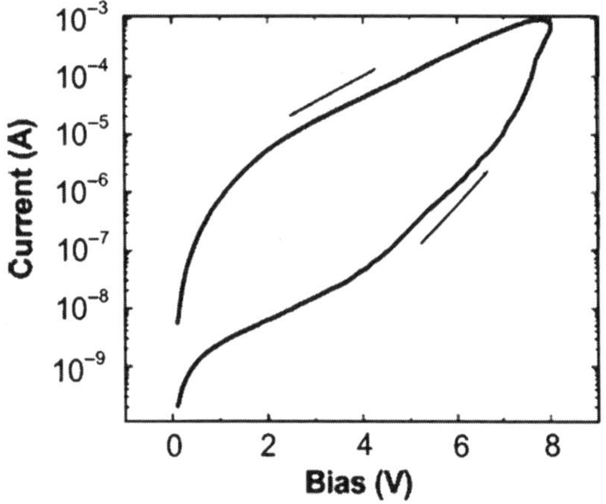

Figure 13. I–V curves of a device Al/Au-2NT NPs + PS/Al. The arrows indicate the voltage-scanning directions. Reprinted with permission from [45], J. Ouyang et al., *Proc. IEEE* 93, 1287 (2005). © 2005, IEEE.

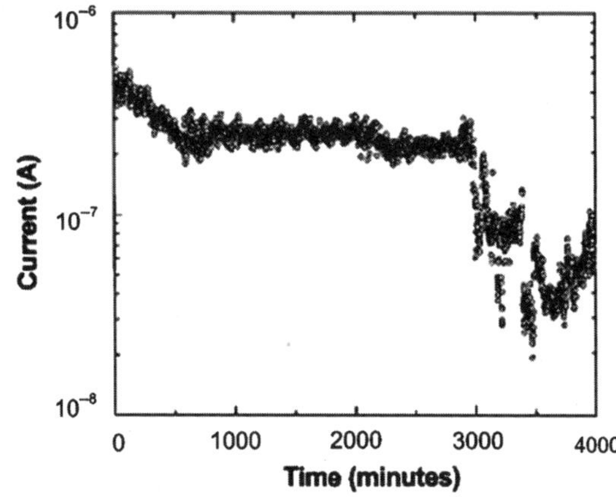

Figure 15. Stress test of a device Al/Au-DT NPs + 8HQ + PS/Al in the ON state at 1 V in nitrogen. Reprinted with permission from [45], J. Ouyang et al., *Proc. IEEE.* 93, 1287 (2005). © 2005, IEEE.

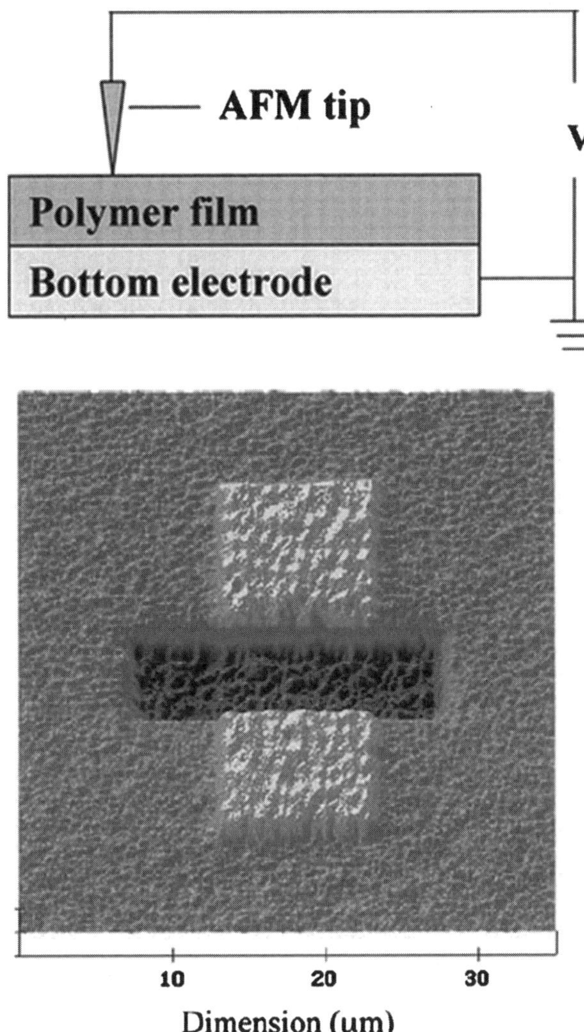

Figure 16. (a) Test configuration for the operation of a device using an AFM tip as the top electrode. Reprinted with permission from [45], J. Ouyang et al., *Proc. IEEE* 93, 1287 (2005). © 2005, IEEE. (b) Scanning surface potential AFM image of an Au-DT NPs + 8HQ + PS film with Al as the bottom electrode and a silicon wafer as substrate. The vertical bar (yellow) was pretreated with a +10 V bias, and the horizontal bar (brown) was pretreated with a −10 V bias. Reprinted with permission from [23], J. Ouyang et al., *Nat. Mater.* 3, 918 (2004). © 2004, Nature Publishing Group.

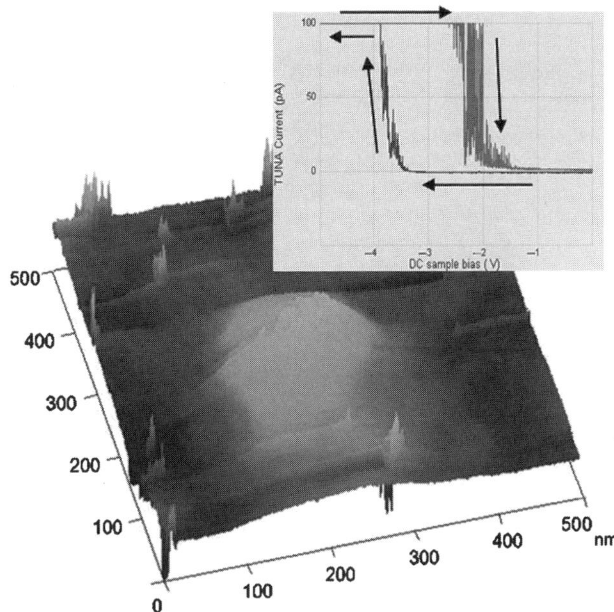

Figure 17. Conductive AFM image and *I–V* curves of a polyaniline nanofiber/gold NP composite. Reprinted with permission from [38], R. Tseng et al., *Nano Lett.* 5, 1077 (2005). © 2005, American Chemical Society.

the middle Al layer was less than 10 nm for the triple-layer devices [21]. Bozano et al. also reported that the device performance was greatly affected by the thickness of the middle Al layer, and most reliable switching properties could be obtained for devices with the middle Al layer between 5 and 10 nm [17]. Reddy et al. carried out a detailed investigation on the effect of the middle Al layer thickness and the size of the NPs on the device performance [18]. Their results are listed in Table 1. The currents in both the ON and OFF states increases continuously with increasing thickness of the middle Al layer. The ON/OFF current ratio is very small for a thin middle Al layer and increases with the increasing thickness until 10 nm. The highest ON/OFF current ratio of 10^5 at 1 V is obtained for the device with a 10-nm thick middle Al layer. The ON/OFF current ratio decreases with a further increase in the thickness of the middle Al layer.

Besides the particle size, in principle, other structural factors (e.g., work function of the metal core and the shell) of the metal NPs in the active layer can affect the electrical behavior because the resistive switches are related to the charging and discharging of the metal NPs under an external electric field [17, 21]. However, no remarkable effect of the metal NPs was observed on the resistive switches in early experimental results. Bozano et al. investigated the electrical behavior of devices glass/Al/Alq_3/NP/Alq_3 with the NPs fabricated from different metals, including Mg, Ag, Cr, and Au, by thermal evaporation [46]. These metals have different work functions, which are between the highest occupied molecular orbital (HOMO) and lowest unoccupied molecular orbit (LUMO) of Alq_3 (Fig. 18). The electrical behavior of the devices was insensitive to the work functions of the metal NPs. Similar investigation was also carried out on the single-layer devices [45]. When Au-DT NPs were replaced with silver NPs capped with 1-dodecanethiol in the active

Table 1. Summary of *I–V* characteristics of ITO/AlQ_3/Al/AlQ_3/Al memristors with different thicknesses of the middle Al layer.

Thickness (nm)	I_{OFF} (A)	I_{ON} (A)	I_{ON}/I_{OFF}
0	9.49×10^{-11}	1.29×10^{-9}	13.6
5	1.43×10^{-10}	3.89×10^{-8}	2.72×10^{2}
10	2.17×10^{-10}	4.14×10^{-5}	1.91×10^{5}
15	3.69×10^{-7}	5.69×10^{-5}	1.54×10^{2}
20	7.72×10^{-5}	1.02×10^{-4}	1.32

Source: Reprinted with permission from [18], V. S. Reddy et al., *Appl. Phys. Lett.* 94, 173304 (2009). © 2009, American Institute of Physics.

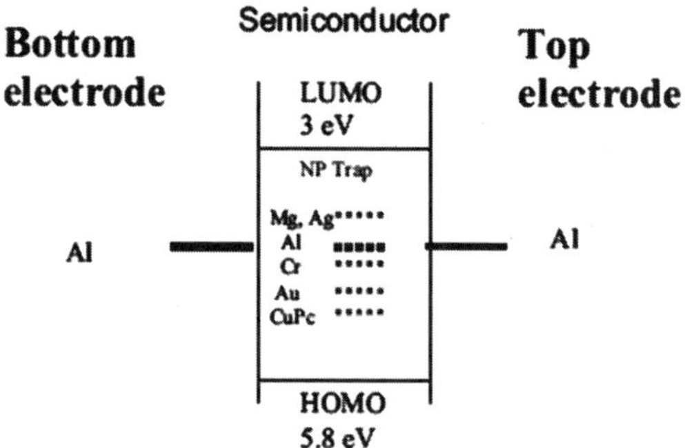

Figure 18. Energy level for different choices of metal NPs for a device Al/Alq_3 (50 nm)/NP/Alq_3 (50 nm). Reprinted with permission from [46], L. D. Bozano et al., *Adv. Funct. Mater.* 15, 1933 (2005). © 2005, Wiley-VCH Verlag GmbH & Co. KGaA.

polymer layer, no salient difference was observed on the electrical behavior of the devices either.

The insensitivity of the electrical behavior to the work function of the metal NP can be attributed to the insulator coating on the metal NP. The metal oxide shell of the metal NPs in the triple-layer devices and 1-dodecanethiol capped on the gold NPs for the single-layer device are insulator. The insulator coating constructs an energy barrier for the metal NPs. When the width of the energy barrier was reduced by short alkanethiols like 1-octanethiol and 1-hexanethiol as the capping molecule of the gold NPs in the polymer layer of the single-layer device, the electrical behavior was almost the same as that for the devices with gold NPs capped with 1-dodecanethiol.

The effect of the capping ligand of the metal NPs on the electrical behavior was observed when conjugated organic molecules were used as the capping ligand of the metal NPs [45, 47]. Figure 19 shows the I–V curves of a device Al/Au-BET NPs + PS/Al (2-benzeneethanethiol [BET]). BET with a conjugated benzene ring can be regarded as an organic semiconductor with a wide band gap. The switch from OFF to ON occurred in the voltage range from 6.2 to 7.8 V, which was less abruptly than that for Al/Au-DT NPs + 8HQ + PS/Al.

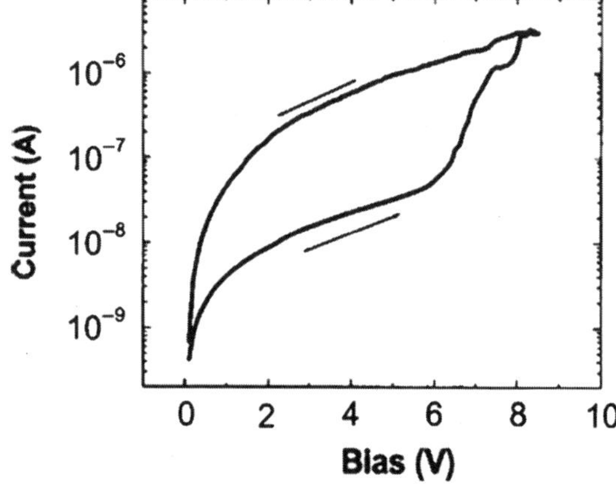

Figure 19. I–V curves of a device Al/Au-BET NPs + PS/Al. The arrows indicate the voltage-scanning directions. Reprinted with permission from [45], J. Ouyang et al., *Proc. IEEE.* 93, 1287 (2005). © 2005, IEEE.

The ligand effect becomes more significant when Au NPs capped with conjugated 2NT were used (Fig. 13). 2NT, which has a conjugated naphthalene ring, is an organic semiconductor with a band gap smaller than BET. The switch of the device Al/Au-2NT NPs + PS/Al was even less abrupt than that of Al/Au-BET NPs + PS/Al, while the current in the ON state of the former was remarkably higher than that of the latter.

2.5. Effect of Electrodes on Resistive Switches

The electrical behavior of many electronic devices is sensitive to the work function of the electrode. The effect of electrode on the resistive switches was investigated for the single-layer and triple-layer devices. Bozano et al. characterized the electrical behavior of triple-layer devices glass/bottom electrode/Alq_3/Al NPs/Alq_3/Al with different metals as the bottom electrode, including Al, Cr, Cu, ITO, Au, and Ni. These metals had different work functions (Fig. 20). No remarkable difference was observed on the electrical behavior of these devices. The single-layer devices with gold NPs capped with alkanethiol also have electrical behavior insensitive to the work function of the electrode [47].

The electrical behavior of the devices becomes sensitive to the electrode when gold NPs capped with conjugated organic ligands are used [48]. Figure 21 shows the I–V curves of such a device glass/Al/Au-2NT NPs + PS/Au with Al and Au as the top and bottom electrodes, respectively. The electrical tests were performed with respective to the bottom Al electrode. This device exhibited bipolar resistive switches sensitive to the electrodes. At the first voltage scan from 0 to 2.5 V, no resistive switch occurred. The current did not exhibit any hysteresis during the subsequent reverse scan from 2.5 to 0 V. However, resistive switch with a rapid current increase took place at the second scan from 0 to −2.5 V. A remarkable hysteresis was observed at the third scan from −2.5 to 0 V. This resulted into the switch of the device from OFF to ON. The device switched back to the ON state in the fourth voltage scans along the positive polarity. It could be switched to the OFF state again by a scan at the negative polarity. The switches between these two resistance states could be repeated numerous times. The resistive switches of

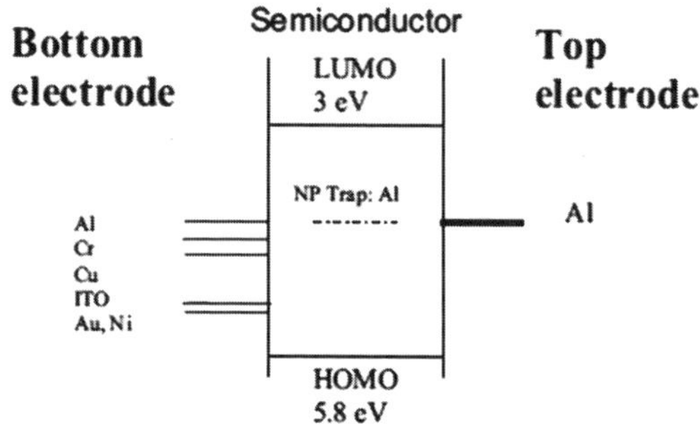

Figure 20. Energy level for different electrodes for a bottom-electrode/Alq_3 (50 nm)/Al (5 nm)/Alq_3 (50 nm) structure. Reprinted with permission from [46], L. D. Bozano et al., *Adv. Funct. Mater.* 15, 1933 (2005). © 2005, Wiley-VCH Verlag GmbH & Co. KGaA.

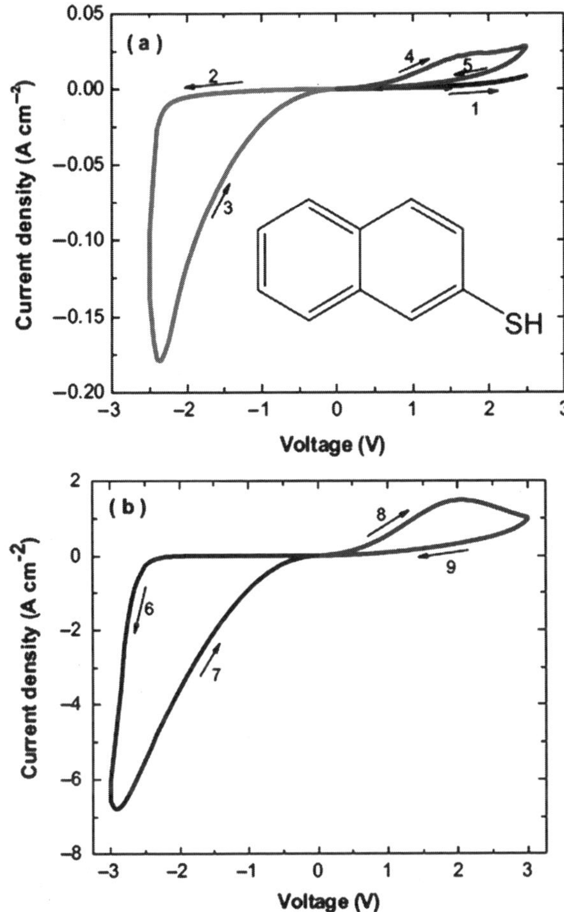

Figure 21. Current density–voltage curves of a device glass/Al/Au-2NT NPs + PS/Au. The arrows indicate the scan directions in the order indicated. Reprinted with permission from [48], J. Ouyang and Y. Yang, *Appl. Phys. Lett.* 96, 063506 (2010). © 2010, American Institute of Physics.

this device are sensitive to the electrodes. The switch from the OFF to ON state happens only at the negative polarity, while the reverse switch occurs merely at the positive polarity.

The dependence of the resistive switches on the electrodes is confirmed by using other metals, such as Cu and Al, to replace Au as the top electrode. As shown in Figure 22, the device glass/Al/Au-2NT NPs + PS/Cu also exhibited electrode-sensitive bipolar resistive switches. But the absolute value of the transition voltage from OFF to ON is higher than that of glass/Al/Au-2NT NPs + PS/Au. On the other hand, a device glass/Al/Au-2NT NPs + PS/Al exhibited a single resistive switch from OFF to ON state along either polarity. It could not return to the ON state by a voltage scan along the opposite or same polarity. The absolute value of the transition voltage was higher than the device with Au or Cu as the top electrode. The switching voltages of these devices are consistent with the work functions of Au (5.1 eV), Cu (4.6 eV), and Al (4.1 eV). The resistive switch is attributed to the charge storage on Au-2NT NPs. The electrode sensitivity of the resistive switches is attributed to the contact potential between the gold NPs and the electrode.

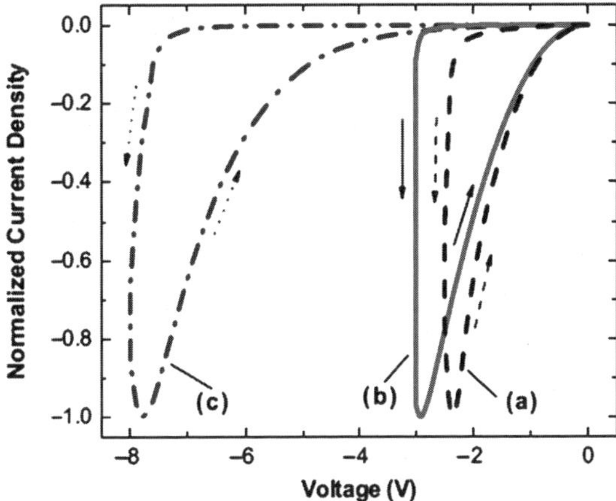

Figure 22. Normalized current density–voltage curves of devices glass/Al/Au-2NT NPs + PS/top electrode with different top electrodes: (a) Au (dashed curves), (b) Cu (solid curves), and (c) Al (dashed-dotted curves). The arrows indicate the scan directions. Reprinted with permission from [48], J. Ouyang and Y. Yang, *Appl. Phys. Lett.* 96, 063506 (2010). © 2010, American Institute of Physics.

2.6. Effect of Polymer Matrix of Single-Layer Devices on Performance

In the early single-layer device, an inert polymer like PS was used as the matrix for the metal NPs and organic semiconductor, so that the matrix polymer does not involve in the resistive switches. When PS was replaced with poly(methyl methacrylate) as the matrix, the electrical behavior of the single-layer device was almost same [45]. Other insulating polymers, such as polyimides, were also used as the matrix [32].

Although the matrix polymer does not involve in the electronic processes during the resistive switches, it can have an effect on the device performance by affecting the distribution of the metal NPs and organic semiconductor in the polymer layer. Two strategies were adopted to make the polymer layer more controllable. One is to use a conjugated polymer as both the matrix and the organic semiconductor. Both poly(3-hexylthiophene) (P3HT) and poly(*N*-vinyl carbazole) (PVK) were used in the active layer of the single-layer devices [49, 50]. Beinhoff et al. also synthesized conjugated poly(biphenylmethylene)s as the matrix for the single-layer devices [51]. Another is to use metal NPs capped with conjugated molecules [48].

An interesting development in the matrix materials is the utilization of biomaterials as the matrix of the single-layer devices [41]. This may bring some biological functions to this kind of resistive-switching device or the applications of resistive-switching devices in biologic systems.

2.7. Mechanisms for Resistive Switches of Hybrid Devices

Although the filament formation between the two electrodes that resulted from metal diffusion is regarded as the resistive switches observed on some inorganic and organic thin films [52–54], many experimental results suggest that the resistive switches observed on the hybrid memristors cannot be attributed to the filament formation. For example, the strong effect of the capping ligand on gold NPs on the resistive switch and the electrode-sensitive bipolar resistive switches cannot be interpreted by the filament formation.

It is generally believed that the resistive switches of the hybrid memristors are related to the charge storage on the NPs. But researchers have disagreed about the detailed mechanism. Three major mechanisms have been proposed:

(a) electric-field-induced charge transfer between NPs and organic semiconductor,
(b) charge trapping on the metal NPs, and
(c) electric-field induced polarization of the middle metal layer for the triple-layer devices.

2.7.1. Electric-Field-Induced Charge Transfer Mechanism

Electric-field-induced charge transfer between NPs and the organic semiconductor has been proposed as the mechanism for the bipolar resistive switches observed on the devices with the active layer consisting of NPs and organic or polymer semiconductor [23, 45]. Conjugated organic compounds and polymers are considered semiconductors, and their conductivity significantly increases after oxidation or reduction. Figure 23 illustrates the electric-field-induced charge transfer between a NP and conjugated 8HQ. The charge transfer results in the charge storage on the NP and a positive or negative charge on the conjugated organic molecule. Consequently, the conductivity of the organic molecule will significantly increase, which accounts for the resistive switch from OFF to ON. A reverse electric field can force both the NPs and the conjugated organic molecule to the neutral state, which results into the resistive switch from ON to OFF. This mechanism is supported by similar resistive switches observed on devices with the admixture of organic donor and organic acceptor in the active layer [55, 56]. It can interpret the bipolar resistive switches and original OFF state of the devices. Electric-field-induced charge transfer was also proposed for gold NPs capped with organic semiconductors, polymer/NP composites, and nanotube/NP composites [45, 47, 57, 58]. A similar electric-field-induced charge transfer was proposed for the resistive switches of the devices with PANi nanofiber/Au NP nanocomposite (Fig. 24) [38].

The organic semiconductor is chemically bonded with the metal core for the metal NPs capped with conjugated organic molecules. The electric field can induce a charge transfer between the capping conjugated organic molecule and the metal core. The electric-field-induced charge transfer can lead to the polarization of the active layer. This is supported by the observation of the asymmetrical electrical behavior on the devices glass/Al/PS + Au-2NT NPs/Al in the ON state (Fig. 25) [48]. The current at −3 V is almost eight times as that at 3 V.

2.7.2. Charge-Trapping Mechanism

Bozano et al. observed the unipolar resistive switches on the triple-layer devices [17]. They found that the resistive switches were similar to that observed on an oxide thin film doped with Au NPs [59]. Thus, the trap-filled model was proposed for the unipolar resistive switches [17, 60]. The switch from ON to OFF is attributed to charge trapping on the metal NPs. The resulting space charge field inhibits the charge injection. This is also used to interpret the resistive switches of a single layer of NPs without an organic semiconductor [41]. It is possible that the charge-trapping model works for the unipolar resistive switches

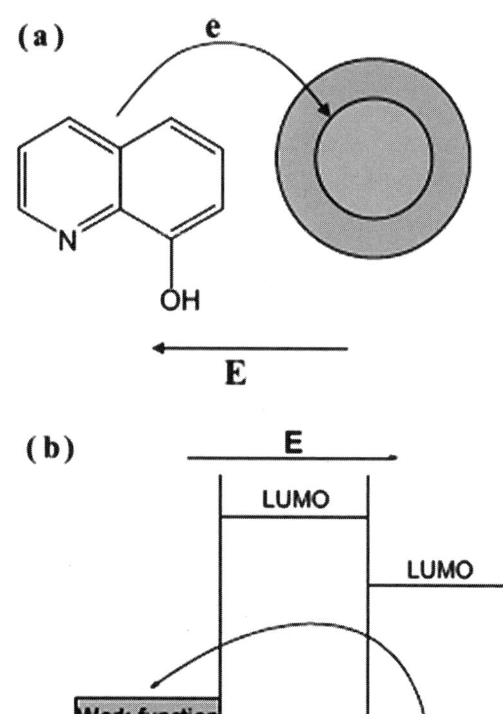

Figure 23. (a) Schematic electron transfer from 8HQ to the core of a gold NP. The inner gray circle indicates the core of the gold NP, and the outer gray ring indicates the capped DT, (b) energy-level diagram of the core of the gold NP, DT, and 8HQ. The two dots on the HOMO of 8HQ stand for two electrons. The straight arrow indicates the direction of the electric field (E), and the curved arrow for the electron transfer from 8HQ to the core of the gold NP. Reprinted with permission from [45], J. Ouyang et al., *Proc. IEEE* 93, 1287 (2005). © 2005, IEEE.

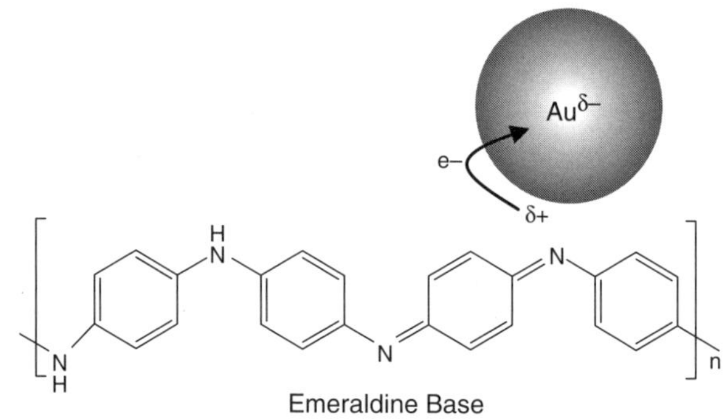

Figure 24. Schematic structure of a polyaniline nanofiber/gold NP composite in the ON state. Reprinted with permission from [38], R. Tseng et al., *Nano Lett.* 5, 1077 (2005). © 2005, American Chemical Society.

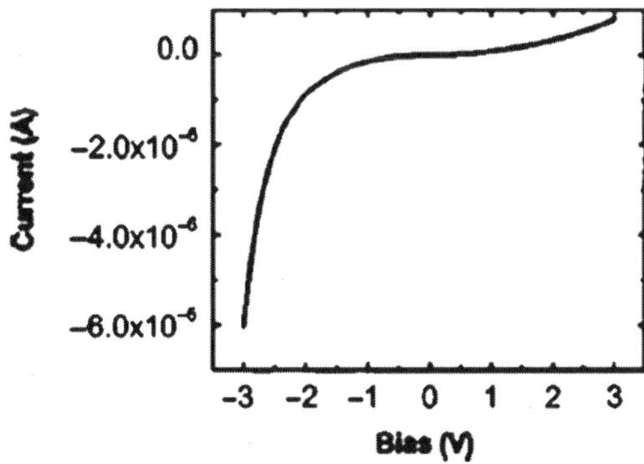

Figure 25. Asymmetric *I–V* curve observed on Al/Au-2NT NPs + PS/Al in the ON state. Reprinted with permission from [47], J. Ouyang et al., *Appl. Phys. Lett.* 86, 123507 (2005). © 2005, American Institute of Physics.

while the electric-field-induced charge transfer is suitable for the bipolar resistive switches of devices with NPs and an organic semiconductor in the active layer. The presence of an organic semiconductor in the active layer makes the devices in the ON state more stable.

Several groups adopted this charge-trapping mechanism for the resistive switches [61, 62]. However, Tang et al. argued that the charge-trapping model is not applicable for the resistive switches because it disregards potential energy changes as a result of the charging process [63]. They argued that the resistive switches were instead due to two-dimensional single-electron tunneling by nanometer metal islands. On the other hand, Rozenberg et al. proposed three types of metal domains in the active film between the top and bottom electrodes: the top domains, the middle domains, and the bottom domains (Fig. 26) [64]. They proposed that the current through the two electrodes was controlled by the charge injection into the top or bottom domains, tunneling through the middle domains, and finally tunneling to another electrode. The charge tunneling between the bottom (or top) domains and the middle domains is much greater than the tunneling between the top and bottom domains. When a voltage produces a large transfer from the middle to the top domains and from the bottom to the middle domains, a switch from OFF to ON takes place. The switch from ON to OFF is attributed to filling the bottom domains and emptying the top ones under a certain voltage, which results into a low probability of carrier transfer into the already-filled bottom domains and the low probability of carrier transfer out of the emptied top domains to the electrode.

2.7.3. Electric-Field-Induced Polarization Mechanism

The electric-field-induced polarization of the middle metal was proposed by Ma et al. to interpret the bipolar resistive switches observed on their triple-layer devices [65, 66]. As shown in Figure 27, the external electric field pushes electrons from some metal NPs into some other metal NPs, which results into positively charged metal NPs at one side and negatively charged NPs at the other side. The charged NPs cause the organic semiconductor to switch from a low

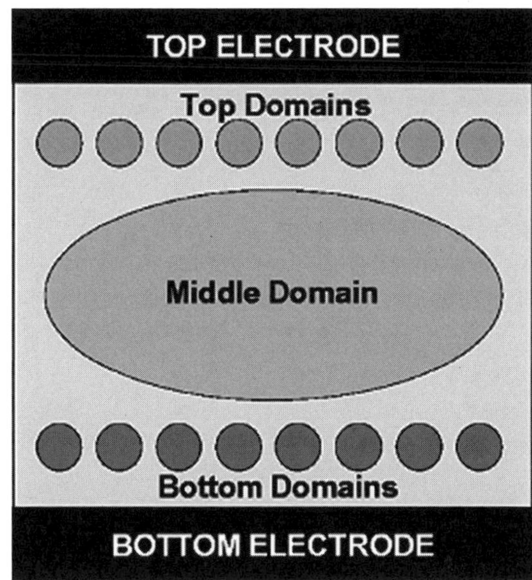

Figure 26. Schematic view of the model with top and bottom electrodes, insulating medium, smaller top and bottom domains, and large middle domains. Reprinted with permission from [64], M. J. Rozenberg et al., *Phys. Rev. Lett.* 92, 178302 (2004). © 2004, American Physical Society.

conductance to a high conductance, i.e., the switch from OFF to ON. A reverse electric field will push the electrons back to the original NPs, resulting in the neutralization of the metal NPs. Consequently, the device switches from ON back to OFF.

All the three mechanisms agree that the resistive switches are the result of charging and discharging of the metal or semiconductor NPs. The charging of the NPs is evidenced

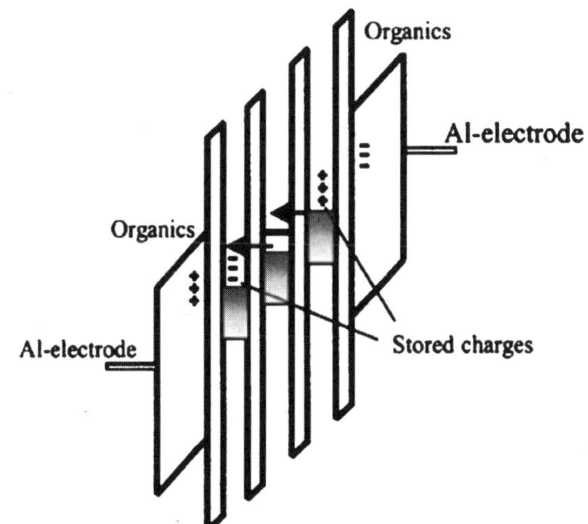

Figure 27. Electrons in the metallic Al NP core tunneling through the energy barrier formed by AIDCN, from metal NP to another NP under the external electric field. The negative charges will be stored at one side and positives charge at the other side. The stored charges subsequently make the organic layers undergo a conductance change and switch the device to the ON state. Reprinted with permission from [21], L. Ma et al., *Appl. Phys. Lett.* 82, 1419 (2003). © 2003, American Institute of Physics.

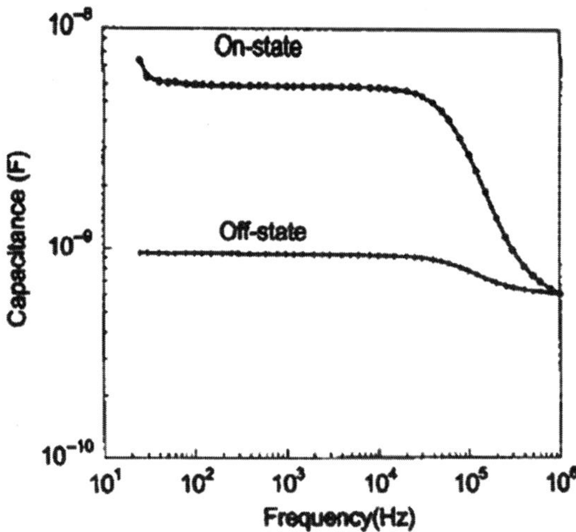

Figure 28. Frequency dependence of capacitances of a device Al/AIDCN/Al/AIDCN/Al in the ON and OFF states. Reprinted with permission from [21], L. Ma et al., *Appl. Phys. Lett.* 82, 1419 (2003). © 2003, American Institute of Physics.

by the capacitances of the devices in the two states [21]. As shown in Figure 28, the device in the ON state has a higher capacitance than in the OFF state. It is more significant in the low frequency range. The high capacitance arises from the charge storage in the NPs.

3. PURE ORGANIC MEMRISTORS

Electric-field-induced resistive switches were also found in devices with only polymers or organic molecules as the active materials. The devices can be classified into two types in terms of the resistive switch mechanism, a (1) donor–acceptor system and (2) charge trapping.

3.1. Organic Donor–Acceptor Organic Memristors

The conductivity of conjugated organic molecules or polymers increases significantly after the oxidation or reduction. For example, charge-transfer complexes of TTF or TCNQ can have high conductivity [4, 5], and many conjugated polymers like polypyrrole, polythiophene, and PANi become highly conductive after oxidation [6]. Photons can also induce a charge transfer between the organic donor and acceptor, which is the principle of organic photovoltaic cells [67]. As mentioned above, the electric field can induce a charge transfer between the organic molecule or polymer and the NP. The charge transfer can also take place when the NP is substituted with an organic donor or acceptor. Figure 29 presents the chemical structure of some organic donors and acceptors.

Chu et al. fabricated devices using methanofullerene [6,6]-phenyl C61-butyric acid methyl ester (PCBM) as the acceptor and TTF as the donor [55]. PS was used as the matrix for the organic donor and acceptor. Reversible resistive switches similar to the hybrid organic memristors were observed. Figure 30 shows the typical I–V curves of such a device. The device turns from OFF to ON at 2.6 V with the abrupt current increase from 10^{-7} A to 10^{-4} A. It is interesting to note that the resistive switches of this device can be bipolar and unipolar. The device could be switched back to the OFF state by applying a higher positive or negative bias (e.g., 9 V or −9 V) as indicated by curve c.

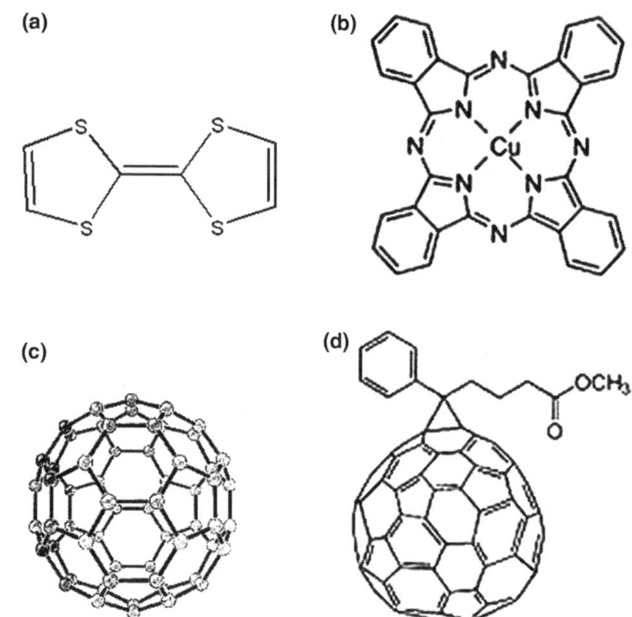

Figure 29. Structure of some organic donors and acceptors: (a) TTF, (b) copper phthalocyanine (CuPc), (c) fullerene, and (d) PCBM.

The resistive switches are attributed to the electric-field-induced charge transfer between PCBM and TTF. The HOMO/LUMO levels are 5.09/2.33 eV [68] and 6.1/3.7 eV for TTF and PCBM [69], respectively. When the electric field exceeds the threshold value, it prompts an electron from the HOMO of TTF to the LUMO of PCBM, giving rise to the switch from OFF to ON. The resistive switch from

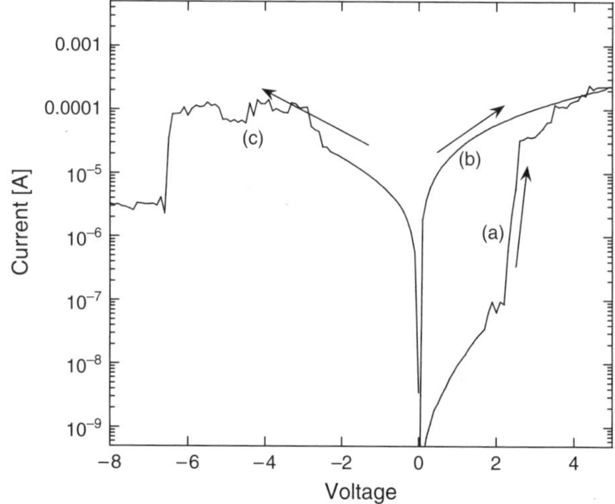

Figure 30. I–V curves of a device Al/PS + PCBM + TTF/Al. (a–c) are the first-, second-, and third-bias scans, respectively. The arrows indicate the voltage-scanning directions. Reprinted with permission from [55], C. W. Chu et al., *Adv. Mater.* 17, 1440 (2005). © 2005, Wiley-VCH Verlag GmbH & Co. KGaA.

the ON to OFF state is the result of the reversal charge transfer between TTF and PCBM. This mechanism is confirmed by the analysis of the conduction mechanisms of the devices in the two states and the alternating current (AC) impedance spectroscopy. The current for the device in the OFF state is due to thermionic emission as evidenced by the linear Log$I$–$V^{1/2}$ relationship (Fig. 31(a)). Thus, the conduction is dominated by a charge injection from the electrode into the active layer. After the device is turned to the ON state, the linear Log$(I/V) - V^{1/2}$ relationship indicates that the conduction mechanism becomes a Poole–Frenkel emission (Fig. 31(b)). However, the charge transport traps thus becomes the dominant conduction mechanism [70, 71]. The Poole–Frenkel behavior is not affected by varying the electrode, which suggests that the charge traps are in the active layer.

The AC impedance spectra of the device in the ON and OFF states are presented in Figure 32. The capacitance in the OFF state is insensitive to the frequency in the range of 20 to 10^6 Hz. The capacitance becomes significantly different in the ON state. The capacitance in the high frequency range of $10^4 \sim 10^6$ Hz is almost the same as in the OFF state, but it is higher than the OFF state by more than one order of magnitude at a low frequency of less than 600 Hz. The higher capacitance at the low frequency range is associated with the electric-field-induced dipole formation between the donor and acceptor.

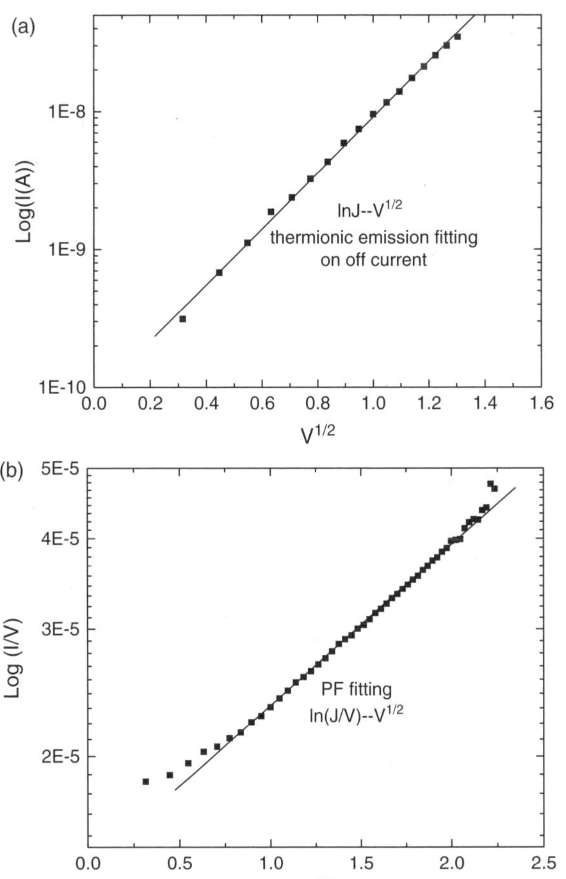

Figure 31. The analysis of I–V curves for the device Al/PS + PCBM + TTF/Al in the (a) ON and (b) OFF states. Reprinted with permission from [55], C. W. Chu et al., *Adv. Mater.* 17, 1440 (2005). © 2005, Wiley-VCH Verlag GmbH & Co. KGaA.

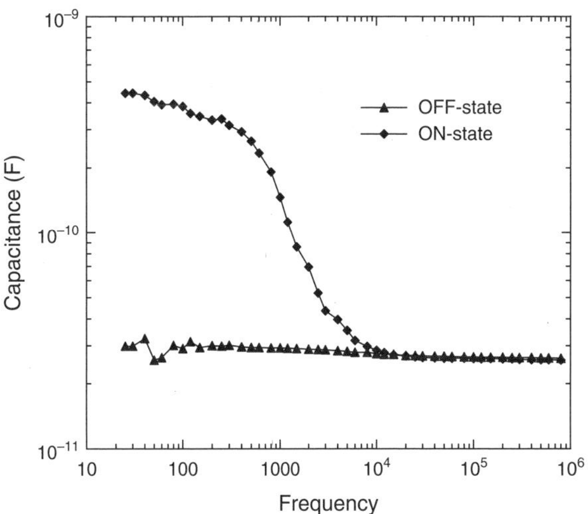

Figure 32. Typical frequency dependence of capacitances of a device Al/PS + PCBM + TTF/Al in the ON and OFF states. Reprinted with permission from [55], C. W. Chu et al., *Adv. Mater.* 17, 1440 (2005). © 2005, Wiley-VCH Verlag GmbH & Co. KGaA.

Besides TTF and PCBM, resistive switches were also observed on devices using other donor–acceptor systems, such as copper phthalocyanine (donor)–fullerenol (acceptor) and polymer donor–organic acceptor systems [72–75].

The donor and acceptor structures can be chemically bonded together in one molecule. A couple of organic molecules consisting of donor and acceptor units were synthesized, and they exhibited resistive switches [76, 77]. Hu et al. synthesized an organic molecule called CPMAB in short (Fig. 33). They observed the resistive switches and studied the structure of CPMAB with microreflection absorption Fourier transform infrared (FTIR) spectroscopy before and after the application of a threshold voltage (Fig. 33). The stretching vibration of the cyano group exhibits a red shift (from 2233.4 cm^{-1} to 2231.0 cm^{-1}) after applying the threshold voltage, which indicates that the cyano group changes from a neutral to a negatively charged state [78–80]. This confirms the electron transfer from the donor unit to the acceptor unit after the resistive switch goes from OFF to ON. Polymers with donor and acceptor units were also synthesized, and they also exhibited resistive switches [81–91].

3.2. Organic Memristors Due to Charge Trapping

Resistive switches were also observed on devices with only one conjugated organic molecule in an inert polymer matrix. These devices usually exhibited unipolar switches with NDR. The mechanisms for the resistive switches are attributed to the charge trapping and detrapping.

Fullerene and its derivatives are nanometer in size and are used for charge trapping [92–94]. Figure 34(a) presents the I–V curves of a device with 5 wt% PCBM blended in PS [93]. The pristine device is in the OFF state and switches

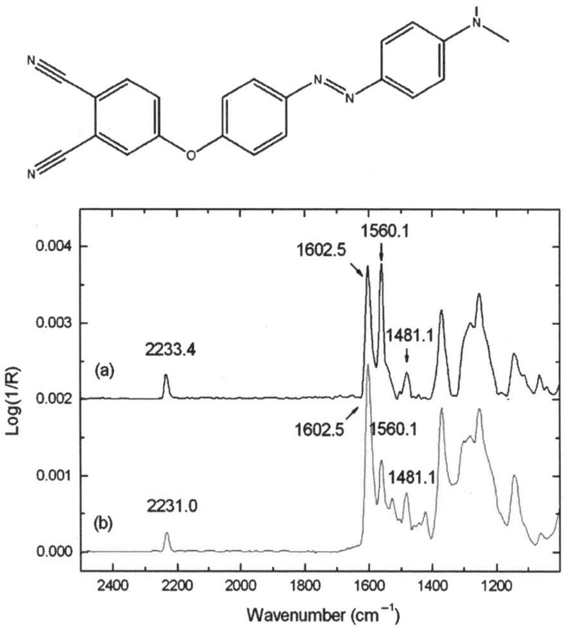

Figure 33. Chemical structure of CPMAB and the microreflection-absorption FTIR spectra of the CPMAB thin film in the (a) ON and (b) OFF states. Reprinted with permission from [77], J. Hu et al., *J. Mater. Chem.* 17, 3530 (2007). © 2007, Royal Society of Chemistry.

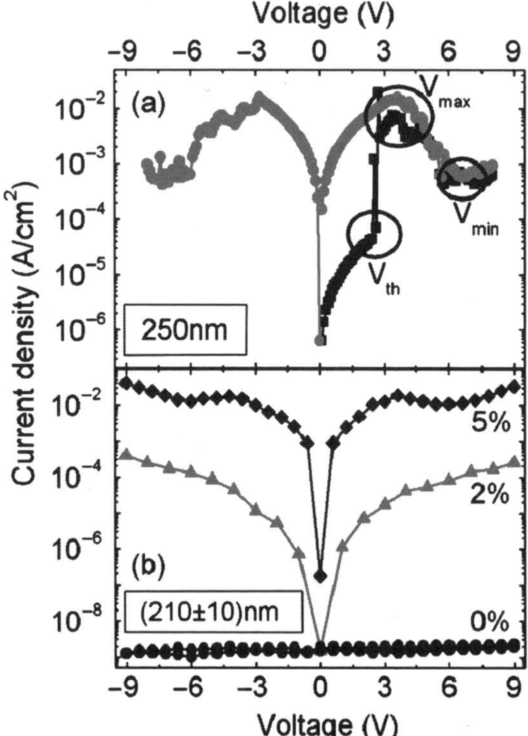

Figure 34. (a) Absolute value of current density (J) as a function of voltage (V) for a Al/5 wt% PCBM + PS/Al device. Squares (■) are the first bias scan from 0 to +8 V and then the circles (●) the second scan from +8 V to −8 V. (b) J–V plot shows the absolute value of current density as a function of voltage for 0 wt% PCBM:PS (circles: ●), 2 wt% PCBM:PS (triangles: ▲) and 5 wt% PCBM:PS (squares: ■) devices. Reprinted with permission from [93], J. K. Baral et al., *Nanotechnology* 19, 035203 (2008). © 2008, IOP Publishing Ltd.

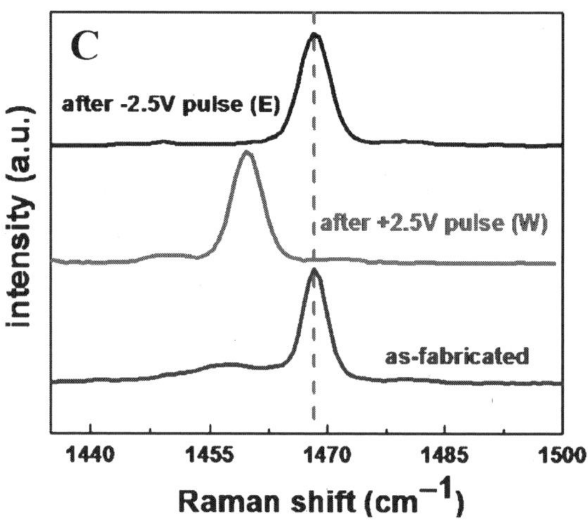

Figure 35. Raman spectra of fullerene in as-fabricate active layer, and the active layer in ON (W) and Off (E) states. Reprinted with permission from [92], S. Paul et al., *Nanotechnology* 17, 145 (2006). © 2006, IOP Publishing Ltd.

to the ON state at approximately 3 V. The NDR appears when the voltage is greater than 5 V. The resistive switches are strongly dependent on the PCBM concentration in PS. No resistive switch was observed when there was no PCBM in PS (Fig. 34(b)).

Paul et al. studied the change on fullerene in polymer before and after the resistive switch with Raman spectroscopy [92]. As shown in Figure 35, the A_{1g} mode appearing at 1469 cm^{-1} for the as-prepared device shifts to a lower wavenumber by 9 cm^{-1} for the device in the ON state. It returns to the original position when the device is erased to the OFF state. The red shift of this Raman band is a strong indication for electron trapping on fullerene during the resistive switch.

Besides fullerene and its derivatives, resistive switches were also observed on polymers with a conjugated unit [95–97] and on polymers with redox-active species [98–100]. The observed resistive switches are also attributed to the charge trapping in these materials.

4. FLEXIBLE ORGANIC MEMRISTORS

Flexible electronic devices are particularly important for special electronic applications, such as foldable and wearable electronics. A wealth of research has been done to develop high-performance flexible electronic devices, such as solar cells, thin-film transistors, photodiodes, light-emitting diodes, and displays [101–105]. The active materials of organic memristors, including NPs, small organic molecules, and polymers, have high mechanical flexibility.

Figure 36 illustrates a flexible organic memristor reported by Ji et al. [106]. Polyethylene terephthalate and polyimide blended with PCBM were used as the substrate and active layer, respectively, so that the device was highly flexible. The device was tested under various degrees of bending (Fig. 37). At the maximum bending condition, i.e., the minimum radius of curvature of 9 mm, the electrical behavior was almost the same as in the flat condition. The bending of the device did not affect the resistive switches. The authors

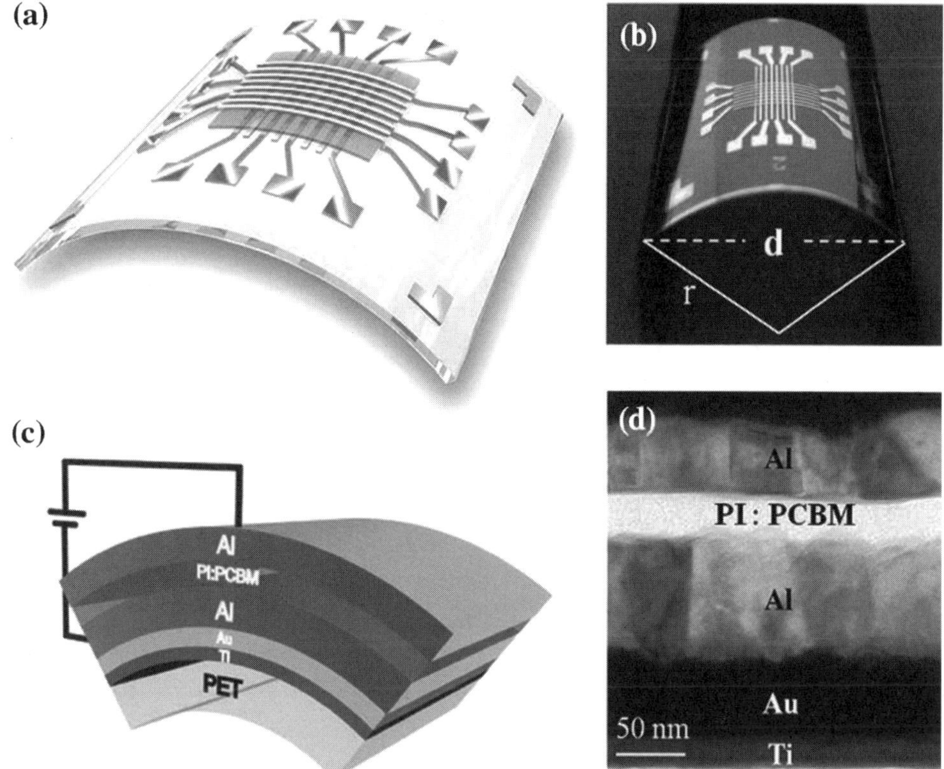

Figure 36. (a) Illustrated and (b) optical images of an 8 × 8 array-type Ti/Au/Al/PI:PCBM/Al flexible organic memory device, (c) schematic view of a Ti/Au/Al/PI:PCBM/Al memory cell, and (d) cross-sectional scanning electron microscopy image of the layers in a memory cell. Reprinted with permission from [106], Y. Ji et al., *Adv. Mater.* 22, 3071 (2010). © 2010, Wiley-VCH Verlag GmbH & Co. KGaA.

also studied the ON/OFF current ratios under various bending conditions and did not observe any remarkable effect when bending the devices.

Lin et al. also demonstrate flexible memristors using polymer-chain-stabilized gold NPs on a plastic substrate [107]. Kuang et al. reported flexible memristors with poly(chloro-para-xylylene) as the active material [108].

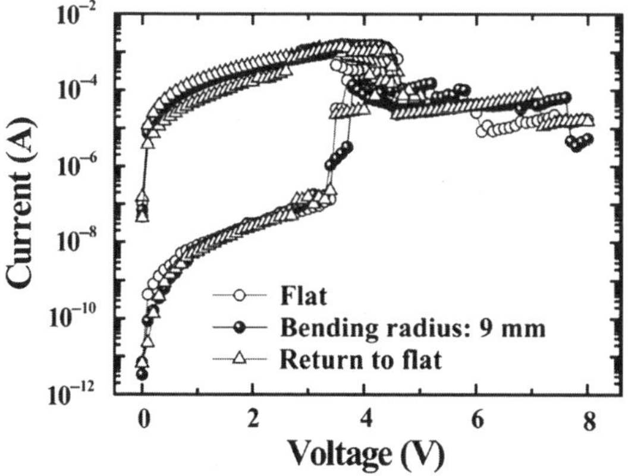

Figure 37. *I–V* curves of a flexible organic memory device as shown in Figure 36. The open circles, filled circles, and open triangles show the *I–V* curves when the device was flat, bent the most (9-mm bending radius condition), and returned to the flat condition after bending, respectively. Reprinted with permission from [106], Y. Ji et al., *Adv. Mater.* 22, 3071 (2010). © 2010, Wiley-VCH Verlag GmbH & Co. KGaA.

Besides memory application, several papers also combined organic memristors with light-emitting diodes in a series [65, 109, 110]. When the memristor was in the ON state, the resistance was small, so that there could be a high current transporting through the light-emitting diodes, thus giving rise to high electroluminescence. There was almost no electroluminescence when the memristor is in the OFF state.

5. CONCLUSIONS AND OUTLOOK

Charge storage or charge trapping in inorganic NPs or conjugated organic molecules or polymers can result into resistive switches of two-terminal devices. These devices can be switched between the ON and OFF states numerous times and have good stability in both states. This renders the strong application of these devices as two-terminal memory devices. These memory devices can have a high response speed and a high density. They can potentially solve the technical difficulties met in the three leading memory technologies: DRAMs, HDDs, and flash memories. They also may have extensive applications in both high-end and low-end systems.

However, to fully explore all the advantages of these devices will take time and will require close collaboration among materials scientists, chemists, and physicists. For example, a large problem to overcome in these devices is their repeatability, which arises from difficulty in precisely controlling the sizes of the NPs and positioning the organic molecules or polymers. There are also technical difficulties when preparing thin films uniformly dispersed with nanometer materials. Thus, different laboratories sometimes report quite different data in the switching voltages, the resistance ratio of OFF to ON, endurance, and retention time of devices. It is believed that all these problems may be solved in the future with the rapid development of organic electronics and nanotechnology.

ACKNOWLEDGMENT

The author would like to thank the Ministry of Education in Singapore for its financial support of this research work (Project No: R-284-000-040-112).

REFERENCES

1. F. So, Ed., "Organic Electronics: Materials, Processing, Devices and Applications." CRC Press, Boca Raton, FL, 2010.
2. D. S. Acker, R. J. Harder, W. R. Hertler, W. Mahler, R. E. Benson, and W. E. Mochel, *J. Am. Chem. Soc.* 84, 3374 (1962).
3. J. B. Torrance, *Acc. Chem. Res.* 12, 79 (1979).
4. J. Ferraris, D. O. Cowan, V. Walakta, Jr, Perlstein, and J. H. Perlstein, *J. Am. Chem. Soc.* 95, 948 (1973).
5. A. A. Bright, A. F. Garito, and A. J. Heeger, *Solid State Commun.* 13, 943 (1973).
6. T. A. Skotheim, Ed., "Handbook of Conducting Polymers." M. Dekker, New York, 1986.
7. J. M. Williams, A. M. Kini, H. H. Wang, K. D. Carlson, U. Geiser, L. K. Montgomery, G. J. Pyrka, D. M. Watkins, J. M. Kommers, S. J. Boryschuk, A. V. S. Crouch, W. K. Kwok, J. E. Schirber, D. L. Overmyer, D. Jung, and M. H. Whangbo, *Inorg. Chem.* 29, 3263 (1990).
8. M. J. Rosseinsky, A. P. Ramirez, S. H. Glarum, D. W. Murphy, R. C. Haddon, A. F. Hebard, T. T. M. Palstra, A. R. Kortan, S. M. Zahurak, and A. V. Makhija, *Phys. Rev. Lett.* 66, 2830 (1991).
9. C. C. Chen, S. P. Kelty, and C. M. Lieber, *Science* 253, 886 (1991).
10. J. Ouyang, *Nano Rev.* 1, 5118 (2010).
11. Y. Yang, J. Ouyang, L. Ma, C. W. Chu, and R. J. Tseng, *Adv. Funct. Mater.* 16, 1001 (2006).
12. J. C. Scott and L. D. Bozano, *Adv. Mater.* 19, 1452 (2007).
13. G. W. Burr, B. N. Kurdi, J. C. Scott, C. H. Lam, K. Gopalakrishnan, and R. S. Shenoy, *IBM J. Res. Dev.* 52, 449 (2008).
14. D. V. Talapin, J. S. Lee, M. V. Kovalenko, and E. V. Shevchenko, *Chem. Rev.* 110, 389 (2010).
15. D. B. Strukov, G. S. Snider, D. R. Stewart, and R. S. Williams, *Nature* 453, 80 (2008).
16. L. P. Ma, J. Liu, and Y. Yang, *Appl. Phys. Lett.* 80, 2997 (2002).
17. L. D. Bozano, B. W. Kean, V. R. Deline, L. R. Salem, and J. C. Scott, *Appl. Phys. Lett.* 84, 607 (2004).
18. V. S. Reddy, S. Karak, and A. Dhar, *Appl. Phys. Lett.* 94, 173304 (2009).
19. S. H. Kang, T. Crisp, I. Kymissis, and V. Bulovic, *Appl. Phys. Lett.* 85, 4666 (2004).
20. F. Li, D. I. Son, J. H. Ham, B. J. Kim, J. H. Jung, and T. W. Kim, *Appl. Phys. Lett.* 91, 162109 (2007).
21. L. Ma, S. Pyo, J. Ouyang, Q. Xu, and Y. Yang, *Appl. Phys. Lett.* 82, 1419 (2003).
22. J. G. Park, W. S. Nam, S. H. Seo, Y. G. Kim, Y. H. Oh, G. S. Lee, and U. G. Paik, *Nano Lett.* 9, 1713 (2009).
23. J. Ouyang, C. W. Chu, C. Szmanda, L. Ma, and Y. Yang, *Nat. Mater.* 3, 918 (2004).
24. C. K. Kim, W. J. Joo, H. J. Kim, E. S. Song, J. Kim, S. Lee, C. Park, and C. Kim, *Synth. Met.* 158, 359 (2008).
25. B. Mukhejee and M. Mukhejee, *Appl. Phys. Lett.* 94, 173510 (2009).
26. W. T. Kim, J. H. Jung, T. W. Kim, and D. I. Son, *Appl. Phys. Lett.* 96, 253301 (2010).
27. D. Y. Yun, J. K. Kwak, J. H. Jung, T. W. Kim, and D. I. Son, *Appl. Phys. Lett.* 95, 143301 (2009).
28. F. Verbakel, S. C. J. Meskers, and R. A. J. Janssen, *Appl. Phys. Lett.* 89, 102103 (2006).
29. D. C. Das and A. J. Pal, *ACS Nano* 2, 1930 (2008).
30. S. Sahu, S. K. Majee, and A. J. Pal, *Appl. Phys. Lett.* 91, 143108 (2007).
31. D. I. Son, J. H. Kim, D. H. Park, W. K. Choi, F. Li, J. H. Ham, and T. W. Kim, *Nanotechnology* 19, 055204 (2008).
32. J. H. Jung, J. H. Kim, T. W. Kim, M. S. Song, Y. H. Kim, and S. Lin, *Appl. Phys. Lett.* 89, 122110 (2006).
33. F. Li, D. I. Son, S. M. Seo, H. M. Cha, H. J. Kim, B. J. Kim, J. H. Jung, and T. W. Kim, *Appl. Phys. Lett.* 91, 122111 (2007).
34. T. H. Kim, E. Y. Jang, N. J. Lee, D. J. Choi, K. J. Lee, J. T. Jang, J. S. Choi, S. H. Moon, and J. Cheon, *Nano Lett.* 9, 2229 (2009).
35. B. C. Das and A. J. Pal, *Small* 4, 542 (2008).
36. M. D. Fischbein and M. Drndic, *Appl. Phys. Lett.* 86, 193106 (2005).
37. B. Ghosh, S. Sahu, and A. J. Pal, *J. Phys. Chem. C* 112, 11290 (2008).
38. R. Tseng, J. Huang, J. Ouyang, R. B. Kaner, and Y. Yang, *Nano Lett.* 5, 1077 (2005).
39. J. Huang and R. B. Kaner, *J. Am. Chem. Soc* 126, 851 (2004).
40. J. Huang, S. Virji, B. H. Weiller, and R. B. Kaner, *Chem. Eur. J.* 10, 1314 (2004).
41. R. J. Tseng, C. Tsai, L. Ma, J. Ouyang, C. S. Ozkan, and Y. Yang, *Nat. Nanotech.* 1, 72 (2006).
42. R. Waser and M. Aono, *Nat. Mater.* 6, 833 (2007).
43. D. S. Jeong, H. Schroeder, and R. Waser, *Electrochem. Solid State Lett.* 10, G51 (2007).
44. W. Wang, T. Lee, and M. A. Reed, *Phys. Rev. B* 68, 035416 (2003).
45. J. Ouyang, C. W. Chu, R. J. H. Tseng, A. Prakash, and Y. Yang, *Proc. IEEE* 93, 1287 (2005).
46. L. D. Bozano, B. W. Kean, M. Beinhoff, K. R. Carter, P. M. Rice, and J. C. Scott, *Adv. Funct. Mater.* 15, 1933 (2005).
47. J. Ouyang, C. W. Chu, D. Sievers, and Y. Yang, *Appl. Phys. Lett.* 86, 123507 (2005).
48. J. Ouyang and Y. Yang, *Appl. Phys. Lett.* 96, 063506 (2010).
49. A. Prakash, J. Ouyang, and Y. Yang, *J. Appl. Phys.* 100, 054309 (2006).
50. P. Y. Lai and J. S. Chen, *Appl. Phys. Lett.* 93, 153305 (2008).
51. M. Beinhoff, L. D. Bozano, J. C. Scott, and K. R. Carter, *Macromolecules* 38, 4147 (2005).
52. W. J. Joo, T. L. Choi, K. H. Lee, and Y. Chung, *J. Phys. Chem. B* 111, 7756 (2007).
53. G. Dearnaley, D. V. Morgan, and A. M. Stoneham, *J. Non-Cryst. Solids.* 4, 593 (1970).
54. D. Tondelier, K. Lmimouni, D. Vuillaume, C. Fery, and G. Haas, *Appl. Phys. Lett.* 85, 5763 (2004).
55. C. W. Chu, J. Ouyang, and Y. Yang, *Adv. Mater.* 17, 1440 (2005).
56. Q. D. Ling, S. L. Lim, Y. Song, C. X. Zhu, D. S. H. Chan, E. T. Kang, and K. G. Neoh, *Langmuir* 23, 312 (2007).
57. F. Li, D. I. Son, S. H. Cho, and T. W. Kim, *Nanotechnology* 20, 185202 (2009).
58. R. J. Tseng, C. O. Baker, B. Shedd, J. Huang, R. B. Kaner, J. Ouyang, and Y. Yang, *Appl. Phys. Lett.* 90, 053101 (2007).
59. J. G. Simmons and R. R. Verderber, *Proc. Roy Soc. A* 301, 77 (1967).
60. H. T. Lin, Z. Pei, and Y. J. Chan, *IEEE Electron. Device. Lett.* 28, 569 (2007).
61. J. Chen and D. Ma, *Appl. Phys. Lett.* 87, 023505 (2005).
62. S. H. Kang, T. Crisp, I. Kymissis, and V. Bulovic, *Appl. Phys. Lett.* 85, 4666 (2004).

63. W. Tang, H. Z. Shi, G. Xu, B. S. Ong, Z. D. Popovic, J. C. Deng, J. Zhao, and G. H. Rao, *Adv. Mater.* 17, 2307 (2005).
64. M. J. Rozenberg, J. H. Inoue, and J. Sánchez, *Phys. Rev. Lett.* 92, 178302 (2004).
65. L. Ma, J. Liu, S. Pyo, and Y. Yang, *Appl. Phys. Lett.* 80, 362 (2002).
66. J. Wu, L. Ma, and Y. Yang, *Phys. Rev. B* 69, 115321 (2004).
67. N. S. Sariciftci, L. Smilowitz, A. J. Heeger, and F. Wudl, *Science* 258, 1474 (1992).
68. N. Martín, E. Ortí, L. Sánchez, P. M. Viruela, and R. Viruela, *Eur. J. Org. Chem.* 1999, 1239 (1999).
69. C. J. Brbec, N. S. Sariciftci, and J. C. Hummelen, *Adv. Funct. Mater.* 15, 11 (2001).
70. C. Laurent and E. Kay, *J. Appl. Phys.* 64, 336 (1988).
71. W. Vollmann and H. U. Poll, *Thin Solid Films* 26, 201 (1975).
72. B. Mukherjee and A. J. Pal, *Chem. Mater.* 19, 1382 (2007).
73. Y. Ma, Y. Wen, J. Wang, Y. Shang, S. Du, L. Pan, G. Li, L. Yang, H. Gao, and Y. Song, *J. Phys. Chem. C* 113, 8548 (2009).
74. J. S. Choi, J. H. Kim. S. H. Kim, and D. H. Suh, *Appl. Phys. Lett.* 89, 152111 (2006).
75. Y. Shang, Y. Wen, S. Li, S. Du, X. He, L. Cai, Y. Li, L. Yang, H. Gao, and Y. Song, *J. Am. Chem. Soc.* 129, 11674 (2007).
76. Y. Ma, X. Cao, G. Li, Y. Wen, Y. Yang, J. Wang, S. Du, L. Yang, H. Gao, and Y. Song, *Adv. Funct. Mater.* 20, 803 (2010).
77. J. Hu, Y. Li, Z. Ji, G. Jiang, L. Yang, W. Hu, H. Gao, L. Jiang, Y. Wen, Y. Song, and D. Zhu, *J. Mater. Chem.* 17, 3530 (2007).
78. J. S. Chappell, A. N. Bloch, W. A. Bryden, M. Maxfield, T. O. Poehler, and D. O. Cowan, *J. Am. Chem. Soc.* 103, 2442 (1981).
79. J. Ouyang, K. Yakushi, T. Kinoshita, N. Nanbu, M. Aoyagi, Y. Misaki, and K. Tanaka, *Spectrochim. Acta Part A* 58, 1643 (2002).
80. J. Ouyang, K. Yakushi, Y. Misaki, and K. Tanaka, *Phys. Rev. B* 63, 054301 (2001).
81. Y. K. Fang, C. L. Liu, C. Li, C. J. Lin, R. Mezzenga, and W. C. Chen, *Adv. Funct. Mater.* 20, 3012 (2010).
82. Y. L. Liu, K. L. Wang, G. S. Huang, C. X. Zhu, E. S. Tok, K. G. Neoh, and E. T. Kang, *Chem. Mater.* 21, 3391 (2009).
83. N. H. You, C. C. Chueh, C. L. Liu, M. Ueda, and W. C. Chen, *Macromolecules* 42, 4456 (2009).
84. Y. L. Liu, Q. D. Ling, E. T. Kang, K. G. Neoh, D. J. Liaw, K. L. Wang, W. T. Liou, C. X. Zhu, and D. S. H. Chan, *J. Appl. Phys.* 105, 044501 (2009).
85. S. G. Hahm, S. Choi, S. H. Hong, T. J. Lee, S. Park, D. M. Kim, W. S. Kwon, K. Kim, O. Kim, and M. Ree, *Adv. Funct. Mater.* 18, 3276 (2008).
86. L. Li, Q. D. Ling, C. Zhu, D. S. H. Chan, E. T. Kang, and K. G. Neo, *J. Electrochem. Soc.* 155, H205 (2008).
87. Q. D. Ling, Y. Song, S. L. Lim, E. Y. H. Teo, Y. P. Tan, C. Zhu, D. S. H. Chan, D. L. Kwong, E. T. Kang, and K. G. Neoh, *Angew. Chem. Int. Ed.* 45, 2947 (2006).
88. X. D. Zhuang, Y. Chen, B. X. Li, D. G. Ma, B. Zhang, and Y. Li, *Chem. Mater.* 22, 4455 (2010).
89. Q. D. Ling, E. T. Kang, K. G. Neoh, Y. Chen, X. D. Zhuang, C. Zhu, and D. S. H. Chan, *Appl. Phys. Lett.* 92, 143302 (2008).
90. K. L. Wang, T. Y. Tseng, H. L. Tsai, and S. C. Wu, *J. Polym. Sic. A* 46, 6861 (2008).
91. Q. D. Ling, W. Wang, Y. Song, C. X. Zhu, D. S. H. Chan, E. T. Kang, and K. G. Neoh, *J. Phys. Chem. B* 110, 23995 (2006).
92. S. Paul, A. Kanwal, and M. Chhowalla, *Nanotechnology* 17, 145 (2006).
93. J. K. Baral, H. S. Majumdar, A. Laiho, H. Jiang, E. I. Kauppinen, R. H. A. Ras, J. Ruokolainen, O. Ikkala, and R. Österbacka, *Nanotechnology* 19, 035203 (2008).
94. S. H. Cho, D. I. Lee, J. H. Jung, and T. W. Kim, *Nanotechnology* 20, 345204 (2009).
95. S. G. Hahm, S. Choi, S. H. Hong, T. J. Lee, S. Park, D. M. Kim, J. C. Kim, W. Kwon, K. Kim, M. J. Kim, O. Kim, and M. Ree, *J. Mater. Chem.* 19, 2207 (2009).
96. M. Vilkman, K. Solehmainen, A. Laiho, H. G. O. Sandberg, and O. Ikkala, *Organ. Electron.* 10, 1478 (2009).
97. J. Chen, L. Xu, J. Lin, Y. Geng, L. Wang, and D. Ma, *Semicond. Sci. Tech.* 21, 1121 (2006).
98. D. M. Kim, S. Park, T. J. Lee, S. G. Hahm, K. Kim, J. C. Kim, W. Kwon, and M. Ree, *Langmuir* 25, 11713 (2009).
99. T. L. Choi, K. H. Lee, W. J. Joo, S. Lee, T. W. Lee, and M. Y. Chae, *J. Am. Chem. Soc.* 129, 9842 (2007).
100. Q. D. Ling, Y. Song, E. Y. H. Teo, S. L. Lim, C. Zhu, D. S. H. Chan, D. L. Kwong, E. T. Kang, and K. G. Heoh, *Electrochem. Solid State Lett.* 9, G268 (2006).
101. Y. Xia, H. Zhang, and J. Ouyang, *J. Mater. Chem.* 20, 9740 (2010).
102. M. Zirkl, A. Haase, A. Fian, H. Schön, C. Sommer, G. Jakopic, G. Leising, B. Stadlober, I. Graz, N. Gaar, R. Schwödiauer, S. B. Gogonea, and S. Bauer, *Adv. Mater.* 19, 2241 (2007).
103. R. Koeppe, P. Bartu, S. Bauer, and N. S. Sariciftci, *Adv. Mater.* 21, 3510 (2009).
104. J. Ouyang, T. F. Guo, Y. Yang, H. Higuchi, M. Yoshioka, and T. Nagatsuka, *Adv. Mater.* 14, 915 (2002).
105. J. Ouyang and Y. Yang, *Adv. Mater.* 18, 2141 (2006).
106. Y. Ji, B. Cho, S. Song, T. W. Kim, M. Choe, Y. H. Kahng, and T. Lee, *Adv. Mater.* 22, 3071 (2010).
107. H. T. Lin, Z. Pei, J. R. Chen, and Y. J. Chan, *IEEE Electron. Device. Lett.* 30, 18 (2009).
108. Y. Kuang, R. Huang, and Y. Tang, *IEEE Electron. Device. Lett.* 31, 758 (2010).
109. R. J. Tseng, J. Ouyang, C. W. Chu, J. Huang, and Y. Yang, *Appl. Phys. Lett.* 88, 123506 (2006).
110. A. A. Zakhidov, B. Jung, J. D. Slinker, H. D. Abruña, and G. G. Malliaras, *Org. Electron.* 11, 150 (2010).

CHAPTER 13

Organic Resistive Switching for Nonvolatile Memory Application

Byungjin Cho[1], Tae-Wook Kim[2], Yongsung Ji[1], Sunghoon Song[1], Takhee Lee[3]

[1] *School of Materials Science and Engineering, Gwangju Institute of Science and Technology, Gwangju 500-712, Korea*
[2] *Korea Institute of Science and Technology, Jeollabuk-Do 565-902, Korea*
[3] *Department of Physics and Astronomy, Seoul National University, Seoul 151-744, Korea*

CONTENTS

1. INTRODUCTION

Information technology (IT) has become an important part of our lives. IT can be seen in the form of mobile phones, personal computers, and many other personal digital assistants. As the complexity of the electronic gadgets increases, miniaturization and data storage become important issues. All IT gadgets require data storages or

ISBN: 1-58883-251-1

Nonvolatile Memories: Materials, Devices and Applications
Edited by Tseung-Yuen Tseng and Simon M. Sze
Volume 2: Pages: 309–334

memories. Conventional memories are implemented on semiconductor-based integrated circuits, such as transistors and capacitors. And there is an increasing demand for higher capacity and device performance, lower power consumption, and lower fabrication cost [1]. However, a number of physical and economic factors are likely to end the continued scaling of current conventional memory devices based on inorganic semiconductors [2]. And, new opportunities are opening up for the development of new memory structures and materials as the industry strives to maintain Moore's Law-based downscaling.

Most of the efforts have been devoted to further scaling of the current two-dimensional (2D) chips with new fabrication techniques, such as imprint template, extreme ultraviolet and immersion lithographies, new structures, such as double-gate, triple-gate and multi-core, and new materials, such as strained silicon, high-dielectrics, and metal gate materials [3]. Another effort has been devoted to the development of the stackable chip, such as through-silicon via that takes chips and memory devices that traditionally sit side by side on a silicon wafer and stacks them together on top of one another [4]. These technologies will extend Moore's Law beyond its expected limits. At the same time, alternative technologies that exploit new materials and concepts to allow better scaling and to enhance the memory performance have been demonstrated by many researchers and engineers. These technologies include ferroelectric random access memory (FeRAM) [5], magnetoresistive random access memory (MRAM) [6], phase-change random access memory (PRAM) [7], and organic/polymer memories [8]. Unlike the current memory technologies with the memory effects associated with a special cell structure, the new technologies are based on electrical bistability of materials arising from changes in certain intrinsic properties, such as magnetism, polarity, phase, conformation, and conductivity, in response to the applied electric field.

In this chapter, we will review two-terminal organic resistive memory, which is based on the resistance change of organic materials sandwiched between two electrodes. First, we briefly address the background knowledge of organic and resistance memory and then general characteristics of the two-terminal organic resistive memory. The attention then shifts to the results of our research, which are summarized in Sections 4 to 7. In Section 4, we discuss general switching characteristics (unipolar and bipolar switching) of organic memory devices developed in our group and Sections 5 to 7 contain integration strategies, performance enhancement techniques, and advanced architectures for practical organic memory applications. Finally, this chapter is summarized and then some perspectives for future progress will be suggested.

2. BACKGROUND

2.1. Brief History of Organic-Based Memory

In the 1960s, there was a significant interest in the electrical properties of amorphous semiconductors due to their unique electrical properties that make them promising materials for memory applications [9]. Electrical switching with memory effects had been observed in a wide variety of inorganic materials [10]. Although the main focus in that era had been placed on inorganic materials, some attention had also been moved to organic and polymer thin films.

In 1970, polymer-based memories, which were based on a thermoplastic resin derived from poly(vinylidene chloride) and polystyrene, were first reported by Sliva and others [11]. Reproducible bistable switching in polymer films prepared by glow-discharge polymerization was also observed by Segui and others [12]. After these pioneering works, a wide variety of polymers by glow-discharge polymerization, electron-beam deposition, or plasma polymerization have been reported to show bistable memory effects. Most of the electrical memory effects observed at the early stage were related to filament formation, but performance was not enough to enable practical applications. Sadaoka and others [13] observed real memory switching in poly(*N*-vinylcarbazole) (PVK) films in 1976 where the memory switching is associated with trapping–detrapping processes arising from the impurities in PVK.

A ferroelectric crystal such as $Pb(Zr,Ti)O_3$ and $Sr\ (Bi,Ta)_2O_9$ maintains a permanent electric polarization that can be repeatedly switched between two stable states by an external bias [5]. The bistability of ferroelectric polarization in a thin film can be exploited to realize a nonvolatile memory. Studies on transition behavior of some ferroelectric polymers began in the 1980s [14]. In 1984, Siradjuddin and others [15] reported results obtained from the studies of electrical conductivity of polyvinylfluoride grown by the isothermal immersion technique. In 1995, Ducharme and colleagues [16] reported a major breakthrough in the fabrication of ferroelectric films by Langmuir–Blodgett technique. The resulting ferroelectric films are estimated to be 1 nm so that the device can be operated even in the very low voltage of 1 V [17]. Polymer FeRAM have been intensively researched, and currently it has become a promising memory technology.

Forrest and others [18] reported a write-once-read-many (WORM) memory in 2003. The memory component is composed of *p–i–n* silicon diode and a conductive polymer fuse of poly(ethylene dioxythiophene [PEDOT]) oxidatively *p*-doped by poly(styrene sulfonic acid [PSS]). High reliability and good compatibility with conventional electronic memory applications was a great achievement. Furthermore, the rectifying property of the silicon diodes can give a possibility to prevent current leakage paths in passive matrix architecture and memory component with fuse-like behavior for data storage has a stable conductance state after electrical transition [18].

The interest in polymer memories has been rapidly developed for the last few years. A large amount of research efforts has been concentrated on this field. It is because of the high possibility that polymer memory can become a potential alternative to the conventional memory technologies. The International Technology Roadmap for Semiconductors (ITRS) has also recognized polymer memory as one of emerging memory technologies since 2005 [8].

2.2. Resistance-Based Memory

Various physical phenomena have been proposed as the basis for new memory technologies. The basic requirements are that the building blocks should have at least two stable states, they can be switched by an external stimulus, and the states can be clearly distinguished during reading-out process. Best candidates for future memory electronics such as MRAM [19], FeRAM [5], and PRAM [7] have been intensively developed and researched. In particular, PRAM is particularly well developed and shows promise for a wide range of applications [7]. Resistive random access memory (RRAM) [20] has also been considered as a potential alternative to conventional Si-based memory.

The resistance-based memories consist of a nanoelectromechanical memory and of a range of metal-insulator-metal (MIM) systems, which show bistable resistance states controlled by external electric stimulation. The conceivable mechanisms of the resistive switching in MIM systems are often comprised of combination of physical and chemical effects. The mechanism can be categorized depending on a dominant contribution by thermal effect, by ionic effect, or by electronic effect [21]. According to the ITRS 2007 edition [22], the resistive switching systems are more specifically categorized into seven parts:

(1) nanoelectromechanical memory,
(2) unipolar fuse/antifuse memory,
(3) ionic memory,
(4) electronic effects memory,
(5) macromolecular memory, and
(6) molecular memory.

Each memory the ITRS suggested was grouped based on the switching mechanism of a resistance change or a particular type of active material.

3. TWO-TERMINAL ORGANIC RESISTIVE MEMORY

Polymer or organic resistive memory consists of a thin film of organic material itself [23] or composites, including embedded components [24, 25] (metal nanoparticles or small molecules) sandwiched between two metal electrodes. This structure can exhibit two stable states of different conductivities at an applied voltage. After conductivity transition occurs, the device can remain in one of two states even after turning off the power.

Advantages of organic memories also include simplicity in device structure, good scalability, low-cost potential, low-power operation, multiple state property, three-dimensional (3D) stacking capability, and large capacity for data storage [26–37]. They also have superior memory parameters such as low operation voltage range, large ON/OFF ratio, nonvolatile memory effect, and fast response time. Such various merits have eventually accelerated the research and development of novel organic resistive memories.

3.1. Device Structures and Switching Characteristics

Generally, organic resistive memory consists of organic layer sandwiched between bottom and top electrodes. Electrical evaluation of unit cell-type device structure is preferred in the early stage of memory development due to the simplicity of device fabrication process (Fig. 1(a)). Next step for the advanced technology of the organic memory is to integrate as many cells in a single chip as possible. A cross-bar structure has been considered as the most ideal architecture for the integration strategy (Fig. 1(b)). All the cross regions between bottom (word lines) and top electrodes (bit lines) are defined as information storage cells in this structure. Three-dimensional staking is also one of the best ways to achieve a great increase in memory cell density (Fig. 1(c)). Despite the advantage that the array structure is simple to make, the reading disturbance between memory cells, called cross-talk interference, which usually results from the current leakage through neighboring cells with low resistances, is unavoidable in such an array structure (Fig. 1(d)). The expected solution to prevent the cross-talk phenomenon is to add a rectifying diode component to each cell (Fig. 1(e)).

A great variety of organic materials has been reported as active media for the information storage cell. In particular,

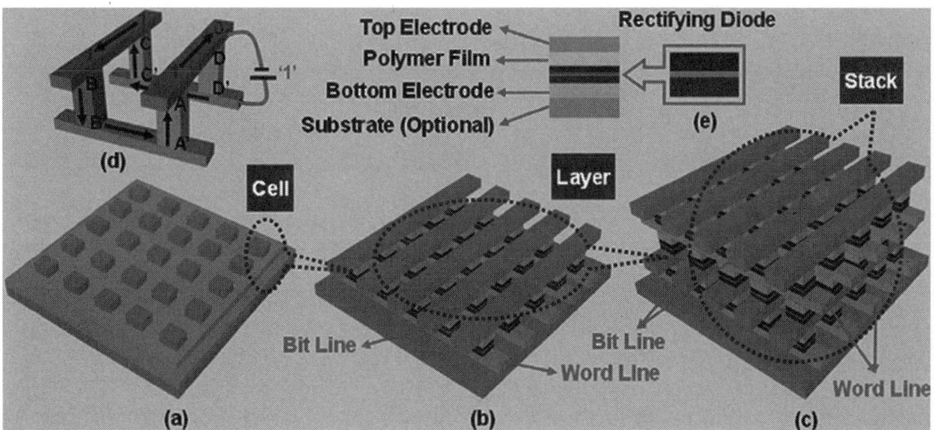

Figure 1. Schematic diagrams of: (a) 5 × 5 testing polymer devices and the basic configuration of a memory cell, (b) a 5 (word line) × 5 (bit line) cross-point memory array, (c) a 2 (stacked layer) × 5 (word line) × 5 (bit line) stacked memory device, (d) parasitic paths in cross-point memories, and (e) rectifying diode integrated to avoid parasitic currents. Reprinted with permission from [110], Q.-D. Ling et al., *Prog. Polym. Sci.* 33, 917 (2008). © 2008, Elsevier.

four architectures have been used for the fabrication of two-terminal organic restive memory devices:

(1) a single-layer device without the nanoparticles (NPs),
(2) a bilayer structure containing two kinds of polymers,
(3) a structure in which nano-traps are placed in the middle of organic layer, and
(4) spun-cast polymer-NP blends in which nano-traps are randomly distributed throughout the entire thickness of the host matrix (Fig. 2(a)).

Electrical switching characteristics of the organic memory device can be basically divided into two categories, volatile or nonvolatile switching, depending on the ability to maintain information (Fig. 2(b)). More specifically, an organic memory device with volatile switching is very similar to dynamic random access memory (DRAM) that needs periodical refreshing to store information (I of Fig. 2(b)). When the power is removed, the device loses its data. However, organic memory device with nonvolatile switching characteristic can store data once it is electrically programmed. Because this kind of memory is similar to conventional flash memory, power is not needed to maintain the information stored in the chip. The nonvolatile switching can be classified into three different kinds according to the current–voltage (*I–V*) characteristics (Fig. 2(b)). The characteristic of II, III, and IV of Figure 2(b) is called a WORM, unipolar, and bipolar switching memory, respectively. The WORM-type can be usually utilized for the memory component of radio-frequency identification card tag, but electrically irreversible switching property limits their memory applications. Depending on the operation voltage polarity, electrically rewritable switching memory is divided into two categories, unipolar and bipolar switching memories. The unipolar memory uses the same voltage polarity, whereas bipolar memory requires different voltage polarity for writing and erasing process. In particular, electrically rewritable switching in the hybrid structure, consisting of diode and memory component, to prevent cross-talk problems can be achieved only by the introduction of unipolar-type switching memory, which will provide a high feasibility for more practical memory applications.

3.2. Possible Mechanisms of Resistive Switching

In this section, we focus on possible switching mechanisms of organic resistive memory, which have been already proposed by many researchers. RRAM is based on the conductivity change of materials in response to the electric field. Generally, conductivity can be defined as a product of the carrier concentration and charge mobility. Therefore, a change of carrier concentration, charge mobility, or both results in a change in the conductivity of materials. Particularly, the conduction mechanism in organic materials is very complex because an amorphous structure in nature cannot be adequately explained on the basis of band model of ordered inorganic materials [38]. The conduction in organic materials is normally explained by intrinsic charge carrier generation in the organic itself and charge carrier injection from electrodes to organic materials. Intrinsic carrier density in organic materials is usually very low and carriers are usually trapped by localized states. Because of the continuous trapping–detrapping process of charge carriers, the time needed for charge transport is normally long [38].

Charge carrier injection at a contact region between electrodes and organic materials is more dominant in RRAM devices. A number of conduction mechanisms such as ohmic

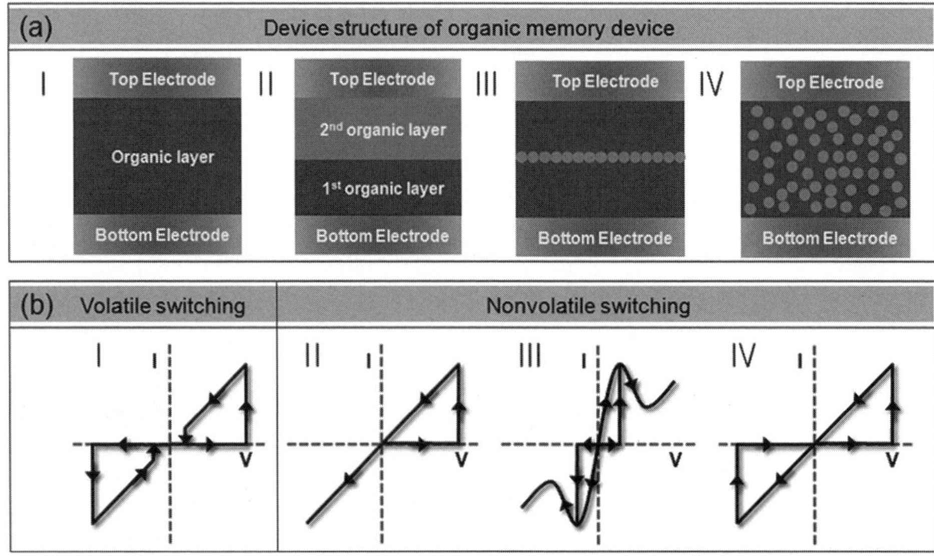

Figure 2. (a) Typical device structures of organic memory device: (I) a single-layer device without the NPs, (II) bilayer structure containing pure two kinds of polymers, (III) structure in which the nano-traps are placed in the middle of organic layer, and (IV) spun-cast polymer-NP blends in which the nano-traps are randomly distributed throughout the entire thickness of the host matrix, (b) typical switching characteristics of organic resistive memory: (I) *I–V* of DRAM-like volatile switching (II) *I–V* curve of write-once-read-many switching (III) *I–V* curve of unipolar switching, and (IV) *I–V* curve of bipolar switching.

conduction, Schottky emission, thermionic emission, space charge-limited current (SCLC), tunneling current, ionic conduction, hopping conduction, and impurity conduction have been proposed to explain the conduction process in organic materials. The current density–voltage and current density–temperature dependencies are summarized in Table 1.

3.2.1. Resistive Switching from Filamentary Conduction Mechanism

In general, when the current of the ON state is highly localized to a small fraction of the device area, the conduction phenomenon is called a filamentary conduction [39, 40]. Although it is hard to elucidate the nature of the localized conducting paths, two kinds of filamentary conduction have been suggested. The one is associated with the carbon-rich filaments formed by the local degradation of organic films [41, 42], and the other one is related to the metallic bridges that result from the migration of electrodes through organic films [39, 43]. If filaments are formed in organic device, the ON state is created, with the conduction characteristics showing a temperature-independent electrical behavior or metallic *I–V* characteristics [44]. It also exhibits a device area-independent behavior, which is due to the formation of much smaller filaments rather than device area [42, 44].

Recently, a wide variety of organic and electrode materials have been employed to study the formation of filaments [45]. The filament formation in a Cu/P3HT/Al device has been reported, which is caused by the penetration of top metal into organic layer under forward bias [45]. The copper ions were generated and drifted into organic layer, which was confirmed by the secondary ion mass spectroscopy analysis [45]. Furthermore, high conductive state showed the typical metallic *I–V* characteristics confirmed by variable temperature experiment, where the resistance increased linearly with the increasing temperature [46]. Metallic filaments can also be produced in devices with composite materials including metal clusters [47]. Homogeneously dispersed Au clusters into PEDOT:PSS or poly(4-hydroxystyrene [PHOST]) was used to make high conducting paths that were thermally induced. Once the high conducting percolation paths were formed in the polymer, the current conduction paths were stable and irreversible, enabling possible WORM memory applications [47].

Table 1. The basic conduction processes in insulators.

Conduction mechanisms	*J–V* characteristics
Ohmic conduction	$J \propto V \exp\left(\frac{-\Delta E_{ae}}{kT}\right)$
Hopping conduction	$J \propto V \exp\left(\frac{\Phi}{kT}\right)$
Schottky emission	$J \propto T^2 \exp\left[\frac{-q(\Phi - \sqrt{qV/4\pi\varepsilon})}{kT}\right]$
Thermionic emission	$J \propto T^2 \exp\left[\frac{-(\Phi - q\sqrt{qV/4d\pi\varepsilon})}{kT}\right]$
Frenkel-Poole emission	$J \propto V \exp\left[\frac{-q(\Phi - \sqrt{qV/4\pi\varepsilon})}{kT}\right]$
Tunnel or field emission	$J \propto V^2 \exp\left[\frac{-4\sqrt{2m}(q\Phi)^{3/2}}{3q\hbar V}\right]$
Direct tunneling	$J \propto \frac{v}{d} \exp\left[\frac{(\text{xpe}\sqrt{2m\Phi})}{\hbar}\right]$
Fowler-Nordheim tunneling	$J \propto V^2 \exp\left[\frac{-4d\sqrt{2m}(\Phi)^{3/2}}{3q\hbar V}\right]$
Ionic conduction	$J \propto \frac{V}{T} \exp\left(\frac{-\Delta E_{ai}}{kT}\right)$
Space-charge-limited current	$J \propto \frac{9\varepsilon_i \mu V^2}{8d^3}$

Source: Reprinted with permission from [110], Q.-D. Ling et al., *Prog. Polym. Sci.* 33, 917 (2008). © 2008, Elsevier.
Notes: Φ = barrier height, V = electric field, T = temperature, ε = insulator dynamic permittivity, m = effective mass, ΔE_{ae} = activation energy of electrons, ΔE_{ai} = activation energy of ions, d = insulator thickness, q = charge and μ is the carries mobility.

3.2.2. Resistive Switching from Space Charge and Traps

If the electrodes/organic materials contact is ohmic and the insulator is trap-free, the accumulation of carriers near the electrode builds up a space charge. Mutual repulsion between individual charges restricts the total charge injected into the sample, and the resulting current is called an SCLC. Space charges may arise from several sources such as injection of electrons and/or holes from electrode, ionized dopants in interfacial depletion regions, and accumulation of mobile ions at electrode interfaces. Traps may be present in the bulk of the material or at interfaces to reduce carrier mobility. When the traps exist at interfaces, they may also affect charge injection into the material.

Electrical bistability of some organic material has been found to be associated with the space charges [48]. Hysteresis characteristic in the *I–V* curves of the ITO/poly[3-(6-methoxyhexyl)thiophene] (P3OMe)/Al structure was observed [48]. It has been proposed that the bistable switching arises from the accumulation of space charges. The space charges accumulate at the metal/polymer interfaces and restrict the electric field. The effect in turn limits the charge injection into the organic layer [49]. The stored charges control the charge injection and lead to hysteresis in *I–V* curve. The conductance switching phenomena have also been observed in organic materials including metal or semiconducting islands that serve as the trapping sites [50]. The common feature of the results is that current abruptly increases at the threshold, reaches a maximum, and then undergoes negative differential region (NDR) to a minimum. It was proposed that the active mechanism is very similar to those observed in inorganic MIM diodes by Simmons and Verderber [51]. The resistive switching was explained in terms of charge trapping on the NPs.

3.2.3. Resistive Switching from Charge Transfer Effects

Generally, a charge transfer (CT) occurs in an electron donor–acceptor system, where there is a partial transfer of electronic charge from the donor to the acceptor moiety. The field-induced transfer is the mechanism that is the most frequently assumed to occur in CT complexes. The electrical memory effect of CT complexes was first observed on Cu-tetracyanoquinodimethane (TCNQ) [52], where Cu is the donor and TCNQ is the organic acceptor. Raman spectroscopy showed that the TCNQ anions in the pristine high resistance film were replaced by neutral TCNQ molecules in the low resistance state (LRS) [53].

Recently, Chu and others [54] reported that a composite film derived from a soluble methanofullerene (PCBM) and tetrathiofulvalene (TTF) dispersed in a polystyrene matrix showed a bistable resistance state. The electronic transition was attributed to an electrical-field-induced charge transfer between TTF and PCBM in the film. Depending on their redox states, TTF and PCBM serve as an electron donor and acceptor, respectively. The energy levels are chosen so that no electron transfer occurs in the ground states. In addition, a low concentration of charge carriers exists in the film so that the film has a low conductivity. A high electric field, however, can facilitate electron transfer from the highest occupied molecular orbital (HOMO) of TTF to the lowest occupied molecular orbital (LUMO) of PCBM. Consequently, the HOMO of TTF and the LUMO of PCBM become partially filled, and TTF and PCBM are charged positively and negatively, respectively. Therefore, a sharp increase in conductivity occurs after the charge transfer [54].

3.2.4. Resistive Switching from Conformation Change Effects

Conductance switching and memory effects of molecular electronic devices often arise from electrically induced conformational changes in molecules or molecular bundles [55]. Devices with Rose Bengal (RB) molecules in the supramolecular matrices using poly(allylamine hydrochloride) as the polyelectrolyte showed conductance switching [56]. However, this phenomenon is not observed in devices based on RB spin-cast films [57]. This is because of the high packing density of the spin-coated film and strong intermolecular interactions where conformational change or rotation of a molecular plane is hindered. In the low bias, reverse bias-induced electro-reduction of RB facilitates the restoration of conjugation in the backbone of the molecule and, hence, switches the molecule to an ON state. Under a large bias, the two perpendicular planes present in RB molecule allow forward-bias induced conformational change, resulting in a conductance recovery to the OFF state [56].

Conductance switching from conformational change effect was also observed in poly(2-[9*H*-carbazol-9-*yl*] ethyl methacrylate [PCz]) and poly(9-[2-([4-vinylbenzyl]oxy) ethyl]-9*H*-carbazole [PVBCz]), which are nonconjugated polymers containing electron-donating carbazole pendant groups [58, 59]. In the absence of a spacer unit between the pendant carbazole group and the main chain, the PVK does not exhibit memory-switching effects [58]. The switching effect in the PCz and PVBCz devices are caused by a field-induced conformational change of the polymers through rotations from the randomly oriented carbazole groups to a more regio-regular arrangement. It is similar to that of the face-to-face conformation of PVK for facilitated carrier delocalization and transport [60]. On the other hand, the differences in memory behavior between PCz and PVBCz can be explained by their inherent differences in the degree of regio-regularity and the ease of conformational relaxation of the field-induced regio-regular carbazole groups in PVBCz.

3.2.5. Resistive Switching from Ionic Conductions

Ionic conduction happens in polymers containing ionic groups. In amorphous polymers, ionic conduction can also occur due to drift of defects from an applied electric field. Ionic conduction is characterized by its high activation energy in comparison with the activation energy for electronic conduction, and the noticeable polarization effect under the action of a direct-current field. In addition, a large transit time for ions is also observed. Activation energies are also found to increase with temperature [38].

Electrically rewritable switching effects from poly(3-hexylthiophene [P3HT]) [61] and a sexithiophene-poly (ethylene oxide [6TPEO]) block copolymer [62] have been reported. The inorganic salts, $LiCF_3SO_3$ and NaCl, serve as the dopants in these studies [61, 62]. The electrical bistability is explained in terms of migration of dopant ions in and out of the P3HT or 6TPEO depletion layer at the aluminum Schottky contact. In the case of 6T-PEO, electrochemical doping of 6T occurs at both electrodes under the forward bias [61, 62]. Near the Al electrode, the 6T is reduced by migration of sodium ions toward the metal electrode (*n*-type doping), while oxidation of 6T occurs near the interface with the PEDOT:PSS electrode, which is related to migration of the chloride ions in the vicinity of the interface (*p*-type doping) [62]. These processes result in the formation of a *p*–*n* junction.

3.3. Requirements for Practical Memory Applications

Specifications of a memory technology are usually described in terms of storage capacity, ON/OFF ratio, speed to write or erase, cycling endurance, retention time, and cost. The performance of the individual cells that comprise the array then should meet the specific requirements to be a commercial product. It should be considered that the active array is connected to a great deal of surrounding circuitry that addresses the desired storage cell, applies the appropriate voltages to write or erase, and senses the ON or OFF state of each cell. This circuitry occupies an area comparable with the memory array itself, which is responsible for a considerable fraction of the cost. It is required to quantify this in terms of "array efficiency:" the fraction of the area devoted to the actual storage cells.

The ON/OFF ratio is related to the value to quantify whether or not the supporting circuitry can distinguish between 0 and 1. This is one of the stringent specifications. More than a factor of 10 is regarded to be sufficient. It is better in terms of memory margin to have as large a value as possible. Many researchers emphasize the value of ON/OFF ratio measured in a single cell. Rather than this, statistical distribution of many cells and many cycles should be considered to be a more important memory parameter. Narrow distribution of each resistance state and large gap between the states are necessary for the best specification of memory.

One of the disadvantages of conventional flash memory is that the time to erase it is several milliseconds. To compete with flash memory in the electronics, it is probably essential to develop a new memory system rewritable in times of a microsecond. In this regards, some of organic resistive memory devices have been demonstrated with the voltage pulse with dozens of nanoseconds [63].

Another weakness of flash memory is that the number of cycling is limited to about 10^6, which prevents its use as core memory. An organic memory device is also very limited to several hundreds of cycles, and thus the poor endurance characteristic should be improved for the practical memory applications. This problem may arise from gradual electrical degradation by oxygen or moisture in air; thus, additional passivation or package process may be a solution for this issue. In particular, an endurance characteristic may be very different in a system that accompanies mass transport (electromigration, electrochemistry, molecular reorientation, NP deformation) compared with one where only charges move (Coulomb blockade, charge-transfer complex) [64].

Generally, DRAM requires data refresh every few milliseconds, which drives the development of a novel nonvolatile memory device. Of course, flash and hard disk drive (HDD) can retain their data for many years. A new WORM organic memory showed the extreme information storage ability. Retention time of about 10^4 seconds was usually demonstrated in rewritable switching memory devices. Nevertheless, the information storage ability is still not comparable with commercial nonvolatile memory devices; thus, a large research effort should be devoted to the retention improvement.

Cost of organic memory is considerably competitive compared with flash or HDD. Cost effective fabrication processes such as spin-coating or printing are available in these organic electronics, which makes the organic memory device attractive. However, irreproducible and degradable device performance gradation in the manufacturing process can prevent achieving the required specifications. This is mainly because of an absence of a clearly defined switching process. Provided that the memory performance is demonstrated and manipulated by well-defined switching mechanisms, price competitiveness of the organic memory will be emphasized.

Generally, organic resistive memory integrated with array form requires novel architecture for reading efficiency improvement. Cross-talk interference in a passive matrix that only includes information storage cells usually occurs due to the leakage of current paths (called sneak paths) through neighboring cells with low resistances in cross-point array structures [65, 66] or an excess of current that may induce electrical damage [67]. This phenomenon disturbs the sensing resistance state of the selected cell. The indicated solution to eliminate this cross-talk is to introduce a switching component (transistor or diode) to each cell [31]. The ITRS also emphasized the combination of a diode or transistor with a resistor in a single chip [22]. The architecture of one diode and one resistor (1D-1R) [18, 25, 68–71] or one transistor and one resistor (1T-1R) [67, 72] can improve reading accessibility in an integrated memory array structure.

4. GENERAL SWITCHING CHARACTERISTICS: UNIPOLAR AND BIPOLAR SWITCHING

4.1. Unipolar Switching of Composites of Poly(9-vinylcarbazole) and Titanium Dioxide Nanoparticles

In this work, organic memory devices using TiO_2 NPs embedded in PVK in the 8 × 8 array structure were fabricated on indium tin oxide (ITO; sheet resistance of ~8 Ω/sq.) on glass substrates [24]. ITO-coated glass substrates were precleaned through a typical ultrasonic cleaning process. ITO electrodes with eight line patterns of 100-μm line-width were prepared as bottom electrodes by conventional photolithography and a subsequent etching process. PVK (molecular weight ~ 1,100,000) and TiO_2 NPs (anatase 5 nm) were used to make a mixture (PVK:TiO_2 = 200:1, 150:1,100:1,10:1, and 1:1 solution volume ratios) of PVK solution (5 mg/ml) and TiO_2 NPs solution (2 mg/ml) dissolved in 1,2 dichloroethane. The PVK:TiO_2 NPs solution was spin-coated at 4,000 rpm for 40 seconds in a N_2-filled glove box. A baking process was then performed on a hotplate in the N_2-filled glove box at 150°C for 2 minutes. The resulting film thickness was estimated to be ~60 nm (for the case of PVK:TiO_2 = 150:1 volume ratio). Then, Al (100-nm thick) electrodes were deposited using an *e*-beam evaporator at a pressure of ~10^{-7} torr. Figure 3(a) shows a schematic cross-sectional view, illustrating the PVK:TiO_2 NPs composite layer sandwiched between the ITO and Al. Aggregates of TiO_2 NPs, having a diameter of 20–40 nm, were observed within the PVK matrix (Fig. 3(b)), and the size of individual TiO_2 NPs was about 3 to 7 nm (Fig. 3(b)). As the PVK:TiO_2 NPs volume ratio changed from 200:1 to 1:1 (i.e., the TiO_2 NPs concentration was increased), the aggregation effect of the NPs became stronger.

Figure 4(a) shows *I–V* characteristics of a memory cell in the 8 × 8 array devices consisting of the ITO/PVK:TiO_2 NPs (volume ratio 150:1)/Al structure. As the voltage increased at the positive bias, the memory device exhibited an abrupt increase of current by three orders of magnitude near 3.4 V (set voltage), indicating a switching effect from a high resistance state (HRS; OFF state) to LRS (ON state; first sweep). The device still remained in the ON state until 5.7 V (reset voltage). Beyond the reset voltage, a sharp reduction of the current happened, showing an NDR behavior (second sweep). The current beyond the NDR region (> 5.7 V) seemed to follow the OFF state. When the *I–V* characteristics were tested again (third sweep), the device showed an almost identical *I–V* curve to what was shown in the first sweep, indicating a rewritable memory effect. Therefore, the device could be set from OFF to ON (writing) by applying a voltage slightly higher than the set voltage and reset from ON to OFF (erasing) by a voltage beyond the NDR region. In this system, the switching can be obtained by successive application of voltages of the same polarity, which is typical of the unipolar memory effect. From the *I–V* results, bistable resistance states at the same voltage could be obtained below the set voltage, and each state remained stable even after the power was turned off, indicating the nonvolatile memory effect. However, there was no resistive

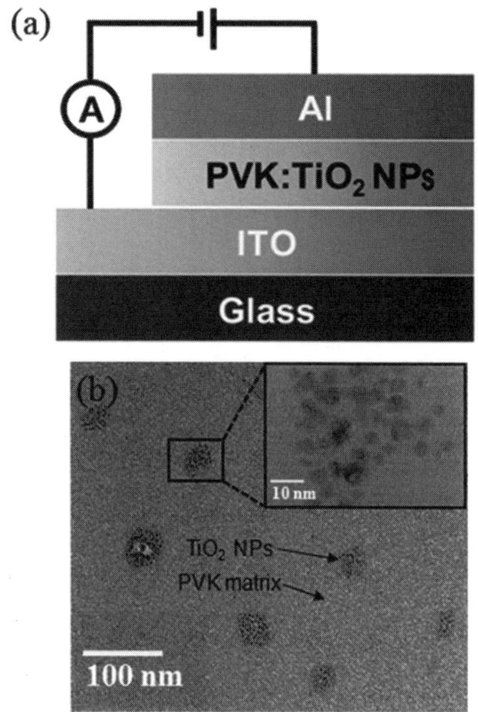

Figure 3. (a) Schematic of the cross-sectional view of ITO/PVK:TiO_2 NPs/Al structure. (b) TEM image of a composite film with PVK:TiO_2 NPs volume ratio of 150:1.

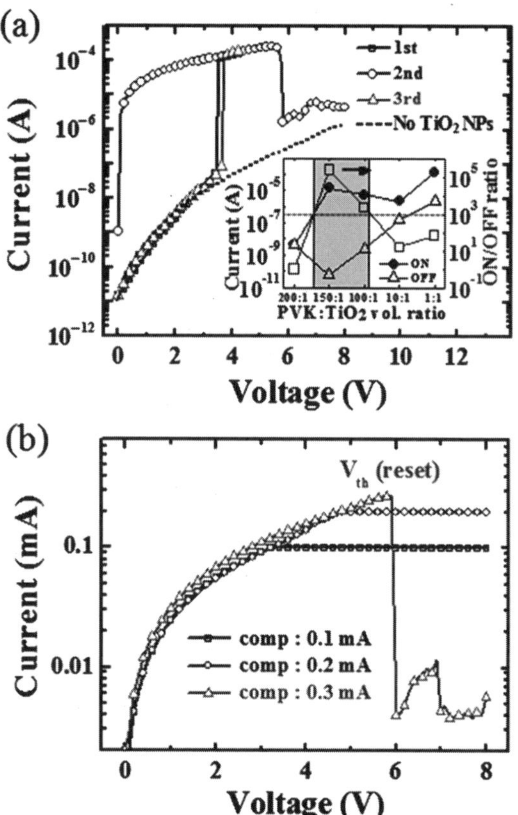

Figure 4. (a) *I–V* characteristics of a ITO/PVK:TiO_2 NPs (volume ratio of 150:1)/Al memory device (line + symbol curves) and ITO/PVK/Al device without TiO_2 NPs (dashed line). The inset shows ON and OFF currents (left axis) and ON/OFF ratio (right axis) measured at 0.5 V as a function of PVK:TiO_2 NPs volume ratio, (b) turn-off process as a function of compliance current.

switching behavior in the devices made with just PVK without TiO_2 NPs (represented by the dashed line in Fig. 4(a)). These effects clearly demonstrate that TiO_2 NPs play an important role in the bistable switching phenomenon.

To study the role of TiO_2 NPs in the bistable switching, we performed *I–V* measurements on devices with different TiO_2NP concentrations. The ON and OFF state currents measured at 0.5 V are displayed as a function of PVK:TiO_2 NPs volume ratio (Fig. 4(a), left axis). It clearly shows that the OFF current gradually increased with increasing TiO_2 NP concentration, while the ON current remained nearly constant regardless of the TiO_2 NP concentration. These different features between the ON and OFF currents eventually resulted in the large variation in the ON/OFF ratios (Fig. 4(a), right axis). In particular, NP concentrations in the range of ~150:1 to 100:1 volume ratio was found to enable high performance organic memory devices with high ON/OFF ratios of more than three orders of magnitude. The TiO_2 NP concentration is a critical factor to determine ON/OFF ratio, and it is one of the key memory parameters. Contrary to OFF currents, ON currents show relatively little variation regardless of TiO_2 NP concentration. It indicates that high current states are due to the introduction of TiO_2 NPs.

Specifically, the current conduction of the ON state is associated with the filamentary conduction model [40]. The model invokes the formation of filaments in the PVK polymer, showing ohmic conduction without thermal activation. The fracture of the filaments is probably a consequence of Joule heating, raising the temperature as a part of the filament. The Joule heating effect gives rise to atomic reorganization. In our device, the filamentary paths are not only made by defects or structural disorder within the PVK polymer. TiO_2 NPs also are involved for the formation of the filamentary paths. Growth of the filamentary paths may mainly occur in the limited region where TiO_2 NPs are distributed. TiO_2 NPs serve as one source of materials that constitute the high conducting paths. It is reasonable to assume that the filament consists of TiO_2 NPs and some kind of defect within the PVK. Note that others have reported the bistability switching in PVK materials [73]. However, the electrode materials, device structures, PVK layer thickness, and charge conduction behavior are different from our devices [74], which may explain different switching properties.

PVK is a well-known hole-transporting polymer [75]. Some reports on polymer memory devices using PVK or PVK composite suggested that holes are major carriers that cause the memory effect [73]. Furthermore, the injection barrier of the hole in the PVK is much lower than that of the electron because of the relatively high HOMO energy level. Thus, holes will be the major charge carriers responsible for the memory effect in our memory devices. On the other hand, PVK mainly functions as a matrix where filamentary paths are formed.

Figure 4(b) shows the turn-off process as a function of the compliance current. Once the ON state was formed, the OFF state could be obtained only when a proper compliance current was applied to the devices. The turn-off process could only be triggered by the appropriate compliance current. The device did not turn to the OFF state if the compliance current was set at 1 mA or 2 mA, but it successfully turned to the OFF state when the compliance current was set larger than 3 mA. A similar compliance dependency of the turn-off process has been reported for the case of memory devices with the Al/PVK/Al structure previously [73]. Our device showed considerable noise fluctuations beyond the NDR region. The noise might have been closely related with rupturing and regrowing of conducting filaments inside the polymer [40]. The number of mobile carriers and their mobility would have provoked noise fluctuations. The considerable noise fluctuations generally occurred within the NDR region [39, 40]. Meanwhile, the noise of our devices appeared after the NDR region (Fig. 4(b)). Note that some reports suggested that the bistability of the organic nonvolatile memory devices result from an interfacial oxide layer such as Al_2O_3 [76, 77]. To minimize the effect of the thin native oxide, the Al top electrode was deposited as soon as possible after the spin-coating of the composite film. In addition, to minimize the effect of O_2 or H_2O, all electrical tests were performed in a nitrogen-filled glove box.

To obtain further information about the switching characteristics of the devices, we studied the correlation between the set current (current at the set voltage) and the reset current (current at the reset voltage). As shown in Figure 5(a), the reset current gradually increased as we increased the set current. This correlation between the reset and set currents can also be utilized to understand the underlying mechanism associated with the filamentary conduction model [73, 78]. It is expected that the higher set current will form stronger filaments. On the other hand, if the stronger filaments are formed, it is relatively hard to break the filamentary current path, and thus, the higher reset current should be expected.

The charge transport mechanism was studied by temperature-variable I–V measurements in a vacuum pressure of $\sim 10^{-3}$ torr. Figure 5(b) shows the Arrhenius plot of each state in the temperature range from 150 to 300 K. The ON and OFF currents were read at 2 V while the temperature was changed at a speed of 2 K/minute. The OFF current is related to a thermally activated transport with an activation energy of ~66 meV. In contrast, the ON current was almost temperature-independent, exhibiting negligible activation energy of ~3 meV. It was also found that the log–log plot of the ON current clearly exhibited the form of $I \sim V$, indicating ohmic characteristics (inset of Fig. 5(b)). These properties of the ON current are mainly attributed to charge tunnelling through filamentary paths induced by a high electric field [40, 76, 79]. Consequently, bistable resistance switching of PVK:TiO_2 NPs devices involves the change of charge conduction mechanism from the thermally activated transport (OFF state) into the tunnelling transport (ON state).

In this work, we demonstrated that organic memory devices with 8 × 8 array cells using titanium dioxide nanoparticles (TiO_2 NPs) embedded within PVK film exhibit bistable resistance states and a unipolar nonvolatile memory effect. TiO_2 NPs were a key factor to induce the bistability, and the concentration of TiO_2 NPs also influenced ON/OFF ratio. From electrical measurements, the switching mechanism of PVK:TiO_2NP devices was closely associated with filamentary conduction model, and it was observed that the OFF state was dominated by thermally activated transport while the ON state followed tunnelling transport.

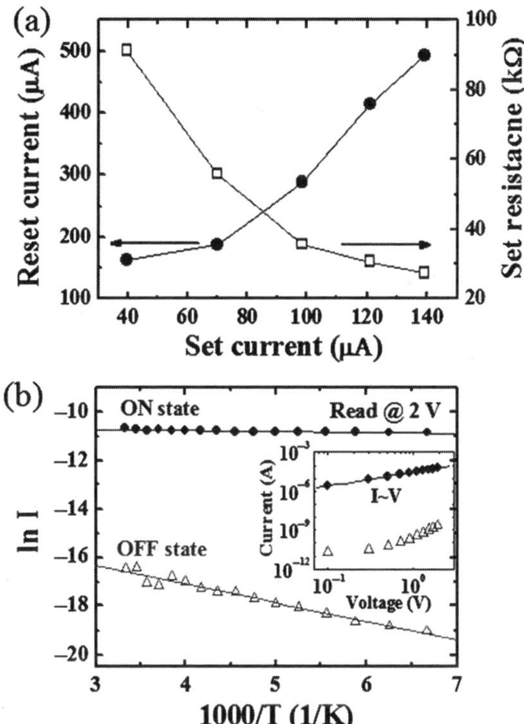

Figure 5. (a) Reset current (left axis) and set resistance (right axis) as a function of set current for a ITO/PVK:TiO_2 NPs (volume ratio of 150:1)/Al memory device, (b) arrhenius plot of ON and OFF currents at temperature range from 150 to 300 K for a ITO/PVK:TiO_2 NPs (volume ratio of 150:1)/Al device. The inset shows the log–log plot of I–V characteristics in the voltage range of 0 to 2 V at 300 K.

4.2. Bipolar Switching of a Polyfluorene-Derivative Single Layer Film

In this work, we demonstrated single component polyfluorene-derivative memory devices. Heavily doped p-type (100) silicon (0.001–0.015 Ω cm) was used as a bottom electrode [23]. After the typical ultrasonic cleaning processes with acetone, methanol, and deionized (DI) water, the silicon wafers were treated with a diluted HF solution to remove the native oxide layer. The polyfluorene derivatives (denoted as WPF-oxy-F), schematically shown in Figure 6(a), were synthesized by a palladium catalyzed Suzuki coupling reaction method [80]. WPF-oxy-F was first dissolved in methanol solvent at a concentration of 5 mg/ml and then was spin coated on p-type silicon substrate. The spin-coating condition was 2,000 rpm for 30 seconds and the resulting thickness of the WPF-oxy-F film was about ~30 nm. Postbaking was performed at 150°C for 20 minutes on a hotplate in a N_2-fiilled glove box. The top electrodes were patterned using a shadow mask that had square patterns of four different sizes: 50 × 50 μm^2, 100 × 100 μm^2, 200 × 200 μm^2, and 400 × 400 μm^2. A memory device structure is schematically illustrated in Figure 6(b). All of

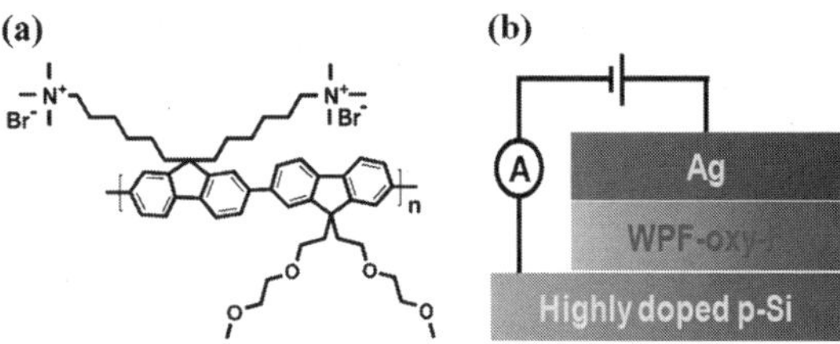

Figure 6. (a) Chemical structure of WPF-oxy-F polyfluorene derivative, (b) schematic of single component WPF-oxy-F memory device.

the electrical characterization was carried out under an ambient condition and in an N_2-filled glove box at room temperature.

Figure 7 shows a typical bipolar switching *I–V* characteristic of a single layer Ag/WPF-oxy-F/p^+Si memory device with a junction area of 50 × 50 μm^2. Bias was applied to the Ag top electrode while p^+Si bottom electrode was ground. When we applied the positive bias from 0 to 5 V, the current increased gradually with the applied bias (Stage 1). Then, a sharp increase of current was observed near a threshold voltage at ~4 V, indicating the transition from an HRS to an LRS. To prevent the device breakdown, a current compliance was set to 1 mA. The low resistance state remained even during the voltage sweep in the negative bias direction from 5 to 0 V (Stage 2). A semilog plot of this *I–V* characteristic (Fig. 7) clearly shows the electrical bistability of WPF-oxy-F with a high ON (LRS)/OFF (HRS) ratio of ~10^4. Although most of the measurement was performed under an ambient condition, any significant degradation phenomenon of the switching behavior was not observed compared with the results measured under the inert gas condition (Fig. 7). When the bias was swept in the negative bias from 0 to −3 V (Stage 3), the current decreased, implying an erasing process from LRS to HRS. After this stage, the device returned to a pristine HRS (Stage 4). Even after the bias was repeatedly applied to the device, the device showed almost identical *I–V* characteristics at the range between −3 V and 5 V, indicating the reversible switching behavior.

To understand the origin of switching behavior, we performed further analysis on WPF-oxy-F memory devices.

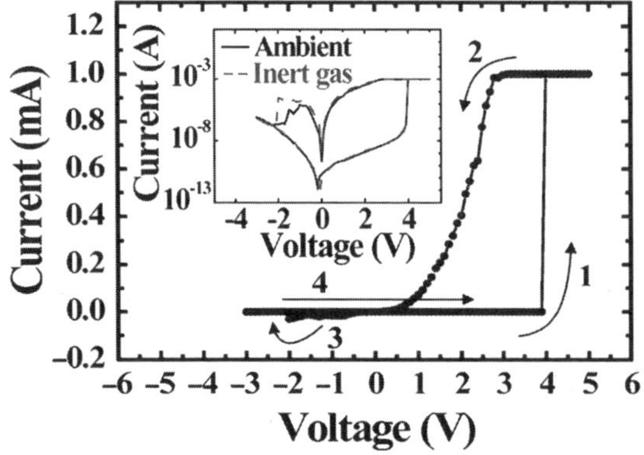

Figure 7. *I–V* characteristics of a WPF-oxy-F memory device. Inset shows the semilog plot of the *I–V* characteristics measured in ambient (solid line) and inert gas condition (dash line). Reprinted with permission from [23], T.-W. Kim et al., *Appl. Phys. Lett.* 92, 253308 (2008). © 2008, American Institute of Physics.

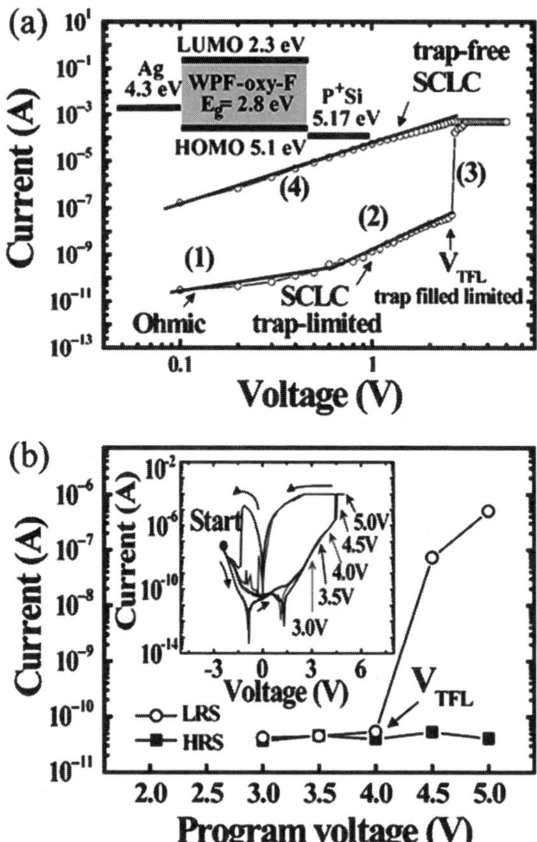

Figure 8. (a) *I–V* characteristics of a WPF-oxy-F memory device in log–log scale. Inset figure shows energy band diagram of WPF-oxy-F memory device, (b) programming voltage dependence of a WPF-oxy-F memory device. Excess bias (V_{th}) required changing the resistance of WPF-oxy-F memory device from HRS to LRS. The inset figure shows stop voltage dependent *I–V* characteristic. Reprinted with permission from [23], T.-W. Kim et al., *Appl. Phys. Lett.* 92, 253308 (2008). © 2008, American Institute of Physics.

The inset in Figure 8(a) shows the energy band diagram of the Ag/WPF-oxy-F/p^+Si device. The LUMO and HOMO of WPF-oxy-F are known to be 2.3 and 5.1 eV, respectively; thus, its bang gap is 2.8 eV [81]. Consideration of the work functions of Ag (4.3 eV) and p^+Si (5.17 eV) reveals that the Ag top contact on WPF-oxy-F shows a very high barrier for the electron transport, whereas the p^+Si contact is efficient for hole injection into the WPF-oxy-F layer. This implies that the electrical conduction for the Ag/WPF-oxy-F/p^+Si devices is mainly dominated by the hole transport.

I–V curves have been usually analyzed to study underlying bistable switching mechanisms in memory devices [82]. For example, by checking the *I–V* relationships of *I–V* curves on the log–log scale, SCLC [81, 83] or filamentary conductions [45, 84] has been suggested as a possible conduction mechanism. Figure 8(a) exhibits a double log plot of the *I–V* curve for a WPF-oxy-F memory device with a junction area of 50 μm × 50 μm. The figure shows four distinct regimes of charge transport behavior, which is similar to results previously reported in some organic memory devices [83, 85]. As shown in Figure 8(a), at a low bias region or ohmic regime (1), the current is linearly proportional to the voltage as a result of the thermally generated free carriers [85]. In this regime, the current density J can be described as

$$J = \frac{qn_0\mu V}{d} \tag{1}$$

where n_0 is the density of free carriers, d is the thickness of the organic layer, and μ is the carrier mobility. At an SCLC trap-limited regime (2), the current is controlled by the traps in the polymer layer through thermally activated hopping conduction [83, 85]. In this regime, the current obeys the Mott-Gurney law as

$$J = \frac{9\varepsilon\varepsilon_0\mu\Theta V^2}{d^3} \tag{2}$$

where Θ is the trapping fraction, ε is the dielectric constant of the polymer, and ε_0 is the permittivity of free space [83, 85]. When the voltage is increased further, the traps in the polymer film will be almost filled by charge carries. This region is described as trap-filled limit regime (3), in which the current flows through thermionic emission and a Fowler-Nordheim conduction mechanism, so that the current increases sharply and the device changes from HRS to LRS [83]. From the single-carrier SCLC conduction theory [85], the tarp density (N_t) in the polymer layer can be explained in terms of a voltage (V_{TFL}) required to fill the traps in the organic layer and is expressed as

$$N_t = \frac{3\varepsilon\varepsilon_0 V_{TFL}}{2qd^2} \tag{3}$$

where q is the electronic charge. After the resistance transition from HRS to LRS, most of the trap sites in the polymer film are filled and the current flow is free from the influence of traps in the polymer film. This region is called a trap-free SCLC regime (4) and the I–V curve fits very well with $I \propto V^2$ [85]. This behavior remains in the subsequent negative bias sweep from 5 to 0 V, indicating that the trap-free SCLC state is kept until the transition from LRS to HRS is made. Based on the analysis of the double log I–V curves, the reversible switching of the WPF-oxy-F memory devices is due to the transition between the trap-limited SCLC and the trap-free SCLC in the WPF-oxy-F film.

Although the conduction mechanism of WPF-oxy-F can be well explained by trap-limited and trap-free SCLC processes, the abrupt jump of current value, which is almost 4 orders of magnitude, is not usual in SCLC conduction [86]. It seems that an additional effect, such as a filamentary conduction, might affect the switching behavior of WPF-oxy-F memory devices as well. Some recent reports on the switching mechanism of organic memory devices well described the formation of metallic filamentary paths resulting from the migration of metal ions from the top electrodes such as silver and copper [45, 84]. In our case, it is also expected that the filamentary conduction may play an important role in the reversible switching behavior.

The switching behavior of an organic memory device based on filamentary conduction can be significantly affected by the threshold voltage, which is the minimum bias required for ionization and migration of metallic electrode [45]. The switching behavior was investigated by changing the program voltage conditions (Fig. 8(b)). Here, the voltage sweep back and forth was made from −2.5 V (start voltage) to 3, 3.5, 4, 4.5, and 5 V (program voltages; Fig. 8(b) [marked with arrows]). The current values at each I–V curve with different program voltages were measured at 0.3 V (read voltage). In the case that the program voltage was less than 4 V, the memory device did not switch and there was no difference between HRS and LRS, with a very similar current level (~10 pA). On the other hand, when the program voltage was larger than 4.0 V, the device started to exhibit switching behavior and LRS showed a current higher than ~100 nA, while HRS was in the current level of ~10 pA. In this voltage range (larger than 4.0 V), the device clearly showed reversible switching behavior, which indicates that it is necessary to over apply the transition voltage to fill the traps and form the metallic filament in the polymer layer. However, as more traps are occupied, the higher the current flows. Therefore, trap-filling process may create high-current paths, which in turn may lead to electromigration and filamentary conduction paths.

Figure 9(a) shows a statistical value of each resistance state of the WPF-oxy-F devices (~120 devices) measured at 0.3 V as a function of junction areas of 50 × 50 μm^2, 100 × 100 μm^2, 200 × 200 μm^2, and 400 × 400 μm^2. The error bar was obtained from standard deviation of resistance values measured in 20–30 devices at each junction area. From this figure, we observed that LRS did not change with the variation of the junction area; instead, the resistance remained about 100 kΩ. In contrast, the resistance

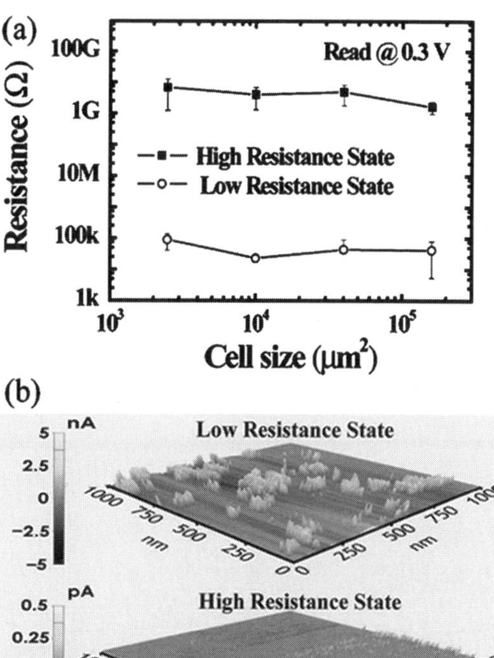

Figure 9. (a) Resistance values of two resistance states HRS and LRS of a WPF-oxy-F memory device as a function of the junction areas, (b) current images of HRS and LRS obtained by CAFM measurement. Reprinted with permission from [23], T.-W. Kim et al., *Appl. Phys. Lett.* 92, 253308 (2008). © 2008, American Institute of Physics.

value of the HRS slightly decreased from 6.8 GΩ to 1.6 GΩ as the junction area increased. To validate this observation, we examined the current images of HRS and LRS with conducting atomic force microscopy (CAFM). Figure 9(b) shows each current image (size of 1×1 μm^2) for HRS and LRS of a WPF-oxy-F layer on p^+Si without a top Ag electrode. An Ag-coated AFM tip was first scanned over the memory junction area under a voltage of 6.5 V applied to the CAFM tip relative to a WPF-oxy-F/p^+Si sample (programming process). Then, the current image of LRS was obtained under a 1.0 V tip bias condition (reading process). Similarly, the current image of HRS was obtained at a 1.0 V tip bias after the CAFM tip was scanned over the junction area under a −3.0 V tip bias (erasing process). The current images were displayed with the same current scale. As shown in these images, the current level of the HRS state is uniformly very small (typically less than ~0.5 pA at 1.0 V). On the other hand, there are localized conduction paths in the current image of LRS. This current image of LRS suggests that switching behavior does not occur uniformly over the junction area.

This work demonstrated bipolar switching behavior of the organic memory device using novel polyfluorene-derivative single layer film. The *I–V* characteristics showed that the WPF-oxy-F single layer film have distinguished two resistance states (ON/OFF ratio of ~10^4). From the analysis of *I–V* curve, area dependent *I–V* characteristics, and current images using conducting AFM, we concluded that the SCLC filamentary conduction is a potential mechanism for reversible switching behavior of WPF-oxy-F memory devices.

5. INTEGRATION STRATEGIES

5.1. Scalable via-Hole Structure

Basic device structures for electrical characterizations of the active polymer memory elements have been demonstrated in the typical form of unit devices or cross-bar-type devices [35, 63]. The junction in such kinds of device structures is defined by the size of the shadow mask during the top electrode metallization; thus, it is usually hard to reduce the active cell size below the submicron scale. Junctions in submicron size have only been characterized by CAFM [87, 88]. However, it is not common to evaluate the detailed memory performance of polymer materials with CAFM because the possible measurements are only limited to *I–V* sweeps or current images that are based on simple contacts or scanning of the conducting tip on the polymer layer.

The scaling issue has been one of the important research topics in many emerging memory technologies. Generally, these memories are based on inorganic materials, which are robust against organic solvent. Therefore, downscaling of such memory devices was successfully demonstrated by using the conventional complementary metal oxide semiconductor (CMOS) process. On the other hand, polymer materials can be easily dissolved by organic solvents; thus, the conventional lithography tool has not been appropriate to pattern polymer materials. Recently, Kwan and others [89] reported a photo cross-linkable copolymer that can be directly patterned using the conventional photolithography process. They successfully demonstrated 4×4 μm^2 memory cells to obtain the potential high-density memory applications [89]. However, this fabrication process is proper only for a specific polymer material that is robust against specific organic solvents. In addition, it is very hard to minimize the feature size to the submicron scale using conventional photolithography techniques. Although various efforts have been devoted to fabrication of organic memory devices with the submicron junction [87, 88], the downscaling of polymer memory devices is still insufficient to achieve high-density memory applications.

There have been few reports on the characterization of organic materials in a submicron scale device structure or on whether the memory performance can be survival in the submicron scale device. In particular, the characterization of the devices with the small feature size will help understanding of the underlying mechanisms of memory operation. In this point of view, scaling is one of the important issues for high-density organic memory applications. Thus, it is essential to understand the scaling effects of organic memory devices from micron scale to sub-micron scale.

In this section, we explain a via-hole structure as a scalable test-bed for switching characterization of organic materials [90]. Organic memory devices with submicron scale were fabricated using an *e*-beam lithography technique. We provide the high-performance resistive switching nonvolatile memory devices in the submicron scale via-hole structure and demonstrate scalability for potential high density memory applications.

Polymer memory devices in a via-hole structure were fabricated on a heavily doped *p*-type (100) silicon (p^+Si) substrate (0.001–0.015 Ω cm). After the typical ultrasonic cleaning process with acetone, methanol, and DI water, the silicon substrate was treated with a diluted HF to remove the native oxide layer. Silicon oxide film with 100-nm thickness was deposited on the silicon substrate using plasma-enhanced chemical vapor deposition. An *e*-beam lithography technique was then used to define the junction area of the organic memory devices in the via-hole structures which have five different areas: 40×40 μm^2, 8.5×8.5 μm^2, 4.5×4.5 μm^2, 1×1 μm^2, 500×500 nm^2, and 200×200 nm^2. To expose the bottom electrode, the silicon oxide film was etched using 6:1 buffered oxide etchant. To fill the via-hole with the organic memory materials, a spin-coating method was used. The wall of the via-hole was inclined as a result of wet etching so that the polymer material could easily fill the via-hole without any pores or defects. Post baking was performed at 150°C for 20 minutes on a hotplate in a N_2-filled glove box. As schematically shown in Figure 10(a), a polymer of WPF-oxy-F was synthesized by a palladium-catalyzed Suzuki coupling reaction method [80]. The typical thickness of the WPF-oxy-F film in the via-hole was measured to be ~70 nm. To make the top electrodes on the polymer layer in the via-hole structure, a 100-nm thick Ag layer was deposited using a shadow mask. *I–V* measurements were carried out using a semiconductor parameter analyzer (Agilent Technology 4155C).

A schematic of the organic memory device with the Ag/WPF-oxy-F/p^+Si layer in the via-hole is shown in Figure 10(b). The active area of the memory device is

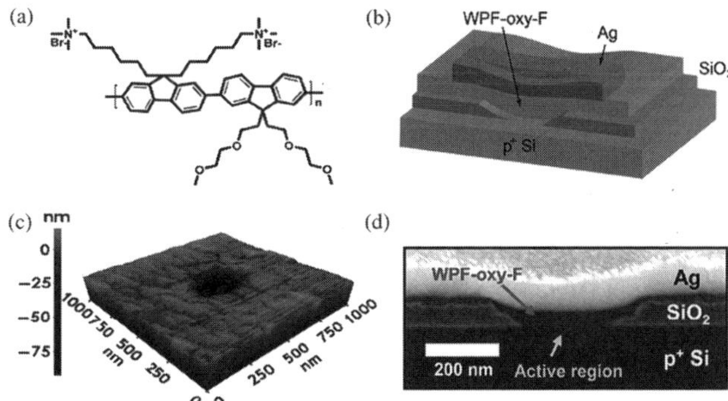

Figure 10. (a) Chemical structure of WPF-oxy-F polyfluorene derivative, (b) schematic of a polymer memory device in a via-hole structure, (c) AFM image of a via-hole of area 200 × 200 nm^2, (d) SEM image of a tilt view of a via-hole polymer memory device. Reprinted with permission from [90], T.-W. Kim et al., *Nanotech.* 20, 025201 (2009). © 2009, Institute of Physics.

defined by the area of bottom electrode (p^+Si). The via-hole region is the only current flow path. Other regions are protected by a SiO_2 layer to prevent leakage paths. Figure 10(c) shows the AFM image of a via-hole device with an active area of 200 × 200 nm^2. Figure 10(d) is the tilted scanning electron microscopy (SEM) image of a organic memory device. We also observed that there was no penetration phenomenon of the Ag (top electrode) into the WPF-oxy-F layer.

Figure 11(a) shows a representative *I–V* characteristic of the organic memory device in the via-hole with an active area of 500 × 500 nm^2. The basic operation of our memory device was well described by the SCLC with filamentary conduction, which is based on the *I–V* characteristics and current images [23]. When a positive bias from 0–5 V is applied to the top electrode, the trap sites within the polymer layer begin to be filled by electrons and more traps become occupied as the current flow increases. The trap filling process contributes to forming high-current paths, which in turn lead to electromigration and filamentary conduction paths [23]. On the other hand, a negative bias on the top electrode breaks the filamentary paths and leaves the trap sites empty, showing an abrupt decrease of current [23]. As shown in Figure 11(b), the current values of each state in all the 28 devices (500 × 500 nm^2) were distributed within an order of magnitude, which indicates excellent device-to-device switching uniformity. This excellent uniformity may result from the decrease of defects at the submicron scale active area. The transition voltages from OFF to ON in most of the submicron scale organic memory devices were distributed in the range between 3.2 and 1.8 V (inset of Fig. 11(b)).

In this work, we demonstrated WPF-oxy-F non-volatile memory devices in a scalable via-hole structure. The devices showed excellent memory performance such as a large ON/OFF ratio of ~10^4 and excellent device-to-device switching uniformity. These electrical characteristics suggest that WPF-oxy-F has potential to be utilized as high-density memory devices. In addition, the scalable via-hole structure is a good test-bed to evaluate the electrical characteristics of polymer memory devices from micron scale to submicron scale.

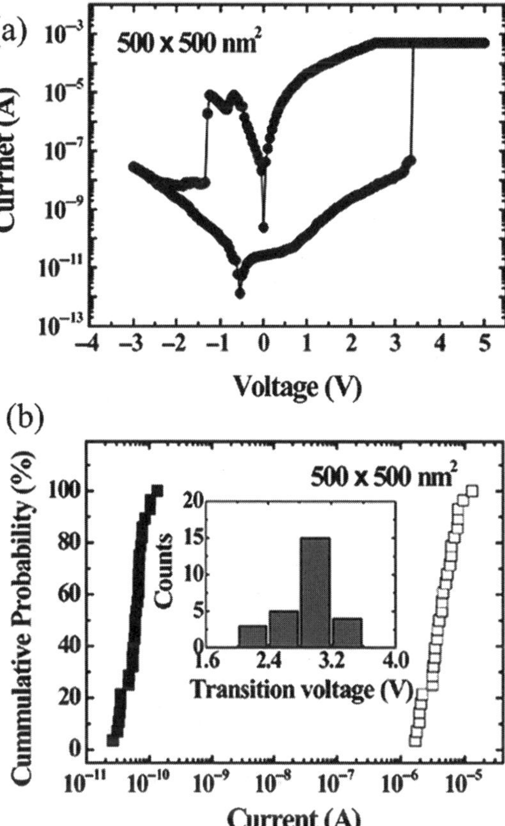

Figure 11. (a) Semilogscale *I–V* characteristics of a polymer memory device with a 500 × 500 nm^2 via-hole, (b) a cumulative probability data set for polymer memory devices with a 500 × 500 nm^2 via-hole (28 devices), showing a good device-to-device switching uniformity. The inset figure shows the histogram of the OFF-to-ON transition for polymer memory devices with a 500 × 500 nm^2 via-hole. Reprinted with permission from [90], T.-W. Kim et al., *Nanotech.* 20, 025201 (2009). © 2009, Institute of Physics.

5.2. Direct Metal Transfer Method

The use of shadow masks to pattern the top electrodes of organic nonvolatile memory devices has limited the memory cell size that has generally been demonstrated to be larger than 100 μm [87, 91]. On the other hand, Yang and others [89] reported a photo cross-linkable copolymer that can be directly patterned using the conventional photolithography process. With the scalability of adapting a conventional photolithography and lift-off process, they demonstrated 4 × 4 μm^2 memory cells [89]. However, it is difficult to apply this method to well-known polymer materials that have no robustness against organic solvents. Therefore, it is necessary to introduce an alternative process that can obtain high memory density and use non-aqueous fabrication methods such as cold-welding [92, 93], micro contact printing [94], or nanoscale transfer printing [95]. Although these processes can be good for pattern transfer, some methods require enormous printing pressure for transferring patterns. Such high pressure may damage the active polymer layer. On the other hand, there are other methods which do not require such high pressure [94, 95]. In particular, pattern transfer methods involving poly dimethyl siloxane (PDMS) stamps do not use high pressure and are also useful due to its conformal contact at the interface between the stamp and the organic layer. But the PDMS-related process generally has some limitation in terms of minimum feature size because of the elastic properties of PDMS stamps. In addition, the PDMS needs additional process steps such as self-assembled ink as an etching mask for subsequent metal etching [94] and a monolayer coating of a chemical linker for chemical bonding between the metal and the substrate [95]. Alternatively, we explain a nonaqueous direct metal transfer (DMT) method for high-density memory applications in this section [96].

Figure 12 shows a fabrication process for cross-bar type polymer non-volatile memory devices using the DMT method. There are four steps to form the top electrode onto the active polymer layer. The first step is the preparation of a glass stamp (Fig. 12(a)). A transparent glass stamp with a line width of 2 μm was fabricated by conventional photolithography and a subsequent etching process. Typical ultrasonic cleaning processes were performed to clean the glass stamp and then the surface of glass stamp was deposited with a monolayer of a releasing material, $CF_3(CF_2)5(CH_2)$ $2SiCl_3$ (tridecafluoro-1,1,2,2-tetrahydroctyltrichlorosilane) in the vapor phase [97]. To easily detach the metallic layer from the glass stamp, an Au layer (35 nm) was deposited on the releasing layer

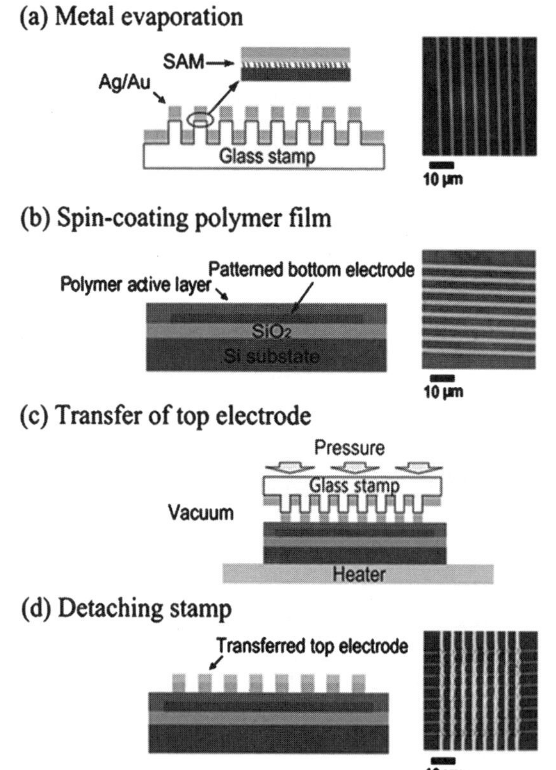

Figure 12. Fabrication process of cross-bar type polymer non-volatile memory devices using the DMT method, (a) metal evaporation on patterned glass stamp, (b) spin-coating of polymer layer on the patterned bottom electrode, (c) transfer of top electrode, (d) detaching the stamp. Reprinted with permission from [96], T.-W. Kim et al., *Nanotech.* 19, 405201 (2008). © 2008, Institute of Physics.

because it has poor adhesion against the releasing layer, and then a Ag layer (40 nm) was deposited on the Au layer. The right image in Figure 12(a) shows an optical image of the prepared glass stamp with eight lines of electrodes. The second step is the preparation of the bottom electrode and spin-coating of the active polymer layer (Fig. 12(b)). The bottom electrodes on the silicon on insulator wafer with a line width of 2 μm for the DMT method were prepared in the same way as the glass stamp. A heavily doped *p*-type poly silicon was used to pattern eight lines of bottom electrodes. Optical images of the bottom electrodes are shown in the right picture in Figure 12(b). Prior to spin-coating of the active polymer layer, the substrate was treated via a diluted HF-last process to remove the native oxide layer. WPF-oxy-F was first dissolved in a mixture of methanol and water with a volume ratio of 3:7 at a concentration of 5 mg/ml. Then, the solution was spin-coated on the patterned bottom electrodes at 4,000 rpm for 30 seconds and the thickness of the WPF-oxy-F film was around 100 nm. To improve film uniformity and to eliminate solvent from the film, postbaking was performed at 150°C for 20 minutes on a hotplate. The third step is transfer of the top electrodes by the DMT method (Fig. 12(c)). The metal-deposited glass stamp was vertically aligned to the bottom electrodes, and then it was pressed onto the WPF-oxy-F layer, which was first heated with 100°C with a pressure of 550 psi for 10 minutes. The final step is detaching the glass stamp (Fig. 12(d)). When the sample was cooled to 80°C, the glass stamp was detached from the organic layer. Finally, the Ag layer was transferred on the WPF-oxy-F layer. The right picture in Figure 12(d) shows the resulting 8×8 cross-bar type organic nonvolatile memory devices, indicating that eight lines of metal top electrodes were well transferred onto the organic layer.

Organic memory devices with the same type of layered structure were also fabricated with the conventional shadow mask method for comparison. However, the line widths of the top and bottom electrodes are typically very large; the line width of our memory devices was about 100 μm. The room temperature *I–V* measurements of the organic memory devices fabricated by the DMT and the shadow mask method were compared.

Figure 13 shows comparison in *I–V* curves of organic memory devices fabricated by both the DMT and shadow mask methods. Both devices showed similar switching characteristics. When we applied a positive bias from 0–5 V to the Ag top electrode, a resistance change was observed at the transition voltage. The current increased gradually with the applied bias (Stage 1). Then, the device was turned on when the bias was increased beyond a certain transition voltage at ~3 V, indicating the writing process from HRS to LRS. After the transition from an HRS to an LRS, the devices remained in the LRS during the voltage sweep in the reverse direction from 5 to 0 V (Stage 2). When the bias was swept continuously in the negative bias direction from 0 to −3 V (Stage 3), the current decreased abruptly, implying erasing process from LRS to HRS. After this stage, the device returned to pristine HRS (Stage 4). When the bias was applied in the positive bias direction repeatedly, the device showed almost identical *I–V* characteristics at the range between −3 and 5 V, indicating reversible resistance

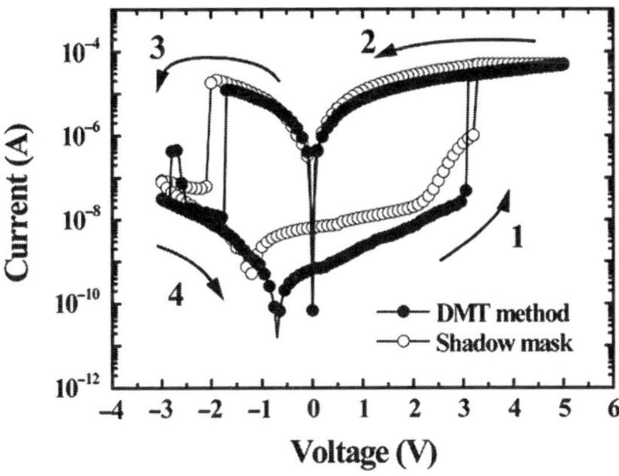

Figure 13. Switching characteristics of memory cells in cross-bar arrays fabricated by the DMT and shadow mask methods. Open circles and filled circles are *I–V* curves for polymer memory devices made by the shadow mask method and the DMT method, respectively. The sweep rate was 50 mV s^{-1} without hold time. Reprinted with permission from [96], T.-W. Kim et al., *Nanotech.* 19, 405201 (2008). © 2008, Institute of Physics.

switching behavior. Both devices showed a high ON/OFF ratio of $\sim 10^3$.

In this work, we have successfully demonstrated that the DMT method is a potential process for fabrication of polymer nonvolatile memory devices with cross-bar architecture. The memory devices in 8 × 8 arrays with cell size of 2 × 2 μm^2 showed almost three orders of magnitude of ON/OFF ratio. The scalability by the DMT method may be promising for high-density, nonvolatile polymer memory applications.

6. PERFORMANCE ENHANCEMENT TECHNIQUES

6.1. Effect of Metal Ions

It is very important to study factors that influence switching behavior. Joo and others [45] determined operation threshold voltage behavior in organic-based memory devices by controlling the ionization of a copper electrode and showed that memory behavior was dependent on field strength and temperature. Ma and colleagues [98] reported organic non-volatile memory devices with controlled copper-ion concentrations within the organic layer. However, the specific effects of metal ions on the switching behavior of organic memory devices have not been thoroughly investigated. In this section, we examine the introduction of additional metal ions and its influences on switching parameters, demonstrating relatively fast transient response time [99].

Single component polyfluorene-derivative memory devices were fabricated in MIM structures on heavily doped *p*-type (100) silicon (p^+ Si) substrates (0.001–0.015 Ω cm). After the typical ultrasonic cleaning processes, silicon wafers were treated with diluted HF to remove the native oxide layer. Poly[(9,9-bis((6′-(*N,N,N*-trimethylammonium)hexyl)-2,7-fluorene)-alt-(9,9-bis(2-(2-methoxyethoxy) ethyl)-fluorene))] dibromide (denoted WPF-oxy-F) and its derivatives (Ca-WPF-oxy-F and Na-WPF-oxy-F) were

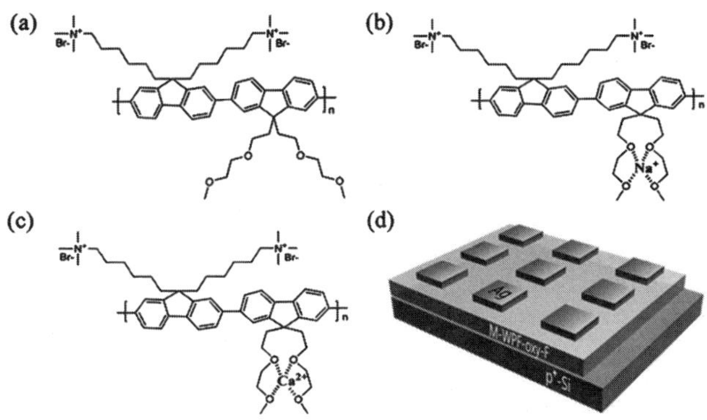

Figure 14. Chemical structures of polyfluorene-derivatives: (a) WPF-oxy-F, (b) Na-WPF-oxy-F, and (c) Ca-WPF-oxy-F, (d) schematic of MIM-type organic nonvolatile memory device. Reprinted with permission from [99], T.-W. Kim et al., *Org. Electron.* 11, 109 (2010). © 2010, Elsevier.

used as an active layer, (Fig. 14) [80]. The three kinds of polyfluorene-derivatives were first spin coated on the highly doped *p*-type silicon substrate and then the resulting films were baked at 150°C for 20 minutes on a hotplate in an N_2-filled glove box. The Ag top electrodes of the MIM devices were patterned with a shadow mask with square patterns of four different sizes: 50 × 50 μm^2, 100 × 100 μm^2, 200 × 200 μm^2, and 400 × 400 μm^2. The memory device structure is schematically shown in Figure 14(d).

To understand the switching mechanism, we characterized the size dependence of the resistance values of both the HRS and the LRS (Fig. 15(a)). The resistance of the polyflourene-derivative with metal ions (Ca- and Na-WPF-oxy-F) clearly scaled with the cell size, indicating that the current flowed through the whole cell area in the HRS [100]. This suggests that the metal ions, which were well dispersed in the polymer layer, acted as current paths, allowing the current to flow through the whole area in the HRS. On the other hand, the resistance values of the three polymer materials in the LRS did not change significantly with cell size due to the formation of localized current paths [101]. Arrangement of dispersed metal ions in the polymer layer with an applied bias can be responsible for this localized current path. However, unlike Ca- and Na-WPF-oxy-F, the resistance of the WPF-oxy-F HRS did not show any clear size dependence (Fig. 6(a)). This behavior in WPF-oxy-F is due to SCLC and localized current flows [23].

To further study the effects of metal ions on memory performance, we measured pulse delay times for the three kinds of polymer memory devices. The inset of Figure 15(b) shows a configuration of thc transient response measurements. We monitored input and output voltage pulses using an oscilloscope, and the relevant data are shown in Figure 15(b). By monitoring output voltage (V_{out}) through a 50 Ω external resistor, we estimated the response times for each polymer memory device. In this analysis, the response time was the delay time between when an input voltage pulse was applied to the device in the HRS and when it switched to the LRS. The transient responses of Ca- and Na-WPF-oxy-F were very similar (~10 μs writing process). On the other hand, the transient response of WPF-oxy-F was ~2 ms, which is a much slower response time. This difference is

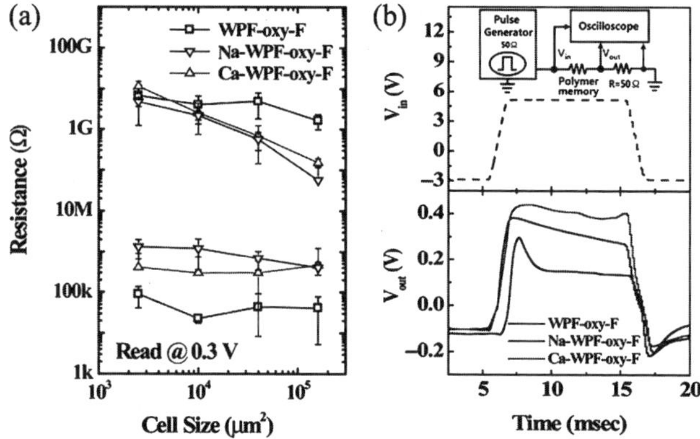

Figure 15. (a) Resistance values of the on and off states of the three kinds of polyfluorene-derivative memory devices as a function of junction area, (b) transient response characteristics of the three kinds of polyfluorene-derivative memory devices. The inset shows the circuit of measurement method. Reprinted with permission from [99], T.-W. Kim et al., *Org. Electron.* 11, 109 (2010). © 2010, Elsevier.

mainly due to the metal ions that make current paths in the polymer layer.

The properties of the three polymer memory devices are summarized in Table 2. Although they show similar memory characteristics (e.g., similar *I–V* hysteresis, room-temperature ON/OFF ratio, and retention time), considerable differences were observed in the threshold voltages, ON/OFF ratios as temperature increases, area dependences, and response times. Thus, metal ions in the polymer layer can play an important role for tuning memory parameters such as operation voltage and response time. One can expect more sophisticated control of organic memory device performance with the use of various metal ions.

In this work, we synthesized WPF-oxy-F with and without metal ions (Ca^{2+} and Na^{+}) and compared the switching behaviors of each polyfluorene-derivative. Although basic memory behavior (*I–V* characteristics and retention) was not significantly affected by the metal ions, Ca-WPF-oxy-F and Na-WPF-oxy-F showed area dependence in the HRS, implying that metal ions assist localized current flow. The threshold voltage of Na-WPF-oxy-F was lower than that of Ca-WPF-oxy-F because of more efficient Na^{+} movement in Na-WPF-oxy-F. In addition, the Ca- and Na-WPF-oxy-F response time was faster than that of WPF-oxy-F, indicating that memory performances could be controlled with the addition of metal ions in the polymer layer.

6.2. Effect of Interfacial Oxide

Interface states between the electrode and the organic film have been considered as an important factor to manipulate the performance of organic electronics [102]. There have been a few reports about some organic memory devices that deal with interface engineering [103, 104]. For instance, the ON/OFF ratio could be significantly enhanced by introducing Ag nanodots between the organic layer and an indium tin oxide surface; the nanodots act as charge-trapping sites [103]. In addition, self-assembled monolayer treatment on the electrode enhances the switching reproducibility by improving the current level distribution [104]. Particularly, we note that native oxides on an Al surface strongly influence the switching characteristics [76, 105], and reproducible switching in organic memory can also be realized through the intentional introduction of an additional oxide film [77]. Nevertheless, up until now, there have been very few detailed studies on the effects of an interfacial oxide on the various memory parameters (ON/OFF ratio, threshold voltage, and endurance). Furthermore, O_2 plasma treatment would be highly preferable because it is a cost-effective method to form the interfacial oxide. O_2 plasma treatment was suggested as the simple approach to enhance memory performance [106].

The organic resistive memory of this work consisted of a composite material of PI:PCBM sandwiched between Al electrodes. To make an active organic layer, BPDA-PPD, used as a PI precursor, was dissolved in NMP (BPDA-PPD:NMP solvent = 1:4 weight ratio). PCBM was also dissolved in NMP at a concentration of 0.5 wt%. A PI:PCBM blending solution was then prepared by mixing the PI solution (2 ml) and the PCBM solution (0.5 ml). Bottom Al electrodes with eight line patterns were deposited using a shadow mask. To create an additional Al oxide layer, the bottom electrodes were treated with O_2 plasma (RF power: 100 W; O_2: 30 sccm; and treatment time: 0, 5, 10, and 20 minutes). The Al oxide surface was also exposed to UV-ozone for 10 minutes to improve the reliability of the organic resistive memory [77]. The PI:PCBM composite solution was then spin coated over the bottom electrodes at 2000 rpm for 40 seconds. The spin-coated film was soft baked at 120°C on a hotplate for 10 minutes to evaporate the solvent and then thermally cured at 300°C under a nitrogen atmosphere for 30 minutes. The typical thickness of the PI:PCBM composite layer was around ~20 nm, which results from transmission electron microscopy (TEM) analysis. A 50-nm thick Al layer was deposited using an *e*-beam evaporator. A completed organic memory device had an 8×8 crossbar array structure with a junction area of 100×100 μm^2. All electrical tests were performed using a semiconductor characterization system (Keithley 4200-SCS) at room temperature in an N_2-filled glove box.

As shown in Figure 16(a), the oxide thickness on the bottom Al electrodes was changed as a function of the O_2 plasma treatment time (0, 5, 10, and 20 minutes). The dispersion value of the oxide thickness was plotted by calculating the statistical average and the standard error of data sets measured from the TEM images of individual devices. Even the device with no treatment had a thin native oxide film (~3.5-nm thick) due to the reaction of residual oxygen gases inside the deposition chamber. The oxide thickness gradually increased according to the treatment time. The increase in the oxide thickness was attributed to the time-induced enhancement of chemical reactions between Al atoms and oxygen molecules. Meanwhile, as the treatment time increased, the interface quality between the Al and the oxide seemed to become worse.

To quantitatively compare the elements of the samples, we analyzed the X-ray photoelectron spectroscopy (XPS) depth profiles of the Al samples treated with O_2 plasma for different lengths of time (0, 5, 10, and 20 minutes). Figure 16(b) exhibits the XPS depth profiles of the samples where Al^{m} $2p$ and O $1s$ are associated with the metallic

Table 2. Summary of basic switching properties of organic non-volatile memory devices with WPF-oxy-F, Ca-WPF-oxy-F, and Na-WPF-oxy-F.

	Band gap [eV]	ON/OFF ratio	V_{th} [V]	Response time [μs]	Retention time [s]	Area dependence of HRS
WPF-oxy-F	2.8	10^4	3.4 ± 0.5	2000	10^4	No
Ca-WPF-oxy-F	2.8	10^4	3.6 ± 0.3	10	10^4	Yes
Na-WPF-oxy-F	2.8	10^4	3.0 ± 0.4	10	10^4	Yes

Source: Reprinted with permission from [99], T.-W. Kim et al., *Org. Electron.* 11, 109 (2010). © 2010, Elsevier.
Notes: HRS = high-resistance state, WPF = polyfluorene derivatives.

Al peak (Al–Al bonds) and the oxygen peak (Al–O bonds), respectively. With plasma treatment time increased, the amount of the oxygen atoms gradually increased throughout the total depth and the amount of the Al atoms decreased. Consequently, 20 minutes of plasma treatment led to the highest oxygen and lowest Al atomic percent values, indicating considerable diffusion of oxygen gas into the Al layer. The diffused oxygen gases contributed to the formation of the Al oxide.

Figure 17(a) shows the *I–V* characteristics of four different organic memory devices. Positive voltages were applied to the top electrode for the resistive switching of our memory devices while the bottom electrode was grounded. After forming process, the devices showed reversible switching behavior between an HRS and LRS. All of the devices had typical unipolar switching behavior, which is achieved by the successive application of voltage with the same polarity [24]. However, the electrical current levels were totally different depending on the plasma treatment time. In particular, the OFF states of the organic memory devices changed more than the ON states. The devices were turned on from an initial HRS (OFF state) to an LRS (ON state) at the threshold voltages (V_{th}). As the voltage increased further, the current of organic device gradually decreased to a minimum value at V_{min}, indicating an NDR. Thus, the devices could be erased with an applied voltage above the V_{min}. During returning to 0 V, the device remained the ON state. From these results, the operation voltages for writing, erasing, and reading were selected to be ~5, 10, and 0.5 V, respectively. These resistive switching phenomena may be associated with the charge-trapping/detrapping mechanism suggested by Simmons and Verderber [51] and Bozano and colleagues [35, 50].

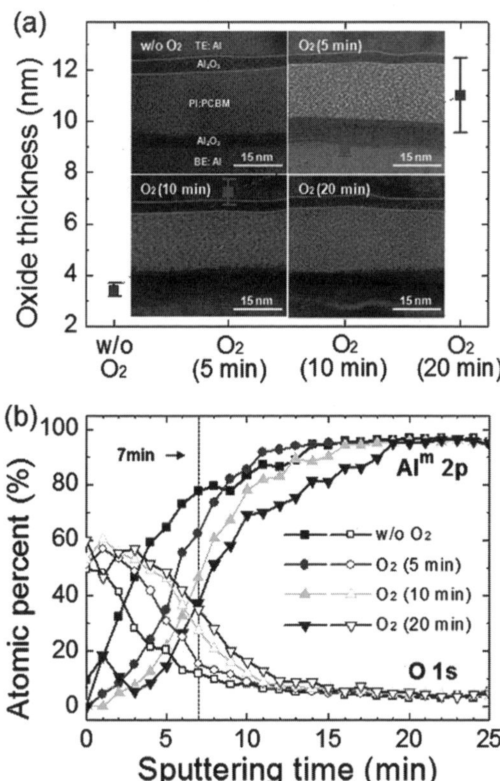

Figure 16. (a) The thickness of Al oxide as a function of the O_2 plasma treatment time: 0, 5, 10, and 20 minutes. The insets show TEM images of each memory device. The top and bottom Al_2O_3 of each TEM image indicate the native Al oxide formed during the deposition of the top electrodes and the interfacial Al oxide with varying thicknesses on the bottom electrodes created by the plasma treatment, respectively, (b) the XPS depth profile of Al^m 2*p* and O 1*s* in the Al samples that were treated for varying times with the O_2 plasma.

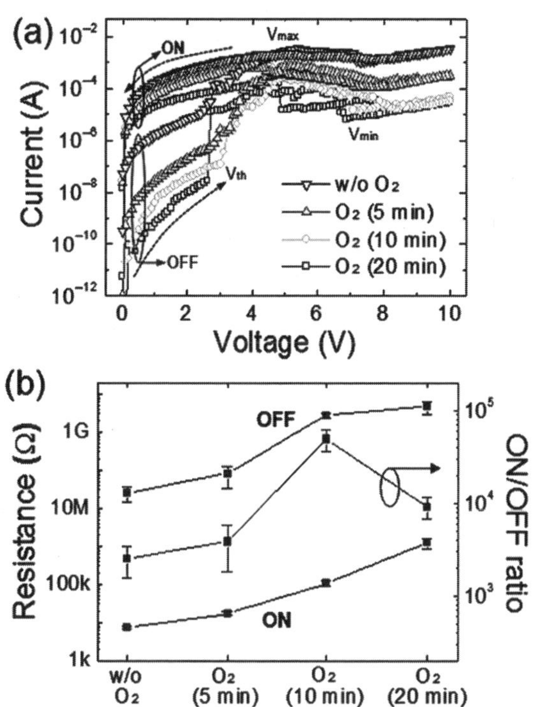

Figure 17. (a) *I–V* characteristics of organic memory devices treated with an O_2 plasma for different lengths of time, (b) the ON and OFF resistances (left *y*-axis) and the ON/OFF ratios (right *y*-axis) as a function of the O_2 plasma treatment time.

The ON and OFF resistances of each device were compared and are shown on the left *y*-axis of Figure 17(b). The dispersion of the resistance values was obtained by calculating the statistical average and standard error of sets of individual memory cells (more than 30 cells at each data point). Both the ON and OFF resistance values showed a gradual increasing trend with increase in the plasma treatment time. For the devices treated with O_2 plasma, a large increase in OFF resistances was observed, which in turn resulted in a high ON/OFF ratio. This indicated that the additional oxide served as a series resistor and considerably affected the initial OFF resistance. Especially, the highest ON/OFF ratio of over 10^4 was obtained in the devices treated for 10 minutes with O_2 plasma (Fig. 17(b)). The OFF resistances did not increase further in the devices with 20 minutes of plasma treatment, which eventually exhibited a decrease in the ON/OFF ratio.

The statistical distribution of the threshold voltages were obtained from 33 randomly selected cells in each organic memory device. Figure 18(a) exhibits the threshold voltage histograms for sets of each device. Almost the same voltage distribution was found in the three types of devices (0, 5, and 10 minutes) treated with plasma for 10 minutes or less. On the other hand, the devices treated with plasma for 20 minutes showed a relatively wide voltage distribution, which was revealed by the large value of the standard deviation. The forming voltages or switching voltages of the organic memory devices are critically dependent on the properties of both the active materials and their interfaces [45, 77, 104]. The wide threshold voltage distribution may be associated with the relatively thick and rough interfacial oxide of the device with longer plasma treatment (Fig. 16(a)). Unfortunately, the wide threshold voltage distribution sometimes leads to failure in turning on the cell. Thus, the plasma treatment time and conditions should be carefully performed to prevent the switching failure.

The performance of each memory device was investigated and compared in terms of endurance cycles. The endurance test was carried out by repetitive sweeping operations of a single cell (Fig. 18(b)). During 150 sweep cycles, the current states of each device remained stable without any significant electrical degradation. On the other hand, the device treated with plasma for 20 minutes showed large fluctuations in the ON resistance values, which is expected to be caused by the poor quality of the oxide interface, as shown in the TEM image. A large number of defect states at the interface can lead to unintentional charge trapping, which eventually makes charge transport unstable.

In this work, we investigated organic resistive memory devices with interfacial oxide layers introduced by using a simple O_2 plasma treatment method. The interfacial oxide thickness increased with the plasma treatment time, which in turn changed the bistable resistance values. The devices undergoing additional plasma treatment exhibited higher ON/OFF ratios than devices with only native oxide. However, the threshold voltage distribution and switching reproducibility degraded in devices treated for long plasma time. In conclusion, the O_2 plasma treatment conditions for the oxide formation should be carefully optimized by considering the essential memory parameters such as the ON/OFF ratio, threshold voltage, and switching reproducibility.

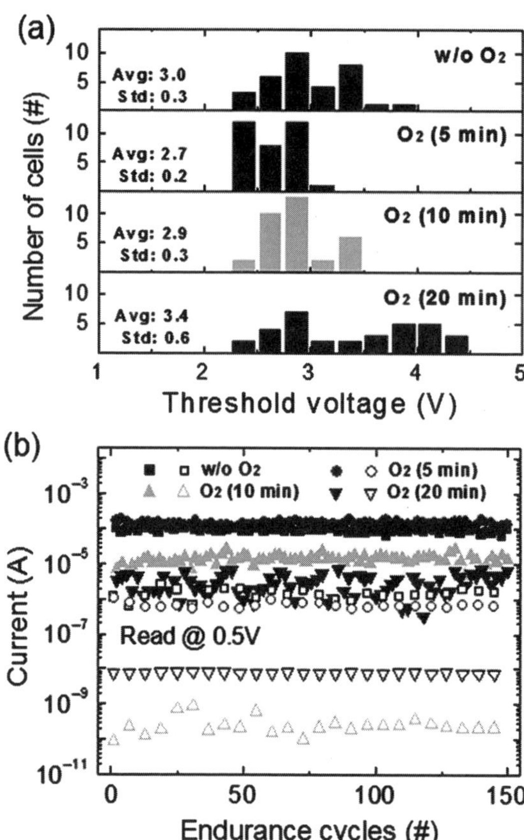

Figure 18. (a) The threshold voltage distributions of organic memory devices treated with an O_2 plasma for different lengths of time, (b) the endurance cycles of the four types of organic memory devices.

7. ADVANCED ARCHITECTURAL CONCEPTS

7.1. Hybrid-Type 1T-1R

Cross-talk phenomenon between memory cells often occurs due to leakage of the current paths (called sneak paths) through neighboring cells with low resistances in cross-point array structures [65, 66] or by an excess of current that may induce electrical damage [67]. This phenomenon disturbs the reading process of the selected cell, which must be absolutely eliminated to realize practical memory application. The ultimate solution to eliminate this cross-talk is introducing a rectifying diode to each cell [31]. ITRS also mentioned the importance of a combination with switching element such as diode and transistor [22]. Consequently, the architecture of a 1D-1R [68, 69] or a 1T-1R [72] can improve reading accessibility in an integrated array memory.

In the field of inorganically based memory, combinations of switch and memory components have been intensively investigated. 1T-1R and 1D-1R circuits have been demonstrated in emerging memory devices such as RRAM and PRAM [65, 67, 107]. On the other hand, the poor processability of organic materials has been considered as one of the major obstacles to achieving more integrated circuitry for practically all organically based electronics applications. For this reason, the feasibility of producing a hybrid-type 1T-1R circuit that consists of an inorganic transistor and a polymer memory was demonstrated in this work [72].

A silicon transistor were fabricated on an n-type (100) silicon substrate (resistivity of 4–6 $\Omega \cdot$ cm). After the isolation was defined, 50 Å thick SiO_2 was formed by dry oxidation to form the gate oxide. Subsequently, 200-nm thick undoped polysilicon was deposited on the gate oxide layer and then gate electrodes were defined by conventional photolithography and wet etching process. Boron implantation was done at 20 keV, followed by a rapid thermal annealing process. The Si-doped Al (1% of Si) electrode layer was deposited on the source electrodes, while the drain electrodes were open for connection to the polymer memory layer. After defining the source and drain electrodes, annealing was performed at 400°C for 30 minutes under nitrogen and hydrogen mixture gas (N_2 97% + H_2 3%) condition. The transistor device structure with a gate width and gate length of 20 μm was finally completed.

As an organic resistor layer, WPF-oxy-F was used and then spin coated on the substrate. Post-baking was performed at 150°C for 20 minutes on a hotplate in a nitrogen-filled glove box. To form electrodes on top of the polymer layer, Ag layer with a line width of 100 μm was deposited using a shadow mask. The junction area of the organic memory is 100 × 100 μm^2. The electrical tests were carried out using a semiconductor parameter analyzer (Agilent Technology 4155C) and pulse generator units (Agilent 41501B PGUs).

The operation of the 1T-1R device is controlled by two electronic parts consisting of a p-channel metal oxide semiconductor field effect transistor (MOSFET) and a organic memory. Figure 19(a) illustrates the schematic and optical image of 1T-1R devices fabricated on a silicon substrate. Figure 19(b) exhibit the schematic of the one-bit cell 1T-1R device and the chemical structure of the organic memory material (WPF-oxy-F). The p-MOSFET device was fabricated by a conventional CMOS process.

An organic nonvolatile memory device with cross-point architecture was fabricated on the drain side (p^+Si) of the Si transistor, which was used as the bottom electrode (Fig. 19(b)). Note that we selected a p-MOSFET device as a switch component instead of fabricating all organically based 1T-1R devices. When the organic transistor and organic memory layers are formed by spin coating or thermal evaporation, they may dissolve each other. It is difficult to integrate both organic transistors and organic resistors into a single chip without damaging the organic active layer or degrading the device. Furthermore, the operating voltage of organic thin film transistors is usually much higher than that of polymer memory devices [108]. For these reasons, we selected the hybrid approach that combined inorganic transistors and organic resistors.

Figure 19(c) represents schematics illustrating the basic operation of the 1T-1R device. When the switching component (p-MOSFET) is turned ON, the current flow from the source to the drain is modulated by the organic memory (1R), which has two stable resistance states: HRS and LRS. We first performed I–V characterizations of the p-MOSFET devices and organic memory devices. Figure 20(a) shows the drain current versus the drain voltage (I_D–V_D) characteristic of the p-MOSFET device and its circuit diagram (inset).

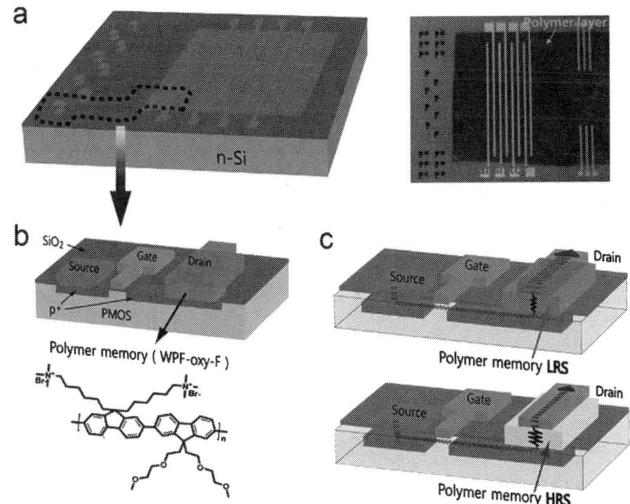

Figure 19. (a) Schematic and optical image of 1T-1R hybrid devices. The area with the black dotted line indicates a silicon transistor (1T) and a polymer memory (1R), (b) schematic of a single 1T-1R device and chemical structure of WPF-oxy-F, (c) Schematics of basic operation of the 1T-1R device. The current flow from source to drain in the 1T-1R device is controlled by the resistance state of the polymer memory device (see text). Reprinted with permission from [72], T.-W. Kim et al., *Adv. Mat.* 21, 2497 (2009). © 2009, WILEY-VCH Verlag GmbH & Co. KGaA, Weinheim.

In order to turn the p-MOSFET device ON, we applied a negative bias to the gate electrode. The drain current was saturated at about −70 μA at a gate bias of −2 V, exhibiting typical long channel p-MOSFET behavior. We also performed I–V characterization of the organic memory device. Figure 20(b) shows a typical bipolar switching behavior. The polymer memory device showed turn-ON and turn-OFF events occurring at ~3 V and −2 V, respectively. In our previous works, we reported WPF-oxy-F polymer as a potential active material for organic memory devices [23, 96].

To evaluate the I–V characteristics of the p-MOSFET combined with the organic memory, we also measured the I_D–V_D and drain current versus gate voltage (I_D–V_G) characteristics of the 1T-1R device. As shown in Figure 21(a), when the organic memory device is in the LRS condition, the 1T-1R device showed a I_D–V_D curve very similar to that of the p-MOSFET device alone, indicating that the memory component in the LRS condition does not affect the operation of the transistor. However, because of the series resistance of both the channel and the polymer memory, the current level in the saturation regime of the 1T-1R device (Fig. 21(a)) was reduced by a factor of ~0.7 compared with the single transistor (Fig. 20(a)) under the same gate bias. In contrast, when the organic memory device is programmed to the HRS, the current flow from the source to the drain in the p-MOSFET device was significantly interrupted by the high resistance of the organic memory device. In the HRS condition, low current of ~10 nA flowed from the source to the drain through the 1T-1R device under a gate bias of −2 V. Similar behavior was also observed in the I_D–V_G characteristic of the 1T-1R device at a fixed drain bias of −0.1 V (Fig. 21(b)). The drain current for the 1T-1R device in the saturation regime was 10 μA (in the LRS condition) and

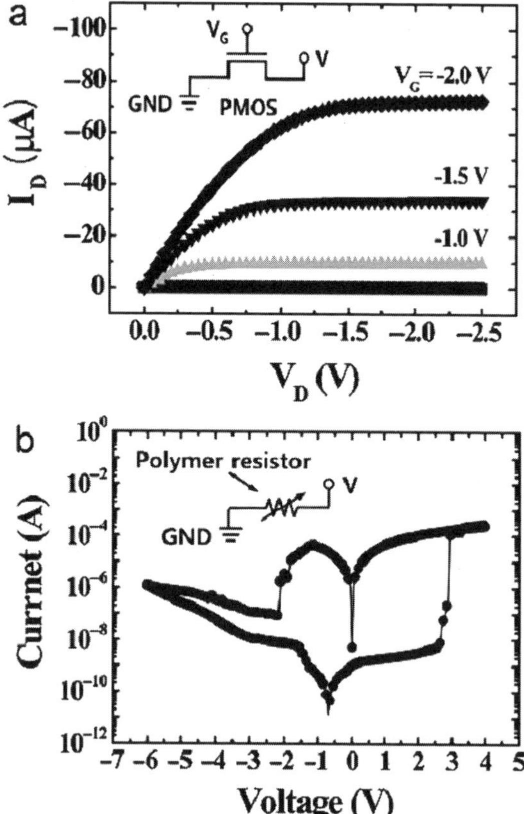

Figure 20. (a) I_D–V_D characteristics of the p-MOSFET device and its circuit diagram, (b) I–V characteristics of polymer memory device and its circuit diagram. Reprinted with permission from [72], T.-W. Kim et al., *Adv. Mat.* 21, 2497 (2009). © 2009, WILEY-VCH Verlag GmbH & Co. KGaA, Weinheim.

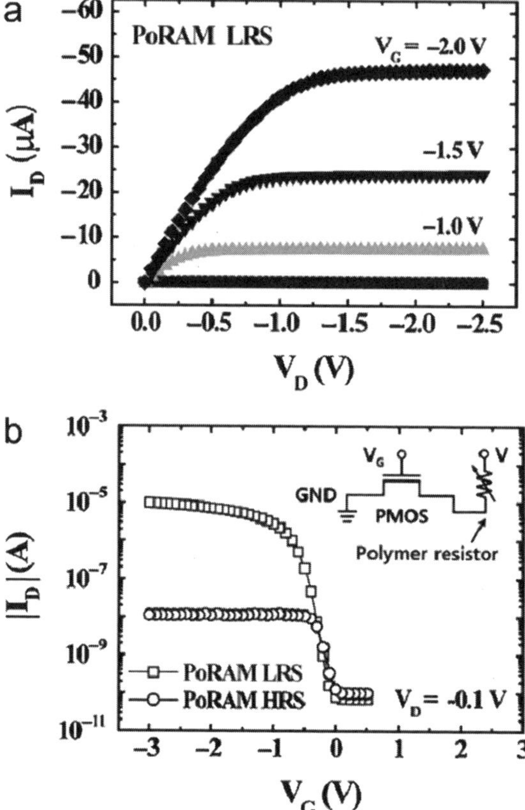

Figure 21. (a) I_D–V_D characteristics of the 1T-1R device, (b) I_D–V_G characteristics of the 1T-1R device with respect to the resistance state of polymer memory device. Reprinted with permission from [72], T.-W. Kim et al., *Adv. Mat.* 21, 2497 (2009). © 2009, WILEY-VCH Verlag GmbH & Co. KGaA, Weinheim.

10 nA (in the HRS condition). The difference of the drain current was about three orders of magnitude. It indicates that the drain current of the 1T-1R device can be controlled by the resistance states of the polymer memory device at a fixed drain bias.

The memory performance of 1T-1R devices was also tested through the endurance of the 1T-1R device by consecutive single voltage pulses (Fig. 22(a)). The LRS and HRS of the polymer memory in the 1T-1R device were alternated by a 5-V pulse (writing process, V_P) and a −4-V pulse (erasing process, V_E) with a pulse duration (τ_p) of 30 and 200 ms, respectively. The current of the 1T-1R device was then read at a fixed gate bias of −1.0 V and a drain bias of −0.1 V. During 50 cycles, the 1T-1R device operated successfully, exhibiting an ON/OFF ratio of more than $\sim 10^3$. The retention test was also investigated under ambient conditions at room temperature (Fig. 22(b)). We measured the I_D–V_G of the 1T-1R device at a fixed gate bias of −1.0 V and a drain bias of −0.1 V when the organic memory is set as either HRS or LRS. The two current values of the 1T-1R device related to the HRS and LRS of the organic memory device were maintained for 10^4 seconds without any serious degradation.

In this work, we successfully demonstrated 1T-1R hybrid-type memory devices. Individual p-MOSFET and polymer memory devices exhibited typical p-channel transistor and bipolar memory properties, respectively. The 1T-1R memory device was successfully switched by applying consecutive voltage pulses. The written or erased data in the 1T-1R device was retained for more than 10^4 seconds.

7.2. Hybrid-Type 1D-1R

Compared with the 1T-1R structure, the 1D-1R architecture is preferred in terms of integration because it occupies less area ($4F^2$, where F is a minimum feature size). Furthermore, the design and fabrication of 1D-1R devices are simpler than 1T-1R devices. The use of an unpatterned storage medium consisting of a phase separated blend of an organic ferroelectric and a semiconducting polymer demonstrated bistable rectifying diodes [109], which has been suggested as being the ultimate solution of the cross-talk problem in organic memories. WORM memory devices combined with a diode [68] or diode-switch organic nonvolatile bistable memory [70] were also demonstrated. However, the electrically irreversible switching of these devices limits their practical applications, which often need a rewritable capability. Electrically rewritable switching in the 1D-1R structure can only be achieved by the use of unipolar-type switching as memory elements that can be set and reset at the same voltage polarity [65, 66, 71]. In addition, as compared with Si-based diode, poor performance and poor reliability

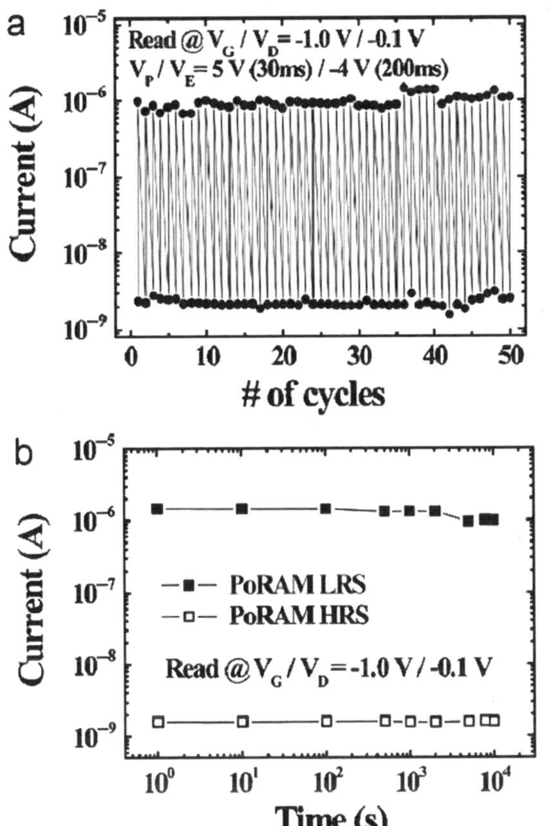

Figure 22. (a) The endurance of the 1T-1R device with consecutive single voltage pulses applied to the polymer memory device. The measurement conditions are a 5 V pulse (writing process, V_P) and a −4 V pulse (erasing process, V_E) with pulse duration (τ_p) of 30 and 200 ms, respectively, (b) the retention. Reprinted with permission from [72], T.-W. Kim et al., *Adv. Mat.* 21, 2497 (2009). © 2009, WILEY-VCH Verlag GmbH & Co. KGaA, Weinheim.

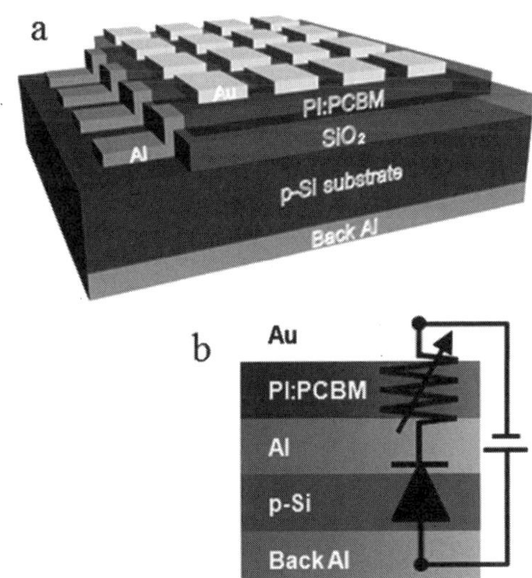

Figure 23. (a) A schematic of 1D-1R hybrid-type memory devices, (b) a schematic of the layered structure and an electronic circuit diagram of the 1D-1R device.

of organic-based diode have been considered as obstacles to reliable operation of the 1D-1R system. Therefore, we have developed a hybrid-type 1D-1R structure combining inorganic diode and organic unipolar memory, which may be preferred [25].

Inorganic Schottky diodes were made on a *p*-type (100) silicon substrate with a resistivity of 8–12 Ω cm. After a typical ultrasonic cleaning process, SiO_2 (with a thickness of 2000 Å) was deposited onto the *p*-Si substrate using plasma-enhanced chemical vapor deposition. The SiO_2 was then patterned by photolithography and wet etching process. To make an ohmic back-contact of the diode, 1000-Å thick Al was deposited onto the back side of the *p*-Si substrate and post-thermal annealing (550°C under an Ar atmosphere for 20 minutes) was performed. Schottky junctions were formed on the front side of the *p*-Si substrate by making Al patterns. Al was also utilized as the bottom electrodes of the organic resistive memory component. The junction area of the Schottky diode was 1 × 1 mm^2.

To make an active layer of organic resistive memory, biphenyltetracarboxylic acid dianhydride *p*-phenylene diamine (BPDA-PPD), used as a polyimide (PI) precursor, was dissolved in *N*-methyl-2-pyrrolidone (NMP) solvent (BPDA-PPD:NMP solvent = 1:3 weight ratio). PCBM was also dissolved in NMP solvent at a concentration of 0.5 wt%. A PI:PCBM composite solution was prepared by mixing the PI solution (2 ml) with the PCBM solution (0.5 ml). The Al surface on the *p*-Si substrate was then exposed to UV-ozone treatment for 10 min to improve reliability of organic resistive memory [77]. The PI:PCBM composite solution was then spin coated and then the coated film was soft baked at 120°C on a hotplate for 10 minutes, followed by a thermal curing process at 300°C under a nitrogen atmosphere for 30 minutes. The resulting thickness was estimated to be ~30 nm. To create the top electrodes of organic memory, a shadow mask with square patterns was aligned with front Al lines and a 50-nm thick Au layer was deposited. The device area of the organic memory was 0.5 × 1 mm^2. The hybrid-type 1D-1R devices, consisting of an organic memory component (Al/PI:PCBM/Au) and an inorganic diode component (*p*-Si/Al), were finally completed. All electrical measurements were done using a semiconductor characterization system (Keithley 4200-SCS) at room temperature in an N_2-filled glove box.

Figure 23(a) showed a schematic of the 1D-1R devices with 16 unit cells. The schematic layer structure and electronic circuit diagram of the devices are illustrated in Figure 23(b). In the 1D-1R devices, the diode component is an inorganic Schottky diode made from Al and *p*-type Si, and the organic resistive memory component consists of a composite material of PI:PCBM composite layer. *I–V* characteristics of the inorganic Schottky diode and organic resistive memory were tested. Figure 24(a) exhibits the *I–V* characteristics of the Schottky diode with its circuit diagram (left inset). The metal-semiconductor junction (Al/*p*-Si) eventually leaded to nonlinear *I–V* curve. The Schottky diode showed excellent rectifying properties with a high rectification ratio (Fig. 24(a)).

Figure 24(b) shows the typical unipolar switching *I–V* curves and its circuit diagram of organic resistive memory. A 1D-1R device with bipolar memory is not erasable due

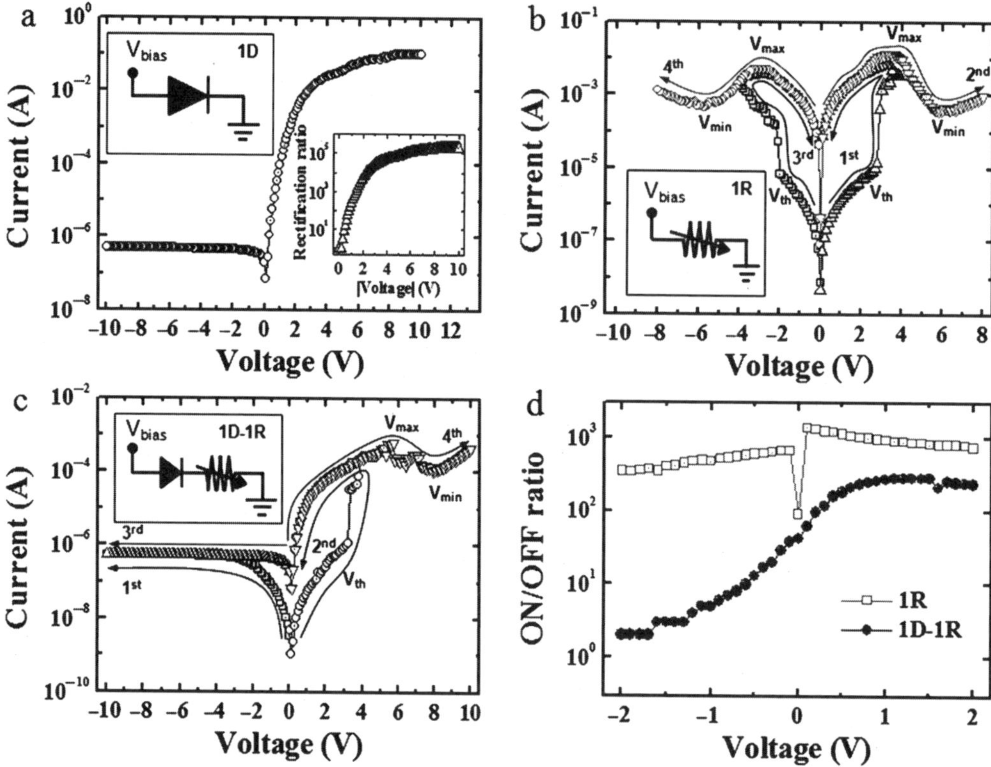

Figure 24. (a) I–V characteristics and circuit diagram (left inset) of an inorganic Schottky diode. Right inset shows the rectification ratio as a function of voltage, (b) I–V characteristics of an organic resistive memory and its circuit diagram (inset). V_{th}, V_{max}, and V_{min} indicate the threshold voltage, the voltage at the local current maximum point, and the voltage at the local current minimum point, respectively, (c) I–V characteristics and circuit diagram (inset) of a 1D-1R memory device, (d) comparison of the ON/OFF ratios for 1R and 1D-1R devices as a function of the applied voltage.

to the suppressed current at the reverse polarity. Therefore, unipolar memory is necessary for the electrically rewritable switching of 1D-1R devices. As shown in Figure 24(b), by double-sweeping the voltage from 0 to 4 V and then back from 4 to 0 V, the device was turned on from an initial HRS (OFF) to an LRS (ON) at the threshold voltage (V_{th} ~ 2.8 V; first curve in Fig. 2(b)). If the voltage increased further from 0 to 8 V, the device remained in the LRS (ON) and then the device experienced a local current maximum (V_{max} ~ 3.3 V), an NDR region, and a local current minimum (V_{min} ~ 5.9 V; second curve). From these results, the operating voltages for writing, erasing, and reading were determined to be ~4, 8, and 1 V, respectively. It is observed that this similar switching property also occurred in the negative voltage regime (third and fourth curves). PI:PCBM composite material was previously reported as a potential active medium for organic memory with thermal robustness as well as multilevel programming capabilities [104]. The resistive switching is related to the charge-trapping mechanism suggested by Simmons and Verderver [51] and Bozano and colleagues [35, 50].

Figure 24(c) shows the I–V characteristic of 1D-1R memory cell (p-Si/Al/PI:PCBM/Au). It clearly shows that the memory and diode function well. Unipolar switching characteristics were observed in forward bias conditions, while the switching in reverse bias conditions was significantly reduced due to the rectifying property of the diode. Specifically, no considerable current flow occurred during the reverse voltage sweep (first curve), while the current increased abruptly at the threshold voltage (V_{th} ~ 3.2 V) in the forward voltage sweep (second curve), indicating a turn-on process from the OFF to ON state. The I–V curve in the subsequent reverse sweep (third curve) was nearly similar to the rectifying current of the diode device alone. The 1D-1R devices were turned off by a forward voltage sweep (fourth curve), resulting in an N-shaped I–V curve (i.e., a local current maximum [V_{max} ~ 5.7 V] followed by NDR and a local current minimum [V_{min} ~ 8 V]). To evaluate the rectifying properties of memory devices connected with the diode component, ON/OFF ratios for 1R and 1D-1R devices as a function of the applied voltage were compared (Fig. 24(d)). The ON/OFF ratio of 1R had nearly the same value regardless of the voltage polarity, which is due to the symmetrical I–V behavior of the 1R (Fig. 24(b)). However, the ON/OFF ratios of 1D-1R devices were significantly different depending on the voltage polarity. This results from a current suppression by the diode device component for the reverse voltage.

It is essential to investigate the device-to-device uniformity of organic memory devices. A statistical analysis of switching characteristics of a set of 35 unit cells was carried out for both 1R and 1D-1R memory devices. Figure 25(a) exhibits the cumulative probability data for each resistance state of the devices. Regardless of the kind of device, both the ON and OFF resistances exhibited a narrow distribution (one to two orders of magnitude). The average resistance

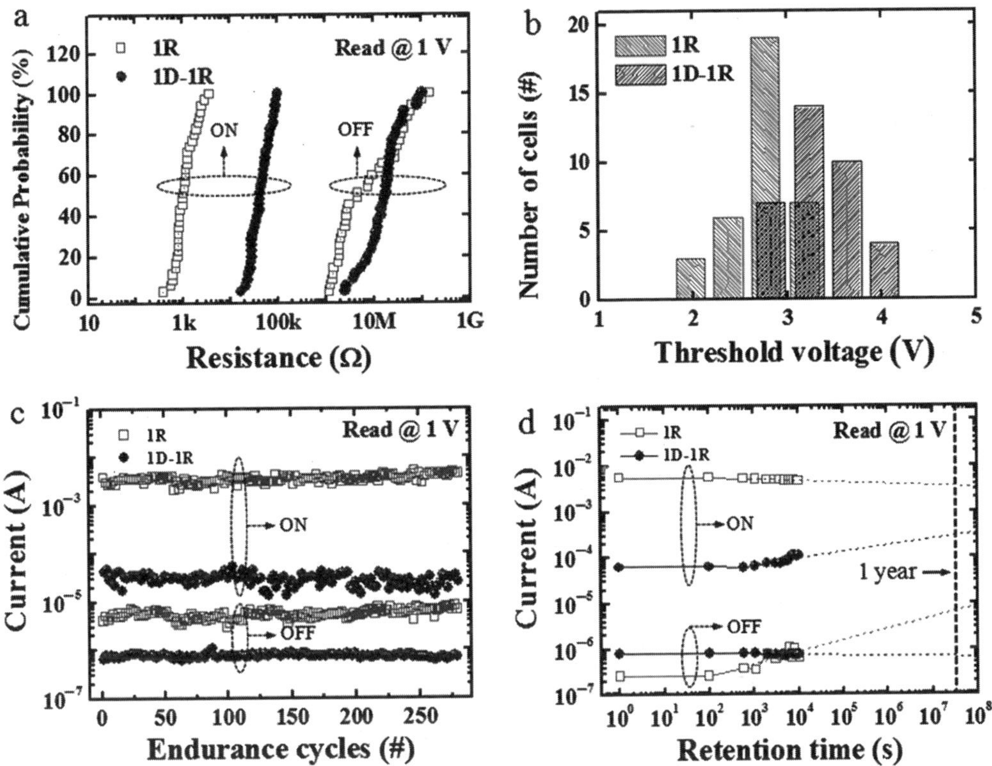

Figure 25. (a) Cumulative probability data of each ON and OFF resistance for 1R and 1D-1R devices. ON and OFF resistances were measured at a voltage of 1 V, (b) comparison of the threshold voltage distributions of 1R and 1D-1R devices, (c) endurance cycles of 1R and 1D-1R devices, (d) detention times of 1R and 1D-1R devices. The extrapolated retention time can be estimated as more than one year.

(~50 kΩ) of the ON state in the 1D-1R devices was higher than that (~1 kΩ) of the 1R devices. This difference is due to the increased series resistance. These results mean that the forward resistance of the diode component affects the ON/OFF ratio in the 1D-1R devices, especially by changing the ON current level. In contrast, the OFF resistance values of the 1D-1R devices were similar to those of the 1R devices, indicating that the OFF resistances are primarily governed by the insulating properties of the organic layer.

We also analyzed the threshold voltage distributions extracted from *I–V* plots of each set of 35 unit cells for both 1R and 1D-1R devices (Fig. 25(b)). The threshold voltages of the 1D-1R devices were little higher than those of the 1R devices. This is likely due to the voltage sharing effect of the series-connected devices (the diode and memory components). The performance of both the 1R and 1D-1R devices was evaluated and compared. The endurance cycling result was obtained by repetitive sweeping operations of a single cell (Fig. 25(c)). During 280 sweep cycles, both 1R and 1D-1R devices maintained two stable current states. To evaluate the capability of retaining information, retention times were tested (Fig. 25(d)). Both 1R and 1D-1R devices provided good retention characteristics (10^4 seconds), with extrapolated retention times of more than 1 year.

The essence of 1D-1R devices is controlling the ON and OFF states of each cell in array-type circuit devices. For example, in integrated-array-type memory devices, parasitic paths can exist in parallel to the selected cell through the neighboring cells if the polymers lack current rectification properties [65, 66]. These paths affect the reading process, causing misreading errors (i.e., cross-talk phenomena). We experimentally observed such reading disturbance in 1R array-type memory devices (Figs. 26(a and b)). Specifically, if (1,2), (2,1), and (2,2) cells were set to the ON states and the (1,1) cell was initially set to the OFF state, the (1,1) cell would be read to be ON resistance (7.9 kΩ) due to the leakage path ([2,1] → [2,2] → [1,2]). This indicates that a specific OFF state can be misread as an ON signal in 1R array devices. This reading disturbance problem can be solved by introducing diode components. If rectifying diode components are integrated into the resistive memory cells, the unintentional leakage path through the (2,2) cell can be prevented and misreading can be avoided. To this end, we demonstrated an array device with 2 × 2 matrix cells that consist of 1D-1R unit cells connected with Au wires (Fig. 26(c)). As illustrated in Figures 26(c and d), even when ON states were set in neighboring cells (i.e., the [1,2], [2,1], and [2,2] cells), the OFF signal of the selected (1,1) cell was successfully read without any electrical interference, showing the desired high resistance of 4.2 M Ω (OFF state). Consequently, accurate cell readings are available only in the 1D-1R array type devices because the diode components suppress the reverse current flow.

This work shows the successful development of 1D-1R hybrid-type devices consisting of an inorganic Schottky diode and organic unipolar memory components. The 1D-1R memory devices have electrically rewritable switching as well as rectifying properties. We constructed array type 1D-1R memory devices where reading disturbance was successfully prevented, making possible an accurate reading process

a

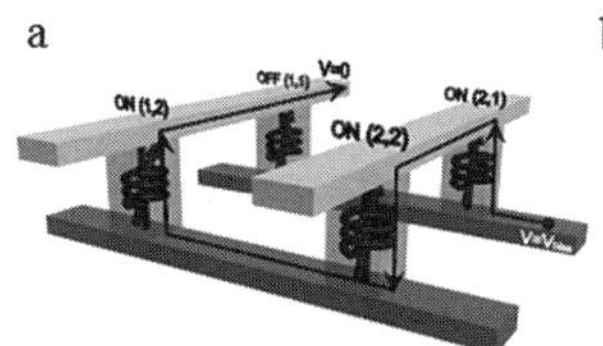

b

Resistance (Ω) in 1R

B/L \ W/L	1	2
1	**7.9 K (ON)**	8.3 K (ON)
2	3.8 K (ON)	12.7 K (ON)

c

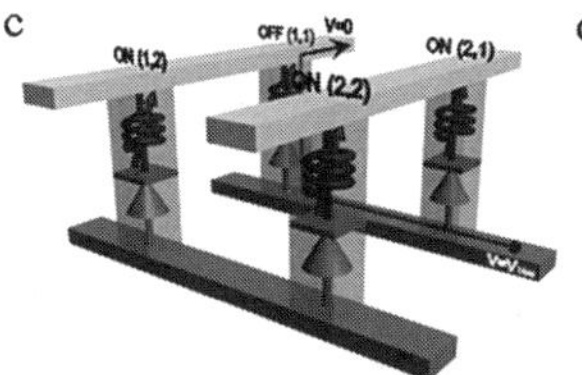

d

Resistance (Ω) in 1D1R

B/L \ W/L	1	2
1	4.2 M (OFF)	27.3 K (ON)
2	24 K (ON)	16.3 K (ON)

Figure 26. (a, b) The reading process of the 1R array type memory device: (a) schematic illustrating the cross-talk interference during reading of an OFF (1,1) cell when neighboring cells ([1,2], [2,1], and [2,2]) were set to the ON state, (b) resistance values of each cell in the 1R device. Each resistance was measured at a voltage of 1 V. The (1,1) cell was misread as an ON signal due to interference from neighboring cells during reading, (c, d) the reading process of the 1D-1R array type memory device: (c) schematic illustrating current flow during reading of an OFF (1,1) cell when neighboring cells ([1,2], [2,1], and [2,2]) were set to the ON state, (d) resistance values of each cell in the 1D-1R device. Each resistance was measured at a voltage of 1 V. The (1,1) cell was accurately read as an OFF signal, demonstrating the absence of the cross-talk problem.

of the selected cell. This enhanced reading capability will advance the development of high-density organic memory applications.

8. CONCLUSION AND PERSPECTIVE

In this chapter, we have reviewed two-terminal organic resistive memories. Several sections in the first part of the chapter present a general overview of the organic memory systems. The focus is then shifted to the advanced approaches such as integration methods, performance enhancement techniques, and advanced architectures (such as 1T-1R and 1D-1R) that have been recently demonstrated in our group. The advanced concepts should be regarded as essential requirements for practical memory applications. In this point of view, this review will provide a meaningful step forward toward future memory application.

For a few decades, organic resistive memory has been intensively investigated due to various merits such as its potential scalability, flexibility, and 3D stackability. Nevertheless, it encounters some challenges. For instance, it is very difficult to analyze the mechanisms responsible for resistance switching and, thus, the responsible mechanism is still a debatable topic. In addition, the performance of organic memories demonstrated so far requires great improvement to be utilized in order to become a practical storage media alternative to conventional flash memory. To solve these issues, further advanced analysis tools should be developed to elucidate the nature of the resistance-switching phenomena. It is also necessary to investigate essential processing factors that influence memory performance and to understand correlation between memory parameters. With solutions for these challenging issues, a goal of the organic resistive memory in the near future will entry into the low-end memory market.

ACKNOWLEDGMENTS

This work was supported by the National Research Laboratory program, National Core Research Center grant, World Class University program of the Korean Ministry of Education, Science and Technology, the Program for Integrated Molecular Systems/GIST, and the IT Research and Development program of MKE/KEIT.

REFERENCES

1. G. Marsh, *Mater. Today* 6, 38 (2003).
2. R. F. Service, *Science* 302, 556 (2003).
3. T. Mikolajick, N. Nagel, S. Riedel, T. Mueller, and K. H. Küsters, *Mater. Sci.-Pol.* 25, 33 (2007).
4. S. Spiesshoefer, Z. Rahman, G. Vangara, S. Polamreddy, S. Burkett, and L. Schaper, *J. Vac. Sci. Technol.* 23, 824 (2005).
5. N. Setter, D. Damjanovic, L. Eng, G. Fox, S. Gevorgian, S. Hong, A. Kingon, H. Kohlstedt, N. Y. Park, G. B. Stephenson, I. Stolitchnov, A. K. Taganstev, D. V. Taylor, T. Yamada, and S. Streiffer, *J. Appl. Phys.* 100, 051606 (2006).
6. J. D. Boeck, W. V. Roy, J. Das, V. Motsnyi, Z. Liu, L. Lagae, H. Boeve, K. Dessein, and G. Borghs, *Semicond. Sci. Technol.* 17, 342 (2002).
7. S. Hudgens and B. Johnson, *MRS Bull.* 29, 829 (2004).
8. International Technology Roadmap for Semiconductors, ITRS, http://www.itrs.net/Links/2005ITRS/Home2005.htm (2005).
9. N. F. Mott, *Adv. Phys.* 16, 49 (1967).
10. S. R. Ovshinsky, *Phys. Rev. Lett.* 21, 1450 (1968).
11. P. O. Sliva, G. Dir, and C. Griffiths, *J. Non-Cryst. Solids* 2, 316 (1970).
12. H. Carchano, R. Lacoste, and Y. Segui, *Appl. Phys. Lett.* 19, 414 (1971).
13. Y. Sadaoka and Y. Sakai, *J. Chem. Soc. Faraday Trans.* 272, 1911 (1976).
14. T. Yagi, M. Tatemoto, and J.-I. Sako, *Polym. J.* 12, 209 (1980).
15. M. Siradjuddin, V. K. Raju, and P. J. Reddy, *Phys. Status. Solidi A* 81, K37 (1984).
16. A. Bune, S. Ducharme, V. Fridkin, L. Blinov, S. Palto, N. Petukhova, and S. Yudin, *Appl. Phys. Lett.* 67, 3975 (1995).
17. T. J. Reece, S. Ducharme, A. V. Sorokin, and M. Poulsen, *Appl. Phys. Lett.* 82, 142 (2003).
18. S. Möller, C. Perlov, W. Jackson, C. Taussig, and S. R. Forrest, *Nature* 426, 166 (2003).
19. S. Tehrani, J. M. Slaughter, E. Chen, M. Durlam, J. Shi, and M. DeHerren, *IEEE Trans. Magn.* 35, 2814 (1999).
20. A. Sawa, *Mater. Today* 11, 28 (2008).
21. R. Waser and M. Aono, *Nat. Mater.* 6, 833 (2007).
22. International Technology Roadmap for Semiconductors, ITRS, http://www.itrs.net/Links/2007ITRS/Home2007.htm (2007).
23. T.-W. Kim, S.-H. Oh, H. Choi, G. Wang, H. Hwang, D.-Y. Kim, and T. Lee, *Appl. Phys. Lett.* 92, 253308 (2008).
24. B. Cho, T.-W. Kim, M. Choe, G. Wang, S. Song, and T. Lee, *Org. Electron.* 10, 473 (2009).
25. B. Cho, T.-W. Kim, S. Song, Y. Ji, M. Jo, H. Hwang, G.-Y. Jung, and T. Lee, *Adv. Mater.* 22, 1228 (2010).
26. Y. Yang, J. Ouyang, L. Ma, R. J. H. Tseng, and C. W. Chu, *Adv. Funct. Mat.* 16, 1001 (2006).
27. L. Fu, L. Cao, Y. Liu, and D. Zhu, Adv. *Colloid Interface Sci.* 111, 133 (2004).

28. C. Li, W. Fan, B. Lei, D. Zhang, S. Han, T. Tang, X. Liu, Z. Liu, S. Asano, M. Meyyappan, J. Han, and C. Zhou, *Appl. Phys. Lett.* 84, 1949 (2004).
29. Y. Yang, L. Ma, and J. Wu, *MRS Bull.* 29, 833 (2004).
30. R. F. Service, *Science* 293, 1746 (2001).
31. J. C. Scott, *Science* 304, 62 (2004).
32. R. J. Tseng, J. Huang, J. Ouyang, R. B. Kaner, and Yang, *Nano Lett.* 5, 1077 (2005).
33. D. T. Simon, M. S. Griffo, R. A. DiPietro, S. A. Swanson, and S. A. Carter, *Appl. Phys. Lett.* 89, 133510 (2006).
34. Y. Song, Q. D. Ling, S. L. Lim, E. Y. H. Teo, Y. P. Tan, L. Li, E. T. Kang, D. S. H. Chan, and C. Zhu, *IEEE Electron. Device. Lett.* 28, 107 (2007).
35. L. D. Bozano, B. W. Kean, M. Beinhoff, K. R. Carter, P. M. Rice, and J. C. Scott, *Adv. Funct. Mat.* 15, 1933 (2005).
36. F. Li, T. W. Kim, W. Dong, and Y.-H. Kim, *Appl. Phys. Lett.* 92, 011906 (2008).
37. F. Li, D.-I. Son, S.-M. Seo, H.-M. Cha, H.-J. Kim, B.-J. Kim, J. H. Jung, and T. W. Kim, *Appl. Phys. Lett.* 91, 122111 (2007).
38. H. S. Nalwa, "Ferroelectric Polymers: Chemistry, Physics, and Applications," Marcel Dekker, New York, 1995.
39. G. Dearnaley, D. V. Morgan, and A. M. Stoneham, *J. Non-Cryst. Solids* 4, 593 (1970).
40. G. Dearnaley, A. M. Stoneham, and D. V. Morgan, *Rep. Prog. Phys.* 33, 1129 (1970).
41. L. F. Pender and R. J. Fleming, *J. Appl. Phys.* 46, 3426 (1975).
42. Y. Segui, B. Ai, and H. Carchano, *J. Appl. Phys.* 47, 140 (1976).
43. W. Hwang and K. C. Kao, *J. Chem. Phys.* 60, 3845 (1974).
44. H. K. Henisch and W. R. Smith, *Appl. Phys. Lett.* 24, 589 (1974).
45. W.-J. Joo, T.-L. Choi, K.-H. Lee, and Y. Chung, *J. Phys. Chem. B* 111, 7756 (2007).
46. W.-J. Joo, T.-L. Choi, J. Lee, S. K. Lee, M.-S. Jung, N. Kim, and J. M. Kim, *J. Phys. Chem. B* 110, 23812 (2006).
47. S. Sivaramakrishnan, P.-J. Chia, Y.-C. Yeo, L.-L. Chua, and P. K. H. Ho, *Nat. Mater.* 6, 149 (2007).
48. H. S. Majumdar, A. Bandyopadhyay, A. Bolognesi, and A. J. Pal, *J. Appl. Phys.* 91, 2433 (2002).
49. S. Das and A. J. Pal, *Appl. Phys. Lett.* 76, 1770 (2000).
50. L. D. Bozano, B. W. Kean, V. R. Deline, J. R. Salem, and J. C. Scott, *Appl. Phys. Lett.* 84, 607 (2004).
51. J. G. Simmons and R. R. Verderber, *Proc. R Soc. London, Ser. A* 301, 77 (1967).
52. R. S. Potember, T. O. Poehler, and D. O. Cowan, *Appl. Phys. Lett.* 34, 405 (1979).
53. E. I. Kamitsos, C. H. Tzinis, and W. M. Risen, *Solid State Commun.* 42, 561 (1982).
54. C. W. Chu, J. Ouyang, J. H. Tseng, and Y. Yang, *Adv. Mater.* 17, 1440 (2005).
55. Z. J. Donhauser, B. A. Mantooth, K. F. Kelly, L. A. Bumm, J. D. Monnell, J. J. Stapleton, D. W. Price, A. M. Rawlett, D. L. Allara, J. M. Tour, and P. S. Weiss, *Science* 292, 2303 (2001).
56. A. Bandyopadhyay and A. J. Pal, *Appl. Phys. Lett.* 84, 999 (2004).
57. B. Mukherjee and A. J. Pal, *Synth. Met.* 155, 336 (2005).
58. E. Y. H. Teo, Q. D. Ling, Y. Song, Y. P. Tan, W. Wang, E. T. Kang, D. S. H. Chan, and C. Zhu, *Org. Electron.* 7, 173 (2006).
59. S. L. Lim, Ling, E. Y. H. Teo, C. X. Zhu, D. S. H. Chan, Kang, and K. G. Neoh, *Chem. Mater.* 19, 5148 (2007).
60. J. Vandendriessche, P. Palmans, S. Toppet, N. Boens, F. C. De Schryver, and H. Masuhara, *J. Am. Chem. Soc.* 106, 8057 (1984).
61. J. H. A. Smits, S. C. J. Meskers, R. A. J. Janssen, A. W. Marsman, and D. M. de Leeuw, *Adv. Mater.* 17, 1169 (2005).
62. F. Verbakel, S. C. J. Meskers, and R. A. J. Janssen, *Chem. Mater.* 18, 2707 (2006).
63. J. Ouyang, C.-W. Chu, C. R. Szmanda, L. Ma, and Y. Yang, *Nat. Mater.* 3, 918 (2004).
64. J. C. Scott and L. D. Bozano, *Adv. Mater.* 19, 1452 (2007).
65. M. J. Lee, Y. Park, D. S. Suh, E. H. Lee, S. Seo, D. C. Kim, R. Jung, B. S. Kang, S. E. Ahn, C. B. Lee, D. H. Seo, Y. K. Cha, I. K. Yoo, J. S. Kim, and B. H. Park, *Adv. Mater.* 19, 3919 (2007).
66. I. G. Baek, D. C. Kim, M. J. Lee, H. J. Kim, E. K. Yim, M. S. Lee, J. E. Lee, S. E. Ahn, S. Seo, J. H. Lee, J. C. Park, Y. K. Cha, S. O. Park, H. S. Kim, I. K. Yoo, U. I. Chung, J. T. Moon, and B. I. Ryu, "IEEE Int. Electron Devices Meet.," New York, p. 750, 2005.
67. K. Kinoshita, K. Tsunoda, Y. Sato, H. Noshiro, S. Yagaki, M. Aoki, and Y. Sugiyama, *Appl. Phys. Lett.* 93, 033506 (2008).
68. E. Y. H. Teo, C. Zhang, S. L. Lim, E.-T. Kang, D. S. H. Chan, and C. Zhu, *IEEE Electron. Device. Lett.* 30, 487 (2009).
69. S.-E. Ahn, B. S. Kang, K. H. Kim, M.-J. Lee, C. B. Lee, G. Stefanovich, C. J. Kim, and Y. Park, *IEEE Electron. Device. Lett.* 30, 550 (2009).
70. H.-T. Lin, Z. Pei, J.-R. Chen, and Y.-J. Chan, *IEEE Electron. Device. Lett.* 30, 18 (2009).
71. M.-J. Lee, S. I. Kim, C. B. Lee, H. Yin, S.-E. Ahn, B. S. Kang, K. H. Kim, J. C. Park, C. J. Kim, I. Song, S. W. Kim, G. Stefanovich, J. H. Lee, S. J. Chung, Y. H. Kim, and Y. Park, *Adv. Funct. Mat.* 19, 1587 (2009).
72. T.-W. Kim, H. Choi, S.-H. Oh, G. Wang, D.-Y. Kim, H. Hwang, and T. Lee, *Adv. Mater.* 21, 2497 (2009).
73. Y.-S. Lai, C.-H. Tu, D.-L. Kwong, and J. S. Chen, *Appl. Phys. Lett.* 87, 122101 (2005).
74. Y. S. Lai, C. H. Tu, D. L. Kwong, and J. S. Chen, *IEEE Electron. Device. Lett.* 27, 451 (2006).
75. Q. D. Ling, S. L. Lim, Y. Song, C. X. Zhu, D. S. H. Chan, E. T. Kang, and K. G. Neoh, *Langmuir* 23, 312 (2007).
76. M. Cölle, M. Büchel, and D. M. de Leeuw, *Org. Electron.* 7, 305 (2006).
77. F. Verbakel, S. C. J. Meskers, R. A. J. Janssen, H. L. Gomes, M. Cölle, M. Büchel, and D. M. de Leeuw, *Appl. Phys. Lett.* 91, 192103 (2007).
78. W. Guan, S. Long, Q. Liu, M. Liu, and W. Wang, *IEEE Electron. Device. Lett.* 29, 434 (2008).
79. W. Tang, H. Shi, G. Xu, B. S. Ong, Z. D. Popovic, J. Deng, J. Zhao, and G. Rao, *Adv. Mater.* 17, 2307 (2005).
80. S.-H. Oh, S.-I. Na, Y.-C. Nah, D. Vak, S.-S. Kim, and D.-Y. Kim, *Org. Electron.* 8, 773 (2007).
81. J. Chen, L. Xu, J. Lin, Y. Geng, L. Wang, and D. Ma, *Appl. Phys. Lett.* 89, 083514 (2006).
82. C.-H. Tu, Y.-S. Lai, and D.-L. Kwong, *IEEE Electron. Device. Lett.* 27, 354 (2006).
83. H.-T. Lin, Z. Pei, and Y.-J. Chan, *IEEE Electron. Device. Lett.* 28, 569 (2007).
84. S. Ssenyange, H. Yan, and R. L. McCreery, *Langmuir* 22, 10689 (2006).
85. M. Arif, M. Yun, S. Gangopadhyay, K. Ghosh, L. Fadiga, F. Galbrecht, U. Scherf, and S. Guha, *Phys. Rev. B* 75, 195202 (2007).
86. A. Carbone, B. K. Kotowska, and D. Kotowski, *Phys. Rev. Lett.* 95, 236601 (2005).
87. S. Paul, A. Kanwal, and M. Chhowalla, *Nanotech.* 17, 145 (2006).
88. J. Kim, S. Cho, S. Choi, S. Baek, D. Lee, O. Kim, S.-M. Park, and M. Ree, *Langmuir* 23, 9024 (2007).
89. W. L. Kwan, R. J. Tseng, W. Wu, Q. Pei, and Y. Yang, "IEEE Int. Electron. Devices Meet.," New York, p. 237, 2007.
90. T.-W. Kim, H. Choi, S.-H. Oh, M. Jo, G. Wang, B. Cho, D.-Y. Kim, H. Hwang, and T. Lee, *Nanotech.* 20, 025201 (2009).
91. J.-S. Choi, J.-H. Kim, S.-H. Kim, and D. H. Suh, *Appl. Phys. Lett.* 89, 152111 (2006).
92. C. Kim, P. E. Burrows, and S. R. Forrest, *Science* 288, 831 (2000).
93. C. Kim, M. Shtein, and S. R. Forrest, *Appl. Phys. Lett.* 80, 4051 (2002).
94. W. M. Lackowski, P. Ghosh, and R. M. Crooks, *J. Am. Chem. Soc.* 121, 1419 (1999).

95. Y.-L. Loo, R. L. Willett, K. W. Baldwin, and J. A. Rogers, *J. Am. Chem. Soc*. 124, 7654 (2002).
96. T.-W. Kim, K. Lee, S.-H. Oh, G. Wang, D.-Y. Kim, G.-Y. Jung, and T. Lee, *Nanotech.* 19, 405201 (2008).
97. G.-Y. Jung, Z. Li, W. Wu, Y. Chen, D. L. Olynick, S.-Y. Wang, W. M. Tong, and R. S. Williams, *Langmuir* 21, 1158 (2005).
98. L. Ma, Q. Xu, and Y. Yang, *Appl. Phys. Lett*. 84, 4908 (2004).
99. T.-W. Kim, S.-H. Oh, J. Lee, H. Choi, G. Wang, J. Park, D.-Y. Kim, H. Hwang, and T. Lee, *Org. Electron*. 11, 109 (2010).
100. G. Pfister and C. H. Griffiths, *Phys. Rev. Lett*. 40, 659 (1978).
101. P. G. Lecomber, A. E. Owen, W. E. Spear, J. Hajto, A. J. Snell, W. K. Choi, M. J. Rose, and S. Reynolds, *J. Non-Cryst. Solids* 77–78, 1373 (1985).
102. H. Ma, H.-L. Yip, F. Huang, and A. K. Y. Jen, *Adv. Funct. Mat*. 20, 1371 (2010).
103. T. Kondo, S. M. Lee, M. Malicki, B. Domercq, S. R. Marder, and B. Kippelen, *Adv. Funct. Mat*. 18, 1112 (2008).
104. B.-O. Cho, T. Yasue, H. Yoon, M.-S. Lee, I.-S. Yeo, U. I. Chung, J.-T. Moon, and B.-I. Ryu, "IEEE Int. Electron Devices Meet.," New York, p. 1, 2006.
105. K. S. Yook, J. Y. Lee, S. H. Kim, and J. Jang, *Appl. Phys. Lett*. 92, 223305 (2008).
106. B. Cho, S. Song, Y. Ji, and T. Lee, *Appl. Phys. Lett*. 97, 063305 (2010).
107. B. S. Kang, S.-E. Ahn, M.-J. Lee, G. Stefanovich, K. H. Kim, W. X. Xianyu, C. B. Lee, Y. Park, I. G. Baek, and B. H. Park, *Adv. Mater*. 20, 3066 (2008).
108. T.-W. Kim, S.-H. Oh, H. Choi, G. Wang, H. Hwang, D.-Y. Kim, and T. Lee, *IEEE Electron. Device. Lett*. 29, 852 (2008).
109. K. Asadi, D. M. de Leeuw, B. de Boer, and P. W. M. Blom, *Nat. Mater*. 7, 547 (2008).
110. Q.-D. Ling, D.-J. Liaw, C. Zhu, D. S.-H. Chan, E.-T. Kang, and K.-G. Neoh, *Prog. Polym. Sci*. 33, 917 (2008).

CHAPTER 14

Nonvolatile Memories for Radiation-Hardened Applications

Xiaoli He[1], Wei Wang[2]
[1]*Institute of Microelectronics, Chinese Academy of Science, Beijing, 100079, China*
[2]*College of Nanoscale Science and Engineering, University at Albany, NY 12203, USA*

CONTENTS

ISBN: 1-58883-251-1

Nonvolatile Memories: Materials, Devices and Applications
Edited by Tseung-Yuen Tseng and Simon M. Sze
Volume 2: Pages: 335–375

1. INTRODUCTION

Radiation-hardened nonvolatile memories are important to aerospace, nuclear, and medical applications. With the scaling trend of CMOS technology, process-induced radiation damages are also becoming a major concern of commercial electronic systems. Thus, the research on radiation effect of nonvolatile memories has recently gained a lot of attention. Specifically, electronic circuits are under constant bombardment by radiation such as energetic electrons, protons, and heavy ions that can upset them or permanently degrade their performance. Typically, a satellite in low-earth orbit would be exposed to a few kilorads of ionizing radiation per year. For higher earth orbits, the dose of radiation can be in the range of several hundreds of kilorads (krad) to megarads (Mrad). These particles can ionize atoms in a material, creating a pulse of electron–hole pairs that cause inadvertent signals in a circuit. This radiation-induced charge can be trapped within the device dielectric and can also introduce defects at material interfaces. In addition to ionization, energetic particles that carry dozens to hundreds of MeV of kinetic energy cause atomic displacement damage in a device. The displacement damage can generate deep traps in a semiconductor that lead to carrier removal or mobility degradation. Thus, radiation-sensitive electronic components used in space usually require shielding, which tends to be heavy and can significantly increase the launch cost of a satellite or a spacecraft. The nonvolatile memory components are typically radiation-sensitive and their radiation effects need careful study to evaluate under different radiation conditions.

This chapter reviews the recent radiation research results on silicon (Si) flash and several emerging nanometer scale memory devices such as ferroelectric random access memory (RAM), magnetoresistive RAM, phase-change RAM, and resistive RAM. These emerging memories have demonstrated many advantages over Si flash in terms of fabrication and device performance, while providing excellent radiation hard properties. These studies will lead to the development of new physics theories and materials/processes to achieve the next generation of radiation hardened memory devices.

In the following sections, the background knowledge of various radiation particles and exposure environments is first reviewed in Section 2. Then, the radiation effects of MOS technology and the existing nonvolatile memories such as Flash are discussed in Sections 3 and 4. Next, recent radiation studies on the emerging nonvolatile memories including ferroelectric RAM (FeRAM), magnetoresistive RAM (MRAM), phase-change RAM (PCRAM), and resistive RAM (ReRAM)/memristor are presented in Sections 5 to 8 respectively. Finally, Section 9 summarizes this chapter and demonstrates that these results will provide an important guideline for the development of future radiation-hardened nonvolatile memories.

2. RADIATION BASICS

2.1. Radiation Particles

Radiation is a process where energy is emitted by one body traveling in a straight line through a medium or through space. It can be either ionizing or non-ionizing, depending on how it affects matter. Non-ionizing radiation includes visible light, heat, radar, microwaves, and radio waves. This type of radiation deposits energy in the materials through which it passes, but it does not have sufficient energy to break molecular bonds or remove electrons from atoms. By contrast, ionizing radiation is more energetic than non-ionizing radiation and includes α particles, β particles, γ rays, X-rays, neutrons, protons, and other heavy ions such as the nuclei of argon, nitrogen, carbon, and other elements [1]. Consequently, when ionizing radiation passes through material, it deposits enough energy to break molecular bonds and displace (or remove) electrons from atoms.

2.1.1. α Particles

α particles are the nuclei of helium atoms, consisting of two protons and two neutrons, i.e., an atomic mass of 4 and a positive charge of 2 units. Because of its large mass and positive charge, an α ray can usually pass only a short distance. A typical α particle energy is 5 MeV with a typical range of 50 mm in air and 23 μm in silicon. A single piece of paper can stop an α ray effectively. α rays are produced following spontaneous decay of certain radioactive atoms, such as radium, plutonium, uranium, and radon. Normally of high energy (in the MeV range), they interact strongly with matter and are heavily ionizing.

2.1.2. β Particles

β particles have the same mass as an electron but may be either negatively (electrons) or positively charged (positrons). With their small size and charge they penetrate matter more easily than α particles but also are more easily deflected. β rays are produced following spontaneous decay of certain radioactive materials, such as tritium (an isotope of hydrogen), carbon-14, phosphorus-32, and strontium-90. Depending on its energy (i.e., speed), a β ray can traverse different distances in water—less than 1 mm for tritium to nearly 1 cm for phosphorus-32. With high velocity, β particles are lightly ionizing.

2.1.3. γ Rays

γ rays consist of photons with a frequency of greater than 10^{19} Hz and no mass or electric charge. γ rays are produced following spontaneous decay of radioactive materials such as cobalt-60 and cesium-137. They are lightly ionizing but highly penetrating. They can be stopped by a sufficiently thick layer of material with a high atomic number, such as lead or depleted uranium.

2.1.4. X-Rays

X-rays have the same characteristics as γ rays, although they are produced differently. When high-speed electrons impact metals, electrons are stopped and release energy in the form of an electromagnetic wave. X-rays produced this way contain a mixture of different wavelengths, whereas γ-ray energy has a fixed value (or two) characteristic to the radioactive material. The way in which X-ray photons interact with matter is identical with γ rays.

2.1.5. Protons

The proton is the nucleus of a hydrogen atom and carries a positive charge of 1 unit. The proton has a mass about 1800 times that of an electron, and thus is more difficult to deflect, with a typical range of several centimeters in air and tens of micrometers in a material, such as aluminum, at energies in the MeV range.

2.1.6. Neutrons

A neutron has the same mass as a proton but has no charge and consequently is difficult to stop. They have the ability to ionize atoms and are the only type of ionizing radiation that can make other objects or material radioactive. Neutron particles are released following nuclear fission (splitting of an atomic nucleus producing large amounts of energy) of high-atomic-number elements such as uranium or plutonium. In fact, it is neutrons that trigger the nuclear chain reaction to detonate an atomic bomb. Neutrons can be slowed down by hydrogenous material, and the capture of a neutron results in the emission of a γ ray. Neutrons are classified according to their energy: thermal (< 1 eV), intermediate, and fast (> 100 eV). Water is an especially effective shield for neutrons.

Table 1 summarizes the mass and charge of the ionizing radiation particles. Figure 1 gives a simple illustration of radiation penetration.

2.2. Radiation Environment

Every electronic device is subjected to radiation. There are various radiation environments that possibly degrade or even ruin electronic devices and systems. In general, radiation environments can be classified as follows: space radiation environment, high-energy physics experiments environment, nuclear reactor environment, terrestrial and man-made environment, and processing-induced radiation environment [1, 2]. Each of these environments is characterized by its own spectrum of particles and energy distribution. Detailed discussion on radiation environments can be found in Refs. [1, 2]. In this section, only the space radiation environment and atmospheric radiation environment will be reviewed in keeping with the subject of space radiation effects on NVM devices.

2.2.1. Space Radiation Environment

The space radiation environment is composed of various energetic particles including protons, electrons, and heavy ions [1–5]. These energetic particles can cause damage to electronic systems in a number of ways. For instance, high

Table 1. Mass and charge of the ionizing radiation particles.

Particle	Rest mass (amu)	Charge
Electron	0.00055	$-e$
Positron	0.00055	$+e$
Proton	1.008	$+e$
Neutron	1.009	0
α	4.004	$+2e$

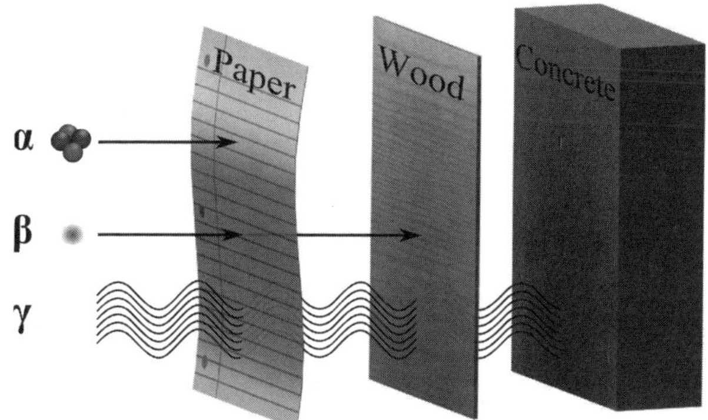

Figure 1. Radiation penetration of α particles, β particles, and γ rays.

energy protons and electrons can cause total-dose ionizing radiation-induced damage, and protons can also cause displacement damage. Heavy ions and high-energy protons can upset system operation and sometimes cause permanent damage to electronics [4, 6–15]. The concentration and types of particles vary significantly with altitude, angle of inclination, and time. Particles present in the space radiation environment can be grouped into two general categories: (1) trapped radiation in the earth's magnetic field, and (2) transient particles from galactic cosmic rays (GCRs) and solar cosmic rays (SCRs) [1–4, 16–18].

2.2.1.1. Trapped Radiation. The earth's magnetic field above the dense atmosphere creates a geomagnetic cavity known as the magnetosphere, which traps a very broad spectrum of energetic charged particles [1–3] and forms trapped radiation belts, as shown in Figure 2. The lower limit of the radiation belts is the earth's atmosphere, as it shields all the trapped particles. The upper limit, however, is less clear and is defined by the minimum intensity in the presence of disturbances of the magnetic field [18]. The trapped radiation belts (or Van Allen belts), discovered by Van Allen and coworkers during the first space missions, consists mainly of electrons up to a few MeV in energy and protons of up to several hundred MeV, although a very small percentage of low-energy heavy ions are also trapped. The charged particles in the radiation belts gyrate spirally around the magnetic field lines, and are reflected back and forth between

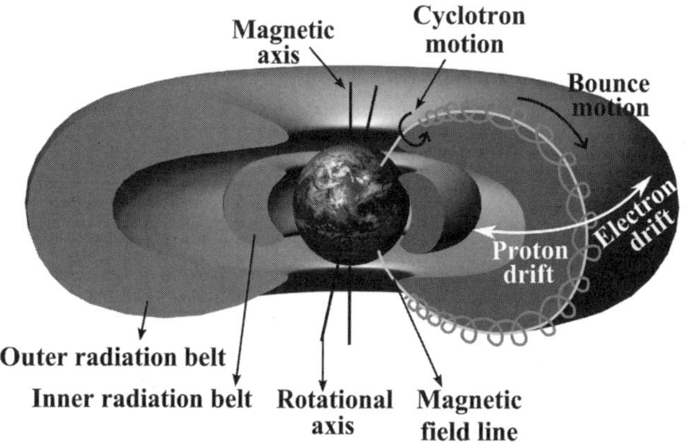

Figure 2. Van Allen radiation belt and the motion of trapped particles in the earth's magnetosphere.

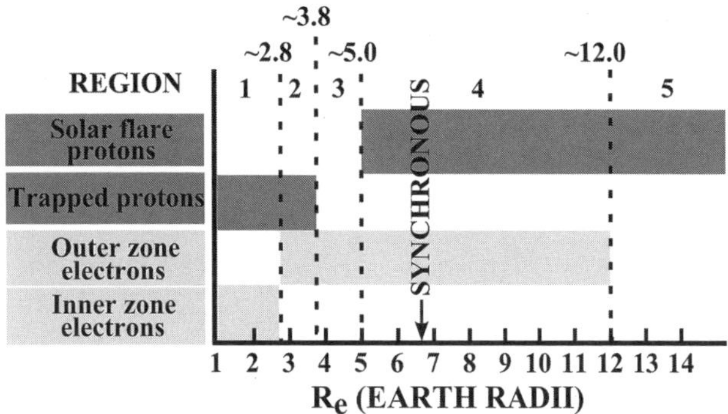

Figure 3. Charged particle distribution in the magnetosphere. Adapted with permission from [3], E. G. Stassinopoulos and J. P. Raymond, *Proc. IEEE* 76, 1423 (1988). © 1988, IEEE.

the poles where the fields are confined [3], as illustrated in Figure 2. Simultaneously, because of their charge, electrons drift eastward while protons and heavy ions drift westward around the earth due to the Lorentz force.

The distribution of charged particles at the equator is presented in Figure 3 [3]. Distances are specified in earth radii, R_e (one R_e is 6380 km). For instance, one earth radius is at the surface of the earth. The magnetosphere can be divided into 5 domains. As the variation in the magnetic field lines occur with latitude (angle of inclination), the boundaries of the domains vary with latitude. Most satellites are operated in near-earth orbits at altitudes from 1 to 10 R_e. Geosynchronous orbit (GEO) is at an altitude of approximately 6.6 R_e. The trapped proton distribution exists primarily in regions 1 and 2 that extends from above 1 R_e to approximately 3.8 R_e. The profile of the trapped proton flux as a function of energy and radial distance is shown in Figure 4 [3]. Protons with energies larger than 10 MeV primarily occupy regions 1 and 2 with the $E > 30$ MeV proton fluxes peaking at approximately 2500 km altitude (at the equator) [5]. As typical spacecraft shielding attenuates protons with energies below 10 MeV, the predominantly low-energy trapped protons trapped above 3.8 R_e are normally ineffective in causing radiation damage. It is noted that the

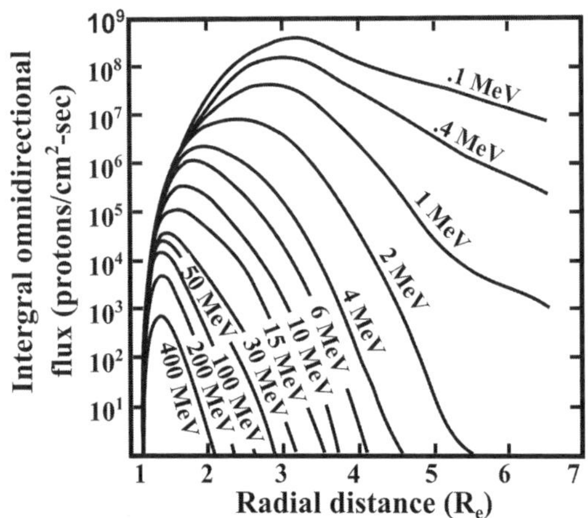

Figure 4. Equatorial radial profiles for proton fluxes. Adapted with permission from [3], E. G. Stassinopoulos and J. P. Raymond, *Proc. IEEE* 76, 1423 (1988). © 1988, IEEE.

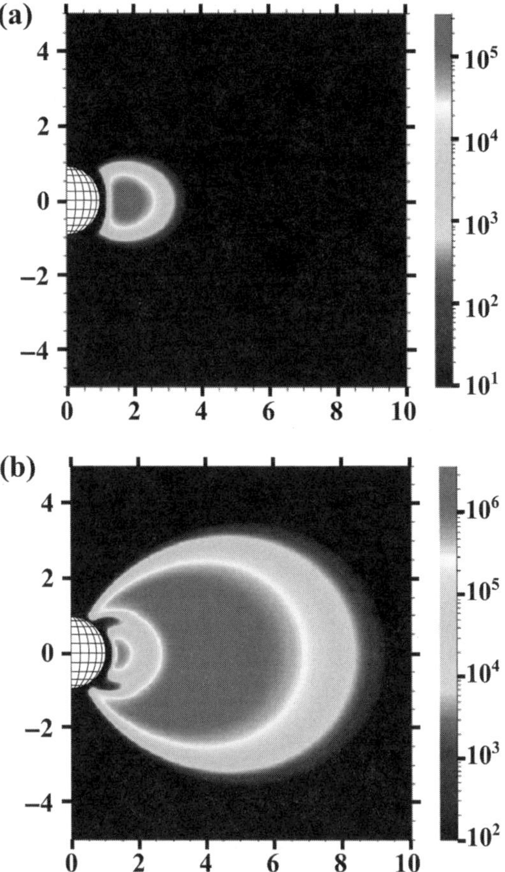

Figure 5. Omni-directional integrated (a) photon fluxes (cm^{-2} s^{-1}) trapped in the radiation belt from NASA AP8 min model (energy > 10 MeV), and (b) electron fluxes trapped in the radiation belt from NASA AE8 max model (energy > 1 MeV). The mapping is done in magnetic coordinates given here earth radii. Reprinted with permission from [18], S. Bourdarie and M. Xapsos, *IEEE Trans. Nucl. Sci.* 55, 1810 (2008). © 2008, IEEE.

altitude corresponding to the proton flux peak decreases with increasing proton energy, and the peak of proton flux with highest energy exists at the lowest relative altitude. As seen in Figure 5(a), a plot of trapped proton fluxes from NASA AP8 min model ($E > 10$ MeV), a single flux maximum is observed for the proton belt. The flux is very stable there. In regions 4 and 5 from about 5 R_e to beyond 14 R_e protons are present, primarily originating from solar fares.

Van Allen belt electrons primarily occupy in regions 1 through 4. The Van Allen belt can be segregated into an "inner zone" and an "outer zone" for electrons. The inner zone extends to about 2.4 R_e and the outer zone from 2.8 to 12 R_e. The gap between 2.5 and 2.8 R_e is the "slot," where the electron flux is usually very low, during magneto-spherically quiet times. The $E > 2$ MeV peak electron fluxes at the equator are at ~2500 km altitude in the inner zone and at 20,000 km altitude in the outer zone [5]. Figure 5(b) [18] gives electron fluxes trapped in the radiation belt from NASA AE8 max model ($E > 1$ MeV), showing the inner and outer belts, i.e., two flux maxima regions. The outer zone electrons have much higher fluxes (10 times higher) and energies (~7 MeV) than the inner zone electrons (< 5 MeV) [3]. Also, the electron populations in the inner belt are relatively stable, but much more variable in the outer belt. The trapped particle population in the outer belt and the slot region can increase the above averages by several orders of magnitude due to changes in the magnetosphere induced by solar and magnetic storms.

In fact, the most intense radiation appears at the Atlantic Ocean off the coast of South America, where the offset and tilt of the geomagnetic axis with respect to the earth's rotation axis cause the anomaly, called South Atlantic Anomaly (SAA, ~300 to ~1200 km from the earth surface) [2, 3, 5, 19]. The intense radiation in the SAA causes damage to many spacecraft in low earth orbit and is a hazard to astronauts there.

The radiation energies and particle fluxes strongly depend on solar activities. The solar cycle is normally divided into two main activity phases: the solar minimum and the solar maximum. On the average, the cycle lasts for 11 year with approximately 4 years of solar minimum and 7 years of solar maximum [18]. Solar particle events occur with greater frequency during the declining phase of solar maximum. Trapped electron fluxes tend to be higher during that declining phase. Trapped proton fluxes in low earth orbit reach their maximum during solar minimum, but when this peak is reached depends on the particular location. GCR fluxes are also at a maximum during solar minimum [18].

The available models of the radiation environment have to take the solar activity into account. Currently AE-8 and AP-8 "NASA" models are the de-facto standard models for electron and proton fluxes in the radiation belts. This is mainly due to the fact that up to now they are the only models completely covering the region of the radiation belts, and having a wide energy range for both protons and electrons. AP-8 gives proton fluxes from 0.1–400 MeV while AE-8 covers electrons from 0.04–7 MeV [20]. These models provide positional or orbit-averaged fluxes and have separate versions for solar minimum and solar maximum. However, large errors may occur in the AP-8 and AE-8 model fluxes where steep gradients in spatial and spectral distribution exist and where time variations are not well understood. A more detailed review of problems with the AP-8 and AE-8 models can be referred to Refs. [18, 20]. Due to the need for trapped particle models with finer time resolution, researchers have developed empirical models using CRRES data to estimate short-term dynamic changes in the particle population: the CRRESPRO, CRRESELE, and CRRESRAD [5, 21, 22]. A number of models developed later, such as PSB97 for low altitude trapped protons [23], LATRM for low altitude trapped protons taking the solar activity into account [24], POLE and IGE-2006 for geostationary electron environment considering solar cycles [25–27]. More models and discussion relative to the various models are reviewed in Refs. [24, 28].

2.2.1.2. Transient Particles. Transient particles from GCRs and solar events can reach near-earth orbiting spacecraft and are particularly hazardous to satellites in polar, highly elliptical, and geostationary orbits.

The GCRs originate outside the solar system and form a background component of radiation that shows a slow cyclical variation with solar activity [29]. They are composed of about 85% protons, 14% α particles, and 1% heavy ions, including all elements of the periodic table. GCRs have low fluxes (generally a few $cm^{-2}\ s^{-1}$), but their energies are high, extending from 10 s MeV up to 100 s of GeV [17]. Those with lower energies are excluded from the solar system by the solar wind. Therefore, GCR fluxes, modulated by the 11-year solar cycle, reach their maximum intensity during solar minimum and drop off by a factor of 2 to 10 at solar maximum [16, 29]. Figure 6 shows the GCR energy spectra for proton, helium, oxygen, iron during solar maximum and solar minimum, indicating that the flux of the ions with $E < 10$ GeV per nucleon is modulated by the solar cycle and solar wind and that the flux peak is around 1 GeV per nucleon [18, 30].

Single Event Effects (SEE) are the main radiation effects caused by GCRs in microelectronics and photonics. The most well-known and used operating model is the Cosmic Ray Effects on Micro-Electronics (CREME). CRÈME96 is the current version [18, 31, 32], similar in approach to a GCR model originated by Badhwar and O'Neill [30]. Both models are based on the diffusion-convection theory of solar modulation. Updates have been presented for both models [33, 34]. A review of historical development of CRÈME has been given by Barth and his co-workers [5]. An example of calculation of SEE rates can be found in Ref. [17].

Superimposed on the GCR background radiations are unpredictable solar energetic particles (SEPs) from solar flare and coronal mass ejection (CME) [5, 18]. Solar flares, accounting for a large part of all solar cosmic rays, are random in nature with higher frequency during solar maximum. These SEPs are similar to GCR particles, composed primarily of protons (90–95%), a minor proportion of alpha particles (5–10%), and some heavy ions and electrons [3]. The number of heavy ions is normally insignificant compared to the GCR heavy ions. In a large solar flare, the number of protons and alpha particles can be greatly enhanced (~10^4 times) over the background GCR spectrum, and the abundance of some heavy ions may increase rapidly (3–4 orders of magnitude) above the galactic background as well. These increases can persist from several hours to days [3].

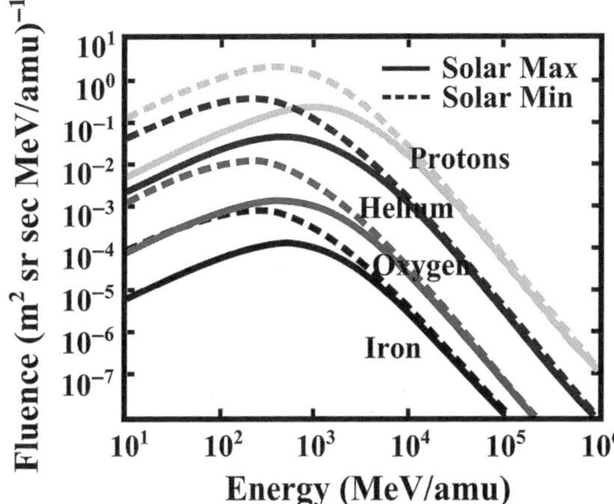

Figure 6. GCR energy spectra for protons, helium, oxygen and iron during solar maximum and solar minimum conditions. Adapted with permission from [18], S. Bourdarie and M. Xapsos, *IEEE Trans. Nucl. Sci.* 55, 1810 (2008). © 2008, IEEE.

The increase of heavy ion fluxes can cause SEE on spacecraft electronics. Typically, after a solar flare occurs, SEPs arrive near the earth within 10 s of minutes to several hours depending on their energy and point of origin on the sun. The peak intensity occurs within 2 hours to one day and decays within a few days to one week (except the ones trapped in the earth's radiation belts). A solar wind usually arrives near the earth within one to two days after a solar flare. As the solar wind strikes the magnetosphere, it can cause disturbances in the geomagnetic fields, compressing them towards the earth. Thus, the solar wind can enhance the total dose that a device receives in a low-earth orbit. Different models have been developed to predict the impact of the solar protons and heavy ions. Detail about the models can be found in Refs. [18, 32, 35].

2.2.2. Geomagnetic Shielding and Atmospheric Radiation Environment

2.2.2.1. Geomagnetic Shielding. The earth's magnetic field acts as an energy filter and provides significant protection from galactic or solar cosmic rays with less than given momentum values at certain altitudes and latitudes. Figure 7 [3] shows the total ion energy required to penetrate the magnetosphere in terms of the dipole parameter L (a dimensionless ratio of the earth's radius, approximately equal to the geocentric distance of a field line in the geomagnetic equator). The charged particles tend to follow the geomagnetic field lines. Near the equator the field lines tend to be parallel to the earth's surface. Thus most energetic ions are defected away [18]. Due to the field lines pointing toward the earth's surface in the polar regions, radiation particles can penetrate deeper.

2.2.2.2. Atmospheric Radiation Environment. As very highly energetic cosmic rays enter the upper atmosphere, they are attenuated through interactions with nitrogen and oxygen atoms in the atmosphere, producing a cosmic ray

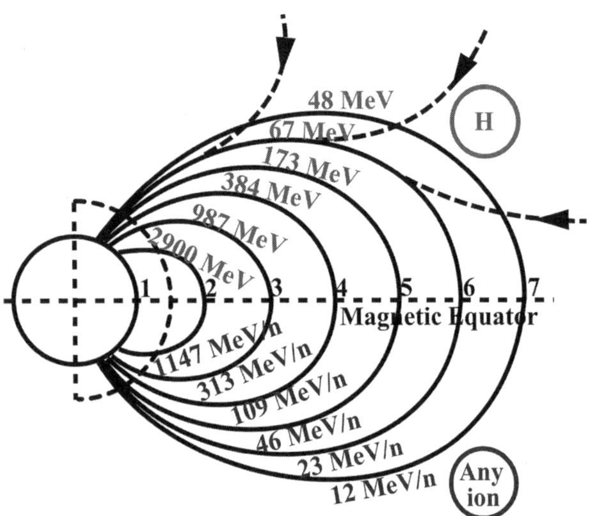

Figure 7. Total energy required to penetrate the magnetosphere. Adapted with permission from [3], E. G. Stassinopoulos and J. P. Raymond, *Proc. IEEE* 76, 1423 (1988). © 1988, IEEE.

shower of secondary particles that also go through the attenuation process. Products of the cosmic ray showers are protons, electrons, neutrons, heavy ions, muons, and pions. In terms of radiation effects in the atmosphere, the most important products are protons and neutrons. The fluxes of protons and neutrons have similar characteristics with respect to energy and altitude variation. Both types of particles have energies reach greater than 1 GeV and flux peak at about 20 km [5]. At the ground level, fluxes of protons and neutrons decreases to hundreds of times lower than peak flux.

2.3. Radiation Measurement

A dose is the amount of radiation energy exposed to or absorbed by a subject. Many radiation monitors measure exposure. The SI unit for exposure is coulomb/kilogram (C/kg), measuring the amount of radiation required to create 1 C of charge of each polarity in 1 kg of matter. The roentgen (R) is an older traditional unit which is almost obsolete, measuring the amount of radiation required to liberate 1 esu of charge of each polarity in 1 cm^3 of dry air and having the following relation Eq. (1):

$$1R = 2.58 \times 10^{-4}\ \mathrm{C/kg} \tag{1}$$

Flux, also known as fluence rate, is the number of particles passing through some defined zone per unit time. The unit of flux is $cm^{-2}\ s^{-1}$. Fluence, another term for radiation exposure dose, is the time-integrated flux of photons or particles with the unit cm^{-2}. As for the flux, the type of particle is also usually stated.

However, the amount of damage done to matter (especially living tissue) by ionizing radiation is more closely related to the amount of energy deposited rather than the charge. This is called the absorbed dose. Absorbed dose (also known as total ionizing dose, TID) is a measure of the energy deposited in a medium by ionizing radiation. The SI unit of radiation absorbed dose is J/kg, which is given the special name Gray (Gy), representing the amount of radiation required to deposit 1 joule of energy in 1 kilogram of any kind of matter.

The rad (radioactivity absorbed dose), is the corresponding traditional unit which is 0.01 J deposited per kg and thus has the relation Eq. (2):

$$100\ \mathrm{rad} = 1\ \mathrm{Gy} \tag{2}$$

As the rad is still an active working unit for most published papers in radiation effects and also for current medical practice, it is also used in this chapter even though Gray is the SI unit. From the definition, one can further describe rad(Si) or rad(SiO_2) for Si and SiO_2, respectively, where absorbed dose, D = fluence × stopping power of the reference material [36]. The stopping power of a material can be obtained by TRIM [37].

3. RADIATION EFFECTS ON ELECTRONIC DEVICES

The semiconductor devices are exposed to a radiation environment with a mix of particles and photons, where ionizing radiation effects cause anomalies and failures for different semiconductor components and circuits. The manner in which ionizing radiation interacts with solid materials depends on the type; kinetic energy; mass and charge state of the incoming particle; and the mass, atomic number, and density of the target material. This section reviews the fundamental ionizing radiation damage mechanisms in a semiconductor device, mainly including TID effects and SEE.

3.1. Total Ionizing Dose Effects

Particles passing through electronic materials deposit a major portion of their energy into materials causing ionization. The amount of energy for ionization that leads to electron–hole pair generation is commonly referred as TID. It is a cumulative long-term ionizing damage due to the interaction of high-energy photons or charged particles (mainly protons and electrons) with device materials [38, 39]. The TID effects include parametric failures (variations in device parameters such as leakage current, threshold voltage, etc.) and functional failures [40]. It is noted that photon-induced TID damage is initiated when electron–hole pairs are generated along the track of secondary electrons emitted via photon-material interactions [39]. Electron–hole pair formation is also an important energy loss mechanism for high-energy electron and ion irradiation in semiconductors or insulators, while it is of secondary importance for neutron exposures [2]. In polymers, the main result of ionization may be the breaking of chemical bonds and the creation of new ones [1]. Those generated electrons and holes with energies higher than the minimum energy required to create an electron–hole pair can generate additional electron–hole pairs. In this manner, a single, high enough energy incident photon, electron, or proton can create thousands or even millions of electron–hole pairs [38, 41].

The minimum energy required for creating an electron–hole pair, E_p, is dependent on the bandgap of the target material [39]. The number of electron–hole pairs generated for a given dose is thus strongly dependent on E_p, and the material density as well. E_p is given for different materials in Table 2, as well as the material densities (ρ) and initial electron–hole pair density generated per rad (k_g) [39, 42]. The latter quantity is obtained from the product of the material density and the deposited energy per rad (1 rad = 100 erg/g = 6.24 × 10^{13} eV/g) divided by E_p [38], i.e., the unit conversion of the above parameters is illustrated Eq. (3) [39]:

$$k_g\left[\frac{\#ep}{cm^3 rad}\right] = 100\left[\frac{erg}{g}\right]\left[\frac{1}{rad}\right]\frac{1}{1.6\times 10^{12}}\left[\frac{eV}{erg}\right] \times \frac{1}{E_p}\left[\frac{\#ep}{eV}\right]\rho\left[\frac{g}{cm^3}\right] \quad (3)$$

Table 2. Electron–hole pair generation energies and pair densities generated by one rad.

Material	Mean E_p (eV)	Density (g/cm^3)	Pair density, generated per rad, k_g (pairs/cm^3)
GaAs	~4.8	5.32	~7 × 10^{13}
Silicon	3.6	2.328	4.0 × 10^{13}
Silicon dioxide	17	2.2	8.1 × 10^{12}

Source: Reprinted with permission from [39], H. J. Barnaby, *IEEE Trans. Nucl. Sci.* 53, 3103 (2006).

The density of electron–hole pairs generated along the tracks of charged particles is proportional to the energy transferred to the target material. Stopping power or linear energy transfer (LET) corresponds to the energy loss per unit length of a particle (dE/dx) that is a function of the mass and energy of the particle, and the target material density [39]. LET has the units of MeV cm^2/g, as the energy loss per unit length of a particle is normalized by the density of the target material. Therefore, the amount of energy (TID) deposited in the material through ionizing interactions can be obtained from the LET function $(dE/dx)/\rho_m$ in MeV cm^2/g, where ρ_m is the density of the material, E the radiation energy, and dx is an elementary trajectory in the material. The LET function can be theoretically expressed by the following Eq. (4) [1, 2, 43]:

$$-\frac{dE}{dx} = 2Pq^4 Z_1^2 Z_2 N_{at}\frac{M_2}{m}\frac{1}{E}\ln\left(\frac{4E}{E_p}\right) \quad (4)$$

Z_1 and Z_2 are respectively the atomic charges of the incident particle and the target material, N_{at} is the atomic density of the target, M_2 the corresponding atomic mass, m and E are the mass and energy of the incident particles, E_p is the mean ionization energy (defined above), q is the electron charge in absolute value, and P the stopping number of the material. Figure 8 [39, 42] shows the stopping power versus particle energy for electrons and protons incident on Si. The absorbed dose is proportional to the integral of the product of the particle fluence and the stopping power over the specimen thickness [36, 42]. The software SRIM/TRIM developed by Ziegler and Biersack calculates the interactions of ions with matter, giving stopping power of different incident ions in different target materials, a distribution of the incident ions in the solid and its parameters (e.g., penetration depth), concentration of vacancies, ionization in the target material, energy deposition rate, etc.

3.2. Single Event Effects (SEE)

SEE have become a major concern for current electronics technology. As electronic components have become smaller in device geometry, lower in operating voltage, and higher in complexity, their sensitivity to SEE has increased [44–47]. When a highly energetic particle strikes sensitive regions of a microelectronic circuit and ionizes the target material along its path, a column of transient electron–hole pairs is created around the particle track. These induced free carriers eventually recombine in a field-free host medium. However, the recombination can be prevented by the intrinsic, strong, internal electric fields, which generate an electrical

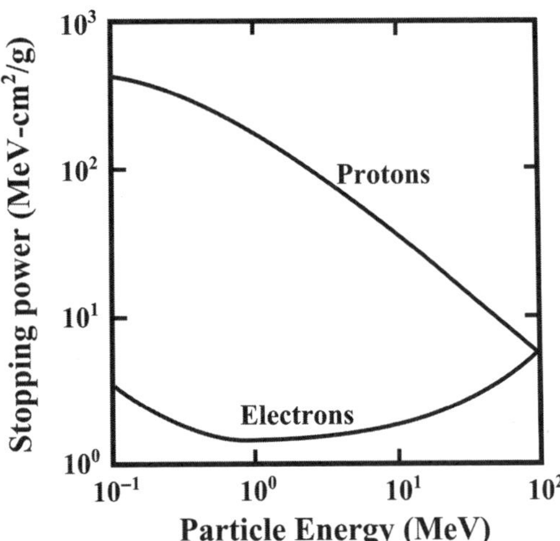

Figure 8. Stopping power for electrons and protons as a function of particle energy. Reprinted with permission from [39], H. J. Barnaby, *IEEE Trans. Nucl. Sci.* 53, 3103 (2006). © 2006, IEEE.

pulse large enough to result in a transient disruption of circuit operation, a change of logic state, or even permanent damage to the device or IC [45, 48]. An excellent overview of historical study of SEE has been given by Dodd and Massengill [45].

There are several known sources of SEE. The major sources for spacecraft or satellite electronics are space radiation including galactic and solar cosmic rays, and trapped particles, described previously [46, 48, 49]. In addition, SEE have to be considered in the atmospheric radiation environment and at the ground level due to α particle generation in packaging materials and because of cosmic ray secondaries, mainly neutrons and photons, as well as thermal neutrons [48, 50–54]. The sources of single event upset (the most common effect in SEEs) are reviewed by Tang and Rodbell [48]. It should be noted that shielding can be used to lower the dose level but is unable to deal with the SEE induced by very high-energy particles. SEE include a wide range of effects. A summary of different types of nondestructive and destructive SEE with corresponding potential sensitive devices or technology can be found in Ref. [49]. The following describes some of the SEEs:

(1) Single event upset (SEU) [48], also known as soft error, is a bit flip in a digital element. It can be induced by either direct ionization from a traversing particle or ionization produced by charged particles and recoil nucleus emitted from a nuclear reaction. These soft errors cause a reset or rewriting of the device with normal function thereafter. The most SEU sensitive digital ICs are very large-scale integration (VLSI) circuits, especially random access memories (RAM).

(2) Single event latchup (SEL) [55] is a low-impedance switching from high impedance for a parasitic *p–n–p–n* structure induced by local electron–hole pair generation. SEL may or may not cause permanent device damage, but it is one of the dominant failure effects of CMOS ICs.

(3) Single event transients (SET) [56, 57], also called digital SET (DSET), are momentary voltage or current disturbances in combinational logic in which a sensitive node is struck by an energetic particle. SETs do not cause an upset in the circuit but may propagate through subsequent circuitry and eventually cause an SEU when they reach a latch or other memory element.

(4) Single event burnout (SEB) can be triggered by the passing of a heavy ion through a MOSFET when biased in its off state. The transient current generated by the incident particles turns on the parasitic bipolar transistor inherent to the MOSFET structure, and a feedback mechanism then causes the second breakdown leading to catastrophic device failure [58, 59].

(5) Single event gate rupture (SEGR) [60] occurs when an energetic particle impinges on a device biased over a critical voltage, causing formation of a conductive path inside the gate oxide.

(6) Single event dielectric rupture (SEDR) will cause an anti-fuse rupture [61].

(7) Single event functional interrupt (SEFI) [62] is caused by a single ion strike, leading to a temporary nonfunctionality (or interruption of normal operation) of the device. SEFI may last if no power reset is done, or in some cases it may last for a finite but rather long time period.

Physical mechanisms responsible for SEE are charge deposition by the energetic particle strike and the subsequent collection of the charge by devices in the region of the particle strike [63]. The charge deposition by direct ionization (usually heavy ions) and indirect ionization (usually lighter particles such as protons and neutrons) can be modeled in the same way using LET [49, 63], energy loss per unit length (MeV/cm or MeV cm^2/g) of a particle as it passes through the target. This is also related to its charge deposition per unit path length (pC/μm). Predicting mission operation is supported by the SEE rate predictions. Models have been developed to describe the physical mechanisms and estimate the probability of the effects [64–73]. A review on physics-based simulation of SEE has been presented by Dodd [45, 63].

3.3. Radiation Effects on MOS Technology and Its Hardening

3.3.1. Radiation Effects on MOS Technology

3.3.1.1. Total Ionizing Dose Effects. Dielectric films with thickness of 2–1000 nm are key components in MOS devices and circuits for different purposes, such as gate oxide, electrical isolation, passivation layers, and spacers. Ionizing radiation can induce significant charge buildup in these dielectric films and at the dielectric film/silicon interfaces, leading to device degradation and failures. The mechanism of device degradation by TID for a *p*-MOS capacitor with a positive applied gate bias is depicted in Figure 9. First, *e–h* pairs are generated along the tracks of charged particles, followed by a prompt recombination of a fraction of the generated *e–h* pairs. The fraction of *e–h* pairs that escape recombination is called the *e–h* yield or charge yield. Electrons having a much higher mobility than holes in oxides will rapidly be swept out of the oxide, while the

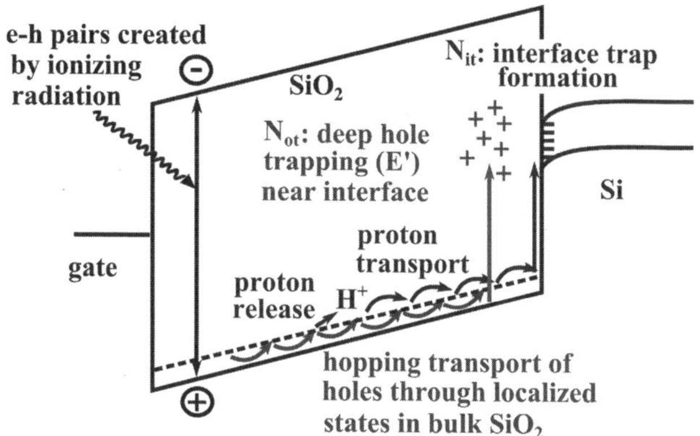

Figure 9. Band diagram of an MOS capacitor with a positive gate bias. Illustrated are the main process in TID damage. Adapted with permission from [39], H. J. Barnaby, *IEEE Trans. Nucl. Sci.* 53, 3103 (2006). © 2006, IEEE.

surviving holes will drift toward the Si/SiO_2 interface by hopping transport via shallow traps in the SiO_2. As the holes approach the interface, a fraction of them may be trapped in the oxide bulk or near the Si/SiO_2 interface, forming a positive oxide-trap charge. Simultaneously, hydrogen ions are likely released as holes and hop through the oxide or trapped near the Si/SiO_2 interface. Another type of ionization defect, positive charged interface traps, is formed when holes at the interface react with hydrogen-containing defects or dopant complexes. More mechanism details can be found in Refs. [39, 41, 74].

For both *n*- and *p*-MOS transistors, oxide-traps of holes are positive, causing negative V_t shifts (ΔV_{ot}). On the other hand, interface traps are positive and lead to negative V_t shifts (ΔV_{it}) for *p*-MOS transistors at threshold. For a *n*-type transistor at threshold, interface traps are dominantly negative, causing positive V_t shifts. The total V_t shift (ΔV_{th}) is the sum of the shifts due to oxide-traps and interface-traps, i.e.,

$$\Delta V_{th} = \Delta V_{ot} + \Delta V_{it}$$

In addition, the radiation-induced charge buildup in gate oxide can cause leakage current to flow in the OFF state/condition, increasing the static power supply current of an IC and potentially inducing an IC failure. The positive charge buildup in the field oxide and SOI buried oxide can cause leakage current through parasitic leakage paths in the transistor. As CMOS scales and the gate oxide thickness is below 6 nm, charge trapping problems in gate oxide, and therefore TID tolerance, are greatly improved, as the positive charges are easily neutralized by electrons tunneling from the gate and/or Si substrate. This leaves charge trapping in field oxide and SOI buried oxide as the primary TID concerns. Figure 10 gives the TID failure level trend for scaling CMOS technologies. The TID hardness has been enhanced from several tens krad(SiO_2) to today's 100–300 krad(SiO_2) for 0.13–0.25 μm CMOS technologies [54]. Another growing concern is particle microdose effects, the total dose effects caused by individual energetic particles. "Stuck bits" are a typical symptom, and they increase with particle fluence.

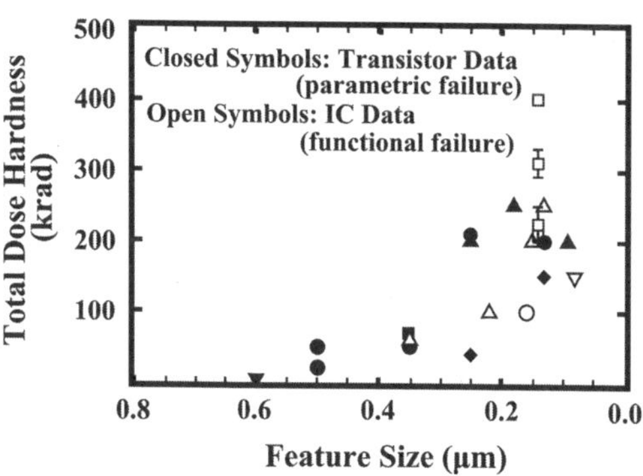

Figure 10. Total ionizing dose failure level scaling trend for digital CMOS technologies. Reprinted with permission from [54], P. E. Dodd et al., *IEEE Trans. Nucl. Sci.* 57, 1747 (2010). © 2010, IEEE.

3.3.1.2. Single Event Effects. As the amount of charge for storing information has continued to decrease, the sensitivity of CMOS devices to single-particle charge collection transients has increased. Figure 11 [54] gives the simulated SEU and SET scaling trends for bulk and SOI CMOS technologies. The threshold LET for both SEU and SET aggressively drops with scaling, and bulk CMOS technologies become sensitive to α particle-induced upsets below 0.25 μm (SOI technologies around 90 nm). Even on the ground level, the sensitivity to neutron induced soft errors has also increased with scaled feature size, as shown in Figure 12 [54] showing the soft error rate for CMOS SRAMs.

3.3.2. Radiation Hardening

It is fairly common knowledge that the fundamental microelectronic building blocks of ICs have been driven by Moore's law to become smaller, faster, and cheaper, allowing more capable computing architectures to become mainstream. Evidence has shown that as modern microelectronics scale down, a higher level of TID tolerance can be reached because of less hole trapping in the thinner oxide [41, 75, 76]. However, TID could also be worsened due to other factors associated with scaling [39, 77]. On the other hand, SEE has become a significant concern in modern

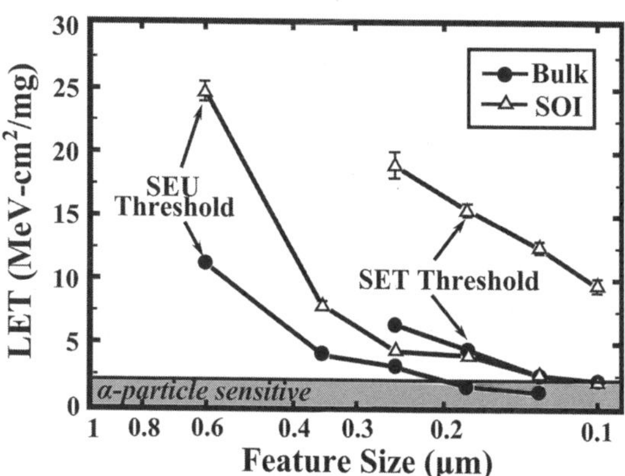

Figure 11. Simulated critical LET for unattenuated transient propagation and SEU threshold LET as a function of scaling for bulk and SOI CMOS technologies. Reprinted with permission from [54], P. E. Dodd et al., *IEEE Trans. Nucl. Sci.* 57, 1747 (2010). © 2010, IEEE.

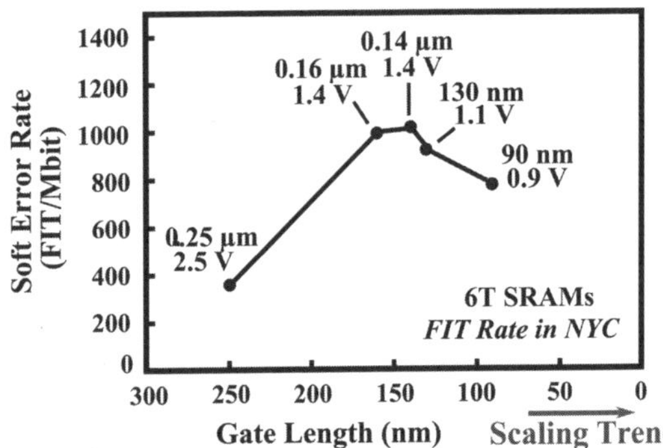

Figure 12. Measured terrestrial neutron SER scaling trend for CMOS SRAMs. Reprinted with permission from [54], P. E. Dodd et al., *IEEE Trans. Nucl. Sci.* 57, 1747 (2010). © 2010, IEEE.

advanced technologies. A lot of effort has been put into the radiation-hardening technology, such as "edgeless" transistor technology [54], hardness by design, layout and process [78–80], reoxide nitrided oxides (RNO) alternate dielectrics [41, 80], ion implantation into buried oxide layer [81], and new materials for radiation hardness such as compound oxides [82, 83].

As the details related to the basic mechanisms of radiation effects in microelectronics are very complicated, there are many radiation-hardening issues and assurance challenges. These include large variation of radiation effects response to different devices' parts [84]; different manufactures and processing; operating temperature, oxide impurities, devices geometry and IC complexities; final packaging processes; radiation conditions including dose, dose rate, and type of radiations; complexes in testing and data analysis; and error rate prediction; among others [54, 79]. In addition, there is no assurance that a given level of hardness is maintained over time [54, 79] since TID hardness is not a parameter that commercial manufacturers monitor.

For radiation-hardened microelectronics, in general, there is a big technology gap between state-of-the-art commercial microelectronics and radiation-hardened microelectronics. While 45-nm technologies have become commercially available today, the most advanced radiation-hardened ICs on the market based on custom processes are at the 150-nm level [54]. More work has to be done for the radiation hardening technology.

4. RADIATION STUDY FOR FLASH NVM

4.1. Introduction to Flash Memories: Storage Mechanism and Structure

Flash memories have been widely used in commercial products and have become the leader among non-volatile memory technologies due to their extremely high density, good retention properties, fast write and read operations, and a transparent user mode [85–87]. The basic structure of an industry-standard flash cell is given in Figure 13. A flash memory cell is based on a MOSFET with a polysilicon layer (floating gate [FG]) interposed between the control gate (CG) and the substrate. The FG is completely surrounded by dielectric oxide. The dielectric layer between the

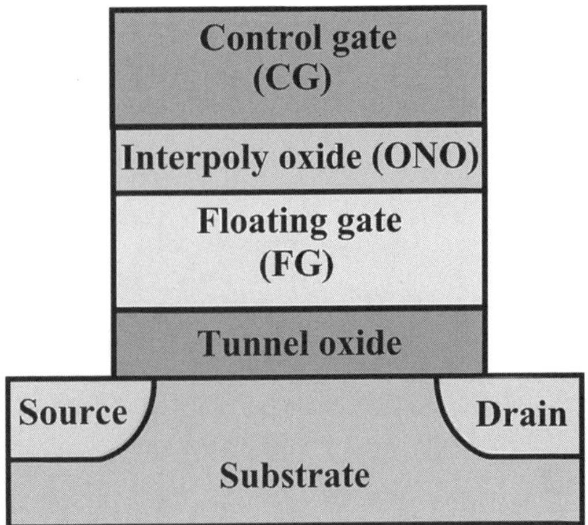

Figure 13. Cross-section of a FG memory cell.

CG and the FG is called interpoly oxide and usually consists of oxide/nitride/oxide (ONO). The layer separating the FG and the substrate is tunnel oxide. By using high electric fields, electrons or holes can pass through the tunnel oxide and can be transferred from or into the FG. As such, the FG can permanently store charges, and the number of charges can change the MOSFET threshold voltage V_{th}. In addition, more bits of information can be stored permanently in a flash memory cell by controlling the number of charges in the FG [88].

Typically, a FG cell is considered in its logical state of "0" (programmed) when it is loaded with charge. Otherwise it is in a logical state of "1" (erased) when charges are removed from FG. This configuration is known as single-level or one-bit-cell storage. To increase the storage density, multi-level storage techniques have also been proposed and commercialized [89, 90]. Figure 14 [90] shows threshold voltage distributions for single-level and multi-level flash memory cells. However, to implement multi-level storage, the control and verify circuitry as well as the programming circuits must have finer resolution for the narrower V_{th} limits.

The charge control on the FG involves two mechanisms: channel hot electron (CHE) injection and Fowler-Nordheim (FN) tunneling. CHE injection is realized when electrons traveling from the source to the drain gain enough energy from the lateral electric field, and a transverse electric field between channel and control gate injects carriers through the oxide. The FN tunneling starts when there is a high electric field through a thin oxide, resulting in electrons passing through the energy barrier itself. A good description of both charge control mechanisms can be found in Ref. [86].

There are two basic structures of flash memory devices, NOR and NAND architecture, as shown in Figure 15. The NOR structure (Fig. 15(a)) allows random access to individual cells, which reduces access time compared to NAND. This comes at the cost of cell areas due to the need for contacts at each drain and source connection [89–91]. For the NOR architecture, erasure is done at the block level through FN tunneling, achieved by applying high programming voltage (V_{pp}) to the source and grounding the CG with the drain floating, as illustrated in Figure 16 [91]. Programming is

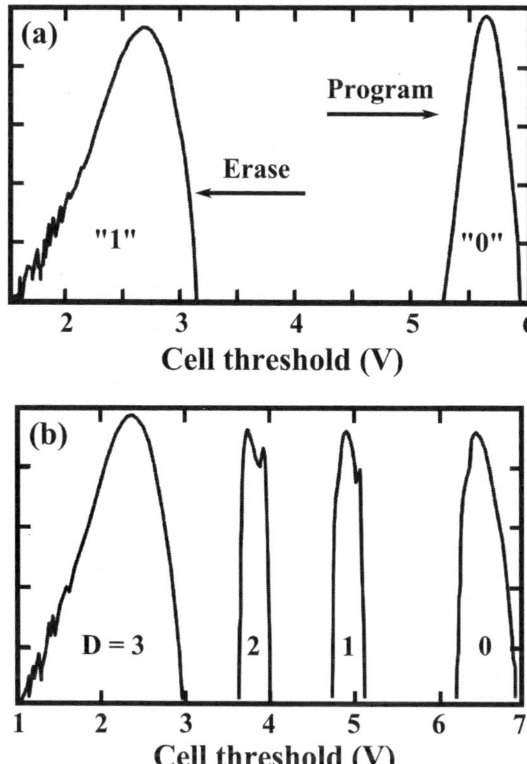

Figure 14. Cell threshold distribution. (a) Single level, (b) multiple level. Reprinted with permission from [90], D. N. Nguyen and L. Z. Scheick, "IEEE Radiation Effects Data Workshop," p. 18, Monterey, CA, 2003. © 2003, IEEE.

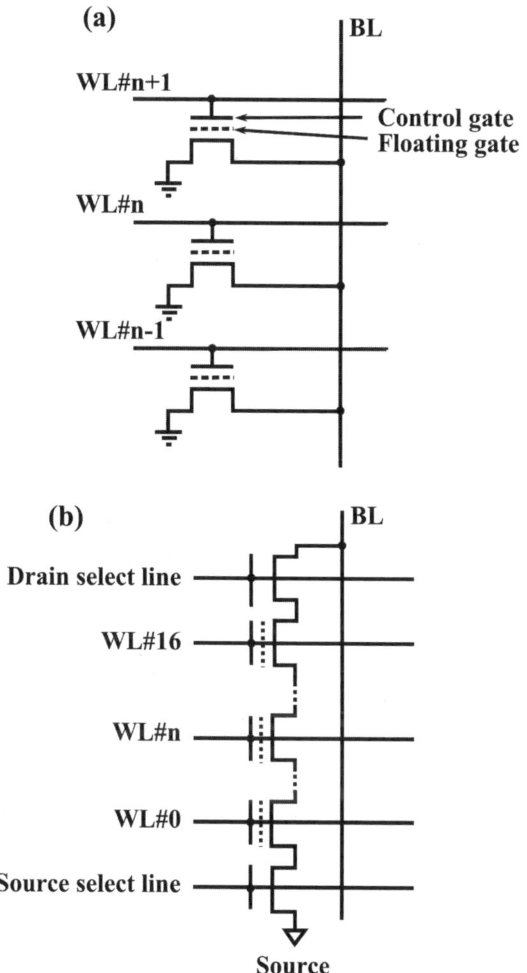

Figure 15. (a) NOR structure with drain and source connections; cells can be accessed directly. (b) NAND structure; cells can only be accessed serially.

performed through CHE injection by grounding the source and applying V_{pp} to the CG (seen in Fig. 16(b)). On the other hand, NAND structures, as seen in Figure 15(b), stack several cells in series with a common bitline, allowing a more compact cell structure compared to NOR. Both erasing and writing operations use FN tunneling, as represented in Figures 16(c and d). This gives more uniform charge transfer between its FG and the substrate [90, 92]. It should be noted that the programming voltage for NAND memory cells is 20 V for erase and write functions, while cells of NOR structure need 12 V for erase and write functions [91, 92]. Because of the high operation voltages, an internal charge pump generator is needed for both types of flash memories.

For space applications, radiation effects of flash memories have been investigated deeply by many researchers [88–90, 92–99]. A flash memory device is an array of FG cells controlled by an embedded state machine and a command state machine, logically organized in blocks and pages [100]. The control circuits including output buffers, charge pumps, and microprocessors have been proved to be the most sensitive part to both TID and SEE experiment. The radiation effects of flash cells have also been investigated, with models built.

For radiation testing for flash memories, different operating modes are usually used [101, 102]:

(1) Static-unbiased mode, in which a pattern is written and verified before exposure, and no bias is applied during the exposure. After exposure, errors are counted.

(2) Static-biased mode, similar to the static-unbiased mode except that bias is maintained during the exposure.

(3) Dynamic read, in which a pattern is written to memory and verified before irradiation, then the pattern is read continuously during irradiation, and errors are counted.

(4) Dynamic read/write, where the initial pattern is continuously read and rewritten during irradiation, and errors are counted.

(5) Dynamic read/erase/write, similar to the dynamic read and read/write, except that a word in error was first erased and then rewritten.

4.2. TID Effects on Flash Memories

Several studies on flash performance under TID experiments have been reported (Refs. [89, 90, 92, 100, 103]). It should be noted that the test results of the commercial devices under radiation are based on the digital outputs and on device parameters available in the user mode. The detailed storage information is inaccessible to the final

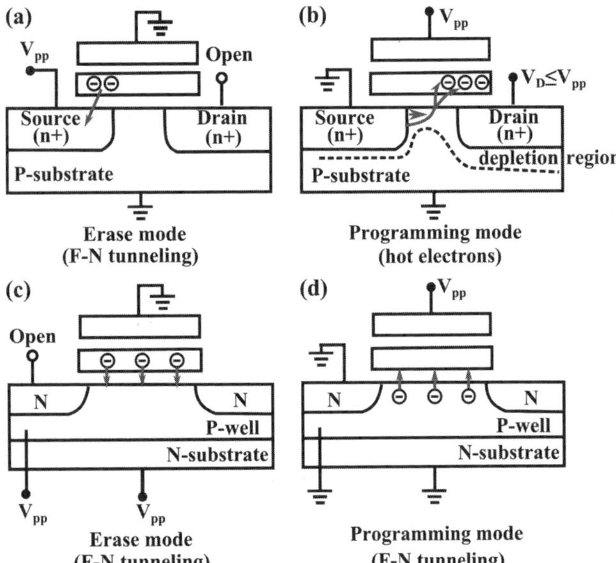

Figure 16. (a) Erase mode and (b) programming mode for NOR flash structures. (c) Erase mode and (d) programming mode for NAND flash structure. Adapted with permission from [91], H. R. Schwartz et al., *IEEE Trans. Nucl. Sci.* 44, 2315 (1997). © 1997, IEEE.

testers due to the confidential information of the DUT of commercial devices. From these reports, the control circuitry has been demonstrated to be the most radiation-sensitive part of commercial devices. In the reports of Nguyen and Johnston [103], the Intel NOR and Samsung NAND devices were tested in erase/write/read (EWR) mode after irradiation in a Static-biased mode with Co-60 at room temperature. During the electrical measurement, the charge pumps are always activated for the Samsung devices to boost its internal supply V_{pp} to 20 V. For the Intel devices, the charge pumps are activated or disabled according to two different voltage conditions. When $V_{dd} = 3.3$ V, $V_{pp} = 5.0$ V, charge pumps are activated; and when $V_{dd} = 5$ V, $V_{pp} = 12$ V, charge pumps are disabled. They found the Samsung devices (with charge pump activated) functionally failed at 10 krad(Si). The Intel devices with the charge pump on failed at 25 krad(Si), while with the charge pump disabled, they worked well at 50 krad(Si) and showed much higher failure level, as presented in Figure 17 [103]. It indicates that the charge pump is the main reason for the failure induced by radiation.

It was also indicated by Nguyen and Johnston that charge pump affects the erase time, as shown in Figure 18 [103]. When activating the charge pump, the erase time increases rapidly at a dose of about 5 krad(Si). However, when disabling the charge pump, the erase time stays stable, even after 30 krad(Si). Figure 19 gives the TID result on 128 Mb Samsung devices in terms of stand-by current under different bias and operation conditions [89]. In the "read" mode, the standby current increased dramatically after biased irradiation at less than 20 krad(Si), while it gradually increases after unbiased irradiation with only a small number of "read" errors up to 100 krad(Si). In the EWR mode, erase mode failure occurs after bias irradiation at 8 krad(Si) and at 45 krad(Si) under unbiased irradiation. This phenomenon was attributed to the radiation-induced threshold voltage

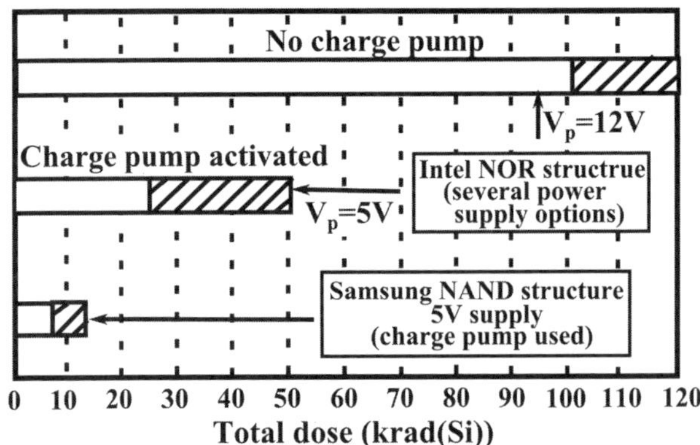

Figure 17. TID failure levels for flash memories in erase/write/read mode. Reprinted with permission from [103], D. N. Nguyen et al., "IEEE Radiation Effects Data Workshop," p. 100, Newport Beach, CA, 1998. © 1998, IEEE.

shifts in the p-MOS transistors in the charge pump circuitry which further reduce V_{out} [89, 103]. The charge pump circuit can be seen in Figure 20 [89]. The different TID failure doses under different operating modes are due to the fact that voltage needed for erasing NAND devices is higher than that for programming, which is further higher than that for reading. Note that charge pumps are not the only radiation sensitive block. Testing errors of devices were also found in the peripheral circuits for page address, output buffers, etc. [87, 102, 104, 105].

On the other hand, ionizing radiation effects on FG arrays, another major part in flash memory devices, have also been investigated during the past years [85, 87, 88, 93, 97, 105–108]. The first model was given by Snyder and co-authors in 1989 for charge loss from FGs [106]. The model considers three contributions, as shown in Figure 21 [106]. Briefly, after radiation, electron–hole pairs are generated in the oxides surrounding the FG. A fraction of them recombine, depending on the oxide electric field. The electrons surviving recombination are quickly swept away from the oxide due to their high mobility, whereas the remaining holes slowly drift toward the FG under the oxide electric

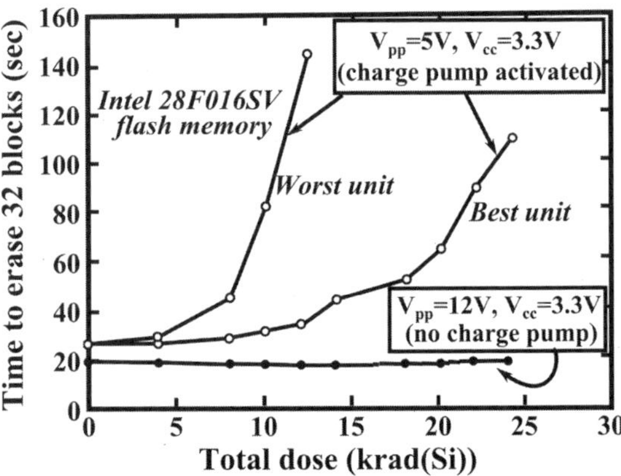

Figure 18. Evolution of the time to erase 32 blocks in an Intel NOR device as a function of the dose. Reprinted with permission from [103], D. N. Nguyen et al., "IEEE Radiation Effects Data Workshop," p. 100, Newport Beach, CA, 1998. © 1998, IEEE.

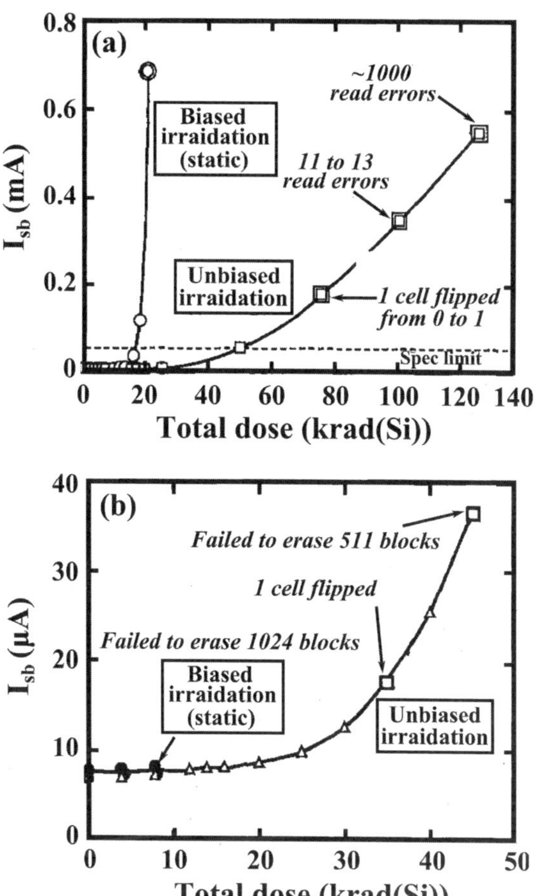

Figure 19. Total dose test results for the 128 Mb Samsung flash device, tested in (a) read mode, and (b) erase/write/read mode. Reprinted with permission from [89], D. N. Nguyen et al., *IEEE Trans. Nucl. Sci.* 46, 1744 (1999). © 1999, IEEE.

field and may be injected into the FG, where they recombine part of the stored electrons (first contribution in Fig. 21(a)). The remaining holes may also be trapped in the oxide (second contribution in Fig. 21(a)). The third contribution is

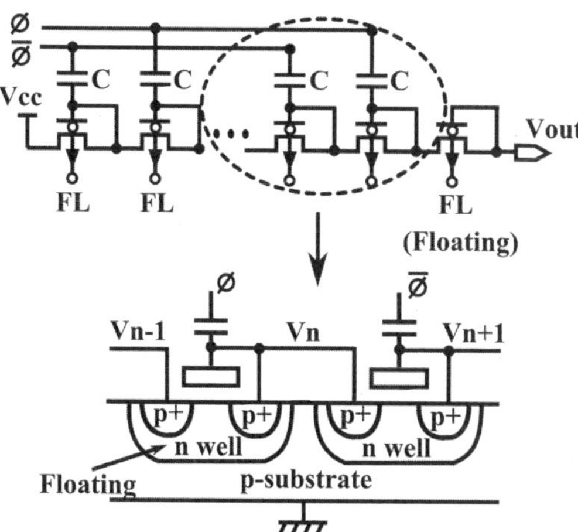

Figure 20. Samsung flash memory charge pump circuit. Reprinted with permission from [89], D. N. Nguyen et al., *IEEE Trans. Nucl. Sci.* 46, 1744 (1999). © 1999, IEEE.

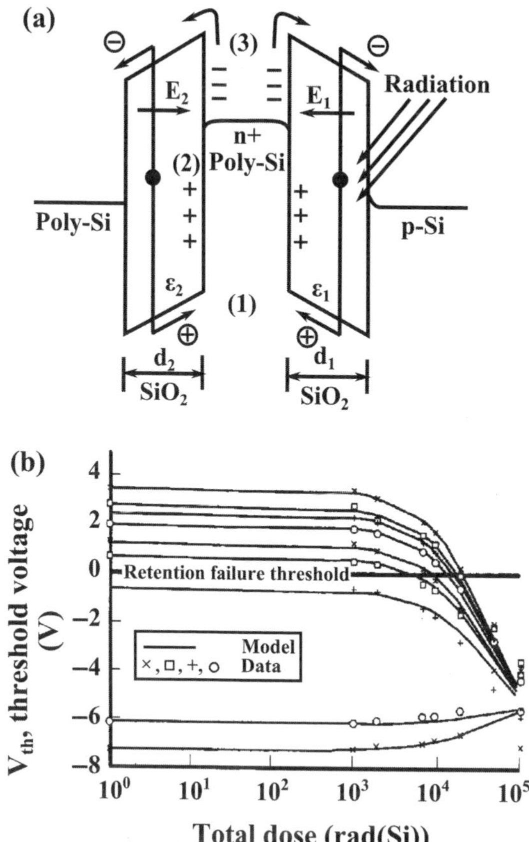

Figure 21. (a) Energy band diagram of the FG when programmed into the excess electron or logic "1". (b) Threshold voltage shifts as a function of total dose. Reprinted with permission from [106], E. S. Snyder et al., *IEEE Trans. Nucl. Sci.* 36, 2131 (1989). © 1989, IEEE.

electron emission, in which the stored electrons escape from the FG when they gain enough energy from the incoming radiation to jump over the oxide barrier. After which, they are quickly swept away by the oxide electric field. All the contributions result in a reduction of the threshold voltage V_{th}. On the other hand, for the erased state when the FG is occupied by holes, the oxide electric fields point in the opposite direction from the programmed state with FG stored with electrons. The electrons generated by irradiation will be injected into the FG, increasing the threshold voltage. This model has been demonstrated to be sufficient to describe experimental data, as shown in Figure 21(b), where the experimental data agrees well with the modeling lines. The size of the window separating the "1" from the "0" states is reduced as TID increases after 1 krad.

In state-of-the-art FG technologies improvement featuring highly scaled size, several aspects have to be considered in the model, including border effects, lateral dimensions of FGs, and the complex ONO sandwich interpoly dielectric [85, 87, 107]. Cellere and co-authors have confirmed that the general ideas of the model are still good to describe charge loss from FGs in the modern flash memories [85, 87, 107]. Based on the Snyder's model and considering the above-mentioned aspects in modern FG technologies, they also proposed a more accurate model, identifying the significance of electron emission mechanism in comparison to charge generation/recombination mechanism [107]. In this model, a multiple ONO stack is used, as shown in Figure 22(a). In terms of charge generation/recombination mechanism, charge trapping in defects is neglected as a first-order approximation in thin oxides (< 10 nm). Secondly, the recombination, thermalization, and electron transit times occur at the same time in thin oxide. In ONO dielectric, only charges generated in the two SiO_2 layers are considered since the charge yield in the nitride is almost 0. Since the height of the FG is comparable with the horizontal ones in modern technologies and the thickness of bottom oxide is comparable with that of the tunnel oxide, holes generated in the bottom SiO_2 can be three times as much as those generated in the tunnel oxide. However, the difference in charge yield is not large, especially when the electric field is larger than 1.5 MV/cm as the charge yield in the bottom SiO_2 layer is lower than that in the tunnel oxide. On the other hand, holes surviving recombination in the top SiO_2 layer are injected into the nitride layer, as well as electrons surviving recombination in the bottom SiO_2 layer, which will be trapped at the interface of nitride and bottom SiO_2. The net charge is 0 if the bottom and top SiO_2 layers have the same thickness. Figure 22(b) [87] shows the charge loss from FG as a function of dose, indicating that charge loss by the top SiO_2 layer is negligible compared to that by the bottom SiO_2 and tunnel oxides. It also shows that the charge loss by the bottom SiO_2 is larger than that by the tunnel oxide. Note that the curve overestimates the charge loss at high dose, as it considers constant oxide electric fields and neglects border effects and electron emission. In terms of electron emission, the number of electrons emitted per unit dose is considered to be linearly dependent on the e_c parameter, accounting for electrons injected from the FG into both the tunnel oxide and ONO.

Using this model, Figure 23(a) [107] gives the comparison of the experimental average values of the V_{th} with the simulated ones as a function of dose, indicating that electron emission has to be considered, especially at high doses. In addition, as the photoemission happens mainly at the surface normal to the incident radiation. Therefore smaller FG results in smaller photoemission, that is, FG devices with smaller gates are less sensitive to TID effects (seen from Fig. 23(b) [107]).

With the same model, Cellere and co-authors have investigated the effects of different TID sources (X-rays, Co-60 γ rays, and protons) on charge loss from FGs, and found out that charge loss from FG when irradiated with X-rays is larger than that when irradiated with γ rays [85, 88], as shown in Figure 24(a) [88]. This phenomenon is attributed

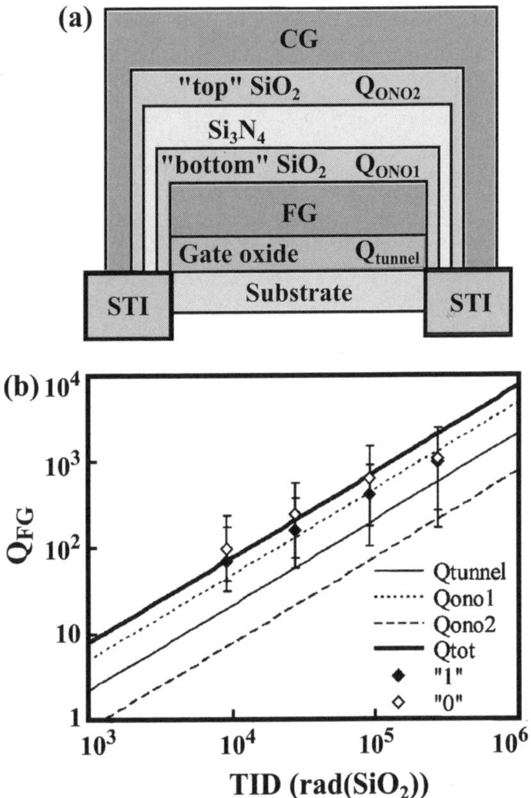

Figure 22. (a) Cross-section of a flash cell with ONO sandwich interpoly dielectric. (b) Calculated (lines) and experimental (points) number of electrons (or holes) lost from FG as a function of dose. Closed symbols: "0," open symbols: "1," error bars are distributions 0.1 and 99.9% values. Reprinted with permission from [87], G. Cellere et al., *IEEE Trans. Nucl. Sci.* 51, 2912 (2004). © 2004, IEEE.

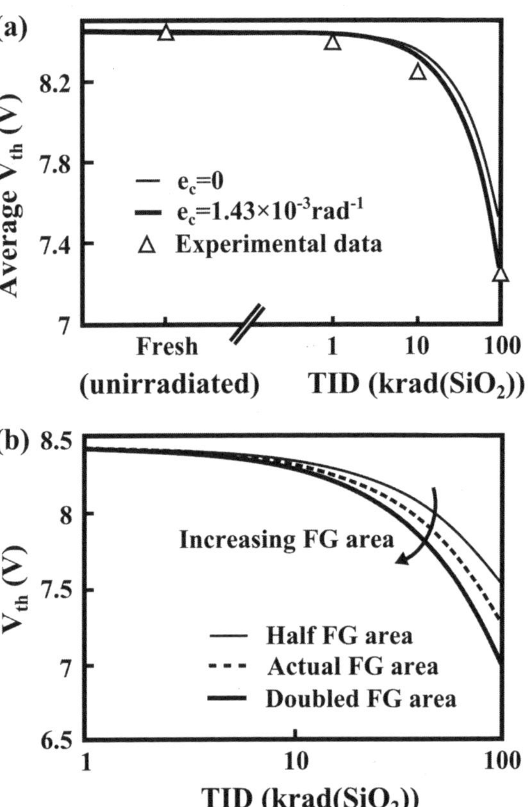

Figure 23. (a) Average value of threshold voltage for devices as a function of total dose (symbols) compared to model results. The thin line corresponds to $e_c = 0$ (no photoemission from FG), while thick line corresponds to calculations using an e_c value. (b) Simulated threshold voltage shift as a function of total dose for different FG area values, demonstrating that devices with lower FG area is less sensitive to TID effects. Reprinted with permission from [107], G. Cellere et al., *IEEE Trans. Nucl. Sci.* 51, 3753 (2004). © 2004, IEEE.

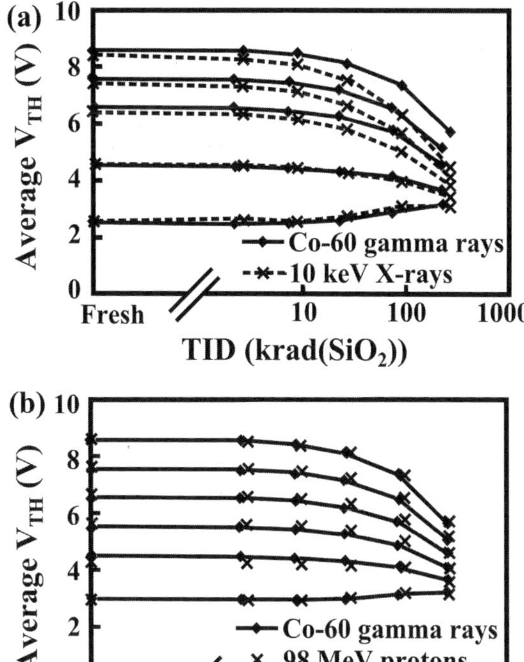

Figure 24. (a) Average threshold voltage of FG cells irradiated with 10 keV X rays and with ^{60}Co γ-rays as a function of total dose. (b) Average threshold voltage of FG cells irradiated with 98 MeV protons and with ^{60}Co γ-rays as a function of total dose. Reprinted with permission from [88], G. Cellere et al., *IEEE Trans. Nucl. Sci.* 54, 1066 (2007). © 2007, IEEE.

to the dose enhancement for lower energy X-rays [85, 88]. Also, charge loss is independent of dose rate in the range of 3–340 rad(SiO_2)/s. For proton irradiation, V_{th} shift is almost independent of the particle energy [88]. For high-energy-proton irradiation, as well as for high-energy-photon irradiation, the charge generation/recombination/transport mechanism largely dominates over electron emission. Thus the evolution of V_{th} according to total dose of protons is almost identical with that of γ rays, as shown in Figure 24(b). Neither of them have dose enhancement effects [88].

Experimental results shows that radiation exposure to a Co-60 source has little effect on the endurance of flash memories under failure level [109], as also predicted by a model based on hole and electron traps. The annealing effect was also checked in Ref. [109], which shows the V_{th} shift had partially recovered but not all the way back to the pre-stress distribution. On this annealing effect, Bagatin and co-authors have proved the error reduction by annealing by investigating the evolution of V_{th} shifts (due to the irradiated FG arrays) in flash memories with both NAND and NOR cells after TID exposure to 10 keV X-ray and 4.2 MeV protons [105]. They concluded that V_{th} shifts of FG cells are due to a combination of charge loss and positive charge trapping in the oxides surrounding FGs, where charge loss gives a permanent V_{th} shift, and charge trapping results in a V_{th} shift recovery because of charge detrapping and neutralization. Studies of the temperature affects after irradiation demonstrate that the number of errors can be modified by operating temperature, and thus accelerated tests may significantly overestimate the error rate in real operating conditions [98, 105, 109]. Claeys et al. have also studied the annealing effects on flash memories irradiated by 1 MeV electrons, 20 MeV protons, and α particles at different temperatures [98]. The findings indicate that *in situ* annealing of the radiation-induced charges or defects may occur during elevated temperature irradiation. Room temperature irradiation is the worst case in terms of the performance parameters; however, they can be recovered by post-radiation annealing.

In the end, TID sensitivity of NAND flash memory building blocks include charge pumps, row-decoders, and FG arrays [93]. It has been found that as TID builds up, read errors show up first due to charge loss and charge trapping in the FG cell, and afterward due to charge pump output voltage reduction, and finally due to row decoder failure, which reveals a difficulty in radiation-hard technology.

4.3. SEE on Flash Memories

Several works have been done with the SEE by heavy ions on flash memories [89–92, 100, 110], where once again the internal complex architecture of flash memories were found to be the most sensitive part. Schwartz et al. [91] revealed that upsets occurred in either controllers, registers, or state machines; and that the threshold LET was around 7 MeV cm^2/mg and the cross-section for functional errors was 10^{-7}~10^{-6} cm^2 for Intel NOR devices. Note that the minimum value above which SEEs are detected is defined as "threshold LET," while cross-section is a measure of the susceptibility of a complex device to SEE, defined as a ratio of the number of errors to the fluence needed to induce them.

Recoverable and complex errors with corresponding recovery methods are listed in Table 3 [91], and no permanent errors were found except catastrophic failure caused by abrupt high power supply currents. For Samsung NAND devices, similar types of complex errors were observed. Due to different architecture, different types of functional errors occurred, as shown in Table 4 [91], in which stuck bits were attributed to ionization damage. The cross-section for these errors was on the order of 10^{-6} cm^2. Fortunately, no errors were ever observed in all devices irradiated in static-unbiased mode, which is the nonvolatile nature of these devices with infrequent reading or writing operations.

Nguyen et al. [89] confirmed the functional failures caused by upsets in the very complex control and state registers, as well as the catastrophic failures in EWR mode. In particular, SEUs in page buffers during irradiation were observed, as indicated in Figure 25 for Samsung 128 Mb NAND structure with a threshold LET 6 MeV-cm^2/mg. Noticeably, a new finding of small numbers of cell state transitions at high LET were found for multi-level flash memory devices. Cross sections of other error types for Samsung NAND and Toshiba NAND were also reported, as shown in Figure 26 [100].

Thresholds between 5 and 12 MeV-cm^2/mg were reported for SEU and SEFI due to the control circuitry in advanced 1 Gb Toshiba NAND flash memories [110] irradiated by a

Table 3. Functional error modes observed for flash memories irradiated in static mode.

Error type	Description	Recovery method
Block clear lockup	Block clear complete status never appears	Power cycling
False block clear	One or more blocks show block clear, even though they are not cleared	Power cycling
Slow block clear	Many passes are required to establish block clear for one or more clocks	Wait (power cycling not req.)
Row/column changes	Large portions of the memory array change state within a short time period, accompanied by block clear lockup	Power cycling
Slow first address programming	After successful block clear, the first address takes many passes and a long time to complete. Subsequent addresses work OK.	Wait
Read lockup	Status bits indicate internal modes and instructions are active, when device is expected to be in the ready state	Power cycling
Write lockup	DATA WRITE status bit stuck in write-error mode during write sequence	Power cycling

Source: Reprinted with permission from [91], H. R. Schwartz et al., *IEEE Trans. Nucl. Sci.* 44, 2315 (1997). © 1997, IEEE.

Co-60 source in static mode. However, during dynamic testing, destructive SEFI were seen. SEL was also found with the threshold LET between 43 and 53 MeV-cm^2/mg when irradiated at 80°C. For Samsung 4 Gb NAND flash memory, Oldhman et al. found results are similar in all test modes, but the SEFI and destructive error cross-sections are orders of magnitude less than the bit upset cross-section, as seen in Figure 27 [101]. In addition, no SEL is found even at temperature up to 70°C. Note that in this study, bit errors

Table 4. Examples of functional errors in the Samsung 16-Mb flash memory.

Error type	Description	Recovery method
Row or column flips	Same values appear in multiple locations for the same bit position	Reinitialize and rewrite
Lockups (self clearing)	Inability to progress beyond read, write, or block clear modes	Reprogramming (EWR); power cycling not required
Lockups (non-clearing)	Inability to exit read, write, or block clear modes	Power cycling followed by reprogramming
Stuck bits	Small number of bits permanently altered	None (permanent effect)

Source: Reprinted with permission from [91], H. R. Schwartz et al., *IEEE Trans. Nucl. Sci.* 44, 2315 (1997). © 1997, IEEE.

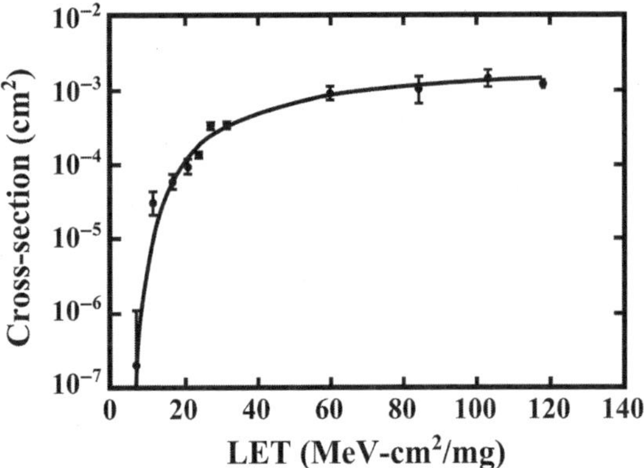

Figure 25. SEU cross-section for the 528-byte buffer register of the Samsung 128 Mb flash memory. Reprinted with permission from [89], D. N. Nguyen et al., *IEEE Trans. Nucl. Sci.* 46, 1744 (1999). © 1999, IEEE.

(DUT32, 33, 34) were normalized per device in order to compare them with SEFI. Later, they also reported that the 4G NAND flash memories from Samsung have good bit error rate, but failed more often at high temperature (70°C) when parts irradiated with high LET ions in the *R*/*E*/*W* test mode [111]. An angular dependence study shows that all the high-temperature failures were at normal incidence, which, together with temperature dependence, was still not well understood. As a fact, in advanced flash memories being scaled, one would expect the SEU cross-section to shrink.

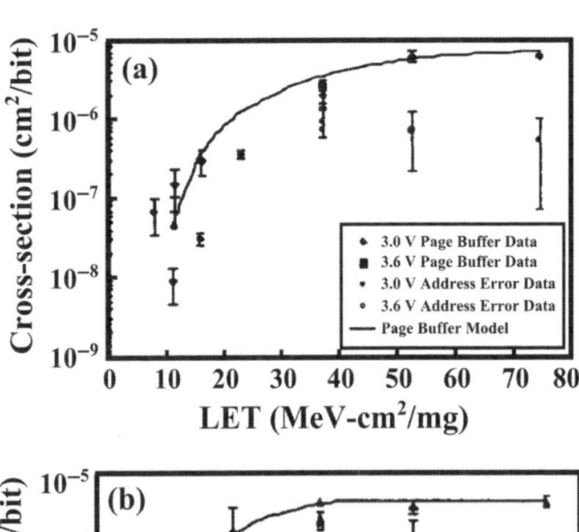

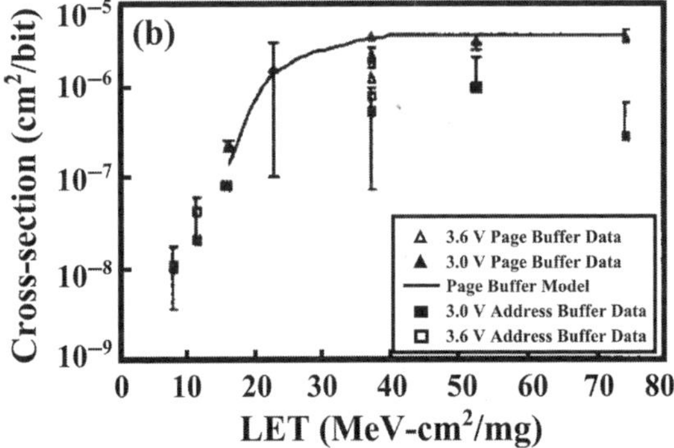

Figure 26. (a) Samsung page and address error cross-section curves. (b) Toshiba page and address error cross-section curves. Reprinted with permission from [100], D. R. Roth et al., "IEEE Radiation Effects Data Workshop," p. 96, Reno, NV, 2000. © 2000, IEEE.

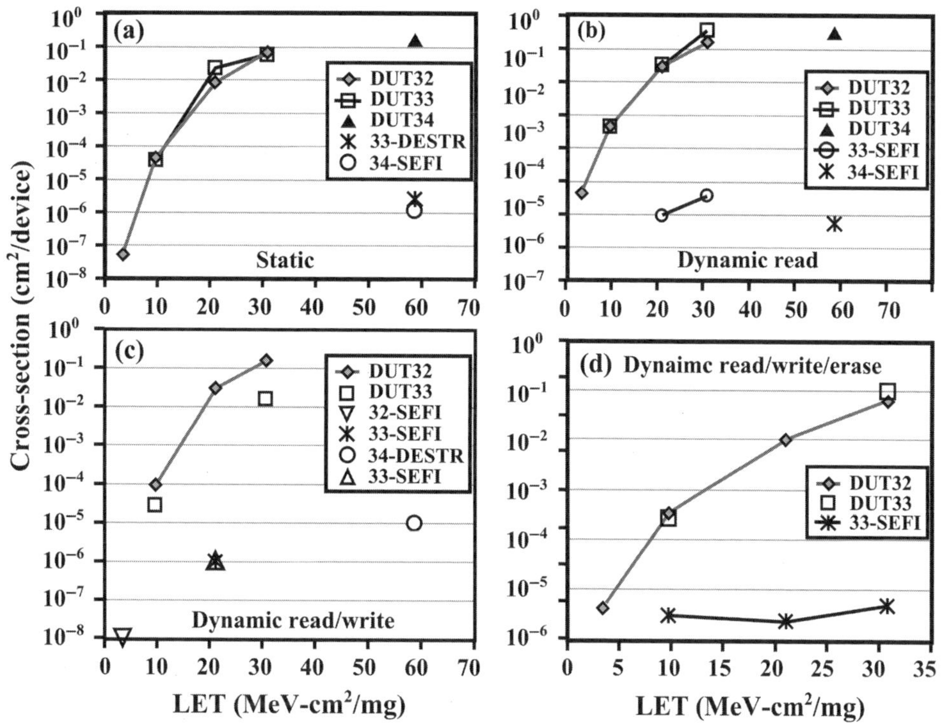

Figure 27. (a) Measured static error cross section, (b) dynamic read upset cross-section, (c) error cross-sections observed in dynamic read/write testing, (d) error cross-sections observed in dynamic read/write/erase testing. Reprinted with permission from [101], T. R. Oldham et al.,"IEEE Radiation Effects Data Workshop," p. 221, Honolulu, HI, 2007. © 2007, IEEE.

By investigating NAND and NOR advanced high-density flash memories from different companies, Irom and Nguyen concluded that the SEU and SEFI cross-section is smaller than the older generation of flash memories [112]. However, functional failures caused by upsets in complex controls and state registers continue to occur [112]. They also observed catastrophic failures in NOR flash, including charge pump failures, and the high current spikes in NAND flashes associated with micro-dose effects. These may become a serious problem as scaling continues and the transistor sizes become comparable to ion track widths.

Although the complex control circuitry has been proved to be very sensitive to ionization radiation, due to the progressive scaling of FGs, the impact from a single ion striking FG arrays has become a concern recently [94, 96, 102, 104, 108, 113–119] and have been modeled [97, 114, 120, 121]. SEUs in both the FG arrays and the page buffers were reported in a modern 1 Gb NAND flash device irradiated by heavy ions, besides SEFIs in the control circuitry [94]. Read errors in devices irradiated in an unbiased testing mode and the reduced retention capability were also reported as a result of charges being leaked out of the FGs of 2-Gb NAND flash memory devices [113]. As shown in Figure 28(a) [97], Cellere et al. associated the tail at lower voltages (negative V_{th} shift comparing to the V_{th} curve pre-radiation) for NOR flash arrays irradiated by I (effective LET ~ 62 MeV cm^2/mg, flux ~ 40 k ions/cm^2 s) to the charge loss caused by one or more ions hitting a FG cell. This induces a local excess of positive charge, lowering the tunnel oxide barrier and enhancing the tunneling current/radiation induced leakage current (RILC). Figure 28(b) shows a secondary peak corresponding to cells hit by single ions. The distance between the main and the secondary peak represents the average V_{th} shift because of the charge loss caused by impact [95, 118, 119]. RILC was further studied by Cellere and co-authors [96, 114, 118, 119], and an accurate model for the charge loss was established, based on phonon trap assisted tunneling. Figure 29(a) shows the tail increasing over time [114, 119]. They attributed it to the charge loss through a local conductive path made by several defects created by heavy-ion irradiation. As given in Figure 29(b), the oxide leakage current grows with the ion LET, as an ion with higher LET can induce more oxide defects and a denser defect track in tunnel oxide in advanced flash technologies using ONO interpoly. Angular dependence of radiation beam indicates that charge loss is smaller for higher beam inclination due to the tilted irradiation, resulting in a longer path across the oxide and therefore lower tunneling probability and smaller leakage current (seen in Fig. 30) [119]. Further details on angular dependence of heavy ions effects in FGs is discussed in Ref. [108].

As a matter of a fact, charge loss is an intrinsic behavior, and V_{th} shift grows not only with ion LET but also with applied electric field across the tunnel oxide [96]. In advanced technologies with very small FGs, single heavy ions can indirectly cause charge loss from FGs even if they do not impact the gate, although the mechanism is not fully understood yet [118]. Finally, Cellere et al. reported that the charge loss from FG arrays is smaller when irradiated with higher energy ions due to the formation of a larger volume of ion tracks by those ions [115]. Therefore, while

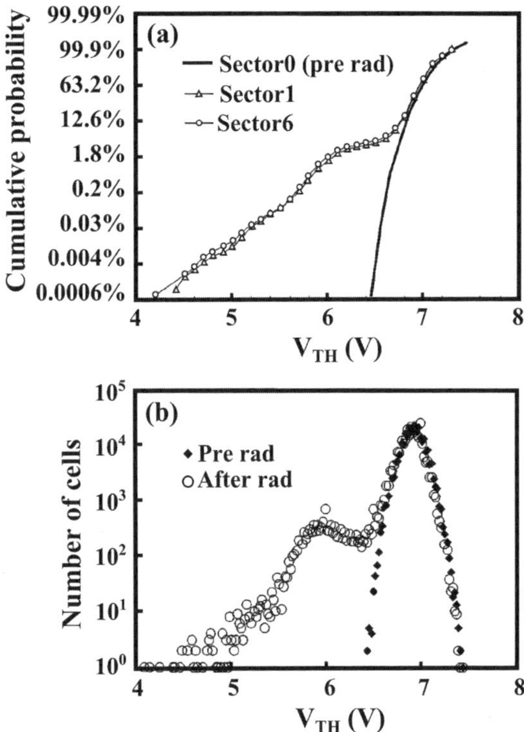

Figure 28. (a) Cumulative distributions of V_{th} for exposed areas of Sector1 and Sector6 of the device after 2×10^7 iodine ions/cm^2. (b) Probability density of threshold voltages for Sector6 before and after irradiation with 2×10^7 iodine ions/cm^2. Reprinted with permission from [97], G. Cellere et al., *IEEE Trans. Nucl. Sci.* 48, 2222 (2001). © 2001, IEEE.

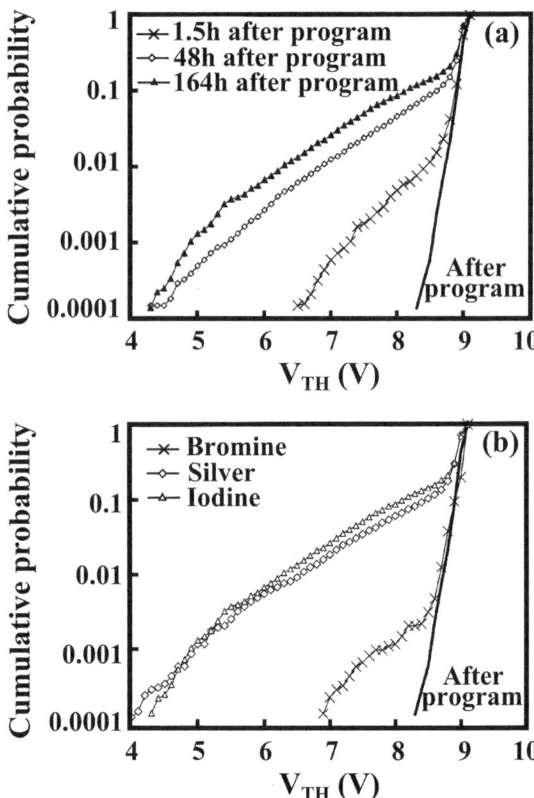

Figure 29. (a) Cumulative distribution of V_{th} for device cells hit by iodine ions after being re-programmed. (b) Cumulative probability of V_{th} for device cells being hit by different ions of bromine (LET = 41 MeV-cm^2/mg), silver (LET = 57 MeV-cm^2/mg), and iodine (LET = 64 MeV-cm^2/mg), immediately after program, and 164 hours after program. Reprinted with permission from [119], G. Cellere et al., *IEEE Trans. Nucl. Sci.* 52, 2144 (2005). © 2005, IEEE.

increasing LET leads to increasing charge loss, the larger energy smoothens and reduces the charge loss increase. Furthermore, titled irradiation with very high energy ions that have larger penetration depth can result in charge loss from multiple or even tens of FGs in highly scaled flash memories [108, 115].

Recently, a new physics-based model, the Transient Carrier Flux (TCF) model, has been proposed by Butt and Alam [120]. A dense cluster of hot electron–hole pairs is generated after a particle strike, with carriers having broad energy distributions which relax back to thermal equilibrium in ~1 psec. The net flux of hot carriers passing over the oxide barriers within ~psec at the FG/oxide interfaces is the dominant mechanism of FG charge loss in a single event strike. Figure 31(a) illustrates the TCF model, showing the energy band profiles of conduction and valence bands along the vertical axis of the FG cell through the gate stack in the programmed state, as well as the energy distributions of the generated electrons and holes in FG, CG, and substrate regions shortly after the strike. The tail of the high energy distribution results in a transient carrier flux into and out of the FG over the tunnel and interpoly oxides. The oxide electrical field E_{ox} in the programmed state favors the flow of electrons out of the FG (represented by the arrows), causing a net loss in the stored FG electrons. Figures 31(b–d) are the simulated results, fitting reasonably well to the experimental results. Figure 31(b) shows the number of electron stored in NAND flash cell (circles) and charge loss tolerance as a function of FG technology design rule, indicating the stored charge and the loss tolerance rapidly reduce with cell scaling which greatly increases the SEU sensitivity of the cells. Figure 31(c) gives the number

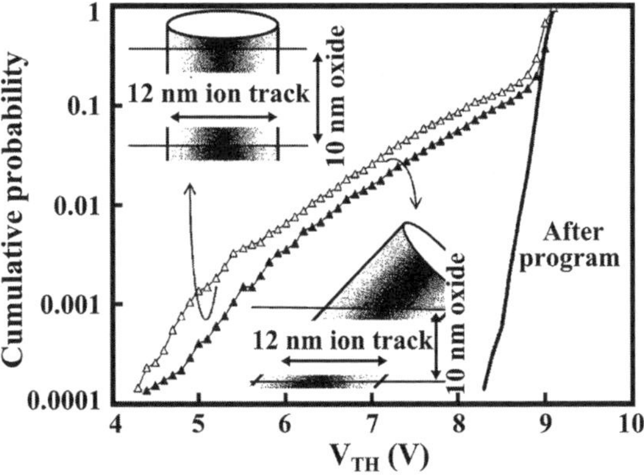

Figure 30. Cumulative distribution of cells being hit by iodine ions, 164 hours after having been re-programmed. Both devices were irradiated with null electric field at different angles with respect to the ion beam (open symbols: 90°, closed symbols: 45°). Inset schematics: tunnel oxide thickness and ion track are in scale. Reprinted with permission from [119], G. Cellere et al., *IEEE Trans. Nucl. Sci.* 52, 2144 (2005). © 2005, IEEE.

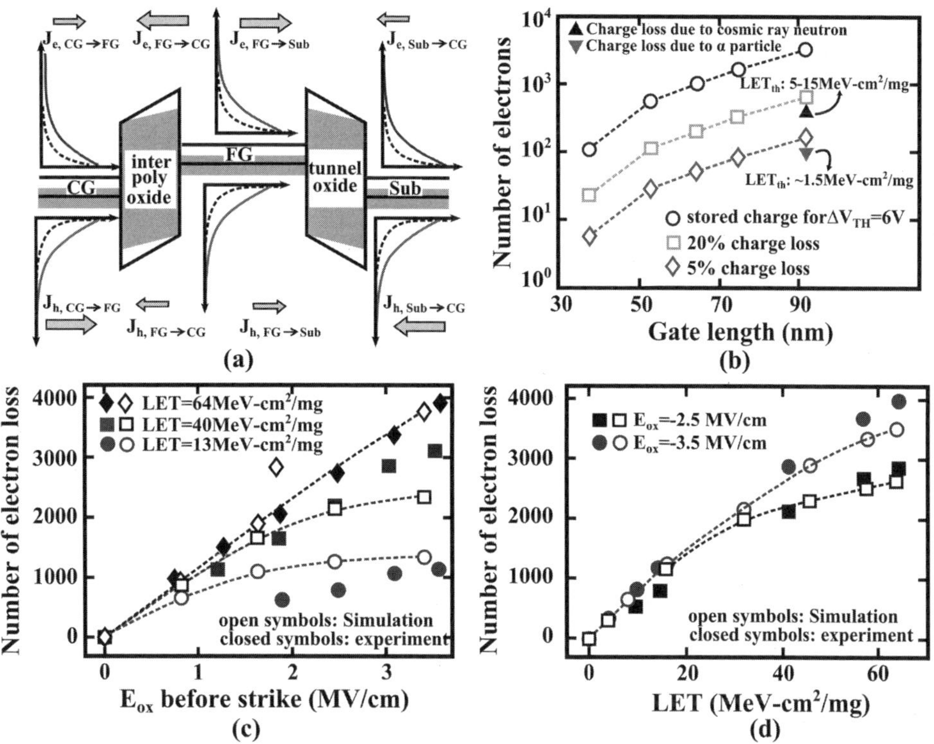

Figure 31. (a) Energy band profiles along the vertical axis through the gate stack of a FG cell in programmed state. The energy distributions of *e–h* pairs generated by a particle strike in CG, FG, and substrate regions and carriers fluxes into and out of the FG are illustrated. (b) Number of electron stored in NAND flash cell (circles) and charge loss tolerance as a function of FG technology design rule. The charge loss tolerance of SLC is assumed to be 20% (squares), while that of MLC is taken as 5% (diamonds). The predicted charge loss due to cosmic ray neutrons and alpha particle strikes (solid symbols) at $E_{ox} = 3$ MeV/cm is shown for comparison. (c) Number of electron loss as a function of E_{ox} for particle strikes having different LETs. (d) Number of electron loss as a function of particle LETs at two different oxide electric fields. Reprinted with permission from [120], N. Z. Butt and M. Alam, "IEEE International Reliability Physics Symposium," p. 547, Phoenix, AZ, 2008. © 2008, IEEE.

of electron loss as a function of E_{ox} for particle strikes having different LETs. The number of electrons loss goes up with increasing E_{ox} because the net electron flux out of FG increases with higher E_{ox}. The number of electron loss as a function of particle LETs at two different oxide electric fields is also shown in Figure 31(d). The number of electrons loss goes up with increasing LET because more carriers are produced as LET is increased, which increases the net electron flux out of FG. Based on this TCF model, a prediction was made that advanced flash memories will become highly sensitive to SEU in the future due to rapidly decreasing charge loss tolerance.

4.4. Other Radiation Effects on Highly Scaled Flash Memories

In order to obtain higher density, the industry trend is to continue with feature-size scaling, and commercial flash memory cells have been scaled down to 50 nm by different manufacturers. The high-density flash memories lead to more condensed internal circuitry and thus more chances of dynamic failure. SEU cross-section for the FG arrays is becoming comparable to that of the control logic, and thus an SEU cross-section can be dominated either by the FG arrays or the control logic [122]. Furthermore, for highly scaled devices, since the ion track structure becomes comparable to the size of critical regions, microdose effects and multi-bit upsets, charge loss from FGs and even RILC, and SEGR may become serious problems. A catastrophic failure associated with high current spikes was reported, caused by energetic ions with high LET hitting charge pump and/or internal circuitry in high density NAND structures [112, 122]. Moreover, the LET threshold for current spikes is smaller with smaller feature size, which means destructive high current spikes and their effects become significant as feature size is scaling down.

It is interesting and worth knowing that nanocrystal-based flash memory (NCM) may provide high radiation tolerance in both TID and SEE, making it an appealing candidate for use in high radiation environments [123–125]. NCMs use a layer of discrete Si nanodots as charge storage elements (seen in Fig. 32 [123]) instead of a floating gate. They feature improved SILC and soft breakdown, better scalability of the thin gate tunnel oxide, and an easy way for multi-bit data storage. TID effects on NCMs were first studied by Petkov and co-workers [124], demonstrating a two-state NCM keeping unchanged dynamic performance up to 15 Mrad(Si). SEE experiment on NAND structures with 0.13 um design rules shows that no NFEI and SEL were observed, but V_{th} distribution had a tail which could be reset, not resulting in any long-term damage [125]. This result is also observed by Cester et al. and they attributed the tail in V_{th} distribution to at least three to four ion hits, which are only partially discharged by the impinging ions [123]. However, the majority

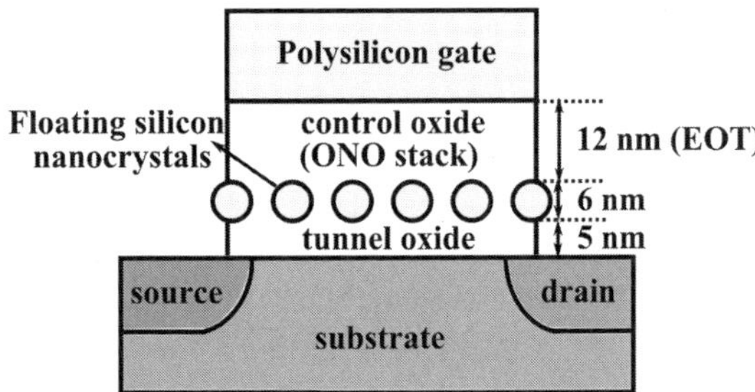

Figure 32. Cross section of the nanocrystal memory cell. Reprinted with permission from [123], A. Cester et al., *IEEE Trans. Nucl. Sci.* 54, 2196 (2007). © 2007, IEEE.

of ions hitting a single NCM cells are unable to produce a noticeable V_{th} shift. Furthermore, despite some cells experiencing multiple hits, NCMs are still functional after the irradiation, and no changes in the retention characteristics were observed. The good robustness to heavy-ion irradiation makes NCMs better than conventional FG memories in terms of radiation tolerance, thus they are an appealing candidate for radiation-harsh environments.

5. RADIATION EFFECTS ON FeRAM

5.1. Introduction to FeRAM

Although today Flash memories are the most prominent NVM due to their high density and low fabrication costs, they also suffer from low endurance, high voltages required for the write operations and difficulties in further scaling. Furthermore, low radiation resistance of Flash becomes another limitation for aerospace applications. Thus, alternative NVM devices have been being explored to replace Flash memories. The first practical applications of FeRAM and MRAM have become commercially available, but still with technological and inherent problems in the scalability. Other emerging NVM memories are being explored to overcome the current bottleneck, among which PCRAM and ReRAM will also be discussed.

The most attractive advantages of FeRAMs are the low power consumption, fast programming times, good retention over a wide temperature range, and virtually unlimited endurance, as well as excellent radiation resistance. The first FeRAM integrated with silicon CMOS was demonstrated in late 1980s [126–128]. The initial FeRAM consisted of 2 transistors and 2 capacitors (2T2C) per bit with a large cell size. Since from the early 1990s especially when the first 256-kb FeRAM using 1 transistor and 1 capacitor cell (1T1C) was reported (Ref. [129]), extensive efforts have been made and many new architectures and circuits/device technologies have been developed to shrink the memory cell and die sizes and to improve FeRAM capacity and better performances. Currently, FeRAMs with capacity up to 60 Mb and design rule down to 0.13 μm have been commercialized. A prototype of high density 128 Mb chain FeRAM with the highest read/write bandwidth of 1.6 Gb/s in all nonvolatile memories has been developed [130, 131], which is comparable to DRAM and very promising as a replacement for DRAM.

FeRAM uses a ferroelectric film as a capacitor for storing data. At present, perovskites lead zirconate–titanate (PZT, $PbZr_xTi_{1-x}O_3$) and layered perovskites strontium bismuth tantalite (SBT, $SrBi_2Ta_2O_9$) are the main materials used in industry. Figure 33 gives the crystal structures of both PZT and SBT. In a PZT perovskite ferroelectric material (Fig. 33(a)), a net spontaneous polarization (or charge displacement) value can result from the Ti/Zr ions movement upward or downward inside the O octahedral depending on the electric field applied, and these metal ions stay there even after the electric field is removed [132–134]. SBT, however, is a layered perovskite consisting of 2 unit cells, one layer of bismuth oxide, and 2 layers of strontium tantalite, and the polarization mechanism is different from that of PZT. As shown in Figure 34(b), when voltage is applied to the electrodes of the capacitor, the 2 layers of O octahedral between BiO_2 layers twist without c-axis movement of Ta in SBT [134]. Thus, charge displacement occurs at each oxygen octahedral as Ta displacements formed relative to the BiO_2 layers. The charge displacements of both PZT (the metal ion movement) and SBT can be sensed as a current flowing between the electrodes of the ferroelectric capacitor, and are usually displayed as hysteresis loops of polarization of the ferroelectric films versus the applied voltage, as typically represented in Figure 34 [134]. The ferroelectric material has 2 stable states, defined as computational "1" and "0,"

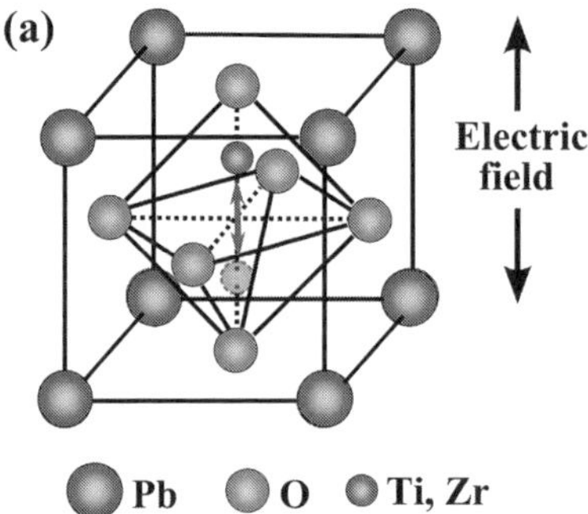

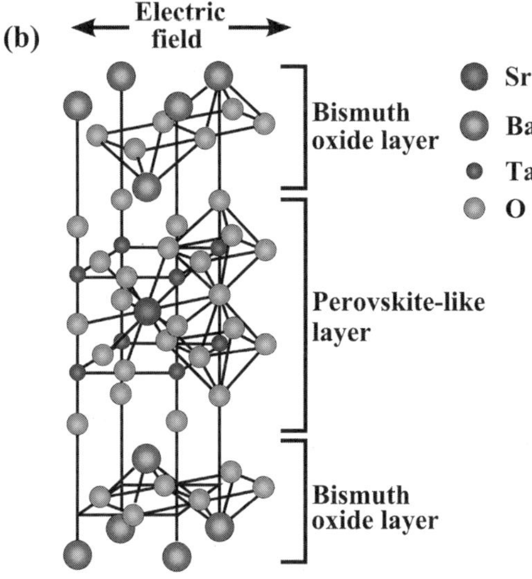

Figure 33. Ferroelectric material molecules used for FeRAM: (a) PZT ($Pb(Zt, Ti)O_3$, Ti or Zr ion moves along c-axis in oxygen octahedral) and (b) SBT ($SrBi_2Ta_2O_9$, two layers of oxygen octahedral twist).

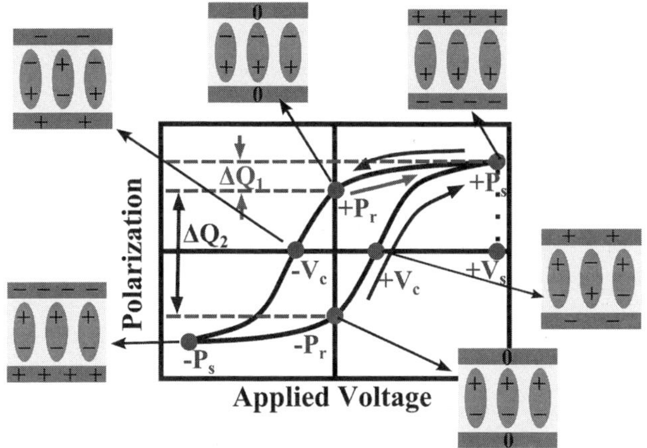

Figure 34. *Q–V* hysteresis loop of a FeRAM cell with the schematic diagram of switching mechanism.

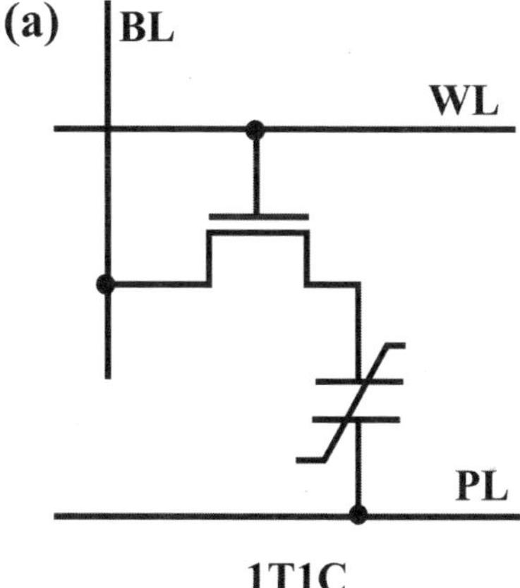

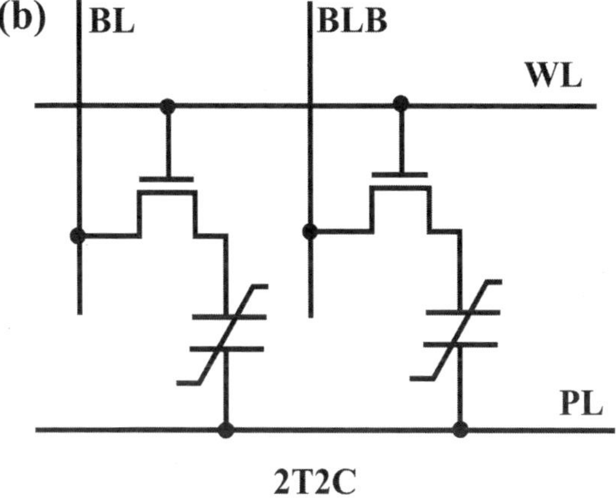

Figure 35. Schematic diagrams of FeRAM bit cells, (a) 1T1C, (b) 2T2C.

when at remanent polarization ($+/-P_r$) states under no bias condition.

The basic of the operations of a ferroelectric capacitor has been described by Kawashima and Cross [134]. In summary, when bias is applied, a polarization switching occurs. Starting from $-P_r$, where it is assumed full polarization and the 3 domains in the schematic (Fig. 34) have the same direction of spontaneous polarization, with increasing positive voltage at the top electrode, a portion of domains start to switch to the other direction and the polarization reaches 0 at coercive voltage $+V_c$. When the applied voltage increases to the saturated voltage $+V_s$, the polarization reaches P_s (saturated polarization) and all domains in the ferroelectric material switch to the opposite direction. The polarization ($+P_r$) remains after the voltage is removed. An opposite switching with similar behavior occurs as negative voltage passes $-V_c$ and $-V_s$, and the $-P_r$ polarization state stays when the negative bias is removed.

The basic FeRAM cell configurations of the conventional 1T1C and 2T2C are given in Figure 35. A transistor is connected to a wordline (WL) to select memory cell. One terminal of the memory cell is connected to a bitline (BL) through the transistor to read/write cell data, and the other terminal is connected to a plateline (PL) to induce the polarization switching. Thus, based on the polarization switching mechanism described above, the FeRAM cell can be written to either "1" or "0" by applying a positive or negative voltage from BL to PL across the capacitor. The reading operation has different methods. The simplest way is to apply a read voltage pulse V_r, and then to detect charge emerging from polarization switching. For example, seen from Figure 34, if the FeRAM cell is in the "$+P_r$" state, when applying a positive voltage pulse, the polarization moves form $+P_r$ to $+P_s$ and then back to $+P_r$, therefore only ΔQ_1 is detected; while if it is at the "$-P_r$" state, the positive electric field induces the polarization switching $-P_r \rightarrow +P_s \rightarrow +P_r$ and the collected charge on electrode, $\Delta Q_1 + \Delta Q_2$, is then detected. The bit information is judged from the difference in the magnitude of the currents. It should be noted that "0" and "1" are arbitrarily defined, such as "1" at $+P_r$ or $-P_r$ and "0" at the opposite. Accordingly, reading voltage may be positive or negative.

Reading is a destructive operation because the readout data have to be rewritten in the memory cell again; it imposes a limitation of endurance of FeRAM, also known as fatigue loss. The causes of fatigue are still in debate but could be due to charge defects, oxygen vacancies, injected interfacial charge, etc. [134]. However, the endurance has been improved to 10^{15} cycles by using conductive metal oxide electrodes such as IrO_x or by using SBT ferroelectric capacitors. Other FeRAM cell degradation issues such as imprint, relaxation, hydrogen degradation, temperature dependent V_c/polarization charge are overviewed in Ref. [134], as well as the developed solutions to them.

Another key challenge is the limited scalability, as a reduction of the cell area of the ferroelectric capacitor gives a deterioration of the detectable charge. The current state-of-the-art FeRAM is limited to 0.13 μm technology with 128 Mb capacity in a chain cell structure [131, 132, 135]. For a higher-level of integration, 3-D stacked FeRAMs have been studied and the effective area of the FeRAM is larger than the unit area of the cell thus compensating for the decrease in signal [136, 137]. However, challenges still exist, such as limited memory capacitor size [132]. Alternative memories based on ferroelectric materials such as ferroelectric field effect transistor (FeFET) and ferroelectric resistive RAM (FRRAM) have also obtained research interest recently [138, 139]. FeFET is in principle a MOSFET with its gate dielectric replaced by a ferroelectric insulator, using spontaneous polarization to control V_t of the channel. This structure with a nondestructive reading is suitable for high density integration and is thus considered to be the ultimate structure for FeRAMs. However, the main disadvantage, poor retention, limited the application in NVMs. FeRAMs change the polarization direction to alter the resistance state of the ferroelectric material. They have a nondestructive readout and have a high potential for scaling, and could be an alternative to FeRAM.

5.2. Radiation Effects on FeRAM

Early investigations of radiation effects on FeRAM focused on PZT-based thin film capacitors, and mixed results were found [140–145]. It was reported that there was no radiation-induced degradation in P_r up to a TID of 10 Mrad(Si) for capacitors cycled during irradiation [144], while Scott et al. studied the PZT capacitors irradiated under a TID in excess of 5 Mrad(Si) and found that the capacitors can fail to maintain the stored polarization charge if the electrodes are shorted during the irradiation [143]. Also, the hysteresis curves became more symmetric after 5 Mrad(Si) irradiation [143]. Later, Schwank et al. [142] claimed that PZT capacitors can survive radiation exposures well in excess of 10 Mrad(Si) with suitable fabrication process. The radiation-induced degradation in P_r and polarization charge after 16 Mrad(Si) irradiation was observed, as well as the different distortions or shifts of the hysteresis curves (see in Fig. 36(a) [142]) depending on the previous polarization state before the devices are irradiated under different bias conditions. The phenomena were attributed to the trapping of radiation-induced charge in the ferroelectric changing the internal polarizing fields and can be recovered by a post-irradiation biased anneal or entirely prevented if the devices are cycled during irradiation. This radiation-induced distortion behavior of hysteresis curves, which can be removed by post-rad cycling, was also observed by other groups [140, 141, 146], and the degradations in P_r and E_c were reported at a TID as low as less than 1 Mrad(Si) [141]. Moreover, reduced radiation-induced degradation can be formed in biased devices during irradiation, comparing to those of nonbiased samples [145, 146] (see Fig. 36(b) [146]). The TID study of PZT capacitors by Moore et al. [147] used a pulse test and distinguished the non-volatile component of the polarization, the retained polarization used for NVM applications, from the total polarization obtained from the traditional hysteresis loop method. As shown in Figure 37(a) [147], the retained polarization decreased with dose and the reduction was 50% at only 1.7 Mrad(SiO_2), indicating that hysteresis loop measurements underestimate the radiation sensitivity of ferroelectric materials. Later, Moore and Benedetto identified a new failure mode, i.e., failure caused by imprint, in FeRAM could occur in a radiation environment [148]. Using the imprint measurement method, they found that the differential polarization degraded even larger than retained polarization (see Fig. 37(b) [148]), indicating that even the retained polarization measurement possibly underestimates the radiation damage to FeRAM cells [148]. In addition, it was reported that ferroelectric thin films are radiation tolerant to neutron fluencies up to 10^{15} neutrons/cm^2 [149].

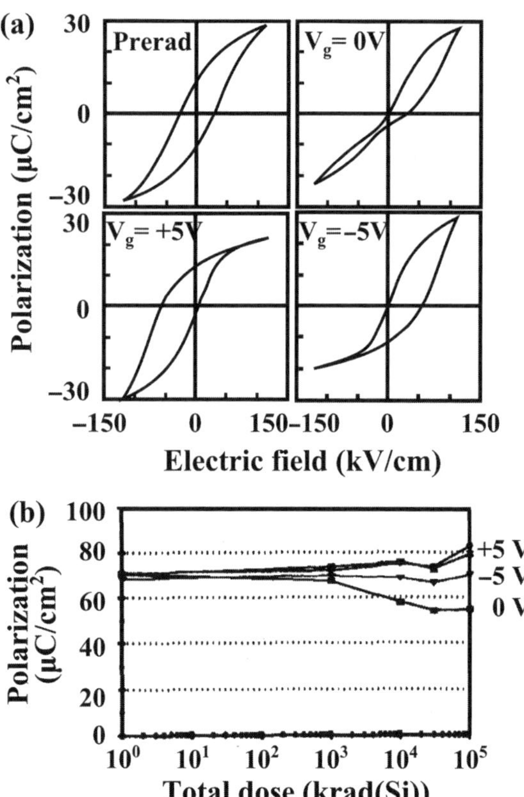

Figure 36. (a) Comparison of the hysteresis curves pre-irradiation and after irradiating to 10 Mrad(Si) with biases of 0, −5 and +5 V. Reprinted with permission from [142], J. R. Schwank et al., *IEEE Trans. Nucl. Sci.* 37, 1703 (1990). © 1990. (b) Polarization versus TID for 3 cases of external bias, 0, −5 V and +5 V. Adapted with permission from [146], Y. M. Coic et al., *IEEE Trans. Nucl. Sci.* 41, 495 (1994). © 1994, IEEE.

Radiation effects on these PZT capacitors were believed to be related to the interaction between radiation-induced charges and the local field in the ferroelectric materials [142, 143]. A charge sheet model was developed and well predicted the capacitor's response to radiation [142]. Charge trapping alters the local polarizing field and thus changes the switching characeristics as a function of applied voltage [142]. A more general analysis of degradiation mechinisms due to irradiation was considered by Leray and the collegues [150]. As a strong local field exists even in the absence of applied external field, radiation-induced electrons/holes are violently separated and then trapped on impurities, lattice point defects, stoichiometric defects, and/or grain boundaries. These trapped charges then form electrostatic boundary conditions and degrade P_r by preventing ferroelectric domains to propagate and/or fractioning the domains and further causing domain wall pinning. However, when the capacitors are biased during irradiation, charges are more likely trapped to the ferroelectric/electrode interfaces, leading to a less efficent wall pinning and thus less degradation in P_r (Fig. 36(b)). On the other hand, the imprint-like degradation (voltage shift seen in Fig. 36(a)) results from screening the polarization state by asymmetric surface trapping at ferroelectric/electrode interfaces or grain walls, which can

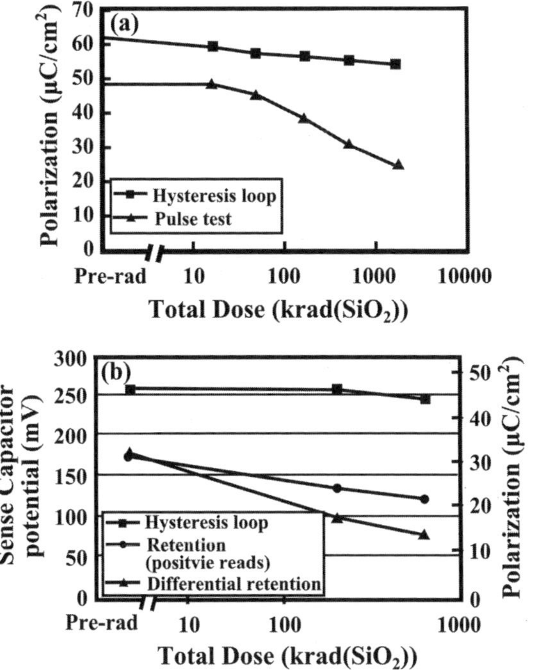

Figure 37. (a) Remanent polarization from hysteresis loop measurements with pulse-retained polarization measuement results at each dose. The two measurements show significantly different levels of radiation-induced damage to the ferroelectric. Reprinted with permission from [147], R. A. Moore et al., *IEEE Trans. Nucl. Sci.* 40, 1591 (1993). © 1993, IEEE. (b) Comparison of polarization versus TID reported by 3 different measurement techniques for PZT samples. Reprinted with permission from [148], R. A. Moore and J. M. Benedetto, *IEEE Trans. Nucl. Sci.* 42, 1575 (1995). © 1995, IEEE.

be easily restored by annealing or cycling due to charge detrapping or redistribution. Especially for biased samples, the radiation-induced charges will be swept out toward the ferroelectric/electrodes interfaces, enhancing the voltage shift. This mechanism of radiation effects on switching kinetics of FeRAM is further supported and evdienced by recent works [151, 152]. Furthermore, neutron radiation effects have been found to induce isolated defects that could trap charges and cause domain wall pinning [146, 149], which could be more severe for small area capacitors where domain wall motion freedom is reduced [146].

Since mid-1990s, the increasing interest and the commercialization of FeRAM have boosted the radiation study on CMOS/FeRAM technologies [146, 153–156] as well as hardened-by-design (HBD) FeRAMs combined with rad-hardened CMOS [133, 157–160], although the first study of irradiated 4-kbit FeRAM was conducted in the early 1990s [140] which demonstrated the functional failures after irradiation were due to the vunerability of underlying CMOS to irradiation. Similar to the first study, the subsequent studies of radiation effects on FeRAMs show that errors or function failures are due to the use of CMOS process while the memories themselves were inherently radiation hard [146, 153, 155, 156]. A TID study of Co-60 and proton radiation on a 64-kbit and a 256-kbit FeRAM device with 2T2C

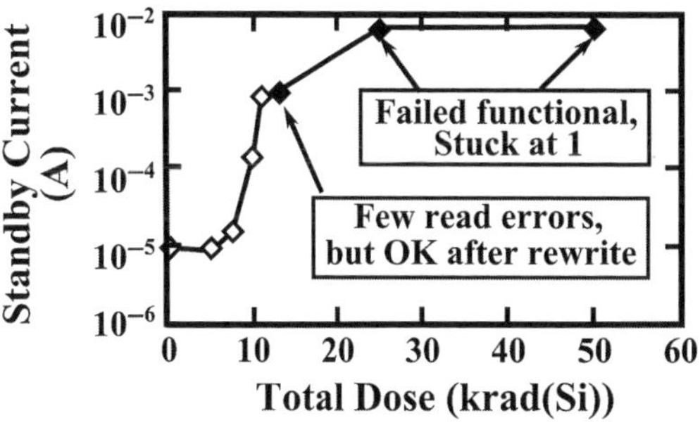

Figure 38. TID effects on 64 Kb FeRAM at 50 rad(Si)/s. Reprinted with permission from [153], D. N. Nguyen and L. Z. Scheick, "IEEE Radiation Effects Data Workshop," p. 57, Vancouver, Canada, 2001. © 2001, IEEE.

structure shows that both devices failed to function after 20–25 krad(Si) when they were biased during irradiation (see Fig. 38 [153]), but still function after 7 Mrad(Si) [153]. Moreover, the radiation results were not affected by 100°C annealing or cycling. A similar TID result was reported for a 128 k × 8 FeRAM with a 0.35 μm CMOS technology except that the device failed at 35 krad(Si) and functionality was recovered after 168 h annealing at 100°C [156]. In terms of SEU, the first testing on a 1 kbit FeRAM device shows the memory is immune to heavy ion irradiation up to an LET of 128 MeV-cm^2/mg [155]. Later, however, it was demonstrated that FeRAM under heavy ion irradiation is sensitive to SEU, with a LET threshold greater than 20 MeV-cm^2/mg, and SEL, with a lowest LET threhold about 10 MeV-cm^2/mg when irradiated in a dynamic mode; but no SEL was observed after proton irradiation [156]. However, PZT degradation is found to be responsible for stuck bits appearing in unbiased devices after irradiation in a recent study on a 32 k × 8 FeRAM with 1T1C structure, while the peripheral circuitry degradation due to irradiation leads to a faster degradation of devices biased during irradiation [154].

As most radiation experiments on a ferroelectric storage element show its inherent tolerance and the radiation hardness of FeRAM is primarily limited to the hardness of the underlying CMOS tehcnology, it is necessary to design the radiation-hardened CMOS circuitry to improve its hardness for space applications. HBD FeRAMs have been developed to assure a high level hardness to TID and SEE without the need for radiation shielding or complex SOI [157–160]. In addition to the rad-hardness design for CMOS circuitry, the design also uses a shunted ferroelectric memory cell, as shown in Figure 39 [160], to reduce the susceptibility to disturbances in harsh environments by holding the voltage across the ferroelectric capacitor near 0 V in the presence of noise coupling to the capacitor plates [157–160]. To evaluate the radiation tolerance of HBD FeRAMs, a radiation testing result for a HBD 1-kbit FeRAM protype with a 0.35 μm CMOS process shows the devices withstand a TID of more than 2 Mrad(Si) and SEL up to an LET of 163 Mg-cm^2/mg with no failures [159]. More recently, high-density radiation-hardened FeRAMs have been designed on a 0.13 or a 0.35 μm CMOS/FeRAM process [157, 158], using a number of HBD techniques, such as *p*-channel transistors in memory arrays, annular *n*-channel gate structures, *p*-type

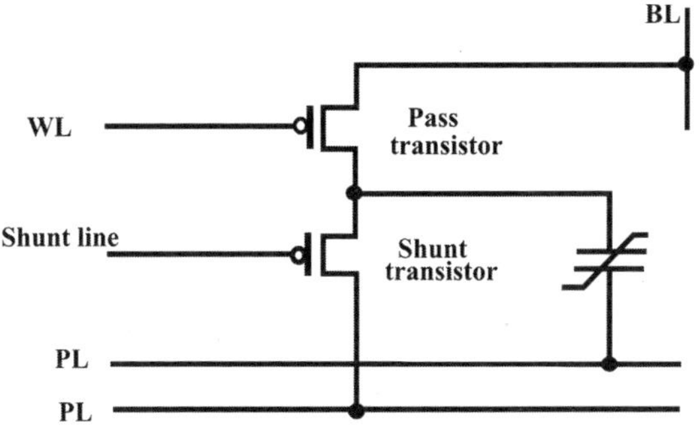

Figure 39. Schematic of shunted ferroelectric memory cell. Reprinted with permission from [160], S. T. Philpy et al., "2004 IEEE Aerospace Conference Proceedings," Vol. 4, p. 2294, Big Sky, Montana, 2004. © 2004, IEEE.

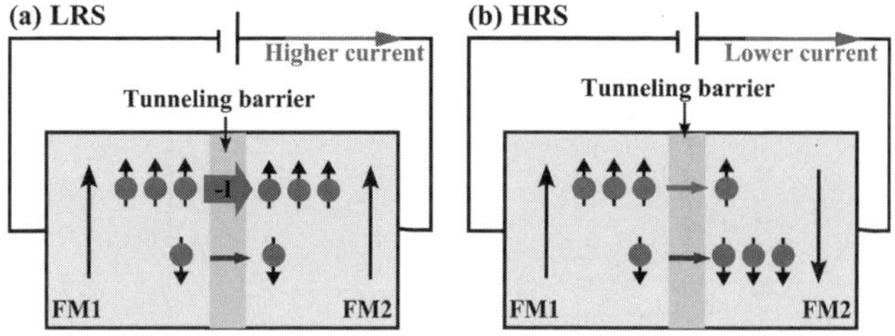

Figure 40. Schematic of the TMR effect in an MTJ. During tunneling, electron spin orientation is preserved and the conductance is proportional to the product of the Fermi level DOS values of the 2 FM electrodes of the same spin orientation. FM1 is the fixed ferromagnetic layer, FM2 the free ferromagnetic layer. (a) Parallel magnetizations of the 2 FM layers giving an LRS. (b) Antiparallel magnetizations corresponding to an HRS.

guard rings, robust/redundant logic gates protecting latches, SEE immune latches, and sense amplifiers [158].

6. RADIATION EFFECTS ON MRAM

6.1. Introduction to MRAM

The concept of magnetic memory dates back to the 1950s, and the earliest mainframe computers broadly used core memories and bubble memories in the following decades. But with the rapid improvements in hard-disk technology and the availability of SRAM, EEPROM, and flash memories, the early old magnetic memories became uncompetitive and faded out of the market. However, in the late 1980s, there emerged a new generation of MRAM employing magnetoresistive (MR) effects with much faster operation speeds than flash and unlimited endurance. MR effects are characterized by the MR ratio, defined by $MR = (R_{high} - R_{low})/R_{low}$, where R_{high} and R_{low} represents the resistance of the device in the high resistance state and low resistance state respectively. Several techniques has been developed, including anisotropic MRAM, giant magnetoresistance (GMR)-based spin valve MRAM and pseudo spin valve MRAM, and tunneling magnetoresistance (TMR)-based magnetic tunnel junction (MTJ) MRAM. Compared to anisotropic and GMR-based MRAM, TMR-based MTJ MRAM has far higher MR ratios (about 20–40%, versus $<2\%$ for anisotropic MRAM and $\sim 7\%$ for GMR-based MRAM) [161, 162]. Thus, TMR-based MTJ MRAM has been intensively studied around the world [162–170], resulting in dramatic improvements of techniques and materials and steadily increased MR values even over 500% [163, 170, 171]. Currently, most major memory device vendors are focused on TMR-based MTJ MRAM. Together with the large MR ratio, the main benefits of nonvolatility, high speed operation, and unlimited read and write endurance make it one of the candidates for the next-generation NVM. In this section, we will mainly discuss TMR-based MTJ MRAMs and their response to radiation.

The basic MTJ structure is composed of two ferromagnetic (FM) layers separated by a thin dielectric tunnel layer (typically <2 nm), as shown in Figure 40. One FM layer of the MTJ is magnetically pinned (i.e., the magnetization does not change direction), called fixed FM layer (FM1 in Fig. 40); the other FM layer has switchable magnetization directions, called free FM layer (FM2 in Fig. 40). With such a thin tunnel layer, quantum mechanical tunneling of electrons through the barrier from one magnetic layer to the other results in a tunneling current through the devices. Due to the nature of the conduction bands in the FM materials, the tunneling current is spin polarized with either spin-up or spin-down electrons. During tunneling, electron spin orientation is preserved so that electrons can tunnel into only the subband of the same spin orientation, as illustrated in Figure 40, and the conductance is proportional to the product of the densities of the two electrodes of the same spin orientation. Therefore, if the magnetization (the majority electron spins) in the free FM layer is parallel to the fixed layer, the resistance is low because the majority spin-aligned electrons in the two FM layers will tunnel more readily through the tunneling barrier; while on the contrary if the magnetization in the free FM layer is anti-parallel to the fixed layer, the resistance is high as the majority spin-aligned electrons in one layer are inhibited from tunneling to the other layer because the spin-aligned electron states are in the minority there [161, 164, 168]. This change in the tunneling resistance with the relative magnetic states of the MTJ is known as TMR. Data can be stored using this TMR effect, and usually read by measuring the tunneling current. The typical TMR effect can be seen in Figure 41 [161], with the tunneling resistance per unit area (RA) as a function of a bitline current I_{BL} that controls the orientation of the magnetization in the free layer. Both the RA and MR ratio are the fundamental properties of MTJ materials. In MRAM applications, the MTJ structures are much more complicated than the basic one mentioned above. Additional layers are usually used to pin the moment of the fixed layer, control dipolar coupling, etc. Different tunnel barrier materials and FM alloys are used in MTJ to optimize their read and write properties [164]. Currently, two major types of magnetic switching in the writing step have been studied, including field-switching and spin-transfer torque (STT) switching.

As shown in Figure 42(a), a fielding switching MRAM device has a MTJ stack, a single transistor and current carrying lines, with the digit line passing under and bitline passing over the MTJ bit. The MTJ bit is typically elongated with the magnetization parallel to the long axis of the bit, called the easy axis; whereas the hard axis is referred to the one

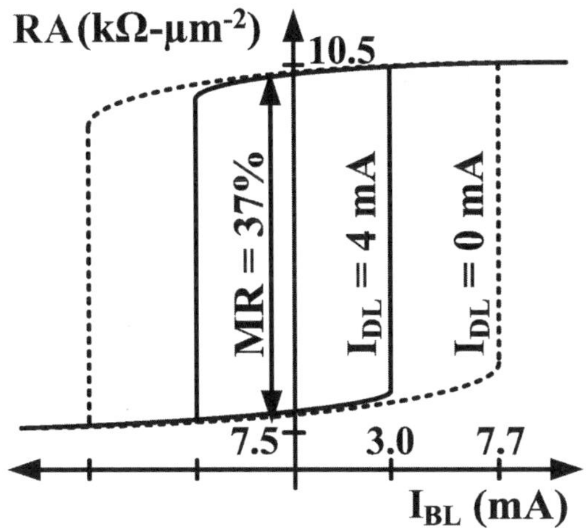

Figure 41. Magnetoresistance tunnel junction hysteresis. Reprinted with permission from [161], B. F. Cockburn, "IEEE International Workshop on Memory Technology, Design and Testing," p. 46, San Jose, CA, 2004. © 2004, IEEE.

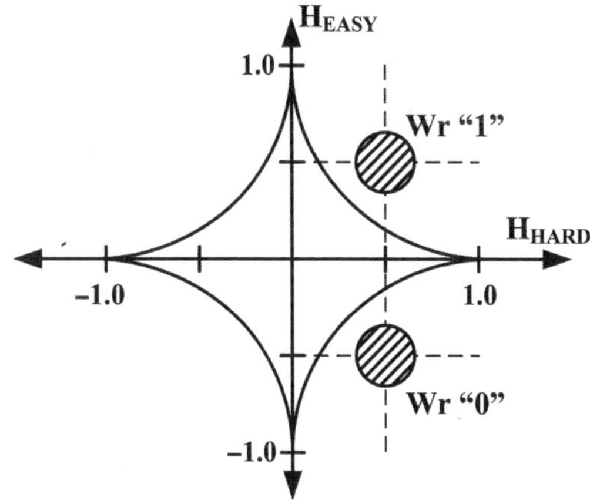

Figure 43. The astroid diagram of conventional MTJ-MRAMs, showing operation regions. Reprinted with permission from [161], B. F. Cockburn, "IEEE International Workshop on Memory Technology, Design and Testing," p. 46, San Jose, CA, 2004. © 2004, IEEE.

perpendicular to the easy axis. Switching is completed by passing currents through the orthogonal digit and bitlines, both of which create magnetic fields acting on the free FM layer of the selected MTJ bit at the cross point. Other bits along the current carrying lines are called the half-selected bits. To read the bit, as given in Figure 42(b), the isolation transistor is turned on to pass a sense current perpendicularly through the MTJ stack. Figure 43 shows the astroid diagram, indicating the switching threshold of the combinations of easy-axis switching field (H_{easy}) and the hard-axis field (H_{hard}) for programming [161]. No programming occurs when the combination of H_{hard} and H_{easy} from the central region in the diagram. The field switching MRAM is designed in such a way that the selected bit always switches but not the half-selected bits, which in fact imposes a challenge for field-switching MRAMs.

The new commercially available toggle MRAM is developed based on the basic MTJ cell, which greatly enhances the operating margins and thus offers much better selectivity. The typical structure of a toggle MRAM is given in Figure 44(a) [164]. The free layer consists of a stack of two or more FM films that are anti-ferromagnetically coupled to each other by means of a spacer layer. Both of the free and fixed layers have the magnetization along an axis of 45 to the bit and digit lines. To program the state, a pulse sequence is applied and causes the coupled FM magnetization components to rotate. Only a single-line current pulse (thus the half-selected bits) cannot switch the bit, increasing the selectivity. The detail about the switching mechanism with the toggle operating condition can be referenced to Ref. [164].

Other approaches such as thermal-assisted switching have been proposed to avoid the half-selected disturbances. Thermal-assisted switching uses an MTJ stack with a strong temperature dependence so that the target bit is selected by heating it to a temperature that significantly lowers its switching field. This method however also introduces new challenges in terms of the complexity of material development and the patterning process, control of thermal conduction, and reliability issues [164].

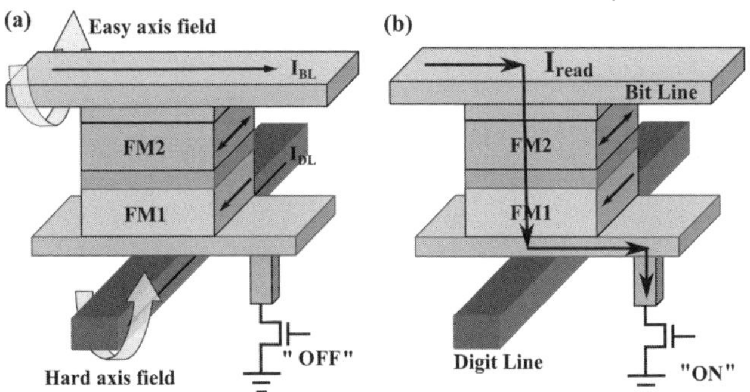

Figure 42. Schematic of conventional MRAM schemes: (a) writing operation with the transistor "OFF" and currents flowing through both the bitline and digit line creating the easy axis field and the hard axis field respectively. (b) Read operation with the transistor "ON". A sensing current is applied to read the resistance of the MTJ.

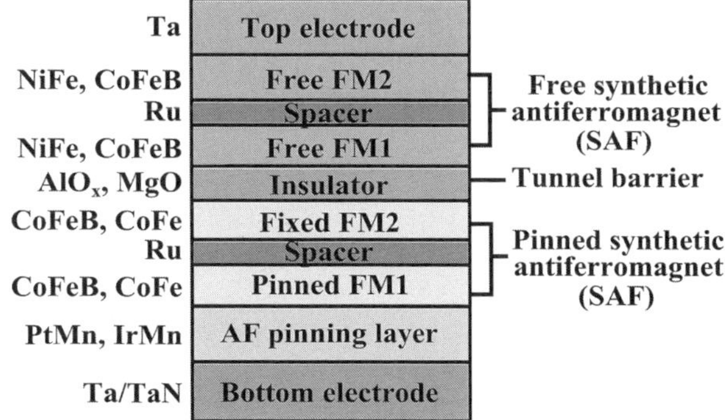

Figure 44. A typical MTJ material stack optimized for toggle MRAM. Reprinted with permission from [164], J. M. Slaughter, *Annu. Rev. Mater. Res.* 39, 277 (2009). © 2009, IEEE. The bottom pinning layer and pinned SAF are used to provide a stable fixed magnetic layer with minimum dipole coupling to the free layer. The free SAF would be replaced by a single FM layer in most other types of MRAM.

Recently, STT MRAM has been intensively investigated and demonstrated to be promising as a universal NVM with low power consumption, high density, fast write and read speed (a few ns), unlimited endurance and excellent scalability [172–174]. The structure of a STT MRAM device connecting an MTJ in series with a transistor is given in Figure 45(a). The details of exactly how the spin current interacts with FM layers leading to switchable magnetic states can be found in Refs. [175, 176]. In summary, electrons leaving a FM layer have a net electron spin moment parallel to the moment of the layer, while electrons reflected from the surface of the electrode are oriented antiparallel to that layer on average. The net spin moment, proportional to both the degree of the polarization and the current density, can generate a spin torque on the local magnetization when the tunneling current arrives at the free FM layer. Depending on the magnitude and direction of the current, switching of magnetization of the storage layer occurs, as illustrated in Figure 45(b) [168]. When a large enough tunneling current is applied in the direction of electrons flowing from the fixed layer to the free layer, the spin torque effect rotates the magnetization of the free layer to a parallel state with respect to the fixed layer; while reversing the direction of the tunneling current, the free layer will be switched to the antiparallel state by the reflected electrons (antiparallel polarized to the fixed layer) from the surface of the fixed layer.

It should be noted that a current density threshold (J_c) exists, above which magnetization switching can occur. J_c can be expressed as Eq. (5) [172]:

$$J_{C0} = \frac{2e\alpha M_s t_F(H + H_k + 2\pi M_s)}{\eta} \quad (5)$$

where the free layer is described by its Gilbert damping constant α, magnetization M_s, the field along the easy axis H, and the effective anisotropy field H_k including magnetocrystalline anisotropy and shape anisotropy. The spin-torque efficiency η depends on the polarization of the tunneling current and the direction of the current. In a typical device with dimensions on the order of 100 nm, the current density threshold is typically in the 10^6–10^7 A/cm^2 range at zero temperature. The main challenge for STT writing mode in high-density and high-speed memory is to reduce the current density threshold.

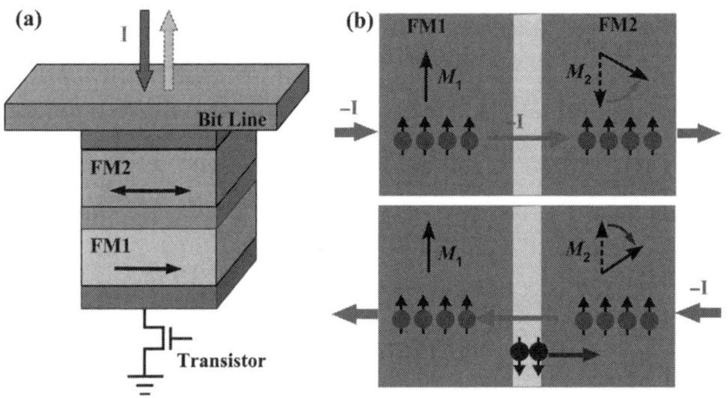

Figure 45. (a) A STT-MRAM cell structure. In MTJ, FM1 is the fixed layer and FM2 the free layer. (b) Schematic diagram of STT effect. Reversing the current direction reverses the spin polarization direction of the tunneling current. If the electron current flows from FM1 to FM2, M2 will rotate to the direction parallel to M1 by the electrons polarized by the FM1; while reversing the tunneling current direction, M2 will rotate to the antiparallel direction to M1 by the reflected electrons antipolarized by the FM1.

6.2. Radiation Effects on MRAM

Unlike most other semiconductor memory technologies, MRAM devices store data with magnetic states, rather than as charge states, and are sensed by measuring the current/resistance without disturbing the magnetic state. Therefore, MRAMs are expected to be inherently radiation resistant, although the radiation responses may vary when MRAMs are made of different materials with different processes and so on.

In the 2000s, radiation effects on MTJ MRAM devices were studied [177–183]. Conraux et al. subjected Al_2O_3-based MTJs with exchange-free (MTJ-1) and exchange-biased (MTJ-2) synthetic antiferromagnet pinned layer to 10 MeV/A swift heavy ion (SHI) bombardment up to total dose of $\sim 10^{13}$ ions/cm^2 [178]. It turns out that MTJs are not fully radiation hard under intense swift heavy ion irradiation. TMR ratios of all the MTJs irreversibly decreased after irradiation with increasing ion fluences (Fig. 46 [178]), as a result of the decrease of antiparallel resistance and the increase of parallel resistance. The author attributes this slight but irreversible degradation to the reducing of spin polarization due to the radiation-induced magnetic domains and defects. Besides, a weak decrease of the tunnel barrier resistance was observed, suggesting limited or spatially localized potential modifications of the tunnel barrier by irradiation. No effect on the magnetic of the MTJ was observed, such as free layer coercivity, interlayer orange-peel coupling, pinned layer exchange bias field. SHI effects on two types of MTJs (exchange bias free), one with undoped Al_2O_3 barrier and the other using Gd-doped Al_2O_3, were also studied by another group under 70 MeV Si ion and 200 MeV Ag ion irradiation [184]. It should be noted that 200 MeV Ag deposit about four times higher energy in the junction layers than the 70 MeV Si ions. Similar reduction of TMR of both types were found upon Si ion irradiation, which were also attributed to the radiation-induced defects and modification of interfaces and layers reducing current polarizing. Note that the doped junction was much more sensitive with a larger TMR reduction, which was expected to be a result of the intermixture of Gd dopant atoms at the FM-barrier interfaces by irradiation, creating additional spin dependent scattering centers. On the other hand, after 200 MeV Ag ion irradiation, both types were completely destroyed, as heavy damage mainly through Co and the barrier layer were induced. Especially for the Gd-doped junction with Ag ion irradiation, large atomic rearrangements occurs due to recoil implantation of different species constituting the junction layers, which leads to the complete destruction of the tunneling properties.

However, it was demonstrated that the exchange bias can be initiated by adjusting the ion dose and the orientation of the pinning direction can be properly changed, as demonstrated for Al_2O_3-based MTJs irradiated by 10/20 keV He^+ ions in a static magnetic field with total dose from 10^{13}

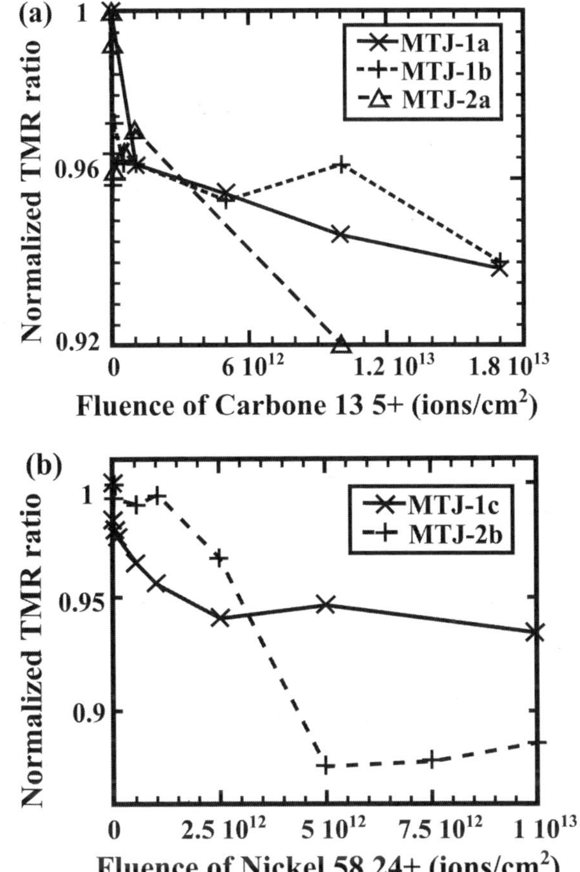

Figure 46. (a) Normalized TMR versus carbon ions fluence. (b) Normalized TMR versus nickel ions fluence. MTJ-1 is MTJs with an exchange-free synthetic antiferromagnet pinned layer and different sizes of 100 um^2 (MTJ-1a) and 400 um^2 (MTJ-1b and MTJ-1c); MTJ-2 is the MTJs with an exchange-biased synthetic antiferromagnet pinned layer and size of 100 um^2 (MTJ-2a and MTJ-2b). Reprinted with permission from [178], Y. Conraux et al., *J. Appl. Phys.* 93, 7301 (2003). © 2003, American Institute of Physics.

to 10^{18} ions/cm^2 [183]. The maximum exchange bias field is about the same as achieved by optimized field cooling. In addition, the free layer experienced a reduction of the coercivity and a slightly increasing ferromagnetic coupling. The side effects of ion bombardment is that RA starts to increase above 5×10^{14} ions/cm^2 (Fig. 47 [183]), whereas TMR increases monotonically with a dose up to 3×10^{15} ions/cm^2 because of the rotation of exchange bias orientation, but starts to decrease slightly under higher doses due to the reduced polarization of the tunneling electrons by higher ion dose-induced structural degradation such as intermixing at the barrier interface and defect formation in the barrier. Unfortunately, the maximum TMR value was reduced from 51.9% to 37.8%. Two years later, they found a remedy for these side effects by showing that a post-annealing step at an optimized temperature after ion bombardment can reduce or even completely recover the damages [185], as the example shows in Figure 48. Noble-gas ion irradiation with low energy (15~105 eV) on Al_2O_3 barrier and its effect on MTJ were also investigated, finding increasing RA and decreasing TMR with ion energy due to the irradiation-induced barrier

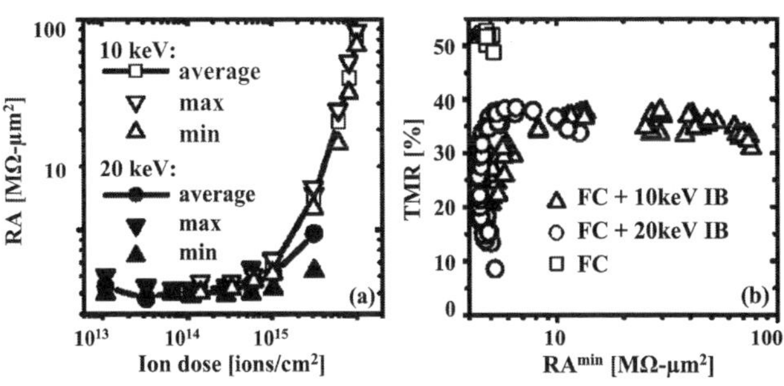

Figure 47. Magnetotransport properties of MTJs for different ion doses and energies: (a) area resistance product RA (external field applied parallel to H_{ion}, $\alpha = 90°$). For each data point an ensemble of 7–9 nominal identical junctions were investigated. The average as well as the minimum and the maximum values of each ensemble are given in the plots. (b) Major loop TMR versus minimum area resistance product RA^{min} for the full range of ion doses for 10 keV/20 keV He^+ ions (external field parallel to H_{ion}, $\alpha = 90°$). Additionally, the data of the reference junctions are plotted (external field parallel to H_{FC}, $\alpha = 0°$). Reprinted with permission from [183], J. Schmalhorst et al., *J. Appl. Phys.* 94, 5556 (2003). © 2003, American Institute of Physics.

widening and defects in the barrier, as well as intermixing at the barrier and electrode interfaces [186, 187].

Recently, Nguyen and Irom investigated the TID and SEL effects on STT-based MTJ MRAM made by Freescale using the JPL (Jet Propulsion Lab) Co-60 facility, and found that the MRAM devices survive the TID up to 60 krad(Si) under read-only radiation testing mode [182]. Room-temperature annealing can help make failed MRAMs functional again, indicating the failures were due to radiation damage to the CMOS circuitry. SEL experiments shows that the MRAM, irradiated in the static mode, are sensitive to SEL, as shown in Figure 49 [182] on the SEL cross-section. The sensitivity to SEL of the MTJ MRAM from Freescale was confirmed with the SEL threshold LET about 10 MeV-cm^2/mg at room temperature and between 7 to 10 MeV-cm^2/mg at 85°C [188]. Another TID study of a NAND MRAM commercial devices also from Freescale has shown that the MTJ MRAMs work normally up to 90 krad(SiO_2) [177, 189], and the failures observed above 100 krad(SiO_2) were also attributed to radiation damage to the CMOS peripheral control logic, rather than the MTJ itself.

Toggle MTJ MRAM devices were studied for TID and heavy ion irradiation effects under X-rays and the JPL Co-60 source (for TID) and heavy ion sources [181], demonstrating that 1 Mbit toggle MRAM has radiation hardness up to 1 Mrad and heavy ion immunity to an LET of 69 MeV-cm^2/mg at fluencies up to 10^8 ions/cm^2. Later, another study of TID and SEL effects on toggle MTJ MRAM devices from Everspin Corporation were performed by irradiating them with the JPL Co-60 source (for TID) and heavy ions (for SEL) in the static read-only mode [180]. No SEL occurred up to an effective LET of 84 MeV-cm^2/mg at any fluences (up to 10^7 ions/cm^2) and no degradation was observed in functional testing. However, TID results (Fig. 50 [180]) shows that the devices were operational up to a lower TID (~75 krad(Si)).

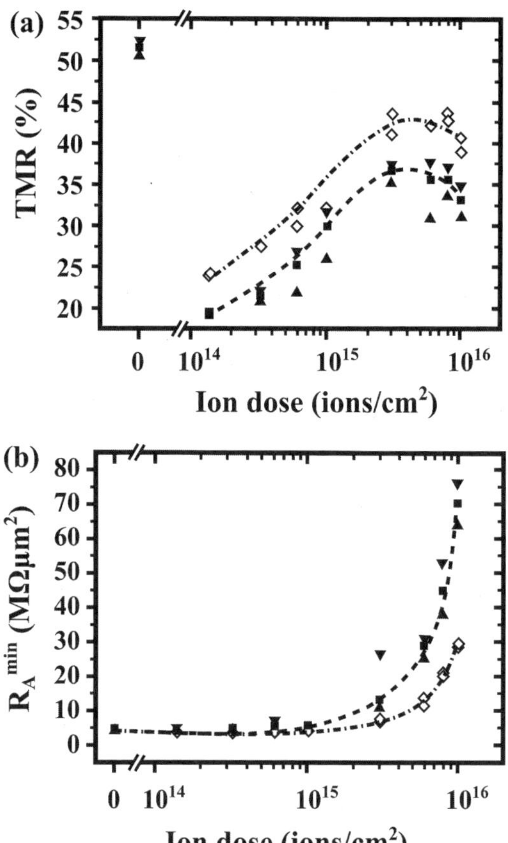

Figure 48. TMR (a) and RA^{min} (b) of MTJs for different ion does before (■: average TMR/resistance, ▼/▲: max./min. measured values) and after post-annealing for 60 min at 548 K (◇: single measurements). Measurement with ion dose 0: $H_{Ext} \parallel H_{FC}$. Measurements with ion dose $\neq 0$: $H_{Ext} \parallel H_{Ion}$. The lines are only a guide for the eye. Reprinted with permission from [185], V. Höink et al., *Appl. Phys. Lett.* 86, 152102 (2005). © 2005, American Institute of Physics.

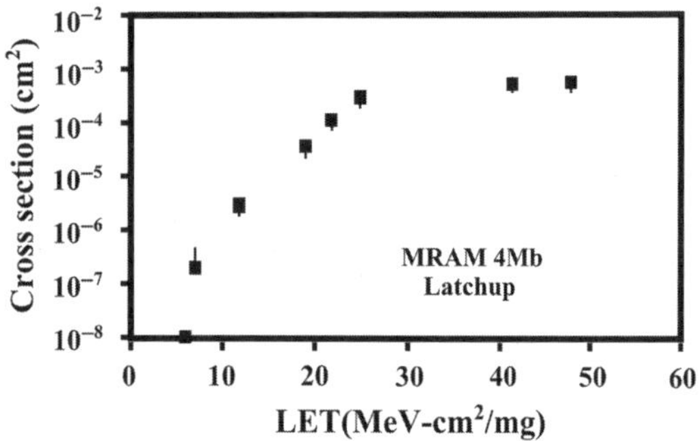

Figure 49. SEL results of the MRAM (static). Reprinted with permission from [182], D. N. Nguyen and F. Irom, "9th European Conference on Radiation and Its Effects on Components and Systems," p. 1, Deauville, 2007. © 2007, IEEE.

7. RADIATION EFFECTS ON PCRAM

7.1. Introduction to PCRAM

PCRAMs or PCMs are one of the most promising candidates for next generation NVM with large cycling endurance, long retention, fast program, and access times, and extended scalability [190–198]. The concept was first introduced in the late 1960s [199], however, commercial interest in its application for NVM boosted in the early 2000s and a lot of integration efforts have been undertaken in PCM technology [200, 201].

The basic structure of a PCRAM device is composed of one phase change material variable resistor and one access device, as shown in Figure 51(a). The access device, used as a selector, can use diodes, bipolar transistors, or MOSFETs, driving the cell in the writing and read-out phases. The resistor is a chalcogenide layer, made by the Group VI elements in the periodic table such as $Ge_2Sb_2Te_5$ (GST), sandwiched by a top metal contact and a resistive bottom electrode. The chalcogenide materials can be made to change phase reversibly between amorphous and crystalline when properly heated and cooled. The amorphous state exhibits high electrical resistivity, while in the crystalline phase, the electric resistivity is much lower, sometimes 3 or 4 orders of magnitude lower. With this peculiar property, PCRAMs use chalcogenides to store rewritable information, "0" (RESET state, corresponding to high resistance) or "1" (SET state, corresponding to low resistance), by changing material phase using a electrical pulse.

Figure 51(b) [200] illustrates the different operations for a PCRAM device using applied voltage pulses. To set the device into its low resistance state (LRS), a 50–100 ns electrical pulse is used to heat a portion of the chalcogenide close to the bottom electrode (the heater) above its crystallization temperature (T_{cryst}), leading to

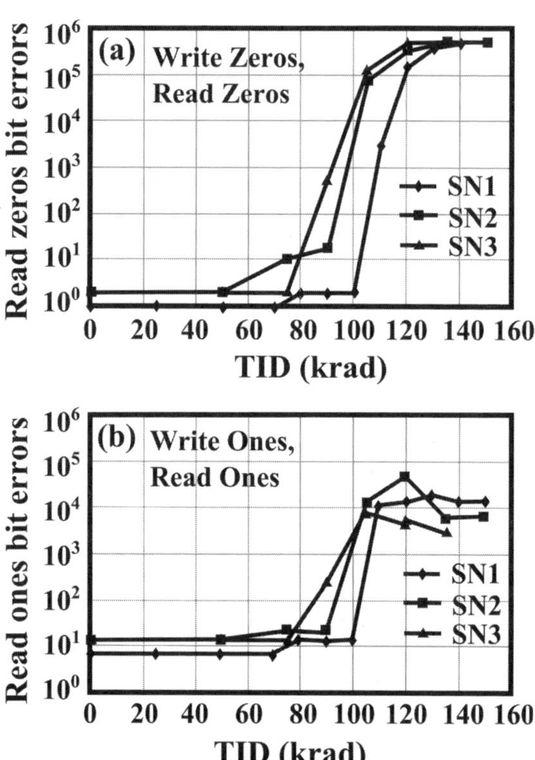

Figure 50. (a) Write Zeros, Read Zeros as a function of TID. (b) Write Ones, Read Ones as a function of TID. Reprinted with permission from [180], J. Heidecker et al., "IEEE Radiation Effects Data Workshop," p. 4, Denver, CO, 2010. © 2010, IEEE.

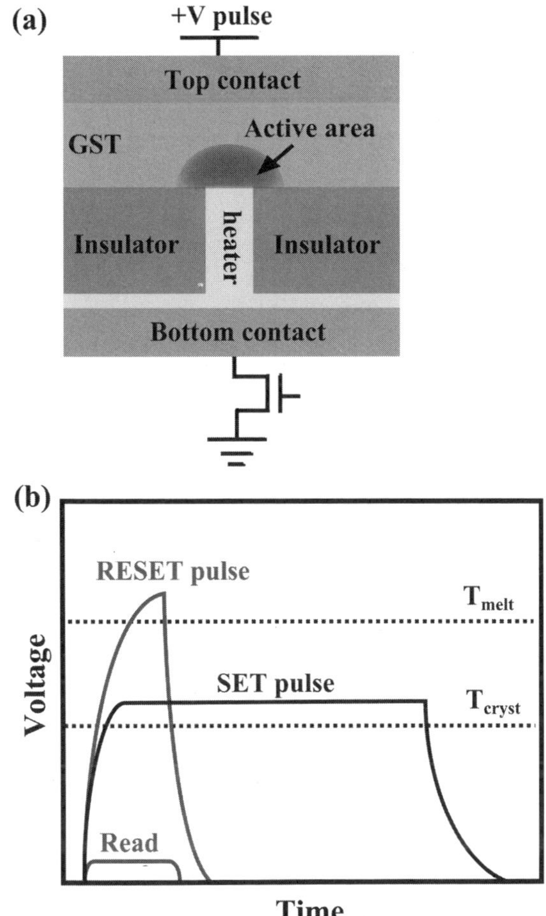

Figure 51. (a) Schematic of a PCM cell composed of a GST and a heater. The phase changing active area is at the interface of the GST and the heater, and the transistor is the access device. (b) Temperature profile when applying a voltage pulse to program a PCM device. Reprinted with permission from [200], G. W. Burr et al., *J. Vac. Sci. Technol. B* 28, 223 (2010). © 2010, IEEE. A "SET" pulse crystallizes a volume of PCM material by heating it above T_{cryst} for a sufficient time; a "RESET" pulse uses a higher voltage pulse to heat this volume to a higher temperature (above T_{melt}) followed by a rapid quenching, leading to a crystalline-amorphous transition. A low voltage is used to read the resistance state without a phase perturbation.

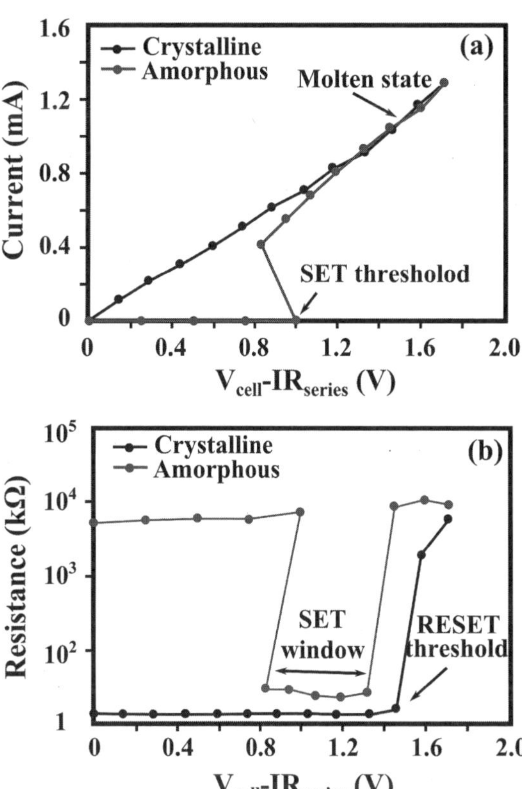

Figure 52. Typical electrical characteristics for a phase change line cell after pulses of 50 ns at 1.75 V and 100 ns at 1.2 V to create the amorphous and crystalline states, respectively. Values of the current (a) and the corresponding resistance (b) for both amorphous and crystalline states are corrected by series resistance. Reprinted with permission from [195], M. H. R. Lankhorst et al., *Nat. Mater.* 4, 347 (2005). © 2005, Nature Group Publishing.

the amorphous-crystalline transition [200, 201]. Set pulses shorter than 50 ns have been reported (Refs. [192, 194]). In the reset operation, crystalline-amorphous transition is obtained by applying a larger electrical pulse, lasting less than 100 ns, with an abrupt cutoff such that chalcogenide close to the heater will be heated above the melting temperature (T_{melt}) and then cooled down quickly. Reading is accomplished by measuring the device resistance at a low voltage so that the device state is not perturbed.

A critical property of phase change materials, so-called threshold-switching phenomenon, makes it possible for the SET programming at a low voltage. Figure 52(a) [195] gives a typical dynamic I–V curve for both the amorphous and crystalline states, although the values of current and voltage parameters may vary for PCRAMs with different phase-change materials. The current is measured for a PCRAM device during a 50-ns pulse with voltage as indicated on the x-axis. Correspondingly, Figure 52(b) shows the resulting resistance after the pulses of Figure 52(a). Seen from the amorphous state, threshold switching exists at around 1 V for the measured cell in Ref. [195], where the phase change material becomes highly conductive. The physics of this effect is still not well understood. A recently reported model with the threshold switching mechanism based on the balance between electron energy gain and relaxation in the hopping transport can serve to predict the sub-threshold characteristics and threshold points for different thickness, temperature, and energy gap of the chalcogenide material [202]. For the highest magnitude pulses where the phase change material is molten, the cell resistance becomes independent of the initial state of the material. This gives the SET window as indicated in Figure 52(b). Multiple resistance states between the minimum and maximum resistance have been demonstrated by properly modulating the electrical pulses used to program the cell [200]. On the other hand, RESET threshold is also apparent from the crystalline state in Figure 52(b). Furthermore, voltages below the threshold voltage allow for an easy and fast reading for the cell state without perturbation. Usually, for a SET operation, the applied current pulse should last long enough to heat the material otherwise the new crystalline phase will return to the highly resistive amorphous state.

Table 5. Some phase change material parameters and the device performance characteristics they influence.

Phase change material parameter	Influence on PCRAM device performance
Crystallization temperature and thermal stability of the amorphous phase	Data retention and archival lifetime Set power
Melting temperature	Reset power
Resistivity in amorphous and crystalline phases	On/off ratio Set and reset current
Threshold voltage	Set voltage and reading voltage
Thermal conductivity in both phases	Set and reset power
Crystallization speed	Set pulse duration (and thus power) Data rate
Melt-quenching speed	Reset pulse duration (and thus power)

Source: Reprinted with permission from [200], G. W. Burr et al., *J. Vac. Sci. Technol. B* 28, 223 (2010). © 2010, American Vacuum Society.

However, for this threshold switching, rather than a threshold voltage, a more accurate description of the underlying physical process is a threshold electric field, which must be surpassed for a success amorphous-crystalline phase transition. The value of threshold electric field is material-dependent. Besides the threshold electric field, there are many other phase change material parameters that can influence the performance of PCRAM devices, which are summarized by Burr et al. in Table 5 [200]. Detail on these parameters as well as its scalability can be referred to Refs. [200, 203].

As PCRAMs store data by a structural phase rather than by an electrical charge and the time-sensitive heating for phase change is much greater than that generated by ionizing radiation, these devices are expected to be tolerant to ionizing radiation effects and displacement [204]. This inherent radiation hardness, together with the appealing device performance, makes it attractive for space-based applications. Both TID and SEE on PCRAMs will be discussed in the following sections.

7.2. Radiation Effects on PCRAM

TID response of PCRAMs was first given by Bernacki et al. [204]. For the radiation study, the devices using a chalcogenide alloy $Ge_2Sb_2Te_5$ (GST) as the phase change material were fabricated in a commercial 0.25 μm CMOS process with radiation-hard CMOS logic. No measurable effect was found on device functionality and retention after irradiation to 1 Mrad(Si) in a static radiation mode under a Co-60 gamma cell. Maimon et al. extended the total dose of Co-60 gamma irradiation up to 2 Mrad(Si) for 64 Kb GST based PCRAMs with a 0.5 μm radiation-hardened CMOS process [205–207]. As shown in Figure 53 [205–207], resistance of the chalcogenide material was not affected by TID. Also, functional test of the memory arrays indicated that no TID induced failures to 2 Mrad(Si). However, it should be mentioned that the 2 Mrad(Si) TID did affect a write current generator circuit, but in general, the integrated PCRAMs have no effect on CMOS transistor characteristics, as well as their response to radiation.

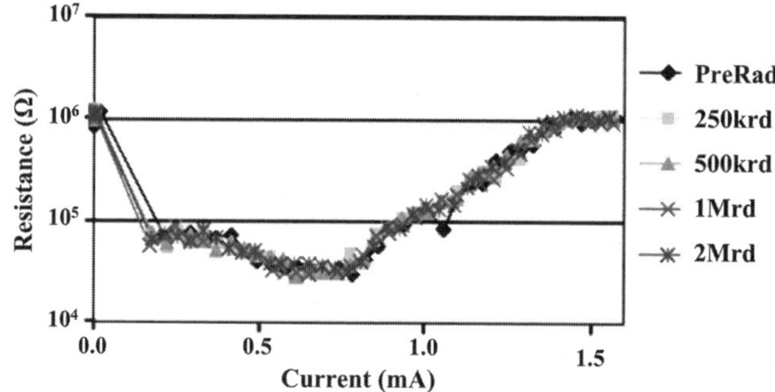

Figure 53. *R–I* curve for typical discrete memory cell. No change was observed to 2 Mrad(Si). Reprinted with permission from [207], J. D. Maimon et al., *IEEE Trans. Nucl. Sci.* 50, 1878 (2003). © 2003, IEEE.

In the same literature, SEE was also studied with heavy ion irradiation, confirming the inherent rad-hardness of PCRAMs. It was demonstrated that no SEU and no SEL occurs to LET_{EFF} 98 MeV cm^2/mg when the devices

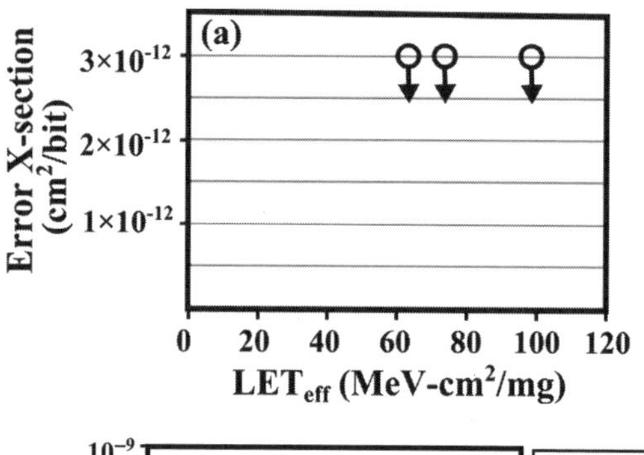

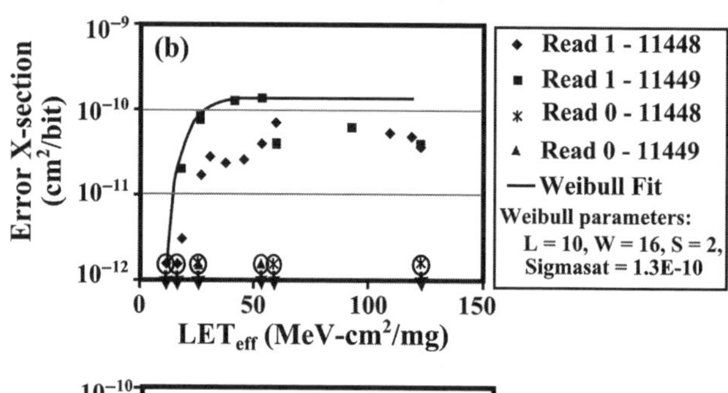

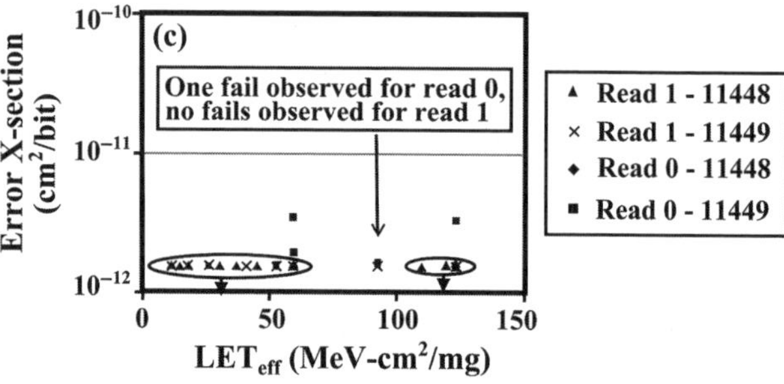

Figure 54. Error cross-section versus LET_{eff}. (a) No upsets were observed during static SEU testing. Cross-section calculated assuming one fail at each LET. (b) Transient read disturbs. Upsets were observed only during dynamic read of the high-resistance memory state. (c) False write observed during dynamic read of low-resistance state. Reprinted with permission from [207], J. D. Maimon et al., *IEEE Trans. Nucl. Sci.* 50, 1878 (2003). © 2003, IEEE.

irradiated in static mode. During dynamic SEE testing to LET_{EFF} 123.2 MeV-cm²/mg, no SEL and SEGR was found in the chalcogenide material itself. However, two SEU modes were observed in this testing mode, read errors and "false writes," which are respectively due to irradiation-induced transient noise in the sense amplifier and write driver circuit, could be avoided by improved circuits. The low cross-sections of the errors are presented in Figure 54 [205–207]. In general, the base semiconductor technology on which the memory is formed should be the major concern for radiation damage.

A 4-Mb prototype chalcogenide RAM (C-RAM) optimized for space applications has been designed and fabricated in a 0.25 μm radiation-hardened CMOS technology by the same group working with BAE Systems, Ovonyx, and the Air Force Research Laboratory [208–210]. A more systematic radiation testing (with second-order radiation effects considered) has been performed [209]. Similar TID and SEE results were demonstrated but with the only failure mode the transient read errors associated with transient upsets in the sense amp and related read circuitry,

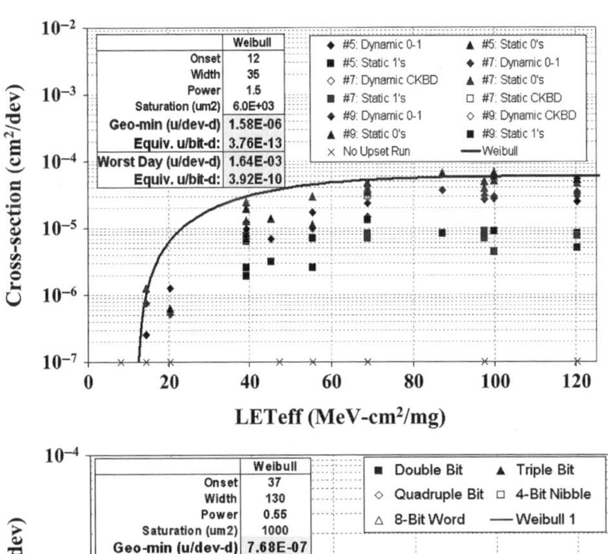

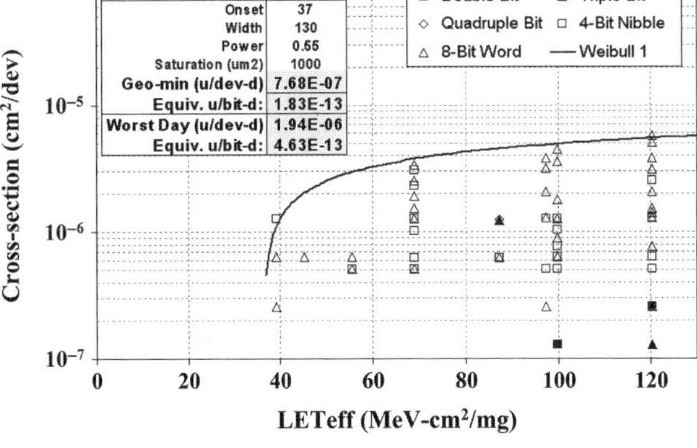

Figure 55. Probability of upsetting (a) a single bit and (b) multiple bits in an 8-bit word due to interaction with a heavy ion found in a typical spacecraft. Note that data were collected from tests at multiple temperatures with various data patterns, test modes and physical orientations. The Weibull curve approximation is meant to cover the worst case encompassing all variations observed during testing. Reprinted with permission from [209], J. Rodgers et al., "9th Annual Non-Volatile Memory Technology Symposium," p. 1, Pacific Grove, CA, 2008. © 2008, IEEE.

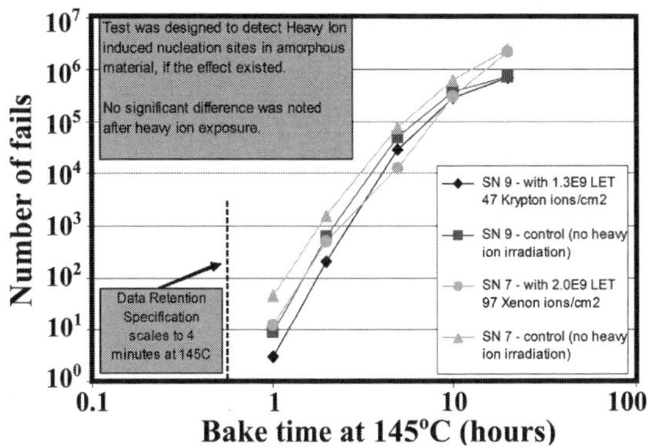

Figure 56. Retention test for PCRAM with and without heavy ion irradiation. Reprinted with permission from [209], J. Rodgers et al., "9th Annual Non-Volatile Memory Technology Symposium," p. 1, Pacific Grove, CA, 2008. © 2008, IEEE.

which further involves correctable single-bit transient read errors and uncorrectable multi-bits transient read errors. Figures 55(a and b) represent the cross-section for single-bit transient read error and multi-bit transient read error respectively [209]. The second-order radiation experiments show that heavy ion striking does not alter the data when devices are unbiased, and also does not affect the stored data retention. The data retention characteristics of C-RAMs with and without heavy ion irradiation are shown in Figure 56 [209], indicating no significant difference exists between both conditions.

The high robustness of 4-Mbit GST-based PCRAM devices against TID up to 30 Mrad(SiO_2) were confirmed by Gasperin et al. by irradiating them with 8 MeV electrons [211]. The observed variation of RESET/SET distribution (seen in Fig. 57 [211]) was attributed to the degradation of the non-rad-hardened MOSFET selectors. Similar results were found in the study of radiation effects by 2 MeV protons and 50 MeV Cu ions (LET $\sim$ 27 MeV cm²/mg) on GST-based PCRAM devices with both MOSFET and BJT selectors [212]. The radiation-induced degradation of the selector transistors accounts for the observed shifts of SET/RESET distributions, although BJT selectors are more robust than MOSFETs to TID, and GST is not highly affected by ionizing particles. Also, the retention experiments indicate unchanged retention characteristics of PCRAMs, while the high temperature annealing experiments shows the possible radiation-induced defects do not influence the GST phase transition process. Recently, the high-radiation hardness of GST-based PCRAMs with a 0.18 μm CMOS technology is again confirmed by a radiation test under Au-197 source [213].

Again, PCRAMs have been demonstrated to be highly robust to radiation effects with high performance. Table 6 [209] summarizes the features of PCRAM designed by BAE Systems for space applications. Therefore, PCRAMs are a prime candidate to replace flash memories for next-generation electronics technology, although several issues still exist and have to be addressed before being commercially used in space missions and applications, such as fabrication process difficulties for high yield and low variability yet combine MLC, "stuck set/reset" in cycling endurance, and cross talk.

Table 6. PCRAM product features for space application.

Minimum read-cycle time 70 ns
Minimum write-cycle time 1000 ns
Single 3.3 V ± 10% power supply

Low operating power
 −290 mW active read (70 ns)
 −140 mW active write (1000 ns)
 −74 mW stand-by

Operating temperature range −40°C to 110°C
Write-cycle endurance 10^5 cycles

Data retention (with ECC)
 −0.3 years at 90°C
 −1.1 years at 85°C
 −3.8 years at 80°C
 −13.5 years at 75°C
 −50 years at 70°C

Radiation levels
 −TID ≥ 1 × 10^6 rad(Si)
 −SEU < 1 × 10^{-11} upsets/bit-day
 −Neutron fluence > 1 × 10^{13} paritcles/cm^2
 −Latchup immune ≤ 120 MeV-cm^2/mg

Source: Reprinted with permission from [209], J. Rodgers et al., "9th Annual Non-Volatile Memory Technology Symposium," p. 1, Pacific Grove, CA, 2008. © 2008, IEEE.

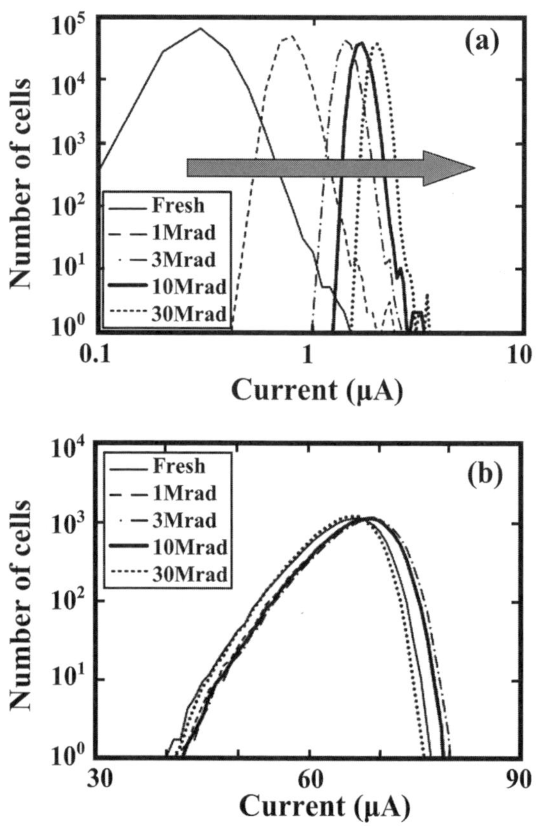

Figure 57. (a) Reset and (b) set read cell distribution measured before irradiation and after each irradiation step. Reprinted with permission from [211], A. Gasperin et al., *IEEE Trans. Nucl. Sci.* 55, 2090 (2008). © 2008, IEEE.

8. RADIATION EFFECTS ON ReRAM/MEMRISTORS

8.1. Introduction to ReRAM/Memristors

In addition to FeRAM, MRAM and PCRAM, a new candidate has emerged recently, ReRAM, with a metal-insulator-metal (MIM) capacitor-like structure, as shown in Figure 58(a). In general, "*M*," used as metal electrodes, can be various metals or electro-conducting non-metal; "*I*," insulating or resistive materials, includes a large variety of metal oxides, higher chalocogenides and organic compounds. MIM cells can be electrically switched between at least 2 different resistance states: high-resistance state (HRS, with high resistance R_{off} or R_H) and low-resistance state (LRS, with resistance R_{on} or R_L). In other words, a MIM cell in its HRS can be set into an LRS by applying a programming (or write) voltage, or otherwise it can be reset from an LRS into an HRS when an erase voltage is applied. The resistance of the cell is then measured by a small bias voltage which does not perturb the state. Furthermore, multilevel switching with more than 2 resistance states have been realized for storage of multiple bits per cell [214–217] when using appropriate voltage pulses or current compliances, which is one of the tempting properties of ReRAMs. In previous literature, excellent and reliable resistive switching performance has been reported, such as high $R_{\text{off}}/R_{\text{on}}$ ratio ($\sim 10^7$), ultrafast programming speed (5 ns), long retention time (> 10 years) and good endurance (10^{15} cycles) [217–219]. Because of its simple structure, a highly scalable cross-bar matrix can be readily achieved only by connecting the word and bitlines, seen in Figure 58(b). The high performance and the excellent scaling potential, together with its good compatibility with CMOS technologies, make ReRAM devices a promising candidate for next-generation NVMs.

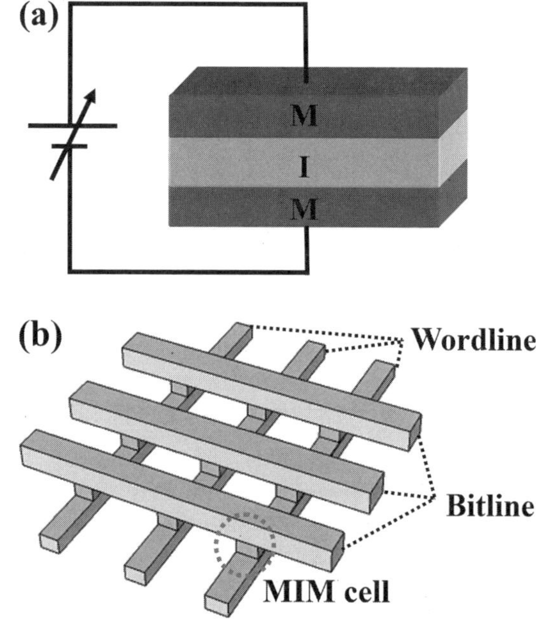

Figure 58. (a) Schematic structure of MIM cell, and (b) its crossbar architecture.

In terms of resistive switching with respect to the applied electrical polarity, ReRAM devices have 2 main switching modes. One is unipolar resistive switching when the switching procedure does not depend on the polarity of the write voltage signal (Fig. 59(a)). The other is bipolar resistive switching, in which SET is accomplished at one voltage polarity and RESET occurs with a reversed voltage polarity (Fig. 59(b)). It should be noted that, for an as-prepared ReRAM device, a "forming" process is usually required to switch the pristine HRS into an LRS by applying a high voltage stress. After the forming process, ReRAM devices are set and reset at a much lower threshold voltage (V_{set}, V_{reset}), respectively.

Several models have been proposed to explain the resistive switching phenomena, such as space charge limited current (SCLC) [220, 221], the formation and rupture of conducting filaments [214], trap charging/discharging [222]. However, the exact and universal mechanism has not yet been clearly understood. In some literatures, resistive switching mechanisms are classified into 2 types: filamentary conducting path and interface conducting path [223]. Another well-accepted classification is the redox-related mechanisms including thermochemical mechanism (TCM) [224], electrochemical metallization mechanism (ECM) [225], and valence change mechanism (VCM) [226, 227], which are reviewed by Waser et al. in detail [228, 229]. TCM effects exist in all transition metal oxides, in which NiO-based ReRAMs have been well studied [224, 230–232]. Briefly, both SET and RESET in TCM ReRAMs are based on thermally triggered formation and rupture of filament mechanism. Filaments have been directly observed [233]. During the SET process (Fig. 60), the device experiences a threshold switching at a weak spot in the dielectric layer inducing a current overshoot at the highly conductive weak spot. This results in local chemical and structural modification by Joule heating, electromigration of melting conductive species of the electrodes and/or the migration of ions and finally a conducting filament connecting the top and bottom electrodes [231]. The filament may consist of defects, stoichiometric deficiency of oxygen (or excess of Ni), and metallic species injected from the electrodes, all of which allow a metallic behavior of electrical

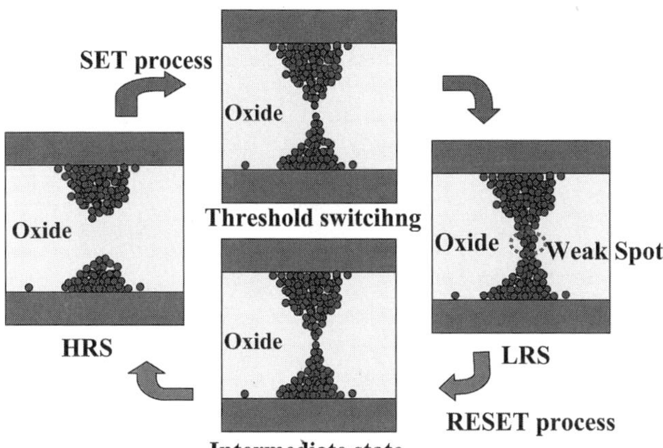

Figure 60. A schematic diagram for the mechanism of resistive switching for TCM.

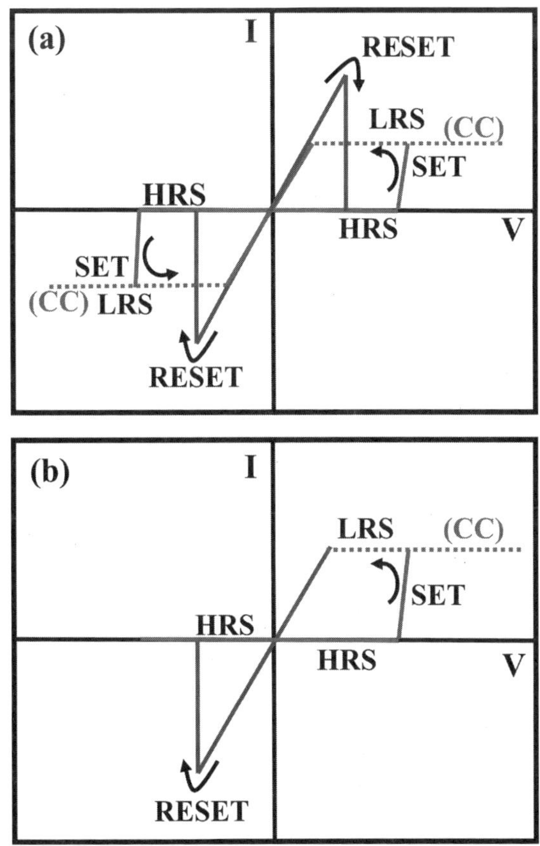

Figure 59. (a) The basic I–V schemes of unipolar switching, and (b) bipolar switching. "CC" is the current compliance, which is a fixed number for SET process.

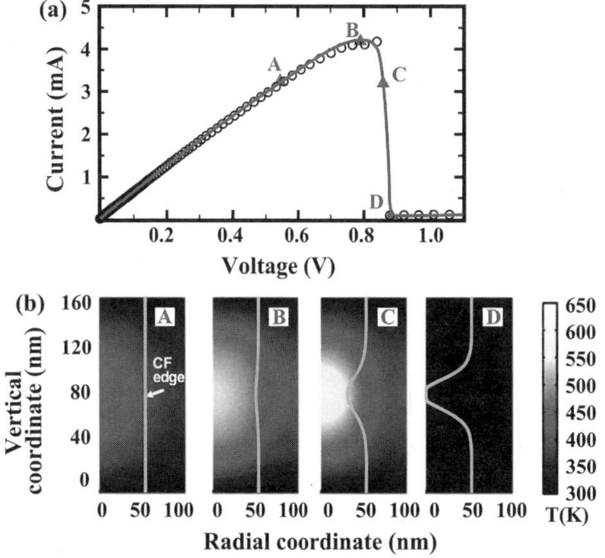

Figure 61. (a) Measured I–V characteristic for a RESET process with the four bias points A at 0.53 V, B 0.78 V, C 0.85 V, and D 0.87 V. (b) Calculated temperature map along a filament for applied voltages at A, B, C, and D labeled in (a). Reprinted with permission from [224], U. Russo et al., *IEEE Trans. Electron Devices* 56, 193 (2009). © 2009, IEEE.

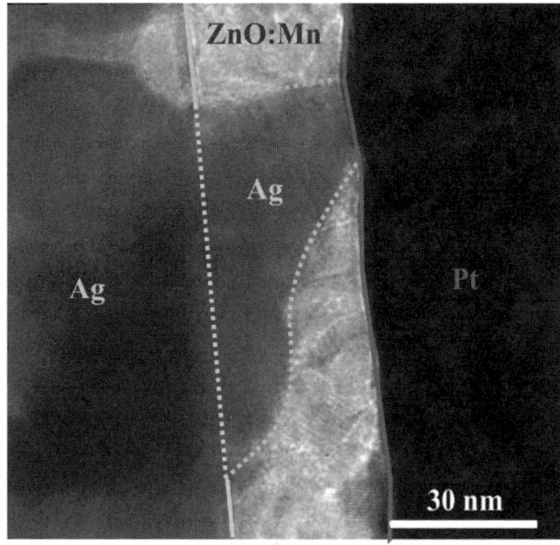

Figure 62. HRTEM image of Ag filament inside Mn-doped ZnO layer. Adapted with permission from [218], Y. C. Yang et al., *Nano Lett.* 9, 1636 (2009). © 2009, American Chemical Society.

conductivity of the filament. The RESET operation (Fig. 60) is driven by Joule heating with a self-accelerating effect during the application of an electrical pulse or sweeping, which enables thermally activated dissolution and/or oxidation of the filament, and thus loss of conductive species. Thus, TCM ReRAM properties are also affected by the heat conduction of the electrodes [232]. Note that the major heating takes place close to the middle of the filament [224, 231]. Figure 61 [224] shows the simulation result for a NiO-based TCM ReRAM, representing the Joule heating with the hot spot at the middle of the filament leading to the rupture of the filament.

When applying a sufficient voltage in an ECM, the electrochemically active metal electrode is dissolved, creating metal ions that migrate to the inert electrode under a high electric field and then are reduced back to metal leading to cathodic deposition. The filament diagram is similar to TCM in Figure 60, except that the weak spot is at the interface of the inert electrode and the oxide, and the formation and rupture of the filament are driven by

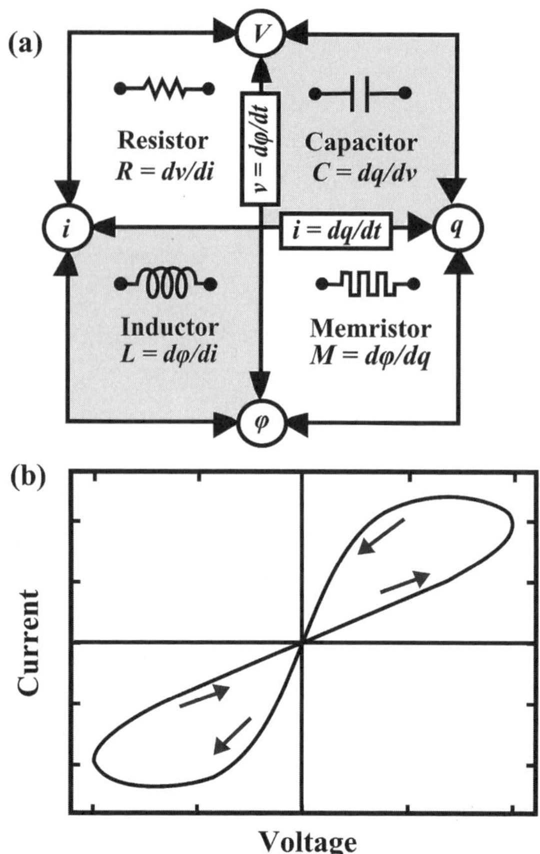

Figure 64. (a) The four fundamental two-terminal circuit elements: resistor, capacitor, inductor, and memristor. Resistors and memristors are subsets of a more general class of dynamical devices, memristems. (b) A typical I–V loop for a memristor device.

electrochemical reactions. SET is completed when a metallic bridge forms inside the oxide and connects both electrodes. RESET is considered an opposite process of SET. Metallic filaments have been experimentally observed by high resolution transmission electronic microscopy (HRTEM) [218, 234], as shown in Figure 62 [218] where Ag filament was

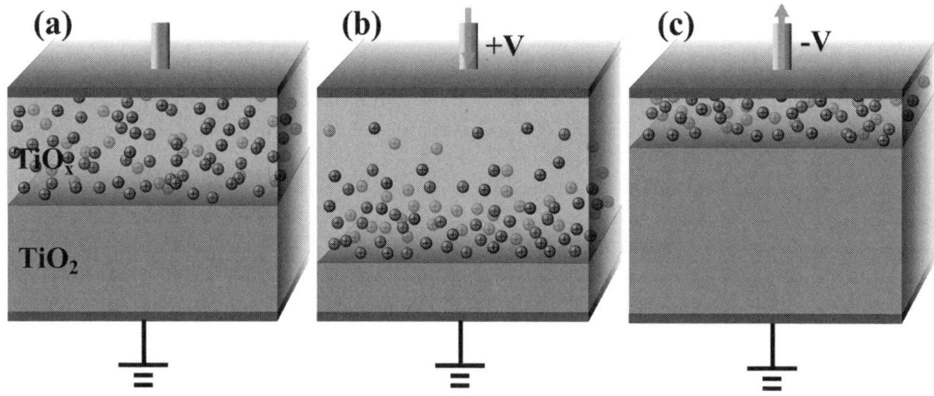

Figure 63. Schematic of resistive switching of a TiO_2-based VCM cell. (a) A pristine memory cell contains a conducting TiO_x layer and a TiO_2 nonconducting layer; (b) when applied positive voltage, the positive charged O vacancies are repelled down to the TiO_2 layer pushing the conducting layer boundary towards the bottom electrode and decreasing the resistance; (c) with a negative bias, O vacancies are pulled out of TiO_2 increasing the resistance of the whole memory cell.

formed in an ZnO:Mn layer. Typically, ReRAMs with an Ag or Cu electrode are in this category.

In VCM, oxygen vacancies, related to oxygen ion defects and positively charged, play a critical role in resistance switching because they are much more mobile than the transition metal ions and can therefore lead to ionic conductivity even at room temperature. There are 2 fundamentally different geometrics of VCM type resistive switching; that is, the filamentary switching scenario and the area distributed switching scenario. In the former scenario, oxygen vacancies accumulate into vacancy chains under electric field, building up a conducting filament inside the oxide. In the latter scenario, resistance switching occurs homogeneously over the entire area of the electrode of the memory cell. As shown in Figure 63(a), the resistive layer contains an insulting TiO_2 layer and a metallic TiO_{2-x} layer. When applying positive voltage (see in Fig. 63(b)) on the top electrode with the bottom electrode grounded, oxygen vacancies are repelled along the electric field direction, increasing the percentage of conducting TiO_{2-x} and thus enhancing the conductivity; whereas the oxygen vacancies are pushed back when negative voltage is applied (Fig. 63(c)), leading to a high-resistance state. Thus, unlike filamentary switching, distributed switching results in a R_{on} proportional to the electrode area [229]. In fact, the concentration equilibrium of oxygen vacancies is determined by the oxygen partial pressure of the ambient atmosphere according to

$$O_O \leftrightarrow \frac{1}{2}O_2(g) + V_O + 2e \qquad (6)$$

where O_O and V_O are oxygen ions at regular lattice sites and oxygen vacancies respectively. The oxygen gas bubble has been experimentally observed during electroforming and SET processes [235]. Recently, nanofilaments of conducting Ti_4O_7 phase have also been observed in TiO_2-based ReRAM [236]. It should be noted that in the filamentary switching mechanism, rather than only a single filament, multiple filaments may form, which makes R_{on} of the device cell size-dependent. VCM memories, $SrTiO_3$- or TiO_2-based ReRAM for instance, are either filamentary switching [226, 227] or area distributed switching [237], or even a combination of both [238].

The TiO_2-based ReRAM mentioned above is also called a memristor. The conception of the memristor is introduced by Leon Chua as the fourth basic circuit element [239, 240] (Fig. 64(a) [241]) with a memristance M and a relation: $d\varphi = M\,dq$, where φ is the magnetic flux and q is the charge. Recently, Strukov and his co-workers first linked the experimental resistive switching with hysteretic I–V characteristics to memristive behavior [241], which has an "8" signature shape of an I–V curve (Fig. 64(b) [241]). Since then, memristive systems have attracted extensive attention, which has been extended to memcapacitor, meminductor systems [242–244]. Furthermore, the CMOS compatible high-density crossbar arrays using a nanoscale a-Si-based memristive system have been demonstrated with excellent yield and performance, indicating the promising potential for next-generation NVMd and for novel forms of electrical circuits, such as synapses in solid-state neuromorphic circuits [245–247].

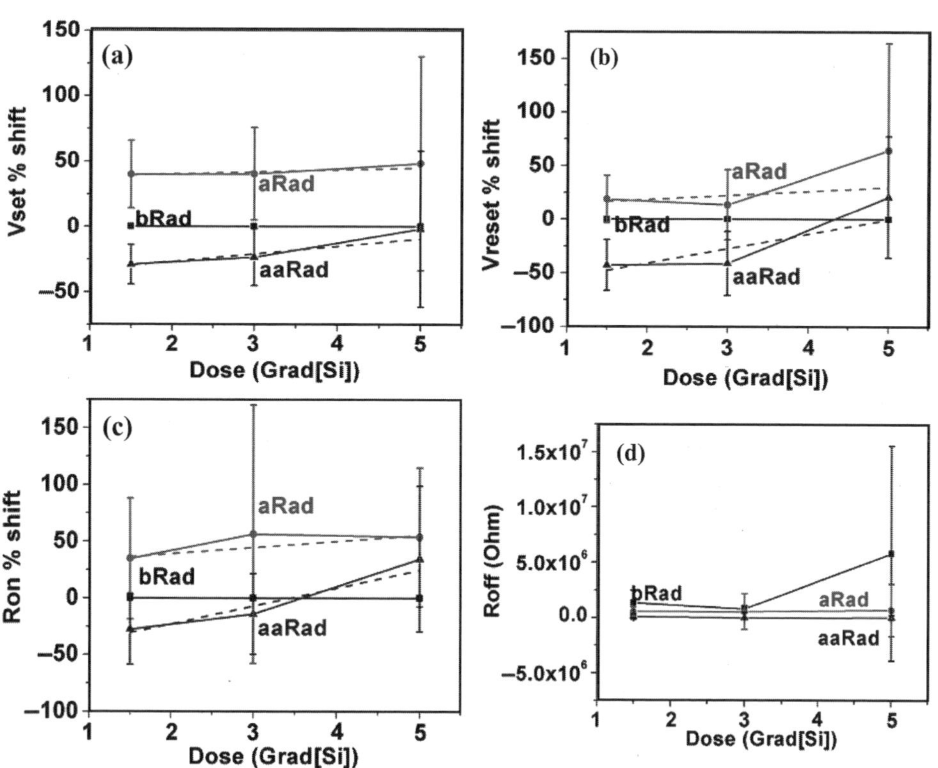

Figure 65. 1.5, 3, and 5 Grad(Si) TID inducing performance changes of Cu/HfO_2:Cu/Pt devices before radiation (brad), immediately after radiation (aRad) and 5 days later after radiation (aaRad). (a) Average shift of V_{set}, (b) average shift of V_{reset}, (c) average shift of R_{on}, and (d) average value of R_{off}. The dashed lines in (a–c) are linear fits for the corresponding shifts. Reprinted with permission from [248], B. Brian et al., *Nanotechnol.* 21, 475206 (2010). © 2010, IOP Publishing.

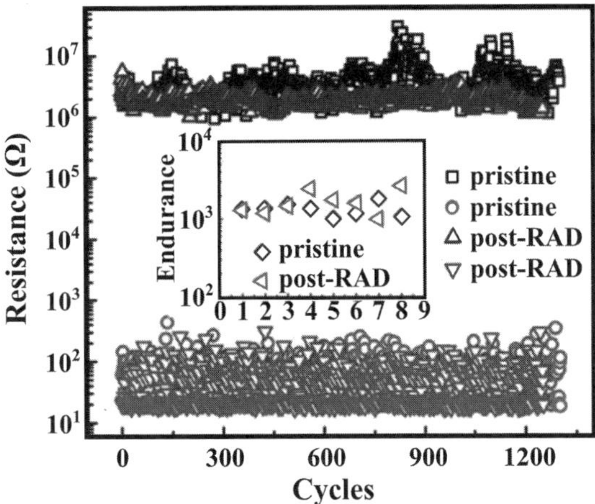

Figure 66. Endurance characteristics for the pristine and postradiation devices. Resistance are stable over 1000 cycles for both types of devices. The endurance results of several devices for both types are shown in the inset. Reprinted with permission from [249], Y. Wang et al., *IEEE Electron Device Lett.* 31, 1470 (2010). © 2010, IEEE.

8.2. Radiation Effects on ReRAM/Memristors

Only a few reports on the radiation response of ReRAM and memristor devices have been published recently. Butcher et al. [248] found that when irradiated under 2 MeV protons with TID of ~Grad(Si), Cu-doped HfO_2-based ReRAM were still functional, but experienced V_{set}, V_{reset}, and R_{on} shifts immediately after the radiation experiments but with rebound effects after 5 days, whereas R_{off} degraded over time after the radiation, as shown in Figure 65 [248]. They attributed the results to an increase of trap densities and defects in the HfO_2 by radiation. With the same ReRAM devices, high stability and no degradation was observed in all performance parameters, such as $V_{set/reset}$, operation speed, endurance, and retention, when irradiated under Co-60 γ ray with a total dose up to 360 krad(Si) [249]. This result indicates HfO_2-based ReRAMs have a radiation hardness up to a total dose of about a few Grad(Si), although a slight degradation occurs with high TID. Figure 66 [249] shows the endurance result with R_{on} and R_{off} before and after radiation. It is interesting that resistance switching properties can be induced by SHI irradiation due to the increased density of defects and thus of metallic filaments inside the oxide layer, demonstrated by the radiation experiment on Li-doped NiO-based junction [250] with 100 MeV Ag = 14 ions bombardment.

Radiation studies on TiO_2 memristive junctions were also done both experimentally and by simulation [251–254].

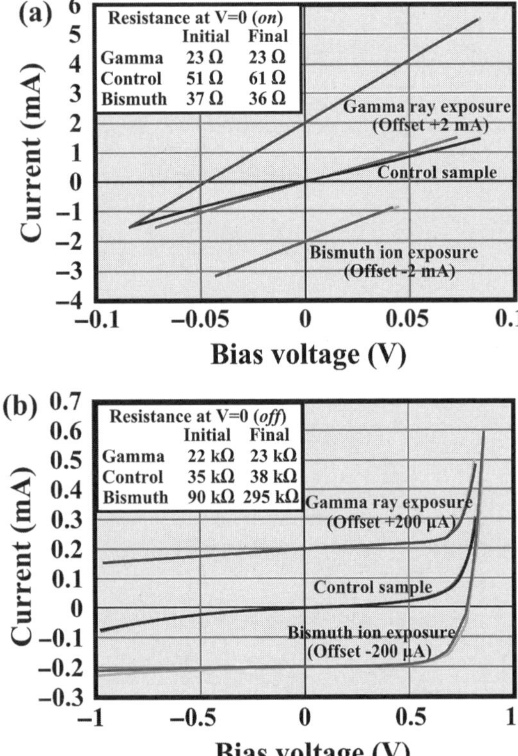

Figure 67. I–V curves of the (a) ON states and (b) OFF states of devices before and after radiation exposure with the dark/light lines denoting the pre-/post-radiation curves, respectively. The γ-ray exposure curves were offset vertically up from the origin and the bismuth ion exposure curves down for clarity. Both the γ- and Bi-ion bombarded samples showed very little change after radiation. Reprinted with permission from [253], W. M. Tong et al., *IEEE Trans. Nucl. Sci.* 57, 1640 (2010). © 2010, IEEE.

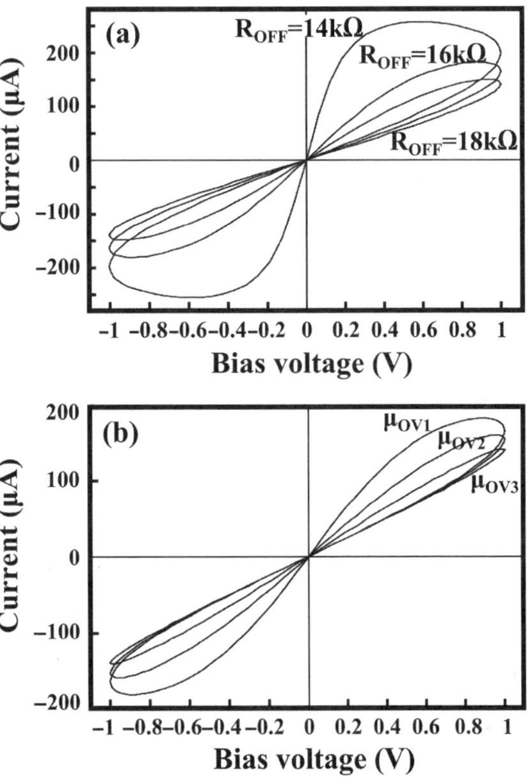

Figure 68. I–V curves of a TiO_2 memristor, plotted for (a) 3 different values of the stoichiometric region resistance: R_{off} = 18 kΩ, 16 kΩ, and 14 kΩ. The decrease in R_{off} is caused by radiation induced emergence of oxygen vacancies in the stoichiometric TiO_2 region; (b) 3 different values of the oxygen vacancy mobility: $\mu_{OV1} = 10^{-10}$ cm^2 v^{-1} s^{-1}, $\mu_{OV2} = 0.8 \times 10^{-10}$ cm^2 v^{-1} s^{-1}, and $\mu_{OV3} = 0.5 \times 10^{-10}$ cm^2 v^{-1} s^{-1}. The decrease in μ_{OV} is caused by the radiation induced presence of oxygen ions and atoms in the oxide. Note that the applied voltage is $v(t) = v_0 \sin(\omega t)$ with $v_0 = 1$ V and $\omega = \pi/10$ s^{-1}.

Experimental results by Tong et al. [253] show that TiO_2 memristive junctions have no degradation (see Fig. 67 [253]) after 45 Mrad(Si) of 1 MeV Co-60 radiation and 23 Mrad(Si) of 941 MeV Bi-ions, due to the insignificant or little TID effects as compared to 1% intrinsic defect dopants, as well as no displacement in the memristor near the surface. Simulations of proton and heavy ion irradiation on TiO_2 memristors [252, 254] show that the TiO_2 memristors of nanosize are immune to ions with energies > 10 MeV. But for ions with certain lower-energies, massive production of oxygen ion/oxygen vacancy pairs in the TiO_2 region will be generated, which influences the device's operation in several ways:

(1) radiation-induced oxygen vacancies in the stoichiometric TiO_2 layer can cause reduced R_{off} and counter-clockwise rotation of the memristor I–V curve and a larger swing in its double-loops (Fig. 68(a) [254]);
(2) the radiation-induced Ti and O ions and interstitial atoms can reduce the mobility of oxygen vacancies and cause clockwise rotation of the I–V curve (Fig. 68(b) [254]);
(3) the displaced oxygen ions may reach the electrodes, forming O_2 gas and leading to permanent disruption of memristor functionality;
(4) when the memristor is used as a switching element of a NVM, the high resistance state can be perturbed by ion bombardment and result in a readout error by a diminished oxygen-poor region.

9. SUMMARY

In this chapter, recent studies of the radiation effects on various nonvolatile memories have been reviewed. Compared with Si flash, several emerging devices such as ferroelectric random access memory (RAM), magnetoresistive RAM, phase-change RAM and resistive RAM have shown potential for performance improvement as well as radiation-hardened properties. Recent results demonstrated that magnetoresistive and resistive RAMs might become the dominant next-generation radiation-hardened memory devices due to their CMOS-compatible fabrication and superior device performance under radiation. As CMOS technologies continue scaling, these emerging nanometer-scale memory devices will open new opportunities to establish many innovative high-performance and reliable electronic systems for aerospace and nuclear industries.

REFERENCES

1. A. Holmes-Siedle and L. Adams, "Handbook of Radiation Effects." Oxford Univercity Press, New York, 1993.
2. C. Claeys and E. Simoen, "Radiation Effects in Advanced Semiconductor Materials and Devices." Springer, Germany, 2002.
3. E. G. Stassinopoulos and J. P. Raymond, *Proc. IEEE* 76, 1423 (1988).
4. D. M. Fleetwood, P. S. Winokur, and P. E. Dodd, *Microelectron. Reliab.* 40, 17 (2000).
5. J. L. Barth, C. S. Dyer, and E. G. Stassinopoulos, *IEEE Trans. Nucl. Sci.* 50, 466 (2003).
6. A. R. Frederickson, *IEEE Trans. Nucl. Sci.* 43, 426 (1996).
7. J. H. Warner, S. R. Messenger, R. J. Walters, G. P. Summers, M. J. Romero, and E. A. Burke, *IEEE Trans. Nucl. Sci.* 54, 196 (2007).
8. J. H. Warner, S. R. Messenger, R. J. Walters, and G. P. Summers, "33rd IEEE Photovoltaic Specialists Conference," p. 1, San Diego, CA, 2008.
9. G. P. Summers, E. A. Burke, P. Shapiro, S. R. Messenger, and R. J. Walters, *IEEE Trans. Nucl. Sci.* 40, 1372 (1993).
10. J. R. Srour and J. W. Palko, *IEEE Trans. Nucl. Sci.* 53, 3610 (2006).
11. S. R. Messenger, M. A. Xapsos, E. A. Burke, R. J. Walters, and G. P. Summers, *IEEE Trans. Nucl. Sci.* 44, 2169 (1997).
12. A. Kalavagunta, A. Touboul, L. Shen, R. D. Schrimpf, R. A. Reed, D. M. Fleetwood, R. K. Jain, and U. K. Mishra, *IEEE Trans. Nucl. Sci.* 55, 2106 (2008).
13. C. J. Dale, P. W. Marshall, E. A. Burke, G. P. Summers, and E. A. Wolicki, *IEEE Trans. Nucl. Sci.* 35, 1208 (1988).
14. M. Beaumel, X. D. Herve, and D. Van Aken, *IEEE Trans. Nucl. Sci.* 57, 2056 (2010).
15. P. E. Dodd, J. R. Schwank, M. R. Shaneyfelt, V. Ferlet-Cavrois, P. Paillet, J. Baggio, G. L. Hash, J. A. Felix, K. Hirose, and H. Saito, *IEEE Trans. Nucl. Sci.* 54, 889 (2007).
16. G. D. Badhwar, *Radiat. Res.* 148, S3 (1997).
17. H. Mavromichalaki, A. Papaioannou, G. Mariatos, M. Papailiou, A. Belov, E. Eroshenko, V. Yanke, and E. G. Stassinopoulos, *IEEE Trans. Nucl. Sci.* 54, 1089 (2007).
18. S. Bourdarie and M. Xapsos, *IEEE Trans. Nucl. Sci.* 55, 1810 (2008).
19. J. R. Heirtzler, *J. Atmos. Sol. Terr. Phys.* 64, 1701 (2002).
20. E. J. Daly, J. Lemaire, D. Heynderickx, and D. J. Rodgers, *IEEE Trans. Nucl. Sci.* 43, 403 (1996).
21. M. S. Gussenhoven, E. G. Mullen, and D. H. Brautigam, *IEEE Trans. Nucl. Sci.* 43, 353 (1996).
22. D. Boscher and S. Bourdarie, *Adv. Space Res.* 28, 1739 (2001).
23. D. Heynderickx, M. Kruglanski, V. Pierrard, J. Lemaire, M. D. Looper, and J. B. Blake, *IEEE Trans. Nucl. Sci.* 46, 1475 (1999).
24. S. L. Huston and K. A. Pfitzer, *IEEE Trans. Nucl. Sci.* 45, 2972 (1998).
25. D. M. Boscher, S. A. Bourdarie, R. H. W. Friedel, and R. D. Belian, *IEEE Trans. Nucl. Sci.* 50, 2278 (2003).
26. A. S. Piet, S. Bourdarie, D. Boscher, and R. H. W. Friedel, *IEEE Trans. Nucl. Sci.* 53, 1844 (2006).
27. A. Sicard-Piet, S. Bourdarie, D. Boscher, R. H. W. Friedel, M. Thomsen, T. Goka, H. Matsumoto, and H. Koshiishi, *Space Weather* 6, S07003 (2008).
28. S. R. Elkington, M. Wiltberger, A. A. Chan, and D. N. Baker, *J. Atmos. Sol. Terr. Phys.* 66, 1371 (2004).
29. M. S. Potgieter, *Space Sci. Rev.* 83, 147 (1998).
30. G. D. Badhwar and P. M. O'Neill, *Adv. Space Res.* 17, 7 (1996).
31. A. J. Tylka, J. H. Adams, Jr, P. R. Boberg, B. Brownstein, W. F. Dietrich, E. O. Flueckiger, E. L. Petersen, M. A. Shea, D. F. Smart, and E. C. Smith, *IEEE Trans. Nucl. Sci.* 44, 2150 (1997).
32. D. L. Chenette, J. Chen, E. Clayton, T. G. Guzik, J. P. Wefel, M. Garcia-Munoz, C. Lopate, K. R. Pyle, K. P. Ray, E. G. Mullen, and D. A. Hardy, *IEEE Trans. Nucl. Sci.* 41, 2332 (1994).
33. P. M. O'Neill, *Adv. Space Res.* 37, 1727 (2006).
34. J. Adams, J. Watts, A. Barghouty, K. Ei-Nemr, C. Malott, and S. Sam, "37th COSPAR Scienctific Assembly." p. 24, Montreal, Canada, 2008.
35. M. A. Xapsos, J. L. Barth, E. G. Stassinopoulos, E. A. Burke, and G. B. Gee, Technical Report, NASA/TP-1999-209763, M-952, NAS 1.60:209763, 1999.
36. S. R. Kulkarni, M. Ravindra, G. R. Joshi, and R. Damle, *Radiat. Eff. Defects Solids* 159, 273 (2004).
37. J. F. Ziegler, J. P. Biersack, and M. D. Ziegler, "SRIM-The Stopping and Range of Ions in Matter." SRIM Co., Maryland, 2008.
38. J. R. Schwank, "31st Annual International Nuclear and Space Radiation Effects Conference," p. 1, Tucson, AZ, 1994.
39. H. J. Barnaby, *IEEE Trans. Nucl. Sci.* 53, 3103 (2006).

40. K. A. LaBel, C. E. Barnes, P. W. Marshall, C. J. Marshall, A. H. Johnston, R. A. Reed, J. L. Barth, C. M. Seidleck, S. A. Kayali, and M. V. O'Bryan, "2000 IEEE Aerospace Conference Proceedings," Vol. 5, p. 535, Big Sky, MT, 2000.
41. J. R. Schwank, M. R. Shaneyfelt, D. M. Fleetwood, J. A. Felix, P. E. Dodd, P. Paillet, and V. Ferlet-Cavrois, *IEEE Trans. Nucl. Sci.* 55, 1833 (2008).
42. J. R. Srour and J. M. McGarrity, *Proc. IEEE* 76, 1443 (1988).
43. R. D. Schrimpf, "Radiation Effects on Embedded Systems." (R. Velazco, P. Fouillat, and R. Reis, Eds.), p. 11, Springer, Netherlands, 2007.
44. R. Ronen, A. Mendelson, K. Lai, L. Shih-Lien, F. Pollack, and J. P. Shen, *Proc. IEEE* 89, 325 (2001).
45. P. E. Dodd and L. W. Massengill, *IEEE Trans. Nucl. Sci.* 50, 583 (2003).
46. R. Perez, *IEEE Trans. Electromagn. Compat.* 50, 455 (2008).
47. J. M. Benedetto, P. H. Eaton, D. G. Mavis, M. Gadlage, and T. Turflinger, *IEEE Trans. Nucl. Sci.* 53, 3462 (2006).
48. H. H. K. Tang and K. R. Rodbell, *MRS Bull.* 28, 111 (2003).
49. S. Duzellier, *Aerosp. Sci. Technol.* 9, 93 (2005).
50. E. Normand, *IEEE Trans. Nucl. Sci.* 43, 461 (1996).
51. E. Normand, *IEEE Trans. Nucl. Sci.* 43, 2742 (1996).
52. J. Olsen, P. E. Becher, P. B. Fynbo, P. Raaby, and J. Schultz, *IEEE Trans. Nucl. Sci.* 40, 74 (1993).
53. C. D. Davidson, E. W. Blackmore, and J. I. Hess, "INTELE 26th Annual International Telecommunications Energy Conference," p. 503, Chicago, IL, 2004.
54. P. E. Dodd, M. R. Shaneyfelt, J. R. Schwank, and J. A. Felix, *IEEE Trans. Nucl. Sci.* 57, 1747 (2010).
55. G. Bruguier and J. M. Palau, *IEEE Trans. Nucl. Sci.* 43, 522 (1996).
56. P. E. Dodd, M. R. Shaneyfelt, J. A. Felix, and J. R. Schwank, *IEEE Trans. Nucl. Sci.* 51, 3278 (2004).
57. J. Benedetto, P. Eaton, K. Avery, D. Mavis, M. Gadlage, T. Turflinger, P. E. Dodd, and G. Vizkelethyd, *IEEE Trans. Nucl. Sci.* 51, 3480 (2004).
58. J. H. Hohl and G. H. Johnnson, *IEEE Trans. Nucl. Sci.* 36, 2260 (1989).
59. S. Liu, M. Boden, D. A. Girdhar, and J. L. Titus, *IEEE Trans. Nucl. Sci.* 53, 3379 (2006).
60. F. W. Sexton, D. M. Fleetwood, M. R. Shaneyfelt, P. E. Dodd, and G. L. Hash, *IEEE Trans. Nucl. Sci.* 44, 2345 (1997).
61. G. Swift and R. Katz, "3rd European Conference on Radiation and Its Effects on Components and Systems," p. 425, Arcachon, France, 1995.
62. R. Koga, S. H. Penzin, K. B. Crawford, and W. R. Crain, "4th European Conference on Radiation and Its Effects on Components and Systems," p. 311, Cannes, France, 1997.
63. P. E. Dodd, *IEEE Trans. Device Mater. Reliab.* 5, 343 (2005).
64. J. Alvarado, E. Boufouss, V. Kilchytska, and D. Flandre, *Microelectron. Reliab.* 50, 1852 (2010).
65. J. R. Brews, M. Allenspach, R. D. Schrimpf, K. F. Galloway, J. L. Titus, and C. F. Wheatley, *IEEE Trans. Nucl. Sci.* 40, 1959 (1993).
66. M. J. Gadlage, R. D. Schrimpf, J. M. Benedetto, P. H. Eaton, D. G. Mavis, M. Sibley, K. Avery, and T. L. Turflinger, *IEEE Trans. Nucl. Sci.* 51, 3285 (2004).
67. G. H. Johnson, J. M. Palau, C. Dachs, K. F. Galloway, and R. D. Schrimpf, *IEEE Trans. Nucl. Sci.* 43, 546 (1996).
68. S. E. Kerns, L. W. Massengill, D. V. Kerns, Jr, M. L. Alles, T. W. Houston, H. Lu, and L. R. Hite, *IEEE Trans. Nucl. Sci.* 36, 2305 (1989).
69. S. Kuboyama, N. Ikeda, T. Hirao, and S. Matsuda, *IEEE Trans. Nucl. Sci.* 51, 3336 (2004).
70. J. C. Pickel, *IEEE Trans. Nucl. Sci.* 43, 483 (1996).
71. M. Turowski, A. Fedoseyev, A. Raman, and K. Warren, "15th International Conference on Mixed Design of Integrated Circuits and Systems," p. 443, Poznan, Poland, 2008.
72. R. A. Weller, M. H. Mendenhall, R. A. Reed, R. D. Schrimpf, K. M. Warren, B. D. Sierawski, and L. W. Massengill, *IEEE Trans. Nucl. Sci.* 57, 1726 (2010).
73. R. A. Weller, R. A. Reed, K. M. Warren, M. H. Mendenhall, B. D. Sierawski, R. D. Schrimpf, and L. W. Massengill, *IEEE Trans. Nucl. Sci.* 56, 3098 (2009).
74. T. P. Ma and P. V. Dressendorfer, "Ionizing Radiation Effects in MOS Devices and Circuits." John Wiley & Sons, New York, 1989.
75. V. Re, L. Gaioni, M. Manghisoni, L. Ratti, V. Speziali, and G. Traversi, "IEEE Nuclear Science Symposium Conference Record," p. 3086, Dresden, Germany, 2008.
76. A. H. Johnston, "4th European Conference on Radiation and Its Effects on Components and Systems," p. 1, Cannes, France, 1997.
77. J. W. Schrankler, R. K. Reich, M. S. Holt, D. H. Ju, J. S. T. Huang, G. D. Kirchner, and H. L. Hughes, *IEEE Trans. Nucl. Sci.* 32, 3988 (1985).
78. R. C. Lacoe, J. V. Osborn, R. Koga, S. Brown, and D. C. Mayer, *IEEE Trans. Nucl. Sci.* 47, 2334 (2000).
79. H. L. Hughes and J. M. Benedetto, *IEEE Trans. Nucl. Sci.* 50, 500 (2003).
80. W. You-Lin and H. Jenn-Gwo, *IEEE Electron Device Lett.* 14, 1 (1993).
81. B.-Y. Mao, C.-E. Chen, G. Pollack, H. L. Hughes, and G. E. Davis, *IEEE Trans. Nucl. Sci.* 34, 1692 (1987).
82. K. E. Sickafus, L. Minervini, R. W. Grimes, J. A. Valdez, M. Ishimaru, F. Li, K. J. McClellan, and T. Hartmann, *Science* 289, 748 (2000).
83. P. J. Sellin and J. Vaitkus, *Nucl. Instrum. Methods Phys. Res. A* 557, 479 (2006).
84. R. L. Pease, *IEEE Trans. Nucl. Sci.* 43, 442 (1996).
85. G. Cellere, A. Paccagnella, A. Visconti, M. Bonanomi, A. Candelori, and S. Lora, *IEEE Trans. Nucl. Sci.* 52, 2372 (2005).
86. P. Pavan, R. Bez, P. Olivo, and E. Zanoni, *Proc. IEEE* 85, 1248 (1997).
87. G. Cellere, A. Paccagnella, S. Lora, A. Pozza, G. Tao, and A. Scarpa, *IEEE Trans. Nucl. Sci.* 51, 2912 (2004).
88. G. Cellere, A. Paccagnella, A. Visconti, M. Bonanomi, S. Beltrami, J. R. Schwank, M. R. Shaneyfelt, and P. Paillet, *IEEE Trans. Nucl. Sci.* 54, 1066 (2007).
89. D. N. Nguyen, S. M. Guertin, G. M. Swift, and A. H. Johnston, *IEEE Trans. Nucl. Sci.* 46, 1744 (1999).
90. D. N. Nguyen and L. Z. Scheick, "IEEE Radiation Effects Data Workshop," p. 18, Monterey, CA, 2003.
91. H. R. Schwartz, D. K. Nichols, and A. H. Johnston, *IEEE Trans. Nucl. Sci.* 44, 2315 (1997).
92. D. N. Nguyen and L. Z. Scheick, "IEEE Radiation Effects Data Workshop," p. 62, Phoenix, AZ, 2002.
93. M. Bagatin, G. Cellere, S. Gerardin, A. Paccagnella, A. Visconti, and S. Beltrami, *IEEE Trans. Nucl. Sci.* 56, 1909 (2009).
94. M. Bagatin, G. Cellere, S. Gerardin, A. Paccagnella, A. Visconti, S. Beltrami, and M. Maccarrone, "IOLTS'07 Proceedings of the 13th IEEE International On-Line Testing Symposium," p. 146, IEEE Computer Society, Washington, DC, 2007.
95. G. Cellere and A. Paccagnella, *IEEE Trans. Device Mater. Reliab.* 4, 359 (2004).
96. G. Cellere, A. Paccagnella, A. Visconti, M. Bonanomi, and S. Beltrami, *IEEE Trans. Nucl. Sci.* 53, 1813 (2006).
97. G. Cellere, P. Pellati, A. Chimenton, J. Wyss, A. Modelli, L. Larcher, and A. Paccagnella, *IEEE Trans. Nucl. Sci.* 48, 2222 (2001).
98. C. Claeys, H. Ohyama, E. Simoen, M. Nakabayashi, and K. Kobayashi, *Nucl. Instrum. Methods Phys. Res. Sect. B* 186, 392 (2002).
99. H. Schmidt, D. Walter, F. Gliem, B. Nickson, R. Harboe-Sorensen, and A. Virtanen, "Radiation Effects Data Workshop," p. 38, Tucson, AZ, 2008.

100. D. R. Roth, J. D. Kinnison, B. G. Carkhuff, J. R. Lander, G. S. Bognaski, K. Chao, and G. M. Swift, "IEEE Radiation Effects Data Workshop," p. 96, Reno, NV, 2000.

101. T. R. Oldham, M. Friendlich, J. W. Howard, M. D. Berg, H. S. Kim, T. L. Irwin, and K. A. LaBel, "IEEE Radiation Effects Data Workshop," p. 221, Honolulu, HI, 2007.

102. T. R. Oldham, R. L. Ladbury, M. Friendlich, H. S. Kim, M. D. Berg, T. L. Irwin, C. Seidleck, and K. A. LaBel, *IEEE Trans. Nucl. Sci.* 53, 3217 (2006).

103. D. N. Nguyen, C. I. Lee, and A. H. Johnston, "IEEE Radiation Effects Data Workshop," p. 100, Newport Beach, CA, 1998.

104. M. Bagatin, S. Gerardin, G. Cellere, A. Paccagnella, A. Visconti, S. Beltrami, R. Harboe-Sorensen, and A. Virtanen, *IEEE Trans. Nucl. Sci.* 55, 3302 (2008).

105. M. Bagatin, S. Gerardin, G. Cellere, A. Paccagnella, A. Visconti, M. Bonanomi, and S. Beltrami, *IEEE Trans. Nucl. Sci.* 56, 3267 (2009).

106. E. S. Snyder, P. J. McWhorter, T. A. Dellin, and J. D. Sweetman, *IEEE Trans. Nucl. Sci.* 36, 2131 (1989).

107. G. Cellere, A. Paccagnella, A. Visconti, M. Bonanomi, P. Caprara, and S. Lora, *IEEE Trans. Nucl. Sci.* 51, 3753 (2004).

108. G. Cellere, A. Paccagnella, A. Visconti, M. Bonanomi, R. Harboe-Sorensen, and A. Virtanen, *IEEE Trans. Nucl. Sci.* 54, 2371 (2007).

109. T. R. Oldham, M. Friendlich, M. A. Carts, C. M. Seidleck, and K. A. LaBel, *IEEE Trans. Nucl. Sci.* 56, 3280 (2009).

110. T. E. Langley and P. Murray, "IEEE Radiation Effects Data Workshop," p. 58, Atlanta, GA, 2004.

111. T. R. Oldham, M. R. Friendlich, A. B. Sanders, C. M. Seidleck, H. S. Kim, M. D. Berg, and K. A. LaBel, "IEEE Radiation Effects Data Workshop," pp. 114–122, Quebec City, QC, 2009.

112. F. Irom and D. N. Nguyen, *IEEE Trans. Nucl. Sci.* 54, 2547 (2007).

113. D. N. Nguyen, S. M. Guertin, and J. D. Patterson, "IEEE Radiation Effects Data Workshop," p. 121, Ponte Vedra, FL, 2006.

114. G. Cellere, L. Larcher, A. Paccagnella, A. Visconti, and M. Bonanomi, "2006 IEEE International Conference on Intergrated Circuit Design and Technology," p. 1, Padova, 2006.

115. G. Cellere, A. Paccagnella, A. Visconti, M. Bonanomi, S. Beltrami, R. Harboe-Sorensen, and A. Virtanen, *IEEE Trans. Nucl. Sci.* 55, 2042 (2008).

116. G. Cellere, A. Paccagnella, A. Visconti, M. Bonanomi, and P. J. McNulty, *Radiat. Prot. Dosim.* 122, 457 (2006).

117. S. M. Guertin, D. M. Nguyen, and J. D. Patterson, *IEEE Trans. Nucl. Sci.* 53, 3518 (2006).

118. G. Cellere, A. Paccagnella, A. Visconti, and M. Bonanomi, *IEEE Trans. Nucl. Sci.* 53, 3291 (2006).

119. G. Cellere, L. Larcher, A. Paccagnella, A. Visconti, and M. Bonanomi, *IEEE Trans. Nucl. Sci.* 52, 2144 (2005).

120. N. Z. Butt and M. Alam, "IEEE International Reliability Physics Symposium," p. 547, Phoenix, AZ, 2008.

121. L. Larcher, *IEEE Trans. Electron Devices* 50, 1246 (2003).

122. F. Irom, D. N. Nguyen, M. Bagatin, G. Cellere, S. Gerardin, and A. Paccagnella, *IEEE Trans. Nucl. Sci.* 57, 266 (2010).

123. A. Cester, N. Wrachien, A. Gasperin, A. Paccagnella, R. Portoghese, and C. Gerardi, *IEEE Trans. Nucl. Sci.* 54, 2196 (2007).

124. M. P. Petkov, L. D. Bell, and H. A. Atwater, *IEEE Trans. Nucl. Sci.* 51, 3822 (2004).

125. T. R. Oldham, M. Suhail, P. Kuhn, E. Prinz, H. S. Kim, and K. A. LaBel, *IEEE Trans. Nucl. Sci.* 52, 2366 (2005).

126. S. S. Eaton, D. B. Butler, M. Parris, D. Wilson, and H. McNeillie, "IEEE International Solid-State Circuits Conference," p. 130, San Francisco, CA, 1988.

127. J. T. Evans and R. Womack, *IEEE J. Solid State Circuits* 23, 1171 (1988).

128. R. Womack and D. Tolsch, "36th IEEE International Solid-State Circuits Conference-Digest of Technical Papers," p. 242, New York, NY, 1989.

129. T. Sumi, N. Moriwaki, G. Nakane, T. Nakakuma, Y. Judai, Y. Uemoto, Y. Nagano, S. Hayashi, M. Azuma, E. Fujii, S. I. Katsu, T. Otsuki, L. McMillan, C. Paz de Araujo, and G. Kano, "41st IEEE International Solid-State Circuits Conference-Digest of Technical Papers," p. 268, San Francisco, CA, 1994.

130. Y. Shimojo, A. Konno, J. Nishimura, T. Okada, Y. Yamada, S. Kitazaki, H. Furuhashi, S. Yamazaki, K. Yahashi, K. Tomioka, Y. Minami, H. Kanaya, S. Shuto, K. Yamakawa, T. Ozaki, H. Shiga, T. Miyakawa, S. Shiratake, D. Takashima, I. Kunishima, T. Hamamoto, and A. Nitayama, "2009 Symposium on VLSI Technology," p. 218, Honolulu, HI, 2009.

131. H. Shiga, D. Takashima, S. Shiratake, K. Hoya, T. Miyakawa, R. Ogiwara, R. Fukuda, R. Takizawa, K. Hatsuda, F. Matsuoka, Y. Nagadomi, D. Hashimoto, H. Nishimura, T. Hioka, S. Doumae, S. Shimizu, M. Kawano, T. Taguchi, Y. Watanabe, S. Fujii, T. Ozaki, H. Kanaya, Y. Kumura, Y. Shimojo, Y. Yamada, Y. Minami, S. Shuto, K. Yamakawa, S. Yamazaki, I. Kunishima, T. Hamamoto, A. Nitayama, and T. Furuyama, *IEEE J. Solid-State Circuits* 45, 142 (2010).

132. D. Takashima, "CMOS Processors and Memories." (K. Iniewski and K. Iniewski, Eds.), Vol. 0, p. 361, Springer, Netherlands, 2010.

133. S. C. Philpy, D. A. Kamp, A. D. DeVilbiss, A. F. Isacson, and G. F. Derbenwick, "2000 IEEE Aerospace Conference Proceedings," Vol. 5, p. 377, Big Sky, MT, 2000.

134. K. Zhang, S. Kawashima, and J. S. Cross, "Embedded Memories for Nano-Scale VLSIs." (K. Zhang, Ed.), p. 279, Springer, United States, 2009.

135. R. Zambrano, *Integr. Ferroelectr.* 53, 247 (2003).

136. L. Goux, G. Russo, N. Menou, J. G. Lisoni, M. Schwitters, V. Paraschiv, D. Maes, C. Artoni, G. Corallo, L. Haspeslagh, D. J. Wouters, R. Zambrano, and C. Muller, *IEEE Trans. Electron Devices* 52, 447 (2005).

137. C. Muller, L. Courtade, C. Turquat, L. Goux, and D. J. Wouters, "7th Annual Non-Volatile Memory Technology Symposium," p. 40, San Mateo, CA, 2006.

138. R. Meyer and R. Waser, *J. Appl. Phys.* 100, 051611 (2006).

139. N. Setter, D. Damjanovic, L. Eng, G. Fox, S. Gevorgian, S. Hong, A. Kingon, H. Kohlstedt, N. Y. Park, G. B. Stephenson, I. Stolitchnov, A. K. Taganstev, D. V. Taylor, T. Yamada, and S. Streiffer, *J. Appl. Phys.* 100, 051606 (2006).

140. J. M. Benedetto, W. M. De Lancey, T. R. Oldham, J. M. McGarrity, C. W. Tipton, M. Brassington, and D. E. Fisch, *IEEE Trans. Nucl. Sci.* 38, 1410 (1991).

141. S. C. Lee, G. Teowee, R. D. Schrimpf, D. P. Birnie, III, D. R. Uhlmann, and K. F. Galloway, *IEEE Trans. Nucl. Sci.* 39, 2036 (1992).

142. J. R. Schwank, R. D. Nasby, S. L. Miller, M. S. Rodgers, and P. V. Dressendorfer, *IEEE Trans. Nucl. Sci.* 37, 1703 (1990).

143. J. F. Scott, C. A. Araujo, H. B. Meadows, L. D. McMillan, and A. Shawabkeh, *J. Appl. Phys.* 66, 1444 (1989).

144. T. F. Wrobel, J. A. Bullington, and L. J. Schwee, *GOMAC Digest of Papers* 13, 267 (1987).

145. J. M. Benedetto, R. A. Moore, F. B. McLean, P. S. Brody, and S. K. Dey, *IEEE Trans. Nucl. Sci.* 37, 1713 (1990).

146. Y. M. Coic, O. Musseau, and J. L. Leray, *IEEE Trans. Nucl. Sci.* 41, 495 (1994).

147. R. A. Moore, J. Benedetto, and B. J. Rod, *IEEE Trans. Nucl. Sci.* 40, 1591 (1993).

148. R. A. Moore and J. M. Benedetto, *IEEE Trans. Nucl. Sci.* 42, 1575 (1995).

149. R. A. Moore, J. M. Benedetto, J. M. McGarrity, and F. B. McLean, *IEEE Trans. Nucl. Sci.* 38, 1078 (1991).

150. J.-L. Leray, O. Musseau, P. Paillet, J.-L. Autran, F. Sodi, and Y.-M. Coïc, *J. Phys. III France* 7, 1227 (1997).

151. L. Courtade, C. Muller, G. Andreoli, C. Turquat, L. Goux, and D. J. Wouters, *Appl. Phys. Lett.* 89, 113501 (2006).

152. D. Wu, A. D. Li, H. Q. Ling, T. Yu, Z. G. Liu, and N. B. Ming, *Appl. Phys. A: Mater. Sci. Process.* 73, 255 (2001).
153. D. N. Nguyen and L. Z. Scheick, "IEEE Radiation Effects Data Workshop," p. 57, Vancouver, Canada, 2001.
154. M. Zanata, N. Wrachien, and A. Cester, *IEEE Trans. Nucl. Sci.* 55, 3237 (2008).
155. J. M. Benedetto, G. F. Derbenwick, and J. D. Cuchiaro, *IEEE Trans. Nucl. Sci.* 46, 1421 (1999).
156. T. Nuns, S. Duzellier, J. Bertrand, G. Hubert, V. Pouget, F. Darracq, J. P. David, and S. Soonckindt, "9th European Conference on Radiation and Its Effects on Components and Systems, p. 1, Deauville, 2007.
157. D. Hayashigawa, D. A. Kamp, and A. D. DeVilbiss, "Non-Volatile Memory Technology Symposium," p. 60, Albuquerque, NM, 2007.
158. D. A. Kamp, A. D. DeVilbiss, G. R. Haag, K. E. Russell, and G. F. Derbenwick, "Non-Volatile Memory Technology Symposium," p. 48, Dallas, TX, 2005.
159. D. A. Kamp, A. D. DeVilbiss, S. C. Philpy, and G. F. Derbenwick, "Non-Volatile Memory Technology Symposium," p. 149, Orlando, FL, 2004.
160. S. T. Philpy, D. A. Kamp, and G. F. Derbenwick, "2004 IEEE Aerospace Conference Proceedings," Vol. 4, p. 2294, Big Sky, Montana, 2004.
161. B. F. Cockburn, "IEEE International Workshop on Memory Technology, Design and Testing," p. 46, San Jose, CA, 2004.
162. S. Tehrani, B. Engel, J. M. Slaughter, E. Chen, M. DeHerrera, M. Durlam, P. Naji, R. Whig, J. Janesky, and J. Calder, *IEEE Trans. Magn*. 36, 2752 (2000).
163. Y. M. Lee, J. Hayakawa, S. Ikeda, F. Matsukura, and H. Ohno, *Appl. Phys. Lett.* 90, 212507 (2007).
164. J. M. Slaughter, *Annu. Rev. Mater. Res.* 39, 277 (2009).
165. J. M. Slaughter, "2007 65th Annual Device Research Conference," p. 245, Notre Dame, IN, 2007.
166. J. M. Slaughter, R. W. Dave, M. DeHerrera, M. Durlam, B. N. Engel, J. Janesky, N. D. Rizzo, and S. Tehrani, *J. Supercond*. 15, 19 (2002).
167. S. Tehrani, "International Electron Devices Meeting," p. 1, San Francisco, CA, 2006.
168. J.-G. Zhu and C. Park, *Mater. Today* 9, 36 (2006).
169. R. Scheuerlein, W. Gallagher, S. Parkin, A. Lee, S. Ray, R. Robertazzi, and W. Reohr, "2000 International Solid-State Circuits Conference, Digest of Technical Papers," p. 128, San Francisco, CA, 2000.
170. S. Yuasa, T. Nagahama, A. Fukushima, Y. Suzuki, and K. Ando, *Nat. Mater.* 3, 868 (2004).
171. Y. Sakuraba, M. Hattori, M. Oogane, Y. Ando, H. Kato, A. Sakuma, T. Miyazaki, and H. Kubota, *Appl. Phys. Lett.* 88, 192508 (2006).
172. Y. Huai, *AAPPS Bull*. 18, 33 (2008).
173. M. Hosomi, H. Yamagishi, T. Yamamoto, K. Bessho, Y. Higo, K. Yamane, H. Yamada, M. Shoji, H. Hachino, C. Fukumoto, H. Nagao, and H. Kano, "IEEE International Electron Devices Meeting," p. 459, Washington, DC, 2005.
174. D. Zhitao, et al., *J. Phys. Condens. Matter* 19, 165209 (2007).
175. M. D. Stiles and J. Miltat, "Spin Dynamics in Confined Magnetic Structures III." (B. Hillebrands and A. Thiaville, Eds.), Vol. 101, p. 225, Springer, Verlag Berlin Heidelberg, 2006.
176. D. C. Ralph and M. D. Stiles, *J. Magn. Magn. Mater.* 320, 1190 (2008).
177. D. J. Cochran, S. P. Buchner, A. B. Sanders, K. A. LaBel, M. A. Carts, C. F. Poivey, T. R. Oldham, R. L. Ladbury, M. V. O'Bryan, and S. R. Mackey, "IEEE Radiation Effects Data Workshop," p. 5, Tucson, AZ, 2008.
178. Y. Conraux, J. P. Nozières, Y. D. Costa, M. Toulemonde, and K. Ounadjela, *J. Appl. Phys.* 93, 7301 (2003).
179. K. J. Hass, G. W. Donohoe, Y. K. Hong, and B. C. Choi, *IEEE Trans. Magn.* 42, 2751 (2006).
180. J. Heidecker, G. Allen, and D. Sheldon, "IEEE Radiation Effects Data Workshop," p. 4, Denver, CO, 2010.
181. R. R. Katti, J. Lintz, L. Sundstrom, T. Marques, S. Scoppettuolo, and D. Martin, "IEEE Radiation Effects Data Workshop," p. 103, Quebec City, QC, 2009.
182. D. N. Nguyen and F. Irom, "9th European Conference on Radiation and Its Effects on Components and Systems," p. 1, Deauville, 2007.
183. J. Schmalhorst, V. Höink, G. Reiss, D. Engel, D. Junk, A. Schindler, A. Ehresmann, and H. Schmoranzer, *J. Appl. Phys.* 94, 5556 (2003).
184. T. Banerjee, T. Som, D. Kanjilal, and J. S. Moodera, *Eur. Phys. J. Appl. Phys.* 32, 115 (2005).
185. V. Höink, M. D. Sacher, J. Schmalhorst, G. Reiss, D. Engel, D. Junk, and A. Ehresmann, *Appl. Phys. Lett.* 86, 152102 (2005).
186. M. D. Sacher, J. Sauerwald, J. Schmalhorst, and G. Reiss, *J. Appl. Phys.* 98, 103532 (2005).
187. J. Schmalhorst and G. Reiss, *Phys. Rev. B* 68, 224437 (2003).
188. M. Elghefari and S. McClure, Jet Propulsion Laboratory Report, National Aeronautics and Space Administration, Pasadena, CA 2008.
189. T. R. Oldham, A. Pham, and M. Friendlich, Online Available http://radhome.gsfc.nasa.gov/radhome/papers/G07OCT_MR2A16A_TID.pdf 2006.
190. S. J. Ahn, Y. J. Song, C. W. Jeong, J. M. Shin, Y. Fai, Y. N. Hwang, S. H. Lee, K. C. Ryoo, S. Y. Lee, J. H. Park, H. Horii, Y. H. Ha, J. H. Yi, B. J. Kuh, G. H. Koh, G. T. Jeong, H. S. Jeong, K. Kinam, and B. I. Ryu, "IEEE International Electron Devices Meeting," p. 907, IEDM Technical Digest, San Francisco, CA, 2004.
191. M. J. Breitwisch, "International Interconnect Technology Conference," p. 219, Burlingame, CA, 2008.
192. G. Bruns, P. Merkelbach, C. Schlockermann, M. Salinga, M. Wutting, T. D. Happ, J. B. Philipp, and M. Kund, *Appl. Phys. Lett.* 95, 043108 (2009).
193. H. F. Hamann, M. O'Boyle, Y. C. Martin, M. Rooks, and H. K. Wickramasinghe, *Nat. Mater.* 5, 383 (2006).
194. K.-F. Kao, C.-M. Lee, M.-J. Chen, M.-J. Tsai, and T.-S. Chin, *Adv. Mater.* 21, 1695 (2009).
195. M. H. R. Lankhorst, B. W. S. M. M. Ketelaars, and R. A. M. Wolters, *Nat. Mater.* 4, 347 (2005).
196. F. Pellizzer, A. Pirovano, F. Ottogalli, M. Magistretti, M. Scaravaggi, P. Zuliani, M. Tosi, A. Benvenuti, P. Besana, S. Cadeo, T. Marangon, R. Morandi, R. Piva, A. Spandre, R. Zonca, A. Modelli, E. Varesi, T. Lowrey, A. Lacaita, G. Casagrande, P. Cappelletti, and R. Bez, "2004 Symposium on VLSI Technology, Digest of Technical Papers," p. 18, Washington, DC, 2004.
197. A. Pirovano, F. Pellizzer, I. Tortorelli, A. Riganó, R. Harrigan, M. Magistretti, P. Petruzza, E. Varesi, A. Redaelli, D. Erbetta, T. Marangon, F. Bedeschi, R. Fackenthal, G. Atwood, and R. Bez, *Solid-State Electron*. 52, 1467 (2008).
198. S. Lai and T. Lowrey, "International Electron Devices Meeting, IEDM Technical Digest," p. 36, Washington, DC, 2001.
199. S. R. Ovshinsky, *Phys. Rev. Lett.* 21, 1450 (1968).
200. G. W. Burr, M. J. Breitwisch, M. Franceschini, D. Garetto, K. Gopalakrishnan, B. Jackson, B. Kurdi, C. Lam, L. A. Lastras, A. Padilla, B. Rajendran, S. Raoux, and R. S. Shenoy, *J. Vac. Sci. Technol. B* 28, 223 (2010).
201. A. L. Lacaita, *Solid-State Electron*. 50, 24 (2006).
202. D. Ielmini, *Phys. Rev. B* 78, 035308 (2008).
203. M. Wuttig and N. Yamada, *Nat. Mater.* 6, 824 (2007).
204. S. Bernacki, K. Hunt, S. Tyson, S. Hudgens, B. Pashmakov, and W. Czubatyj, *IEEE Trans. Nucl. Sci.* 47, 2528 (2000).
205. J. Maimon, K. Hunt, J. Rodgers, L. Burcin, and K. Knowles, "2004 IEEE Aerospace Conference Proceedings," Vol. 4, p. 2306, Big Sky, Montana, 2004.

206. J. Maimon, K. Hunt, J. Rodgers, L. Burcin, and K. Knowles, *AIP Conference Proceedings* 699, 639 (2004).
207. J. D. Maimon, K. K. Hunt, L. Burcin, and J. Rodgers, *IEEE Trans. Nucl. Sci.* 50, 1878 (2003).
208. L. Bin, A. Bumgarner, D. Pirkl, J. Stobie, W. Neiderer, M. Graziano, L. Burcin, T. Storey, B. Orlowsky, K. K. Hunt, J. Rodgers, and J. Maimon, "7th Annual Non-Volatile Memory Technology Symposium," p. 64, San Mateo, CA, 2006.
209. J. Rodgers, J. Maimon, T. Storey, D. Lee, M. Graziano, L. Rockett, and K. Hunt, "9th Annual Non-Volatile Memory Technology Symposium," p. 1, Pacific Grove, CA, 2008.
210. T. Storey, K. K. Hunt, M. Graziano, B. Li, A. Bumgarner, J. Rodgers, and L. Burcin, "Non-Volatile Memory Technology Symposium," p. 97, Dallas, TX, 2005.
211. A. Gasperin, N. Wrachien, A. Paccagnella, F. Ottogalli, U. Corda, P. Fuochi, and M. Lavalle, *IEEE Trans. Nucl. Sci.* 55, 2090 (2008).
212. A. Gasperin, A. Paccagnella, J. R. Schwank, G. Vizkelethy, F. Ottogalli, and F. Pellizzer, *IEEE Trans. Nucl. Sci.* 55, 3189 (2008).
213. L. Wu, X. Zhou, Z. Song, J. Lian, F. Rao, B. Liu, S. Song, W. Liu, X. Liu, and S. Feng, *Phys. Status Solidi A* 207, 2395 (2010).
214. M. Liu, Z. Abid, W. Wang, X. He, Q. Liu, and W. Guan, *Appl. Phys. Lett.* 94, 233106 (2009).
215. S.-S. Sheu, P.-C. Chiang, W.-P. Lin, H.-Y. Lee, P.-S. Chen, Y.-S. Chen, T.-Y. Wu, F. T. Chen, K.-L. Su, M.-J. Kao, K.-H. Cheng, and M.-J. Tsai, "2009 Symposium on VLSI Circuits," p. 82, Kyoto, Japan, 2009.
216. D. Shang, C. Chen, Q. Wang, Z. Wu, W. Zhang, and X. Li, *J. Mater. Res.* 23, 302 (2008).
217. Y. Wang, Q. Liu, S. Long, W. Wang, Q. Wang, M. Zhang, S. Zhang, Y. Li, Q. Zuo, J. Yang, and M. Liu, *Nanotech.* 21, 045202 (2010).
218. Y. C. Yang, F. Pan, Q. Liu, M. Liu, and F. Zeng, *Nano Lett.* 9, 1636 (2009).
219. S. H. Jo and W. Lu, *Nano Lett.* 8, 392 (2008).
220. A. Chen, S. Haddad, Y. C. Wu, Z. Lan, T. N. Fang, and S. Kaza, *Appl. Phys. Lett.* 91, 123517 (2007).
221. Q. Liu, W. Guan, S. Long, M. Liu, and J. Chen, *J. Appl. Phys.* 92, 012117 (2008).
222. S. Seo, M. J. Lee, D. H. Seo, E. J. Jeoung, D.-S. Suh, Y. S. Joung, I. K. Yoo, I. R. Hwang, S. H. Kim, I. S. Byun, J.-S. Kim, J. S. Choi, and B. H. Park, *Appl. Phys. Lett.* 85, 5655 (2004).
223. A. Sawa, *Mater. Today* 11, 28 (2008).
224. U. Russo, D. Ielmini, C. Cagli, and A. L. Lacaita, *IEEE Trans. Electron Devices* 56, 193 (2009).
225. C. Schindler, G. Staikov, and R. Waser, *Appl. Phys. Lett.* 94, 072109 (2009).
226. M. Janousch, G. I. Meijer, U. Staub, B. Delley, S. F. Karg, and B. P. Andreasson, *Adv. Mater.* 19, 2232 (2007).
227. K. Szot, R. Dittmann, W. Speier, and R. Waser, *Phys. Status Solidi RRL* 1, R86 (2007).
228. R. Waser and M. Aono, *Nat. Mater.* 6, 833 (2007).
229. R. Waser, R. Dittmann, G. Staikov, and K. Szot, *Adv. Mater.* 21, 2632 (2009).
230. C. Cagli, D. Ielmini, F. Nardi, and A. L. Lacaita, "IEEE International Electron Devices Meeting," p. 1, San Francisco, CA, 2008.
231. C. Cagli, F. Nardi, and D. Ielmini, *IEEE Trans. Electron Devices* 56, 1712 (2009).
232. S. H. Chang, S. C. Chae, S. B. Lee, C. Liu, T. W. Noh, J. S. Lee, B. Kahng, J. H. Jang, M. Y. Kim, D.-W. Kim, and C. U. Jung, *Appl. Phys. Lett.* 92, 182507 (2008).
233. J. Y. Son and Y.-H. Shin, *Appl. Phys. Lett.* 92, 222106 (2008).
234. Z. Xu, Y. Bando, W. Wang, X. Bai, and D. Golberg, *ACS Nano* 4, 2515 (2010).
235. J. J. Yang, et al., *Nanotechnol.* 20, 215201 (2009).
236. D.-H. Kwon, K. M. Kim, J. H. Jang, J. M. Jeon, M. H. Lee, G. H. Kim, X.-S. Li, G.-S. Park, B. Lee, S. Han, M. Kim, and C. S. Hwang, *Nat. Nanotechnol.* 5, 148 (2010).
237. J. J. Yang, M. D. Pickett, X. Li, A. A. Ohlberg Douglas, D. R. Stewart, and R. S. Williams, *Nat. Nanotechnol.* 3, 429 (2008).
238. R. Muenstermann, T. Menke, R. Dittmann, and R. Waser, *Adv. Mater.* 22, 4819 (2010).
239. L. Chua, *IEEE Trans. Circuit Theory* 18, 507 (1971).
240. L. O. Chua and K. Sung Mo, *Proc. IEEE* 64, 209 (1976).
241. D. B. Strukov, G. S. Snider, D. R. Stewart, and R. S. Williams, *Nature* 453, 80 (2008).
242. D. Biolek, Z. Biolek, and V. Biolkova, "European Conference on Circuit Theory and Design," p. 249, Antalya, 2009.
243. M. Di Ventra, Y. V. Pershin, and L. O. Chua, *Proc. IEEE* 97, 1717 (2009).
244. Y. V. Pershin and M. Di Ventra, *Electron. Lett.* 46, 517 (2010).
245. S. H. Jo, K.-H. Kim, and W. Lu, *Nano Lett.* 9, 870 (2009).
246. S. H. Jo, T. Chang, I. Ebong, B. B. Bhadviya, P. Mazumder, and W. Lu, *Nano Lett.* 10, 1297 (2010).
247. Y. V. Pershin and M. Di Ventra, *Neural Networks* 23, 881 (2010).
248. B. Brian, X. He, M. Huang, Y. Wang, Q. Liu, H. Lv, M. Liu, and W. Wang, *Nanotechnol.* 21, 475206 (2010).
249. Y. Wang, H. Lv, W. Wang, Q. Liu, S. Long, Q. Wang, Z. Huo, S. Zhang, Y. Li, Q. Zuo, W. Lian, J. Yang, and M. Liu, *IEEE Electron Device Lett.* 31, 1470 (2010).
250. U. S. Joshi, S. J. Trivedi, K. H. Bhavsar, U. N. Trivedi, S. A. Khan, and D. K. Avasthi, *J. Appl. Phys.* 105, 073704 (2009).
251. S. Kim, O. Yarimaga, S.-J. Choi, and Y.-K. Choi, *Solid-State Electron.* 54, 392 (2010).
252. N. Marjanovic, M. Vujisic, K. Stankovic, and P. Osmokrovic, *Radiat. Eff. Defects Solids* 166, 1 (2011).
253. W. M. Tong, J. J. Yang, P. J. Kuekes, D. R. Stewart, R. S. Williams, E. DeIonno, E. E. King, S. C. Witczak, M. D. Looper, and J. V. Osborn, *IEEE Trans. Nucl. Sci.* 57, 1640 (2010).
254. M. Vujisic, K. Stankovic, N. Marjanovic, and P. Osmokrovic, *IEEE Trans. Nucl. Sci.* 57, 1798 (2010).

CHAPTER 15

Nonvolatile Quantum Memory

Oleksandr Voskoboynikov
National Chiao Tung University, 1001 Ta Hsueh Rd., Hsinchu 30010, Taiwan

CONTENTS

1. INTRODUCTION

The continuous miniaturization of integrated circuits brings a tremendous reduction of the number of electrons representing one bit of information. An extrapolation of this trend suggests that an atomic scale might be reached by around 2020, and quantum effects on bit writing, storing, and reading can no longer be ignored. The information technology developers will be forced to drastically change the paradigm of computation by creating computer systems that rely on quantum effects. Therefore, the development of quantum information science and technology is decisive for the future computer technology.

The earliest discussion on the concept of quantum computing was performed by Benioff, who demonstrated a Hamiltonian model of the Turing machine [1], and Feynman, who proposed local Hamiltonians to be used as logically reversible gates and a configuration of ballistic quantum networks [2]. Deutsch [3] developed the quantum network approach within the linear algebra terminology. Quantum computing has become more practical and accessible after works of Shor on large number factoring [4] and Grover on the database search [5].

The development of the field of quantum information research opens up a number of new opportunities in the information technology area. Combining material science, physics, mathematics, and computer science, quantum informatics has developed from a visionary idea to one of the most fascinating areas of quantum mechanics. After a few decades of quantum computing extensive development, the list of publications in this field is increasing very fast, which reflects the growing interest that the field has received. The basic ideas and principles of quantum information and computing are presented in numerous reviews, monographs, and tutorials (see, e.g., Refs. [6–23] and references therein).

Quantum computing, quantum cryptography, and quantum teleportation are three branches of potential 21st century quantum informatics. This includes data processing

ISBN: 1-58883-251-1

Nonvolatile Memories: Materials, Devices and Applications
Edited by Tseung-Yuen Tseng and Simon M. Sze
Volume 2: Pages: 377–400

possibilities unique for the quantum world and those leading to new computation algorithms, safe methods for the transmission of coded messages, and teleportation of information. In this field, the experimental realization of an operational quantum computer is still a challenge. At the same time, such applications as cryptography and quantum communication are already implemented and tested [24]. (We should stress that the components used for the commercial realizations of quantum cryptography deviate from the theoretical quantum models in the security level [25].)

It is believed that a core quantum computer (as well as a classical one) should consist of three essential parts:

(1) a memory, which holds the current quantum information;
(2) a processor, which performs operations on the information; and
(3) some sort of input/output interfaces, which introduce the initial and extract the final quantum information.

Among those parts, quantum memory is an essential building block for all quantum computing, information, and communication applications. Conventional classical (even in a nano-scale) information storages (memories) by definition cannot store the complete quantum information about quantum mechanical system state configurations. Therefore, we should build and use quantum storages on the base of physical systems inherently controlled by quantum mechanics. On the other hand, the ultimate goal of quantum computing is to obtain practical solutions to be implemented in the classical world. So, quantum information applications require transport of quantum information between the preferred quantum storage systems and "bridges" between the quantum storages and classical environment. Light is a very good candidate for the quantum information transport and bridge, but it is rather hard to localize it in quantum storages. (We will discuss some recent achievements for the quantum memory of light [26, 27] later in this review). Material systems are more appropriate for local quantum memory storages, but storing and retrieving quantum states in material systems without corrupting the information it carries is an important challenge for the field of the quantum information processing.

In general, practical realizations of quantum memory (including basic memory carriers, basic programming, erasing mechanisms, etc.) are strongly connected to specific quantum information processing to be implemented. The application of quantum physical principles to the field of computing leads to the concept of a quantum memory storage, in which data are stored not as bits in conventional memory, but as a combined quantum state of many two-state systems of quantum bits. Today, according to the physical quantum bit (qubit) realizations, different physical systems are proposed as quantum computing candidates. Among them, we should mention (see, e.g., Refs. [7, 15, 22, 26–35]) nuclear spins in molecules, trapped ions and atoms, photonic systems, superconductor-based systems, quantum dots and impurities in solids, ballistic electrons in meso-structures, carbon-based nanomaterials, single electron devices, semiconductor spintronic systems, magnetic nano-particles, and others. However, all promising candidates for the quantum memory realization suffer from the same practical pitfall. They rely on particles and molecules that are extremely sensitive to the environment; therefore, any such system can store the quantum information only for seconds (the best results claim minutes), and the more particles and ions are added to a system, the quicker its ability fades. Moreover, subsequent detections and storages would destroy a part of the quantum information because measurement/output disturbs quantum mechanical states.

In a classical computer, memory is determined by the expectation value of its register contents (classical bits). A classical bit in the memory is presented by a great number of particles, which guarantees that the uncertainty of the measurement (readout) is small enough to make errors practically impossible. The logical state of a classical memory register is determined by the states of all bits the register contains. Satisfying the classical Boolean logic, those bits can be changed locally, i.e., independently from one another. The state of an n bit register can therefore be described by n binaries.

In a quantum computer, information is represented as a collective quantum state of many subsystems. Within the simplest quantum memory implementation, each subsystem is described by two quantum states (qubit). In the Dirac notation, the states are presented as $|0\rangle$ and $|1\rangle$ vectors in the two dimensional Hilbert space. Those can be two states of the polarization of quantum particles' spins, the polarization of photons, or any two ground and excited states of a quantum system. According to the quantum superposition principle, we can fully describe any state $|A\rangle$ of the quantum system (any vector in the Hilbert space) as

$$|A\rangle = a_0 \cdot |0\rangle + a_1 \cdot |1\rangle$$

where a_0 and a_1 are two complex numbers representing the state in the complex vector space spanned by $|0\rangle$ and $|1\rangle$ satisfying the following condition

$$|a_0|^2 + |a_1|^2 = 1$$

It is obvious that this interpretation stands in contradiction to the classical Boolean logic, where intermediate states between 0 and 1 are not possible. A quantum memory register containing n qubits cannot be presented as a common state of n isolated qubits. Moreover, it is not even possible to define the state of an isolated qubit from the register. Manipulations (readout) on a single qubit affect the complex amplitudes of the overall state and have a global character in the memory. A system of n qubits has a Hilbert state space of 2^n dimension. Accordingly, we can store any number A in our quantum memory register as long as we have enough qubits, just as we can store any number A in a classical register as long as we have enough classical bits to represent that number. A quantum register composed of n qubits requires 2^n complex numbers completely describes a vector in the Hilbert space. This means that, in principle, the memory storage can process an exponentially greater amount of information in a quantum register than in a classical memory register of the same number of the basic bits. An ideal quantum memory can be exponentially denser than its classical counterpart.

To perform a massive quantum computing we are urgent for the ability of a quantum memory register to exist in a superposition of base quantum states (qubits). Therefore, one of the key hurdles to building a large quantum memory storage is maintaining the coherence of the many (n) individual qubits. A quantum memory register can exist in a superposition of states. Since the number of possible states is 2^n, in principle we could perform in one operation on a quantum computer what would take an exponential number of operations on a classical computer. This is the essence of the incredible theoretical power of the quantum information processing.

In a classical memory, the formal description of the inner state and the measurement (readout) of this state is the same, and it is given by the binary values of the concerned bits. Moreover, the measurement can be performed so that it does not affect the state. In contrast, the measurement of a quantum memory state reduces (collapses) the state. Therefore, it is principally not possible to measure the state of a quantum register itself. We can only estimate the expectation value of qubits by repeated measurements under the same conditions.

Now, we should distinguish the theoretically developed and proven quantum memory (as a paradigm) and its physical realization (as physical quantum memory storage). To obtain a practical and realistic quantum memory device, we should satisfy a few very basic requirements:

- Quantum memory storage should be equipped with a fast access input/output interface to ease write and read processes.
- Quantum memory storage should have a long enough storage time (quantum bits should not decay too fast).
- Quantum memory should be scalable and large number of qubits should be equally easy to store.

We can consider nonvolatile quantum memory storages' properties and perspectives in a glance using conventional classical nonvolatile memory characteristics (see, e.g., other chapters of this book and Refs. [36, 37] and references therein). According to a conversional definition, a nonvolatile memory does not lose its data when the system or device is turned off. In classical computer systems the nonvolatile memory is typically used for the task of secondary storage or long-term persistent storage.

For the classical nonvolatile memory, the length of time that the memory can retain the data unpowered is the property called *retention*. Actually, the retention time is the measure of nonvolatility, and this is the most important property of the nonvolatile memory. When the retention time is less than 1 second a classical memory is called "a volatile memory." A classical nonvolatile memory is typically specified as meeting unpowered retention time of 10 years (in worst cases). The retention of the memory depends on physical realization peculiar to a given technology approach. Each classical nonvolatile technology makes use of some physical attribute to achieve nonvolatility, and the particular mechanism employed brings with it a number of technology specific characteristics.

The normal write/read processes result in stresses of the storage those eventually degrade the properties of the memory or corrupt the memory content. The ability of a device to resist physical corruption and degradation is defined as *endurance*. It is quantified as a minimum number of erase/write cycles that the device can be expected to survive. The modern industry has used 100,000 cycles as the minimum competitive endurance requirement.

Some classical memory technologies perform destructive readout processes and the reading destroys the data. For other classical technologies, readout can be accomplished with nondestructive readout and the reading does not significantly disturb the data. The destructive readout memory has the disadvantage of requiring that every read operation must be followed by an operation to restore the data.

It was already mentioned that quantum memory is extremely sensitive to the environmental conditions. Keeping conventional definitions we should admit that the actual *retention* realized in quantum computer systems is of a few seconds (minutes), and it is strongly limited by the quantum decoherence processes. Although this time is obviously not compatible with the classical requirements, it is still reasonably long in the quantum world, where the quantum computing is performing. We also can hope for significant improvements of quantum memory retention with further development of quantum memory technologies.

The quantum memory *endurance* strongly depends on the actual physical material background of the memory storage. Since it is not possible to nondestructively measure a quantum system's state (the quantum memory noncloning theorem), we should assign quantum memory to the destructive readout memory and take into account all the post-read operations for the quantum data restoration. Nevertheless, if we are only interested in the final results of quantum information processing, there is no need for the intermediate determination of the quantum memory status, so only the start input and final output state should be given. Therefore, at least for the secondary storage systems, the nonvolatile quantum memory can be reasonably used.

In this review, we discuss some important properties of quantum memory and its prospects to satisfy in the future main requirements for the nonvolatile memory implementation. The purpose of this discussion is to provide the perspective necessary for understanding the basic principles of the quantum memory and its present day practical status. The emphasis is on an overview, rather than on the specifics of implementation. The principles of quantum computing, i.e., quantum superposition and quantum correlation that yield quantum entanglement, are discussed. Then, provisional properties of quantum memory will be illustrated, and the power and future development of nonvolatile quantum memory will be suggested, together with the application to the measurement, instrumentation, and control.

2. QUANTUM COMPUTATION AND QUANTUM MEMORY

Quantum computing is concerned with the processing of quantum states. In quantum systems, the amount of available quantum memory increases exponentially with the size of the system. Quantum mechanics allows us to accommodate extremely large state spaces. In this chapter, we will briefly discuss most important facts that we need to understand quantum memory and its characteristics.

2.1. Basic Principles of Quantum Theory

2.1.1. Mathematical Foundations of Quantum Theory

2.1.1.1. Hilbert Space. In quantum theory, states of physical systems are represented by *vectors* $|\psi\rangle, |\phi\rangle, |\chi\rangle, \ldots,$ (in fact, *rays*) in an n-dimensional Hilbert space $\mathcal{H}^{(n)}$ [13, 17, 18, 39–43]. (We use the Dirac notation [38] and only consider vector spaces of finite dimensionalities, but the concepts described in this subchapter are not restricted only to finite dimensional vector spaces). It is a linear vector space over the field of complex numbers **C**; the vectors can be added together or multiplied by scalars and the results of these operations are also elements of the Hilbert space (*superposition principle*). For instance:

$$|\psi\rangle = c_1|\phi\rangle + c_2|\chi\rangle \tag{1}$$

where the operation of addition (+) is invertible, commutative, and associative. Hilbert space $\mathcal{H}^{(n)}$ includes a *zero element* equivalent for all vectors. For a Hilbert space $\mathcal{H}^{(n)}$ we can assign a dual space $\mathcal{H}^{*(n)}$ ($\langle\psi|$, $\langle\phi|$, $\langle\chi|, \ldots$) and the *bra*

$$|\psi\rangle = \begin{pmatrix} c_0 \\ c_1 \\ \ldots \\ c_{n-1} \end{pmatrix}$$

and *ket*

$$\langle\psi| = (c_0^* \, c_1^* \, \ldots \, c_{n-1}^*)$$

vectors are related by the Hermitian conjugation.

$$|\psi\rangle = (\langle\psi|)^\dagger, \quad \langle\psi| = (|\psi\rangle)^\dagger \tag{2}$$

Note that for vector spaces of infinite dimensionalities we can write the bra- and ket-vectors as infinitely dimensional row- and column-vectors.

For each pair of vectors in $\mathcal{H}^{(n)}$ we define the *scalar (inner) product* of two vectors in $|\psi\rangle$ and $|\phi\rangle$ as a bilinear form (complex number),

$$C\{\phi, \psi\} = \langle\phi|\psi\rangle \tag{3}$$

This bilinear form has the following properties:

$$\begin{gathered} C\{\psi, \psi\} \in \mathbf{R} \\ C\{\psi, \psi\} \geq 0 \quad \text{and} \quad C\{\psi, \psi\} = 0 \quad \text{only if} \quad |\psi\rangle = 0 \\ \langle\phi|\psi\rangle = (\langle\psi|\phi\rangle)^\dagger \end{gathered} \tag{4}$$

Using the inner product defines on $\mathcal{H}^{(n)}$ we can define a *norm* $\|\psi\| = \sqrt{\langle\psi|\psi\rangle}$, distance $\|\psi - \phi\|$, and, on this basis, a topology of the Hilbert space. In quantum mechanics, elements of $\mathcal{H}^{(n)}$ of the norm 1 are called *pure states* and they correspond to the quantum states of a closed quantum system.

2.1.1.2. Vector Transformations in a Hilbert Space. A *linear operator* $\hat{O}$ acts on the nonzero vector $|\psi\rangle$ and transforms $|\psi\rangle$ into another vector $|\tilde{\psi}\rangle$,

$$|\tilde{\psi}\rangle = \hat{O}|\psi\rangle \tag{5}$$

Clearly, the opposite transformation $|\tilde{\psi}\rangle \Rightarrow |\psi\rangle$ is presented by the *inverse operator* $\hat{O}^{-1}$, such as

$$\hat{O}\hat{O}^{-1} = \hat{O}^{-1}\hat{O} = \hat{I}$$

where $\hat{I}$ is the *identity operator*, $\hat{I}|\psi\rangle = |\psi\rangle$.

An operator $\hat{O}$ can be written in terms of the *outer product* of those two vectors ($|\tilde{\psi}\rangle\langle\psi|$):

$$\hat{O} = \frac{|\tilde{\psi}\rangle\langle\psi|}{\|\psi\|^2} \tag{6}$$

Certain elements $|\phi\rangle$ among the vectors of a Hilbert space on which the action of an operator is simply a rescaling ($|\tilde{\phi}\rangle = o|\phi\rangle$, $o \in \mathbf{C}$),

$$\hat{O}|\phi\rangle = o|\phi\rangle$$

is called an *eigenvector* of that operator, and o is the corresponding *eigenvalue*.

An operator is called a *Hemitian conjugate* (or just *Hemitian*) if $\hat{O}^\dagger = \hat{O}$ or $(|\tilde{\psi}\rangle\langle\psi|)^\dagger = |\psi\rangle\langle\tilde{\psi}|$. Eigenvalues of a Hemitian operator are real:

$$\begin{aligned} 0 &= \langle\phi|\hat{O}^\dagger - \hat{O}|\phi\rangle = \langle\phi|o^* - o|\phi\rangle \\ &= (o^* - o)\langle\phi|\phi\rangle \Rightarrow o^* = o \end{aligned}$$

Two eigenvectors of a Hemitian operator $|\phi_1\rangle$ and $|\phi_2\rangle$ with different eigenvalues o_1 and o_2 are orthogonal: $\langle\phi_1|\phi_2\rangle = 0$.

An operator is called *unitary* if $\hat{O}^\dagger\hat{O} = \hat{O}\hat{O}^\dagger = \hat{I}$. Clearly, the unitary operator does not change the norm of the vector:

$$\hat{O}|\psi\rangle = |\phi\rangle \Rightarrow \langle\phi|\phi\rangle = \langle\psi|\hat{O}^\dagger\hat{O}|\psi\rangle = \langle\psi|\psi\rangle$$

If two operators $\hat{O}$ and $\hat{O}^\dagger$ *commute*, i.e., $\lfloor\hat{O}, \hat{O}^\dagger\rfloor \equiv \hat{O}\hat{O}^\dagger - \hat{O}^\dagger\hat{O} = 0$, the operator $\hat{O}$ is called *normal.* Obviously, an operator that is Hermitian and unitary is normal.

A case of particular importance is that when in (6) $|\tilde{\psi}\rangle = |\psi\rangle$ and $\|\psi\| = 1$. Then the operator $\hat{P}_\psi = |\psi\rangle\langle\psi|$ acts as the *projector* onto the vector $|\psi\rangle$

$$\hat{P}_\psi|\phi\rangle = |\psi\rangle\langle\psi|\phi\rangle \tag{7}$$

and $\langle\psi|\phi\rangle$ is the *component* (*projection*) of $|\phi\rangle$ along $|\psi\rangle$.

2.1.1.3. Basis in a Hilbert Space. Two vectors $|\psi\rangle$ and $|\phi\rangle$ are called *orthogonal* if $\langle\phi|\psi\rangle = 0$. If $\{|0\rangle, |1\rangle, \ldots, |n-1\rangle\}$ ($\langle i|j\rangle = \delta_{ij}$) is an *orthonormal basis* of vectors in $\mathscr{H}^{(n)}$, we can write for each vector $|\psi\rangle$ of $\mathscr{H}^{(n)}$:

$$|\psi\rangle = \sum_{i=0}^{n-1} \alpha_i |i\rangle \tag{8}$$

where $\alpha_i = \langle i|\psi\rangle$ are components of the vector in the given basis (and α_i^* are components for the corresponding bra vector $\langle\psi|$). For a pure state,

$$\sum_{i=0}^{n-1} |\alpha_i|^2 = 1$$

The scalar product of two vectors,

$$|\psi\rangle = \sum_{i=0}^{n-1} \alpha_i |i\rangle \quad \text{and} \quad |\phi\rangle = \sum_{i=0}^{n-1} \beta_i |i\rangle$$

can be written as

$$\langle\phi|\psi\rangle = (\beta_0^* \, \beta_1^* \ldots \beta_{n-1}^*) \begin{pmatrix} \alpha_0 \\ \alpha_1 \\ \ldots \\ \alpha_{n-1} \end{pmatrix} = \sum_{i=0}^{n-1} \beta_i^* \alpha_i \tag{9}$$

The *outer product* of those two vectors is

$$|\phi\rangle\langle\psi| = \begin{pmatrix} \beta_0 \\ \beta_1 \\ \ldots \\ \beta_{n-1} \end{pmatrix} (\alpha_0^* \alpha_1^* \ldots \alpha_{n-1}^*)$$
$$= \begin{pmatrix} \beta_0\alpha_0^* & \beta_0\alpha_1^* & \ldots & \beta_0\alpha_{n-1}^* \\ \beta_1\alpha_0^* & \beta_1\alpha_1^* & \ldots & \beta_1\alpha_{n-1}^* \\ \ldots & \ldots & \ldots & \ldots \\ \beta_{n-1}\alpha_0^* & \beta_{n-1}\alpha_1^* & \ldots & \beta_{n-1}\alpha_{n-1}^* \end{pmatrix} \tag{10}$$

In general, an action of any linear operator $\hat{O}$ (5) is given in terms of components of a matrix formed by a certain basis: $O_{ij} = \langle i|\hat{O}|j\rangle$. For instance, a transformation

$$|\psi\rangle = \sum_{i=0}^{n-1} \alpha_i |i\rangle$$

into another vector,

$$|\tilde{\psi}\rangle = \sum_{i=0}^{n-1} \tilde{\alpha}_i |i\rangle$$

is presented by the following vector components' transformation:

$$\tilde{\alpha}_i = \sum_{j=0}^{n-1} O_{ij} \alpha_j$$

For a Hemitian operator: $O_{ij}^* = O_{ji}$. the projector operator onto $|i\rangle$ then is

$$\hat{P}_i = |i\rangle\langle i| \tag{11}$$

satisfying

$$\hat{P}_j \hat{P}_i = \hat{P}_j \delta_{ij} \tag{12}$$

If $\mathscr{H}^{(m)}$ is a subspace of $\mathscr{H}^{(n)}$ $(m \leq n)$ and $\{|0\rangle, |1\rangle, \ldots, |m-1\rangle\}$ is an orthonormal basis of this subspace, then the projector onto $\mathscr{H}^{(m)}$ is

$$\hat{P}_{\mathscr{H}^{(m)}} = \sum_{i=0}^{m-1} |i\rangle\langle i| \tag{13}$$

and the *completeness relation* for $\mathscr{H}^{(n)}$ reads

$$\hat{P}_{\mathscr{H}^{(n)}} = \sum_{i=0}^{n-1} |i\rangle\langle i| = \hat{I}$$

In a Hilbert space, every normal operator $\hat{O}$ has a set of orthonormal eigenvectors $\{|i_o\rangle\}$ (associated with the eigenvalues o_i), which is *complete*:

$$\sum_{i=0}^{n-1} |i_o\rangle\langle i_o| = \hat{I} \tag{14}$$

That means that every vector $|\psi\rangle$ in the Hilbert space can be decomposed:

$$|\psi\rangle = \sum_{i=0}^{n-1} \zeta_i^o |i_o\rangle$$

The action of the operator $\hat{O}$ on such a vector can be written as

$$\hat{O}|\psi\rangle = \sum_{i=0}^{n-1} \zeta_i^o o_i |i_o\rangle$$

If we consider now the action of the projection operators $\hat{P}_i^o = |i_o\rangle\langle i_o|$ on the vector $|\psi\rangle$, we find that the action of the operator $\hat{O}$ can be replaced with the accumulated action of the projection operators (*spectral decomposition* of the operator):

$$\hat{O} = \sum_{i=0}^{n-1} o_i \hat{P}_i^o \tag{15}$$

If for two operators $\hat{O}_1$ and $\hat{O}_2$, their commutator $\lfloor \hat{O}_1, \hat{O}_2 \rfloor$ is 0, this is a necessary and sufficient condition for the existence of a complete set of basis vectors $\{|i_o\rangle\}$ that are simultaneous eigenvectors of $\hat{O}_1$ and $\hat{O}_2$ associated with the eigenvalues o_{1i} and o_{2i}.

2.1.1.4. Tensor Product of Hilbert Spaces. Let $\mathcal{H}_1^{(n)}$ and $\mathcal{H}_2^{(m)}$ be two n and m-dimensional Hilbert spaces. The *tensor product* $\mathcal{H}_1^{(n)} \otimes \mathcal{H}_2^{(m)}$ can be composed from them yielding a $(n \times m)$-dimensional Hilbert space $\mathcal{H}^{(n\times m)} = \mathcal{H}_1^{(n)} \otimes \mathcal{H}_2^{(m)}$, where any $|\chi\rangle \in \mathcal{H}^{(n\times m)}$ can be written as $|\chi\rangle = |\psi\rangle \otimes |\phi\rangle$ for some $|\psi\rangle \in \mathcal{H}_1^{(n)}$ and $|\phi\rangle \in H_2^{(m)}$. If $|\psi\rangle = \sum_{i=0}^{n-1} \alpha_i |i_1\rangle$ and $|\phi\rangle = \sum_{i=0}^{m-1} \beta_i |i_2\rangle$ then the tensor product $|\chi\rangle$ is a vector,

$$|\chi\rangle = |\psi\rangle \otimes |\phi\rangle = \begin{pmatrix} \alpha_0\beta_0 \\ \cdots \\ \alpha_0\beta_{m-1} \\ \alpha_1\beta_0 \\ \cdots \\ \alpha_1\beta_{m-1} \\ \cdots \\ \alpha_{n-1}\beta_{m-1} \end{pmatrix} \tag{16}$$

with the basis $\{|0_1\rangle \otimes |0_2\rangle, |0_1\rangle \otimes |1_2\rangle, \ldots, |(n-1)_1\rangle \otimes |(m-1)_2\rangle\}$. Note that a vector $|i_1\rangle \otimes |j_2\rangle$ from the basis of the Hilbert space $\mathcal{H}^{(n\times m)}$ also can be presented in literature as $|i\rangle \otimes |j\rangle$, $|i \otimes j\rangle$, or $|i, j\rangle$.

Consider now a vector $|\chi\rangle$ in the Hilbert space $\mathcal{H}^{(n\times m)} = \mathcal{H}_1^{(n)} \otimes \mathcal{H}_2^{(m)}$. Using the tensor product basis $\{|i\rangle \otimes |j\rangle\}$ we can present the vector as:

$$|\chi\rangle = \sum_{i,j=0}^{n-1,\,m-1} \mu_{ij} |i\rangle \otimes |j\rangle \tag{17}$$

2.1.1.5. Density Operator. Let $\hat{O}_1$ be an operator that acts on vectors from a subspace $\mathcal{H}_1^{(n)}$ of the Hilbert space $\mathcal{H}^{(n\times m)}$:

$$\hat{O}_1|\chi\rangle = \sum_{i,j=0}^{n-1,\,m-1} \mu_{ij} \hat{O}_1 |i\rangle \otimes |j\rangle$$

We calculate a matrix element of $\hat{O}_1$:

$$\begin{aligned}\langle\chi|\hat{O}_1|\chi\rangle &= \sum_{i',j'=0}^{n-1,\,m-1} \sum_{i,j=0}^{n-1,\,m-1} \mu^*_{i'j'}\mu_{ij} \langle j'| \otimes \langle i'|\hat{O}_1|i\rangle \otimes |j\rangle \\ &= \sum_{i',i,j=0}^{n-1,\,n-1,\,m-1} \mu^*_{i'j}\mu_{ij} \langle i'|\hat{O}_1|i\rangle \\ &= \sum_{i,i'=0}^{n-1,\,n-1} \rho_{ii'} (O_1)_{i'i} = Tr(\hat{\rho}\,\hat{O}_1) \end{aligned} \tag{18}$$

where $Tr(\hat{O})$ stands for the trace of an operator $\hat{O}$. Equation 18 defines the *density operator* (reduced density operator) of the sub-space $\mathcal{H}_1^{(n)}$:

$$\rho_{ii'} = \sum_{j=0}^{m-1} \mu_{ij}\mu^*_{i'j} \tag{19}$$

The density operator is clearly Hermitian ($\rho = \rho^\dagger$), positively defined ($\langle\psi|\hat{\rho}|\psi\rangle \geq 0$), and it has unit trace:

$$Tr(\hat{\rho}) = \sum_{j=0}^{m-1} |\mu_{ij}|^2 = \| \psi \|^2 = 1 \tag{20}$$

We assume that, the system described by $\mathcal{H}^{(n\times m)}$ is closed (pure). In addition, the density operator of a pure state obeys $\hat{\rho}^2 = \hat{\rho}$.

2.1.2. Quantum Physics Foundations of Quantum Memory

The principles of quantum physics accumulate and generalize the results of numerous experiments. Based on this solid knowledge, quantum physics plays a fundamental role in the modern understanding, description, and application of natural phenomena. In this subchapter we present basic principles (postulates) and some of the corollaries and related definitions of terms indispensable for understanding and exploration of the quantum memory issue.

2.1.2.1. Basic Concepts. Quantum mechanics is essentially a statistical theory. It explains and predicts physical system properties on the foundation of statistics. Unlike classical mechanics, quantum mechanics cannot completely define the future behavior of a physical system. The reason why is that the difference between the two ways of description (classical and quantum) is more than a technical matter and it is hidden in the measurements we use to determine the state of the system. Classical physics assumes that the influence of the measuring process on the investigated system can be made arbitrarily small. This is no longer true for microscopic systems when the tools of the measurement and their influence on the system states cannot be neglected [40, 43, 44]. Therefore, using quantum theory we can define only *probabilities* with which these states of the system occur. Consequently, the theoretical description of quantum mechanics is based on the *wave function* (*state vector*) paradigm. Within this paradigm, a complex Hilbert space $\mathcal{H}^{(n)}$, called the *state space*, is associated with any quantum system (in general $\mathcal{H}^{(n)}$ is of infinite dimension, but in quantum information theory we operate with spaces of finite dimensions). Conventionally, the state vectors (wave functions) $|\psi\rangle$ in $\mathcal{H}^{(n)}$ are assumed to be normalized: $\|\psi\|^2 = 1$. We can choose a one-dimensional subspace (a ray) in our Hilbert space that corresponds to any state of the system under consideration. The states described by rays are called *pure*. Vectors from this subspace differ only by a nonzero complex scalar $|e^{i\nu}| = 1$, $\nu \in \mathbf{R}$ (e.g., $|\psi\rangle$ and $e^{i\nu}|\psi\rangle$), υ is called the *relative phase,* and describe the same physical state.

If $|\psi\rangle$ and $|\varphi\rangle$ describe two different states of the system, the *probability amplitude* to obtain as a result the state $|\psi\rangle$ when measuring the state $|\phi\rangle$ is

$$a_\psi(\phi) = \langle\psi|\phi\rangle \tag{21}$$

which is the *component* of $|\phi\rangle$ along $|\psi\rangle$. The *probability* to find the system in the state $|\psi\rangle$ when measuring the state $|\phi\rangle$ in quantum physics is defined as

$$P_\psi(\phi) = |a_\psi(\phi)|^2 = |\langle\psi|\phi\rangle|^2 \tag{22}$$

From the mathematical point of view, that means that we have to project $|\phi\rangle$ onto $|\psi\rangle$ to obtain the probability $P_\psi(\phi)$ (which is a physical characteristic of the system's state). According to our definition, the mathematical operation corresponding to the experimental measurement of the physical system's state is a projection.

2.1.2.2. Observables. The quantum states of a physical system are characterized by *observables*. Those are outcomes (experimental data) of experiments with a minimum level of uncertainty. In quantum theory, each observable $\mathcal{O}$ is represented by the corresponding Hermitian operators $\hat{O}$ on the Hilbert space $\mathcal{H}^{(n)}$ representing the physical system. We omit here discussions of the ways in which this correspondence is realized (e.g., Refs. [38, 40, 43]).

The measurement of an observable $\mathcal{O}$ (a physical property or characteristic) of the system has a result o_i, which is one of the real eigenvalues of $\hat{O}$ associated with the eigenvector (eigenstate) $|i_o\rangle$. Assuming for the simplicity here that the eigenvalues $\{o_i\}$ are nondegenerated, we obtain from Eq. (15) that o_j is an exact value of the observable $\mathcal{O}$ if the quantum system is in the eigenstate $|j_o\rangle$. If the system is in a state $|\psi\rangle$ composed from $|i_o\rangle$ as

$$|\psi\rangle = \sum_{i=0}^{n-1} a_i(\psi)|i_o\rangle$$

the probability to find the system in $|i_o\rangle$ is

$$P_i(\psi) = |a_i(\psi)|^2 = |\langle i_o|\psi\rangle|^2 \tag{23}$$

and the *expectation value* (theoretically predicted) value of $\mathcal{O}$ can be presented as

$$\mathcal{O}_\psi = \sum_{i=0}^{n-1} P_i(\psi)\, o_i = \langle\psi|\hat{O}|\psi\rangle \tag{24}$$

Immediately after the measurement, the quantum system is found in a state $|i_o\rangle$, which is an eigenstate of $\hat{O}$ with the measured eigenvalue o_i. In other words, the event of the measurement projects the system state onto the state $|i_o\rangle$; therefore, it corresponds to the projector operator $\hat{P}_i^o = |i_o\rangle\langle i_o|$. Two mutually exclusive measurement-outcomes correspond to two orthogonal projection operations (projectors):

$$\hat{P}_i^o\hat{P}_j^o|\psi\rangle = \delta_{ij}|i_o\rangle$$

In the measurement we automatically *collapse* the quantum state of the system onto one ($|\psi\rangle \Rightarrow |i_o\rangle$) from the basis [40, 45]. Instead of a set of probabilistically possible states we obtain one, well-defined state. Following immediate measurements of the system's state will lead to $|i_o\rangle$ with probability 1. This fact is confirmed by numerous experimental observations, and this means that the results of a measurement are defined by the preparation (initialization) of the system's state. The conditions under which a state is prepared have different impacts on the final result. The initialization conditions are important to predict the actual evolution of the system. However, there are no general rules to make a decision of which conditions are substantial. An analysis of a particular physical situation is always required. We also should realize that the statistical description of expectation values in Eq. (24) also represents a fundamental requirement to verify the probabilistic predictions from Eq. (24): we should be able to replicate a quantum state for many identical quantum systems or to prepare the state according to the same prescriptions many times in the same system.

The statistical spread of the measurement results (expectation values of an observable $\mathcal{O}$) can be expressed in terms of the expectation values of *standard deviations*

$$\Delta\mathcal{O} = \sqrt{\langle\psi|(\hat{O}-\mathcal{O}_\psi)^2|\psi\rangle} = \sqrt{\langle\psi|\hat{O}^2|\psi\rangle - \mathcal{O}_\psi^2}$$

For two observables $\mathcal{O}_1$ and $\mathcal{O}_2$, the Heisenberg's *uncertainty principle* states that

$$\Delta\mathcal{O}_1\cdot\Delta\mathcal{O}_2 \geq \frac{1}{2}\langle\psi|[\hat{O}_1,\hat{O}_2]|\psi\rangle \tag{25}$$

Uncertainty is a fundamental property of quantum systems. The inequality (25) suggests, e.g., that if a large number of identical quantum systems are prepared in the same quantum state $|\psi\rangle$ and the independent measurement gives dispersions $\{\mathcal{O}_{1\psi},\Delta\mathcal{O}_1\}$ and $\{\mathcal{O}_{2\psi},\Delta\mathcal{O}_2\}$, while the expectation values obey Eq. (25).

2.1.2.3. Evolution of Pure Quantum States. The evolution in time of a closed quantum system is described by the quantum state vector $|\psi\rangle$ evolution in the Hilbert space $\mathcal{H}^{(n)}$. The superposition principle implies that the evolution is governed by a linear equation, which is postulated in quantum theory as the *Schrödinger equation*

$$i\hbar\frac{\partial}{\partial t}|\psi(t)\rangle = \hat{H}|\psi(t)\rangle \tag{26}$$

where the linear operator $\hat{H}$ is called the *Hamiltonian* and $\hbar$ stands for the Dirac constant. The operator $\hat{H}$ is a Hermitian operator corresponding to the classical Hamiltonian and it represents an observable, which is the energy E of the system.

According to Eq. (26) the expectation value of a time-independent operator $\hat{O}$ changes in time as

$$\frac{d}{dt}\mathcal{O}_\psi = -\frac{i}{\hbar}\langle\psi(t)|[\hat{O},\hat{H}]\,|\psi(t)\rangle \tag{27}$$

On the other hand, the time evolution of a quantum state $|\psi(t)\rangle \Rightarrow |\psi(t')\rangle$ (without losses of the overall probability: $\|\psi(t')\| = \|\psi(t)\|$) can be described by a unitary operator (*propagator*), $\hat{U}(t',t)$:

$$|\psi(t')\rangle = \hat{U}(t',t)\,|\psi(t)\rangle \tag{28}$$

The operator $\hat{U}(t',t)$ possesses the group properties of $\hat{U}(t'',t) = \hat{U}(t'',t')\hat{U}(t',t)$, $\hat{U}(t,t') = \hat{U}^{-1}(t',t)$, and obviously, $\hat{U}(t,t) = \hat{I}$. Using that we can present the Schrödinger equation in the following form:

$$i\hbar\frac{d}{dt}\hat{U}(t,t') = \hat{H}(t)\hat{U}(t,t') \tag{29}$$

A formal solution of this equation can be written as

$$\hat{U}(t, t') = \hat{P}_D \exp\left[-\frac{i}{\hbar}\int_{t'}^{t}\hat{H}(\tau)\,d\tau\right] \tag{30}$$

where $\hat{P}_D$ is the chronologic operator introduced by Dyson [46].

In many important cases where the quantum physics is invariant under the time translations, the operator $\hat{U}(t', t)$ should depend only on the time difference $\hat{U}(t', t) = \hat{U}(t' - t)$ and the Hamiltonian is independent of time. In this case, the energy of the quantum system has a definite value of E and the change of the quantum states in time (all of them belong to the same ray of $\mathscr{H}^{(n)}$) can be presented by the relative phase:

$$|\psi(t)\rangle = \exp\left[-\frac{i}{\hbar}Et\right]|\chi\rangle \tag{31}$$

where $|\chi\rangle$ is time independent vector with norm 1. The Schrödinger equation can be transformed into its stationary (time independent) form:

$$\hat{H}|\varphi\rangle = E|\varphi\rangle \tag{32}$$

and the propagator (30) can be written as:

$$\hat{U}(t - t') = \exp\left[-\frac{i}{\hbar}\hat{H}(t - t')\right] \tag{33}$$

According to (32) eigenvectors of the Hamiltonian form an orthonormal basis $\{|\chi_i\rangle\}$ for $\mathscr{H}^{(n)}$ with the associated eigenvalues $\{E_i\}$ and any state from $\mathscr{H}^{(n)}$ can be expanded in this basis with time dependent coefficients:

$$|\psi(t)\rangle = \sum_{i}^{n-1} \alpha_i(t)\,|\chi_i\rangle \tag{34}$$

where

$$\alpha_i(t) = \exp\left(-\frac{i}{\hbar}E_i t\right)$$

If the quantum system at time t' was in one of the eigenstates $|\phi_j\rangle$ of the Hamiltonian then $\alpha_i(t') = \delta_{ij}$ and at a later time,

$$|\psi(t)\rangle = \hat{U}(t - t')\,|\phi_i\rangle = \exp\left[-\frac{i}{\hbar}E_j(t - t')\right]|\phi_i\rangle \tag{35}$$

Therefore, the propagator is just a phase factor of the state.

2.1.2.4. Evolution of Mixed Quantum States. If two (or more) quantum subsystems associated with the Hilbert spaces $\{\mathscr{H}_i^{(n_i)}, i = 1, 2, \ldots, k\}$ composed into a quantum system associated with $\mathscr{H}^{(N)} (N = \prod_{i=1}^{k} n_i)$ a genetic mixed quantum state of $\mathscr{H}^{(N)}$ expanding Eq. (17) can always be prepared as a mixture:

$$|\psi\rangle = \sum_{i,j,\ldots,p=0}^{n_1-1, n_2-1, \ldots, n_k-1} \mu_{i,j,\ldots,p}\, \overbrace{|i\rangle \otimes |j\rangle \cdots \otimes |p\rangle}^{k} \tag{36}$$

When our quantum system is an ensemble (mixture) of subsystems, or for the quantum subsystem of our interest (or experimental accessibility) the preparation history is uncertain, it is convenient to use the density operator instead of the pure state description.

In many cases we can separate our ensemble of subsystems in two parts, the subsystem of our interest associated with $\mathscr{H}^{(n)}$ and the rest associated with $\mathscr{H}^{(m)}$. It follows from the reduced density operator (of the sub-system $\mathscr{H}^{(n)}$) definition and properties that it can be written as:

$$\hat{\rho} = \sum_{i=0}^{n-1} \rho_i |i_\rho\rangle\langle i_\rho| \tag{37}$$

where ρ_i is an eigenvalue of the density operator and $|i_\rho\rangle$ is the corresponding eigenvectors. The density operator eigenvalues can be used to represent any mixed state by the state vectors for the quantum subsystem of our interest. In quantum information theory it is called a purification, which refers to the *Schmidt purification theorem:*

$$|\psi\rangle = \sum_{j}^{n-1} \sqrt{\rho_i}|i_\rho\rangle \otimes |i_\rho\rangle \tag{38}$$

The expectation value of an observable $\mathscr{O}$ associated with the operator $\hat{O}$ (which is defined on the subspace $\mathscr{H}^{(n)}$) according to Eq. (18) is given by

$$\mathscr{O}_\psi = \langle\psi|\hat{O}|\psi\rangle = Tr(\hat{\rho}\,\hat{O}) \tag{39}$$

The Gleason's theorem [47] states that the most general description of quantum systems can be given by the density operator. In an appropriate orthonormal basis $\{|i\rangle\}$, the density operator can be presented as:

$$\hat{\rho} = \sum_{i=0}^{n-1} P_i |i\rangle\langle i| \tag{40}$$

where P_i represents the probability to find our quantum subsystem in the state $|i\rangle$ $(\sum_i P_i = 1)$.

The fidelity F of two quantum states $|\psi\rangle$ and $|\phi\rangle$ is defined as the probability to find the system in the state $|\psi\rangle$ when measuring the state $|\phi\rangle$. According to Eq. (22), it is:

$$F(\psi, \phi) = |\langle\psi|\phi\rangle|^2 \tag{41}$$

We can use this definition to have a qualitative measure when comparing pure and mixed states. For a pure state $|\psi\rangle$ and a mixed state presented by the density operator $\hat{\rho}$, the fidelity reads

$$F(\psi, \hat{\rho}) = \langle\psi|\hat{\rho}\psi\rangle \tag{42}$$

More generally speaking, for two mixed states $\hat{\rho}_1$ and $\hat{\rho}_2$, Eq. (42) leads to the following expression (the Uhlmann's theorem [13])

$$F(\hat{\rho}_1, \hat{\rho}_2) = \left(Tr\sqrt{\hat{\rho}_1^{1/2}\hat{\rho}_2\hat{\rho}_1^{1/2}} \right)^2 \tag{43}$$

Clearly, $0 \le F \le 1$ and it is 1 only when $\hat{\rho}_1 = \hat{\rho}_2$.

The time evolution of the density operator $\hat{\rho}(t)$ (and accordingly the time evolution of the expectation values for the mixed systems) is defined by the Schrödinger Eq. (26). So, we define the initial (at the moment $t' = 0$) density operator as

$$\hat{\rho}(0) = \sum_{i=0}^{n-1} P_i |i(0)\rangle\langle i(0)|$$

and the states $\{|i(t)\rangle\}$ evolve according to Eq. (28) by a unitary operator $\hat{U}(t', t) = \hat{U}(0, t) \equiv \hat{U}(t)$. The density operator evolution is defined as

$$\hat{\rho}(t) = \sum_{i=0}^{n-1} P_i \hat{U}(t)|i(0)\rangle\langle i(0)|\hat{U}^{\dagger}(t) = \hat{U}(t)\hat{\rho}(0)\hat{U}^{\dagger}(t) \tag{44}$$

By differentiating Eq. (44), the *von Neumann master evolution equation* for the density operator can be readily obtained as:

$$i\hbar \frac{d\hat{\rho}(t)}{dt} = [\hat{H}, \hat{\rho}(t)] \tag{45}$$

Here we should emphasize again that the density operator has two important properties: it is Hermitian and it evolves. Therefore, according to the general quantum description of observables, we can assign a corresponding observable to the density operator. It has been shown [39, 40, 48] that the corresponding observable is the classical phase space density. Therefore, the thermodynamic partition function Z, energy E, and the von Neumann entropy S_N (a proper extension of the Shannon entropy [49] onto quantum systems) can be presented by the density operator:

$$Z = Tr(\hat{\rho}) = Tr\left[\exp\left(-\frac{\hat{H}}{k_B T}\right)\right]$$

$$E = k_B T^2 \frac{\partial}{\partial T} \ln Z; \quad \text{and}$$

$$S_N = k_B\left(\ln Z - T\frac{\partial}{\partial T}\ln Z\right) = -k_B Tr(\hat{\rho}\ln\hat{\rho}) \tag{46}$$

where k_B is the Boltzmann constant, and T stands for temperature. It follows from the expressions above that a quantum system can be described by the following density operator

$$\hat{\rho} = N\exp\left(-\frac{\hat{H}}{k_B T}\right) \tag{47}$$

where a normalization constant N should be defined from Eq. (20).

Unlike for classical systems, a quantum state cannot be cloned by universal (independent on the state) unitary transformations (reproduced one or many times without losses in the probability) [50, 51]. This very important statement is known as *"the quantum non-cloning theorem."* We consider an unknown quantum state $|\phi_{S_1}\rangle$ of a quantum system S_1 (associated with a Hilbert space $\mathscr{H}_1^{(n)}$) to be copied state onto a quantum state $|\varphi_{S_2}\rangle$ of another quantum system S_2 (associated with a Hilbert space $\mathscr{H}_2^{(m)}$). The evolution (cloning) of the states vector $|\phi_{S_1}\rangle \otimes |\varphi_{S_2}\rangle \Rightarrow |\phi_{S_1}\rangle \otimes |\phi_{S_2}\rangle$ of the composed system $S_1 \otimes S_2$ (associated with a Hilbert space $\mathscr{H}_1^{(n)} \otimes \mathscr{H}_2^{(m)}$) is provided by a unitary operator $\hat{U}$ as the following:

$$\hat{U}|\phi_{S_1}\rangle \otimes |\varphi_{S_2}\rangle = |\phi_{S_1}\rangle \otimes |\phi_{S_2}\rangle$$

If this operation is a universal, we should be able to clone another quantum state $|\tilde{\phi}_{S_1}\rangle$ of S_1:

$$\hat{U}|\tilde{\phi}_{S_1}\rangle \otimes |\varphi_{S_2}\rangle = |\tilde{\phi}_{S_1}\rangle \otimes |\tilde{\phi}_{S_2}\rangle$$

Performing the inner product of those two operations, we obtain

$$\begin{aligned}\langle\varphi_{S_2}| \otimes \langle\phi_{S_1}|\hat{U}^{\dagger}\hat{U}|\tilde{\phi}_{S_1}\rangle \otimes |\varphi_{S_2}\rangle &= \langle\varphi_{S_2}| \otimes \langle\phi_{S_1}|\tilde{\phi}_{S_1}\rangle \otimes |\varphi_{S_2}\rangle \\ &= \langle\phi_{S_2}| \otimes \langle\phi_{S_1}|\tilde{\phi}_{S_1}\rangle \otimes |\phi_{S_2}\rangle\end{aligned}$$

which leads to

$$\langle\phi|\tilde{\phi}\rangle = \langle\phi|\tilde{\phi}\rangle^2$$

and suggests that the unitary cloning is possible only if $|\phi_{S_1}\rangle = |\tilde{\phi}_{S_1}\rangle$ (for only one chosen state) or $\langle\phi_{S_1}|\tilde{\phi}_{S_1}\rangle = 0$ (only for orthogonal states), which is not generally a universal operation. Therefore, no universal unitary evolution can produce identical copies of an unknown quantum state.

The impossibility of a universal cloning procedure strongly distinguishes quantum memory from classical memory. For the classical memory, each classical bit (state) on the memory register can be copied by a universal copy-operation. In contrast, the quantum memory output reading always requires extra conditions and operations to be copied without unrecoverable losses.

Fortunately, the noncloning theorem does not forbid a possibility to approximately copy the quantum register (some time with a very high level of approximation). "The quantum copy machine" [52, 53] can perform a universal copying of the original quantum states into two identical copies with the maximum average fidelity $F_{\max}(\phi_{\text{in}}, \phi_{\text{out}})$ between the input $|\phi_{\text{in}}\rangle$ and output $|\phi_{\text{out}}\rangle$ states.

The noncloning theorem has broad practical implications in the quantum information processing such as lending security to quantum key distribution.

2.2. Qubits

2.2.1. Computational Qubit

An elementary (simplest, basic) quantum object, which can be used to store quantum information, is quantum bit or *qubit.* A qubit is a vector $|\psi\rangle$ in a two-dimensional Hilbert space $\mathscr{H}^{(2)}$ corresponding to a two-state quantum system.

It can be fully described by a superposition of two orthonormal vectors in the Hilbert space $\mathscr{H}^{(2)}$ labeled

$$|0\rangle = \begin{pmatrix} 1 \\ 0 \end{pmatrix} \quad \text{and} \quad |1\rangle = \begin{pmatrix} 0 \\ 1 \end{pmatrix}$$

$$|\psi\rangle = \alpha_0|0\rangle + \alpha_1|1\rangle \tag{48}$$

This is a generic pure state with the norm of the vector to be one:

$$|\alpha_0|^2 + |\alpha_1|^2 = 1 \tag{49}$$

The value of a qubit (the primitive binary quantum value, *computational qubit*) is an observable Q corresponding to the Hermitian operator

$$\hat{Q} = \sum_{i=0,1} i|i\rangle\langle i| = \begin{pmatrix} 0 & 0 \\ 0 & 1 \end{pmatrix} \tag{50}$$

The expectation value of $\hat{Q}$ is

$$Q = \langle\psi|\hat{Q}|\psi\rangle = |\alpha_1|^2$$

and it gives the probability to find the system in state $|1\rangle$ if a measurement is performed on the qubit. This ensures that the probability to find the system in the state $|0\rangle$ or $|1\rangle$ is $|\alpha_0|^2$ or $|\alpha_1|^2$, respectively.

The most important difference between quantum memory agent (qubit) and its classical counterpart (*cbit*, classical bit) primarily arises from the realization superposition principle (Eq. [48]): the qubit can be measured with certain probability in one of an infinite number of states, whereas a cbit is capable of being in only one of two exclusive states. On the other hand, information presented by the quantum memory agent (a single unknown qubit state) cannot generally be retrieved by a single measurement. An ensemble of identical quantum systems must be prepared and measured to obtain an appropriate expectation value with certain probability.

2.2.2. Pauli Representation

Any quantum system with two quantum states can be used for a physical implementation of a qubit. Few examples were realized in experiments, including the two orthogonal polarizations of a photon, spin states of electrons and other spin-half particles, two close energy states in atoms, ions, quantum dots, and quantum dots molecules, and superconducting circuits, among others. The mathematical models and evolution operations of all quantum two-state systems are isomorphic to each other and to two dimensional *"isospin"* states [54], which are also described by vectors in $\mathscr{H}^{(2)}$, acted on by the symmetry Lie group SU(2) [55]. Just as is in the case for a regular electron's spin, an isospin is described by two quantum numbers: the total isospin and the component of the spin vector in some direction. Therefore, the genetic pure two quantum state systems also can be treated in the *Pauli representation*, where we introduce an orthonormal basis of two ("up" and "down") isospin's states,

$$|\uparrow\rangle = |0\rangle = \begin{pmatrix} 1 \\ 0 \end{pmatrix} \quad \text{and} \quad |\downarrow\rangle = |1\rangle = \begin{pmatrix} 0 \\ 1 \end{pmatrix} \tag{51}$$

The coefficients α_0 and α_1 in Eq. (48) can be parameterized, taking into account the state normalization $\|\psi\| = 1$:

$$\alpha_1 = \cos\frac{\theta}{2}, \quad \alpha_1 = \exp(i\varphi)\sin\frac{\theta}{2} \tag{52}$$

where the angular parameters θ and φ are attributed to the standard directional angles of a three-dimensional real unit vector,

$$\mathbf{n} = (\sin\theta\cos\varphi, \sin\theta\sin\varphi, \cos\theta) \tag{53}$$

Therefore, the unit ray $|\psi\rangle$ describing the pure state in the Hilbert space, $\mathscr{H}^{(2)}$, is mapped uniquely (one-to-one) to a unit vector $\mathbf{n}$ on the unit *Poincaré sphere* (*Bloch sphere*) besides an overall phase:

$$|\psi\rangle \equiv |\mathbf{n}\rangle = \cos\frac{\theta}{2}\,|\uparrow\rangle + \exp(i\varphi)\sin\frac{\theta}{2}\,|\downarrow\rangle = \begin{pmatrix} \cos\frac{\theta}{2} \\ \exp(i\varphi)\sin\frac{\theta}{2} \end{pmatrix} \tag{54}$$

For a given pure state (Eq. [54]) in which the isospin is directed of polar angle θ, a measurement of the distinguished isospin polarization $\hat{\sigma}_z$ leads to $|\uparrow\rangle$ with probability $\cos^2\theta/2$ and to $|\downarrow\rangle$ with probability $\sin^2\theta/2$.

The isospin polarization (actual $\mathbf{n}$-vector direction) can be represented by Hermitian projection operators introduced by Pauli:

$$\begin{aligned} \hat{\sigma}_x &= |\uparrow\rangle\langle\downarrow| + |\downarrow\rangle\langle\uparrow| = \begin{pmatrix} 0 & 1 \\ 1 & 0 \end{pmatrix} \\ \hat{\sigma}_y &= i(|\downarrow\rangle\langle\uparrow| - |\uparrow\rangle\langle\downarrow|) = i\begin{pmatrix} 0 & -1 \\ 1 & 0 \end{pmatrix} \\ \hat{\sigma}_z &= |\uparrow\rangle\langle\uparrow| - |\downarrow\rangle\langle\downarrow| = \begin{pmatrix} 1 & 0 \\ 0 & -1 \end{pmatrix} \end{aligned} \tag{55}$$

The Pauli operators in Eq. (55) are Hermitian by definition with some useful properties:

$$Tr\hat{\sigma}_i = 0; \quad \lfloor\hat{\sigma}_i, \hat{\sigma}_j\rfloor = 2i\varepsilon_{ijk}\hat{\sigma}_k$$

where ε_{ijk} is the Levi-Civita symbol.

It is known that the SU(2) group is locally isomorphous with the SO(3) group; therefore, if $|\psi\rangle$ is subjected to a SU(2) transformation, $\mathbf{n}$ undergoes an orthogonal rotation belonging to SO(3). Indeed, the expectation values of those operators in the state of Eq. (54) are:

$$\begin{aligned} \langle\mathbf{n}|\hat{\sigma}_x|\mathbf{n}\rangle &= \sin\theta\cos\varphi = n_x \\ \langle\mathbf{n}|\hat{\sigma}_y|\mathbf{n}\rangle &= \sin\theta\sin\varphi = n_y \\ \langle\mathbf{n}|\hat{\sigma}_z|\mathbf{n}\rangle &= \cos\theta = n_z \end{aligned} \tag{56}$$

Any unitary operation on qubits (the ray rotations) can be in general reduced to 2×2 unitary matrices of the SU(2) form, so, apart from an arbitrary phase factor, any single-qubit unitary operator can be written in the form

$$\hat{U}(\boldsymbol{\delta}) = \exp\left(-\frac{i}{2}\boldsymbol{\delta}\cdot\hat{\boldsymbol{\sigma}}\right) = \hat{I}\cos\frac{\delta}{2} - i\frac{\boldsymbol{\delta}\cdot\boldsymbol{\sigma}}{\delta}\sin\frac{\delta}{2} \quad (57)$$

where $\boldsymbol{\delta}$ represents the vector of the rotation and $\hat{\boldsymbol{\sigma}} = (\hat{\sigma}_x, \hat{\sigma}_y, \hat{\sigma}_z)$. The action of the unitary operator from Eq. (57) upon a state vector $|\mathbf{n}\rangle$ in Eq. (54) is equivalent with the spatial rotation of the three-dimensional polarization vector $\mathbf{n}$ in Eq. (53), which is presented by an orthogonal three-dimensional spatial rotation operator $\hat{\mathbf{R}}(\boldsymbol{\delta})$ as the following:

$$\hat{U}(\boldsymbol{\delta})|\mathbf{n}\rangle = |\hat{\mathbf{R}}^{-1}(\boldsymbol{\delta})\,\mathbf{n}\rangle \quad \text{and} \quad \hat{U}(\boldsymbol{\delta})\boldsymbol{\sigma}\hat{U}^{\dagger}(\boldsymbol{\delta}) = \hat{\mathbf{R}}(\boldsymbol{\delta})\hat{\boldsymbol{\sigma}} \quad (58)$$

The density operator (matrix) corresponding to the pure state of Eq. (54) can be written as

$$\hat{\rho} = |\mathbf{n}\rangle\langle\mathbf{n}| = \frac{1}{2}(\hat{I} + \mathbf{n}\cdot\hat{\boldsymbol{\sigma}}) = \frac{1}{2}\begin{pmatrix} n_z & n_x - in_y \\ n_x + in_y & 1 - n_z \end{pmatrix} \quad (59)$$

and the expectation value of the isospin polarization along the direction $\mathbf{n}_1$ is

$$\langle\hat{\sigma}_{n_1}\rangle = Tr(\hat{\sigma}_{n_1}\hat{\rho}) = \mathbf{n}_1\cdot\mathbf{n} \quad (60)$$

In general, if a pure isospin state is polarized in direction $\mathbf{n}$ and we measure certain $\hat{\sigma}_m$ along $\mathbf{m}$ direction, the state $\mathbf{n}$ collapses to $\mathbf{m}$ with the probability, which is equivalent with the fidelity of those states,

$$p(\mathbf{n}\to\mathbf{m}) = F_{\mathbf{nm}} = |\langle\mathbf{m}|\mathbf{n}\rangle|^2 = \cos^2\frac{\vartheta}{2} \quad (61)$$

where $\cos\vartheta = \mathbf{n}\cdot\mathbf{m}$.

Any operator $\hat{O}$ associated with the observable $\mathcal{O}$ for a two-state isospin quantum system can be presented in terms of the Pauli matrices:

$$\hat{O} = o_0\hat{I} + \mathbf{o}\cdot\hat{\boldsymbol{\sigma}} \quad (62)$$

where o_0 is a real number and $\mathbf{o}$ is a real vector. Therefore, the commutator of two operators $\hat{O}_1$ and $\hat{O}_2$ is

$$\lfloor\hat{O}_1, \hat{O}_2\rfloor = 2i(\mathbf{o}_1\times\mathbf{o}_2)\cdot\hat{\boldsymbol{\sigma}} \quad (63)$$

Following Eq. (62), the computational qubit operator in Eq. (50) also can be written in the Pauli representation as

$$\hat{Q} = \frac{1}{2}(\hat{I} - \hat{\sigma}_z) \quad (64)$$

The general Hamiltonian matrix describing two component isospin states in external fields can be written as [56]:

$$\hat{H} = E_0\hat{I} + \mathbf{E}\cdot\hat{\boldsymbol{\sigma}} \quad (65)$$

where E_0 is the ground state energy and the vector $\mathbf{E} = (E_x, E_y, E_z)$ represents the system energy changes when the external field acts along x, y, z direction accordingly. The von Neumann density operator evolution in Eq. (45) for the Hamiltonian (65) takes the following form

$$\frac{d\hat{\rho}}{dt} = -\frac{i}{\hbar}\mathbf{E}\cdot[\hat{\boldsymbol{\sigma}}, \hat{\rho}] = \frac{1}{\hbar}(\mathbf{E}\times\mathbf{n})\cdot\hat{\boldsymbol{\sigma}} \quad (66)$$

Mixed (nonpure) states also can be described within the Pauli presentation as vectors (rays) $|\mathbf{r}\rangle$ inside the Poincaré sphere ($\|\mathbf{r}\| \leq 1$). Using the relations from Eqs. (56) and (59) we can obtain the density operator and the expectation value of the isospin polarization for the mixed states:

$$\hat{\rho} = \frac{1}{2}(\hat{I} + \mathbf{r}\cdot\hat{\boldsymbol{\sigma}}) \quad \text{and} \quad \mathbf{r} = Tr\hat{\boldsymbol{\sigma}}\hat{\rho} \quad (67)$$

2.3. Entanglement, Qubit Processing, and Decoherence

2.3.1. General Concept

In classical physics each individual state of noninteracting subsystems (combined into one system) can be described locally (separately) like an individual component. Therefore, the complexity of the description of classical systems grows linearly with the number of components. A quantum system, combined from k quantum subsystems (each of n_i dimensionality), is described by vectors in Eq. (36) in $\mathcal{H}^{(N)}(N = \prod_{i=1}^{k} n_i)$ Hilbert space. For instance, a complex classical system of n *cbits* (n classical noninteracting subsystems) associates with a vector space of $2n$-dimension. In contrary, a complex quantum system of n *qubits* (n quantum noninteracting subsystems) associates with a Hilbert space of 2^n-dimension. Within the quantum description, the extra dimensions are formed by *entangled quantum states*. The *entanglement* is an inherent property of complex quantum systems that was already realized by Schrödinger [57] and it manifests the power of a quantum computer and pitfalls of building it. Quantum subsystems can be in a sharing state of close coupling with each other and it is not possible to describe one of the subsystems in isolation. Even when the entangled quantum subsystems are separated, a change of quantum state of one of the entangled subsystems nonlocally affects the other subsystems' quantum states.

The essence of the quantum entanglement is that some quantum states of a complex quantum system in Eqs. (17) or (36) cannot be expressed as a tensor product of the states of its subsystems. To demonstrate that, we consider a case of two subsystems S_1 (associated with a Hilbert space $\mathcal{H}_1^{(n)}$) and S_2 (associated with a Hilbert space $\mathcal{H}_2^{(m)}$) combined into a composite quantum system S. Choosing two pure states,

$$|\psi_1\rangle = \sum_{i=0}^{n-1}\alpha_i|i_1\rangle; \quad \sum_{i=0}^{n-1}|\alpha_i|^2 = 1 \quad \text{and}$$

$$|\psi_2\rangle = \sum_{i=0}^{n-1}\beta_i|i_2\rangle; \quad \sum_{i=0}^{m-1}|\beta_i|^2 = 1$$

we can obtain a joint product state of the following form:

$$|\psi\rangle = \sum_{i=0,\,j=0}^{n-1,\,m-1}\alpha_i\beta_j|i\rangle\otimes|j\rangle \quad (68)$$

For the quantum system S in the state of Eq. (68), the unitary transformations performed on one subsystem do not affect the state of the other subsystem.

However, not any joint state (68) is the most general product state (17). A state $|\chi\rangle = \sum_{i,j}^{n-1,m-1} \mu_{ij}|i\rangle \otimes |j\rangle$ where μ_{ij} *cannot be presented* as $\mu_{ij} = \alpha_i\beta_j$ is called an *entangled pure state*. Otherwise, it is called a *separable pure state*. Therefore, the entangled state $|\chi\rangle$ is not *factorable* (*separable*) into a state vector $|\psi_1\rangle \in \mathcal{H}_1^{(n)}$ and a state vector $|\psi_2\rangle \in \mathcal{H}_2^{(n)}$.

For two mixed quantum states chosen from two subsystems S_1 and S_2 the entanglement or inseparability can be defined with density operators of the subspaces $\hat{\rho}_1$ and $\hat{\rho}_2$. A density operator $\hat{\rho}$ for the system $S = S_1 \otimes S_2$ *is separable* if it can be written in the following separable form

$$\hat{\rho} = \sum_{i=1}^{n\times m} p_i \hat{\rho}_1^i \otimes \hat{\rho}_2^i; \quad p_i \geq 0, \; \sum_{i=1}^{n\times m} p_i = 1 \tag{69}$$

where $\hat{\rho}_i^j$ represent a mixed state j for a subsystem i. Otherwise, the mixed states of subsystems S_1 and S_2 are *entangled*.

The entanglement of complex quantum systems can be measured by the Shannon (von Neumann) entropy (Eq. [46]):

$$S_S = -k_B \sum_{i=1}^{n\times m} p_i \log p_i \tag{70}$$

The entropy vanishes when all $p_i = 0$ except only one state $i = i_0$: $p_i = \delta_{ii_0}$ and the complex system's state is not entangled by definition. If the state probability distribution is uniform, $p_i = p$, the entropy (Eq. [70]) is maximal and the state (Eq. [17]) is *maximally entangled*.

For two subspaces, $\mathcal{H}_1^{(n)}$ and $\mathcal{H}_2^{(m)}$, with the same dimension $n = m$ a maximally entangled state (*the Bell state*) reads

$$|\psi\rangle = \frac{1}{\sqrt{n}} \sum_{i=0}^{n-1} \exp(i\gamma_i)|i\rangle \otimes |j\rangle \tag{71}$$

where $\exp(i\gamma_i)$ is a phase factor. The corresponding reduced density operators are

$$\hat{\rho}_1 = \hat{\rho}_2 = \frac{1}{n}\hat{I} \tag{72}$$

The entanglement (*quantum nonlocality*) was actually first discussed in the famous Einstein–Podolskv–Rosen (EPR) thought experiment [58]. Bell [59] has shown theoretically that nonlocal correlations between separated (but entangled) quantum systems can be stronger than any classical mechanism can provide. This result was experimentally confirmed in the quantum mechanical description of the nature favor (see, e.g., Ref. [60] and references therein).

The quantum entanglement is thought to be one of the most important and efficient tools of quantum information processing enabling, e.g., teleportation, cryptography, and quantum memory. At the same time, the role of the entanglement in quantum computation is still under debate [61]. Actually, it is a basic resource of quantum information. However, to keep quantum memory coherent, the quantum states entangled within the memory unit must be kept well isolated, to avoid entanglement with the environment. Therefore, the quantum entanglement is one of the major pitfalls for the practical realization of the quantum computing.

2.3.2. Entangled Qubits

Let us consider a quantum state of two isospins performed in pure states $|\uparrow\rangle$ and $|\downarrow\rangle$. In the Pauli representation, the general pure entangled two qubit state can be written as

$$\begin{aligned}|\psi\rangle &= \alpha_{\uparrow\uparrow}\,|\uparrow\rangle\otimes|\uparrow\rangle + \alpha_{\downarrow\downarrow}\,|\downarrow\rangle\otimes|\downarrow\rangle \\ &\quad + \alpha_{\uparrow\downarrow}\,|\uparrow\rangle\otimes|\downarrow\rangle + \alpha_{\downarrow\uparrow}\,|\downarrow\rangle\otimes|\uparrow\rangle\end{aligned} \tag{73}$$

which also can be presented as

$$|\psi\rangle = \beta_1|\Psi^+\rangle + \beta_2|\Psi^-\rangle + \beta_3|\Phi^+\rangle + \beta_4|\Phi^-\rangle \tag{74}$$

by using the following orthonormal Bell's basis,

$$\begin{aligned}|\Phi^\pm\rangle &= \frac{1}{\sqrt{2}}(|\uparrow\rangle\otimes|\uparrow\rangle \pm |\downarrow\rangle\otimes|\downarrow\rangle) \\ |\Psi^\pm\rangle &= \frac{1}{\sqrt{2}}(|\uparrow\rangle\otimes|\downarrow\rangle \pm |\uparrow\rangle\otimes|\downarrow\rangle)\end{aligned} \tag{75}$$

Each of the four Bell states from Eq. (75) have this important properties: it can be transformed into any other by a single isospin unitary transformation, and the expectation value of a single isospin is zero. The polarization of the isospins are completely correlated for $|\Phi^\pm\rangle$ and completely anticorrelated for $|\Psi^\pm\rangle$.

Another orthonormal basis for the two qubit Hilbert space can be formed by

$$\begin{array}{ll} |\Psi^-\rangle & \text{“singlet”} \\ |\Psi^+\rangle, \dfrac{1}{\sqrt{2}}(|\Phi^+\rangle \pm |\Phi^-\rangle) & \text{“triplet”} \end{array} \tag{76}$$

Two latter states from the triplet are uncorrelated and not entangled.

A measure of the entanglement in two arbitrary pure isospins can be presented by the fidelity F in Eq. (61). The fidelity of two entangled mixed isospins (Eq. [67]) $\hat{\rho}_1$ and $\hat{\rho}_2$ takes a simple form of Eq. (43),

$$F = Tr(\hat{\rho}_1\hat{\rho}_2) + 2\sqrt{\det(\hat{\rho}_1)\det(\hat{\rho}_2)} \tag{77}$$

where $\det(\hat{\rho})$ stands for the determinant of the 2×2 matrix associated with Eq. (67). If one of the two isospins, $\hat{\rho}_2$, is in an unknown state (Eq. [72]; maximally mixed, Bell's state) the fidelity of Eq. (43) then reads

$$F = \frac{1}{2}Tr(\hat{\rho}_1) + \sqrt{\det(\hat{\rho}_1)} \geq \frac{1}{2} \tag{78}$$

In a quantum information process a very large number of qubits (isospins) may be entangled. Therefore, the range of variation in the possible entangled states grows rapidly. For instance, for three qubits one can already perform states with a pair of entangled qubits but not entangled with the third. There is no common single analytically computable measure of entanglement for mixed multi-qubit states [61]. However, following Eq. (71) we can present two maximally entangled states [62]: the Greenbrg–Horn–Zeilinger (GHZ) state,

$$|\mathrm{GHZ}\rangle = \frac{1}{\sqrt{2}}(|\uparrow\rangle\otimes|\uparrow\rangle\otimes|\uparrow\rangle + |\downarrow\rangle\otimes|\downarrow\rangle\otimes|\downarrow\rangle) \tag{79}$$

and Werner state,

$$| W\rangle = \frac{1}{\sqrt{3}}(|\uparrow\rangle\otimes |\uparrow\rangle\otimes |\downarrow\rangle + |\uparrow\rangle\otimes |\downarrow\rangle\otimes |\uparrow\rangle + |\downarrow\rangle\otimes |\uparrow\rangle\otimes |\uparrow\rangle) \tag{80}$$

For four or more qubits, the entanglement consideration becomes even more complicated. For instance, the qubits can be entangled in pairs, but the first pair cannot be entangled with the second one.

2.3.3. Logical Operation with a Single Qubit

The quantum information processing is based on the manipulations of qubits. Each of the manipulations is performed by *a quantum logic gate*, which presents reversible (unlike classical gates) transformations on qubits. A quantum gate on a qubit is a unitary matrix-operator, $\hat{U}$, from Eq. (57). As it was mentioned before, the transformation of a qubit by a unitary quantum gate can be mapped onto a three-dimensional rotation of the corresponding polarization vector. Clearly, the Pauli matrices themselves present unitary quantum gates denoted by $\hat{X} \equiv \hat{\sigma}_x, \hat{Y} \equiv \hat{\sigma}_y, \hat{Z} \equiv \hat{\sigma}_z$ [2]. Other important single qubit transformations (gates) are the *identity gate* $\hat{I}$, the *Hadamard gate*

$$\hat{H} = \frac{1}{\sqrt{2}}\begin{pmatrix} 1 & 1 \\ 1 & -1 \end{pmatrix} \tag{81}$$

and *phase shift gate*

$$\hat{R}(\varphi) = \begin{pmatrix} 1 & 0 \\ 0 & \exp(i\varphi) \end{pmatrix} \tag{82}$$

The gates $\hat{X}, \hat{Y}, \hat{Z}$, and $\hat{H}$ perform elementary single-qubit logical operations, e.g.,

$$\hat{X}|0\rangle = |1\rangle, \quad \hat{X}|1\rangle = |0\rangle \tag{83}$$

$$\hat{Y}|0\rangle = i|1\rangle, \quad \hat{Y}|1\rangle = -i|0\rangle \tag{84}$$

$$\hat{Z}|0\rangle = |0\rangle, \quad \hat{Z}|1\rangle = -|1\rangle \tag{85}$$

and

$$\hat{H}|0\rangle = \frac{|0\rangle + |1\rangle}{\sqrt{2}}, \quad \hat{H}|1\rangle = \frac{|0\rangle - |1\rangle}{\sqrt{2}}. \tag{86}$$

The isospin polarization rotations in Eqs. (53) and (54) of about x, y, and z axes also can be presented by the elementary gates

$$\begin{aligned}
\hat{R}_x(\alpha) &\equiv \exp\left(-i\frac{\alpha}{2}\hat{X}\right) = \begin{pmatrix} \cos\frac{\alpha}{2} & -i\sin\frac{\alpha}{2} \\ -i\sin\frac{\alpha}{2} & \cos\frac{\alpha}{2} \end{pmatrix} \\
\hat{R}_y(\alpha) &\equiv \exp\left(-i\frac{\alpha}{2}\hat{Y}\right) = \begin{pmatrix} \cos\frac{\alpha}{2} & -\sin\frac{\alpha}{2} \\ \sin\frac{\alpha}{2} & \cos\frac{\alpha}{2} \end{pmatrix} \\
\hat{R}_z(\alpha) &\equiv \exp\left(-i\frac{\alpha}{2}\hat{X}\right) = \begin{pmatrix} \exp\left(-i\frac{\alpha}{2}\right) & 0 \\ 0 & \exp\left(i\frac{\alpha}{2}\right) \end{pmatrix}
\end{aligned} \tag{87}$$

Clearly, any unitary gate transformation rotates the isospin polarization vector $\mathbf{n}$ keeping the qubit state $|\mathbf{n}\rangle$ on the Poincaré sphere. Therefore, by the operations $\hat{H}$ and $\hat{R}(\varphi)$ it can be proved that we can perform all single-qubit operations, and they form a set of *universal* single-qubit gates. For instance,

$$\begin{aligned}
\hat{X} &= \sqrt{2}\hat{H} - \hat{R}(\pi) \\
\hat{Y} &= i\hat{X}\hat{R}(\pi) \\
\hat{Z} &= \hat{R}(\pi)
\end{aligned} \tag{88}$$

and the cumulative result of the subsequent transformations $\hat{R}(\pi/2 + \varphi)\hat{H}\hat{R}(\varphi)\hat{H}$ of the state $|0\rangle$ is the generic single-isospin state $|\mathbf{n}\rangle$ from Eq. (54).

2.3.4. Multi-Qubit Quantum Gates

A single qubit gate is unable to generate, change, or demolish entanglement in a multi-qubit system called a *quantum register* that consists of a labeled series of qubits. Clearly, to generate and manipulate entangled states we should implement general unitary transformations using associated elementary multi-qubit gates. In the quantum information processing the computational qubit and isospin (physical state in a quantum system) are equivalent. Therefore, a quantum register containing more than one qubit cannot be described by simply presenting the states of each separated qubit. Manipulations on a single qubit change the quantum state of the overall quantum register.

Let us now consider the creation of entanglement with the very important two-qubit example of the controlled NOT (CNOT, or XOR) quantum gate. This gate is a transformation on both a control qubit $|\psi\rangle_C$ (first qubit) and on a target $|\psi\rangle_T$ (second qubit). The action of this gate is to control the state of $|\psi\rangle_T$ according to the actual state of $|\psi\rangle_C$. The CNOT gate complements $|\psi\rangle_T$ if $|\psi\rangle_C = |1\rangle_C$ and if $|\psi\rangle_C = |0\rangle_C|\psi\rangle_T$ remains unchanged:

$$\begin{aligned}
\hat{U}_{\text{CNOT}}|1\rangle_C \otimes |0\rangle_T &= |1\rangle_C \otimes |1\rangle_T \\
\hat{U}_{\text{CNOT}}|1\rangle_C \otimes |1\rangle_T &= |1\rangle_C \otimes |0\rangle_T \\
\hat{U}_{\text{CNOT}}|0\rangle_C \otimes |0\rangle_T &= |0\rangle_C \otimes |0\rangle_T \\
\hat{U}_{\text{CNOT}}|0\rangle_C \otimes |1\rangle_T &= |0\rangle_C \otimes |1\rangle_T
\end{aligned} \tag{89}$$

The unitary operator $\hat{U}_{\text{CNOT}}$ in the Pauli matrix representation can be written as:

$$\begin{aligned}
\hat{U}_{CNOT} &= |0\rangle_C\langle 0|_C \otimes \hat{I}_T + |1\rangle_C\langle 1|_C \otimes \hat{X}_T \\
&= \begin{pmatrix} \hat{I}_C & 0 \\ 0 & \hat{X}_T \end{pmatrix} = \begin{pmatrix} 1 & 0 & 0 & 0 \\ 0 & 1 & 0 & 0 \\ 0 & 0 & 0 & 1 \\ 0 & 0 & 1 & 0 \end{pmatrix}
\end{aligned} \tag{90}$$

It is clear, that the operator $\hat{U}_{\text{CNOT}}$ cannot be decomposed into a tensor product of two single-qubit operators. The CNOT quantum gate realization makes it possible to define the state $|\psi\rangle_C$ if $|\psi\rangle_T$ is prepared in the $|0\rangle_T$ state. In addition, it is the inverse of itself since $(\hat{U}_{\text{CNOT}})^2 = \hat{I}$.

Most importantly, the CNOT gate is able to perform entanglement of two qubits and to disentangle them in reverse. For example, the entanglement of a quantum state is preconfigured by Eq. (86):

$$|h^{+}\rangle_C \equiv \hat{H}|0\rangle_C = \frac{1}{\sqrt{2}}(|0\rangle_C + |1\rangle_C)$$

and the $|0\rangle_T$ into the Bell states (Eq. (75)) reads:

$$\hat{U}_{\mathrm{CNOT}}|h^{+}\rangle_C|0\rangle_T = \frac{1}{\sqrt{2}}(|0\rangle_C \otimes |0\rangle_T + |1\rangle_C \otimes |1\rangle_T) = |\Phi^{+}\rangle_{CT}$$
$$\hat{U}_{\mathrm{CNOT}}|\Phi^{+}\rangle_{CT} = |h^{+}\rangle_C|0\rangle_T \tag{91}$$

We can see more general that:

$$\hat{U}_{\mathrm{CNOT}}(\alpha_1|0\rangle + \alpha_2|1\rangle)_C|0\rangle_T = \alpha_1|0\rangle_C \otimes |0\rangle_T + \alpha_2|1\rangle_C \otimes |1\rangle_T$$
$$\hat{U}_{\mathrm{CNOT}}\alpha_1|0\rangle_C \otimes |0\rangle_T + \alpha_2|1\rangle_C \otimes |1\rangle_T = (\alpha_1|0\rangle + \alpha_2|1\rangle)_C|0\rangle_T \tag{92}$$

The CNOT gate belongs to a large class of the controlled unitary (CU) gates,

$$\hat{U}_{CU} = \begin{pmatrix} \hat{I} & 0 \\ 0 & \hat{U} \end{pmatrix} \tag{93}$$

where the unitary operator $\hat{U}$ can be chosen as a single qubit gate from Eqs. (81)–(87).

One more important unitary two qubit gate $\hat{U}_S$ is able to reverse (swap) the sequence of the qubits,

$$\hat{U}_S|\psi\rangle_1 \otimes |\psi\rangle_2 = |\psi\rangle_2 \otimes |\psi\rangle_1 \tag{94}$$

It is called a SWAP gate:

$$\begin{aligned}\hat{U}_S &= \frac{1}{2}(\hat{I}_1 \otimes \hat{I}_2 + \hat{\sigma}_1 \otimes \hat{\sigma}_2) \\ &= \frac{1}{2}(\hat{I}_{12} + \hat{X}_1 \otimes \hat{X}_2 + \hat{Y}_1 \otimes \hat{Y}_2 + \hat{Z}_1 \otimes \hat{Z}_2) \\ &= \begin{pmatrix} 1 & 0 & 0 & 0 \\ 0 & 0 & 1 & 0 \\ 0 & 1 & 0 & 0 \\ 0 & 0 & 0 & 1 \end{pmatrix}\end{aligned} \tag{95}$$

The SWAP gate obviously does not introduce any entanglement between the qubits.

It can be shown that three universal quantum gates—the Hadamar gate from Eq. (81), the phase-shift gate from Eq. (82), and the CNOT gate from Eq. (90)—can be used together to implement an arbitrary unitary operation on the quantum state space of n qubits (quantum register) [13]. For instance, all of the Bell states from Eq. (75) can be produced form $|0\rangle_{C,T}$ states through the following successions:

$$|0\rangle_C|0\rangle_T \overset{\hat{H}_C}{\Longrightarrow} \frac{1}{\sqrt{2}}(|0\rangle_C + |1\rangle_C)|0\rangle_T \overset{\hat{U}_{CNOT}}{\Longrightarrow} |\Phi^{+}\rangle_{CT}$$
$$|0\rangle_C|0\rangle_T \overset{\hat{X}_T}{\Longrightarrow} |0\rangle_C|1\rangle_T \overset{\hat{H}_C}{\Longrightarrow} \frac{1}{\sqrt{2}}(|0\rangle_C + |1\rangle_C)|1\rangle_T \overset{\hat{U}_{CNOT}}{\Longrightarrow} |\Psi^{+}\rangle_{CT}$$
$$|0\rangle_C|0\rangle_T \overset{\hat{X}_C}{\Longrightarrow} |1\rangle_C|0\rangle_T \overset{\hat{H}_C}{\Longrightarrow} \frac{1}{\sqrt{2}}(|0\rangle_C - |1\rangle_C)|0\rangle_T \overset{\hat{U}_{CNOT}}{\Longrightarrow} |\Phi^{-}\rangle_{CT} \tag{96}$$
$$|0\rangle_C|0\rangle_T \overset{\hat{X}_C}{\Longrightarrow} |1\rangle_C|0\rangle_T \overset{\hat{X}_T}{\Longrightarrow} |1\rangle_C|1\rangle_T$$
$$\overset{\hat{H}_C}{\Longrightarrow} \frac{1}{\sqrt{2}}(|0\rangle_C - |1\rangle_C)|1\rangle_T \overset{\hat{U}_{CNOT}}{\Longrightarrow} |\Psi^{-}\rangle_{CT}$$

The GHZ state from Eq. (76) can also be performed using the CNOT gate as the following,

$$\begin{aligned}|0\rangle_C(|0\rangle \otimes |0\rangle)_T &\overset{\hat{H}_C}{\Longrightarrow} \frac{1}{\sqrt{2}}(|0\rangle_C + |1\rangle_C)(|0\rangle \otimes |0\rangle)_T \\ &\overset{\hat{U}_{CNOT}}{\Longrightarrow} \frac{1}{\sqrt{2}}[|0\rangle_C \otimes (|0\rangle \otimes |0\rangle)_T \\ &\qquad + |1\rangle_C \otimes (|1\rangle \otimes |0\rangle)_T] \\ &\overset{\hat{U}_{CNOT}}{\Longrightarrow} \frac{1}{\sqrt{2}}[|0\rangle_C \otimes (|0\rangle \otimes |0\rangle)_T \\ &\qquad + |1\rangle_C \otimes (|1\rangle \otimes |1\rangle)_T]\end{aligned} \tag{97}$$

It is common now to use quantum logical circuits equipped with the quantum gates to represent the quantum information processes (multi-qubit transformations) [11, 14].

2.3.5. Decoherence, Error Correction, and Quantum Register Measurement

Ideal quantum information processing is performed in ideal Hilbert spaces, which correspond in quantum theory to isolated quantum systems (quantum registers). There are very few general reasons resulting in deviations (some are time crucial) of a quantum information processing from the ideal flow: the quantum system (quantum register) differs from the idealized models used in quantum theory; quantum gates are not perfect and they lead to nonunitary transformations; and the quantum mechanical systems (quantum registers) are not perfectly isolated from the environment.

Most crucial is that the quantum registers must be kept isolated to avoid entanglement with the environment. The entropy of such a system has to remain constant since no heat dissipation is possible; therefore, state changes have to be adiabatic, which requires that all of the quantum data processing are reversible and the quantum information is appropriately conserved. In reality, quantum systems (quantum registers) are always in various interactions with the environment. Those interactions lead to irreversible changes in the quantum registers, which cause a loss of information encoded and stored in the registers. The entanglement between a quantum system and the environment leads the quantum system to change its state over time randomly from the observer point of view. In addition, any desirable access to the quantum memory disturbs the quantum register. *Decoherence* is a resulting process in which the environment causes various (uncontrollable) changes (transitions, relaxations) in the quantum registers. Those lead to a decay of the phase coherence and degrade the quantum information [12, 44, 45, 63]. Thus, one of the most important objectives in quantum memory research is to find a way to keep quantum registers in coherent states for a reasonably long time.

Decoherence means many aspects of quantum state degradation due to interactions of the system with the environment and sets the *maximum time* available for quantum memory use. As a very basic example, this is the time required for a pure qubit state [18, 63],

$$\hat{\rho}_0 = (\alpha|0\rangle + \beta|1\rangle)(\alpha^*\langle 0| + \langle 1|\beta^*) \tag{98}$$

to decay into a qubit state mixed with the environment described by the following diagonal density operator,

$$\hat{\rho} = |\alpha|^2|0\rangle\langle 0| + |\beta|^2|1\rangle\langle 1| \tag{99}$$

The interaction of the quantum register (qr) with the environment (ev) should be described in terms of the common register and environment density operator $\hat{\rho}_{qr\otimes ev}$. The density operator of the quantum register $\hat{\rho}_{qr}$ has to be obtained as a reduced one:

$$\hat{\rho}_{qr} = Tr_{ev}(\hat{\rho}_{qr\otimes ev}) \tag{100}$$

The correct description of the quantum system (quantum register) dynamics must take into consideration the decoherence processes. When the system-environment coupling is weak, this can be done by introducing a more general form of the system from the von Neumann master Eq. (45) for $\hat{\rho}_{qr}$. The most popular assumption is the Markovian approximation [18, 64] when the master equation for an open to the enlargement quantum system can be written as:

$$\frac{d\hat{\rho}_{qr}(t)}{dt} = -\frac{i}{\hbar}[\hat{H}_{qr}, \hat{\rho}_{qr}(t)] + \frac{1}{2\hbar}\sum_j\{[L_j\hat{\rho}_{qr}(t), L_j^\dagger] + [L_j, \hat{\rho}_{qr}(t)L_j^\dagger]\} \tag{101}$$

where the Hamiltonian $\hat{H}_{qr}$ describes the isolated quantum system (quantum register) and L_j stands for the Lindblad operator [64], which describes the effect of the system interaction with the environment. It also determines the dynamics of each jth channel of the dissipation (emission or absorption process).

As a simple example of the Lindbland's description, let us consider an isospin system whose Hamiltonian (65) is

$$\hat{H}_{qr} = -\frac{E}{2}\hat{\sigma}_z \tag{102}$$

and E denotes the energy difference between the ground state $|\uparrow\rangle$ and the exited state $|\downarrow\rangle$. For the simplest model, the only dissipation channel is a single Lindblad operator corresponding to the dissipation process $|\downarrow\rangle \Rightarrow |\uparrow\rangle$ and can be parameterized by only one characteristic constant Γ as the following:

$$\hat{L} = \sqrt{\Gamma}\begin{pmatrix} 0 & 1 \\ 0 & 0 \end{pmatrix} \tag{103}$$

The Lindblad equation then reads

$$\frac{d}{dt}\begin{pmatrix} \rho_{\uparrow\uparrow} & \rho_{\uparrow\downarrow} \\ \rho_{\uparrow\downarrow} & \rho_{\downarrow\downarrow} \end{pmatrix} = \frac{i}{\hbar}E\begin{pmatrix} 0 & \rho_{\uparrow\downarrow} \\ \rho_{\uparrow\downarrow} & 0 \end{pmatrix} + \frac{\Gamma}{\hbar}\begin{pmatrix} \rho_{\uparrow\uparrow} & -\frac{1}{2}\rho_{\uparrow\downarrow} \\ -\frac{1}{2}\rho_{\downarrow\uparrow} & -\rho_{\uparrow\uparrow} \end{pmatrix} \tag{104}$$

where we omit the index qr. The equation can be readily solved for a certain initial condition (at the time of the channel's opening $\hat{\rho}(0) = \hat{\rho}^0$):

$$\rho_{\uparrow\uparrow}(t) = \rho^0_{\uparrow\uparrow} + \rho^0_{\downarrow\downarrow}(1 - e^{-(\Gamma/\hbar)t}), \quad \rho_{\uparrow\downarrow}(t) = \rho^0_{\uparrow\downarrow}e^{(1/\hbar)(iE-(\Gamma/2))t}$$
$$\rho_{\downarrow\downarrow}(t) = \rho^0_{\downarrow\downarrow}e^{-(\Gamma/\hbar)t}, \quad \rho_{\downarrow\uparrow}(t) = \rho^0_{\downarrow\uparrow}e^{(1/\hbar)(-iE-(\Gamma/2))t} \tag{105}$$

According to this result, the off-diagonal components of the isospin density operator or coherence of the qubit state from Eq. (98) decays with the time constant $T_2 = 2T_1 = 1/\Gamma$. This also shows that the coherence decay process in this model is slower than the amplitude damping process.

Most important for any quantum computer elements (quantum gates, quantum circuits, quantum memory registers, etc.) is the ratio of "decoherence decay time/the element operation time." In general, this ratio is defined by the physical realization of the certain element. For some realizations of the quantum registers, decoherence time T_2 may be as short as few microseconds. This is not necessarily a big problem because the gates operation time can be much shorter than the decoherence time (the typical gate operation time is of about ps). However, this range the decoherence time is unacceptably short for nonvolatile quantum memory.

Moreover, even when the initial states of quantum memory registers are uncorrelated with the environment we could not expect to operate a quantum memory with perfect accuracy. If the real gate transformation $\hat{U}$ causes a small deviation $\hat{u}$ from an ideal unitary $\hat{U}_0$ ($\hat{U} = \hat{U}_0[1 + \mathrm{O}(\hat{u})]$) after a certain number of gate applications, these deviations will generate a serious failure. To prevent the errors from piling up, we have to perform a correction procedure for the quantum information and keep our quantum register out of the dissipative processes. As mentioned above, error detection/correction is difficult in the quantum world since we cannot reliably clone an arbitrary qubit. Nevertheless, there are several ways to effectively prolong decoherence time dynamically. For instance, a closed-loop control method incorporates introduced and developed quantum error correcting codes (QECC) [4, 12, 13]. Most of the methods, however, require extra qubits (enchantment of quantum registers) and dynamical control of them [65]. By restoring quantum registers irrespective of the nature of decoherence and errors we remove some results of the entanglement between the quantum register and the environment.

In classical memory, reading a memory register is not even regarded as a formal part of the computation. The state of the classical memory register is not affected by the reading.

A quantum information processing starts with the quantum registers' initialization performed by quantum gates according to the quantum "initialization" algorithm [34]. The gates use some advanced physical process that puts the system into an entangled state. There is only one way to extract information from the quantum register, i.e., to measure it. We can only measure probability on the actual state of the register. However, the action of the measurement of the quantum state (extracting information from the quantum register) is irreversible (it collapses the quantum state). The post-measurement quantum register contains no traces on the premeasurement register. There is no way to reconstruct the register input after finding of the output.

To perform the probability measurement we should to produce a chain of unitary transformations to prepare the quantum register into a certain configuration where significant information has a significant probability or to prepare many equivalent quantum registers at the same quantum state and measure them in parallel. In both approaches above, decoherence remains the number one problem. Nevertheless, a variety of contributions in the area of quantum error correcting codes, fault tolerant computation concatenated codes, and quantum repeaters show that reliable memory transmission and processing of quantum information in time and space are, in principle, possible. Therefore, realistic investigations of the sources and forms of decoherence as well as of the impacts it can cause are highly important for a practical realization of quantum memory.

3. POSSIBLE PHYSICAL REALIZATIONS

A number of physical systems are under investigation for their suitability to implement quantum information processing. The main requirements (*Di Vincenzo criteria*) for a physical system to be a considerable candidate for practical realization in "hardware elements" of a quantum computer were formulated by Di Vincenzo as the following [66, 67]:

— It should be a physical system well presenting a qubit ("isospin") that can be scaled to form an appropriate quantum register;
— A proper initialization of quantum register (a formation of the ground state) should be performed;
— A quantum register should possess long enough decoherence time to ensure all of the register transformations with minimal error probability;
— A universal set of quantum gates for one- and two-qubit unitary transformations should be implemented; and
— A measurement of the states of individual qubits within the quantum register should be performed with very low-error probability.

In addition to quantum computation, quantum communication applications require the ability to interconvert stationary and flying qubits and transmit them between specified locations.

Among those criteria, most important for the quantum memory "hardware" implementation is that we obviously need a technology that enables us to store entangled qubits for a long enough time to complete interesting computation tasks or to delay them until an appropriate time. We also need efficient and reliable methods to generate (initialize) and measure quantum memory registers.

Nonvolatile quantum memory storage should have a specifically long decoherence time, T_2, so it must be very well isolated from the environment to minimize decoherence errors. Meanwhile, this is one of the most difficult challenges in the realization of quantum information processing (specifically for quantum computation).

Since the theoretical proposal of quantum computation, there has been much effort in the development of quantum qubits and their storages. As mentioned before, any quantum system with two quantum states can be kept well separated from other quantum states, which can be used for a physical implementation of quantum computation. At present, a number of physical systems are under investigations for the implementation of a quantum memory register. Among them are:

(1) Nuclear magnetic resonance on molecules;
(2) Ions or atoms trapped by electric and magnetic fields or intensive laser beams;
(3) Photonic systems that have been implemented with optical and infrared photons;
(4) Superconducting circuits;
(5) Electron and nuclear spins localized in solid state structures and other unique realizations [7].

The most important elements and features of nonvolatile quantum memory are summarized in Table 1. The are compared with their classical counterparts. There we'll also describe in brief some actual schemes of the physical implementation of quantum memory.

3.1. Nuclear Magnetic Resonance on Molecules

Magnetic resonance is a spectroscopic technique that investigates the spin degrees of freedom of nuclear and electron spins. Magnetic moments associated with the spins and whether a magnetic field is applied to the system the energy of these magnetic moments depends on their orientation with respect to the field. The case of nuclear magnetic resonance (NMR) technology [68] (computations and theoretical descriptions about them are good examples of quantum computation models and methods [18, 69]). A typical NMR setting performs excitations of the nuclear spins with a strong static magnetic field that is controlled by radiofrequency, and it measures their electromagnetic response. The canonical example of a NMR qubit is a two-level quantum system ("isospin") of the nuclear spin in the magnetic field about 10 T [70]. Nuclear spins used in NMR quantum computing are typically the spin-1/2 nuclei of ^{1}H, ^{13}C, ^{19}F, ^{15}N, ^{31}P, or ^{29}Si atoms in molecules of liquid solutions. The method was first proposed for small quantum operations [71]. To form a valuable quantum register, a molecular sample should be chosen appropriately and carefully designed to ensure quantum information storage. Each nuclear spin can be addressed individually by the external magnetic field and it can be tuned to a chosen

Table 1. Elements and features of nonvolatile quantum memory.

	Nonvolatile classical memory	Nonvolatile quantum memory
Agent	Classical bit	Qubit
Amount of information	Binary: 0 or 1	Infinite amount (in principle)
Multiagent systems	Linear growth of information in a classical register	Exponential growth of information in a quantum register (entanglement)
Write	Routine classical operation	Initialization
Read	One time routine operation	Probability measurement
Processing	Permutations (classical gates)	Unitary transformations (quantum gates)
Information received	State of each bit in a register	Probability of a qubit state in quantum memory register
State after reading	Does not change	Collapsed
Retention	~10 years (unpowered retention)	At the present: Form ~ns to ~few minutes (limited by the decoherence time T_2)
Endurance	$\sim 10^6$	Nondeterminable at the present
Data retrieving	Destructive or nondestructive	Only destructive (noncloning theorem)
Conditions	Design, materials, methods	Design, materials, methods + low temperature, external fields, etc.

frequency range. Entanglement is achieved through interspin exchange interactions inside the molecule and two-qubit quantum gates can be performed by detuning the spin rotation frequency [69, 70]. This relatively favorable situation led to several proposals and some experimental realizations [72]. One-qubit operations (with a very high fidelity of about 0.999) were implemented using radiofrequency pulses. Two-qubit operations (CNOT gate and SWAP gate with fidelity of about 0.995) are realized by using the spin-exchange interactions between nuclei [73].

The obvious advantage of the NMR quantum qubit register is that the NMR technique is very well developed and NMR spectrometers are commercially available within a wide range of parameters.

The most important issue is that quantum registers are actually very small fractions of the molecular samples. Therefore, the register is principally formed by mixed states. That makes the register description to be a very complicated task when the number of involved qubits grows. Although scalability is often mentioned as the main problem of NMR-based quantum computation, the NMR technique made it possible to manipulate up to 12 qubits [74]. Solid-state NMR approaches [75] allow us to obtain control over, in principle, a much larger number of qubits. Moreover, in the solid state, the spins can be highly polarized by techniques such as polarization transfer from electronic spins [76, 77]. A variety of architectures have been proposed for solid-state NMR quantum computing [33, 34, 78]. For instance, a nitrogen-vacancy (NV) defect center in a diamond coupled to a cluster of ^{13}C spins as a quantum processor has been proposed [31, 79, 80].

Decoherence time for NMR liquid systems depends on the molecule employed as a quantum register. Actual decoherence time is relatively large compared with the gate operation time; it achieves about 2 seconds at room temperature [73]. Theoretically, it can reach up to 100 seconds [18, 70]. This is still not suitable to implement a long-term quantum storage. The most important and irresolvable problem for nonvolatile quantum memory implementation is that NMR quantum memory cannot be realized without strong external magnetic fields.

3.2. Trapped Ions and Atoms

Being inherently quantum mechanical objects themselves, atomic systems are good "quantum information storages." The main problem is keeping data stored under control (allocate, manipulate, and retrieve) in this memory. Among many energy states in atomic systems, we always can define two states as a ground state and excited state of the system with a very long lifetime of qubit (isospin) properties [7, 18, 78, 81–83]. Therefore, trapped atomic ions were first proposed as quantum computing and quantum memory candidates [83]. In the most advanced experiments, ions are kept by electric fields in a high-vacuum chamber. With such a device, ions can be confined along the longitudinal axis in the center of the chamber where the ions form a string under the action of laser cooling [15, 16, 78, 82, 84–86]. The ion string provides a quantum register with the quantum information stored in the individual electronic states of the ions.

It was demonstrated that by using electromagnetic traps, the ionic systems can be kept isolated from its environment and coherence of the associated quantum register can also be controlled quite well. When ions are trapped by electrical (or magnetic) fields [87], their charges allow us to address the positions of the ions and the spatial motion in the trap with high precision. Because of their strong electrostatic interaction, the spatial displacement of one ion transfers to the other one. The ions confined in electromagnetic traps have their internal electronic degrees of freedom—qubits—but they also have external degrees of freedom, which are associated with their spatial collective motion within the trap, that can be used to carry and convey information. Via side Doppler laser cooling [88, 89] the ions can be cooled to a temperature $T < 10$ μK so that each collective vibration mode is very likely to occupy its quantum ground state. The internal quantum states exhibit very long coherence times; the relaxation time of excited states can reach more than 1 second, or even up to 10 minutes for hyperfine atomic states [88, 89], and the spatial motional states have typical lifetimes of about 10^2 milliseconds [90, 91]. The external laser pulse can induce an entanglement of the internal and external degrees of freedom [83], so one-qubit and two-qubit CNOT gates can be implemented with fidelity up to 0.9994 [82]. The writing and reading of the information are also done with short laser pulses.

The record for trapped ion qubit entanglement is currently presented in the 8-qubit W-state [92]. As the number of ions in a trap increases, we face difficulties. The addition of each ion adds three external vibrational modes. It soon becomes nearly impossible to select the desired vibrational mode. There is some prospect that this approach still can be scaled to relatively large size when an ion-trap system must incorporate arrays of interconnected traps, each holding a small number of ions. The information carriers between traps might be photons. Future improvement is expected using the technique of segmented linear Paul traps, which allow shuttling ions from a "processor" unit to a "memory" section [93]. In addition, miniaturization and integration of segmented linear ion traps is rapidly progressing [82, 84].

The main advantages of trapped ions may be that it is relatively easy to read the results from individual ions. The main difficulties at this time are to control the gate operations with sufficient precision and to increase the number of trapped ions.

Neutral atoms [7, 15, 18, 78, 84, 86] are also promising candidates for the quantum memory realization, first of all because of their very weak entanglement with the environment and that the decoherence time of this system is relatively long (up to 2 seconds) [94]. Similar to ions, a large number of neutral atoms can be trapped and cooled to very low temperatures (up to nK) in a standing modulated laser field (optical lattices [87]), where the manipulation of the atoms can be done with very high precision [95, 96]. In addition, individual addressing and readout were recently demonstrated [96].

Inside of the optical lattice the atoms interact because they all couple to the normal modes of the electromagnetic field in the cavity (instead of the vibrational modes as in the ion traps). When putting the laser out of tune, the atoms can interact in the external states of atoms and external vibrational states.

Realization of multi-qubit entangled quantum registers is challenging because the atoms interact very weakly with each other. Therefore, it was proposed to control mediated interatomic interactions by either optical dipole–dipole coupling [97] or ground state collisions [98, 99]. A proposal for fast quantum gates based on interactions between Rydberg atoms (an atom with a large principal number and a maximal orbital number and very large electric dipole moments) [100] and another based on magnetic spin–spin interaction [101] can be used to realize suitable two-qubit gates.

We should note that despite much progress in recent years, trapped ions and atoms quantum memory require a combination of very sophisticated techniques and quite intensive and precise magnetic, electric, and optical fields. With all of this, the decoherence time remains very short in terms of long-living memory conditions. This makes quantum nonvolatile memory based on this technology very problematic—at least for the present.

3.3. Photonic Systems

Two orthogonal independent photon polarizations can be associated with two isospin directions and are used like two primary qubit states. In addition to amplitude and polarization, a vector wave also has a phase, which we can characterize as a linear superposition of the qubit component and as an arbitrary directed isospin [13, 17, 26, 27, 78]. Photons are commonly used in other quantum systems described here as very robust, quick, and almost universal carriers of quantum information. They can propagate over long distances in optical fibers with well-preserved coherence. Nowadays phonons can be obtained with precise timing, well-defined polarization, and pulse–shapes in the quantum regime from deterministic sources of single photons [102, 103]. A quantum register combined from photons can be used for quantum information distribution (distributed quantum memory, quantum teleportation) and for implementation of various quantum algorithms in quantum optical processors. Modern efficient photon detectors perform projective (quantum non-demolition [104, 105]) measurement and retrieve each qubit from the quantum register with a very high precision.

It was thought for a long time that realization of multi-qubit quantum gates is impossible within the linear optics and requires nonlinear interaction between two photons, an interaction that is typically very small in bulk materials [78]. However, recently an approach was demonstrated that can use quantum multi-qubit logic operations for simple linear optical elements, such as beam splitters and phase shifters [8, 106]. Few multi-qubit gates were demonstrated with this approach.

Very recently, integrated quantum photonic circuits that can continuously and accurately tune the degree of quantum photonic interference with fidelity up to 0.98 and decoherence time 0.1 ms were performed with nonlinear optical effects [107, 108].

Most of the photonic quantum memory storages require a quantum memory register of light to be mapped onto a long-lived material objects (ionic, atomic, solid state, etc.) and then (on demand) the quantum information can be converted again into the flying photonic qubits [26, 109, 110]. For this process to be efficient, there must be a strong coupling between the light and atomic systems, which are actually nonoptical but rather material carriers for the storages (as described in other sections).

Recently, several promising proposals toward this goal, based on the electromagnetically induced transparency (EIT) in atomic media [110–112], have been reported (Refs. [26, 113–117]). EIT is a nonlinear optical phenomenon observed in atoms of a warm gas [113, 114], in an atomic Mott insulator [116] and in solid media (Pr doped crystal of Y_2SiO_5) [116, 117] as well. Because the light can drastically reduce its speed in media under the EIT conditions, the effect can be used as a basis for the quantum memory applications. A photonic quantum memory cell is controlled by the EIT effect with a control field [26, 118, 119]. When the informative photonic pulse propagates inside the EIT cell, the control field can be switched off, which reduces the speed of light and the quantum information can be stored as a collective optical media excitation. The quantum information can be retrieved if the control field is switched on again. It was demonstrated that the photonic quantum information of light can be stored in a magnetically trapped thermal cloud of sodium atoms with the decay time of 0.9 ms [119, 120] and in Pr doped crystal of Y_2SiO_5 up to 2.3 seconds [27, 117]. EIT-based quantum storages still have an important drawback because of background noise in the retrieved signal. To decrease the noise we have to balance the quantum storage efficiency (fidelity) and lifetime.

Although the EIT photonic quantum storage decoherence time is still quite short, it was already demonstrated that it can perform in a quantum storage when the control field is switched off. This property makes the EIT photonic quantum memory more suitable for possible future nonvolatile applications.

3.4. Superconducting Circuits

In context of the implementation of the quantum information processing, solid-state systems are very attractive because of their compactness, scalability, and compatibility with existing technology. Here, qubits are constructed from collective electrodynamic modes of macroscopic electrical elements, rather than microscopic degrees of freedom. For an integrated circuit to behave quantum, the first requirement is the absence of dissipation. Over the past decade, these systems have become key players in experimental studies of macroscopic coherence and decoherence (see e.g., Refs. [121, 122]).

Superconducting materials (with zero resistance) demonstrate inherent collective macroscopic quantum mechanical properties owed to a quantum liquid formed by Cooper pairs, i.e., pairs of electrons held together by a coupling to lattice vibrations [123, 124]. Those prominent quantum properties can be used for the realization of superconducting qubit systems operated at temperatures close to absolute zero. Superconducting qubits are solid-state electrical circuits based on the Josephson tunnel junction [125]. The simplest superconducting integrated circuit can be described like the LC loss-less harmonic oscillator [15, 17, 18, 22, 63, 78, 85, 126]. Quantum state energies of the harmonic oscillator are known to be equidistant, all transitions between neighboring excited states are degenerated, and it is impossible to assign only one excitation as a support for the qubit. To isolate an appropriate pair of ground and excited states (isospin), we should introduce strong nonlinear effects into the circuit. The Josephson tunnel junction (made of two superconductors, which are separated by a thin layer of insulating materials) behaves as a pure nonlinear inductance (the Josephson element [125]). There are three main strategies to prepare superconducting qubit involving only one Josephson element, and they lead to three fundamental basic types of closely related, but distinct superconducting qubits: charge, flux, or phase qubits [126–128].

The charge qubit consists of a small superconducting volume called the Cooper pair box that is connected to the circuit by a Josephson junction [129–132]. The charge superconducting qubit uses the charging energy to define its two states, while the smaller Josephson energy provides the transfer between them. The potential of the charge qubit has been already confirmed [128, 132].

Quantum information can be also associated with two states of distinct magnetic flux ("up" or "down") through a superconducting ring [128, 133, 134]. The quantum state of the flux isospin can be measured locally with high precision by a superconducting quantum interference device (SQUID) [135, 136].

The phase-qubit can be performed in a current-biased Josephson junction [125, 128]. The flow of such a current does not even require the application of an external voltage. The difference of superconducting wave function phase for the pair of the junction electrodes is controlled by the current-biased Josephson equation [125], which corresponds to the superconducting pair interacting with an effective "washboard" potential [15, 123, 126, 128]. The phase qubit is formed by two of the lowest energy states in a local minimum of the potential.

In contrast to their microscopic counterparts, mesoscopic superconducting qubits tend to be well coupled, which makes them appealing from the point of view of implementation of quantum gates and valuable quantum memory registers. The manipulation (and measurement) of the state of the superconducting qubits can be performed by using appropriate microwave pulses. In such a manner, basic superconducting quantum gates were demonstrated [137–139].

For large-scale quantum memory register, more sophisticated coupling schemes should be developed. One of them is presented by "quantum bus" arrays with selective frequency control [128, 140–144]. At the present, the four qubit quantum register has been performed [145].

The intrinsic limitation on the coherence time of superconducting qubits results from low-frequency noise, which arises from three principal sources: fluctuations in the transparency of the Josephson junction, random hopping of electrons between traps on the surface of the superconducting films, and magnetic-flux fluctuations [128]. Considerable improvement in the Josephson junction technology allowed to increase decoherence times in recent experiments from $\sim$1 ns up to $\sim$4 μs and three-qubit GHZ state with fidelity up to 0.88 have been demonstrated [128, 146–148].

For the superconducting quantum registers, the promise of scalability to large numbers of qubits is fully controlled by the superconducting technology and improvements in the quality of the oxide layers. Two main obstacles for nonvolatile should be noted for quantum memory implementation on the basis that semiconductor qubits still have a relatively short decoherence time and extremely low temperature conditions. The first problem can only be resolved by sufficiently improved technology and the second one can be eventually resolved in the future with applications of modern high-temperature superconducting materials [149].

3.5. Quantum Dots and Spins Localized in Solids

Quantum dots are nanosized solid-state objects that possess atom-like properties because they can localize and confine electrons in three dimensions in such a way that their energies become discrete. Those "artificial atoms" are very promising in various interesting device applications in optics, optoelectronics, quantum cryptography, and quantum computing [7, 121, 122, 150–152]. Advances in modern semiconductor technologies make it possible to produce semiconductor nanoobjects (quantum dots, nanorings, quantum dot molecules, quantum dot posts, nanorods, etc.) within a wide range of geometrical shapes and material parameters and investigate their properties in details [152–161]. Although artificial atoms can be realized in many semiconductor systems, we should mention two most important and developed types: quantum dots formed by full electrostatic control on the basis of two-dimensional semiconductor structures [7, 121, 122, 152, 157, 158, 162] and self-assembled semiconductor quantum dots [150, 151, 154, 157]. Quantum dots can be fabricated close enough together and assembled into large arrays where they can be coupled to external electromagnetic fields. Single and many isospins as well can be stored and manipulated in these structures of typical sizes from 5 nm to 1 μm. Isospin quantum registers can be performed in quantum dots on the base energy states of charged particles [157, 163], electron and hole spin states [78, 157, 162, 164, 165], and states of excitons [78, 166, 167] confined in the system. Highly selective near-field optical spectroscopy [168] can be used as a probing technique for those nanosystems. However, quantum dot qubits generally need very low temperatures (form mK to few K) to be stored and controlled. Complex dissipative irreversible processes are inherent to solid-state media. Nevertheless, quantum dot qubits can remain coherent for long enough to perform many quantum operations [157, 158]. For instance, to form a spin two-qubit gate the exchange coupling between two adjacent quantum dots [162, 164, 165, 169] and, more recently, the ultrafast laser techniques to achieve optical control [169, 170] have been employed. Unfortunately, electronic spins in most popular quantum dot systems are based on III–V semiconductor materials that suffer from relatively strong spin-orbit interaction and fluctuating magnetic fields produced by atomic nuclear spins, which couples with the electron through the hyperfine interaction (random "Overhauser field") [157, 171]. This limits the spin's decoherence time in III–V semiconductor quantum dots to 3 μs [7, 157, 169]. Very recently it was demonstrated that for electrostatic GaAs quantum dots one can substantially increase (up to 200 μs) the coherence times using the Hahn echo effect by applying small magnetic field ($\sim$0.4 T) to the system [171]. Nevertheless, for the future applications it is also desirable to form quantum dot qubits based on other materials, where spin-orbit coupling and Overhauser field are considerably weaker. One of the possible solutions is to use nuclear spin free silicon and germanium [78, 172, 173].

In complete analogy to the quantum dot, electron or nuclear spins on isolated impurities in silicon can possess long decoherence times. It was demonstrated that the spin decoherence time for electrons bound to phosphorus impurities in isotopically pure ^{28}Si can reach 0.6 seconds [7]. Using 7 T superconducting solenoid NMR magnet long-living spin coherence times at room temperature (up to 25 seconds) were also demonstrated for individual nuclear spins of ^{29}Si isotopes in purified ^{28}Si [7, 174].

Carbon materials (specifically diamonds) are also nuclear spin-free with vanishing spin-orbit coupling. Therefore, synthetic isotopically enriched ^{12}C diamonds are promising candidates for realization of a robust relatively long time coherence ($\sim$2 ms) for electron spins localized on nitrogen-vacancy (NV) centers [7, 31, 79, 80, 175–177]. Recent experiments demonstrated the potential of diamond NV centers quantum register scalability, even in room temperature [80].

Possible implementations of nonvolatile quantum memory on the base of solid-state electron or nuclear spins could be a very practical solution in a view of highly developed modern semiconductor technologies. Although some systems (for instance NV centers) do not require for severe temperature conditions, present coherence achieved times still should be substantially extended.

4. CONCLUSIONS AND PERSPECTIVES

Although quantum information theory has a relatively short history, it has become an emerging and rapidly growing discipline. Multidisciplinary research in this field is attracting increasing attention from both the academic and industry communities. Impressive progress toward practical realizations of quantum information processing in various physical systems has been recently demonstrated.

While current quantum registers have at most 12 qubits, it will be necessary to increase this number to at least 40 (which is equivalent to 1 TB classical memory) before quantum computers can perform tasks that cannot be solved by classical computers. If quantum computers with 50–100 qubits can be built, they will open a new era in computational physics and engineering for much more realistic modeling and simulations. This should provide us with the most incredible development in our understanding of the behavior and properties of big ensembles of quantum particles. A 300-qubit quantum memory register can store information that is equivalent to about 10^{90} complex numbers, which exceeds the estimated number of atoms in the universe available now for observation. Therefore, the quantum computer (if it will actually happen) should have the theoretical capability of simulating and memorizing any finite physical system.

Quantum information processing cannot be realized without appropriate quantum memory storages. However, building such a long-lived quantum memory storage is extremely challenging. Decoherence due to interaction with the environment is a key problem. All present quantum memory schemes are very sensitive to the surrounding environment, limiting how long they can store data. In addition, the imperative requirements for the quantum memory register scalability to many hundreds of entangled qubits bring up huge difficulties. In Table 2 we summarize the most recent information relevant to realizations of quantum memory described in the previous chapter.

Most important are values of achieved decoherence times. At the present, from a conventional classical computing point of view, the best decoherence time values (up to few minutes) allow us to rank existing quantum memory as a dynamical memory or very short nonvolatile memory.

We should clarify that the time scale in the quantum (atomic) world is very different from our macro-world's time scale. For instance, a natural atomic time unit is of about 2.4×10^{-17} seconds, which is the time for light to pass 72 hydrogen atoms in a row ($\sim$7.2 nm). Note that the record for the shortest time interval measured is 12 attoseconds [178], or 2 atomic units. In this scale the decoherence time of 2 seconds is an incredibly long time, which makes a quantum memory accessible for 10^{17} times. On the other hand, today's commercially available computers have a clock cycle time of almost 0.3 ns, which also allows "to check" a quantum memory register up to 10^9 times before it decays. Nevertheless, before nonvolatile quantum memory becomes practical, it is important to reduce the complexity of experimental

Table 2. Qubits for quantum memory.

Physical qubit	Number of entangled qubits	Decoherence time	Control and conditions
Molecular spins	12	2 s	NMR technique High magnetic fields Room temperature
Trapped ions	8	1 s–10 min	Strong electromagnetic fields Low temperature (mK)
Neutral atoms	2	2 s	Strong electromagnetic fields Low temperature (nK–μK)
Photons	2	0.1 ms–2.3 s	Materials with strong nonlinear optical effects
Superconducting circuits	3	1 ns–4 μs	Low temperature (mK)
Quantum dots	2	3 μs–200 μs	External fields Low temperature (K)
Phosphorous impurity bound electron in silicon	–	0.6 s	Materials with special properties NMR technique
Nuclear spins of ^{29}Si isotopes	–	25 s	Materials with special properties NMR technique
Nitrogen vacancy spins in diamonds	2	2 ms	Materials with special properties Room temperature

implementations, improve their robustness, and drastically enhance decoherence times.

Despite the exponentially growing literature in the field, it is not yet identified (even on the research level) what the best physical implementation of a quantum memory register will be. Of the many proposed technologies for quantum memory registers, solid-state systems (including the electromagnetically induced transparency control of light memory in crystals, superconducting circuits, and localized electrons and spins) have perhaps the greatest potential for scalability and eventual commercialization because of their small sizes, straightforward fabrication methods, and robustness. Other technologies and hybrid architectures for quantum computation and memory, including interfaces between them, also seem very promising. Among them we should also mention here ballistic electrons in semiconductor, low-dimensional semiconductor structures [179–182], ferrite particles [30], organic materials [184], carbon-based nanosystems [185, 186], quantum dots near plasmonic nanostructures [187], electronic spins coupled with a superconducting resonator [188–190], hybrid superconductor–quantum dot devices [191], molecular ensembles coupled to a high-Q stripline cavity [192], and others [7].

In general, individual qubits cannot be encoded in physical systems of macroscopic size without irreducible losses. Therefore, the hybrid approach can also include a proper combination of classical and quantum hardware that can be realized in "multiscale" classical-quantum systems. In such a combined classical-quantum memory, all quantum processes in quantum registers should be performed inside the system core of quantum scale and the informative connections between the core- and macro-world can be controlled by a classical computer interface.

Nobody can predict whether the problems experienced with the practical implementations of a large, robust, and a long-time lived without external power quantum memory can be overcome. To build even a small nonvolatile quantum storage device, we have to possess direct control over matter at the quantum level. The knowledge that large quantum registers can be coherently controlled and manipulated for a long time at the quantum level is both a powerful stimulus and one of the greatest challenges facing theoretical and experimental physics. Real progress in this field is possible with the decisive development of nanotechnology.

The nonvolatile quantum memory storage's physical realization is the long-term goal, and it requires cross-disciplinary efforts in physics, mathematics, computer science, engineering, and material science. It is too early to designate a system to be an implemented winner. Before this can happen, tremendous difficulties must be overcome. Therefore, practical, robust nonvolatile quantum memory may more than a decade away.

REFERENCES

1. P. Benioff, *J. Statistical Phys.* 22, 563 (1980).
2. R. P. Feynman, *Optics News* 11, 11 (1985).
3. D. Deutsch, *Proc. Royal Soc. London A* 425, 73 (1989).
4. P. W. Shor, "Proceedings of the 35th Annual Symposium on Foundations of Computer Science," p. 124, IEEE Computer Society Press, Los Alamitos, California, 1994.
5. L. K. Grover, *Phys. Rev. Lett.* 79, 325 (1997).
6. C. H. Bennett and D. P. DiVincenzo, *Nature* 404, 247 (2000).
7. T. D. Ladd, F. Jelezko, R. Laflamme, Y. Nakamura, C. Monroe, and J. L. O'Brien, *Nature* 464, 45 (2010).
8. P. Kok, W. J. Munro, K. Nemoto, T. C. Ralph, J. P. Dowing, and G. J. Milburn, *Rev. Mod. Phys.* 79, 135 (2007).
9. G. P. Berman, G. D. Doolen, R. Mainieri, and V. I. Tsifrinivich, "Introduction to Quantum Computers." World Scientific, Singapore, 1998.
10. H.-K. Lo, S. Popescu, and T. Spiller, "Introduction to Quantum Computation and Information." World Scientific, Singapore, 2000.
11. G. Benenti, G. Casati, and G. Strini, "Principles of Quantum Computation and Information." Vol. I, World Scientific, Singapore, 2004.
12. G. Benenti, G. Casati, and G. Strini, "Principles of Quantum Computation and Information." Vol. II, World Scientific, Singapore, 2007.
13. M. A. Nielsen and I. L. Chuang, "Quantum Computation and Quantum Information." Cambridge University Press, Cambridge, UK, 2004.
14. S. M. Barnett, "Quantum Information." Oxford University Press, Oxford, UK, 2009.
15. G. Chen, D. A. Church, B.-G. Englert, C. Henkel, B. Rohwedder, M. O. Scully, and M. S. Zubairly, "Quantum Computing Devices, Principles, Designs, and Analysis." Charman and Hall/CRC, Taylor and Francis Group, New York, 2007.
16. P. Lambropoulos and D. Petrosyan, "Fundamentals of Quantum Optics and Quantum Information." Springer, Berlin, 2007.
17. M. Le Bellac, "A Short Introduction to Quantum Information and Quantum Computation." Cambridge University Press, Cambridge, UK, 2006.

18. M. Nakahara and T. Ohmi, "Quantum Computing: From Linear Algebra to Physical Realizations." CRC, Taylor and Francis Group, New York, 2008.
19. L. Diósi, "A Short Course in Quantum Information Theory." Springer, Berlin, 2007.
20. G. Auletta, M. Fortunato, and G. Parisini, "Quantum Mechanics." Cambridge University Press, Cambridge, UK, 2009.
21. P. Kaye, R. Laflamme, and M. Mosca, "An Introduction to Quantum Computing." Oxford University Press, Oxford, UK, 2008.
22. Z. Meglicki, "Quantum Computing Without Magic Devices." The MIT Press, Cambridge, 2008.
23. G. Jaeger, "Quantum Information." Springer, New York, 2007.
24. D. Stucki, N. Walenta, F. Vannel, R. T. Thew, N. Gisin, H. Zbinden, S. Gray, C. R. Towery, and S. Ten, *New. J. Phys.* 11, 075003 (2009).
25. L. Lydersen, C. Wiechers, C. Wittmann, D. Elser, J. Skaar, and V. Makarov, *Nature Photon.* 4, 686 (2010).
26. A. I. Lvovsky, B. C. Sanders, and W. Tittel, *Nature Photon.* 3, 706 (2009).
27. M. P. Hedges, J. J. Longdell, Y. Li, and M. J. Sellars, *Nature* 465, 1052 (2010).
28. M. Stoneham, *Physics* 2, 34 (2009).
29. C. Nayak, S. H. Simon, A. Stern, F. Freedman, and S. Das Sarma, *Rev. Mod. Phys.* 80, 1083 (2008).
30. E. O. Kamentskii and O. Voskoboynikov, "Trends in Quantum Computing Research." Chap. 10, Nova Science Publishers, New York, 2006.
31. P. Neumann, N. Mizuochi, F. Rempp, P. Hemmer, H. Watanabe, S. Yamasaki, V. Jacques, T. Gaebel, F. Jelezko, and J. Wrachtrup, *Science* 320, 1326 (2008).
32. J. J. Longdell, M. J. Sellars, and N. B. Manson, *Phys. Rev. Lett.* 93, 130503 (2004).
33. B. E. Kane, *Nature* 393, 133 (1998).
34. D. P. DiVincenzo, *Nature* 393, 113 (1998).
35. D. D. Awschalom, D. Loss, and N. Samarth, Eds., "Semiconductor Spintronics and Quantum Computation." Springer, Berlin, 2002.
36. B. Jacob, S. W. Ng, D. T. Wang, and S. Rodriguez, "Memory Systems, Cache, DRAM, Disk." Elsevier, Amsterdam, 2008.
37. J. E. Brewer and M. Gill, Eds., "Nonvolatile Memory Technologies. Emphasis on Flash." John Wiley & Sons, Inc. Hoboken, New Jersey, 2008.
38. P. Dirac, "The Principles of Quantum Mechanics." Oxford University Press, Oxford, UK, 1982.
39. D. Hilbert, J. von Neumann, and L. Nordheim, *Math. Ann.* 98, 1 (1928).
40. J. von Neumann, "Mathematical Foundations of Quantum Mechanics." Princeton University Press, Princeton, 1955.
41. W.-H. Steeb, "Wavelets, Hilbert Spaces, Wavelets, Generalized Function and Quantum Mechanics." Kluwer Academic Publisher, Dordrecht, 1998.
42. J. Blank, P. Exner, and M. Havlíček, "Hilbert Space Operators in Quantum Physics." Springer Science + Business Media B.V., New York, 2008.
43. L. D. Landau and E. M. Lifshitz, "Quantum Mechanics. Non-Relativistic Theory." Elsevier, Oxford, 2005.
44. V. B. Braginsky and F. Ya. Khalili, "Quantum Measurement." Cambridge University Press, Cambridge, 1992.
45. J. A. Wheeler and W. H. Zurek, Eds., "Quantum Theory and Measurement." Princeton University Press, Princeton NJ, 1983.
46. F. J. Dyson, *Phys. Rev.* 75, 1736 (1949).
47. A. M. Gleason, *Jour. Math. Mech.* 6, 885 (1957).
48. R. P. Feynman, "Statistical Mechanics: A Set of Lectures." Perseus Books Group, New York, 1998.
49. C. E. Shannon, *Bell Sys. Tech. J.* 27, 623 (1948).
50. D. Dieks, *Phys. Lett. A* 92, 271 (1982).
51. W. K. Wooters and W. H. Zurek, *Nature* 299, 802 (1982).
52. V. Bužek and M. Hillery, *Phys. Rev. A* 54, 1844 (1996).
53. N. Gisin and S. Massar, *Phys. Rev. Lett.* 79, 2153 (1997).
54. W. Heisenberg, *Zeitschrift Für Physik.* 77, 1 (1932).
55. B. Cassen and E. U. Condon, *Phys. Rev.* 50, 846 (1936).
56. O. Voskoboynikov and C. M. J. Wijers, *J. Comp. Theor. Nanosci.* 7, 1723 (2010).
57. E. Schrödinger, *Annalen Der Physik.* 81, 109 (1926).
58. A. Einstein, B. Podolsky, and N. Rosen, *Phys. Rev.* 47, 777 (1935).
59. J. S. Bell, *Physics* 1, 195 (1964).
60. A. Aspect, *Nature* 398, 189 (1999).
61. R. Horodecki, P. Horodecki, M. Horodecki, and K. Horodecki, *Rev. Mod. Phys.* 81, 865 (2009).
62. W. Duer, G. Vidal, and J. I. Cirac, *Phys. Rev. A* 62, 062314 (2000).
63. M. Schlosshauer, "Decoherence and the Quantum-to Classical Transitions." Springer, Berlin, 2007.
64. G. Lindblad, *Commun. Math. Phys.* 48, 119 (1976).
65. S. Imre and F. Balázs, "Quantum Computing and Communications." John Wiley & Sons, England, 2005.
66. D. P. DiVincenzo, *Fortschr. Phys.* 48, 771 (2000).
67. D. P. DiVincenzo, *Quant. Info. Comp.* 1, 1 (2001).
68. R. S. Macomber, "A Complete Introduction to Modern NMR Spectroscopy." John Wiley and Sons, New York, 1998.
69. L. M. K. Vandersypen and I. L. Chuang, *Rev. Mod. Phys.* 76, 1037 (2004).
70. I. S. Oliveira, R. Sarthour, Jr, T. Bonagamba, E. Azevedo, J. C. C. Freitas, and E. R. deAzevedo, "NMR Quantum Information Processing." Elsevier, Amsterdam, 2007.
71. D. G. Cory, A. F. Fahmy, and T. F. Havel, *Proc. Natl. Acad. Sci. USA* 94, 1634 (1997).
72. M. A. Nielsen, E. Knill, and R. Laflamme, *Nature* 396, 52 (1998).
73. C. A. Ryan, M. Laforest, and R. Laflamme, *New J. Phys.* 11, 013034 (2009).
74. C. Negrevergne, T. S. Mahesh, C. A. Ryan, M. Ditty, F. Cyr-Racine, W. Power, N. Boulant, T. Havel, D. G. Cory, and R. Laflamme, *Phys. Rev. Lett.* 96, 170501 (2006).
75. C. A. Ryan, O. Moussa, J. Baugh, and R. Laflamme, *Phys. Rev. Lett.* 100, 140501 (2008).
76. C. P. Slichter, "Principles of Magnetic Resonance." 3rd edition, Springer-Verlag, Berlin, 1990.
77. M. Mehring, J. Mende, and W. Scherer, *Phys. Rev. Lett.* 90, 153001 (2003).
78. H. O. Everitt, Ed., "Experimental Aspects of Quantum Computing." Springer, New York, 2005.
79. J. Wrachtrup, S. Y. Kilin, and A P Nizovtsev, *Opt. Spectrosc.* 91, 429 (2001).
80. P. Neumann, R. Kolesov, B. Naydenov, J. Beck, F. Rempp, M. Steiner, V. Jacques, G. Balasubramanian, M. L. Markham, D. J. Twitchen, S. Pezzagna, J. Meijer, J. Twamley, F. Jelezko, and J. Wrachtrup, *Nature Phys.* 6, 249 (2010).
81. H. Häffner, C. F. Roos, and R. Blatt, *Phys. Rep.* 469, 155 (2008).
82. R. Blatt and D. Wineland, *Nature* 453, 1008 (2008).
83. J. I. Cirac and P. Zoller, *Phys. Rev. Lett.* 74, 4091 (1995).
84. W. P. Schleich and H. Walther, Eds., "Elements of Quantum Information." Wiley-VCH Verlag, Weinheim, 2007.
85. J. Stolze and D. Suter, "Quantum Computing. A Short Course from Theory to Experiment." Wiley-VCH Verlag, Weinheim, 2004.
86. I. Bloch, *Nature* 453, 1016 (2008).
87. W. Paul, *Rev. Mod. Phys.* 62, 531 (1990).
88. H. J. Metcalf and P. van der Straten, "Laser Cooling and Trapping." Springer-Verlag, New York, 1999.
89. J. H. Wesenberg, R. J. Epstein, D. Leibfried, R. B. Blakestad, J. Britton, J. P. Home, W. M. Itano, J. D. Jost, E. Knill, C. Langer, R. Ozeri, S. Seidelin, and D. J. Wineland, *Phys. Rev. A* 76, 053416 (2007).
90. J. J. Bollinger, D. J. Heinzen, W. M. Itano, S. L. Gilbert, and D. J. Wineland, *IEEE Trans. Instrum. Meas.* 40, 126 (1991).
91. P. T. H. Fisk, M. J. Sellars, M. A. Lawn, C. Coles, A. G. Mann, and D. G. Blair, *IEEE Trans. Instrum. Meas.* 44, 113 (1995).

92. H. Häffner, W. Hänsel, C. F. Roos, J. Benhelm, D. Chekal-kar, M. Chwalla, T. Körber, U. D. Rapol, M. Riebe, P. O. Schmidt, C. Becher, O. Gühne, W. Dür, and R. Blatt, *Nature* 438, 643 (2005).
93. D. Kielpinski, C. Monroe, and D. J. Wineland, *Nature* 417, 709 (2002).
94. P. Treutlein, P. Hommelhoff, T. Steinmetz, T. W. Hänsch, and J. Reichel, *Phys. Rev. Lett.* 92, 203005 (2004).
95. J. Beugnon, C. Tuchendler, H. Marion, A. Gaëtan, Y. Miroshnychenko, Y. R. P. Sortais, A. M. Lance, M. P. A. Jones, G. Messin, A. Browaeys, and P. Grangier, *Nature Phys.* 3, 696 (2007).
96. K. D. Nelson, X. Li, and D. S. Weiss, *Nature Phys.* 3, 556 (2007).
97. G. K. Brennen, C. M. Caves, P. S. Jessen, and I. H. Deutsch, *Phys. Rev. Lett.* 82, 1060 (1999).
98. D. Jaksch, H.-J. Briegel, J. I. Cirac, C. W. Gardiner, and P. Zoller, *Phys. Rev. Lett.* 82, 1975 (1999).
99. O. Mandel, M. Greiner, A. Widera, T. Rom, T. W. Hänsch, and I. Bloch, *Nature* 425, 937 (2003).
100. D. Jaksch, J. I. Cirac, P. Zoller, S. L. Rolston, R. Côté, and M. D. Lukin, *Phys. Rev. Lett.* 85, 2208 (2000).
101. L. You and M. S. Chapman, *Phys. Rev. A* 62, 052302 (2000).
102. B. Lounis and M. Orrit, *Rep. Prog. Phys.* 68, 1129 (2005).
103. T. M. Babinec, B. J. M. Hausmann, M. Khan, Y. Zhang, J. R. Maze, P. R. Hemmer, and M. Lončar, *Nature Nanotech.* 5,195 (2010).
104. P. Grangier, J. A. Levenson, and J. P. Poizat, *Nature* 396, 537 (1998).
105. G. Nogues, A. Rauschenbeutel, S. Osnaghi, M. Brune, J. M. Raimond, and S. Haroche, *Nature* 400, 239 (1999).
106. E. Knill, R. Laflamme, and G. J. Milburn, *Nature* 409, 46 (2001).
107. J. C. F. Matthews, A. Politi, A. Stefanov, and J. L. O'Brien, *Nature Photo.* 3, 346 (2009).
108. J. L. O'Brien, A. Fukusawa, and J. Vučković, *Nature Photo.* 3, 687 (2009).
109. C. Simon, M. Afzelius, J. Appel, A. Boyer de la Giroday, S. J. Dewhurst, N. Gisin, C. Y. Hu, F. Jelezko, S. Kröll, J. H. Müller, J. Nunn, E. S. Polzik, J. G. Rarity, H. De Riedmatten, W. Rosenfeld, A. J. Shields, N. Sköld, R. M. Stevenson, R. Thew, I. A. Walmsley, M. C. Weber, H. Weinfurter, J. Wrachtrup, and R. J. Young, *Eur. Phys. J.* 58, 1 (2010).
110. K. Hammerer, A. S. Sørensen, and E. S. Polzik, *Rev. Mod. Phys.* 82, 1041 (2010).
111. M. Fleischhauer, A. Imamoglu, and J. P. Marangos, *Rev. Mod. Phys.* 77, 633 (2005).
112. M. D. Eisaman, A. André, F. Massou, M. Fleischhauer, A. S. Zibrov, and M. D. Lukin, *Nature* 438, 837 (2005).
113. K. J. Boller, A. Imamoglu, and S. E. Harris, *Phys. Rev. Lett.* 66, 2593 (1991).
114. A. Javan, O. Kocharovskaya, H. Lee, and M. O. Scully, *Phys. Rev. A* 66, 013805 (2002).
115. U. Schnorrberger, J. D. Thompson, S. Trotzky, R. Pugatch, N. Davidson, S. Kuhr, and I. Bloch, *Phys. Rev. Lett.* 103, 033003 (2009).
116. A. V. Turukhin, V. S. Sudarshanam, M. S. Shahriar, J. A. Musser, B. S. Ham, and P. R. Hemmer, *Phys. Rev. Lett.* 88, 023602 (2002).
117. J. J. Longdell, E. Fraval, M. J. Sellars, and N. B. Manson, *Phys. Rev. Lett.* 95, 063601 (2005).
118. A. V. Gorshkov, A. André, M. Fleischhauer, A. S. Sørensen, and M. D. Lukin, *Phys. Rev. Lett.* 98, 123601 (2007).
119. N. B. Phillips, A. V. Gorshkov, and I. Novikova, *Phys. Rev. A* 78, 023801 (2008).
120. C. Liu, Z. Dutton, C. H. Behroozi, and L. V. Hau, *Nature* 409, 490 (2001).
121. T. Heinzel, "Mesoscopic Electronics in Solid State Nanostructures." Wiley-VCH Verlag, Weinheim, 2007.
122. T. Ihn, "Semiconductor Nanostructures: Quantum States and Electronic Transport." Oxford University Press, Oxford, 2010.
123. D. R. Tilley and J. Tilley, "Superfluidity and Superconductivity." Adam Hilger Ltd., Bristol, 1986.
124. M. Tinkham, "Introduction to Superconductivity." Krieger, Malabar, 1985.
125. B. D. Josephson, "Superconductivity." (R. D. Parks, Ed.), Marcel Dekker, New York, 1969.
126. B. Ruggiero, P. Delsing, C. Granata, Y. Pashkin, and P. Silvestrini, Eds., "Quantum Computing in Solid State Systems." Springer, New York, 2006.
127. J. Q. You and F. Nori, *Physics Today* 58, 42 (2005).
128. J. Clarke and F. K. Wilhelm, *Nature* 453, 1031 (2008).
129. M. Büttiker, *Phys. Rev. B* 36, 3548 (1987).
130. V. Bouchiat, D. Vion, P. Joyez, D. Esteve, and M. H. Devoret, *Physica Scripta T* 76, 165 (1998).
131. Y. Nakamura, Yu. A Pashkin, and J. S. Tsai, *Nature* 398, 786 (1999).
132. Y. Makhlin, G. Schrön, and A. Shnirman, *Rev. Mod. Phys.* 73, 357 (2001).
133. K.-J. Boller, A. Imamoglu, and S. E. Harris, *Phys. Rev. Lett.* 66, 2593 (1991).
134. J. R. Friedman, V. Patel, W. Chen, S. K. Tolpygo, and J. E. Lukens, *Nature* 406, 43 (2000).
135. J. Clarke, *Sci. Amer.* 271, 46 (1994).
136. J. Clarke and A. I. Braginski, Eds. "The SQUID Handbook: Fundamentals and Technology of SQUIDs and SQUID Systems." Vol. 1, Wiley, Weinheim, 2004.
137. M. Steffen, M. Ansmann, R. C. Bialczak, N. Katz, E. Lucero, R. McDermott, M. Neeley, E. M. Weig, A. N. Cleland, and J. M. Martinis, *Science* 313, 1423 (2006).
138. T. Yamamoto, Yu. A. Pashkin, O. Astafiev, Y. Nakamura, and J. S. Tsai, *Nature* 425, 941 (2003).
139. J. H. Plantenberg, P. C. de Groot, C. J. P. M. Harmans, and J. E. Mooij, *Nature* 447, 836 (2007).
140. Y. Makhlin, G. Schön, and A. Shnirman, *Nature* 398, 305 (1999).
141. L. F. Wei, Y. X. Liu, and F. Nori, *Phys. Rev. B* 71, 134506 (2005).
142. J. Lantz, M. Wallquist, V. S. Shumeiko, and G. Wendin, *Phys. Rev. B* 70, 140507 (2004).
143. A. Blais, R.-S. Huang, A. Wallraff, S. M. Girvin, and R. J. Schoelkopf, *Phys. Rev. A* 69, 062320 (2004).
144. A. O. Niskanen, K. Harrabi, F. Yoshihara, Y. Nakamura, S. Lloyd, and J. S. Tsai, *Science* 316, 723 (2007).
145. M. Grajcar, A. Izmalkov, S. H. W. van der Ploeg, S. Linzen, T. Plecenik, Th. Wagner, U. Hübner, E. Il'ichev, H.-G. Meyer, A. Y. Smirnov, P. J. Love, A. M. van den Brink, M. H. S. Amin, S. Uchaikin, and A. M. Zagoskin, *Phys. Rev. Lett.* 96, 047006 (2006).
146. P. Bertet, I. Chiorescu, G. Burkard, K. Semba, C. J. P. M. Harmans, D. P. DiVincenzo, and J. E. Mooij, *Phys. Rev. Lett.* 95, 257002 (2005).
147. L. DiCarlo, J. M. Chow, J. M. Gambetta, L. S. Bishop, B. R. Johnson, D. I. Schuster, J. Majer, A. Blais, L. Frunzio, S. M. Girvin, and R. J. Schoelkopf, *Nature* 460, 240 (2009).
148. J. A. Schreier, A. A. Houck, J. Koch, D. I. Schuster, B. R. Johnson, J. M. Chow, J. M. Gambetta, J. Majer, L. Frunzio, M. H. Devoret, S. M. Girvin, and R. J. Schoelkopf, *Phys. Rev. B* 77, 180502 (2008).
149. R. N. Bhattacharya and M. P. Paranthaman, Eds., "High Temperature Superconductors." Wiley-VCH Verlag, Weinheim, 2010.
150. L. Jacak, P. Hawrylak, and A. Wojs, "Quantum Dots." Springer, Berlin, 1998.
151. D. Bimberg, Ed., "Semiconductor Nanostructures." Springer, Berlin, 2008.
152. T. Chakraborty, "Quantum Dots: A Survey of the Properties of Artificial Atoms." Elsevier, Amsterdam, 1999.
153. G. W. Bryant and G. S. Solomon, Eds., "Optics of Quantum Dots." Artech House, MA, 2005.

154. S. M. Reimann and M. Manninen, *Rev. Mod. Phys.* 74, 1283 (2002).
155. J. Stangl, V. Holý, and G. Bauer, *Rev. Mod. Phys.* 76, 725 (2004).
156. F. Boxberg and J. Tulkki, *Rep. Prog. Phys.* 70, 1425 (2007).
157. R. Hanson, L. P. Kouwenhoven, J. R. Petta, S. Tarucha, and L. M. K. Vandersypen, *Rev. Mod. Phys.* 79, 1217 (2007).
158. F. Henneberger and O. Benson, Eds., "Semiconductor Quantum Bits." Pan Stanford Publishing, Singapore, 2009.
159. G. Konstantatos and E. H. Sargent, *Nature Nanotech.* 5, 391 (2010).
160. J. M. Garsía, G. Medeiros-Ribeiro, K. Schmidt, T. Ngo, J. L. Feng, A. Lorke, J. Kotthaus, and P. M. Petroff, *Appl. Phys. Lett.* 71, 2014 (1997).
161. B. C. Lee, O. Voskoboynikov, and C. P. Lee, *Physica E* 24, 87 (2004).
162. J. R. Petta, A. C. Johnson, J. M. Taylor, E. A. Laird, A. Yacoby, M. D. Lukin, C. M. Marcus, M. P. Hanson, and A. C. Gossard, *Science* 309, 2180 (2005).
163. T. Hayashi, T. Fujisawa, H. D. Cheong, Y. H. Jeong, and Y. Hirayama, *Phys. Rev. Lett.* 91, 226804 (2003).
164. D. Loss and D. P. DiVincenzo, *Phys. Rev. A* 57, 120 (1998).
165. J. M. Elzerman, R. Hanson, L. H. W. van Beveren, B. Witkamp, L. M. K. Vandersypen, and L. P. Kouwenhoven, *Nature* 430, 431 (2004).
166. M. Bayer, P. Hawrylak, K. Hinzer, S. Fafarad, M. Korkusinski, Z. R. Wasilewski, O. Stern, and A. Forchel, *Science* 291, 451 (2001).
167. C. Piermarocchi, P. Chen, Y. S. Dale, and L. J. Sham, *Phys. Rev. B* 65, 075307 (2002).
168. L. Novotny and B. Hecht, "Principles of Nano-Optics." Cambridge University Press, Cambridge, 2006.
169. D. Press, T. D. Ladd, B. Zhang, and Y. Yamamoto, *Nature* 456, 218 (2008).
170. D. Kim, S. G. Carter, A. Greilich, A. S. Bracker, and D. Gammon, *Nature Phys.* 7, 223 (2011).
171. H. Bluhm, S. Foletti, I. Neder, M. Rudner, D. Mahalu, V. Umansky, and A. Yacoby, *Nature Phys.* 7, 109 (2011).
172. Y. Hu, H. O. H. Churchill, D. J. Reilly, J. Xiang, C. M. Lieber, and C. M. Marcus, *Nature Nanotech.* 2, 622 (2007).
173. D. Culcer, Ł. Cywiński, Q. Li, X. Hu, and S. Das Sarma, *Phys. Rev. B* 82, 155312 (2010).
174. T. D. Ladd, D. Maryenko, Y. Yamamoto, E. Abe, and K. M. Itoh, *Phys. Rev. B* 71, 14401 (2005).
175. G. Balasubramanian, P. Neumann, D. Twitchen, M. Markham, R. Kolesov, N. Mizuochi, J. Isoya, J. Achard, J. Beck, J. Tissler, V. Jacques, P. R. Hemmer, F. Jelezko, and J. Wrachtrup, *Nature Mat.* 8, 383 (2009).
176. R. Hanson, V. V. Dobrovitski, A. E. Feiguin, O. Gywat, and D. D. Awschalom, *Science* 320, 352 (2008).
177. T. Gaebel, M. Domhan, I. Popa, C. Wittmann, P. Neumann, F. Jelezko, J. R. Rabeau, N. Stavrias, A. D. Greentree, S. Prawer, J. Meijer, J. Twamley, P. R. Hemmer, and J. Wrachtrup, *Nature Phys.* 2, 408 (2006).
178. S. Koke, C. Grebing, H. Frei, A. Anderson, A. Assion, and G. Steinmeyer, *Nature Photon.* 4, 462 (2010).
179. A. Bertoni, P. Bordone, R. Brunetti, C. Jacoboni, and S. Reggiani, *Phys. Rev. Lett.* 84 5912 (2000).
180. J. Harris, R. Akis, and D. K. Ferry, *Appl. Phys. Lett.* 79, 2214 (2001).
181. R. Ionicioiu, G. Amaratunga, and F. Udrea, *Int J. Modern Phys. B* 15, 125 (2001).
182. L. Yu and O. Voskoboynikov, *Solid State Comm.* 145, 447 (2008).
183. S. Nadj-Perge, S. M. Frolov, E. P. A. M. Bakkers, and L. P. Kouwenhoven, *Nature* 468, 1084 (2010).
184. S. Sanvito, *Nature Nanotech.* 2, 204 (2007).
185. B. Treuzettel, D. V. Bulaev, D. Loss, and G. Burkard, *Nature Phys.* 3, 192 (2007).
186. N. Mason, M. J. Biercuk, and C. M. Marcus, *Science* 303, 655 (2004).
187. M. L. Andersen, S. Stobbe, A. S. Sørensen, and P. Lodahl, *Nature Phys.* 7, 215 (2011).
188. H. Wu, R. E. George, J. H. Wesenberg, K. Mølmer, D. I. Schuster, R. J. Schoelkopf, K. M. Itoh, A. Ardavan, J. J. L. Morton, and G. A. D. Briggs, *Phys. Rev. Lett.* 105, 140503 (2010).
189. D. I. Schuster, A. P. Sears, E. Ginossar, L. DiCarlo, L. Frunzio, J. J. L. Morton, H. Wu, G. A. D. Briggs, B. B. Buckley, D. D. Awschalom, and R. J. Schoelkopf, *Phys. Rev. Lett.* 105, 140501 (2010).
190. Y. Kubo, F. R. Ong, P. Bertet, D. Vion, V. Jacques, D. Zheng, A. Dréau, J.-F. Roch, A. Auffeves, F. Jelezko, J. Wrachtrup, M. F. Barthe, P. Bergonzo, and D. Esteve, *Phys. Rev. Lett.* 105, 140502 (2010).
191. S. De Franceschi, L. Kouwenhoven, C. Schönenberger, and W. Wernsdorfer, *Nature Nanotech.* 5, 703 (2010).
192. P. Rabl, D. DeMille, J. M. Doyle, M. D. Lukin, R. J. Schoelkopf, and P. Zoller, *Phys. Rev. Lett.* 97, 033003 (2006).

CHAPTER 16

Search for Frontrunners Among Emerging Non-Volatile Memory Technologies: STTRAM or RRAM or Others

Alois Gutmann[†], Jin-Ping Han[‡]
Infineon Technologies, 2070 Rt. 52, Hopewell Junction, NY 12533, USA

CONTENTS

[†]Present address: 205 Rollingwood Drive, Athens, GA30605, USA.
[‡]Present address: IBM SRDC, 2070 Rt. 52, MS 30A, Hopewell Junction, NY 12533, USA.

ISBN: 1-58883-251-1

Nonvolatile Memories: Materials, Devices and Applications
Edited by Tseung-Yuen Tseng and Simon M. Sze
Volume 2: Pages: 401–442

1. INTRODUCTION

In psychology, memory is the ability of an organism for short or long term storage, retention, and recall of information and experiences [1]. During information processing the formation, storage, and retrieval of memory is achieved in three stages: Registration or encoding (receiving, processing, and combining received information); Storage (creation of a permanent record of the encoded information); Retrieval or recollection (recall of stored information in response to some cue for use in a subsequent process or activity).

In an extension to non-psychological fields, for some time the term "memory" has been borrowed to refer to computer data storage by computer components and recording media which retain digital data used for computing. It is one of the fundamental components of all modern computers. Coupled with a central processing unit (CPU), it enables the execution of encoding or registration, storage (often referred to as "write"), and retrieval (also termed "read") in basic computer models introduced since the 1940s [2].

In computing, memory refers to the physical devices used to store data or programs in a systematic way, such as binary code, on a temporary or permanent basis for use in an electronic digital computer. The semiconductor technology has been the main stream of current primary/secondary computer memory making use of integrated circuits consisting of silicon-based transistors.

There are two main types of memory: volatile and non-volatile. Volatile memory retains its stored data only when the power is on and loses its data when the power is off. The contents of this type of memory may be quickly and easily updated and changed. Non-volatile memory (NVM) retains its storage even when the power is turned off. Although the stored information in most non-volatile memories may be changed, the process involved is much slower than that for volatile memory.

This publication contains six subsequent sections. In Section 2, the currently established volatile and non-volatile memory technologies are described as an overview of all available options and to set a benchmark for novel device types. Section 3 describes innovative NVM technologies that have already progressed to commercial products by mid-2011. Sections 4 and 5 are dedicated to "emerging" NVM options, i.e., to innovative technologies that are still in a development/pre-production stage. Particular emphasis will be given to the development of Spin-Transfer-Torque (STT) MRAMs and Resistive RAMs (ReRAMs or RRAMs), which are considered to be the two most promising types of non-volatile memories based on inorganic switching materials. A shorter discussion of NVMs based on organic switching materials is included at the end of Section 6.

2. ESTABLISHED MEMORY TECHNOLOGIES

2.1. Volatile Memory

Volatile memory requires power to maintain the stored information. Random access memory (RAM) is a common type of volatile semiconductor technology, either static RAM (SRAM) or dynamic RAM (DRAM) devices. SRAM data can be retained without requiring periodical refreshment. Yet SRAMs still belong to the class of volatile memories since all data is lost when power is turned off, typically bi-stable latching circuitry is applied to store each bit. In DRAMs, on the other hand, charges used for data storage may leak out and thus information will vanish automatically without refreshing. Because of this refresh requirement, this type of memory devices is termed as "dynamic," as opposed to SRAM and other static memories. The advantage of a DRAM is its simple structure, with only one transistor and a capacitor (1T/1C) per bit, compared to six transistors (6T) for each bit in a conventional SRAM. This difference accounts for the substantial price difference between these two types of memory. DRAMs can be manufactured with very high densities. On the other hand, SRAMs can provide faster access to data and require less standby power.

The DRAM cell's basic layout of one transistor and one capacitor (1T-1C) was invented in 1967 by Dennard [3] as shown schematically in Figure 1. Information is stored in the DRAM cell by means of the presence or absence of a charge in the capacitor. An individual DRAM cell is selected or unselected by turning on or off the word line transistor by increasing or decreasing the gate voltage since the word line is connected to the gate. The information is then transferred between the bit line (data line) and the storage capacitor.

The charge, and hence the data stored in a DRAM cell, is lost if the chip's power supply is switched off. The stored charge can also gradually leak out due to mechanisms such as junction leakage, access transistor sub-threshold leakage, and the need for dielectric capacitance balance in order to attain a data retention time long enough to survive the standby period between refresh cycles. The capacitance requirement, in particular, imposes a severe scaling limit on conventional DRAM devices.

In order to overcome these shortcomings, many researchers have resorted to other innovative ways to produce volatile memory functionality for VLSI applications, such as advanced-random access memory (A-RAM) [4, 5], twin transistor RAM (TTRAM) (a new type of computer memory in development by Renesas [6, 7]), and zero-capacitor RAM (Z-RAM), a novel technology developed by Innovative Silicon [8]. However, all these new approaches have to overcome severe technical challenges.

A SRAM [9] cell typically uses six transistors to store and access one bit as shown in Figure 2. The four transistors (T1, T2, T3, and T4) in the center form two cross-coupled inverters (1 n-channel and p-channel transistor each). This storage

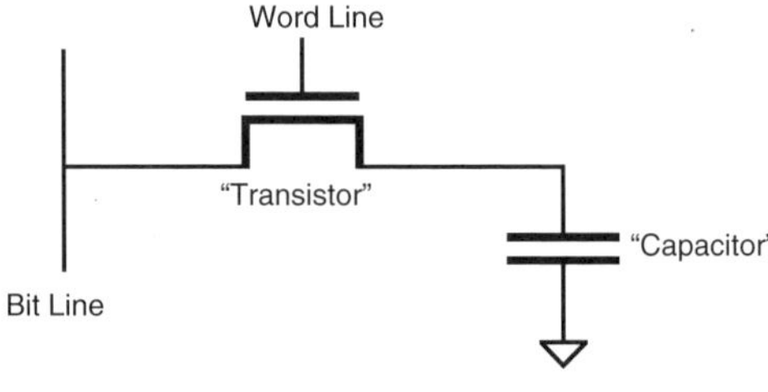

Figure 1. Schematic representation of the basic 1 transistor/1 capacitor DRAM cell.

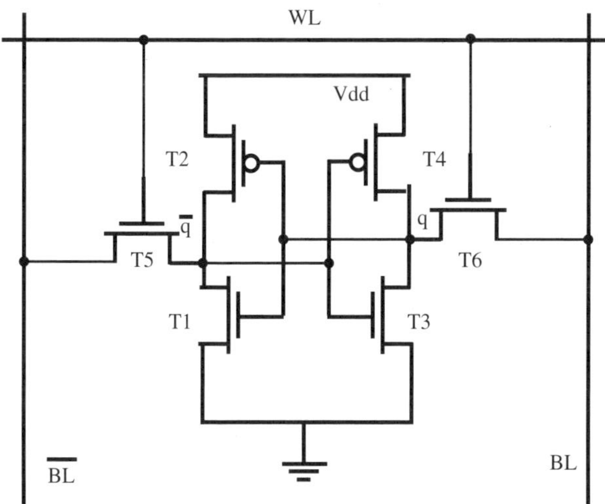

Figure 2. Six-transistor CMOS SRAM cell.

cell has two stable states denoted as "0" and "1". Two additional access transistors (T5 and T6, both *n*-channel transistors) are used to control access to the storage cell during read and write operations. When the cell is not addressed, the two access transistors are closed and the data is kept to a stable state, latched within the flip-flop. The word line (WL in figure) that controls the two access transistor gates enables access and control whether the cell is connected to the bit lines (BL) or not.

During read accesses, the bit lines are actively driven high and low by the inverters in the SRAM cell. This improves SRAM bandwidth compared to DRAMs—in a DRAM, the bit line is connected to storage capacitors and charge sharing causes the bit line to swing upwards or downwards. The symmetric structure of SRAMs also allows for differential signaling, which makes small voltage swings more easily detectable. Commercial SRAM chips accept all address bits at a time while commodity DRAMs have the address multiplexed in two halves, i.e., higher bits followed by lower bits, over the same package pins in order to keep their size and cost down. This difference contributes to the speed advantage of SRAM versus DRAM devices.

The data in a SRAM cell is volatile since power has to be provided in order to maintain the information. However, the data does not "leak away" like in a DRAM, thus the SRAM does not require a refresh cycle.

2.2. Classic Non-Volatile Memory

Non-volatile memory doesn't require power to retain the stored information, in other words, the data will not be lost when the power is off. Examples of non-volatile memory include compact disks (CD), various version of read-only memory (ROM), flash memory, SONOS, most types of magnetic computer storage devices (e.g., hard disks, floppy disks, and magnetic tape), optical disks, and early computer storage methods such as paper tape and punched cards. Upcoming non-volatile memory technologies include FeRAM, PRAM, MRAM, RRAM (e.g., CBRAM), Racetrack memory, NRAM, Millipede, etc. Our focus will be on well-established non-volatile memories and the currently dominating flash memory.

2.2.1. Early-Version NVM (CD, Mask ROM, PROM, EPROM and EEPROM)

2.2.1.1. Compact Disk (CD). Beside semiconductor IC-based ROMs, discussed later, there exist quite a few typical optical non-volatile storage media ROM options as for example compact disks (CD) [10]. Read-only memory (CD-ROM) allows only reading of data (analogous to masked ROM). CD-R is a 'Write Once Read Many' device (analogous to PROM), while CD-RW supports erase-rewrite cycles (analogous to EEPROM). Both are designed for backwards-compatibility with CD-ROM.

The first audio compact disk was demonstrated in 1982 by Philips and Sony, claiming the use of light for reading the digital information stored in the relief of the disk surface. A compact disk contains clear polycarbonate material, coated with a reflective metal, and a layer of clear lacquer for protection. CD-ROMs have been widely adopted for PC applications due to their convenience and adequate data capacity. In some cases, particularly large programs are now stored on DVD as well as CD.

2.2.1.2. Mask ROM. Mask ROM [11] has its contents pre-programmed and part of the chip masked off during the photolithography process by the integrated circuit manufacturer; therefore its data cannot be changed any more by the user. The main advantages of a mask ROM are its compact size and low manufacturing costs. However, any design error in data or code will require a costly replacement by a corrected mask ROM. Mask ROM in PCs are mainly used to permanently store fixed microcodes in microprocessors or firmware in microcontrollers, but offer much less flexibility for other memory application.

2.2.1.3. Programmable ROM (PROM). PROM, also called one-time programmable ROM (OTP NVM), was initially invented in 1956 by Tsing and Henrich and commercialized in 1969 [12, 13]. It allows users to program its contents exactly once by physically altering its structure via a special device called a PROM programmer. Typically, this device uses high voltages to permanently destroy or create internal links (fuses or anti-fuses) within the chip. PROM can only be programmed once.

2.2.1.4. Erasable Programmable Read-Only Memory (EPROM). EPROM was invented by Frohman of Intel in 1971 [14]. EPROM was made possible by the invention of floating gate transistors or FGMOSFETs, which are briefly discussed in the Section 2.2.2. A set of arrays of such transistors form an EPROM, which can be individually programmed electrically. The operation principle of EPROM is fairly simple. When applying a voltage higher than the threshold voltage (V_t), electrons can tunnel through the insulator and be stored at the floating gate area (write or rewrite). Since the quality of the gate-end insulator is high, the stored charges cannot leak out easily. Ultraviolet light (UV) can reset or erase the base state of an EPROM to all "1" or "0" because the UV photons can have sufficient energy to push electrons through the insulator and return the base state into a ground state. Unlike PROM, an EPROM can be repeatedly reset to its un-programmed state by exposure to strong ultraviolet light penetrating though a transparent fused quartz window (generally for 10 minutes or longer). After programming, the window is typically covered with a label to prevent accidental erasure. Repeated exposure to UV light will eventually wear out an EPROM. The endurance of most EPROM chips exceeds 1000 cycles of erasing and reprogramming.

2.2.1.5. Electrically Erasable Programmable Read-Only Memory (EEPROM). EEPROM was invented in 1983 [15]. EPROM's obvious drawbacks—UV is not a practical source for the device operation and not easy to control—triggered development of an improved version of EPROM, "electrically" erasable programmable read-only memory (EEPROM), sometimes called E^2PRAM. Instead of using UV, a more convenient high power pulse is employed to drive the electrons through the insulator. Its entire data content (or that of selected areas) can be electrically erased, then rewritten electrically. Writing or flashing an EEPROM occurs at much slower speed (milliseconds per bit) than reading from a ROM or writing to a RAM (nanoseconds in both cases). Another disadvantage of EEPROMs is their propensity to high-power induced mechanical degradation. Therefore EEPROM retention time (the period during which the memory retains its state) is short, in the order of 10^5 cycles. However, this problem has been overcome by adding a standard SRAM whereby the EERPROM can back up each of its bits when power is off, and the data can be loaded back to EERPROM when power is up. This back-and-forth data transferring memory chip is also called "NOVRAM." The memory state of the floating-gate transistor is maintained for as long as the charge is not leaked out or otherwise diminished. Typically the commercial floating-gate EEPROM products all have specifications of over 10 years of retention time.

2.2.2. Current Dominating Version: Flash Memory

Flash memory, invented by Toshiba in the mid-1980s [16, 17], is an updated version of EEPROM and makes much more efficient use of the chip area and can be erased and reprogrammed thousands of times without damage. The first commercial NOR-type flash chip was introduced by Intel in 1988. NAND flash from Toshiba and Samsung followed in 1989. Flash memory offers faster read access and higher endurance than previous versions of EEPROM. It is non-volatile too, and therefore it has become a powerful and cost-effective solid-state storage technology dominating in mobile electronics devices and other consumer application markets. A flash memory stores the information in an array of unit cells or floating gate transistors.

2.2.2.1. Floating Gate Transistor (FGMOSFET). The invention of floating gate transistors or FGMOSFETs brought a revolutionary change for the NVRAM [18]. The FGMOSFET is a field effect transistor comprised of a conventional MOSFET and at least one capacitor on top used to couple control voltages to the floating gate, while the metal or poly layer of the original MOSFET serves the floating gate as the charge storage unit and the bottom electrode of the top capacitor. The schematic view is shown in Figure 3. To program it, a high voltage is applied to the control gate in order to induce electrons to tunnel through the insulating dielectric layer (e.g., oxide or oxide-nitride) into the floating gate, which impedes the subsequent operation of the control gate. The "0" or "1" is stored by the voltage polarity on the control gate. Since insulating oxide surrounds the floating gate entirely, charge trapped on the floating gate cannot leak out. The charge stored on the floating gate can be modulated by applying voltages to the source, drain, substrate, and control gate terminals.

The functional principles of flash memory are based on the modulations of an electric charge that is carried by electrons and stored in the gate of FGMOSFET. The charging state of the gate affects the threshold voltage of the transistor, which can be sensed and taken to code for binary zeros and ones. Toggling the state of a memory cell requires voltage bursts with amplitudes large enough to move electrons across the barriers that surround the gate in a MOS transistor. A charge pump is commonly used to build up the required voltages. This buildup takes considerable time, and as a result the (block) write time for typical flash memory devices are around 100 microseconds, which is four orders of magnitude above the (byte) writing times found in current SRAMs.

The main drawbacks of floating-gate based technology include:

(1) relatively high voltage operation compared to those required for DRAM, SRAM, and logic devices,
(2) relatively long programming time (typically more than 1 μsec) and erase time (typically even much longer than the programming time),
(3) relatively high power consumption, and
(4) limited endurance (typically less than 1 million program/erase cycles).

2.2.2.2. Flash NAND and NOR. The high voltages that are required to program a flash device cause degradation with every write cycle. Scaling the flash devices down aggravates this issue. Although the memory cells get smaller, the programming voltages cannot be reduced. At present, typical flash devices are specified for 5,000 writing operations per sector. In order to maximize the life time of a flash device, many flash controllers implement strategies for "wear leveling," which will distribute write operations so that the number of write operations are balanced across physical sectors and the life span of the device is not shortened by a single sector having accumulated a large number of write cycles. In older versions of flash memory devices, each cell used to store one bit of data, but newer versions, i.e., multi-level cell devices (MLC), can store more than 1 bit per cell, due to the fact that the number of electrons placed on the floating gate of a cell can be varied.

Examples of simple NAND and NOR flash [19] wiring structures are shown in Figures 4(a and b). With a NOR gate flash device, each cell has one end connected directly to a bit line and the other end connected to ground. When one of the word lines is set to high, the corresponding FGMOSFT pulls the output bit line low. In NAND gate flash, the cells in block are connected in series, while the Bit Line selector

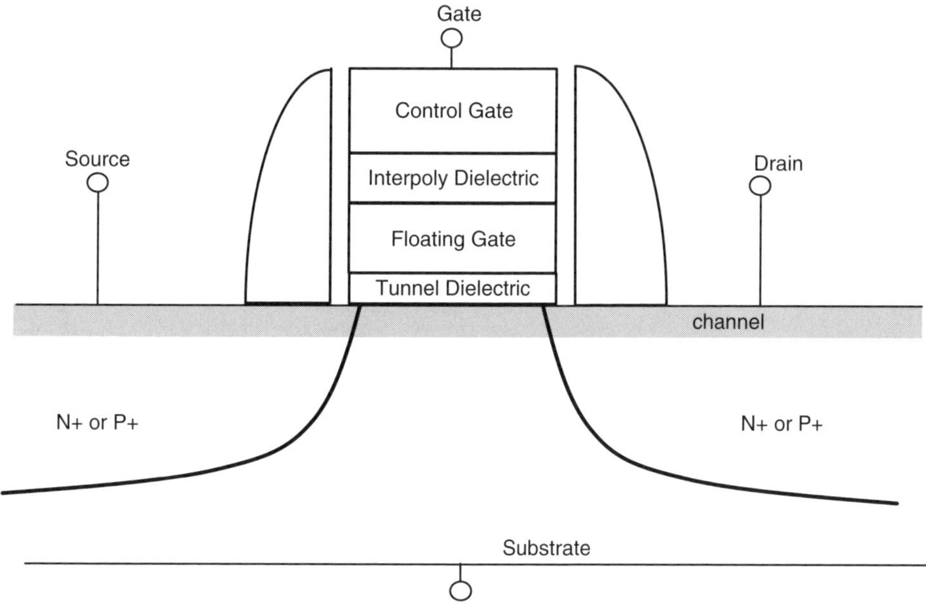

Figure 3. Schematics of floating gate transistor (first used as EPROM unit cell, then used in flash technology).

and Ground selector are connected at two ends. Only if all word lines are set high, the bit line is pulled low. NAND flash has a very small cell size that enables a low cost-per-bit of stored data. It offers higher density and lower cost per bit than NOR flash and so exhibits faster erase and write times. However, its *I/O* interface allows only sequential access to data, and thus it has been primarily utilized as a high-density mass data storage medium in consumer devices such as USB solid-state disk drives and digital still cameras, while being less useful for computer memory.

NOR flash has a full address/data (memory) interface that allows random access to any location. Due to its relatively long erase and write times it has typically been used for program code storage that does not require updating frequently, such as computer's BIOS or the firmware of set-top boxes in PDAs and mobile phones, etc. NOR-based flash was the basis of early flash-based removable media. Compact flash cards were originally based on it, although this application moved to the cheaper NAND flash option later on.

Recent development work opened an opportunity for NAND to become an alternative for some traditional NOR-based applications (in order to benefit from the above described advantages for NAND) as well as for combinations of NAND and NOR for today's full-featured smart phones that incorporate cameras, music, video, gaming, internet, and other functionalities.

A comparison of some key parameters of conventional single Level Cell (SLC) NOR versus NAND is given in Refs. [20, 21] as well as in Table 1.

In industrial devices, flash memory has been widely used in the following areas: security and military systems, embedded computers, solid-state disk drives, networking and communication products, wireless communication devices, retail management products (e.g., handheld scanners), and medical apparatus, etc.

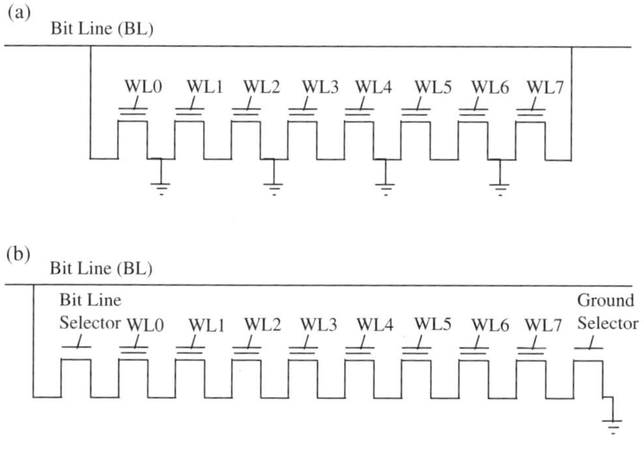

Figure 4. Simple wiring circuitry based on floating gate transistors (a) NOR; (b) NAND.

3. NOVEL NVM TECHNOLOGIES IN PRODUCTION

Currently, innovative non-volatile memory technologies with faster programming speeds, lower programming voltages, and much longer endurance still remain a goal of ongoing research and development. Alternatives that have been explored include ferroelectric memories where the polarization state of a ferroelectric capacitor can be switched and sensed (FRAM) [22, 23], thin film magnetic memories where the giant magneto-resistive effect or magnetic tunnel junctions can be used to store and sense non-volatile data (MRAM) [24], and ovonic unified memories (OUM, also called phase change memories (PCM)) where the resistance of a chalcogenide glass layer in series with a transistor can be switched and sensed [25]. Resistive switching random access memories (RRAM) is another popular emerging

Table 1. NOR versus NAND comparison.

Parameter	Conventional SLC NOR	Conventional SLC NAND
Capacity	16 Mb–2 GB	512 Mb–32 GB
XIP (code execution)	Easy	Hard
Performance erase	Very slow	Fast
Write	Slow	Fast
Read	Fast	Fast
Life span	Only 10% of NAND	10 times longer than NOR
Erase cycle range	10,000 to 100,000	10 times higher than NOR
Interface	Full memory interface	*I/O* mapped only, indirect access
Access method	Random access	Sequential
Standby power	Low	Medium low
Active power	Medium high	Low
Hardware easy-of-use	Easy	Complicated
Full system integration (hardware and software)	Easy	Hard, simplistic driver may be ported
Cost-per-bit	High	Very low
Application	Code storage; limited data storage; eXcuteInPlace	Program/data mass storage
Comments		DiskOnChip(NAND/MLC NAND-based) have pros of NAND and NOR for both code and data storage application

memory technology that utilizes electro- or thermochemical effects to induce resistive switching (RS) [26]. RRAM and STTRAM technology will be discussed in more detail in Sections 4 and 5.

3.1. Ferroelectric RAM (FeRAM or FRAM)

FeRAM or FRAM is a random access memory similar to conventional DRAM but uses a remanent polarization of a ferroelectric layer to achieve non-volatile functionality while volatile data storage relies on charging/discharging a dielectric layer. Among these innovative memory types, FRAM has by far the longest development history, yet so far it gained only fractions of a percent in semiconductor market share. Beginning in the 1950s, serious attempts were made to develop digital memories from ferroelectrics, particularly in bulk film form. A fabrication method and experimental results from metal/ferroelectric/Si (MFS) transistors were first reported by Wu in 1974 [27], although with major problems reported due to carrier injection at the interface, materials intermixing, and interface traps. Between 1975 to 1985 several high-quality thin film deposition techniques were developed, such as sputtering, sol–gel, and MOD (metal-organic deposition) methods [28], which stimulated the birth of the first integrated ferroelectric memory device in 1988: a 1T/1C (1 transistor/1 capacitor) 256 bit device using sol–gel $Pb(Zr,Ti)O_3$ (PZT)] [29]. The first 256 kb ferroelectric non-volatile memory 1T/1C cell with 100 ns r/w time at an operating voltage of 3 V, fabricated with MOD spin-on $SrBi_2Ta_2O_9$ (SBT) capacitor followed in 1994 [30]. Especially through the 1990s and in early 2000 research in FRAM had been actively conducted by Ramtron, Toshiba, Fujitsu, Hitachi, Texas Instruments, and Infineon, among others. At present, capacitor structure-based FRAM devices with capacities up to 256 Mbit have been developed and planning to be mass-produced by Fujitsu and OKI.

Limited write-erase cycles ($\sim 10^6$) and the need for high voltage (power) are drawbacks of flash and EEPROM, while FRAMs offer significant improvements regarding both problems. For example, endurance over as many as 10^{16} write-erase cycles has been reported for 3.3 V devices. Disadvantages for FeRAM are, on the other hand, much lower storage densities than flash devices, storage capacity limitations, and higher cost. These shortcomings have been a major set-back for FRAM market growth and further FRAM related development work.

Compared to conventional semiconductor memories, FRAM makes use of rather "exotic" materials for the purpose of storing information, i.e., ferroelectric crystals. Such crystals are unusual in having an atom (or more than one atom) in each unit cell that can occupy one of two energy states, both of which are stable. These two energy states of the ferroelectric crystal exhibit opposite electric polarizations and can be switched by the application of a voltage of appropriate polarity and magnitude. The bi-stable property of the crystals enables them to represent digital "1" and "0" by means of these two energy states. The conventional FRAM cell structure is composed of a ferroelectric MFM (metal-ferro-metal) capacitor for data storage and a MOSFET (metal-oxide-semiconductor field effect transistor) for cell selection, as shown in Figure 5. This configuration is often referred to as a 1T-1C (1 transistor-1 capacitor) cell structure. It is quite similar to the 1T-1C DRAM cell described earlier, except that the capacitor is made of ferroelectric materials exhibiting a memory hysteresis effect. Depending on the data on the bit line (BL), the data will be stored in state "0" or "1". The read operation is performed through the word line (WL), which selects the cell to be read, and the data line (DL), which reveals if the data is "1" or "0". The readout operation of the 1T-1C cell is destructive. To preserve the stored value read, the sense amplifier on the bit line detects the read signal, and then writes the original state back into the cell. This is equivalent to the "refresh" operation performed on DRAM cells.

An 1-transistor memory cell based on a metal-ferro-electric-insulator-semiconductor FET structure (or MFIS-FET) (see Fig. 6(a)) does not require a storage capacitor

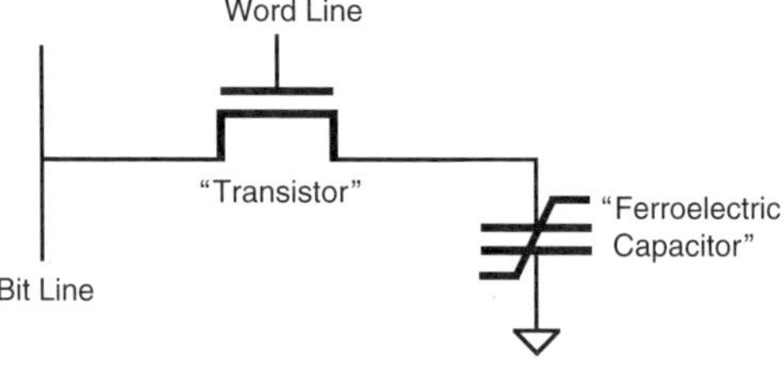

Figure 5. A schematic representation of the basic 1 transistor/1 capacitor FRAM cell.

and hence offers much higher memory density than the 1T-1C cell described above. It utilizes the remnant polarization of a ferroelectric thin film to modulate the conduction states of a channel on a Si substrate between the source and drain. Another device alternative, operating similar to a floating gate transistor, is a MFMISFET structure, as shown in Figure 6(b).

Figure 7 shows the basic operation principle of 1-T FeRAM. To program the memory cell, one applies a gate pulse of appropriate polarity and amplitude. As shown in the top left inset figure, a positive gate pulse will cause an upward polarization of the ferroelectric film, which in turn causes the transistor channel to be inverted and the transistor to be turned on. This corresponds to the memory state "1". Similarly, as shown in the top right inset figure, a negative gate pulse will cause a downward polarization of the ferroelectric film, which in turn causes the transistor channel to be depleted and the transistor to be turned off. This corresponds to the memory state "0". To read out the stored data, a zero gate voltage is applied, and the drain current I_d will be relatively large if a "1" state is stored, while I_d will be very small or nearly zero if a "0" state is stored.

It is highly desirable in principle to build a non-volatile memory device based on this single-FET structure to serve both as the storage element and its sensing device with a non-destructive readout operation. In practice, however, many challenges have held back progress towards this goal for nearly three decades ever since Wu first reported the experimental results on the use of ferroelectric-gate FET as a non-volatile memory device [27]. In particular, the grossly insufficient retention time has kept MFISFET from qualifying as a non-volatile memory device. Despite the efforts of many researchers over several decades, the longest retention times reported in the literature are only a few hours to a few days [31]. The maximum reported retention time was 30 days [32], which is still far from the 10-year retention requirement for current non-volatile semiconductor memory products. Retention times for MFMISFET structures are longer by comparison, but also still far below the required values. Therefore few commercial non-volatile FET-type FeRAM products have been made available so far, explaining why FeRAM production amounts only to a very small portion of the total semiconductor market.

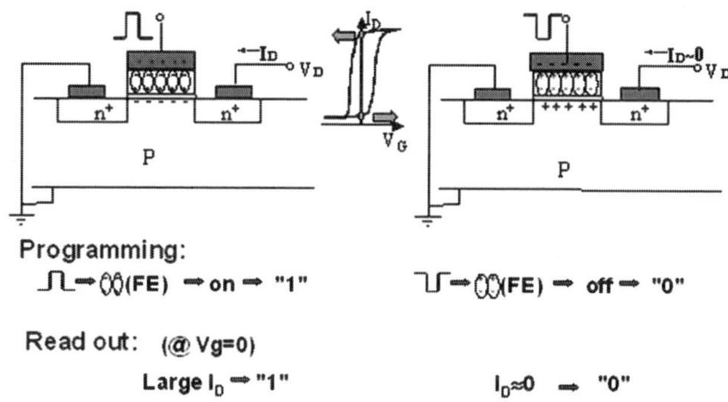

Figure 7. Operation principle of the basic 1 transistor FeRAM cell based on MFISFET.

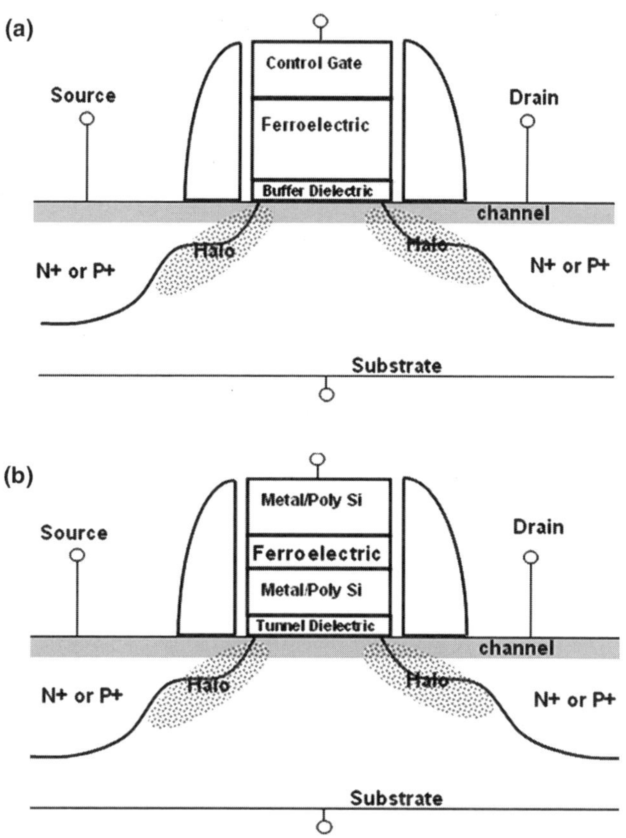

Figure 6. A schematic representation of the basic 1 transistor FeRAM cell based on (a) MFISFET, (b) MFMISFET structure.

Although not qualified as a non-volatile memory device, the MFISFET structure is nevertheless very attractive as a DRAM cell, the FEDRAM (FErroelectric DRAM) cell [33, 34]. A refresh operation is provided from time to time to restore the memory, which may be fading with time because of the finite retention time [35].

3.2. Phase-Change Memory (PCM)

PCM, also known as ovonic unified memory, is a type of non-volatile memory that utilizes chalcogenide materials that can be "switched" between two states, crystalline and amorphous, after electric current induced heat is applied. The semiconducting behavior of chalcogenide glasses was first described by Kolomiets and Gorunova in 1955 [36]. However, the first patent for an application to utilize the phase-change properties was filed one decade later by Ovshinsky [37, 38]. A phase-change memory device was described in a Ph.D. thesis by Sie in 1969 [39]. Both works demonstrated the feasibility of integrating a chalcogenide film with a diode array as a phase change memory device. Although Ovshinsky claimed the first reliably operating PCM device, various issues mostly related to material quality and power consumption held back successful commercialization of the technology for a few decades that followed. After a long gap of almost 30 years, Ovonyx, Inc. was formed in 1999 to commercialize PCM technology. A year later, both Intel and STMicroelectronics licensed technology from Ovonyx. Between 2003 and 2005, patents related to PCM devices where filed by a large number of technology companies including Elpida, Hitachi, Infineon, Macronix, Matsushita, Mitsubishi, Remesas, and Sony. Towards the end of this period, the first successful PCM technology implementations were announced, namely 64 [40], 256 [41], and 512 megabit [42] devices by Samsung (in 2004, 2005, and 2006, respectively). In 2008, Intel and STMicroelectronics began to provide samples of four-state multi-level PCMs to their customers [43]. Intel also demonstrated the cross-point PCM [44]. In December 2009, Numonyx announced a device with 1 gigabit capacity [45]. In 2010, Samsung shipped a 65-nm version of its 512 megabit PCM device as NOR replacement for mobile phones [46]. The storage density of 512 megabit PCM chips offered by Samsung remained significantly smaller than those of contemporary flash devices exhibiting overall capacities as high as 64 gigabit, but it was superior to other technologies aiming to replace flash, such as MRAM or FRAM, which could offer much lower capacities.

Chalcogenide alloy materials [47] contain one or more elements from Group VI of the periodic table, while the Group VI elements form predominantly twofold-coordinated covalent chemical bonds that can produce linear, tangled, polymer-like clusters in the melt. This increases the viscosity of the liquid inhibiting the atomic motion necessary for crystallization. The chalcogenide material that has been most thoroughly investigated for memory applications is an alloy of germanium (Ge), antimony (Sb), and tellurium (Te). The acronym of the material is GST. The stoichiometry of the elements in the alloy is 2Ge, 2Sb, 5Te. GST loses its crystallinity when heated above its melting point (about 600°C). When cooled down from temperatures above the melting point, GST settles into an amorphous state that is characterized by a high electrical resistance. A schematic diagram of two PCM memory cells is shown in Figure 8. The amorphous state has a high resistance state that is typically taken to represent a binary "0", whereas the crystalline state has a low resistance and is used to represent a binary "1". The switching frequency of a memory device based on GST is limited by the time required to complete this phase transition, which in turn depends on temperature. The cooler the material, the longer it takes to crystallize as shown in Figure 9(a). GST crystallization times are commonly around 50–100 ns [48], which is longer than a few nanoseconds switching times of current conventional DRAM. Switching times being less than 20 ns or even as short as 5 ns [49] have been reported.

Besides the amorphous and crystalline states described above, two distinct, partially crystalline states have been demonstrated in chalcogenide materials. As a result, four different material phases, each distinguishable by its electrical properties, can be utilized for PCM devices. Four states allow for the coding of two bits in a single memory cell and hence a doubling of memory density.

The amorphous phase of chalcogenide alloy has a high electrical resistance at low electric fields, as seen in Figure 9(b) [50]. With increasing voltage, conductivity is initially ohmic, then starts to grow exponentially [51]. When a threshold voltage V_{th} is exceeded, the material switches rapidly into a highly conductive "dynamic" ON state. The dynamic ON state stays as long as a enough holding current passes through the device. The device can then be programmed to the RESET state by applying a shorter but larger current pulse to a bit in the polycrystalline state in order to melt the programmed volume of chalcogenide alloy and to have a fast enough falling edge to permit the molten programmed volume of material to cool

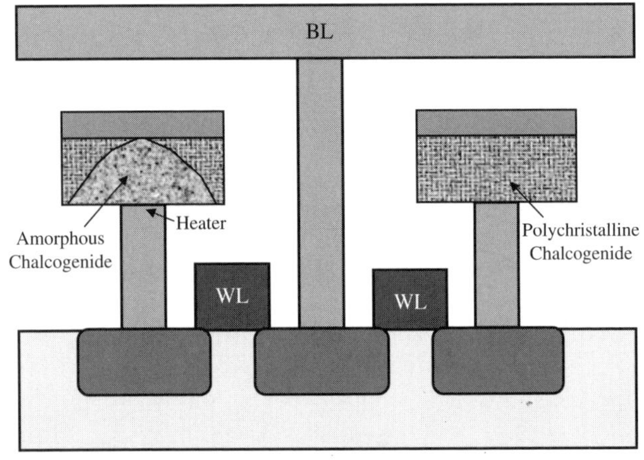

Figure 8. Schematic diagram of two PCM memory cells in a low resistance crystalline state and in a high resistance amorphous state.

(a)

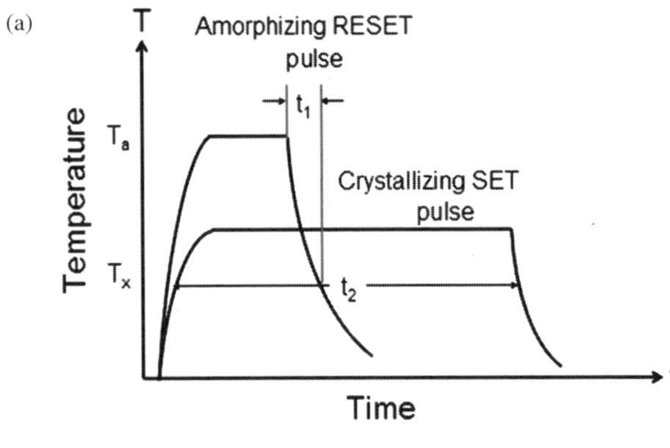

(b)

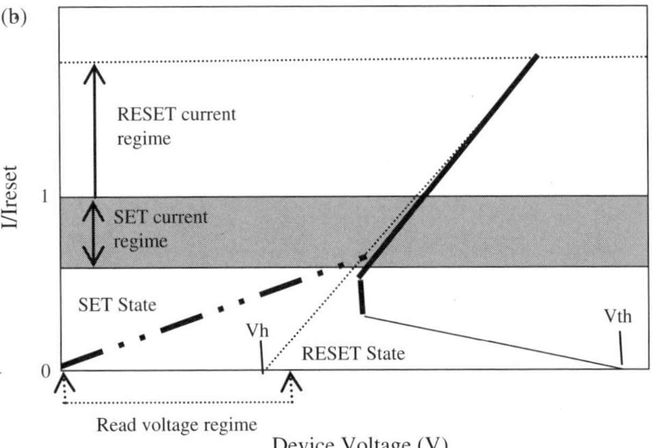

Figure 9. (a) Schematic temperature-time relationship during programming in a PCM device. (b) Current–voltage characteristics for a PCM cell element in both the RESET (amorphous, high-resistance) and SET (crystalline, low-resistance) states.
Notes: T_a: amorphization, and T_x: crystallization temperatures; V_h: holding voltage, and V_{th}: switching threshold voltage.

fast enough to vitrify [52]. Threshold switching has been explained [53] in terms of electric-field-induced filling of the charged valence alternation pair traps, which alters the recombination kinetics.

PCM offers a range of potential advantages over flash memory devices, but some serious drawbacks must be resolved.

A potential advantage for PCM devices is that write cycles being several orders of magnitude above the limit for flash memories can be achieved. The high voltages that are required to program a flash device cause degradation with every write cycle, while the device degradation in PCM are related to physical mechanisms of GST such as thermal expansion during programming, material (in particular metal) migration, and unknown processes. The data stored in a PCM device is much more stable than that in a flash memory one. Flash devices suffer from charge leakage that corrupts the stored data over time, while it has been estimated that a PCM memory could retain its data for much longer time than flash at an operating temperature of 85°C [54]. The higher stability of PCM devices also extends to radiation resistance, but the electron charges trapped in the gate of a flash device are susceptible to radiation exposure. PCM devices, on the other hand, have the potential to meet higher radiation specifications.

Sensitivity to high temperatures limits PCM to be integrated only in a mild temperature BEOL process, while high soldering temperatures are potential source for damaging the devices. Programming the memory cells of PCM devices requires high current densities ($> 10^7$ A/cm^2) inside the phase-change material. In order to achieve these densities, device designs have shrunk the active areas to sizes that are much smaller than those of the driving transistors. As a result, the heater and sometimes even the phase-change material itself have to be packaged in sub-lithographic dimensions. The costs associated with these measures are disadvantages of PCM devices compared to flash technology.

Probably the biggest challenge for phase change memory is its long-term resistance and threshold voltage drift [55]. The resistance of the amorphous state slowly increases, following a power law. This severely limits the ability for multilevel operation (a lower intermediate state would be confused with a higher intermediate state at a later time) and could also jeopardize standard two-state operation if the threshold voltage increases beyond the design value.

3.3. Conventional Magnetic Field-Induced MRAM

The development of anisotropic magnetoresistive (AMR) thin films [56] in 1971, the discovery of giant magnetoresistance (GMR) in 1988 [57, 58] (awarded a Nobel Prize in 2007), and the development of magnetic tunnel junctions (MTJs) [59, 60] in the early 1990s opened different technical avenues to create magnetoresistivity, thereby boosting ideas for a new NMV concept, namely magnetoresistive random access memory (MRAM) technology. MRAM devices utilize magnetic field/current induced changes of the magnetization direction in a magnetic layer in order to store information while an accompanying change in magnetoresistivity is used for the information readout.

The operation margin of MRAMs is driven by the total signal change expressed by the magnetoresistance ratio, MR, which is the change in resistance divided by the minimum resistance. Due to their distinct advantage regarding MR, as discussed below, MTJ-based MRAMs have become the favored technology path, rather than avenues using AMR or GMR materials. The fact that resistance values of MTJs can be adjusted to the kΩ range in order to allow easy impedance matching with CMOS transistors (preferably used as selection components in MRAMs)—while this is not the case for GMR films with their much lower resistance in the 10^{-2} to 10^{-1} Ω range—favors also the usage of MTJs.

The first publications on MTJ-based MRAMs appeared around the turn of the century [61, 62]. Figure 10 shows a simplified schematic drawing of the architecture of a conventional MRAM cell and the corresponding read and write mechanisms. The MTJ, being the "heart" of the MRAM cell, consists of two ferromagnetic (FM) layers separated by an insulator layer of ultra-thin thickness allowing tunneling of electrons through the barrier if a bias voltage is applied between two metal electrodes in contact with the upper and lower ferromagnetic layers. The tunneling current is influenced by the relative orientation of magnetization in the two FM plates. More electrons will tunnel through the barrier if the magnetizations of the FM layers are in parallel orientation, corresponding to a state of lower magnetoresistance. Higher magnetoresistance of the MTJ, on the other hand, is established in case of anti-parallel magnetic orientation of the FM layers.[a]

The tunnel barrier must be very thin (< 2 nm) in order to arrive at a suitable resistance value because the tunnel resistance depends exponentially on the barrier thickness, it must be free of pinholes and its thickness must be highly uniform [63].

The tunnel magnetoresistance ratio, TMR, defined in a similar manner to MR, is as follows:

$$\text{TMR} = (R_{\text{ap}} - R_p)/R_p$$

where R_{ap} is the electrical resistance in anti-parallel state, and R_{p} is the electrical resistance in parallel state. TMR depends on the material choices for the FM layers as well as barrier and can be improved by processing optimizations of the materials involved. Moreover it increases with lower temperature and lower bias voltage.

Amorphous aluminum oxide was the first material used as MTJ barrier. Co–Fe, Co–Ni, and Ni–Fe alloys, frequently

[a] Tunnel magnetoresistance is related to spin polarizations of the ferromagnetic layers. In first approximation it can be understood based on a two-band model in which the *d*-band on both electrode sides is split up into a band for spin-up electrons (i.e., electrons with spin orientation parallel to the external magnetic field) and a band for spin-down electrons. If the two FM layers are in parallel magnetic alignment to each other, then electron tunneling across the barrier occurs from majority-band to majority-band and from minority-band to minority-band. On the other hand, in case of anti-parallel FM alignment, majority/minority band electrons are forced to migrate into the minority/majority band of the opposing electrode. The comparatively lower number of states available for tunneling between FM layers in anti-parallel alignment causes the observed increase in tunneling resistance.

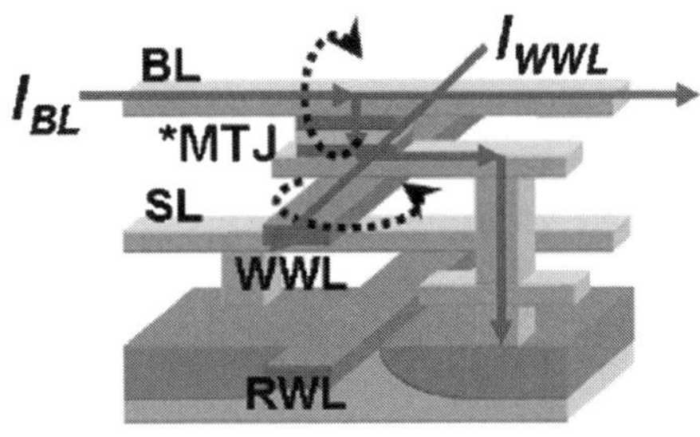

Figure 10. Conventional MRAM cell operating via FIMS. Note: schematic views of cell architecture. Reprinted with permission from [243], International Technology Roadmap for Semiconductors, Semiconductor Industry Asso., 2010 Ed., available online at www.itrs.net/reports.html. © 2010, International SEMATECH, Austin, USA.

with additives (e.g., Pt, Cr, Ta, Nb, Tb, B, O) to adjust the magnetic properties, are possible material choices for the ferromagnetic layers employed in MRAM MTJs. TMR values in the 20–50% range could be obtained in case of optimized AlO_x thickness and optimized oxidation conditions. In combination with CoFeB as FM layer, TMR signals could be further raised up to 70% [64]. More recently (2004), a shift to crystalline MgO as tunnel barrier material [65, 66] occurred, which brought along a further drastic increase of TMR to $\geq 200\%$, with record values around 400–600% (e.g., for bccCo/MgO/bcc Co [67]). The improvement with crystalline MgO barriers relies on the filtering of tunnel electrons according to the symmetry of their wave functions, as predicted by theoretical work [68]. This drastic step-by-step (T)MR improvement in comparison to MR values of around 2% obtained with initially using AMR films or about 20% for weakly coupled GMR films with 2–3 magnetic layers explains why the MTJ approach is favored for MRAM devices.

The magnetic orientation of one of the ferromagnetic (FM) layers in the MTJ, termed the reference layer or "pinned" layer, is fixed (pinned), generally by direct exchange coupling (see e.g., Ref. [69]) with an adjacent antiferromagnetic (AF) layer consisting, for example, of FeMn, PtMn, or IrMn. The magnetization direction of the other non-pinned FM layer, the so-called "free layer," remains changeable.

High density MRAM architecture can be achieved by organizing dense MRAM arrays in grids of orthogonally aligned conducting lines, with an individual bit being positioned in the intersection of a particular line-column pair. Selectivity is provided by a transistor or a diode in series with the MTJ. Transistor application is the preferred choice since transistors can provide higher current saturation for the same cell size. The maximum cell current change (read margin) is obtainable if the current through the bit is limited by the MTJ resistance and not by the transistor saturation current. Alternative MRAM architectures without transistor or diode elements have been proposed [70, 71], which suffer, however, from drawbacks of higher design complexity or higher area demand for readout circuitry.

To read an individual MRAM bit, the corresponding selection transistor allows current flow through the addressed MTJ, which is used for the measurement of its resistance in comparison to a reference value that has been set between the high (R_{high}) and low (R_{low}) resistance of the MTJ. This allows determining whether the magnetic orientation of the free layer is in parallel or in antiparallel alignment to that of the pinned layer. The dispersion for both R_{high} and R_{low} have to be minimized to ensure the required read margin. Read access time as well as RC time constant are determined by the bit resistance (with typical values around 10 kΩ), allowing ns access times [72, 73]. Typical read voltages are around 300 mV.

Writing of cells, i.e., setting of the orientation of the magnetization of the free layer, has been achieved in the first generation of MRAM devices by a method based on the Stoner-Wohlfarth model [74] of coherent magnetization rotation in single domain particles. The easy axis field, H_e, necessary to reverse magnetization is reduced by applying simultaneously a second field, H_h, aligned perpendicularly along the hard axis. Selective switching of one individual bit can occur for H_e and H_h fields, which lie inside an asteroid defined by the equation:

$$H_e^{2/3} + H_h^{2/3} \geq (2\ K/M_s)^{2/3}$$

with K being the effective anisotropy constant (accounting for crystalline and shape anisotropies) and M_s, the saturation magnetization.

Coherent reversal is achievable within a few ns (3–7 ns). In the ideal case only the bit under the cross-point of the pair of orthogonally aligned write lines through which currents are passed should be affected. However, the bits adjacent to the target bit see about half of the threshold magnetic field. The risk for false writes in the vicinity of the targeted cell increases with shrinking device size. This so-called "half-select" issue establishes a severe scaling obstacle for the Stoner-Wohlfarth writing approach, excluding its application beyond 90 nm. Moreover a high sensitivity of the switching field to shape variations, edge roughness, and material anisotropy render it difficult to find field values suitable for large bit arrays. Last but not least, current pulses of several mA are required to achieve the necessary magnetic field values of 50 Oe in MTJs. Estimates indicate that with shrinking cross-section of the conduction lines the current density would eventually surpass the electromigration limit (around 10^6 A/cm^2), creating another obstacle for aggressive device scaling.

Various solution attempts with partial success were made in the period from 1998–2005 to resolve the narrow operating window observed in the case of Stoner-Wohlfarth writing [75] which included the application of special bit shapes [76, 77], the reduction of vortex formation to alleviate demagnetization effects along the storage layer edges [78], or the use of synthetic ferromagnetic (SF) storage layers (two ferromagnetic layers coupled antiferromagnetically by a Ru spacer) in order to increase single domain character and to lower the sensitivity to shape anisotropy [79, 80]. In spite of these short-comings, at least one commercial product based on this concept has made it to the market, namely a 4 Mb MRAM fabricated by Freelance since 2006.

In order to avoid the half-select issue, the Stoner-Wohlfarth scheme was eventually replaced by the Toggle concept (analyzed in detail in Refs. [81, 82]), involving a new writing approach proposed by Savchenko et al. [83]. This new approach offered a significantly wider write operation margin at the expense of higher power requirements. A schematic representation of a toggle cell and the layout of its programming (write) lines are shown in Figure 11.

The free layer of a conventional toggle cell consists of a synthetic antiferromagnetic (SAF) tri-layer stack comprising 2 ferromagnetic layers separated by an antiferromagnetic coupling (AFC) Ru layer, which maintains their antiparallel alignment to each other. The easy axis of a cell is aligned mid-angle (45°) between the directions of bit line and word lines, aligned orthogonally to each other. Consequently, a magnetic field emanating from only one program line cannot induce switching of the bit under program conditions. The dependencies of the operating window on current field and AFC strength [84] are depicted schematically in Figures 12(a and b). The writing point is set between the spin-flop field and the saturation field, taking into account their distributions (as indicated by "6σ" in Figure 12(a)). A 4-step sequence of current pulses through two program lines (PL1 and PL2), as shown schematically in Figure 13 toggles the free layer between the two magnetization states.

Prototypes of 4 Mbit toggle MRAM cells were fabricated in 2003–2004 [85, 86]. In 2005, integration of a 1T1MTJ (1 transistor/1 MTJ) 90 nm toggle cell (with 0.29 μm^2 cell size) module into a 90 nm CMOS process flow was successfully demonstrated [87], indicating scalability to 90 nm technology. The MRAM module insertion did not have any detrimental effects on the performance of transistor gates and the backend with low-k dielectrics. The Cu interconnects were covered with highly permeable magnetic materials (so-called "cladding" layers) in order to increase the local effective fields. The field on the back of the current line aligns the magnetization of the cladding layer, generating a stray field which strengthens the effective field on one side of the current line while it weakens the field on the opposite side. Cladding is most effective when the sidewalls and the bottom of the conducting lines are covered. Under optimum conditions doubling of the effective field strength due to cladding has been achieved. The power requirement for MRAM operation could be reduced by thinning the barrier

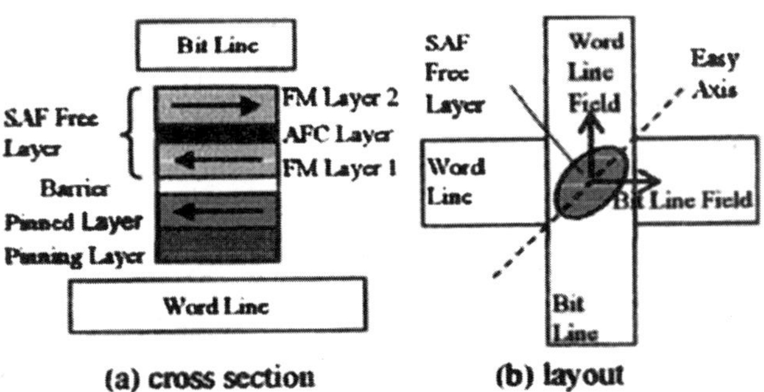

Figure 11. Schematics of toggle MRAM cell architecture and layout. (a) Cross-section of toggle MRAM cell (b) 45° orientation of magnetic bit with respect to programming lines. Reprinted with permission from [84], T. Suzuki et al., "VLSI Tech. Dig.," p. 188, 2005. © 2005, IEEE.

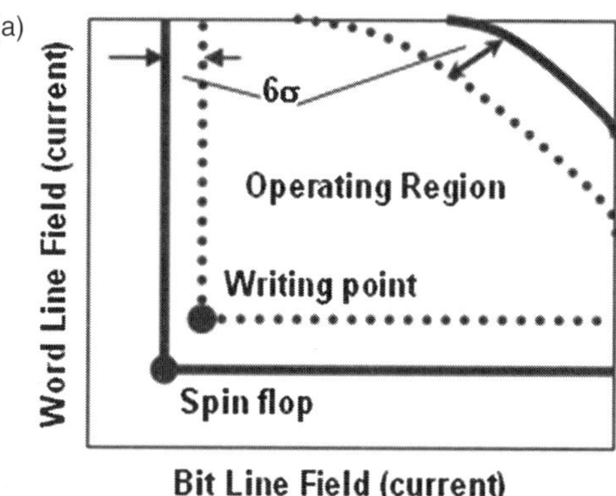

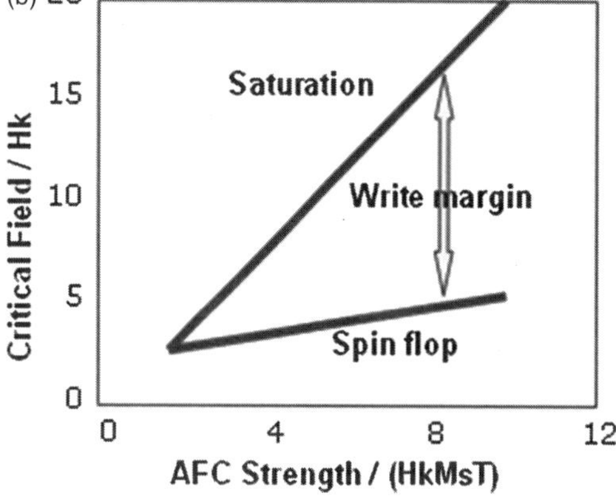

Figure 12. Dependencies of operation window of toggle cell. (a) On program current fields and (b) on AFC strength. Reprinted with permission from [84], T. Suzuki et al., "VLSI Tech. Dig.," p. 188, 2005. (Redrawn) © 2005, IEEE.

thickness, thus lowering the resistance x area product (RA) of the barrier to 1 Ω μm^2 [86].

A major issue for further scaling of the MRAM toggle concept turned out to be the reduction of the writing current without drawbacks in write margin and thermal stability. A decrease in AFC strength will lower the write current requirement but such an approach seems questionable for further scaling because the concomitant decreases in saturation magnetization compromises the available write margin [88], as shown in Figure 3(b). An innovative MRAM toggle cell stack concept incorporating 4 (rather than 2) antiferromagnetically coupled ferromagnetic layers [84] promised a larger write margin, better thermal stability, and a potential reduction of the switching current by a factor of 2. All in all, at the penalty of higher switching energies, advanced toggle cell approaches seemed to offer improved scalability by 1–2 nodes as compared to the Stoner-Wohlfarth scheme, however, not beyond 65 nm.

Toggle-mode MRAM chips with 4 Mbit density and a cell size of 1.26 μm^2 were available on the market in 2006. By 2010, 16M MRAM devices with access times around 35 ns, MRAMs with emphasis on high speed (200–250 MHz range) and low supply voltage (1.8 V) capability for interfacing with next-generation logic controllers, MRAMs for aerospacial applications, as well as first embedded MRAM products were being manufactured. In June 2010 Menta and LIRMM (both from Montpellier, France) announced

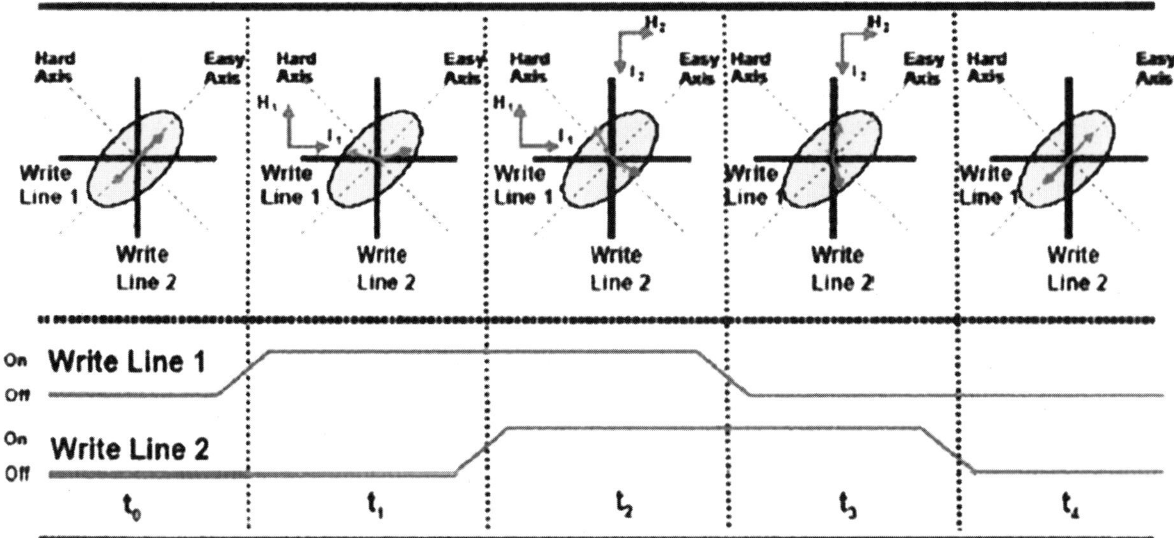

Figure 13. Four-step sequence of toggle cell switching special sequence of current pulses through write line 1 and write line 2 rotates magnetic bit by 180° to opposite magnetization. Reprinted with permission from [94], I. L. Prejbeanu et al., *J. Phys.: Condens. Matter* 19, 165218 (2007). © 2007, Elsevier.

the tape-out of the world's first MRAM-based field programmable gate array (FPGA). A few million MRAM chips were sold in 2011, with demand increasing. The fabrication of conventional MRAM devices based on 65 nm technology is expected to start in 2012, but subsequent nodes will definitely be dominated by STT technology (see Section 4.2).

4. EMERGING NVM TECHNOLOGIES—MRAM INNOVATIONS

4.1. Thermally Assisted MRAM

Avoidance of thermally activated bit switching to ensure good data retention as well as lowering of the power consumption remained tough challenges for conventional MRAM scaling. The thermal stability of MRAM devices is quantified by the dimensionless ratio (α) of the energy barrier (E_b) between two stable magnetic configuration versus the thermal energy capable to induce bit switching. Until recently $\alpha \geq 65$ [39, 89] had been a commonly accepted requirement to guarantee the industry standard of 10-year data retention, even at commercial operation temperatures up to 70°C, yet an even higher α value (≥ 75) is deemed necessary for the Gbit density regime (see also Section 4.2.2.4). Due to the linear dependence of E_b on the volume of the magnetic material in a bit, however, it has become more difficult to meet this target as MRAM cell size is scaled down. The adverse effect of reduced magnetic volume must be compensated by higher anisotropy, leading to an increase of the switching field. Thus a compromise has to be found between bit stability and write current, rendering the desired reduction in power consumption more difficult for the above described conventional MRAM concepts.

A solution that provides these needed improvements regarding write selectivity, data retention, and power consumption, came along with the arrival of a new MRAM concept, namely the thermally assisted MRAM (TA-MRAM), also called thermal select MRAM (TS-MRAM) in the literature. The first publications on demonstrations of TA-MRAMs with cell sizes of a few μm^2, requiring current pulse times as low as 10 ns, appeared in the literature in 2004 [90, 64].

The TA-MRAM approach uses the fact that the required switching field can be significantly lowered when heating the free layers of an MRAM element above or close to the magnetic ordering temperature. For MRAMs operating via field-induced switching programming of a TA-MRAM bit occurs by combination of Joule heating and magnetic reorientation under the influence of an applied magnetic field. (The TA concept is also applicable to spin-polarized current based MRAM operation, as discussed in Section 4.2). Once an open select transistor allows current to flow through the MTJ, inelastic relaxation of hot electrons can raise the temperature in the free layer within nanoseconds by 150°C and more, enabling magnetization switching during cool-down to the stand-by temperature. Material properties (thermal conductivity, specific heat) determine heat and cooling times, ranging generally from 3–5 ns for the former and from 10–20 ns for the latter. Thus total programming cycle times can be kept within 20–30 ns. Typical write conditions are: a heating voltage pulse of 2 V, 20 ns and a magnetic field of 20 Oe.

In the early 2000s, different proposals have been made as to how to make use of the basic concept of thermally assisted MRAMs. Initial design proposals [77, 92] suggested the usage of a low Curie point ferromagnetic material as the storage layer. With a heating element the free layer is heated slightly above its Curie point. During the initial cool-down phase setting of the magnetization direction occurs very rapidly at a temperature just below the Curie point under the influence of a magnetic field created by current flow through the so-called digit line. Alternative schemes employed exchange-biased storage layers. When the free layer/antiferromagnet (AF) bilayer is heated above a critical "blocking" temperature, T_b, the pinning of the free layer disappears and its magnetization can be reversed by a small magnetic field created by current through a single digit line. The design options following this line of thought differ with respect to the way the heating of the cells is achieved. For one option [92] two orthogonally aligned current lines are used to heat an individual cell and to generate the write field. Other publications and patents (e.g., [78, 79]) propose direct heating via write current flow through the MTJ. For the first mentioned approach, heating is indirect (causing higher power consumption) and dependent on heat diffusion (inducing prolonged write times). For the alternative and more favorable approach, the heat is generated locally within the tunnel magnetoresistive junctions. A junction architecture exhibiting application of exchange bias for both the free layer and the reference layer has been also developed [79]. Write scheme, hysteretic behavior, and MTJ architecture for such an advanced TA-MRAM (with exemplary material choices) are illustrated in Figure 14 [93]. In this case, the blocking temperature of the reference layer has to be significantly higher than that of the free layer, so that the thermally assisted switching in the storage layer does not affect the magnetization of the reference layer. Material choice (e.g., IrMn, PtMn, RhMn, FeMn) and fine tuning the thickness of the antiferromagnetic layers allow the desired difference in blocking temperatures to be obtained, with the write temperature being set between the two blocking temperatures, typically around 200°C. Using 5–6 nm thick IrMn for exchange biasing, $T_b s$ for free layers can be shifted into the 150–160°C range, for example, while application of 25 nm IrMn or 20 nm PtMn produce blocking temperatures of 210°C and 300°C, respectively, for reference layers. Since the exchange biased free layer exhibits higher intrinsic anisotropy, shape anisotropy can be

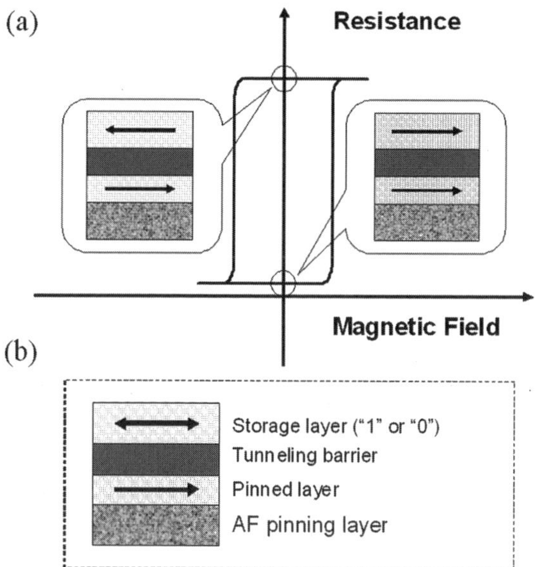

Figure 14. Schematics of thermally assisted MRAM cell operating via field induced magnetization switching (a) hysteresis loops of storage layer before and after writing (b) insert of storage area description Redrawn after [93], B. Dieny et al., *Int. J. Nanotechnol.* 591 (2010).

reduced, allowing lower bit aspect ratios, even down to 1:1. This contributes to reduction of the switching field, and consequently of power consumption. The variation of critical dimensions of circular patterns can be better controlled during lithographic patterning (and etching as well) than that of elliptical shapes.

A further contribution to lower power consumption has been made by the partial coverage of the MTJs with thermal barriers. Such barriers made of low conductivity materials (e.g., BiTe or GeSbTe with thermal conductivities of 1.5 W/mK and 0.5 W/mK, respectively [94]) help to confine the generated heat within the junctions.

The temperature rise in MTJs is determined by the achievable power density, P_d, which itself depends on pulse width (time) and write voltage. Since $P_d = (RA)\ j^2 = (V^2/RA)$—with R and A being the resistance and area of the MTJ, respectively, while j and V are the current density and the voltage drop across the junction—optimization efforts [95, 96] to maxima P_d focused on the development of barriers with low RA and high break-down voltage (since the break-down voltage limits the maximum possible voltage drop across the junction). One optimization goal is to maintain comparable write times of 3–7 ns as achieved with the Stoner-Wohlfarth (SW) approach [97]. Write current requirements (for both magnetic field and heat production) for TA-MRAMs decrease with shrinking bit length while the opposite is true in the case of SW-MRAMs. Simulations results [94], shown in Figure 15, indicate a significant difference between these two MRAM type/writing modes for bit lengths below 100 ns, with write currents needed for TA-MRAMs being lower by a factor of 20 and more. This clearly points out the much more favorable write current scaling outlook for the TA-MRAM concept.

Multi-level programming capability for the TA MRAM concept has been demonstrated by a novel MRAM architecture [98]. This architecture implemented an additional field-generating word line under the MTJ, aligned perpendicular to the bit line and parallel to the standard word line. This allows the free layer orientation to be set in 4 angular directions, corresponding to 4 different MR levels. Four equidistant resistance levels could be demonstrated for 70 nm MTJ width. With the 2-bit/cell operation offered by

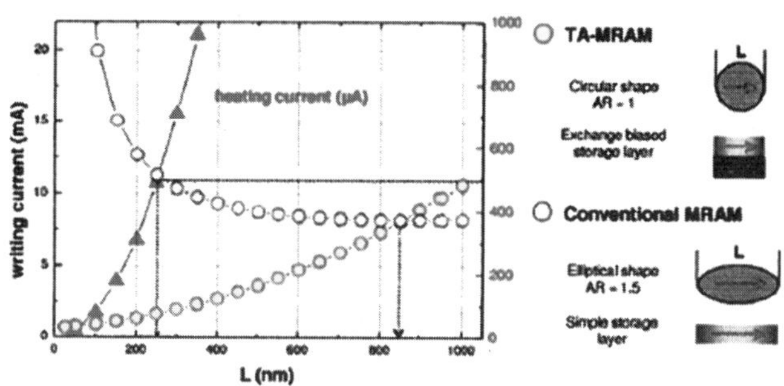

Figure 15. Simulation of write current requirements as a function of bit length (L) comparison of conventional Stoner-Wohlfarth architecture with thermally assisted (TA) MRAM architecture.

Note: Total current represents current required for 2 orthogonal write lines in SW case, and for magnetic field and cell heating in TA MRAM case. Reprinted with permission from [94], I. L. Prejbeanu et al., *J. Phys.: Condens. Matter* 19, 165218 (2007).

this advanced cell concept, a 70% increase in effective bit density could be achieved for the 65 nm technology node.

In summary, the main advantages derived from an advanced TA-MRAM involving direct heating and (double) exchange-biased SAF structures can be listed as follows:

- Selectivity is not an issue any longer because only the selected heated MTJs are written, whereas non-heated MTJs remain unaffected by the magnetic field due to the exchange bias.
- Immunity against write disturbance is very high because the stored magnetization orientation can only be erased in the simultaneous presence of magnetic field and heat.
- Exchange bias anisotropy ensures high thermal stability and satisfactory data retention behavior.
- Since only one magnetic field is required for writing, the power consumption is lower as compared to the case of Stoner-Wohlfarth writing, in spite of the necessity to heat the cell. The scalability outlook regarding power consumption is promising.

4.2. Spin-Transfer-Torque MRAM (STTRAM)

4.2.1. Spin-Torque-Transfer Basics

Utilization of spin-transfer-torque (STT), described below, allows magnetization reversal by a spin-polarized current without application of an external field. The potential of STT to induce magnetic domain-wall movement was already considered by Berger in 1978 [99] and a few years later indeed observed experimentally [100]. In 1996 both Berger [101] and Slonczewski [102] predicted independently that the current flow across a metallic multilayer (FM/non-FM barrier/FM) could produce STT strong enough to reorient the magnetization within a ferromagnetic (FM) layer. A year later Slonczewski [103] pursued an extensive patent application for possible commercial applications. Spin-transfer induced magnetization switching was first demonstrated for all-metal pillars in the late 1990s [104, 105] and eventually for MTJs [106] in 2004.

The phenomenon of STT in a tri-layer consisting of two magnetic layers separated by a non-magnetic spacer layer (non-magnetic metal or insulating tunnel barrier) can be described shortly here (more detailed explanations of the complexities of the effect may be found in Refs. [107, 108]).

When passing through the first magnetic layer, the current becomes spin-polarized as a result of spin-dependent scattering phenomena in this layer. (Spin filtering can occur either in transmission or reflection.) The spin-polarized conduction electrons then drift through the spacer layer and reach the interface to the 2nd magnetic layer. The current entering this receiving magnetic layer is subjected to further spin filtering whenever the magnetization orientation of the 2nd magnetic layer is not collinear with that of the 1st magnetic layer. In this case the spins of the transmitted electrons process incoherently around the magnetization direction of the receiving electrode. The resulting spin polarization reorientation generates an incoming flow of angular momentum which is transferred to the local magnetization of the 2nd magnetic layer and exerts a torque on it. (Magnetic excitation of the first magnetic layer by STT can be impeded by application of either a higher film thickness or exchange biasing). Using typical materials, STTRAM devices must be fabricated with lateral dimensions below 250 nm in order to ensure that the threshold for STT-excitation becomes effective at a lower current than the threshold for Oersted-field driven reorientation (correlation to device radius, r, for the latter, but to r^2 for the former).

The strength of the spin transfer torque becomes sufficient to induce magnetization reversal if a critical current density is reached. Application of the Landau–Lifshitz–Gilbert equation with consideration of all spin-transfer terms gives [93]:

$$j_{\text{crit,in-plane}} = (2e/h)(\alpha t_F/P)[(\mu_o M_s^2/2) + 2K]$$

with
e-electron charge
h-Planck constant
α-Gilbert damping
t_F-thickness of ferromagnetic layer
P-current polarization
μ_o-vacuum permeability
M_s-saturation magnetization
K-uniaxial anisotropy of the storage (free) layer

Excellent scalability is a major asset for the STTRAM approach since spacial control capability is significantly better for local currents than for local magnetic fields induced by current lines. Feasibility of cell sizes as small as 6 F^2—in particular for perpendicular STTRAM elements (discussed below)—has been predicted, as well illustrated in Figure 16 showing the schematic cross-sections of 2 adjacent STTRAMs integrated over CMOS circuitry. With the first generation of STTRAM prototype devices, the magnetization directions were aligned parallel to the substrate (in-plane STT (I-ST)) and the magnetization was fixed for the bottom electromagnetic layer (in the so-called "bottom-pinned" (BP) STTRAM). Subsequent technology advancements leading to deviations from this conventional

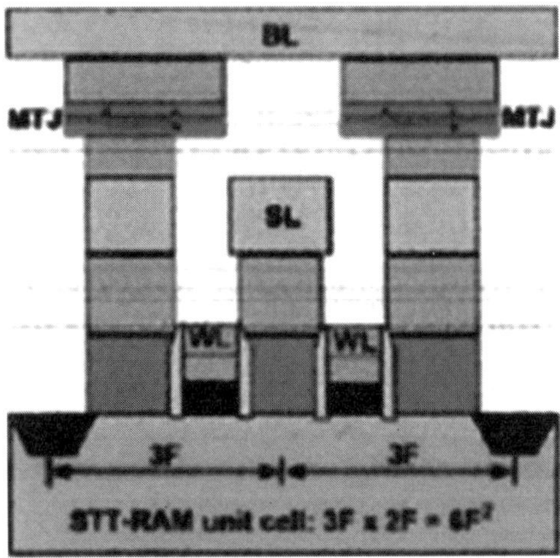

Figure 16. Schematic cross-sections of two STTRAM cells integrated with CMOS architecture (with indication for 6 F^2 capability for both I-ST and P-ST MRAM configurations). Reprinted with permission from [119], A. Driskill-Smith et al., "2010 Symp. VLSI Techn. Dig. Tech. Papers," p. 51, 2010. © 2010, IEEE.

STTRAM architecture (e.g., P-ST MRAM) will be discussed in the following paragraphs.

4.2.2. STT Technology Improvements

During the last few years, several STT technology innovations have been introduced in order to further improve the scalability of STTRAM devices and to enhance their performance by addressing critical parameters like power consumption, switching speed, internal stress in the tunnel barrier, an undesired supply current asymmetry effect, as well as thermal stability and cell-to-cell cross-talk.

4.2.2.1. Capability for Multi-Level Operation. A reduction in effective cell size has been projected for multi-level operations. First reports on the fabrication of a multi-level-cell (MLC) spin-transfer torque memory prototype with series-connected MTJs as well as of corresponding 2-step write and read techniques appeared in the literature in 2010 [109], demonstrating 4-level operation for 70 × 140 nm and 70 × 150 nm sized MTJs in series. Schematic views of the used process flow and an exemplary configuration are shown in Figures 17(a and b). The size of the lower-lying MTJs was controlled by as self-aligned technique utilizing the width of the spacer along the sidewalls of the upper-lying MTJs to determine the width of the lower-lying (wider) MTJs. The costs of the additional process steps to stack MTJs on top of each other was estimated to be attractively low, being about 5% of the costs of a 3-metal CMOS process flow for adding a 2nd MTJ level, and less than 4% for adding a 3rd level on top of the 2nd. The stack MTJ approach allows therefore a drastic reduction in costs/bit, at the expense of a moderate increase in complexity.

4.2.2.2. Reduction of Program Current and Critical Current Density. Since magnetization switching depends on a critical current density (current/area), the write current requirement scales with shrinking cell size, in contrast to the Stoner-Wohlfarth approach for which the opposite is true. A reduction in write current brings not only an obvious reduction in power consumption but further contributes to improved scalability because it reduces the size requirements for write transistors.

Efforts to gain write current reduction and high read signals have aimed at the development of MTJs with low RA, high breakdown voltage, and high TMR values [110, 111]. Furthermore, the programming current could be reduced by usage of CoFeB as ferromagnetic material [112], bringing improvement due to a reduction of the saturation magnetization, or by an increase of STT efficiency, e.g., by the incorporation of 2 pinned layers with opposite magnetization on both sides of the free layer of the MTJ stack [113]. Such an arrangement will provide additional contributions of the spin-polarized current originating from either transmission or reflection from each of the two pinned layers, irrespective of the chosen current polarity. In order to avoid the effects of the pinned layers on STT cancelling each other out, the resistance of the two spacer layers separating the free layer from the two pinned layers must be different.

Typical critical current densities for magnetization reversal, which have to be obtained at voltages below the breakdown voltage of the tunnel barrier, are in the range of 10^6–10^7 A/cm^2. A reduction of the critical current density alleviates the electrical stress in the tunnel barrier. Values close to 1×10^6 A/cm^2 could be achieved without loss in thermal stability for conventional bottom-pinned 1T1MTJ MRAMs by employment of dual barrier MTJ (DMTJ) devices [114, 115].

4.2.2.3. Alleviation of Direction Dependent Asymmetry Effect. For a conventional bottom-pinned STTRAM, the critical current density depends on the direction of switching, with $I_c(P \rightarrow AP)$ being generally 20–50% higher than $I_c(AP \rightarrow P)$. Moreover there also exists a current direction dependent asymmetry in the current supply capability of the select transistor. Corresponding Splice simulations results [116] are shown in Figure 18. For the bottom-pinned 1T1MTJ MRAM architecture this current supply asymmetry unfortunately affects the more (current) demanding $P \rightarrow PA$ switching. Two technology innovations have been proposed in the literature recently as options to meet the $I_c(P \rightarrow PA)$ current requirement more easily. Employment of a reverse-connected 1T1MTJ MRAM architecture [117], as explained in Figure 19, alleviates the asymmetry problem by shifting the "source degeneration" issue to the less critical $AP \rightarrow P$ switching. This proposed solution goes, however,

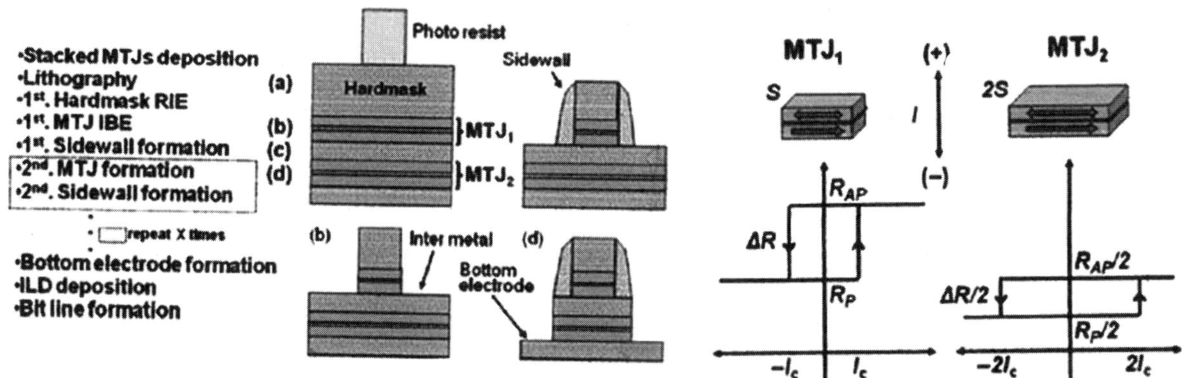

Figure 17. Process flow, schematic cross-section and MTJ configuration of STTRAM memory with series-stacked MTJs (from Ref. [59]).
Note: Example for area(MTJ1) = area(MTJ2)/2. Reprinted with permission from [109], T. Ishigaki et al., "2010 Symposium on VLSI Tech. Dig. Techn. Papers," p. 47, 2010. © 2010, IEEE.

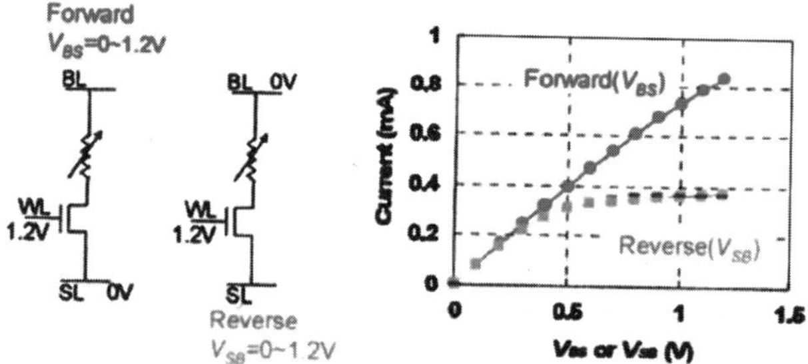

Figure 18. Spice simulations of *I–V* curves for 1T1MTJ STTRAM indicating current direction dependent asymmetry. Reprinted with permission from [116], Y. M. Lee et al., "VLSI Tech. Dig.," p. 49, 2010. © 2010, IEEE.

along with a cell area penalty due to the need for additional connection lines required for the reverse-connection of the cell.

This drawback can be avoided by an alternative approach, namely the application of a so-called "top-pinned" RAM cell architecture developed recently [116]. In a top-pinned MTJ stack the free layer is closer to the transistor than the reference layer, while the opposite is true for the conventional bottom-pinned MRAM structure. Exemplary stacks for bottom-pinned (BP) and top-pinned (TP) MTJS with corresponding material choices are depicted in Figure 20. For both stack types (BP or TP), the magnetoresistance (MR) ratio of the MTJ depends strongly on the storage layer thickness as well as on the choice of material for the metal layer adjacent to the free layer (FL) (see Fig. 21). Ru and Ta are seemingly suitable, but not Cr or Pt. For the same FL thickness MRs of TP-MTJs were found to be higher than those of BP-MTJs, due to the difference in thickness of the dead layer of the FL formed by intermixing during sputtering [118].

The experimental data from TP STTRAMs fabricated in 45 nm technology [117] indicate improved switching performance for TP MTJs when compared to BP MTJs, however, the retention characteristics of the TP STTRAM prototypes still need to be further improved. 512 bit arrays

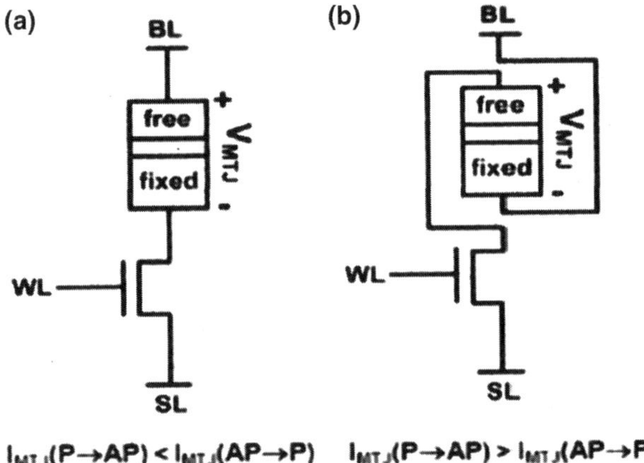

Figure 19. STTRAM architecture comparison: conventional cell (a) versus reverse-connected cell (b). Note difference in current supply behavior. Reprinted with permission from [117], C. J. Lin et al., "IEDM Techn. Dig.," p. 279, 2009. © 2009, IEEE.

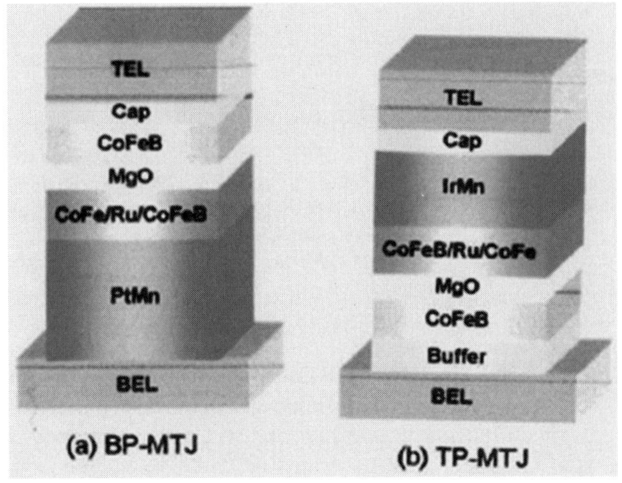

Figure 20. Schematic cross-sections of MTJ architecture alternatives (a) bottom-pinned MTJ (BP-MTJ) (b) top pinned MTJ (TP-MTJ). Reprinted with permission from [116], Y. M. Lee et al., "VLSI Tech. Dig.," p. 49, 2010. © 2010, IEEE.

of these 45 nm TP STTRAMs exhibited a 100% success rate for parallel and antiparallel states at 1 V bias, whereas even at a comparatively higher bias of 1.6 V switching to the antiparallel state failed for about 4/5 of the bits of BP STT MTJ cells.

4.2.2.4. Perpendicular STTRAM—A Major Asset. Undesired thermal activation of bits, endangering 10-year

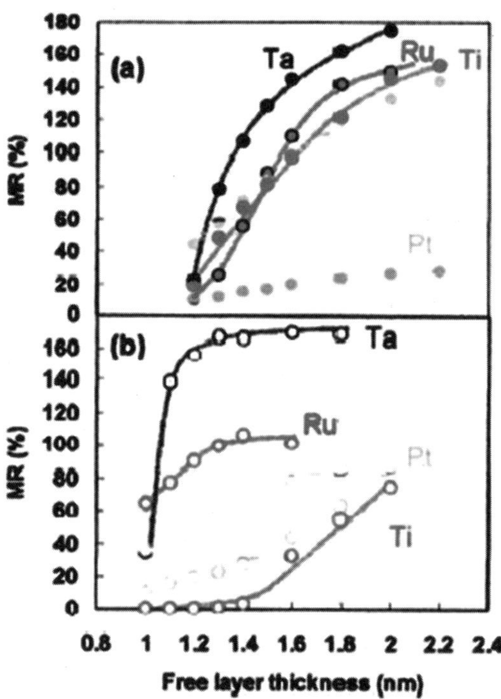

Figure 21. Magnetization ratio (MR) as a function of free layer thickness for (a) BP-MTJs and (b) BP-MTJs. Dependence on free layer thickness and choice of metal adjacent to the free layer. Reprinted with permission from [116], Y. M. Lee et al., "VLSI Tech. Dig.," p. 49, 2010. © 2010, IEEE.

data retention, remerges as critical problem once further MRAM miniaturization drives MTJ widths below 100 nm. Measurements of thermal stability of STTRAM chips by various techniques [119] revealed read disturbance rates higher than expected from STT theory, implying that for the 1 Gbit MRAM generation the thermal stability ratio Δ target will have to be raised to > 75 to ensure 10-year data retention.

The thermal activation energy (E_a) for bit switching depends on the volume (v), saturation magnetization (M_s) and magnetization anisotropy (H_k) of the MRAM storage layer as follows: $E_a = 1/2(vM_sH_k)$. A reduction in free layer volume as a result of MRAM cell size scaling will lead to an undesired decrease of E_a. This problem could potentially be alleviated by compensating increases of M_s or H_k, but such approaches face certain limitations. Material optimization to increase the uniaxial anisotropy, for example, can be hampered by an accompanying rise in Gilbert damping, necessitating an increase in write current as drawback. Several publications during 2006–2008 [120–123] point, on the other hand, to distinct benefits to be derived from the application of "perpendicular magnetization" in so-called perpendicular ST MRAM (P-ST MRAM) devices. A comparison of the I-ST and P-ST concepts is schematically drawn in Figure 22. In P-ST MRAM cells, the magnetization orientations of the storage layer and reference are aligned perpendicular to the substrate, whereas the first generation of STTRAMs exhibited magnetization directions parallel to the substrate (in-plane STT (I-ST)). The direction of the axis around which spin precession occurs is aligned parallel to the substrate for I-ST MRAMs, but perpendicular to the substrate for P-ST MRAMs. Pinning the reference layer to perpendicular magnetization orientation is achieved by covering at least the side surfaces of the reference layer (or capping it) with suitable anti-ferromagnetic material.

For a comparable shrink in cell volume from one node to the next one, the application of the P-ST concept offers the distinct advantage of allowing the use of thicker free layers with the benefits of better scalability (smaller foot-print) and improved thermal stability as compared to I-ST MRAMs. The critical switching current for P-ST MRAM operations is:

$$j_{\text{crit,perpendicular}} = (2e/h)(\alpha t_F/P)[2K_{\text{eff}}]$$

will be lower than $j_{\text{crit,in-plane}}$ (see above) for I-ST-MRAM operation, when assuming comparable K values, consequently promising an advantage regarding power consumption.

Proposals for obtaining higher perpendicular magnetic anisotropy include using $L1_0$-crystalline alloys [123] like FePt (with suitable damping constant) as FL material, or building the free layer as a multi-level stack of ultra-thin magnetic layers, e.g., 5 × Co/Ni [121]. The latter approach delivers very high surface-induced perpendicular anisotropy with an effective H_k around 5 kOe, whereas the shape anisotropy in the storage layers of I-ST MRAM cells produces much lower H_k values in the range of 0.5–1.5 kOe. Simulation results for the MTJ widths below 100 nm [122] indicate scalability advantages with respect to data retention as well as switching current requirement, as shown in Figures 23 and 24. They predict that an aggressive thermal stability target corresponding to $E_a = 85\ k_bT$ can be met even for an MTJ width of 20 nm when using the P-ST concept, whereas the I-ST concepts fails already for MTD widths < 30 nm. For widths of 28 nm and 20 nm an advantage in switching current by factors of 5 (28 nm) and 3 (20 nm) has been predicted (comparison for identical E_a values, achieved by adjustment of the free layer thickness), with low write current values around 30 μA. Experimental data from a P-ST MRAM prototype [124] cell with capped perpendicular reference layer, MgO as tunnel barrier layer and an $L1_0$-alloy (proposed in Ref. [125]) as ferromagnetic material for the free layer confirmed the P-ST potential for low programming currents and fast switching times. The $L1_0$ alloy was deposited with DC magnetron sputtering at a temperature close to 400°C. By ion milling using a hardmask circular cell shapes with diameters in the range of 50–55 nm could be patterned. These P-ST MRAM devices exhibited magnetization switching at currents of about 50 μA and high speed switching times around 4 ns.

In summary, when compared to I-ST MRAM technology, the P-ST MRAM approach promises lower switching currents, better scalability due to smaller MTJ and select transistor sizes, and low magnetic cell-to-cell interaction.

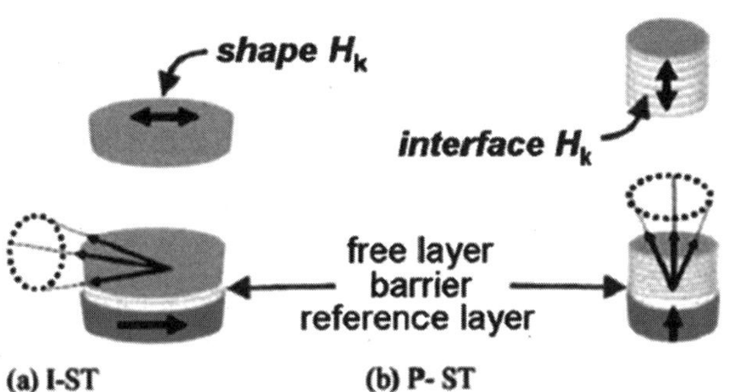

Figure 22. Comparison of in-plane (I-ST) and perpendicular-to-plane (P-ST) STT switching concept. Note dotted lines indicate magnetization precession when a writing current is applied. Reprinted with permission from [122], U. K. Klostermann et al., "IEDM Techn. Dig.," p. 187, 2007. © 2007, IEEE.

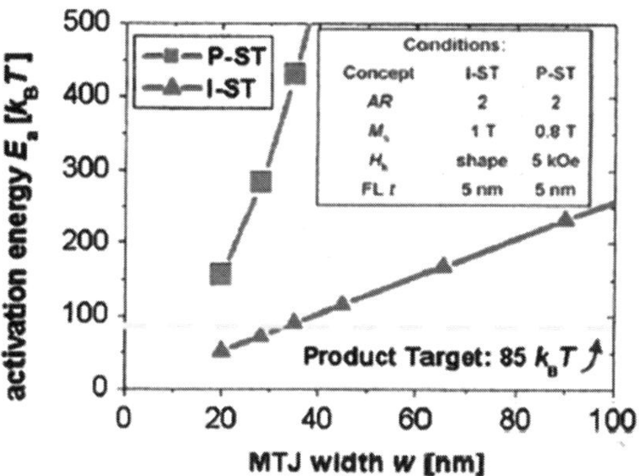

Figure 23. Simulation results regarding scalability of data retention for I-ST and P-ST MRAMs. Reprinted with permission from [122], U. K. Klostermann et al., "IEDM Techn. Dig.," p. 187, 2007. © 2007, IEEE.

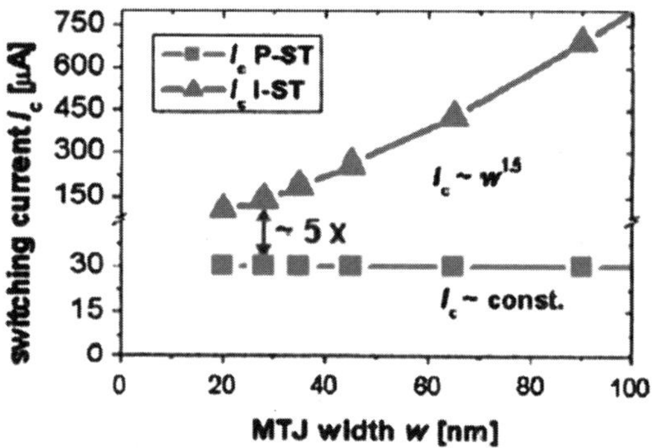

Figure 24. Simulation results regarding scalability of required write current for I-ST and P-ST MRAMs. Note free layer thickness was adjusted to match E_a. Reprinted with permission from [122], U. K. Klostermann et al., "IEDM Techn. Dig.," p. 187, 2007. © 2007, IEEE.

4.2.2.5. Combination of Thermal Assist and STTRAM Concepts. The thermal assist concept, the benefits of which had been described in Section 4.1, can be applied to either I-ST or P-ST MRAM devices. In TA-STTRAMs the current flowing through the PTJ has to carry out a double function to induce the spin-torque transfer and the heating in the cell. Therefore, the following compatibility requirement between power and current density has to be met: the critical current density for STT must result in a power density sufficient to unblock the exchange biased storage layer. Furthermore, the MTJ resistance area (RA) product must be sufficiently low ($< 10\ \Omega\ \mu m^2$) so that the STT critical current does not lead to pulse voltage exceeding the tunnel break-down voltage. Consistent magnetization reversal within 30 ns could be demonstrated in thermally assisted I-ST MRAM prototypes with 140 nm cell diameter [126], when applying voltage pulses of ± 1.1 V. Extension of the TA-STT concept to MRAM stacks with perpendicular magnetization electrodes is under way, being the option that seems most promising regarding scalability and performance.

4.2.3. Outlook for STTRAM Technology

Early STTRAM prototypes exhibit advantages regarding cell area, W/E times as well as write/read voltages when comparing their specifications with those of contemporary conventional MRAMs (see Table 3 in Section 7). For perpendicular STTRAM devices, possibly in combination with vertical select transistors, a cell size limit of 6 F^2 has been projected to be actually viable (see Table 4). The arrival of the STTRAM concept has certainly infused new confidence that there exists after all a viable scaling path for MRAM technology. The combination of the thermal assist concept with the perpendicular STTRAM approach might provide an avenue for ultimate performance. The arrival of 65 nm STTRAM products is expected for 2012, with 32 nm devices to follow by 2014/2015. Recent (2011) STTRAM-related announcements include the teaming-up of Crocus and Russia's state-owned investment group Rusnano to build a factory in Russia, and a collaboration between Renesas and Grandis regarding 65 nm STTRAM development.

4.3. Nanodot/Nanoring Magnetic Elements and Magnetic Vortex Memories

With tighter packing of conventional elliptically shaped magnetic bits stray field energy and shape anisotropy energy increase distinctly, necessitating a rise in switching field and thus power consumption. Circular magnetic elements, such as disks (cylinders) or rings, have been proposed (e.g., [127–129]) as an alternative due to their promise for reduced sensitivity to magnetic cross-talk or lower power consumption, as explained in the following.

One of the equilibrium configurations of soft magnetic materials in thin sub-micron-sized magnetic elements of square or circular shape is the so-called vortex state. Vortex-state magnetic structures were predicted by theory and in 2000 observed for the first time in thin nanodots [130]. In the out-of-plan region of a magnetic vortex structure, depicted in Figure 25 [131], the static magnetization is curling in-plane in clockwise or anti-clockwise manner, while its core region with a typical exchange length of 5–10 nm exhibits magnetization aligned perpendicularly to the dot plane with bimodal polarity (either up or down). The combination of 2 possible curling configurations of the out-of-core region (helicity) with 2 possible magnetization alignments of the core (polarity) yields 4 different nanodot ground states that are energetically equivalent in absence of an external field, which breaks the symmetry. Since no magnetic charges exists at the perimeter of its closed domain, a vortex state does not produce any magnetic stray field. The bistable polarity, the high magnetic stability that can only be destroyed in the presence of strong magnetic fields, and the insensitivity to magnetic cross-talk—allowing very high packing density of cells—render vortex-state technology a promising candidate for memory application. The curling magnetic field induced by a current perpendicular to the plane will align the helicity of the out-of-core region with its own helicity. A magnetic field along the plane normal will align the magnetization of the core parallel to its own direction. For both scenarios the out-of-core helicity and the magnetization direction of the core will both change signs during switching, but chirality will be conserved.

Figure 25. Illustration of magnetization orientation in vortex-state of nanostructure. Note curling in-plane magnetization of out-of-core region versus out-of-plane magnetization direction in core region. Reprinted with permission from [131], A. Wachowiak et al., *Science* 298, 577 (2002). © 2002, The American Physical Society.

Vortices exhibit two independent magnetic parameters, namely polarity and chirality, and could therefore in principle become the basis for quarternary bits allowing data storage as "0", "1", "2" and "3". However, until recently the path towards such novel technology has been impeded by the inability to consistently control both polarity and chirality. Reliable control of polarity can be obtained fairly easily, however, chirality control has been hampered by random switching of chirality between its two alternate states. Successful chirality stabilization without any performance draw-backs could eventually be obtained by the introduction of a circular exchange bias, as demonstrated in 2009 for nanodots with a permalloy (Py)/IrMn bilayer [132]. Such minidisks were annealed and subsequently cooled below the blocking temperature of IrMn (without any external field), hereby imprinting the vortex configuration of the permalloy layer into the IrMn layer. Under the influence of the then established circular exchange bias, the vortex of an individual Py/IrMn nanodisk maintains a single chirality during the magnetization reversal. Thus the goal of stable and controllable chirality has been achieved.

When applying a spin-polarized current pulse, STT is the dominant factor driving magnetization switching, while a minor contribution comes from a circular Oersted field (<20 Oe) at the outer boundary of the annular layer. STT enables direct switching of magnetization in all parts of the ring, and reversal is highly consistent. Therefore, spin-polarized current switching seems to be a particularly promising switching mode when combined with the application of nanorings as magnetic elements. By 2007 nanorings MTJS with minimum outer diameters of 100 nm and minimum widths down to 20 nm could be patterned, employing electron beam lithography and Ar-ion beam milling [133]. However, it remains to be clarified whether reliable magnetization behavior can still be obtained once the outer diameters of nanorings are shrunk much more aggressively (e.g., to the sub-20 nm regime). Lacking scalability would render the nanoring approach a technological cul-de-sac.

A prototype of magnetic vortex memory involving frequency controlled resonance has been developed recently [134]. The underlying concept is depicted in Figure 26. The employed nanodisks had a diameter of 500 nm and a thickness of 44 nm and were separated by a distance of 10 μm. They were made of epitaxially grown NiMnSb(001), a material with desirably ultra-low damping constant ($\alpha = 0.002$). In the presence of a static magnetic field (H) applied along the axis of the vortex-core a splitting will occur in the frequency of the gyroscopic motion of the vortex-core magnetization around its equilibrium position depending on core polarity, whereas no such splitting exists for $H = 0$. The difference in frequencies for the two core polarities, $f_+ - f_-$, is proportional to the strength of the applied field H. With the help of a microwave field with in-plane magnetic orientation (as described with the vector h in Fig. 26) and tunable frequency, the polarity of an individual nanodot can be addressed selectively by setting the MW frequency in resonance with the gyroscopic frequency of either the p^+ or p^- vortex core polarity. When the amplitude of such set MW field surpasses a critical value and the vortex

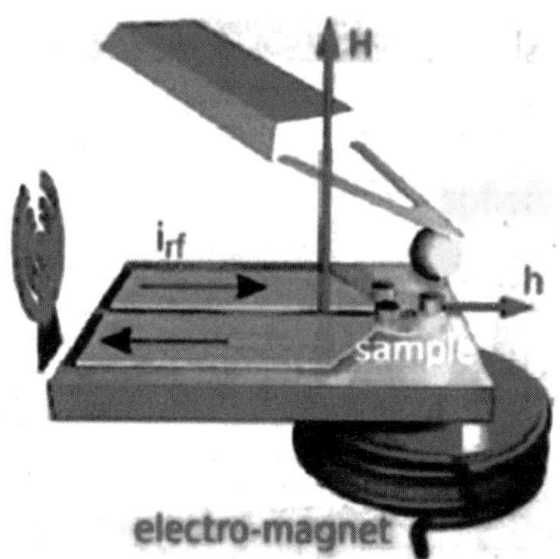

Figure 26. Principle of operation for frequency controlled magnetic vortex memory. Note H is the static magnetic field along axis of vortex-core; h is the microwave field with in-plane magnetic orientation. Reprinted with permission from [134], B. Pigeau et al., *Appl. Phys. Lett.* 96, 132506 (2010). © 2010, American Institute of Physics.

core precession speed exceeds a threshold value, core polarity reversal occurs. Once reverted, the newly created state is not any longer in resonance condition, thus its polarity cannot be switched back.

5. EMERGING NVM TECHNOLOGIES—RESISTIVE RAM (ReRAM or RRAM)

The majority of R&D activities towards innovative non-volatile memories (NVM) capable of competing with and to possibly replace contemporary flash devices in information technology applications has been dedicated to explorations of materials exhibiting a reversible change in resistance derived from various effects such as phase change, ferroelectric tunneling, thermochemical, electrochemical, or magnetoresistive effects, or molecular switching, etc. By convention, the nomenclature "resistive switching random access memories"—abbreviated ReRAM or RRAM—has been reserved for NVM devices that utilize electronic, electrochemical, or thermochemical effects to induce resistive switching (RS). An RRAM cell is a capacitor-like structure comprising an insulator or semiconductor material sandwiched between metal electrodes that can be switched between two stable resistive states, driven by voltage/current pulses. RRAMs have become attractive R&D objects aiming at future NVM applications due to their comparatively simple device structure, compatibility for integration with CMOS device architecture, and promising performance and scalability.

This section focuses on this class of devices. Resistive switching materials and corresponding mechanisms will be addressed, followed by a discussion on manufacturing and operational issues and possible improvement options, starting hierarchically with RRAM stacks and then moving on to cross-point arrays. Finally, a short outlook on the potential timeline for first RRAM products will be given.

5.1. RRAM Materials and Mechanisms

The RS materials used in RRAMs are generally metal oxides, although organic materials are also possible. (Resistive switching involving organic materials will be discussed shortly in a separate section on Macromolecular and Polymer Memory Devices). In 1962 hysteretic resistive switching in a metal-insulator-metal (MIM) system was first observed by Hickmott on oxide insulators [135]. Occasional publications on resistive switching in binary oxides, such as Al_2O_3, NiO, SiO_2 or VO_2, were followed by more extensive RRAM research in the 1980s, predominantly on transition metal oxides. Renewed R&D activities, starting in the late 1990s, included a.o. studies on more complex oxides with perovskite type crystal structure. In the meantime publications on resistive switching phenomena have accumulated for a wide variety of inorganic materials including binary oxides of Cu [136, 137], Ni [138–142], Fe [143], W [144–146], V [147], Nb [148–152], Ta [153, 154], Ti [155–159], Zr [160, 161], Hf [162–165], and perovskite oxides such as $Pr_{1-x}Ca_xMnO_3$ (PCMO) [166–169], Cr-doped $SrTiO_3$ [170, 171], $SrZrO_3$ [42, 173], or $Pb(Zr_xTi_{1-x})O_3$ [174].

RRAMs exhibit reversible switching between a high resistance state (HRS) and a low resistance state (LRS) under the influence of voltage or current pulses. In most (but not all) cases such switching capability does, however, not yet function in as-fabricated RRAM cells but has to be initiated by high voltage stress during an "electro forming" (EF) step, which induces a soft break-down in the switching material, thereby causing resistance to drop by orders of magnitude. In order to avoid hard dielectric break-down, which will eliminate any subsequent switching capability, the EF current has to be limited by current compliance from a control circuit. During a so-called "set process" an RRAM cell is shifted from the HRS (OFF) state to the LRS (ON) state by application of a threshold voltage (set voltage), whereby the current may again be limited by current compliance. The reverse shift from LRS to HRS occurs in the "reset process" upon application of a higher current and a voltage below the set voltage.

A classification of RRAM schemes can be carried out based on differences in behavior with respect to the dependency on voltage/current polarity and cell size: in unipolar (symmetric) resistive switching (URS) the switching direction does not depend on the polarity of the applied voltage but only on its amplitude. With bipolar (antisymmetric) resistive switching (BRS), on the other hand, HRS → LRS and LRS → HRS switching require the application of opposite voltage polarities. No or weak dependence of the switching current on cell size/electrode pad size points to localized switching in filamentary conduction paths, whereas linear or almost linear dependence points to a homogeneous distribution of the switching effect within the bulk of the switching materials or along its interface(s). Schematic representations of *I–V* characteristics for URS and BRS and filamentary and interface-type switching are shown in Figures 27 and 28, respectively.

The wide variety of inorganic and organic RS materials combined with variations in the choice of top and bottom electrodes as well as process modifications have produced an intimidating amount of *I–V* plots and promising

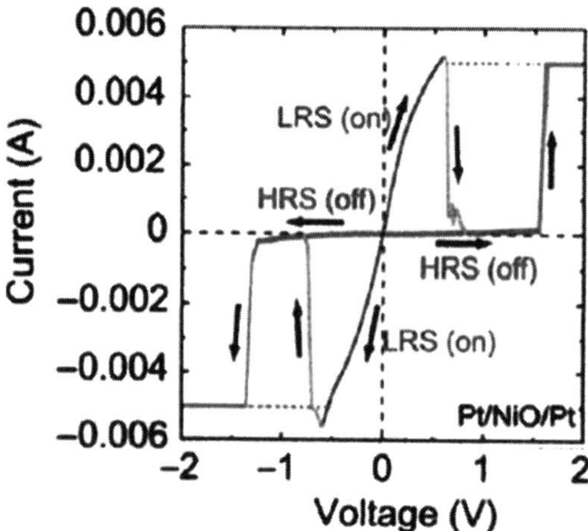

Figure 27. *I/V* curve for unipolar switching in Pt/NiO/Pt cell. Reprinted with permission from [194], A. Sawa, *Mater. Today* 11, 28 (2008). © 2008, Elsevier.

performance data for prototype devices, but added difficulty to the task of gaining an in-depth understanding of the complex interactions between chemical, electrical, and thermal effects causing resistive switching. Over the years, RS has been linked to various phenomena such as thermoelectrical effects [175–177], electrochemical metallization processes [178, 179], tunneling barrier variation [180], field induced charge injection by Fowler-Nordheim tunneling trapped at insulator sites leading to a modification of the electrostatic barrier of the MIM structure [181], trapping at interface states affecting adjacent Schottky barriers at the metal/semiconductor interface [182, 183], trapping at Au nanoclusters in polymers [184], electronic charge injection induced metal-insulator (Mott) transition [185–187], ion drift and diffusion migration in solid electrolytes [188]., a.o. Some types of RS systems are clearly dominated by one particular driving force as the origin of switching. With other ones, different driving mechanisms may overlap in a complementary or competing manner, exhibiting dependencies on structural surrounding (choice of electrodes), chemical

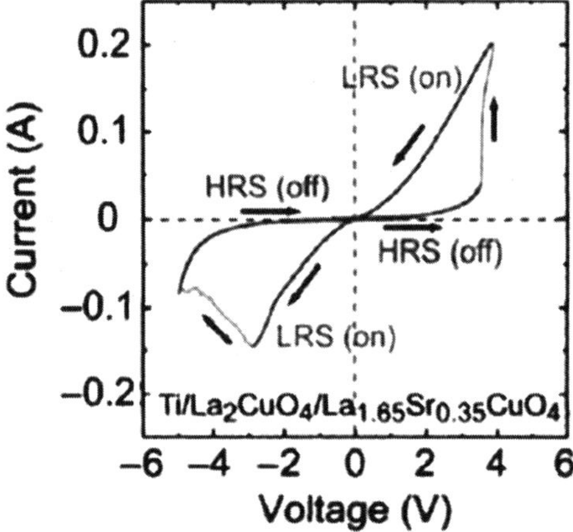

Figure 28. *I/V* curve for bipolar switching in $Ti/La_2CuO_4/La_{1.65}Sr_{0.35}CuO_4$ cell. Reprinted with permission from [194], A. Sawa, *Mater. Today* 11, 28 (2008). © 2008, Elsevier.

composition (oxidation state), or the voltage/current applied during electroforming. Some binary oxides, for example, can exhibit either unipolar or bipolar switching, as discussed below. If a thermoelectrical/thermochemical effect dominates, the RRAM device will generally exhibit unipolar switching behavior. On the other hand, if the dominating mechanism induces a redistribution and drift of charged species, bipolar switching will be observed. A clean-cut classification of switching schemes seems rather difficult, however, an attempt of classification, based on the dominating mechanism involved, will be made in the following. Devices following the first two of the below discussed categories of switching mechanisms are frequently summarized in the literature under the term "Redox RRAM" because their switching mechanisms are all driven by redox reactions.

5.1.1. Thermoelectrical (Fuse/Antifuse) Switching

The basic concept of fuse/antifuse switching due to percolative formation and fracture of filamentary conducting paths is well established although the details of the involved mechanism(s) are insufficiently understood so far. Unipolar fuse/antifuse switching is exhibited, for example, by single or bilayer films of binary oxides like NiO [177, 189, 190], TiO_2 (22), or Ta_2O_5/TiO_2 [191]. Bipolar filamentary switching has also been observed, e.g., in films of Cu_xSi_yO [192] or Fe-doped $SrTiO_3$ [193]. Direct evidence for the formation of localized conductive filaments (CF) via electron microscopy imaging has been reported for a planar configuration of copper oxide between Pt electrodes [194]. *I–V* measurements for NiO based RRAM elements [177], showing weak dependence of I_{SET} on cell size (I_{SET} values of 0.5, 1, and 4 mA corresponded to cell sizes of 0.05, 0.56, and 9.4 μm^2, respectively, i.e., an 8-fold increase of I_{SET} was related to a much larger cell area variation by a factor close to 200) have been interpreted to support a localized filamentary conduction mechanism in contrast to interface-type switching. Resistance measurements by Menke et al. [193] of two mechanically divided portions of an electroformed sample showed reduced resistance for only one of the separated parts while the other one remained in its initial (pre-forming) high-Ohmic state. This confirmed that the electroforming process for this particular system (Nb:STO BE/1 at.%Fe:STO/Pt TE) was local in nature and not encompassing the whole device area.

The basic model for fuse/antifuse switching assumes a soft break-down of the dielectric material during the electroforming process leading to a network of filament-like conducting paths between top and bottom electrode, resulting in significantly lower resistance. The filament may contain electrode material transported into the insulator, consisting of decomposed or chemically modified insulator material (e.g., sub-oxides) [195] or consisting of carbon from residual organics [196]. A voltage sweep applied during the reset process induces local disconnection of CFs by high Joule dissipation [176], which enhances the thermally activated diffusion of defects or atomic species constituting the CF, leading to CF rupture and a high-*R* state. For 5 nm thick NiO wires a rise in filament temperature up to around 450°C K has been estimated for $I = 200$ nA [177]. Cagli et al. [189] interpreted results from NiO-based RRAM devices as evidence that the reset process is initiated by threshold switching, a reversible transition from high to low resistance generally observed in Poole-Frenkel controlled semiconductors [197].

The set operation restores the low-resistance CF(s). A sudden rise in current at the beginning of the set process was correlated to a (calculated) temperature spike to > 2000°C. Such high local temperatures should enable structural modifications in NiO leading to CF formation, e.g., via thermal or electrochemical redox reactions [198, 199]. A recent (2010) paper by Lee et al. [200] was dedicated to the study of filamentary switching in NiO films. The authors conclude that a formation of metallic filaments occurs in two steps: a migration of oxygen vacancies driven by a high electric field in the forming step or the "ON" transition, followed by a reduction of Ni atoms in proximity to the oxygen vacancies. XPS data exhibited a neutral metallic peak for all NiO films which showed switching behavior. Filament rupture was attributed to the migration of oxygen vacancies away from the filament and oxidation of Ni atoms to recover the NiO bulk-like coordination. Schematics of the proposed mechanism and oxidation states [200] for both filament formation and rupture are shown in Figure 29.

The compliance current value during electroforming of RRAM devices seems to play a crucial role in deciding on the nature of the observed switching mechanism. Jeong et al. [201] observed unipolar fuse/antifuse switching in $Pt/TiO_2/Pt$ elements if the forming compliance current (CC) exceeded 1 mA, whereas bipolar switching was obtained for CC < 0.1 mA. Evidently a critical current to induce sufficiently high local temperatures must be reached in order to ensure that thermochemical effects take over the dominating role in defining the observed switching mode. When applying a voltage sweep with CC > 3 mA, the switching mode of TiO_2 could be altered from BRS to URS, but this change was irreversible and a return to BRS was not any longer possible.

Undesirable resistance fluctuations related to intermediate resistance states—most likely corresponding to additional filaments formed successively in case of incomplete 1st filament formation—have been observed after the set operation in case the set current remained below a critical value, I_{SET}, which is the threshold current to ensure a reproducible R_{ON} state [177].

5.1.2. Bipolar Ion/Vacancy Migration Driven Switching

This type of bipolar switching relies on redox reactions and the migration/drift of highly mobile ions or vacancies (or a combination of both). Thermal effects do not play any significant role, in contrast to fuse/antifuse switching, but filament formation/rupture based switching is observed for one particular sub-category, namely for the case of conductive bridge (CB) switching. Polarity-dependent memory switching following the CB mechanism was first reported by Hiroshe and Hiroshe [202] in 1976 for Ag-photodoped amorphous As_2S_3. In general this particular switching scheme utilizes a MIM structure incorporating a solid electrolyte layer as ion-conducting material,

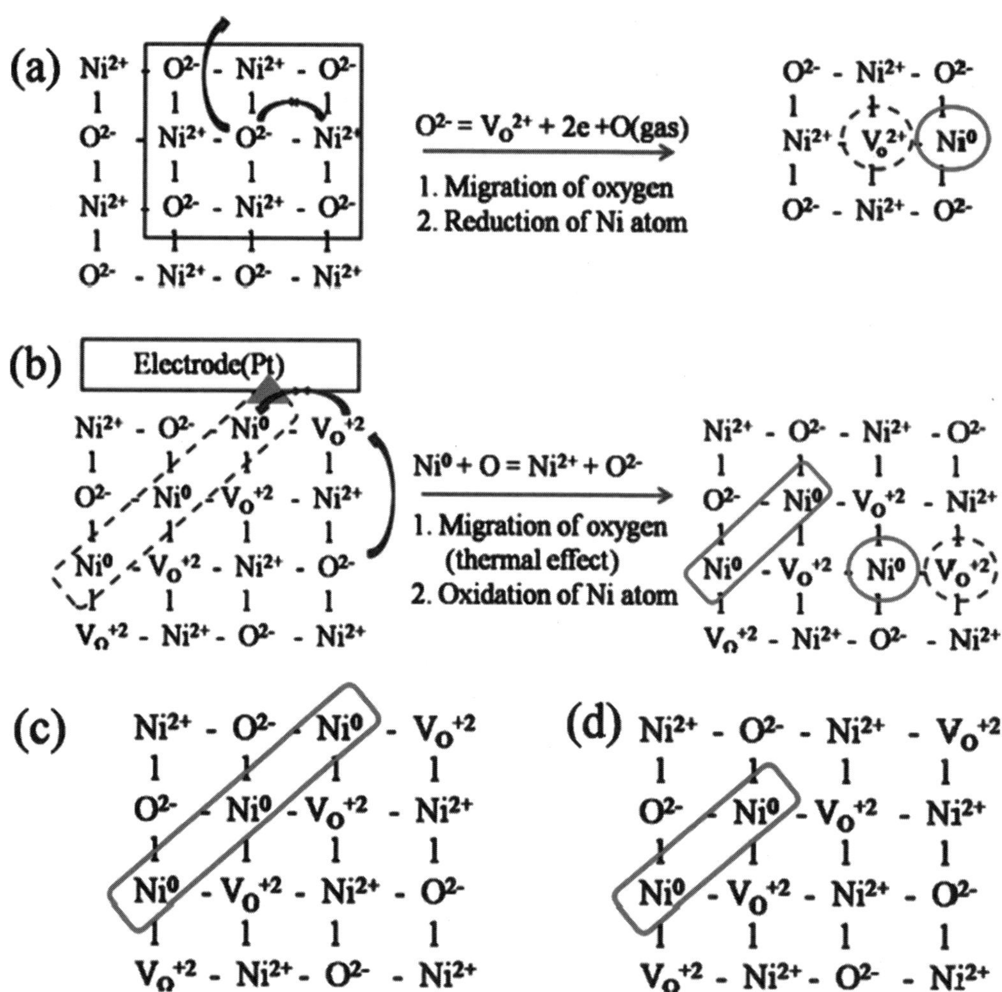

Figure 29. Mechanism for formation and rupture of filaments in NiO films, (a) formation mechanism, (b) rupture mechanism, (c) oxidation states corresponding to filament formation, and (d) oxidation states corresponding to rupture. Reprinted with permission from [200], H. D. Lee et al., *Phys. Rev. B* 81, 193202 (2010). © 2010, The American Physical Society.

sandwiched between an electrochemically active metal electrode and an inert metal counter-electrode. The basic mechanism of operation is explained for the system Ag/Ag_2S/Pt by Eq. (1) and Figure 30 [203]:

$$Ag^+(Ag_2S) + e^- \underset{\text{oxidation}}{\overset{\text{reduction}}{\rightleftharpoons}} Ag \tag{1}$$

With the inert electrode biased as cathode, highly mobile Ag^+ ions migrate through the ion conducting Ag_2S to the cathode where they are reduced to metallic Ag. The accumulating reduced metal leads to the growth of Ag dendrites in direction to the anode.

Simultaneously metal ions of the electrochemically active electrode are oxidized and released to the ion-conducting electrolyte, thus ensuring continuous availability of metal cations for electrochemical deposition at the cathode. Eventually the growing metal dendrite forms a highly conducting bridge between the electrodes, thus switching the device to its ON state. Upon reversal of the polarity of the bias voltage metal atoms are oxidized to positive ions at the surface of the filament. They dissolve until the conducting bridge is finally interrupted (OFF state). Opening and closing the conducting bridge requires different voltages. Recent electrochemical simulations [204] could explain this asymmetry as the result of different electric field distributions, as the morphology of the dendrite-electrode plane configuration changes during the transition from closed to disrupted conducting bridge.

Resistive switching is most easily achieved if the sandwiched material in the MIM structure is either an ion conductor for the redox reactive material (e.g., Ag_2S for Ag^+ [205]), or it is a compound with high solubility for the migrating cation, like GeSe [178, 179, 206] for Ag ions, or SiO_2 [207], or WO_3 [144] for Cu ions. Ag/(ZnCd)S/Pt [208] is another example for an RRAM system operating by CB type switching.

Conductive bridge switching is unique among the various RRAM switching types as it does not require any electroforming process. Using current compliance during the set operation the targeted ON resistance can be tailored over several orders of magnitude [206, 207]. Switching can be obtained in the 10 ns regime. Switching voltage (few

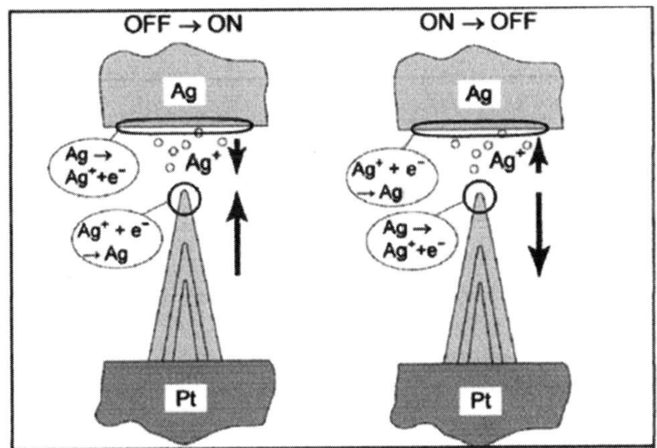

Figure 30. Schematics of resistive switching mechanism in Ag^+/Ag_2S based conductive bridge RRAM cell. Reprinted with permission from [203], R. Waser, "IEDM Techn. Dig.," p. 289, 2008. © 2008, IEEE.

100 mV s) and current (sub-100 pA possible) requirements can be kept low, with the promise for low power consumption. Integration of a 2 Mbit Ag/$GeSe_x$/W RRAM device into 90-nm CMOS technology could be successfully demonstrated [179] with good read and program control. In this case the standard *W* plug of the underlying CMOS architecture may be used as the bottom electrode of the RRAM element built on top. (The latter work reported functional RRAM devices with GeSe widths as small as 20 nm).

An innovative type of switching element based on CB formation was developed by Terabe et al. [209] using an electronic and ionic mixed conductor for one of the electrodes and a vacuum nanogap as the insulator between the electrodes. The Pt top electrode of this particular system is separated by a 1 nm wide gap from a Ag_2S layer capping the underlying Ag bottom electrode. Metal filament growth from Ag_2S across the nanogap (see Fig. 31) can be controlled with atomic precision.

Separation of control line from conduction line by three-terminal devices in which the formation and dissolution of a metal filament is controlled by the gate electrode bias, has been successfully demonstrated for liquid [210] and, later on, solid [211] electrolyte-based systems. Such devices should widen the chances for practical applications of solid electrolyte switches.

Another sub-category of devices that follow non-thermal switching mechanisms driven by redox reactions and the migration of ions/defects (generally oxygen anions and oxygen vacancies) exhibits an interface-type of switching, as seen, for example, with certain binary oxides and more complex oxides. In 2007 Odagawa et al. [212] were the first to suggest a redox reaction-driven switching mechanism in magnetite (Fe_3O_4) films. A year later direct experimental evidence for a switching mechanism of that nature was derived from the analysis of the HRS and LRS states of Pt/TaO_x/Pt test samples [154]. Using hard X-ray photoemission spectroscopy (HX-PES) as a non-destructive technique allowed the investigation of the Ta 4*d* band at the buried TaO_x/anode interface, which had been confirmed as the location of switching using a method developed by Muraoka et al. [213]. The HX-PES data exhibited an increase of the ratio of $Ta_2O_{5-\delta}/TaO_{2-\beta}$ from HRS to LRS, indicating that $Ta_2O_{5-\delta}$ in HRS had been reduced to $TaO_{2-\beta}$ in LRS ($Ta_2O_{5-\delta}$ and $TaO_{2-\beta}$ being phases close to Ta_2O_5 and TaO_2, respectively, but with some oxygen deficiency). The oxygen content in the TaO_x films could be influenced by a post-deposition anneal in O_2 ambient. The O/Ta ratio was found to be higher in the vicinity of the anode as compared to the bulk TaO_x. When using different metals as electrode material in the metal/TaO_x/metal stacks, significant differences with respect to the stability of resistive switching were discovered, further evidence for the important role of the metal-oxide interface. RRAM elements containing electrodes of metals with high work function like Ir or Pt exhibited stable RS, whereas memory cells with low-WF metals showed unstable switching behavior. Based on the available *I–V* and physical analysis data, resistive switching in Pt/TaO_x/Pt was explained by a change in barrier height between TaO_x and the anode as the result of an electric field driven redox reaction. Schematic representations of the potential energy curve of the TaO_x redox pair and the change of barrier height are depicted in Figures 32(a and b) [154]. During the reset operation, when a positive voltage is applied to the anode, O^{2-} anions migrate from the bulk TaO_x towards the anode, accumulate at the oxide/metal interface and induce the oxidation of $TaO_{2-\beta}$ to $Ta_2O_{5-\delta}$. The increase of the $Ta_2O_{5-\delta}$ component at the expense of $TaO_{2-\beta}$ enlarges the band gap and increases the barrier height. Application of a negative voltage at the anode during the set operation, on the other hand, results in reduction of $Ta_2O_{5-\delta}$ and a concomitant decrease in barrier height.

5.1.3. Switching Based on Electronic/Electrostatic Effects

Charge carrier injection and trapping/detrapping phenomena that either modify the band structure of the bulk insulator in a MIM structure or induce changes in the properties of the interface between insulator and metal electrodes have been invoked as the root cause for resistive switching in certain RRAM devices. Already in 1967 the first model of this kind was developed by Simmons and Verderber [181] to explain resistive switching in Au/SiO/Al. Their model assumes injection of Au ions into SiO during the forming process to introduce a band of localized impurities within the bandgap of the insulator. Electrons can migrate through SiO by tunneling between adjacent trapping sites. After all traps in SiO have been filled by injected electrons (trap filled limit) a drastic rise in current is noted and the device state shifts from HRS to LRS. A return to HRS is possible after the release of the trapped charges.

Bipolar switching was also observed with Al/TiO_x/Al devices [157]. By clever biasing experiments the Al top electrode/TiO_x interface was identified as the switching location (and not the TiO_x bulk). Al reacts with the underlying TiO_x during deposition, competing for oxygen and thereby inducing oxygen vacancies in the border region of TiO_x [214]. These oxygen vacancies may act as traps. The *I–V* characteristics were interpreted in terms of a trap-controlled space-charge limited current model and the

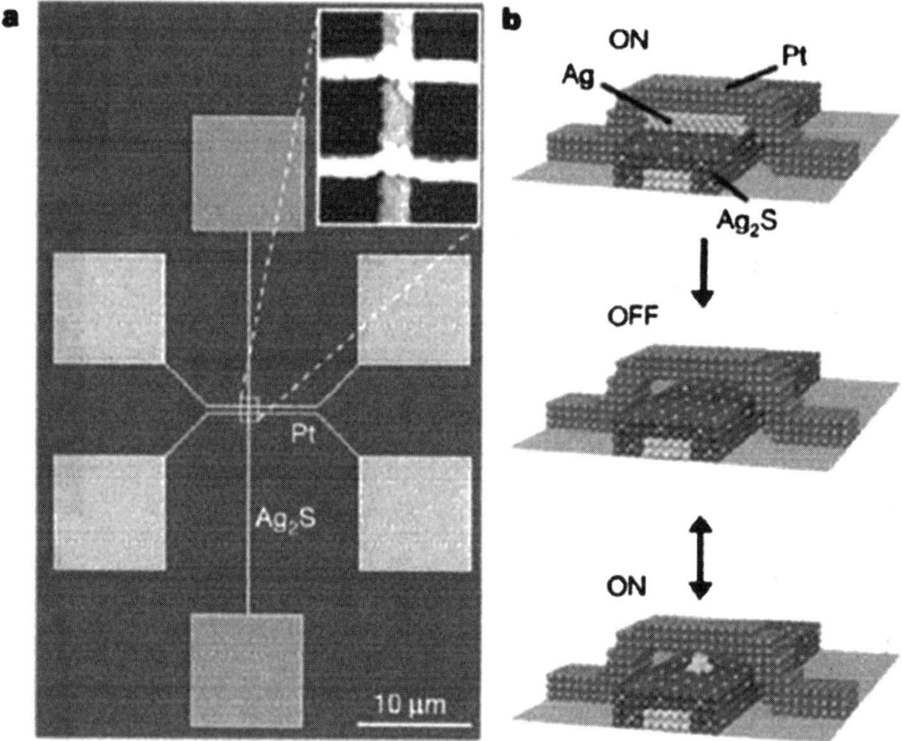

Figure 31. Atomic switch utilizing conductive bridge formation across nanogap of about 1 nm width for device fabrication, (a) SEM image: crossing point of 150 nm thick Ag_2S wire and two Pt wires of 100 nm width; (b) schematics of switching mechanism: as-formed switch-on state (top), switched-off state (center) and switched-on state after initial switching-off process (bottom). Reprinted with permission from [209], K. Terabe et al., *Nature* 433, 47 (2005). © 2005, Nature Publishing Group.

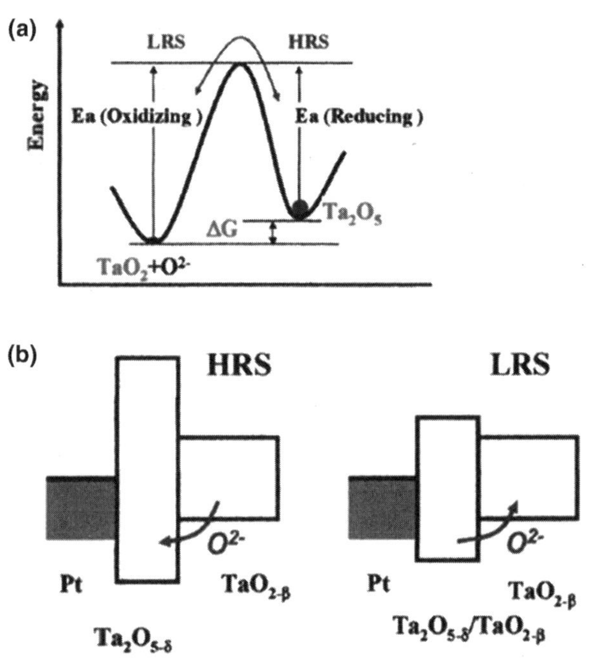

Figure 32. Oxygen ion migration and redox reaction driven resistive switching in Pt/TaO_x/Pt RRAM cell. (a) Potential energy curve of TaO_x redox pair; (b) change in barrier height at TaO_x/anode interface accompanying redox reaction. Reprinted with permission from [154], Z. Wei et al., "IEDM Tech. Dig.," p. 293, 2008. © 2008, IEEE.

observed resistive switching in Al/TiO_x/Al was attributed to a capture-release process of injected electrons at traps along the interface to the Al top electrode.

Sawa et al. [183, 194] carried out extensive studies to elucidate the nature of bipolar switching involving RRAM devices containing perovskite type oxides. Experiments employing $Pr_{0.7}Ca_{0.3}MnO_3$ (PCMO) as representative for a *p*-type oxide semiconductor and Nb-doped $SrTiO_3$ (Nb:STO) as *n*-type semiconductor showed existence or non-existence of switching behavior depending on the choice of metal for the top electrode (TE). Ti, Au, and $SrRuO_3$ (SRO) with work functions of −4.1, −5.1 and −5.3 eV, respectively, were selected as TE materials. With more negative TE work function, the contact resistance between metal and PCMO decreased, whereas the contact resistance between metal and Nb:STO became higher. Only Ti/PCMO, Au/Nb:STO, and SRO/Nb:STO exhibited rectification and hysteretic behavior, indicative of resistive switching, whereas the other TE/oxide combinations did not. These observations pointed to the metal/semiconductor interface as the location of switching in the investigated stacks and were related to differences in a Schottky-like barrier at the interface caused by changes in contact resistance under the influence of the applied voltage. The conventional Schottky model correlates changes in contact resistance to changes of the potential profile of the depletion layer at the barrier. It predicts capacitance to be inversely proportional to the width of the depletion layer, W_d. *C–V* curves measured for the Ti/PCMO interface (see Fig. 33(a) [194]) indicated

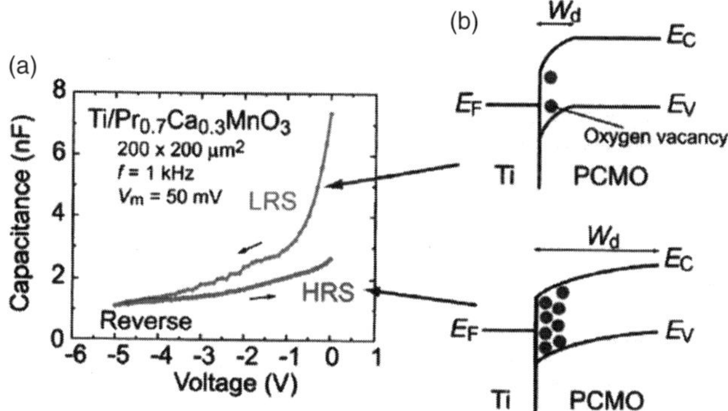

Figure 33. Resistive switching in Ti/$Pr_{0.7}Ca_{0.3}MnO_3$ (PCMO)/$SrRuO_3$ RRAM device (a) *C–V* curve for Ti/PCMO interface: CLRS > CHRS; (b) modulation of depletion layer width, W_d, at Ti/PCMO interface as function of electric field driven oxygen vacancy migration. Reprinted with permission from [194], A. Sawa, *Mater. Today* 11, 28 (2008). © 2008, Elsevier.

hysteretic behavior, with the capacitance, C, being lower for HRS as compared to LRS (at $V = 0$). Thus, electron tunneling through the barrier is expected to be easier in the LRS case. Migration of oxygen vacancies in the vicinity of the interface (see Fig. 33(b)) is assumed to be the driving mechanism for the change in W_d. Sawa et al. found indirect experimental evidence for the impact of oxygen vacancies by comparing *I–V* curves of as deposited RRAM devices versus those of samples subjected to annealing at 400°C in O_2 ambient, which should reduce the concentration of oxygen vacancies at the metal/oxide interface. In PCMO as *p*-type oxide semiconductor oxygen vacancies will act as acceptor scavengers, in *n*-type Nb:STO as effective donors. A reduction in oxygen vacancies due to post-deposition treatment in O_2 should therefore cause a narrowing of the depletion layer at the PCMO/TE interface, but a widening for the Nb:STO case. Corresponding changes in contact resistance, going in opposite direction for PCMO and Nb:STO, have indeed been observed by Sawa et al. for their O_2-annealed RRAM structures.

RRAM devices exhibiting switching mechanisms based on charge injection/trapping are difficult to optimize with respect to all parameters of merit. There exists a trade-off between switching speed and ON/OFF ratio. Moreover, at low voltages (<1 V) and high device densities, long retention times were found to be incompatible with short write/read pulses (<100 ns). Potential scaling limitations by the defect trap density and dead times in the range of ms to s are further concerns.

A somewhat atypical example for bipolar interfacial switching was detected in the literature for Pt/NiO/$SrRuO_3$ (-Pt/NiO/Pt shows URS!-), which has been attributed to interfacial Schottky barrier changes involving the migration of Ni (and not oxygen) vacancies [215].

Rather than assuming changes in the oxide valence state and the Schottky-like interface barrier, metal-insulator transition (MIT) [216, 217], also called Mott transition, has been invoked as an alternative explanation for bipolar resistive switching in oxides of certain transition metals. First arguments along this line were made in 2005/2006 to explain experimental results [185, 186] and theoretical work on MIT was done too (83) [218].

In a correlated insulator, electrons are prevented from conducting by Coulomb repulsion between them. However, a transition from insulating to metallic state can be induced by an increase of temperature, pressure, or doping level, which will enable electrons to escape their sites, leave electron holes behind and become conducting electrons. Various lower oxides, such as Fe_3O_4, Ti_2O_3, NbO_2, or VO_2 (e.g., Ref. [219]), exhibit this phenomenon of metal-insulator-transition, which goes along with a sharp and reversible change in conductivity by several orders of magnitude. It can be induced thermally at a certain transition temperature, T_{tr} (being, for example, ~340 K for VO_2 and 400–600 K for Ti_2O_3). Since the coexistence of lower oxides beside the highest oxide during RRAM device fabrication and operation seems thermodynamically feasible, the formation of such lower oxides has been postulated to occur during the electroforming step, with subsequent voltage-driven switching between an insulating HRS (OFF) state and a metallic LRS (ON) state.

Oka and Nagaosa [218] used a density matrix renormalization group approach (DMRG) combined with a modified Poisson's equation to calculate the potential in a metal strongly correlated electron system (SCES) interface and found 3 possible solutions representing an Ohmic junction, a Schottky barrier, and a MIT (Mott) transition. For the MIT case, the model showed the emergence of a quantum well at the interface of a hole doped Mott insulator and an electrode with low work function (or at the interface of an electron doped Mott insulator and an electrode with a high work function), i.e., the formation of a metallic region sandwiched between two insulating layers of a Mott insulator and a band insulator. Applying the theoretical model to resistive switching devices, a region with coexisting metallic and insulating phases, corresponding to the ON and OFF state, respectively, was predicted if a certain potential boundary condition was met. The model demonstrated switching between these two states by applying a voltage bias to the electrode and predicted also the appearance of a hysteresis loop in the *I–V* characteristics.

MIT-induced resistive switching does not show any pad size dependency and filamentary switching behavior has been confirmed at least for some cases. With Mott transition-based switching, the filamentary build-up of the switching material seems to be limited to a thin layer close to the metal/oxide interface, whereas traditional fuse/antifuse switching is generally attributed to filament formation across the whole oxide bulk from bottom to top metal electrode. Switching phenomena that may be explainable by MIT-transition seem therefore to hold an intermediate position between interfacial and filamentary switching, as they exhibit certain characteristics of both of these switching types.

What concerns performance, RRAMs operating via MIT-induced switching exhibit generally comparatively low ON/OFF ratios <10. The relatively high switching energy required for this device type raises concerns regarding power consumption.

5.2. RRAM Element Improvement Options

A reduction in electroforming voltage and reset current, tighter distribution of resistance values of HRS and LRS for improved sensing margin, and improved reliability and retention are improvement targets for future RRAM devices. Such improvement may result from judicious selection of RRAM MIM materials, modifications of the RRAM stack layers, scaling by reduction of the resistive film thickness, or by device architecture innovations resulting in smaller contact areas and reduced switching volume, or—last but not least—by doping and defect control.

Irrespective of its obviously appreciated impact to lower the power consumption, a reduction of the reset current becomes a prerequisite for high density RRAM device architectures with transistors as selection devices because the maximum possible current through transistors decreases with shrinking transistor size. Improvement in switching uniformity is considered to be particularly important for RRAMs exhibiting filamentary switching because the stochastic nature of the filament formation/rupture may degrade the switching uniformity as RRAM devices are further scaled down.

One popular option for performance improvement for either unipolar or bipolar switching RRAMs are resistive film treatments or RRAM stack modifications that enhance the concentration of oxygen or metal vacancies within the RRAM stack which, as described earlier, play an important role in many resistive switching mechanisms. In 2005 Seo et al. [139] reported the influence of the post-deposition anneal of DC reactive sputtered polycrystalline NiO films in Ar/O_2 ambient at 300°C (@50 mT). Increasing the partial pressure of oxygen resulted in more Ni vacancies (producing *p*-type semiconducting behavior [220] in the NiO films, which lowered their resistance. Seo et al. tested RRAM elements containing a NiO trilayer consisting of a center layer of higher resistance embedded in two NiO layers of comparatively lower resistance. The idea behind this approach was that formation and rupture of filaments can be easily induced in regions with higher R, while the low-R part of the NiO trilayer may preserve its initial conductivity during the switching procedure. I_{RESET} could be drastically reduced to 100 μA for the NiO trilayer while 10 mA were required for a RRAM stack containing only a (single-layer) high-R NiO film. This advantage came at the cost of lower ON/OFF ratio (as R_{HRS} was lowered). R_{HRS} was moreover found to be dependent on the excess voltage over the reset voltage. Minimization of the reset voltage variation went along with improved distribution of R_{HRS}.

A decrease in reset current and tighter reset voltage distribution were also reported for a Ta/Ru BE/NiO/Ru/TA TE stack when subjecting deposited NiO films (PVD at 300°C) to a subsequent post-plasma-oxidation (PPO) treatment in N_2O/He at 350°C [221]. Higher oxygen content worked best. PPO led moreover to improved film surface roughness. A beneficial influence—again leading to lower reset current and reduced reset voltage variation—was also noted for a $Ru/Ta_2O_5/TiO_2$/RuRe RRAM stack [191] when subjecting the TiO_2 layer to plasma oxidation. In this case the performance improvement, which was highest for low oxidation conditions, was attributed to a lowering of the activation energy for oxygen vacancy formation.

For RRAMs operating via a bipolar resistive switching mechanism, performance improvement has been achievable by introduction of an addition layer in the MIM structure or by modification of the switching material itself. Lee et al. [162] reported, for example, about the beneficial impact of a reactive Ti getter layer inserted between TiN and HfO_x in an RRAM element with HfO_x sandwiched between TiN electrodes. A TiO_x intermediate layer is formed in this case by reaction with oxygen ions from the adjacent HfO_x layer, while the bordering HfO_x region becomes oxygen-deficient and enriched in oxygen vacancies. The forming voltage was found to depend strongly on HfO_x film thickness (see Fig. 34) and decreased for thinner films. For the case of very thin HfO_x (3 nm) even electroforming-free operation was obtainable, accompanied by switching times of 5 ns, very high ON/OFF ratios exceeding 1000, and fairly low operation voltage (< 3 V). Other work [163] using the same RRAM stack confirmed forming-less operation when employing ultra-thin switching films (3 nm HfO_x). The scaling in RS film thickness produced again favorable operation parameters: switching time ≤ 10 ns, V_{SET} and $V_{RESET} < 1.5$ V, $I_{SET} \sim 200$ μA, and a sensing margin > 100.

Benefits from an inserted 5–10 nm thick Ti getter layer could also be gained for the RRAM system $TiN/Ti/TiO_2/TiN$, as reported during the SSDM Conference 2010 [222]. Annealing at 400°C after the deposition of the top electrode converted the sputtered Ti layer into TiON by reaction with the surrounding TiN and TiO_2. Without Ti cap the stack exhibited lower conductivity (due to a lower concentration in oxygen vacancies) and large switching variations. In the presence of the oxygen vacancy-rich TiO_{2-x} layer the switching properties were, however, significantly improved. The number of additionally created oxygen vacancies could be regulated by the Ti film thickness, allowing an adjustment of the ON/OFF ratio. The decrease in R_{HRS} led to a decrease in the ON/OFF ratio, similarly as observed with HfO_2-based systems with a Ti insertion layer.

Performance improvements may be also obtainable by employing so-called "bilayer" RRAMs elements, i.e.,

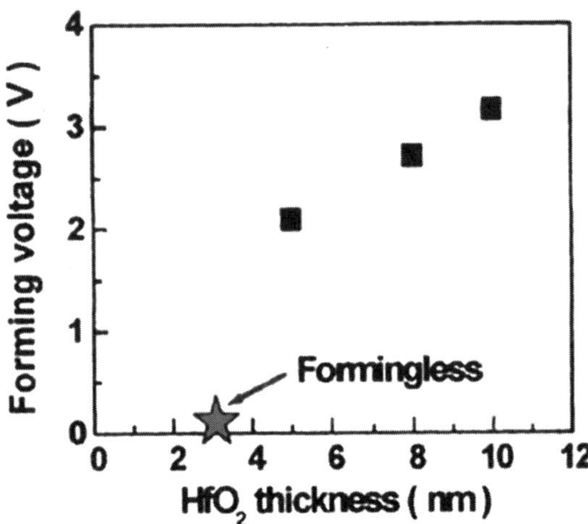

Figure 34. Dependence of electroforming voltage of $TiN/TiO_x/HfO_x$/TiN RRAM device on HfO_2 film thickness. Reprinted with permission from [162], H. Y. Lee et al., "IEDM Tech. Dig.," p. 297, 2008. © 2008, IEEE.

RRAMs containing a bilayer of two different oxide layers sandwiched between the metal electrodes, as for example the system BE/HfO_2/ZrO_x/TE [223]. A prototype of such an RRAM device containing a HfO_2/ZrO_x bilayer was built following the deposition-in-via approach. The process flow involved ALD deposition of Hf and sputtering of Zr (with thicknesses of, for example, 3 nm and 7 nm, respectively). The choice of the top electrode influenced the stability of switching. Zr or Hf TEs lead to stable switching with low V_{FORM} (V_{FORM} could be reduced from 3 V to below 1 V by lowering the HfO_2 thickness. Zr and Hf TEs produced unstable switching. No switching was observed when employing a Sm TE).

I–V curve representative and a schematic drawing of the presumed switching mechanism are shown in Figures 35(a and b). In the initial state an intermediate layer of oxygen vacancy-rich HfO_x is formed at the interface between HfO_2 and ZrO_x. In the set state (LRS) a conducting filament is formed, accompanied by O^{2-} ion migration to the Pt top electrode. In the reset state (HRS) the tunnel barrier between HfO_x and ZrO_x is controlled by the reset voltage. When switching to the reset state, CF disrupture is presumed to occur only in the oxygen vacancy-enriched HfO_x layer while the CFs formed in HfO_2 remain intact. This should explain the observed remarkable improvement in reproducibility from sweep to sweep. The *I–V* curves of the 1st and the 1000th sweep deviated only slightly from each other, as shown in Figure 35(a). As compared to the data from a RRAM containing a single layer of HfO_2, the bilayer RRAM system delivered significantly

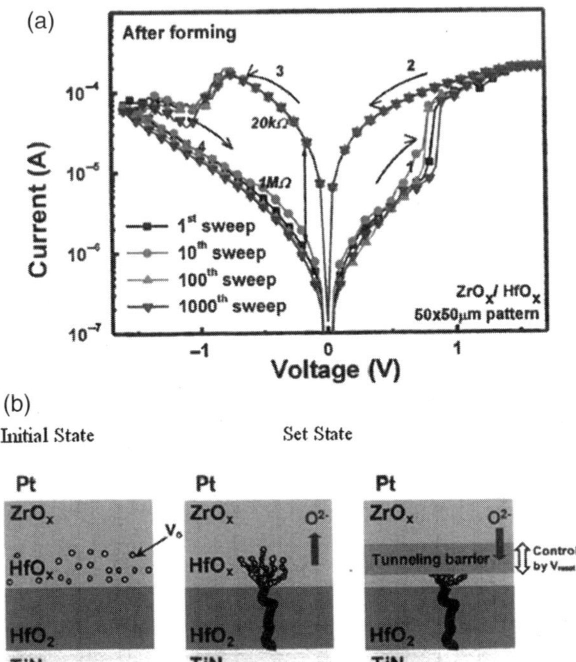

Figure 35. Resistive switching in TiN/HfO_2/HfO_x/ZrO_x/TiN RRAM "bilayer RRAM" stack (a) *I/V* characteristics, and (b) proposed mechanism. Note V_o is the oxygen vacancy. Reprinted with permission from [223], J. Lee et al., *Microelectr. Eng.* 88, 1113 (2011); "New Nonvolatile Memory Workshop," Tsingchu, 2010. © 2010, Elsevier.

tighter distributions of V_{SET}, V_{RESET}, R_{HRS}, and R_{LRS}, the widths of the resistance distributions, for example, were reduced by factors of 5–10.

Another example for the influence of the choice of the electrode material on switching behavior is given by Chien et al. [224], discussing the results for the TE/WO_3/W BE system with fixed W bottom electrode and varying top electrode material. Usage of low work function metals as top electrode materials, like Ti, TiN, W or Al, resulted in high forming current whereas employment of high-WF top electrode materials like Ni or Pt led to lower I_{FORM}. Analysis of *I–V* curves of the initial states suggested a SCLC-based switching mechanism for the RRAMs with low-WF metal and involvement of thermionic emission if a high-WF top electrode was used.

A beneficial change in vacancy density relevant to the underlying resistive switching mechanism can also be obtained by modification of the resistive material itself. Wang et al. [192], for example, reported a novel Cu_xSi_yO resistive memory with excellent data retention and resistance distribution, its performance being clearly better as compared to that of a Cu_2O-based RRAM. Cu_2O is a metal-deficient *p*-type semiconductor with Cu vacancies (V_{Cu}) as main defect type. It shows filamentary conduction by carrier hopping between localized Cu vacancy defects. The improvement for Cu_xSi_yO versus Cu_2O was attributed to a stabilizing effect of Si incorporation on V_{Cu} (its activation energy being 5 times higher in Cu_xSi_yO than in Cu_2O). Excellent retention stability was found when using a Ni top electrode. This was ascribed to a low driving force for intermixing at the interface due to the small difference in free energies of the oxides of W and Ni. Good read disturb immunity was observable for < 0.6 V.

Finally, improved switching uniformity seems also obtainable by modifications of the device architecture. Patent applications by Hynix in 2008 and 2010 [225, 226] propose a deposition-in-via approach whereby the resistive material between the top and bottom electrodes does not fill the whole via but is only aligned along the sidewalls of the via while the via center is filled with an oxide exhibiting a high threshold voltage (e.g., Al_2O_3). Thus, the shape of the resistive material forms a hollowed cylinder rather than a filled cylinder, amounting to an effective reduction in contact area between metal electrodes and the switching oxide. Nb_2O_5 or NbO_2 [225] or a trilayer of NbO_x/NiO/NbO_x [226] were suggested as material choices for the latter. Improved *R* distributions have been reported when applying the patent application ideas of Hynix.

A recently proposed novel RRAM architecture with "*U*-type" cell structure [227] follows a very similar idea. In this approach the switching material covers the sidewall as well as the bottom of a via hole, but the contact area to the top electrode is again limited to an annular cross-section. The reduction in contact area and the funneling of the carrier flow within a cross-section of small lateral dimensions evidently improve switching uniformity, supposedly by better control of filament formation and a reduced number of formed filaments. Possibly the change in resistor behavior due to the shrinkage of its cross-section, inducing different local current densities and altered temperature distributions, may play a more important role than the mere number of filaments.

U-structured RRAM cells delivered a slight reduction of I_{RESET}, a significant decrease of V_{FORM} (to about 1 V for an RS film thickness of 5 nm), V_{SET}, and V_{RESET}, allowing even electroforming-less operation. The similarities in improvement as compared to the positive effects of RS film thickness reduction in a planer RRAM stack are not surprising.

Reduction of contact area by a lower electrode contact comprising a carbon nanotube (bundle), either SWCNTB or MWCNT, has been proposed in a patent application in 2009 [228]. Claims regarding lower I_{RESET} and improved R_{HRS} and R_{LRS} distributions have been made.

5.3. RRAM Stack Manufacturing

There are several options available to built RRAM stacks. Corresponding patent applications have been filed recently (e.g., see Refs. [229–231]). One approach involves dry etching of the MIM stack [229], followed by its encapsulation in insulating oxide, oxide CMP, via etching to the top of the RRAM stack and plug formation to the next wiring level. A schematic cross-sectional drawing of an RRAM element built by such a dry etching-based approach over the drain region of a selection transistor is shown exemplarily in Figure 36. Regions of resistive material film exposed to etch gases may undergo undesired structural (surface roughness) or compositional changes. If a noble metal like Pt is employed as electrode material, dry etching of such metals will require using advanced etch tools allowing operation at elevated temperatures (e.g., 400–500°C) to enable removal of low-volatility etch products. Etching of noble metals, e.g., of Pt top electrode (with TiN on top of it as antireflective layer to keep lithography related CD variations in check) may often produce a less perfect taper angle in the etched MIM stack as compared to etched profiles of more conventional materials. Resulting differences between the areas of bottom and top electrodes may degrade the device performance (switching margin).

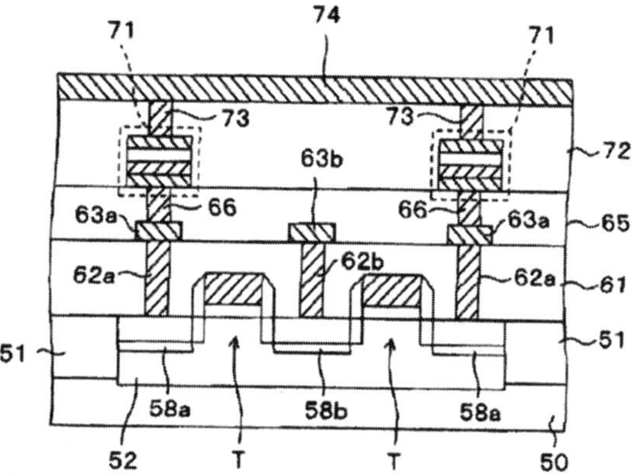

Figure 36. Schematic cross-section of dry-etch-patterned RRAM element built over drain region of selection transistor. Note 71 is the $Pt/NiO_x/Pt$ element patterned via dry-etch approach, 72 is the encapsulating oxide, 66 and 73 are the W plugs, 63b is the writing ground, and 74 is the bit line. Reprinted with permission from [229], H. Noshiro and K. Kinoshita (Fujitsu), U.S. Patent Application Publication US2010/0083487 A1, April 8, 2010. © 2010.

What concerns the deposition of switching materials, binary oxides (e.g., of Ni, Ti, Al, W, or Zr) can be deposited—generally at room temperature—using PVD sputtering or magnetron sputtering of metal oxide targets, employing source gases like Ar, He, or N_2/O_2 at 1–100 mT pressure. Similar process conditions, although occasionally at elevated temperatures, can be used for the deposition of perovskite-type oxides [232].

Due to the issues mentioned above for dry etching-based RRAM stack fabrication, another approach relying on the deposition of the switching material in via holes seems to be more favored as it avoids detrimental edge effects. For this second method, special precautions are required to achieve high directionality in deposition, thereby ensuring that material deposition occurs mainly at the bottom of via holes rather than along their sidewalls. Collimators with aspect ratios between 1–5 or DC bias of several 100 s of Volts have been employed for that purpose (88) [232]. Another option is the application of ionized metal plasma PVD (IM-PVD) (86) [116], which can be used for the deposition of electrode as well as metal oxide materials. The deposition-in-via approach can also be employed for the deposition of organic switching materials. Metal doped TCNQ, for example, can be deposited via thermal or e-beam evaporation, or via co-evaporation of solid TCNQ and dopant pellets. Spin coating of doped-TCNQ solutions at < 1000 RPM, with a subsequent hold time for solidification, is another viable deposition technique.

For $Al/TiO_2/Al$ devices (23) [157] better device reliability has been reported for RRAM devices built using the deposition-in-via method as compared to application of a so-called "crossbar" approach that may also suffer from detrimental edge effects. With the latter technique, the resistive switching material is deposited over the etched bars of Al bottom electrodes, followed by Al top electrode deposition.

A further method for the build-up of RRAM elements involves the formation of the resistive switching oxide layer by oxidation of the corresponding metal. NiO (or TiO_2), for example, can be formed by oxidation of deposited Ni (or Ti), either in a furnace at 350°C (for 20 mins) or via an RTA process at 400°C (for 1 min) [231]. RTA enables better thickness control. Plasma oxidation in RF or DC source plasma in O_2 or Ar/O_2 ambient can be applied (1–100 mT, RT–300°C) as an alternative.

Such oxidation will occur only along the sidewalls of the metal plate to be oxidized if the top surface of the latter is covered by an insulating material during that stage of manufacturing (e.g., by insulator INSF1 marked in the exemplary device cross-section shown in Fig. 37). Fujitsu has developed a device architecture and a related process flow [231] that results in the formation of four separated small volumes of switching material positioned along the four sidewalls of an oxidized Ni plate with square-shaped footprint. Each of these separated volumes of switching material will require a somewhat different electroforming voltage, V_F. By limiting V_F to a value that suffices to achieve soft break-down for any of the 4 switching volumes, higher values of V_F can be suppressed. This is advantageous since a lower V_F reduces the probability of failure of transistors connected in series to RRAM elements. Improved device reliability has indeed been observed when a V_F distribution shift to the lower side

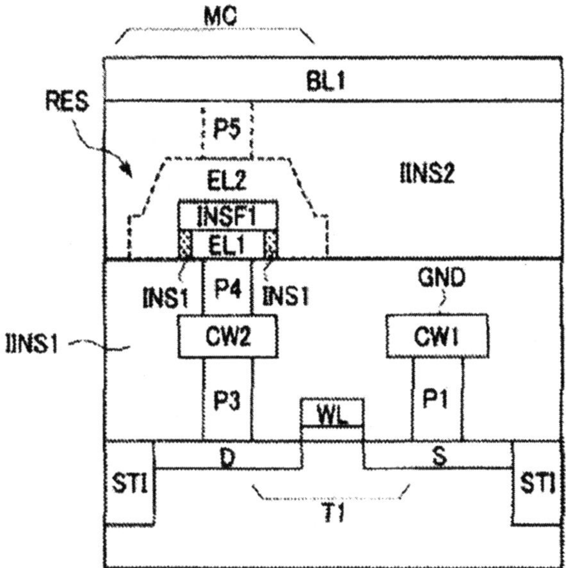

Figure 37. Schematic cross-section of RRAM element with resistive switching layer built by sidewall oxidation of metal pad. RES is the RRAM element, T1 is the selection transistor, EL1 is the Ni pad, INS1 is the NiO_x formed by sidewall oxidation of Ni, EL2 is the Pt top electrode, IINS1 and INSF1 are the insulating films of CVD SiO_2, P4 and P5 are the *W* plugs. Figure 12, Reprinted with permission from [231], H. Noshiro (Fujitsu), U.S. Patent Application Publication US2010/0027319 A1, February 4, 2010. © 2010.

was obtained. The small lateral dimensions of the switching material produced by sidewall oxidation of metal may contribute to improved switching uniformity, as discussed in the following section.

Applying the deposition-in-via technique, the diameter of etched vias can be reduced by the deposition of a sidewall liner, thus allowing the manufacturing of RRAM stacks with sizes below the available lithographic patterning capability. Although being no solution to increased device density, this approach nevertheless allows systematic studies aiming at an understanding of the change of properties and performance with shrinking RRAM element size.

5.4. RRAM Cross-Point Arrays: Issues and Possible Solutions

Cross-point array architecture, i.e., the positioning of individual cells at the cross-points of regularly spaced densely packed arrays of word lines and bit lines in orthogonal alignment to each other, is the design of choice for obtaining non-volatile memory arrays of high packing density. The capability to selectively read an individual cell within a cell array requires the incorporation of selection devices (either transistors or diodes) or rectification by alternative means, since a conventional high-density 0T (or 0D) 1R-cross-point structure of RRAM elements would face a severe read-out issue for the following reason: there exist many parallel conducting paths connecting each word line with each bit line, and only one of them passes through the node to be addressed. For random storage of "0"s and "1"s many of $(M-1) \times (N-1)$ possible "sneak paths" in an array of M rows and N columns will pass through at least 3 nodes in ON state. The superposition of such sneak currents would easily overwhelm the desired signal from the target cell. However, even in the shortest sneak path there will exist one RRAM element through which the current runs "backwards," and therefore the current can be reduced if this element is rectifying. With increasing array density and accordingly higher number of rows and columns the rectification ratio will have to be raised.

Selection capability for individual RRAM cells can be provided via connection to transistors or rectifying diodes, or by innovative RRAM devices with built-in diode functionality, which has been proposed in the literature recently (2010). The figures of merit for any offered solution are performance (e.g., achievable rectification ratio), ease of manufacturing, involved costs, and the impact on device density. Transistors with laterally aligned source and drain sections require more footprint than diodes built in vertically stacked layers, therefore the latter ones offer a better promise to achieve a 4 F^2 cell size ultimately desired for non-3D stacked RRAM devices. Various options to resolve the read-out issue, applicable for either unipolar or bipolar switching RRAM devices, are discussed in the rest of this section.

Lee et al. [234] proposed a low-temperature grown Pt/*p*-NiO_x/*n*-TiO_x/Pt diode as a suitable switching element for unipolar switching (e.g., NiO based) RRAMs. This type of diode exhibited good rectification characteristics at room temperature, with a rectification ratio of 10^5 at $+/-3$ V and a turn-on voltage of 2 V. A year later Lee et al. [162] announced that even more improvement may be derived from the usage of *p*-CuO_x/*n*-$InZnO_x$ diodes which deliver a current density increase by 2 orders of magnitude ($> 10^4$ A/cm^2) as compared to *p*-NiO_x/*n*-TiO_x diodes. While epitaxial Si-based diodes require high processing temperatures and are difficult to grow on metallic layers, the proposed semiconductor-based Pt/*p*-NiO_x/*n*-TiO_x/Pt diode can be manufactured at a processing temperature below 300°C, rendering it a suitable candidate for incorporation in 3D stackable cross-point structures.

Chang et al. [235] proposed a SiO_2-based RRAM device with built-in diode functionality as a solution to provide isolation for unipolar RS devices without a need for either a transistor or diode. This device exhibits diode rectifying characteristics for both set and reset states. They produced a schematics drawing of the structure of such a 0T1R RRAM cell and its perceived programming mechanism, involving a sequence of soft breakdown (SBD), hard breakdown (HBD), reset and set steps. The SBD induces percolation paths between the Si substrate and the poly gate. During a subsequent hard breakdown of poly Si from the N^+ gate breaks through the thin tunnel oxide, a phenomenon called "dielectric breakdown induced epitaxy" (DBIE) occurred. Severe Joule heating to temperatures close to the melting point of Si ($T_{crit} \sim 1400$°C) induced by the reset current and the migration of O^{2-} ions into the molten Si led to the formation of a Si-rich oxide layer once the current is turned off and the temperature drops. During set operation at lesser current and lower Joule heating as compared to the reset operation, Si filaments through oxide form in a process similar to electromigration. This set/reset switching between Si filament and SiO_2 establishes the memory switching behavior. The reset operation significantly lowers the forward current and enables a wide sensing margin over 3 orders of magnitude. High temperature retention of both HRS and LRS over more than 1000 h of baking at 150°C could be demonstrated, as well as good read disturb immunity. However, the required set and reset voltages of -7 V and -9 V, respectively, are high, with negative impact on power consumption. The cycling test data published in 2010 did not exceed 100 unipolar cycles.

With respect to device innovations offering built-in rectification properties applicable to bipolar switching devices, Jo et al. [236] presented a novel $Pr_{0.7}Ca_{0.3}MnO_3$ (PCMO)/Al-based switching memory with self-formed Schottky barrier due to a redox reaction at the PCMO/Al interface. The *I–V* curves of such a device can be separated into three regions. In region I the curve shows Schottky diode-like behavior in the LRS state, indicative of a metal-semiconductor (MS) structure. Region II indicates metal-oxide-semiconductor (MOS) behavior in the HRS state, going along with the formation of AlO_x. Region III is a transition region changing MS to MOS, or MOS to MS. Owing to AlO_x formation by oxidation at the PCMO/Al interface, the *I–V* characteristics are similar to that of a conventional MOS device. Using appropriate biasing conditions for the selected and unselected cells, the stability for read and set/reset operations were determined for worst case conditions. It was found that the read operation was limited by unselected cells while the set stability was restricted by HRS and the reset stability by LRS. Fabricated prototype devices with 50 nm electrode diameter exhibited read stability through 10^5 pulses (at read time of 10 μs) and set/reset stability through at least 10^4 pulses under worst case conditions (see Fig. 38). Such results, although not fully satisfactory, seem encouraging for initial data.

Another option to provide rectification properties for bipolar switching RRAM devices was offered by Waser et al. [237], namely the back-to-back connection of ZrO_x/HfO_x-based RRAM elements, i.e., the series-connection of $Pt/ZrO_x/HfO_x$/BE with BE/HfO_x/ZrO_x/Pt. Each of the two combined devices acts alternately as a selection device during voltage sweeps of either positive or negative bias. The read-out margin was found to be significantly improved. In comparison to a $Pt/ZrO_x/HfO_x$/BE control sample, the back-to-back connected device allowed the integration of 20 times more word lines.

Read-out accuracy can moreover be improved by circuitry modifications. The particular state (HRS or LRS) of an individual RRAM cell state is determined by comparison of the read current signal with a reference current, I_{REF}. Improvement in read accuracy is obtainable by applying a current reference circuit including at least 3 (rather than 1) RRAM reference cells coupled in parallel with another to provide a better defined averaged reference current to the sense amplifier circuits [238, 240]. Moreover a shift of the reference current value away from the midpoint between current values representing "0" and "1" has been proposed [222] to provide benefits if the resistance distribution of one of the states is significantly broader than the other.

Furthermore a design and write procedure to allow high-speed write-in based on RRAM-only architecture (without

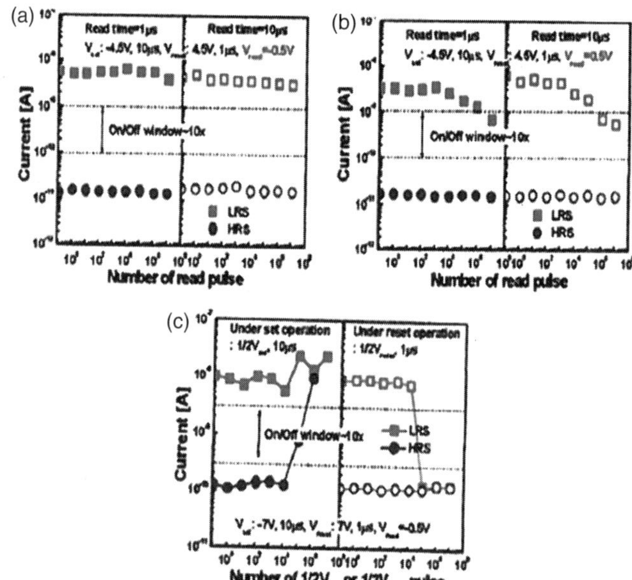

Figure 38. $Pr_{0.7}Ca_{0.3}MnO_3/AlO_x$ based resistive switching memory with self-formed Schottky barrier for application in cross-point structure without selection devices. Note the disturbance under selected (a) and unselected (b) cell operation, as well as the ISET and IRESET distributions (c) under worst case conditions. Reprinted with permission from [236], M. Jo et al., "VLSI Tech. Dig.," p. 53, 2010. © 2010, IEEE.

involvement of SRAMs) has been proposed in a 2010 patent application [241].

More specific auxiliary circuits may come into play for special types of resistive switching memory. For copper sulfide-based conductive bridge memory, for example, a special control circuit has been designed [242] with the goal to alleviate the negative effects of "overprogramming" of nanobridge formation/dissolution. Excessive thickening or excessive dissolution of a bridge may lead to a longer programming time for the subsequent program step or result in degraded cycling endurance due to an increase of stress on the switches. The auxiliary circuit monitors the voltage drop on a memory cell and thereby ensures timely completion of the on-going programming step before overprogramming can occur.

5.5. Current Status of RRAM R&D and Commercialization

The International Technology Roadmap for Semiconductors (ITRS) of 2009 [243] lists the following minimum requirements for near future RRAM products: cell area 10 F^2, read time ≤ 15 ns, data retention ≥ 10 years (presumably at 85°C), endurance $\geq$ 1E5 cycles, and read operation voltage ≤ 2.5 V. With respect to best projections for RRAMs it gives the following values: read time < 10 ns, write/erase times < 20 ns, endurance $\geq$ 1E6 cycles, write operation voltage 3 V, read operation voltage 0.7 V, and a cell area size of 5 F^2 with feature sizes of 5–10 nm. Other important requirements [244] are $I_{RESET} \leq 100$ μA, ON/OFF ratio ≥ 10, scalability down to 4 F^2, a minimum feature size of ultimately 5–10 nm, 3D-stacking capability, as well as CMOS compatibility. A compilation of RRAM performance data extracted from selected literature from 2005 to 2010 [245–249] is shown in Table 2. Although far from complete, this table gives a rough assessment of the performance of recent test chips versus the perceived requirements on an industry product. Three messages can be read from these data: First, that unipolar switching RRAMs do generally require higher reset currents (exception: NiO trilayer [139]) than bipolar switching RAMs and that they offer higher ON/OFF ratios. In Table 2, data for CB RAMs (although exhibiting bipolar switching too) have been listed separately from data related to non-CB BRS RAMs. Second, that the best of the listed (non-CB)BRS/CB RAM results already meet or come very close to meeting all of the above mentioned performance requirements. For some systems individual targets are even significantly exceeded (e.g., very low I_{RESET} and $V_{SET/RESET}$, V_{READ} values for CB RAMs, switching times of 2–4 ns and endurance over 1E8 – 1E9 cycles for particular BRS RAMs).

Third, although the best results are excellent and very encouraging, these performance data have only been obtained from kbit–Mbit [179] test chips exhibiting densities still several orders of magnitude away from the target range. Several of these test chips have been built in 180 nm or 90 nm CMOS technology. The smallest active cell sizes studied were in the range of 20–30 nm, but the corresponding pitch sizes were not shrunk correspondingly.

Thus, although RRAM R&D has made significant progress over the past decade, RRAM technology is still immature and with respect to its roadmap for attractive product densities still years behind competing NVM technologies. Nevertheless, RRAM development work is being pursued by more than a dozen companies worldwide, a mixture of well-established companies and start-ups including, for example Adesto Technologies, 4DS, Elpida, Fujitsu, Hewlett Packard, Hynix, IBM, NEC, Samsung, Sharp, Spansion, and Unity Semiconductor. The latter one has entered a joint RRAM development program with Micron in the meantime and has announced extremely aggressive plans for 1 Gbit test chips in 2012–2014 and terabit (!!) RRAM products after 2014. Elpida and Sharp have also entered RRAM co-development, aiming at commercial products in 2013.

RRAM employment is envisioned for either embedded or stand-alone NVM applications. Embedded devices, exhibiting a 1T1R (1 transistor, 1 resistor) cell structure, may be used for code as well as data storage. The industry trend points to using TMO-based bipolar switching RRAMs or conductive bridge RAMs for such applications needing high operation speeds. Stand-alone RRAMs, targeting for data storage applications, on the other hand will be built as 3D cross-point arrays to achieve maximum density. Transition metal or perovskite-type oxides are the preferred material choices to ensure operation at sufficiently low power. Node selection is achieved by incorporation of diodes (1D1R cell structure) since the build-in of transistors is forbidden by

Table 2. Compilation of RRAM device data from literature (2005–2010).

Switching type	System	I_{reset} [μA]	V_{reset} [V]	V_{set} [V]	V_{read} [V]	Switching time [ns]	ON/OFF ratio	Retention time	Endurance cycles	Reference	Year of public	Comments
URS	$Ru/Ta_2O_5/TiO_x/RuRe$	~200	0.45–0.65	1.5–2.8			~100	>120 hrs (100°C)	1E5	[191]	2010	
URS	$Ru/NiO/WO_x/W$	1000	~0.5	~1.0			~1000			[245]	2009	
	$Pt/TiO_2/Pt$	3E4 – 5E4			0.3		≥ 1000			[201]	2007	but, I_{reset} < 1 mA (BRS)
URS	?/NiO/?	≥ 500	~0.5	~1.0						[177]	2006	I_{set} = 0.5 mA in 180 nm for cell area of CMOS 0.05 μm^2
URS	$?/NiO/Pt/Ti/SiO_2/Si$	~100							1E5	[139]	2005	NiO trilayer varying O content
BRS	$TiN/Ti/HfO_x/TiN$	25	−1.5	1.5		≤ 10	≥ 100	≥ 10 yrs (150°C)	1E8	[163]	2010	1 kbit
BRS	$Ni/WO_3/W$	~180			0.6			≥ 10 yrs (115°C) 1600 hrs (150°C)	1E4	[228]	2010	
BRS	$TaN/Cu_xSi_yO/M1$		−1.0	2.0			≥ 50	≥ 10 yrs (150°C)		[192]	2010	
BRS	$Pt/Al/Pr_{0.7}Ca_{0.3}MnO_3/Pt$						~10		≥ 1E4 (set oper.)	[240]	2010	V_{set} = −4.5 V 50 nm diameter
BRS	$?/WO_3/?$	~100	−1.5	2.0		2	≥ 10		≥ 1E8	[246]	2009	
BRS	$?/TiO_2/Ta_2O_5/?$	200	−1.5	4.0			≥ 1000	≥ 10 yrs (150°C)	1E6	[247]	2009	
BRS	$Pt(Ir)/Ta_2O_5/Pt(Ir)$	≤ 170	−1.5	2.0		≤ 10	≥ 10	≥ 10 yrs (85°C)	1E9	[154]	2008	8 kbit
BRS	$TiN/TiO_2/HfO_x/TiN$	→25	<1.5			5	~1000	≥ 10 yrs (200°C)	1E6	[162]	2008	
CB	$TE/TiTe_x/Cu–GeSbTe/TiTe_x/SiO_2/BE$	30–90	−1.0	2.0	+/− 0.6		≥ 30	200 hrs (150°C)	2E5	[248]	2010	for 200 nm diameter in 180 nm CMOS
CB	$Ag/GeSe_x$		−0.2	0.2	0.15					[249]	2007	
CB	Ag/GeSe/W	≤ 20	−0.2		0.15	≤ 50		≥ 10 yrs (150°C)	1E6	[179]	2007	2 Mbit in 90 nm CMOS
CB	Cu_2S					5E3 – 3.2E4				[242]	2005	1 kbit in 180 nm CMOS

space constraints. Successful stacking of 1D1R arrays has already been demonstrated. For example, Lee et al. [162] reported on 2-stack RRAM devices in 2007.

Several serious issues still have to be addressed along the difficult path toward commercialization of RRAM technology. Hopefully the wide range of possible materials can be narrowed down quickly to the few most promising ones to focus the industry resources to find an improved understanding of the mechanisms and trade-offs involved. Bipolar switching materials, for example, promise lower power consumption than unipolar switching materials, but the need for two voltage/current polarities renders the circuit design more complex. Loss of switching stability and uniformity is of particular concern with filamentary RRAMs, while a fatigue issue as a result of oxygen ion diffusion is expected when applying RRAMs operating via a non-filamentary switching mechanism. Long-term stability in stochiometry will be very critical for the latter device class. Irrespective of the material choice, all parameters degrading switching uniformity, e.g., the density of material defects, film roughness, or CD variations due to patterning, will have to be monitored more tightly and be improved with device size. Material choices will be determined not only by device performance but also by the ease and boundary conditions of material processing. NiO, for example, is favored by many, yet it is a material that is difficult to etch. More mature processing know-how exists, for example, for HfO_2, already established as high-k gate material. Low-thermal-budget processing will be required to avoid device integration issues. This will practically exclude noble metal electrode materials. In general CMOS compatibility must be maintained for all materials and processes. Degradation mechanisms must be studied more carefully and suitable reliability models have to be developed in order to guarantee adequate retention properties. Reliability improvement will be of particular importance for RRAM devices targeting code storage applications. And finally, of paramount importance, cost-of-ownership for mass production must be brought down rigorously.

6. EMERGING NVM TECHNOLOGIES—MOLECULAR AND POLYMER NON-VOLATILE MEMORY DEVICES

Non-volatile memory devices containing films of polymers or molecules sandwiched between metal electrodes have gained considerable interest over the last years. Molecular or polymer films can be cheaply deposited on substrates by various techniques, such as spray, spin or dip coating, or ink-jet printing. The low cost of processing is therefore one attractive feature of "molecular memories" or "polymer memories," others are the promise for easy scalability—in principle down to individual molecules in the case of molecular memories—and their unique suitability for special applications like flexible electronics. A wide variety of organic materials (see review article by Scott and Bozano (2007) which contains an extensive literature list [250]) has been investigated for NVM applications. The switching mechanisms in operation may induce either a capacitance change or a resistance change in the device structure.

One way to obtain memories operating via the capacity change mode is to sandwich between the capacitor electrode organic films that can be electrochemically oxidized or reduced under the influence of an applied electric field, such as ferrocene-derivates [251, 252] or metallo-porphyrine compounds [251, 253]. Under the influence of an electrical bias, carriers will tunnel in and out of the redox molecules and change the amount of charge in these molecules. The organic species employed are chemically bonded to one of the capacitor plates. Ferrocene compounds, for example, may be attached to the substrate via aliphatic linker chains. Modification of the length of such links will alter the requirement for the programming voltage.

An alternative option to obtain a capacitance change-driven memory is the incorporation of a ferroelectric organic film, e.g., poly(vinyliden difluoride) (PVDF) or a co-polymer of PVDF with trifluoroethylene [254], between the capacitor electrodes. The bistable ferroelectric polarization of such materials can be directed towards either of the biased capacitor plates, and the polarization orientation is reversible if the applied voltage is high enough. Organic ferroelectric materials have not only been employed for 2-terminal devices but also for 3-terminal devices, such as ferroelectric field-effect transistor (FeFET) structures [255]. For this application also non-fluorine-containing compounds, like a polyvinylalcohol/fullerene compound [256] mixture, have been employed, besides the materials mentioned above. Currently the switching times of devices using ferroelectric organic materials are 1–3 orders of magnitude longer than a benchmark target of 1 μs, a minimum requirement for flash replacement.

Organic materials usable for NVMs that operate via resistance change outnumber those that induce capacitance change by far. The organic semiconductors used as insulator in metal-insulator-metal (MIM) structures include molecular compounds (e.g., anthracene [257], tetracene [258], certain fluorescent dyes [259, 260], and homogeneous, e.g., polystyrene [261]), polyacrylates [261], or polybiphenyls [262] or non-homogeneous macromolecular/polymer compounds created by glow-discharge of benzene [263, 264], acetylene [264], or styrene [264]. A Pb/glow-discharged poly(divinylbenzene)/Pb element showed resistance changes by several orders of magnitude at operation voltages equal to or below 2 V, however, the retention time was half an hour [254] only and damage after switching was observed.

More complex material choices for molecular/polymer memories include donor–acceptor complexes and conjugated oligomers/polymers doped with electron donors or acceptors.

In donor–acceptor complexes organic donor compounds like tetracyanoquinodimethane (TCNQ) or 2-amino-4,5-imidazoledicarbonitrile [265] may be coupled with Cu or be combined with an organic acceptor [266, 267]. CuTCNQ, in particular, has been researched in detail using various investigation techniques [268–270]. Mixed-valence conduction [268] and the formation/rupture of Cu filaments [271] have been suggested as switching mechanisms, but these explanations remain controversial.

Purely organic donor–acceptor complexes have also been investigated. Such materials may be manufactured by simply mixing the components [266, 267], by incorporation of the components in host polymers [272], or by deposition of organic bilayer systems [273]. Further options are the attachment of both acceptor and donor functionalities on the same molecule [274] or on the backbone of a polymer [275].

With conjugated oligomers/polymers doped with electron donors or acceptors—NaCl containing polyphenylacetylene [276] is an example for this material class—the resistance switching is attributed to bias-induced electrochemical oxidation/reduction of the conjugated compound, enabling a switching between a conductive and a non-conductive state. On the other hand, for systems containing rotaxene (a dumbbell shaped molecule threaded through a "macrocyle") [277], bipyridine or nitrophenyl complexes field-induced changes in conformational structure have been invoked to cause modification of the electronic barrier height and thus the resistance of the devices, although the switching mechanism remains controversial. With bipyridine bridged between two Au electrodes, the shape of the bipyridine molecule may be changed as a result of physical distortion. Fabrication of the top contact without degradation of the molecule, electrode shortening, and metal migration are issues to be addressed with such extremely scaled molecular memories. A cross-bar point array of rotaxene-containing elements has been built with an interconnect pitch of 33 nm, which corresponds to a density of 10^{11} bits/cm^2 [277].

Organic–inorganic hybrid systems, such as host polymers including inorganic nanoparticles (NPs) of Ag, Pt, or ZnO (a.o.), as well as polymer-nanocrystal memories containing metal oxide coated nanocrystals of Ni, Al, or Au, have gained considerable interest during the past years. The investigation of such systems was initiated by the observation of bistable switching in film stacks comprised of a "floating" metallic layer between two organic semiconductors [278], and the subsequent insight that a separation of the metal into disconnected particles would allow the optimum utilization of the observed phenomena. Polystyrene [184], dimethylanthracene [280], polyfluorene with cyano ligands [281], or conjugated polymers like poly(3-hexylthiophene) [282] are examples for host polymers employed in these hybrid systems. Metallic nanoparticles are often coated with metal oxide acting as a tunnel barrier or a colloid stabilizer. Uncoated Au nanoparticles can be stabilized by bonds to amino or thiol ligands of the surrounding polymer. Surface functionalization by an amino-terminated self-assembled monolayer (SAM) had been employed in the manufacturing of Au NP-pentacene memory transistors [283], leading to a density of 2–5 × 10^{10} NP/cm^2 (with estimated 40–100 charges/NP), which is 4–5 times higher than in absence of surface functionality. The observed ON/OFF ratio was ~3 × 10^4 and the threshold voltage shift was 22 V, whereas a reference device without Au nanoparticles exhibited a V_t shift of about 2 V only and a much lower ON/OFF ratio of ~2.2. This striking difference is the result of different switching mechanisms in operation.

The majority of devices containing NP/polymer layers show negative differential resistance for a voltage range above the switching threshold. It has been verified that NPs contribute to on-state conductance. This fact was interpreted to be the result of charge-carrier hopping between NPs and could also explain the generally weak influence of the employed organic material on the device properties. Charge-trapping on NPs will lead to the build-up of a space-charge field that can inhibit further charge injection and influence the flow of mobile carriers to varying extent, depending on the magnitude of the external electric field applied. A model related to this so-called "Couloumb blockade" effect was first developed by Simmons and Verderber [181] and was later extended by Tang et al. [285]. The extended model led to a better fit between experimental results and theoretical predictions. Highly correlated electron effects have been suggested as an alternative mechanism [286].

Au NPs were also employed for an actively addressable 16-byte organic non-volatile bistable memory (ONBM) device on plastic substrate [287], purportedly the first of its kind reported in the literature. Its chemistry, device architecture, and the operation sequence are depicted in Figure 39. Such a device aims at applications for flexible electronics. No change in electronic performance occurred during compressive stress tests down to a bending radius of 5 mm.

In general 3D stacking and integration into CMOS processing are possible with macromolecular-nanocrystal memory systems. Such devices offer rather high ON/OFF ratios, but severe weaknesses are long programming times (up to ms range) and very short retention times. For Au NP based memories devices, for example, retention times ranging from about 1 h to a few days have been reported.

The electrical characteristics of memory devices utilizing the above mentioned organic switching material options vary strongly from group to group, but even within the same material class. Frequently, the investigation of the intrinsic properties of such systems suffers from lacking reproducibility of the switching behavior due to various effects like pinhole formation, contamination, non-homogeneity of

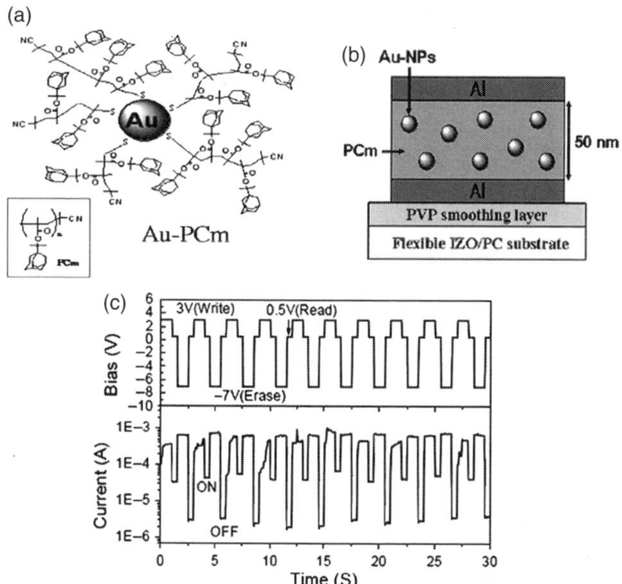

Figure 39. 16-Byte ONBM array on plastic substrate (a) chemistry, (b) schematics of device structure, and (c) write-read-erase-read sequence. Reprinted with permission from [287], H.-T. Lin et al., "IEDM 2007 Proc.," p. 233 (S9-P6), 2007. © 2007, IEEE.

the films, or damage during top electrode deposition, a.o., which render the determination of the actual root causes of the switching behavior rather difficult. Some of the invoked switching mechanisms, such as filamentary conduction via metallic bridges [288] or high mobility paths, electrochemical processes in doped conducting polymers [276], or trap-controlled tunneling [289], are similar to those discussed with inorganic RRAM devices, others are specific to the organic nature of the switching material, as for example field-induced electron/hole transfer in charge-transfer complexes, resistance change due to configuration changes in molecules, or the formation of carbonaceous filaments in plasma polymerized films [264]. For a few systems, as for example devices with Al/polymer/Al stacks, evidence for localized currents flowing through filamentary structures was deduced from the appearance of "hot spots" in infrared microscopy images. Upon cycling such hot spots reappeared at the same locations. For MIM structures involving Al electrodes, the originally plausible assumption that switching originated within the polymer had to be discarded because it turned out that the resistive switching occurs actually in native aluminum oxide formed over Al, whereas the role of the polymer is limited to the prevention of catastrophic breakdown of the device. Reproducible switching [290] could be obtained in Al (bottom electrode)/20 nm Al_2O_3/80 nm spirofluorene polymer/Ba/Al (top electrode) stacks in which native aluminum oxide was deliberately replaced by a sputtered Al_2O_3 layer of controlled thickness. I/V characteristics of this system as well as test results regarding current density stability are depicted in Figure 40(a–b). A forming step with an electrical field of 10^9 V/m is required to initiate soft break-down of the Al_2O_3 which changes the resistive behavior of the structure to non-linear field switchable resistance. The programming field changes the resistance of the filament formed in Al_2O_3 via migration of oxygen. Erase, write, and read steps are carried out at different voltages. $V_{erase} > V_{write} > V_{read}$, are approximately 9, 5, and 0.5 V, respectively. Long switching dead times in the range of ms, sensitivity to oxygen, and high erase and write voltages are serious concerns for such polymer memories containing Al_2O_3 films.

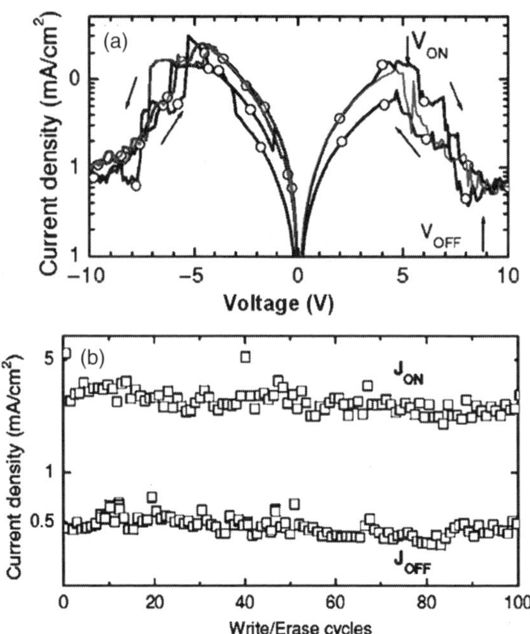

Figure 40. I/V characteristics and cycling behavior of polymer memory containing Al_2O_3 film (stack: Al/20 nm Al_2O_3/80 nm polymer/Ba-Al) (a) I/V characteristics after electroforming step (1st scan is the black line, 2nd scan is the gray line, V_{on} and V_{off} are the voltages used for switching) (b) reproduciblity of current densities during 100 write/erase cycles (+0.5 V read pulse after +5 V write pulse (for 100 ms) or +10 V erase pulse (for 100 ms)). Reprinted with permission from [290], F. Verbakel et al., *Appl. Phys. Lett.* 91, 192103 (2007). © 2007, The American Institute of Physics.

Device data confirming sufficiently good performance of organic material-based RRAMs for all relevant figures of merit are still lacking. Power consumption (assuming a switching energy/bit <1 nJ) and ON/OFF ratio requirements are unlikely to become performance-limiting factors. More difficult challenges will be to achieve the current density target (a value of 4 A/cm^2 has been estimated for a low-performance benchmark device of 1 μm^2 size exhibiting read times around 1 μs [250]) to ensure sufficient separation of the resistance distributions of LRS and HRS states, to improve rectification properties, and to meet retention and endurance requirements. Future research efforts will have to focus on the elimination of artifacts and aim at a better understanding of the switching and transport mechanisms as the basis to enable an accurate assessment of performance trade-offs, e.g., between switching and retention times, or between retention time and ON-state current. With respect to endurance, systems involving only charge transport will behave quite differently than devices involving mass transport phenomena.

With respect to processing issues, better solutions must be found to alleviate the danger of degrading the polymer/molecular layer during the deposition of the top electrode. Frequently liquid electrolyte contacts are employed which are not compatible with IC processing. Solubility of the deposited organic film in the solvents of subsequent lithography or multi-level stack formation steps is another issue which could, however, be alleviated by the development of composite films containing a thermally curable polyimide component [291] or of single-component polymers that can be cross-linked under the influence of UV light [292].

All in all, usage of macromolecular/polymer memory devices on an industrial scale seems to be even farther out than the manufacturing of RRAM devices based on inorganic switching materials. Nevertheless, during the past decade, R&D activities in this field have been driven by the hope to create at low manufacturing costs "smart" memory polymers of high density with optimally tailored properties to enable switching between stable states, addressability, and charge storage. Assuming scaling capability—in the extreme, down to individual molecules—the organic layer of a molecular memory should not be the limiting factor for scaling, but the density of its interconnects. For a 32 nm interconnect pitch, corresponding to 16 nm technology, densities around 100 Gbit/cm^2 could be expected in principle. Joint research activities have been started, for example, between Intel and Thin Film Technologies (Sweden), AMD and Coatue

(MA), Hewlett Packard and Princeton University, by Lucent Technologies' Bell Laboratories, and Philips and Eindhoven University of Technology. Potential applications are low-end replacement for standard NAND flash devices, or polymer memory devices for identification tags, etc.

7. OVERALL CONCLUSION

Expectations that further scaling of DRAM and flash devices might face insurmountable obstacles when reaching the 20–10 nm minimum feature size range have induced wide-spread R&D efforts by semiconductor vendors and academic research institutes over the past decade to develop innovative non-volatile memory device types. Uncertain about the most promising avenue, several (about 9) companies are pursuing development of two (in rare cases even more) of the four non-volatile memory technology options involving inorganic switching materials: FeRAM, PCM, MRAM, RRAM. The majority of the companies are developing only one new technology, including a few start-ups that were founded to focus on one particular innovative NVM option. By mid-2011 about 20 companies were involved in MRAM development, however not all of them with the intention to go into device manufacturing later on, more than a dozen in RRAM R&D and about 10 in PCM development. RRAM had gained momentum, while it had become already too late for tentative newcomers to jump onto the PCM wagon. Regarding MRAM R&D, the industry focus has shifted away from scaling-limited magnet-field induced MRAM to STTRAM technology. After more than 10 years of FeRAM device manufacturing history, FeRAM density values are still only in the lower Mbit range and FeRAM related R&D work has lost steam, in view of the better scaling capability provided by competing technologies. Yet several companies have become involved in research activities on organic ferroelectric compounds. As for polymer/molecular memories in general, its seems doubtful that organic material-based systems will ever meet the long-term retention and reliability requirements expected from devices to compete with and possibly even replace high-performance flash. But nevertheless polymer/molecular memories might gain ground eventually as cost-effective solutions for low- and mid-performance products and for applications with unique requirements (e.g., flexible electronics).

PCM, STTRAM, and RRAM remain as serious contenders to gain significant portions of the market of non-volatile memory devices in the near or mid-term future. A very competitive NVM product market can be expected during the next decade, as representatives of these three innovative NVM technologies will be launched generation after generation. Performance characteristics of the various device types will vary, but the ever expanding list of potential applications will ensure that suitable product-customer matches will be found. Timeliness to market and performance will determine the near- and mid-term success of the individual products. PCM technology has seemingly a time advantage of about 3 years on the product density roadmap when compared to MRAM technology. One Gbit PCMs should be on the market by late 2011/2012, while MRAM devices might pass the 1 Gbit barrier sometime in 2014/2015. In that time frame, one company announced a 4 Gbit *p*-STTRAM, however, by mid-2011 the very first generation of STTRAMs—most likely with densities in the 16–64 Mbit range—had not yet reached the market. RRAM technology is even farther behind in the R&D race towards device commercialization and corresponding product roadmaps are still rather vaguely defined. First available RRAM devices (of yet unspecified density, most likely of the bipolar mode type), might be introduced in 2012/2013. An announcement for terabit RRAM products "after 2014" (or 2015 at the earliest) cannot be realistically assessed until 2013.

Table 3 [243, 293] contains information about the performance of available NVM products and experimental results from prototypes of emerging technology options, reflecting the status obtained by 2007/2008. An estimate on the ultimate performance characteristics of the contending technologies is given in Table 4 [293]. The data in these two

Table 3. Performance of product or prototype devices of NVM technologies (status 2007/2008).

Parameter	Unit	NAND flash	Trapping charge	FeRAM	Conv. MRAM magnetic field-induced	STTRAM	PCM	Fuse/Antifuse RRAM	Nanoionic RRAM	Electrical effects RRAM	Macro-molecular memories	Molecular memories
Feature size	nm	90	65	180	90	50	65	180	90	1000	250	30
Cell area	F^2	5	6	22	20	16	5		8			
Read time	ns	50	14	45	20	~40	60		< 50		~10	
W/E time	ns	100–1000	2E4 – 2E6	10	20	2	50–120	5–10	5	100	10	2E8
Write cycles		> 1E15	> 1E15	E14	> 3E16	> 1E12	E8	> 1E6	> 1E9	> 1E3	> 1E6	> 2E3
Read voltage	V	2	1.6	0.9–3.3	1.5	0.7	3	0.4	0.15	0.7	1	0.5
Write voltage	V	15	7–9	0.9–3.3	1.5	+/− 1	3	0.5–1	0.6–0.2	3–5	+/− 2	+/− 1.5
Retention time	yr	> 10	> 10	> 10	> 10	> 10	> 10	0.7– >10	> 10	> 1	0.5	0.2
Write energy/bit	J	> 1E – 14	> 1E – 13	3E – 14	7E – 11	4E – 12	5E – 12	1E – 12	5E – 14	1E – 9	1E – 13	

Source: Reprinted with permission from [243], International Technology Roadmap for Semiconductors (ITRS). http://www.itrs.net/reports.html, ITRS 2009 Ed. 2009 ITRS Table Files Links, Focus B Tables, Table ERD5 "Emerging Research Resistance-Based Memory Devices—Demonstrated and Projected Parameters; © 2009, International SEMATECH, Austin, USA" from [293], www.itrs.net/reports.html click 2010 Update/2010 Future Memory Devices Workshop Summary, Appendix 3, © 2009, International SEMATECH, Austin, USA.

Table 4. Projections for ultimate performance of flash and innovative NVM technologies.

Parameter	Unit	NAND flash	STTRAM	Nanothermal fuse/antifuse RRAM + PCM	Nanoionic RRAM	Electrical effects RRAM	Macro-molecular memories	Molecular memories
Feature size	nm	16	7–10	5–10	5–10	5–10	5–10	5
Cell area	F^2	2.5	6	8–5	8–5	8–5	8–5	5
Read time	ns		< 10	< 10	< 10	< 10	< 10	< 10
W/E time	ns	E4	< 2	< 10	< 20	< 20	< 10	< 40
Write cycles		> 1E16	> 1E16	> 1E16	> 1E16	> 1E16	> 1E16	> 1E16
Read voltage	V	0.1–0.5	< 0.5	< 0.5	< 0.2	0.7	0.7	0.3
Write voltage	V	18–20	< 1	0.5–1	< 0.5	< 3	< 1	0.08
Retention time	yr	> 10	> 10	> 10	> 10	> 10	worse*	worse**
Write energy/bit	J		1E − 13	< 1E − 13 (PCM)	1E − 15	1E − 10		2E-19

* and **:The statements of ITRS experts in the original table provided by International SEMATECH were "Not known" for both columns which were modified by the authors to "worse," based on the expectation that retention times of >10 years are unlikely to be achieved with macromolecular or molecular devices. For the former device type (*), for example, retention times have not exceeded 6 months so far (2009/2010 status).

Source: Reprinted with permission from [293], www.itrs.net/reports.html click 2010 Update/2010 Future Memory Devices Workshop Summary, Appendix 3, © 2009, International SEMATECH, Austin, USA.

tables have been extracted from ITRS Roadmap 2009 and 2010 publications.

A few insights can be derived from Table 3. While already impressively small cell areas of 5 F^2 and 8 F^2 could be demonstrated for PCM and nanoionic RRAM devices, respectively, FeRAM has evidently already lost the scaling race. STTRAM prototypes exhibited the shortest write time requirement (2 ns) of all contending technology options and their endurance (> 1E12) was higher by at least 3 orders of magnitude as compared to PCM or the best RRAM option. Sub-1 V voltage operation (for write/erase/read) could be demonstrated for Redox RRAM and STTRAM devices while PCM products operated around 3 V. When comparing RRAM device types only, electric effects RRAMs fared worse with respect to all listed parameters of merit, thus future R&D activities will probably primarily concentrate on redox RRAMs ("nanothermal" and "nanoionic" RRAMs in the terminology of the ITRS experts). Nanoionic RRAMs exhibited lower write and read voltage and lower write energy requirements and offered better endurance when compared to (nanothermal) fuse/antifuse RRAM devices. Retention lifetimes for fuse/antifuse devices did not exceed 8 months, yet their unipolar switching mechanism renders them attractive because their circuitry has to take account of only 1 current polarity. What concerns (macro)molecular memories, their retention times were found to be even worse, namely in the range of 2–6 months only. The organic nature of their switching layers will make it much more difficult and most likely impossible to meet a > 10 year retention lifetime target.

When looking at the projection of the ultimate performance of competing device technologies, as shown in Table 4, the differences between the various device types become smaller than in the experimentally verified performance data from 2007/2008. Surely R&D people will work very hard to alleviate the perceived performance weaknesses of their target technology. Yet, it has to be said that performance predictions for device generations to be manufactured more than a decade later will in general reflect best case scenarios. The predictions will gain in precision over time as the impact of pending issues with increased device shrinkage can be assessed in a more quantitative manner. The validity of concerns that RRAM devices exhibiting filamentary switching may suffer from retention/endurance degradation with scaling, for example, will become only verifiable once aggressive cell size targets are actually reached. Possibly even processing related factors, e.g., a varying degree of influence of the patterning technology for very small feature sizes, may contribute to performance differentiation between the competing technologies. Nevertheless, Table 4 predicts some performance differences between the 3 major technology contenders, namely, read, write, and erase times stay within a range of 10–20 ns in general, only the *W/E* times for STTRAM devices are even lower (2 ns). As already seen for experimental data of 2007/2008, nanoionic RRAMs maintain their read and write voltage requirement advantage versus both nanothermal devices (fuse/antifuse RRAMs and PCMs lumped together) and STTRAMs. Best-case predictions with respect to the ultimately achievable minimum feature size and cell area limit MRAM devices to 7 nm and 6 F^2, respectively, while 5 nm and 5 F^2 are considered possible for both the PCM and STTRAM technologies. The more conservative predictions assume an ultimate feature size of 10 nm for all of the listed technology options, only molecular memories fare better in principle (5 nm). A technology outlook for the year 2022, by the ERD-ERM work group of ITRS [294], supports the indication that MRAM devices, due to their complex stack structure of 10–12 layers, will be somewhat more difficult to shrink than PCM devices. A minimum feature size of 22 nm and a cell size of 20 F^2 is predicted for STTRAMs, while the corresponding values are 18 nm and 4.8 F^2, respectively, for PCM memories. This amounts to a density advantage by a factor of 6 for PCMs versus STTRAMs. In case this prediction holds, the currently existing back-log of about 3 years for the STTRAM behind the PCM technology on the device density roadmap will probably not be fully erased nor at least significantly reduced during the next decade.

RRAMs reported in conference publications during 2008–2010 have most likely raised the industry interest for this particular device technology option. Since RRAM stacks are much simpler than those of advanced MRAM structures, manufacturing costs for RRAMs will be lower than those for MRAMs. They are also expected to be lower in comparison to those for PCM memories with more complex switching material and more severe packaging demands. Assuming comparable device performance, this would be a decisive argument to favor RRAM versus MRAM or PCM technology. However, the enhanced attention of the industry to RRAM technology may derive not solely from its own perceived merits but might also be the result of apparent weaknesses of the alternatives, already farther matured technologies. Some analysts claim that phase change memories have run into power consumption issues recently, which purportedly induced many labs to put more emphasis on RRAM-related research. There are indications that the scaling of MRAM devices to the next generation is somewhat later than original industry announcements, probably primarily caused by the need to drive the recently developed STT approach to production quality. The comparatively lower level of maturity of RRAM technology might thus turn into an (at least temporary) advantage to attract more attention and more industry resources, as many of its own problems related to the manufacturing of commercial high density RRAM devices are still waiting to surface. IMEC has announced its intention to fabricate RRAM devices with feature sizes smaller than 20 nm by 2011, thereby employing an EUV lithography pre-manufacturing exposure tool available on site. Results like this would provide a better assessment of the ultimate potential of RRAM technology.

It will require a tremendous amount of commitment and hard work to push any NVM technology currently in development to a dominating position in a post-flash era. Flash technology should not be written off too early because the semiconductor industry will provide abundant resources in order to extend this established technology as far as possible. RRAM technology has been the latest in line with respect to the start of serious R&D efforts towards commercialization for NVM applications. Nevertheless, with the current, rather limited, knowledge available, it looks like a very strong contender. Can RRAM technology win the race to become a viable option to replace flash technology in the sub-15 (or 10) nm feature size regime? Can the last horse scrambling out of the start-house actually win the competition? With horse races it has happened before. Rarely, but it has happened.

REFERENCES

1. H. Ebbinghaus, "Memory; a Contribution to Experimental Psychology." (Trans. by H. A. Kuger and C. E. Bussenius), Dover Publications, Inc., New York 1964 (Originally published, 1885).
2. J. P. Eckert, J. W. Mauchley, H. Goldstein, and J. Brainerd, Desc. ENIAC and Comments on Electronic Digital Computing Machines, The Applied Mathematics Panel Report No. 171. 2R, Univ. Pennsylvania, Philadelphia, 1945.
3. R. H. Dennard, U.S. Patent 3387286, 1968.
4. N. Rodriguez, F. Gamiz, and S. Cristoloveanu, Patent Number: FR09/52452, Institut Nationalle de la Propiété Industrielle, 2009.
5. N. Rodriguez, S. Cristoloveanu, and F. Gamiz, "Proc. 2009 IEEE Int. SOI Conf.," p. 1, Foster City, CA, 2009.
6. F. Morishita, H. Noda, T. Gyohten, M. Okamoto, T. Ipposhi, S. Maegawa, K. Dosaka, and K. Arimoto, "Proc. IEEE Custom Integrated Circuits Conf. (CICC)," San Jose, CA, 2005.
7. F. Morishita and K Arimoto, Semiconductor memory device, US Patent 7652927, 2010.
8. S. Okhonin, M. Nagoga, J. M. Sallese, and P. Fazan, "SOI Conf. 2001 IEEE International, Digital Object Identifier: 10. 1109/SOIC. 2001. 958032," p. 153, 2001.
9. K. Ochii, M. Matsui, and O. Ozawa, Static random access memory, United States Patent 4901284, 1990.
10. H. Nakajima, "Digest of Tech. Papers, 36th IEEE Int. Solid-State Circuits Conf. (ISSCC)," New York, 1989, p. 60.
11. T. Shirato, Mask ROM-type semiconductor memory device, U.S. Patent 4500975, 1985.
12. C. W. Tsing and W. H. Henrich, Storage matrix, U.S. Patent 3,028,659, 1962.
13. D. J. Mcelroy, Method of making a high density floating gate electrically programmable ROM, U.S. Patent 4151021, 1979.
14. D. Frohman-Bentchkowsky, "IEEE ISSCC Tech. Dig.," p. 80, 1971.
15. W. Johnson, G. Perlegos, A. Renninger, G. Kuhn, and T. Ranganath, "IEEE ISSCC Dig. Tech.," p. 152, 1980.
16. F. Masuoka, M. Asano, H. Iwahasi, and T. Komuro, "1984 IEDM Tech. Dig.," p. 464, 1984.
17. F. Masuoka and H. Iizuka, Semiconductor Memory Device and Method for Manufacturing the Same, U.S. Patent 4531203, 1985.
18. D. Kahng and S. M. Sze, *The Bell System Tech. J* 46, 1288 (1967).
19. P. Paven, R. Bez, P. Ovivo, and E. Zanoni, "Proc. IEEE," p. 85, 1997.
20. http://www.pdl.cmu.edu/SDI/2009/slides/Numonyx.pdf.
21. http://www2.electronicproducts.com/NAND_vs_NOR_flash_technology-article-FEBMSY1-feb2002-html.aspx.
22. O. Auciello, J. F. Scott, and R. Ramesh, *Physics Today* 51, 22 (1998).
23. G. F. Derbenwick and A. F. Isaacson, *IEEE Circuits and Devices* 17, 20 (2001).
24. K. Inomata, *IEICE Transactions on Electronics* E84c, 740 (2001).
25. S. Lai and T. Lowrey, "2001 IEDM Tech. Dig.," p. 803, 2001.
26. I. G. Baek, M. S. Lee, S. Seo, M. J. Lee, D. H. Seo, D.-S. Suh, J. C. Park, S. O. Park, H. S. Kim, I. K. Yoo, U-In Chung, and J. T. Moon, "IEDM Tech. Dig.," p. 587, 2004.
27. S. Wu, *IEEE Trans. Electron Device* ED21, 499 (1974).
28. C. P. D. Araujo, J. F. Scott, and G. W. Taylor, "Ferroelectric Thin Films: Synthesis and Basic Properties." Gordon and Breach Publishers, Amsterdam, 1996.
29. S. S. Eaton, D. B. Butler, M. Paris, D. Wilson, and H. McNeile, "IEEE, Intl. Solid-State Circuit Conf. (ISSCC), Digest of Technical Papers," San Francisco, 1988, p. 130.
30. T. Sumi, N. Moriwaki, G. Nakane, T. Nakakuma, Y. Judai, Y. Uemoto, Y. Nagano, S. Hayashi, M. Azuma, E. Fujii, S.-I. Katsu, T. Otsuki, L. McMillan, C. Paz de Araujo, and G. Kano, "Dig. Tech. Papers, IEEE Intl. Solid-State Cir. Conf.," San Francisco, February, 1994, p. 268.
31. K.-H. Kim, J.-P. Han, S.-W. Jung, and T. P. Ma, *Electron Devic. Lett.* 23, 82 (2002).
32. K. Aziwa, Y. Kawashima, and H. Ishiwara, *Mater. Res. Soc. Symp. Proc.* 80, 113 (2005).
33. T. P. Ma and J.-P. Han, U.S. Patent 6067244, 2000.
34. J.-P. Han and T. P. Ma, *Integr. Ferroelectr.* 27, 1053 (1999).
35. T. P. Ma and J.-P. Han, *Electron Dev. Lett.* 23, 386 (2002).
36. N. A. Goriunova and B. T. Kolomiets, *Zurn. Techn. Fiz.* 25, 2069 (1955).
37. S. R. Ovshinsky, Symmetrical Current Controlling Device, U.S. Patent 3271591, 1966.
38. S. R. Ovshinsky, *Phys. Rev. Lett.* 21, 1450 (1968).
39. C. H. Sie, Memory Devices Using Bistable Resistivity in Amorphous As–Te–Ge Films, Ph.D. Dissertation, Iowa State University, Proquest/UMI Publication #69-20670, Ann Arbor, January, 1969.
40. S. J. Ahn, Y. J. Song, C. W. Jeong, J. M. Shin, Y. Fai, Y. N. Hwang, S. H. Lee, K. C. Ryoo, S. Y. Lee, J. H. Park, H. Horii, Y. H. Ha, J. H. Yi, B. J. Kuh, G. H. Koh, G. T. Jeong, H. S. Jeong, K. Kim,

and B. I. Ryu, "IEEE International Electron Devices Meeting 2004," IEDM Technical Digest, San Francisco, CA, 2004, p. 907.
41. S. J. Ahn, Y. N. Hwang, Y. J. Song, S. H. Lee, S. Y. Lee, J. H. Park, C. W. Jeong, K. C. Ryoo, J. M. Shin, J. H. Park, Y. Fai, J. H. Oh, G. H. Koh, G. T. Jeong, S. H. Joo, S. H. Choi, Y. H. Son, J. C. Shin, Y. T. Kim, H. S. Jeong, and K. Kim, "2005 Symposium on VLSI Technology," Digest of Technical Papers, Kyoto, Japan, 2005, p. 98.
42. J. Oh, J. Park, Y. Lim, H. Lim, Y. Oh, J. Kim, J. Shin, J. Park, Y. Song, K. Ryoo, D. Lim, S. Park, J. Kim, J. Kim, J. Yu, F. Yeung, C. Jeong, J. Kong, D. Kang, G. Koh, G. Jeong, H. Jeong, and K. Kim, "IEDM Tech. Dig.," p. 49, 2006.
43. http://www.technologyreview.com/Infotech/20148/?a = f.
44. D. Kau, S. Tang, I. V. Karpov, R. Dodge, B. Klehn, J. A. Kalb, J. Strand, A. Diaz, N. Leung, J. Wu, S. Lee, T. Langtry, K. Chang, C. Papagianni, J. Lee, J. Hirst, S. Erra, E. Flores, N. Righos, H. Castro, and G. Spadini, "IEDM Tech. Dig.," p. S27, 2009.
45. G. Servalli, "IEDM Tech. Dig.," p. 113, 2009.
46. http://www.samsung.com/us/aboutsamsung/news/newsIrRead.do?news_ctgry=irnewsrelease&page=1&news_seq=18828&rdoPeriod=ALL&from_dt = &to_dt=&search_keyword=.
47. H. Fritzsche, *Annu. Rev. Mater. Sci.* 2, 697 (1972).
48. R. Bez, "IEDM Tech. Dig.," p. 89, 2009.
49. W. Gawelda, J. Siegel, C. N. Afonso, V. Plausinaitiene, A. Abrutis, and C. Wiemer, *J. Appl. Phys*. 109, 123102 (2011).
50. M. Gill, T. Lowrey, and J. Park, "ISSCC 2002 Tech. Dig.," Vol. 12, p. 4, 2002.
51. D. K. Reinhard, F. O. Arntz, and D. Adler, *Appl. Phys. Lett*. 23, 521 (1973).
52. S. Hudgens and B. Johnson, *MRS Bull*. 29, 829 (2004).
53. A. Pirovano, A. Lacaita, A. Benvenuti, F. Pellizzer, and R. Bez, *IEEE Trans. Electron. Dev.* 51, 452 (2004).
54. A. Pirovano, A. Redaelli, F. Pellizzer, F. Ottogalli, M. Tosi, D. Ielmini, A. L. Lacaita, and R. Bez, *IEEE Trans. Device and Materials Reliability* 4, 422 (2004).
55. D. Ielmini, A. L. Lacaita, and D. Mantegazza, *IEEE Trans. Electron Dev*. 54, 308 (2007).
56. R. P. Hunt, *IEEE Trans. Mag*. 7, 150 (1971).
57. M. Baibich, J. M. Broto, A. Fert, F. Nguyen Van Dau, F. Petroff, P. Etienne, G. Creuzet, A. Friederch, and J. Chazelas, *Phys. Rev. Lett*. 61, 2472 (1988).
58. P. Grünberg, German Patent DE3820475 (C1), Issued December 1989, or U.S. Patent US4949039A, Issued August, 1990.
59. T. Miyazaki and N. Tezuka, *J. Magn. Magn. Mater*. 139, L231 (1995).
60. J. S. Moodera, L. R. Kinder, T. M. Wong, and R. Meservey, *Phys. Rev. Lett*. 74, 3273 (1995).
61. R. Scheuerlein, "ISSCC Dig. Tech. Papers," p. 128, 2000.
62. P. K. Naji, M. Durlam, S. Tehrani, J. Calder, and M. F. DeHerrera, "ISSCC Dig.," p. 122, 2001.
63. M. Julliere, *Phys. Lett*. 54A, 225 (1975).
64. D. Wang, C. Nordman, J. M. Daughton, Z. Qian, and J. Fink, *IEEE Trans. Magn*. 40, 2269 (2004).
65. S. Yuasa, T. Nagahama, A. Fukushima, Y. Suzuki, and K. Ando, *Nat. Mater.* 3, 868 (2004).
66. S. S. P. Parkin, C. Kaiser, A. Pan Cula, P. M. Rice, B. Hughes, M. Samant, and S. H. Yang, *Nat. Mat.* 3, 862 (2004).
67. S. Yuasa, A. Fusushimo, H. Kubota, Y. Suzuki, and K. Ando, *Appl. Phys. Lett*. 89, 042505 (2006).
68. W. H. Butler, X.-G. Zhang, T. C. Schulthess, and J. M. MacLaren, *Phys. Rev. B* 63, 054416 (2001).
69. W. H. Meiklejohn and C. P. Bean, *Phys. Rev*. 105, 904 (1957).
70. F. Z. Wang, *Appl. Phys. Lett*. 77, 2036 (2000).
71. Y. Zheng, X. Wang, D. You, and Y. Wu, *Appl. Phys. Lett*. 79, 2788 (2001).
72. H. Boeve, J. Das, L. Lagae, P. Peumans, C. Bruynscraede, K. Dessein, L. V. Melo, R. C. Sousa, P. P. Freitas, G. Borghs, and J. D. Boeck, *IEEE Trans. Magn*. 35, 282 (1999).
73. J. M. Daughton, *J. Appl. Phys*. 81, 3758 (1997).
74. E. C. Stoner and E. P. Wohlfarth, *Phil. Trans. R. Soc. London A* 24, 599 (1948).
75. M. Yoshikawa, T. Kai, M. Amano, E. Kitagawa, T. Nagase, M. Nakayama, S. Takahashi, T. Ueda, T. Kishi, T. Tsuchida, S. Ikegawa, Y. Asao, H. Yoda, Y. Fukuzumi, K. Nagahara, H. Numata, H. Hada, N. Ishiwata, and S. Tahara, *J. Appl. Phys.* 97, 10P508 (2005).
76. R. C. Sousa, I. L. Prejbeanu, D. Stanescu, B. Rodmacq, O. Redon, B. Dieny, J. Wang, and P. P. Freitas, *J. Appl. Phys*. 95, 6783 (2004).
77. R. S. Beech, J. A. Anderson, A. V. Pohm, and J. M. Daughton, *J. Appl. Phys*. 87, 6403 (2000).
78. D. W. Abraham and P. L. Trouilloud, U.S. Patent 6,385,082 B1, 2001.
79. B. Dieney and O. Redon, Patent WO2003043017, 2003.
80. J. P. Nozieres, B. Dieny, O. Redon, R. C. Sousa, and I. L. Prejbeanu, Patent WO200508671, 2004.
81. D. C. Worledge, *Appl. Phys. Lett*. 84, 4559 (2004).
82. H. Fujiwara, S. Y. Wang, and M. Sun, *J. Appl. Phys.* 9, 10P507 (2005).
83. L. Savchenko, B. N. Engel, N. D. Rizzo, M. DeHerrera, and J. Janesky, U.S. Patent 6,545,906 B1, April, 2003.
84. T. Suzuki, Y. Fukumoto, K. Mori, H. Honjo, R. Nebashi, S. Miura, K. Nagahara, S. Saito, H. Numata, K. Tsuji, T. Sugibayashi, H. Hada, N. Ishiwata, Y. Asao, S. Ikegawa, H. Yoda, and S. Tahara, "VLSI Tech. Dig.," p. 188, 2005.
85. M. Durlam, D. Addie, J. Akerman, B. Butcher, P. Brown, J. Chan, M. DeHerrera, B. N. Engel, B. Feil, G. Grynkewich, J. Janesky, M. Johnson, K. Kyler, J. Molla, J. Martin, K. Nagel, J. Ren, N. D. Rizzo, T. Rodriguez, L. Savtchenko, J. Salter, J. M. Slaughter, K. Smith, J. J. Sun, M. Lien, K. Papworth, P. Shah, W. Quin, R. Williams, L. Wise, and S. Tehrani, "IEDM Tech. Dig.," p. 995, 2003.
86. B. N. Engel, J. Akerman, B. Butcher, R. W. Dave, M. DeHerrera, M. Durlam, G. Grynkewich, J. Janesky, S. V. Pietambaram, N. D. Rizzo, J. M. Slaughter, K. Smith, J. J. Sun, and S. Therani, *IEEE Trans. Magn*. 41, 132 (2005).
87. M. Durlam, T. Andre, P. Brown, J. Calder, J. Chan, R. Cuppens, R. W. Dave, D. Ditewig, M. DeHerrera, B. N. Engel, B. Feil, C. Frey, D. Galpin, B. Garni, G. Grynkewich, J. Janeski, G. Kerszykowksi, M. Lien, J. Martin, J. Nahas, K. Nagel, K. Smith, C. Subramanian, J. J. Sun, J. Tamin, R. Williams, L. Wise, S. Zoll, F. List, R. Fournel, B. Martino, and S. Tehrani, "VLSI Tech. Dig.," Vol. 10B-2, p. 186, 2005.
88. H. Fujiwara, S. Y. Wang, and M. Sun, *Trans. Magn. Soc. Jpn*. 4, 121 (2004).
89. J. Akerman, M. DeHerrera, M. Durlam, B. Engel, J. Janesky, F. Mancott, J. Slaughter, and S. Tehrani, Magnetic tunnel junction based magneto-resistive random access memory, Chapter 5 in "Magnetoelectronics," edited by M. Johnson, Elsevier Inc., San Diego, CA, 2004, p. 231.
90. I. L. Prejbeanu, W. Kula, K. Ounadjela, R. C. Sousa, O. Redon, B. Dieny, and J. P. Nozieres, *IEEE Trans*. 40, 2625 (2004).
91. J. Wang and P. P. Freitas, *Appl. Phys. Lett*. 84, 945 (2004).
92. J. M. Daughton and A. V. Pohm, *J. Appl. Phys*. 93, 7304 (2003).
93. B. Dieny, R. C. Sousa, J. Hérault, C. Papusoi, G. Prenat, U. Ebels, D. Houssameddine, R. Rodmacq, S. Auffret, D. Buda-Prejbeanu, M. C. Cyrille, B. Delaët, O. Redon, C. Ducruet, J.-P. Nozières, and I. L. Prejbeanu, *Int. J. Nanotechnol*. 7, 591 (1970).
94. I. L. Prejbeanu, M. Kerekes, R. C. Sousa, H. Sibuet, O. Redon, B. Dieny, and J. P. Nozieres, *J. Phys.: Condens. Matter* 19, 165218 (2007).
95. Y. Yang, Y. Jiang, S. Abe, T. Ochiai, T. Nozaki, A. Hirohata, N. Tezuka, and K. Inomata, *Phys. Rev. Lett*. 92, 167204 (2004).

96. H. Meng, J. Wang, Z. Diao, and J.-P. Wang, *J. Appl. Phys. AP* 97, 10C926 (2005).
97. R. H. Koch, J. G. Deak, D. W. Abraham, P. L. Trouilloud, R. A. Altman, Y. Yu, and W. J. Gallagher, *Phys. Rev. Lett.* 81, 4512 (1998).
98. R. Leuschner, U. K. Klostermann, H. Park, F. Dahmani, R. Dittrich, C. Crigis, K. Hernan, S. Mege, C. Park, M. C. Clech, G. Y. Lee, S. Bournat, L. Altimime, and G. Müller, "IEDM Techn. Dig.," p. S6P5, 2006.
99. L. Berger, *J. Appl. Phys.* 49, 2156 (1978).
100. P. P. Freitas and L. Berger, *J. Appl. Phys.* 57, 1266 (1985).
101. L. Berger, *Phys. Rev. B* 54, 9359 (1996).
102. J. Slonczewski, *J. Magn. Mater.* 159, L1 (1996).
103. J. Slonzewski, U.S. Patent #5, 695, 864, December 9, 1997.
104. M. Tsoi, A. G. M. Jansen, J. Bass, W.-C. Chiang, M. Seck, V. Tsoi, and P. Wyder, *Phys. Rev. Lett.* 80, 4281 (1998).
105. J. E. Wegrowe, D. Kelly, Y. Jaccard, P. Guittienne, and J. P. Ansermet, *Europhys. Lett.* 45, 626 (1999).
106. Y. Huai, F. Albert, P. Nguyen, M. Pakala, and T. Valet, *Appl. Phys. Lett.* 84, 3118 (2004).
107. D. L. Mills and J. A. C. Bland, Eds., "Nanomagnetism: Ultrathin Films, Multilayers and Nanostructures." Elsevier, Amsterdam, 2006.
108. D. Ralph and M. D. Stiles, *Journal of Magnetism and Magnetic Materials* 320, 1190 (2008).
109. T. Ishigaki, T. Kawahara, R. Takemura, K. Ono, K. Ito, H. Matsuoka, and H. Ohno, "2010 Symposium on VLSI Tech. Dig. Techn. Papers," p. 47, 2010.
110. Y. Jiang, S. Abe, T. Ochiai, T. Nozaki, A. Hirohata, N. Tezuka, and K. Inomata, *Phys. Rev. Lett.* 92, 167204 (2004).
111. H. Meng, J. Wang, Z. Diao, and J.-P. Wang, *J. Appl. Phys.* 97, 10C926 (2005).
112. H. Kano, K. Bessho, Y, Higo, K. Obha, M. Hashimoto, T. Mizuguchi, and M. Hosomi, "INTERMAG Europe 2002, Digest of Technical Papers," p. BB4, 2002.
113. B. Dieny and O. Redon, U.S. Patent #6,950,335B2, and FR2832542 2005.
114. Y. Huai, M. Pakala, Z. Diao, and Y. Ding, *Appl. Phys. Lett.* 87, 222510 (2005).
115. Z. Diao, A. Panchula, Y. Ding, M. Pakala, S. Wang, Z. Li, D. Apalkov, H. Nagai, A. Driskill-Smith, L.-C. Wang, E. Chen, and Y. Huai, *Appl. Phys. Lett.* 90, 132508 (2007).
116. Y. M. Lee, C. Yoshida, K. Tsunoda, S. Umehara, M. Aoki, and T. Sugii, "VLSI Tech. Dig.," p. 49, 2010.
117. C. J. Lin, S. H. Kang, Y. J. Wang, K. Lee, X. Zhu, W. C. Chen, X. Li, W. N. Hsu, Y. C. Kao, M. T. Liu, W. C. Chen, Y. C. Lin, M. Nowak, N. Yu, and L. Tran, "IEEE International Electron Devices Meeting 2009," IEDM Technical Digest, Baltimore, MD, 2009, p. 279.
118. Y. H. Wang, W. C. Chen, S. Y. Yang, K.-H. Shen, C. Park, M.-J. Kao, and M.-J. Tsai, *J. Appl. Phys.* 99, 08M307 (2006).
119. A. Driskill-Smith, S. Watts, V. Nikitin, D. Apalkov, D. Druist, R. Kawakami, X. Tang, X. Luo, A. Ong, and E. Chen, "2010 Symp. VLSI Techn. Dig. Tech. Papers," p. 51, 2010.
120. X. Zhu and J.-G. Zhu, *IEEE Trans. Magn.* 42, 2739 (2006).
121. S. Mangin, D. Ravelosona, J. A. Katine, M. J. Carey, B. T. Terris, and E. E. Fullerton, *Nat. Mater.* 5, 210 (2006).
122. U. K. Klostermann, M. Angerbauer, U. Grüning, F. Kreupl, M. Rüehrig, F. Dahmani, M. Kund, and G. Müller, "IEDM Techn. Dig.," p. 187, 2007.
123. N. Nakayama, T. Kai, N. Shimomura, M. Amano, E. Kitagawa, T. Nagase, M. Yoshikawa, T. Kishi, S. Ikegawa, and H. Yoda, *J. Appl. Phys.* 103, 07A710 (2008).
124. T. Kishi, H. Yoda, T. Kai, T. Nagase, E. Kitagawa, M. Yoshikawa, K. Nishiyama, T. Daibou, M. Nagamine, M. Amano, S. Takahashi, M. Nakayama, N. Shimomura, H. Aikawa, S. Ikegawa, S. Yuasa, K. Yakushijii, H. Kubota, A. Fukushima, M. Oogane, T. Miyazaki, and K. Ando, "IEDM Techn. Dig.," p. 309, 2008.
125. M. Yoshikawa, E. Kitagawa, T. Nagase, T. Daibou, M. Nagamine, K. Nishiyama, T. Kishi, and H. Yoda, *IEEE Transactions on Magnetics* 44, 2573 (2008).
126. J. Herault, M. Souza, Y. Hadj-Larbi, M.-T. Delaye, R. Sousa, L. Prejbeanu, and B. Dieny, "CF-06 IEEE Intermag. Conf.," Sacramento, CA, 2009, p. 101.
127. R. P. Cowburn, D. K. Koltosv, A. O. Adeyeye, M. E. Welland, and D. M. Ticker, *Phys. Rev. Lett.* 83, 1042 (1999).
128. M. Schneider, H. Hoffmann, S. Otto. T. Haug, and J. Zweck, *J. Appl. Phys.* 92, 1466 (2002).
129. J.-G. Zhu, Y. Zheng, and G. A. Prinz, *J. Appl. Phys.* 87, 6668 (2000).
130. T. Shinjo, T. Okuno, R. Hassdorf, K. Shigeto, and T. Ono, *Science* 289, 930 (2000).
131. A. Wachowiak, J. Wiebe, M. Bode, O. Pietzsch, M. Morgenstern, and R. Wiesendanger, *Science* 298, 577 (2002).
132. M. Tanase, A. K. Petford-Long, O. Heinonen, K. S. Buchanan, J. Sort, and J. Nogues, *Phys. Rev. B* 79, 014436 (2009).
133. Z. C. Wen, H. X. Wei, and X. F. Han, *Appl. Phys. Lett.* 91, 122511 (2007).
134. B. Pigeau, G. de Loubens, O. Klein, A. Riegler, F. Lochner, G. Schmidt, L. W. Molenkamp, V. S. Tiberkevich, and A. N. Slavin, *Appl. Phys. Lett.* 96, 132506 (2010).
135. T. W. Hickmott, *J. Appl. Phys.* 33, 2669 (1962).
136. W.-Y. Wang and S.-W. Rhee, *Appl. Phys. Lett.* 91, 232907 (2007).
137. A. Chen, S. Haddad, Y.-C. Wu, T.-N. Fang, Z. Lan, S. Avanzino, S. Pangrle, M. Buynoski, M. Rathor, W. Cai, N. Tripsas, C. Bill, M. VanBuskirk, and M. Taguchi, "IEEE International Electron Devices Meeting 2005," IEDM Technical Digest, Washington, DC, p. 746, 2005.
138. J. F. Gibbons and W. E. Beadle, *Solid State Electron.* 7, 785 (1964).
139. S. Seo, M. J. Lee, D. H. Seo, S. K. Choi, D.-S. Suh, Y. S. Joung, I. K. Yoo, I. S. Byun, I. R. Hwang, S. H. Kim, and B. H. Park, *Appl. Phys. Lett.* 86, 093509 (2005).
140. I. G. Baek, D. C. Kim. M. J. Lee, H.-J. Kim, E. K. Yim, M. S. Lee, J. E. Lee, S. E. Ahn, S. Seo, J. H. Lee, J. C. Park, Y. K. Cha, S. O. Park, H. S. Kim, I. K. Yoo, U.-I. Chung, J. T. Moon, and B. I. Ryu, "IEDM Tech. Dig.," p. 746, 2005.
141. S. Seo, M. J. Lec, D. H. Seo, E. J. Jeoung, D.-S. Sun, Y. S. Joung, I. K. Yoo, I. R. Hwang, S. H. Kim, I. S. Byun, J.-S. Kim, J. S. Choi, and B. H. Park, *Appl. Phys. Lett.* 85, 5655 (2004).
142. J. C. Bruyere and B. K. Chakraverty, *Appl. Phys. Lett.* 16, 40 (1970).
143. R. C. Morris, J. E. Christopher, and R. V. Coleman, *Phys. Rev.* 184, 565 (1969).
144. C. Schindler, S. C. P. Thermadam, R. Waser, and M. N. Kozicki, *Trans. Electr. Dev.* 54, 2762 (2007).
145. M. N. Kozicki, C. Gopalan, M. Balakrishnan, and M. Mitkova, *Trans. Nanotech.* 5, 535 (2006).
146. A. Chen, S. Haddad, and Y.-C. Wu, *Electr. Dev. Lett.* 29, 38 (2008).
147. B. P. Zakharchenya, V. P. Malinenko, G. B. Stefanovich, M. Yu Terman, and F. Chudnovskii, *Pisma Zh. Tekh. Fiz. (Sov. Tech. Phys. Lett.)* 11, 108 (1985).
148. W. R. Hiatt and T. W. Hickmott, *Appl. Phys. Lett.* 6, 106 (1965).
149. B. Lalevic, N. Fuschillo, and W. Slusark, *IEEE Trans. Electron. Dev.* ED-22, 965 (1975).
150. G. C. Vezzolli, *J. Appl. Phys.* 36, 184 (1965).
151. S. H. Shin, T. Halperin, and P. M. Raccah, *J. Appl. Phys.* 48, 3150 (1977).
152. T. W. Hickmott, *J. Vac. Sci. Technol.* 6, 828 (1969).
153. K. L. Chopra, *J. Appl. Phys.* 36, 184 (1965).
154. Z. Wei, Y. Kanzawa, K. Arita, Y. Katoh, K. Kawai, S. Muraoka, S. Mitani, S. Fujii, K. Katayama, M. Iijima, T. Mikawa, T. Ninomiya, R. Miyanaga, Y. Kawashima, K. Tsuji, A. Himeno, T. Okada, R. Azuma, K. Shimakawa, H. Sugaya, T. Takagi,

R. Yasuhara, K. Horiba, H. Kumigashira, and M. Oshima, "IEDM Tech. Dig.," p. 293, 2008.

155. F. Argall, *Solid State Electron*. 11, 535 (1968).

156. G. H. Kim, J. H. Lee, J. Y. Seok, S. J. Song, J. H. Yoon, M. H. Lee, K. M. Kim, H. D. Lee, S. W. Ryu, T. J. Park, and C. S. Hwang, *Appl. Phys. Lett*. 98, 262901 (2011).

157. L. E. Yu, S. Kim, M.-K. Ryu, S.-Y. Choi, and Y. K. Choi, *IEEE Electr. Dev. Lett*. 29, 331 (2008).

158. J. R. Jameson, Y. Fukuzumi, Z. Wang, and P. Griffin, *Appl. Phys. Lett*. 91, 112101 (2007).

159. G. Taylor and B. Lalevic, *Solid State Electron*. 19, 669 (1976).

160. S. Kim, I. Byun, I. Hwang, J. Kim, J. Choi, B. H. Park, S. Seo, M.-J. Lee, D. H. Seo, D.-S. Suh, Y. S. Joung, and I.-K. Yoo, *Jp. J. Appl. Phys., Part* 2 44, L345 (2005).

161. A. Beck, J. G. Bednorz, C. Gerber, C, Rossel, and D. Widner, *Appl. Phys. Lett.* 77, 139 (2000).

162. H. Y. Lee, P. S. Chen, T. Y. Wu, Y. S. Chen, C. C. Wang, P. J. Tzeng, C. H. Lin, F. Chen, C. H. Lien, and M.-J. Tsai, "IEDM Tech. Dig." p. 297, 2008.

163. D. S. Lee, Y. H. Sung, I. G. Lee, J. G. Kim, H. Sohn, and D.-H. Ko, *Appl. Phys. A: Material Science & Processing* 102, 997 (2011).

164. Y. H. Tseng, S. S. Chung, S. Shin, S. S.-M. Kang, H. Y. Lee, and M. J. Tsai, *SSDM10*, Paper E-9-2 (2010).

165. T.-H. Hou, K.-L. Lin, J. Shieh, J.-H. Lin, C. T. Chou, and Y.-J. Lee, *Appl. Phys. Lett*. 98, 103511 (2011).

166. A. Baikalov, Y. Q. Wang, B. Shen, B. Lorenz, S. Tsui, Y. Y. Sun, Y. Y. Xue, and C. W. Chu, *Appl. Phys. Lett*. 83, 957 (2003).

167. A. Sawa, T. Fujii, M. Kawasaki, and Y. Tokura, *Appl. Phys. Lett*. 85, 4073 (2004).

168. A. Odagawa, H. Sato, I. H. Inoue, H. Akoh, M. Kawasaki, Y. Tokura, T. Kanno, and H. Adachi, *Phys. Rev. B Condens. Matter* 70, 224403 (2004).

169. S. Q. Liu, N. J. Wu, and A. Ignatiev, *Appl. Phys. Lett*. 76, 2749 (2000).

170. Y. Watanabe, J. G. Bednorz, A. Bietsch, Ch. Gerber, D. Widmer, A. Beck, and S. J. Wind, *Appl. Phys. Lett*. 78, 3738 (2001).

171. K. Szot, W. Speier, G. Bihlmayer, and R. Waser, *Nat. Mater.* 5, 312 (2006).

172. J. W. Park, K. Jung, M. K. Yang, J.-K. Lee, D.-Y. Kim, and J.-W. Park, *J. Appl. Phys*. 99, 124102 (2006).

173. K. C. Park and S. Basavaiah, *Solid-State Electron*. 7, 785 (1964).

174. J. R. Contreras, H. Kohlstedt, U. Poppe, R. Waser, C. Buchal, and N. A. Pertsen, *Appl. Phys. Lett.* 83, 4595 (2003).

175. U. Russo, D. Ielmini, C. Cagli, A. L. Lacaita, S. Spiga, C. Wiemer, M. Perego, and M. Fanciulli, "IEDM Techn. Dig.," p. 775, 2007.

176. T. N. Fang, S. Kaza, S. Haddad, An Chen, Y.-C. Wu, Z. Lan, S. Avanzino, D. Liao, C. Gopalan, S. Choi, S. Mahdavi, M. Buynoski, Y. Lin, C. Marrian, C. Bill, M. VanBuskirk, and M. Taguchi, "IEEE International Electron Devices Meeting 2006," IEDM Technical Digest, San Francisco, CA, 2006, pp. S30P6.

177. D. C. Kim, S. Seo, S. E. Ahn, D.-S. Suh, M. J. Lee, B.-H. Park, I. K. Yoo, I. G. Baek, H.-J. Kim, E. K. Yim, J. E. Lee, S. O. Park, H. S. Kim, U.-I. Chung, J. T. Moon, and B. I. Ryu, *Appl. Phys. Lett*. 88, 202102 (2006).

178. M. Kund, G. Bettel, C.-U. Pinnow, T. Rohr, J. Schumann, R. Symanczyk, K.-D. Ufert, and G. Müller, "IEDM Techn. Dig.," p. 754, 2005.

179. S. Dietrich, *IEEE J. Solid-State Circ*. 42, 839 (2007).

180. M. Terai, Y. Sakotsubo, Y. Saito, S. Kotsuji, and H. Hada, *Jap. J. Appl. Phys.* 49, 04DD19 (2010).

181. J. G. Simmons and R. R. Verderber, *Proc. R. Soc. Lond. A* 301, 77 (1967).

182. T. Fujii, M. Kawasaki, A. Sawa, H. Akoh, Y. Kawazoe, and Y. Tokura, *Appl. Phys. Lett*. 86, 012107 (2005).

183. A. Sawa, T. Fujii, M. Kawasaki, and Y. Tokura, *Appl. Phys. Lett*. 88, 232112 (2006).

184. J. Y. Ouyang, C. W. Chu, C. R. Szmanda, L. P. Ma, and Y. Yang, *Nat. Mater*. 3, 918 (2004).

185. R. Fors, S. I. Khartsev, and A. M. Grishin, *Phys. Rev. Lett. B* 71, 045305 (2005).

186. G. I. Meijer, U. Staub, M. Janousch, S. L. Johnson, B. Delley, and T. Neisius, *Phys. Rev. B* 72, 155102 (2005).

187. D. S. Kim, Y. H. Kim, C. E. Lee, and Y. T. Kim, *Phys. Rev. B* 74, 174430 (2006).

188. D. Strukov, G. S. Snider, D. R. Stewart, and R. S. Williams, *Nature* 453, 80 (2008).

189. C. Cagli, D. Ielmini, F. Nardi, and A. I. Lacaita, "IEDM Techn. Dig.," Vol. 289, p. 301 (2008).

190. M. Kawai, K. Ito, M. Ichikawa, and Y. Shimakawa, *Appl. Phys. Lett*. 96, 072106 (2010).

191. Y. Sakotsubo, M. Terai, S. Kotsuji, Y. Saito, M. Tada, Y. Yabe, and H. Hada, "2010 Symp. VLSI Techn. Dig. Technical Papers," p. 87, 2010.

192. M. Wang, W. L. Juo, Y. L. Wang, L. M. Yang, W. Zhu, P. Zhou, J. H. Yang, X. G. Gong, Y. Y. Lin, R. Huang, S. Song, Q. T. Zhou, H. M. Wu, J. G. Wu, and M. H. Chi, "Symp. VLSI Tech. Dig. Tech. Papers," Vol. 89, p. 90, 2010.

193. T. Menke, P. Meuffels, P. Dittmann, K. Szot, and R. Waser, *J. Appl. Phys*. 105, 066104 (2009).

194. A. Sawa, *Mater. Today* 11, 28 (2008).

195. F. A. Chudnovskii, L. L. Odynets, A. L. Pergament, and G. B. Stefanovich, *J. Solid State Chem*. 12, 95 (1996).

196. H. Pagnia and N. Sotnik, *Phys. Stat. Sol.* 108, 11 (1988).

197. D. Ielmini, D. Mantegazza, A. L. Lacaita, A. Pirovano, and F. Pellizer, *IEEE Electron Dev. Lett*. 26, 799 (2005).

198. K. Kinoshita, T. Tamura, M. Aoki, Y. Sugiyama, and H. Tanaka, *Appl. Phys. Lett*. 89, 103509 (2006).

199. K. M. Kim, B. J. Choi, and C. S. Hwang, *Appl. Phys. Lett*. 90, 242906 (2007).

200. H. D. Lee, B. Magyari-Köpe, and Y. Nishi, *Phys. Rev. B* 81, 193202 (2010).

201. D. S. Jeong, H. Schroeder, and R. Waser, *Solid-State Lett*. 10, G51 (2007).

202. Y. Hiroshe and H. Hiroshe, *J. Appl. Phys.* 47, 2767 (1976).

203. R. Waser, "IEDM Techn. Dig.," p. 289, 2008.

204. X. Guo, C. Schindler, S. Menzel, and R. Waser, *Appl. Phys. Lett*. 91, 133513 (2007).

205. M. Balakrishnan, M. N. Kozicki, C. Gopolan, and M. Mitkova, "Dev. Res. Conf. Dig.," Santa Barbara, CA, June, 2008, p. 47.

206. C. Schindler, M. Meier, R. Waser, and M. N. Kozicki, "2007 Symp. Non-Volatile Memory Tech.," p. 82, 2007.

207. C. Schindler, M. Weides, M. N. Kozicki, and R. Waser, *Appl. Phys. Lett*. 92, 122910 (2008).

208. Z. Wang, P. B. Griffin, J. McVittie, S. Wong, P. C. McIntyre, and Y. Nishi, *IEEE Electron Dev. Lett*. 28, 14 (2007).

209. K. Terabe, T. Hasegawa, T. Nakayama, and M. Aono, *Nature* 433, 47 (2005).

210. F. Q. Xie, I. Nittler, C. Obermair, and T. Schimmel, *Phys. Rev. Lett.* 93, 128303 (2004).

211. N. Banno, T. Sakamoto, T. Hasegawa, K. Terabe, and M. Aono, *Jpn. J. Appl. Phys*. 45, 3666 (2006).

212. A. Odagawa, Y. Katoh, Y. Kanzawa, Z. Wei, T. Mikawa, S. Muraoako, and T. Takagi, *Appl. Phys. Lett*. 91, 133503 (2007).

213. S. Muraoka, K. Osano, Y. Kanzawa, S. Mitani, S. Fujii, K. Katayama, Y. Katoh, Z. Wei, T. Mikawa, K. Arita, Y. Kawashima, R. Azuma, K. Kawai, K. Shimakawa, A. Odagawa, and T. Takagi, "IEDM Techn. Dig.," p. 779, 2007.

214. H. Y. Jeong, M. K. Ryu, S.-Y. Choi, and J. Y. Lee, "Proc. MRS Spring Meeting," San Francisco, CA, 2007, p. 242.

215. J. S. Choi, J.-S. Kim, I. R. Hwang, S. H. Hong, S. H. Jeon, S.-O. Kang, B. H. Park, D. C. Kim, M. J. Lee, and S. Seo, *Appl. Phys. Lett*. 95, 022109 (2009).

216. N. F. Mott, "Metal-Insulator-Transitions." Taylor & Francis, London, 1974.
217. J. M. Honig, "The Metal and Non-Metal States of Matter." (B. P. Edwards and C. N. R. Rao, Eds.), Taylor and Francis, London, p. 261, 1985.
218. T. Oka and N. Nagaosa, *Phys. Rev. Lett*. 95, 266403 (2005).
219. M. M. Qazilbash, M. Brehm, B.-G. Chae, P.-C. Ho, G. O. Andreev, B.-J. Kim, S. J. Yun, A. V. Balatsky, M. B. Maple, F. Keilmann, H.-T. Kim, and D. N. Basoc, *Science Mag*. 318, 1750 (2007).
220. B. Lalevic, N. Fuschillo, and B. Leung, *Phys. Status Solidi A* 23, 61 (1974).
221. K. Okamoto, M. Tada, K. Ito, Y. Saioto, S. Ishida, and H. Hada, "SSDM2010 Conf.," Miyagi, Japan, 2009, Paper E-9-3.
222. S. J. Kim, M. G. Sung, W. G. Kim, J. Y. Kim, J. H. Yoo, J. N. Kim, B. G. Gyun, J. Y. Byun, M. S. Joo, J. S. Roh, and S. K. Park, "SSDM2010 Conf.," Tokyo, Japan, 2010, Paper E-9-4.
223. J. Lee, M. Jo, D.-J. Seong, J. Shin, and H. Hwang, *Microelectr. Eng.* 88, 1113 (2011); "Proceedings of 17th Biennial International Insulating Films on Semiconductors Conference," Grenoble, France.
224. W. C. Chien, Y. C. Chen, F. M. Lee, Y. Y. Lin. E. K. Lai, Y. D. Yao. J. Gong, S. F. Horng, C. W. Yeh, S. C. Tsai, C. H. Lee, Y. K. Huang, C. F. Chen, H. F. Kao, Y. H. Shih, K. Y. Hsieh, and C.-Y. Lu, "SSDM2010 Conf.," Tokyo, Japan, 2010, Paper E-8-4.
225. T. H. Kim (Hynix), U.S. Patent Application US2010/0124810 A1, May 20, 2010.
226. T. H. Kim (Hynix), "Non-volatile memory device and fabrication method thereof," U.S. Patent Application US2008/0083916 A1, April 10, 2008.
227. K. C. Ryoo, J.-H. Oh, S. Jung, H. Jeong, and B.-G. Park, "SSDM2010 Conf.," Paper E-5L, 2010.
228. Y. T. Hwang, U.S. Patent Application US2009/0302301 A1, December 10, 2009.
229. H. Noshiro and K. Kinoshita (Fujitsu), U.S. Patent Application Publication US2010/0083487 A1, April 8, 2010.
230. Y. J. Lee, U.S. Patent Application Publication US2010/0167462 A1, July 1, 2010.
231. H. Noshiro (Fujitsu), U.S. Patent Application Publication US2010/0027319 A1, February 4, 2010.
232. C. H. Ho, E. K. Lai, and K. Y. Hsieh, U.S. Patent 7,595,218 B2, September 29, 2009.
233. M.-J. Lee, S. Seo, D.-C. Kim, S.-E. Ahn, D. H. Seo, I.-K. Yoo, I.-G. Baek, D.-S. Kim, I.-S. Byun, S.-H. Kim, I.-R. Hwang, J.-S. Kim, S.-H. Jeon, and B. H. Park, *Adv. Mater*. 19, 73 (2007).
234. M.-J. Lee, Y. Park, B.-S. Kang, S.-E. Ahn, C. Lee, K. Kim, W. Xianyu, G. Stefanovich, J.-H. Lee, S.-J. Chung, Y.-H. Kim, C.-S. Lee, J.-B. Park, and I.-K. Yoo, "IEDM Tech. Dig. 2007," p. 771, 2007.
235. K.-P. Chang, H.-T. Lue, K.-Y Hsieh, and C.-Y. Lu, "SSDM2010 Conf.," Tokyo, Japan, 2010, Paper E-8-2.
236. M. Jo, D. Seong, S. Kim, J. Lee, W. Lee, J.-B. Park, S. Park, S. Jung, J. Shin, D. Lee, and H. Hwang, "VLSI Tech. Dig.," p. 53, 2010.
237. E. Linn, R. Roezin, C. Kügeler, and R. Waser, *Nat. Mater.* 9, 403 (2010).
238. H.-J. Kim (Samsung), U.S. Patent Application US2007/0140029 A1, June 21, 2007.
239. H.-J. Kim (Samsung), U.S. Patent US7,495,984 B2, February 24, 2009.
240. H.-J. Kim (Samsung), U.S. Patent Application Publication US2009/0135642 A1, May 28, 2009.
241. M. Aoki (Fujitsu Limited), U.S. Patent Application Publication US20010/0157655 A1, June 24, 2010.
242. S. Kaeriyama, T. Sakamoto, H. Sunamura, M. Mizuno, H. Kawaura, T. Hasegawa, K. Terabe, T. Nakayama, and M. Aono, *IEEE J. Solid-State Circ*. 40, 168 (2005).
243. International Technology Roadmap for Semiconductors (ITRS). http://www.itrs.net/reports.html, ITRS 2009 Ed., 2009 ITRS Table Files Links, Focus B Tables, Table ERD5 "Emerging Research Resistance-Based Memory Devices—Demonstrated and Projected Parameters." International SEMATECH, Austin (2009).
244. I.-G. Baek, September 2010, Process Dev. Team/RRAM PJT, Samsung Electronics Co. "SEMATECH 7th Int. Symp. Adv. Gate Stack Tech.," Troy, N.Y., USA, 2010.
245. G. H. Oh, Y. L. Park, J. I. Lee, D. H. Im, J. S. Bae, D. H. Kim, D. H. Ahn, H. Horii, S. O. Park, H. S. Yoon, I. S. Park, Y. S. Ko, and J. T. U.-In Chung, "Symp. VLSI Techn. Dig.," p. 26, 2009.
246. W. C. Chien, Y. C. Chen, E. K. Lai, Y. Y. Lin, K. P. Chang, Y. D. Yao, P. Lin, J. Gong, S. C. Tsai, C. H. Lee, S. H. Hsieh, C. F. Chen, Y. H. Shih, K. Y. Hsieh, R. Liu, and C.-Y. Lu, "Proc. SSDM," p. 1206, 2009.
247. M. Terai, S. Kotsuji, H. Hada, N. Iguchi, T. Ichihashi, and S. Fujieda, "2009 IEEE Int. Reliability Phys. Symp. (IRPS)," Washington, D.C., USA, 2009, p. 134.
248. Y.-Y. Lin, F.-M. Lee, Y.-C. Chen, W.-C. Chien, C.-W. Yeh, K.-Y. Hsieh, and C. Y. Lu, "VLSI Tech. Dig.," p. 91, 2010.
249. R. Waser and M. Aono, *Nat. Mater*. 6, 833 (2007).
250. J. C. Scott and L. D. Bozano, *Adv. Mater.* 19, 1452 (2007).
251. Q. Li, G. Mathur, S. Gowda, S. Surthi, Q. Zhao, L. Yu, J. S. Lindsey, D. F. Bocian, and V. Misra, *Adv. Mater*. 16, 133 (2004).
252. K. M. Roth, J. S. Lindsey, D. F. Bocian, and W. G. Kuhr, *Langmuir* 18, 4030 (2002).
253. K. M. Roth, N. Dontha, R. B. Dabke, D. T. Gryko, C. Clausen, J. S. Lindsey, D. F. Bocian, and W. G. Kuhr, *J. Vac. Sci. Technol. B* 18, 2359 (2000).
254. L. V. Gregor, *Thin Solid Films* 2, 235 (1968).
255. H. E. Katz, X. M. Hong, A. Dodabalapur, and R. Sarpeshkar, *J. Appl. Phys*. 91, 1572 (2002).
256. G. H. Gelinck, A. W. Marsman, F. J. Touwslager, S. Detayesh, D. M. DeLeeuw, R. C. Naber, and P. W. Blom, *Appl. Phys. Lett.* 87, 092903 (2005).
257. A. R. Elsharkawi and K. C. Kao, *J. Phys. Chem. Solids* 38, 95 (1975).
258. A. Szymanski, D. C. Larson, and M. M. Labes, *Appl. Phys. Lett.* 14, 88 (1969).
259. A. Bandyopandhyay and A. L. Pal, *Chem. Phys. Lett*. 371, 86 (2003).
260. M. Kushida, Y. Imaizumi, K. Harada, and K. Sugita, *Thin Solid Films* 509, 149 (2006).
261. H. K. Henisch and W. R. Smith, *Appl. Phys. Lett*. 24, 589 (1974).
262. L. D. Bozano, B. W. Kean, N. Beinhoff, K. R. Carter, and J. C. Scott, *Adv. Funct. Mater*. 15, 1933 (2005).
263. H. Carchano, R. Lacoste, and Y. Segui, *Appl. Phys. Lett.* 19, 414 (1971).
264. L. F. Pender and R. J. Fleming, *J. Appl. Phys.* 46, 3426 (1975).
265. L. P. Ma, Q. F. Xu, and Y. Yang, *Appl. Phys. Lett*. 84, 4908 (2004).
266. M. Ouyang, S. M. Hou, H. F. Chen, and K. Z. Wang, *Phys. Lett. A* 235, 413 (1997).
267. H. J. Gao, K. Sohlberg, Z. Q. Xue, H. Y. Chen, S. M. Hou, L. P. Ma, X. W. Fang, S. J. Pang, and S. J. Pennycook, *Phys. Rev. Lett*. 84, 1780 (2000).
268. R. S. Potember, T. O. Poehler, and D. O. Cowan, *Appl. Phys. Lett*. 34, 405 (1979).
269. T. Oyamada, H. Tanaka, K. Matsushige, H. Sasebe, and C. Adachi, *Appl. Phys. Lett*. 83, 1252, (2003).
270. E. I. Kamitsos, C. H. Tsinis, and W. M. Risen, *Solid State Commun*. 42, 561 (1982).
271. C. Sato, S. Wakamatsu, K. Tadokoro, and K. Ishii, *J. Appl. Phys*. 68, 6535 (1990).
272. C. W. Chu, J. Ouyang, J.-H. Tseng, and Y. Yang, *Adv. Mater.* 17, 1440 (2005).
273. M. Lauters, B. McCarthy, D. Sarid, and G. E. Jabbour, *Appl. Phys. Lett.* 87, 231105 (2005).
274. L. P. Ma, W. J. Jang, Z. Q. Xue, and S. J. Pang, *Appl. Phys. Lett.* 73, 850 (1998).

275. Q. Ling, Y. Song, S. J. Ding, C. Zhu, D. S. Chan, D.-L. Kwong, E.-T. Kang, and K.-G. Neoh, *Adv. Mater.* 17, 455 (2005).
276. J. H. Krieger, S. V. Trubin, S. B. Vaschenko, and N. F. Yudanov, *Synth. Met*. 122, 199 (2001).
277. J. E. Green, J. W. Choi, A. Boukai, Y. Bunimovich, E. Johnston-Halperin, E. Delonno, Y. Luo, B. A. Sheriff, K. Xu, Y. S. Shin, H.-R. Tseng, J. F. Stoddart, and J. R. Heath, *Nature* 445, 414 (2007).
278. L. P. Ma, J. Liu, S. M. Pyo, D. Sieves, and Y. Yang, *Appl. Phys. Lett*. 86, 123507 (2003).
279. J. Ouyang, C.-W. Chu, C. Szmanda, L. P. Ma, and Y. Yang, *Nat. Mater.* 3, 918 (2004).
280. J. Ouyang, C.-W. Chu, R. J.-T. Tseng, A. Prakash, and Y. Yang, *Proc. IEEE* 93, 1287 (2005).
281. T. Ouisse and O. Stefan, *Org. Electron*. 5, 251 (2004).
282. A. Prakash, J. Ouyang, J. L. Lin, and Y. Yang, *J. Appl. Phys*. 100, 054309 (2006).
283. C. Novembre, D. Guerin, K. Lmimouni, C. Gamrat, and D. Vuillaume, *Appl. Phys. Lett*. 92, 103314 (2008).
284. J. G. Simmons and R. R. Verderber, *Proc. R. Soc. London, Series A* 391, 77 (1967).
285. W. Tang, H. Shi, G. Xu, B. S. Ong, Z. D. Popovic, J. Deng, J. Zhao, and G. Rao, *Adv. Mater*. 17, 2307 (2005).
286. J. Wu, L. Ma, and Y. Yang, *Phys. Rev. B* 69, 115321 (2004).
287. H.-T. Lin, Z. Pei, J.-R. Chen, C.-P. Kung, Y.-C. Lin, C.-M. Teng, and Y. J. Chan, "IEDM 2007 Proc.," Washington D.C., USA, 2007, p. 233 (S9-P6).
288. G. Dearnaley, D. V. Morgan, and A. M. Stoneham, *J. Non-Cryst. Solids* 4, 593 (1970).
289. R. E. Thurstans and D. P. Oxley, *J. Phys. D* 35, 802 (2002).
290. F. Verbakel, S. Meskers, R. Janssen, H. Gomes, A. Vandenbiggelaar, and D. M. de Leeuw, *Appl. Phys. Lett*. 91, 192103 (2007).
291. B. Cho, T. Yasue, H. Yonn, M. Lee, I. Yeo, U. Chung, J. Moon, and B. Ryu, *IEDM*, DOI: IEDM 2006, 346729 (2006).
292. W. L. Kwan, R. J. Tseng, W. Wu, Q. Pei, and Y. Yang, "IEDM Tech. Dig.," p. 237, 2007.
293. www.itrs.net/reports.html click 2010 Update/2010 Future Memory Devices Workshop Summary, Appendix 3.
294. www.itrs.net/reports.html click 2010 Update/2010 Future Memory Devices Workshop Summary, Appendix 1a.

Index

A

B

C

ISBN: 1-58883-251-1

Nonvolatile Memories: Materials, Devices and Applications
Edited by Tseung-Yuen Tseng and Simon M. Sze
Volume 2: Pages: 443–447

J

K

L

M

N

O

P

Q

R

S

T

U

Z